The Bristol and Gloucestershire Archaeological Society
Gloucestershire Record Series

Hon. General Editor
C. R. Elrington, M.A., F.S.A., F.R.Hist.S.

VOLUME 17

Catalogue of Berkeley Castle Muniments (1)

A CATALOGUE
OF THE
MEDIEVAL MUNIMENTS
AT
BERKELEY CASTLE

EDITED BY BRIDGET WELLS-FURBY

FIRST OF TWO VOLUMES

The Bristol and Gloucestershire Archaeological Society

2004

The Bristol and Gloucestershire Archaeological Society
Gloucestershire Record Series

© The Bristol and Gloucestershire Archaeological Society 2004

ISBN 0 900197 60 9

British Library Cataloguing in Publication Data.
A catalogue record for this book is available from the British Library.

Printed in Great Britain by J. W. Arrowsmith Ltd., Winterstoke Road, Bristol BS3 2NT

CONTENTS

FOREWORD

I am delighted to write a foreword to this *Catalogue*. Ever since my ancestor, Robert FitzHarding, was granted the Honour of Berkeley in 1153 our muniments have been central to the affairs of my family. They date from that grant and are unique as the only archives in England which are contemporary with the building in which they are still stored. Moreover they are not merely of local importance. Some of my ancestors played a leading role in English history in medieval times, being at Runnymede for Magna Carta, having custody of the ill-fated Edward II, negotiating with Richard II for his abdication and fighting at Creçy and Agincourt. They also held lands in most counties at various times and won the last private battle in England, close by at Nibley Green, on 20 March 1470. And at least one, Thomas (IV), was an outstanding patron of scholarship, commissioning John de Treviza to translate into English Higden's *Polychronichon*, a popular textbook on history and geography, so that intelligent laymen could read it.

But despite the importance of the muniments, and the value placed upon them by my family, this is the first proper catalogue of any part of them to be published. A special 'Evidence House' was built to house them, probably early in the reign of the first Queen Elizabeth, and two generations later the family's historian, John Smyth, gathered and arranged them as part of his researches. However, over the next century and a half they became scattered and disordered, a prey to dirt, damp, mould, insects, rodents, theft, vandalism and deliberate destruction. Their survival in their present state owes much to the 5th Countess, who seems to have supervised the work of W. F. Shrapnell, a self-taught antiquary, employed at the Castle around 1800–1810. His lists remained the best descriptions of many of the documents until the 1980's.

At some time during the 19th century the muniments were moved out of the 'Evidence House' into what is now the private chapel. (The present Muniment Room was built by the 8th Earl in about 1926.) Soon after the creation of the Historical Manuscripts Commission a short report on them was published, and perhaps that and the publication of Smyth's *Lives of the Berkeleys* by this Society in 1883 persuaded Lord Fitzhardinge to ask an antiquary, Edward Peacock, to list the deeds and rolls. Illness prevented him from completing the task which was brought to conclusion by I. H. Jeayes. (Their methods are discussed below, Introduction, p. l.) The resulting catalogue of the Select Series was privately printed in 1892. Until today it has been the only published guide to the muniments.

The great achievement of this present *Catalogue* is to re-create, as far as is now possible, the original archival groupings of the documents. It shows how, by dynastic marriage and careful purchases, my family built up a large and varied holding of land, sadly squandered by William, Marquess of Berkeley. This *Catalogue* has been many years in the making and is now the standard guide to those muniments dated before the death of the Marquess in February 1492. It will remain so for ever. I hope that maybe someone will eventually produce a continuation, listing the much larger number of my family's documents which survive for the period since 1492.

Although a full list of acknowledgements follows, I offer my personal thanks to several people and organisations without whose efforts this monumental work could not have been achieved. First, I am deeply conscious of the time and scholarship devoted by Dr Bridget Wells-Furby over many years to compiling the *Catalogue*. She is the only person who could have done this, using the knowledge which she acquired during research for her doctoral thesis. But she could not have done it without the funding generously awarded by the British Academy, to whom I also offer profound thanks. Thirdly, I am grateful for the long and fruitful relationship between successive owners of the Castle and the Bristol and Gloucestershire Archaeological Society, of which this *Catalogue* is only the latest of many examples. I wish to record my deep gratitude to the Trustees of the National Manuscripts Conservation Trust for their financial support for several conservation and filming projects. Finally I thank the Gloucestershire Record Office for hosting these projects and for advice on the storage and management of my family's muniments over the last fifty years.

Berkeley Castle   JOHN BERKELEY
October 2003

ACKNOWLEDGEMENTS

My thanks and those of the Bristol and Gloucestershire Archaeological Society are gratefully aknowledged to the British Academy for awarding the major research grant which funded the cataloguing of the muniments; to Mr. Berkeley and the Trustees of the Berkeley Will Trust for their support and especially for placing whole classes of documents temporarily in the Gloucestershire Record Office so that they could be worked on continuously with a wide range of reference books to hand; to the Gloucestershire Record Office for hosting the project and to the staff there for their advice and friendship; to the staff of various other record offices for advice given at long distance; and to the National Manuscripts Conservation Trust for awarding grants towards the conservation and filming of the documents to enable the most fragile to be consulted safely.

In addition I should like to express my personal thanks to Professor Chris Given-Wilson, of the University of St. Andrews, who set me on the path which has led to the publication of the *Catalogue* by suggesting the Berkeleys as the subject of research for my doctoral dissertation; to Mr. David J. H. Smith, honorary general secretary of the Bristol and Gloucestershire Archaeological Society and former county archivist of Gloucestershire, who obtained the grants which made possible the initial work on the *Catalogue* at Gloucester in 1991–2 and has, at every stage in the compilation of the *Catalogue*, provided guidance and advice; and to the Society for including the *Catalogue* in its distinguished Gloucestershire Record Series.

I should further like to thank Professor Christopher Elrington, honorary general editor of the Record Series, for his constant enthusiasm and encouragement, and particularly for his work on the index; Dr. Samantha Letters, Dr. Rowena Archer and Dr. Simon Payling for their generous assistance with, respectively, the Segraves, the Mowbrays and the Willoughbys; Dr. Oliver Padel for his essential help with Cornish place-names; and, at a domestic level, my mother, Mrs. Sheila Harvey, and my father-in-law, Mr. Hans Wells-Furby, who have lived with the Berkeleys for too many years.

Dennington, Suffolk   BRIDGET WELLS-FURBY
March 2004

LIST OF ABBREVIATIONS

Besides those in common use, the following abbreviations may require elucidation.

BCM	Berkeley Castle Muniments. (For the abbreviations used as shelfmarks, see below, p. lxi)
BIHR	*Bulletin of the Institute of Historical Research* (later called *Historical Research*)
BL	British Library
BL Harl. MS 4748	British Library, Cartulary of the honour of Segrave
Barkley	Sir Henry Barkley, 'The Earlier House of Berkeley', *TBGAS* viii (1883–4)
Blomefield, *Norfolk*	Francis Blomefield, *Essay Towards a Topographical History of the County of Norfolk* (2nd edn., 11 vols., 1805–10)
Bridges, *Northants.*	John Bridges, *History and Antiquities of the County of Northampton* (3 vols., 1759–91)
CChR	*Calendar of Charter Rolls* (6 vols., Public Record Office, 1903–27)
CCR	*Close Rolls of the Reign of Henry III* (14 vols.) and *Calendar of Close Rolls* (47 vols., Edward I to Henry VII, Public Record Office, 1911–63)
CFR	*Calendar of Fine Rolls* (22 vols., Public Record Office, 1911–62)
CIM	*Calendar of Inquisitions Miscellaneous* (7 vols., Public Record Office, 1916–68)
CIPM	*Calendar of Inquisitions Post Mortem* (21 vols., Public Record Office, 1904–2002)
CIPM Hen. VII	*Calendar of Inquisitions Post Mortem, Henry VII* (3 vols., Public Record Office, 1898–1955)
CLibR	*Calendar of Liberate Rolls* (6 vols., Public Record Office, 1916–64)
CMR	*Calendar of Memoranda Rolls, 1326–7* (Public Record Office, 1968)
CPL	*Calendar of Papal Registers: Letters* (15 vols., Public Record Office, 1893–1978)
CPR	*Calendar of Patent Rolls* (54 vols. to the end of Henry VII, Public Record Office, 1893–1916)
Cal. Doc. Irel.	*Calendar of Documents relating to Ireland* (5 vols., Public Record Office, 1875–86)
Cat. Anct. D.	*Descriptive Catalogue of Ancient Deeds in the Public Record Office* (6 vols., Public Record Office, 1890–1915)
Copinger, *Suffolk Manors*	W. A. Copinger, *The Manors of Suffolk* (7 vols. 1905–11)
Cornwall Fines, 1195–1377; 1377–1461	*Cornwall Feet of Fines*, vol. i, 1195–1377; vol. ii, 1377–1461 (Devon and Cornwall Record Society, 1914, 1950)

Curia Regis Rolls	*Curia Regis Rolls* (19 vols., Public Record Office, 1922–2002)
d.s.p.	died *sine prole* (i.e. without issue)
Devon CRO	Devon County Record Office
Dorset Fines, 1327–1485	*Full Abstracts of Feet of Fines relating to the County of Dorset [1327–1485]* (Dorset Records vol. 10, 1910)
Ekwall, *Dict. of Eng. Place-Names*	Eilert Ekwall, *The Concise Oxford Dictionary of English Place-Names* (4th edn., 1960)
Ellis	C. A. Ellis, note and pedigree in Smyth, *Lives of the Berkeleys*, i. 19–20
Farrer	William Farrer, *Honors and Knights' Fees* (3 vols., 1923–5)
Feud. Aids	*Inquisitions and Assessments relating to Feudal Aids* (6 vols., Public Record Office, 1899–1920)
Fryde, *Fall of Edward II*	Natalie Fryde, *The Tyranny and Fall of Edward II, 1321–1326* (1979)
GAR	Berkeley Castle Muniments, General Account Rolls
GC	Berkeley Castle Muniments, General Charters
GCR	Berkeley Castle Muniments, General Court Rolls
GEC	*The Complete Peerage*, ed. G. E. C[ockayne] (14 vols., 1910–98)
GIPM	*Abstracts of Inquisitiones post mortem for Gloucestershire, 1236–1413* (3 vols., issued jointly by the Bristol and Gloucestershire Archaeological Society and the British Record Society Index Library, vols. xxx, xl, xlviii, 1903–14)
GMR	Berkeley Castle Muniments, General Miscellaneous Rolls
GRR	Berkeley Castle Muniments, General Rental Rolls
GSUB	Berkeley Castle Muniments, General Series Unbound Books
Genealogist	*The Genealogist*: a quarterly magazine (1877–1922)
Great Cartulary	Berkeley Castle Muniments, The Great Cartulary (BCM SB 10)
Hist. of Parl. 1386–1421	J. S. Roskell, Linda Clark and Carole Rawcliffe, *The History of Parliament: The House of Commons 1386–1421* (4 vols., 1992)
Historical Research	See *BIHR*
Hutchins, *Dorset*	John Hutchins *The History and Antiquities of the County of Dorset* (4 vols., 1861–70)
Jeayes	*Descriptive Catalogue of the Charters and Muniments in the possession of the Rt. Hon. Lord Fitzhardinge, at Berkeley Castle*, compiled by Isaac Herbert Jeayes (1892)
Lysons, *Magna Britannia*	Daniel and Samuel Lysons, *Magna Britannia* (1874)
McFarlane, *Collected Essays*	K. B. McFarlane, *England in the Fifteenth Century: Collected Essays* (1981)
Morant, *Essex*	Philip Morant, *History and Antiquities of the County of Essex* (1816)

n.d.	no date
Nichols, *Leics.*	John Nichols, *History and Antiquities of the County of Leicester* (4 vols. in 8 parts, 1795–1811)
PNGlos	A. H. Smith, *The Place-Names of Gloucestershire* (English Place-Name Society, 4 vols., 1964–5)
PRO	Public Record Office, Kew, London
Pole, *Devon*	Sir William Pole, *Collections towards a Description of the County of Devon* (1791)
Proc. Som. Arch. & Nat. Hist. Soc.	*Proceedings of the Somerset Archaeological and Natural History Society*
Radford, 'Tretower'	C. A. Raleigh Radford, 'Tretower: The Castle and the Court', *Brycheiniog* (The Brecknock Society), vi (1960)
Reg. Bransford	*Calendar of the Register of Wolstan de Bransford, Bishop of Worcester, 1339–49* (Worcestershire Historical Society, 1966)
Reg. Cobham	*Register of Thomas de Cobham, Bishop of Worcester, 1317–27* (Worcestershire Historical Society, 1930)
Reg. Drokensford	*Calendar of the Register of John de Drokensford, Bishop of Bath and Wells (A.D. 1309–1329)* (Somerset Record Society vol. 1, 1887)
Reg. Giffard	*Register of Bishop Godfrey Giffard, 1268–1301* (2 vols., Worcestershire Historical Society, 1898, 1902)
Reg. Hallum	*The Register of Robert Hallum, Bishop of Salisbury, 1407–17* (Canterbury and York Society, part cxlv, 1982)
Reg. Shrewsbury	*The Register of Ralph of Shrewsbury, Bishop of Bath and Wells, 1329–1363* (Somerset Record Society, vols. 9 and 10, 1896)
Rot. Litt. Claus.	*Rotuli Litterarum Clausarum in turri Londinensi asservati* (Record Commission, 2 vols., 1833–4)
Rot. Parl.	*Rotuli Parliamentorum* (6 vols., 1783, and index vol., 1832)
Rudder, *Glos.*	Samuel Rudder, *A New History of Gloucestershire* (1779)
SB	Berkeley Castle Muniments, Select Books
SC	Berkeley Castle Muniments, Select Charters
SR	Berkeley Castle Muniments, Select Rolls
SRS	Somerset Record Society
St Augustine's Cartulary	*The Cartulary of St Augustine's Abbey, Bristol* (Bristol and Gloucestershire Archaeological Society, Gloucestershire Record Series, vol. 10, 1998)
Sanders, *English Baronies*	I. J. Sanders, *English Baronies: a Study of their Origin and Descent, 1086–1327* (1960)
Saul, *Knights and Esquires*	Nigel Saul, *Knights and Esquires: the Gloucestershire Gentry in the Fourteenth Century* (1981)

Smyth	John Smyth of Nibley, *The Lives of the Berkeleys, with a Description of the Hundred of Berkeley* (The Berkeley Manuscripts, 3 vols., Bristol and Gloucestershire Archaeological Society; vols. i–ii, 1883, are the *Lives of the Berkeleys*; vol. iii, 1885, is *The Hundred of Berkeley*)
Somerset Fines, 1196–1307; 1307–46; 1347– 99; 1399–1461	*Pedes Finium, commonly called Feet of Fines, for the County of Somerset, 1196–1307*; [second series] *1307–46*; [third series], *1347–99*; [fourth series], *1399–1461* (Somerset Record Society, vols. vi, xii, xvii, xxii, 1892–1906)
Staffs. Hist. Collections	*Collections for a History of Staffordshire* (published by the William Salt Archaeological Society, later the Staffordshire Record Society)
TBGAS	*Transactions of the Bristol and Gloucestershire Archaeological Society*
temp.	*tempore* (i.e. in the time of)
VCH	*Victoria History of the Counties of England* (for all counties; in progress)
Wilts. Fines, 1272– 1327; 1327–77	*Abstracts of Feet of Fines relating to Wiltshire for the reigns of Edward I and Edward II* (Wiltshire Archaeological and Natural History Society, Records Branch vol. i, 1939); *for the reign of Edward III* (Wiltshire Record Society vol. xxix, 1974)
Wilts. IPM	*Abstracts of Wiltshire Inquisitions post mortem, 1242–1326; 1327–77* (British Record Society Index Library and Wiltshire Archaeological and Natural History Society, 2 vols., 1908, 1914)

INTRODUCTION

THE BERKELEY LORDS TO 1492 AND THE DEVELOPMENT OF THE ESTATE

For three and a half centuries the Berkeleys of Berkeley maintained their position in the upper ranks of the English aristocracy. Only the Plantagenets rivalled their ability to continue to produce male heirs and the Berkeleys' achievements were imperilled only by the apparently selfish actions of the last lord of the medieval period, William (d. 1492), who bartered the ancient patrimony of the family for the meretricious, and merely temporary, attractions of a marquessate. The development of the estate falls naturally into three periods. In the first, from *c.* 1140 to *c.* 1280, the Berkeleys acquired the lordship of Berkeley and consolidated their local position. In the second, from *c.* 1280 to 1417, overlapping the era of 'high farming' in the earlier part, they greatly extended their estate by purchase and by acquiring the Lisle estate through marriage. The third, rather dismal period, from 1417 to 1492, was dominated by the efforts of the heirs male to retain their estate in the face of determined opposition by the heirs general but culminated in the fortuitous inheritance of half of the Mowbray estate and the promotion to exalted rank. At all times the marriages of the lords and the families which they produced had the most significant impact, although in differing ways.

First Period: *c.* 1140–1280

Robert FitzHarding (d. 1170)

Robert, founder of the baronial family of Berkeley, was a younger son of Harding son of Eadnoth, otherwise Harding de Meriet. Harding witnessed a royal charter in 1086 and was still alive *c.* 1125,[1] and from his eldest son, Nicholas (d. *c.* 1170), the Meriets of Merriott in Somerset descended.[2] Robert established himself as a merchant at Bristol, becoming provost of the town and acquiring a number of manors to add to that of Fifehead in Dorset which he had from his father.[3] From Robert earl of Gloucester he purchased the manors of Bilswick and Bedminster (now in Bristol) and the three Somerset hundreds of Portbury, Bedminster and Hartcliff, just south of Bristol; from others the manors of Leigh (a member of Bedminster), Portbury, Weare, Tickenham and Pawlett in northern Somerset, Bray (Devon) and South Cerney and Acton (Glos.).[4] As an associate of the earl of Gloucester, the Empress Maud's half-brother and greatest supporter, he took Maud's side against Stephen, and Maud and her son 'made use of the purse of this Robertt in that wantfull tyme of theirs'.[5] The tradition that Henry II rewarded his services immediately on his succession with the grant of 'Berkeley and Berkeley Herness' has recently been challenged by the finding that the early charters purporting to record the grants are forgeries.[6] Berkeley Herness was royal demesne but had been held at an annual fee farm rent of £500 17s. 2d. by a family earlier

---

[1] For a useful summary of references to Eadnoth and Harding see Ann Williams, *The English and the Norman Conquest* (1995).

[2] B. W. Greenfield, 'Meriet of Meriet and Hestercombe', *Proc. Som. Arch. & Nat. Hist. Soc.* xxviii (1882), 99–215. Smyth, i. 15, says that Robert was the eldest son, and Nicholas a younger. Eadnoth was called 'the staller' from the position which he held under Edward the Confessor.

[3] Ellis (cf. above, p. xvii).

[4] Below, pp. 420–1, 429, 517, 524, 528, 535; Smyth, i. 34–5. Bedminster was later held of the Clare earls of Gloucester and then of the Despensers: *CIPM* v, no. 538, p. 338; ix, no. 428, p. 338.

[5] Smyth, i. 22.

[6] N. Vincent, 'New Charters of Henry II as Duke of Normandy', *Historical Research* (forthcoming); R. B. Patterson, 'Ducal and Royal *Acta* of Henry Fitz Empress in Berkeley Castle', *TBGAS* cix (1991), 117–26, upheld the authenticity of the charters; cf. below, p. 2.

called of Berkeley.[1] Those Berkeleys, who had been staunch in support of Stephen from their castle at Dursley, were dispossessed of Berkeley in 1147. Robert FitzHarding is not named as possessing Berkeley until 1166, and may have acquired Berkeley shortly before, some years after the beginning of Henry II's reign.

FitzHarding died in 1170 as a canon of St. Augustine's Abbey, which he had founded some thirty years earlier on his manor of Bilswick just outside the borough of Bristol. He had endowed the abbey with the manors of Bilswick, Almondsbury, Ashleworth, South Cerney, Cromhall, Fifehead Magdalen, Horfield and Leigh,[2] later adding the advowsons of all the churches in Berkeley Herness (Berkeley, Wotton, Beverston, Ashleworth and Cromhall).[3] His wife Eve, whom he married before 1130,[4] founded a priory of nuns, St. Mary Magdalen's in Bristol, and, following her husband's example, retired there, dying as prioress in March 1173, and being buried with her husband at St. Augustine's.[5]

If there was ill-feeling between the former holders of Berkeley Herness and the new ones it was ameliorated, to some extent at least, by an agreement for a double marriage thought to have taken place in 1153–4 but perhaps some ten years later.[6] FitzHarding's eldest son Maurice married Alice, daughter of Roger de Berkeley of Dursley, and his daughter Helen married Roger's eldest son, another Roger. Alice brought with her the manor of Slimbridge, and Helen took the manor of Dursley to Roger de Berkeley. Dursley was to be held directly of the king and, in addition, Roger held Ozleworth, half of Newington and the lands of Bernard Capelli, for which he did no service to FitzHarding.[7] Although the arrangement solved the immediate strife, as late as 1278 FitzHarding's great-grandson Maurice (II) paid £200 to Henry de Berkeley, great-great-grandson of Robert and Helen, for a quitclaim of the lordship of Berkeley,[8] and the transfer caused other complications. For instance, the Berkeleys of Dursley had granted advowsons and lands in the Herness to Kingswood, Gloucester and Reading abbeys, resulting in disputes as late as 1224.[9]

Having acquired the large and valuable lordship, by whatever means, FitzHarding gave away a large proportion of it, either out of generosity or in the hope of securing supporters of his title to the estate. Besides his grants to St. Augustine's, he had a large family for which to provide. To his brother Elias he gave 2 hides of land in Combe and Huntingford, both within the later manor of Wotton under Edge.[10] To his second daughter Aldena or Alditha he granted the small sub-manor of Kingscote (also in Wotton) on her marriage to

---

[1] Smyth, i. 22–5, 30. 'Herness' means 'obedience, a jurisdiction, a district obedient to a single jurisdiction': *PNGlos* ii. 207. The chronicler Walter Map says that it was worth £500 a year: Smyth, iii. 3.

[2] Smyth, i. 35–6; *St Augustine's Cartulary*, pp. xiv–xxii. Almondsbury, Ashleworth, Horfield and Cromhall were, later, detached portions of the lordship of Berkeley.

[3] Below, p. 19; Smyth, i. 35–6, 39, 60, 66.

[4] One of their younger sons, Henry, was evidently born by the early 1130s: below, p. xxiii.

[5] Smyth, i. 42–4.

[6] Below, p. 281; Smyth, i. 3–5, 33, 55, 72–3. Maurice de Berkeley's eldest son Robert was not born until *c*. 1165.

[7] As recorded in the Red Book of the Exchequer, 1166: Smyth, i. 28.

[8] Smyth, i. 143; below, p. 3.

[9] Smyth, i. 33, 69; iii. 124; *Curia Regis Rolls* xi, nos. 698, 1006, 1392, 2870.

[10] Below, p. 352; Smyth, i. 16; iii. 147, 234–5. That in Combe, which had been purchased by FitzHarding, passed through a younger son of Elias whose descendants adopted the name of de Combe, and that in Huntingford passed to the Veel family by marriage to Maud, daughter and heir of Harding, Elias's eldest son. Maud's second cousin Robert (II), lord 1190–1220, granted to her and Geoffrey le Veel more lands in free marriage, including two assarts in Michaelwood Chase, which in 1205–6 the king confirmed: Smyth, iii. 37, 238.

Nigel FitzArthur of Clapton (Som.).[1] FitzHarding's third daughter Margaret married Odo FitzWilliam and was granted lands in Dursley parish to add to Odo's manor of Woodmancote in the same parish.[2]

FitzHarding had four younger sons, Robert, Nicholas, Henry and Thomas (see Pedigree 1). Henry and Thomas were clerks. Thomas became archdeacon of Worcester, and Henry (d. 1188) dean of Mortain in Normandy and archdeacon of Exeter, having been treasurer to Henry II as duke of Normandy.[3] He was also presented to all the churches of Berkeley Herness by the first abbot of St. Augustine's.[4] On Nicholas (d. 1189) his father settled the manors of Hill and Nympsfield from the Herness, and from outside it the manor of Tickenham and other manors and lands in Somerset.[5] Nicholas married Ala, said to be a daughter and coheir of Guy FitzTecius, who brought him another manor in Tickenham and other lands in Somerset, in Elmore (Glos.) and in Cambridgeshire.[6] His son and heir Roger died in 1230. Roger's son and heir Nicholas ('FitzRoger') married one Sibyl who was heir to the Gloucestershire manor of Elmore.[7] This family did not adopt a fixed surname until the 14th century when the long life of John FitzNichol (who succeeded his father in 1312 and died in 1375) prompted his grandson and heir Thomas to continue the use of FitzNichol.

Nicholas's brother Robert, usually called Robert de Weare, received more generous treatment from his father. FitzHarding granted to him the manors of Beverston, King's Weston and Elberton in Berkeley Herness, those of Over, Redwick and Northwick elsewhere in Gloucestershire, and in Somerset the manors of Weare and Pawlett, with the three hundreds.[8] Robert married, first, Hawise, the twice-widowed but still childless daughter and heir of Robert de Gurney, who brought him the Somerset manors of Barrow and Englishcombe. She had a daughter Eve but was dead by 1168.[9] By 1182 Robert had bought the wardship of his second wife, Avice, daughter of Robert de Gaunt and heir of her mother Alice Paynel.[10] Avice died in 1192 in the lifetime of her father, and in 1193–4 and 1194–5 Robert was paying 33 marks to have the lands of Alice Paynel.[11] Robert died in 1195 leaving as his heir his son by Avice, Maurice, usually called de Gaunt although he

---

[1] Smyth, i. 58, 65; iii. 251–2; Ellis; *CIM* i, no. 1291. In the 13th century the manor probably passed to a younger son, since it was held by a family who used the surname of Kingscote, while the manors of Clapton and Ashcombe (Som.) descended with another line surnamed Arthur: *CIM* i, no. 1291; *CIPM* iii, no. 371, pp. 248–9; v, no. 538, pp. 338–9; below, pp. 435, 525–6, 535.

[2] Odo's descendant, Thomas FitzOdo (d. 1274), left a son and heir aged nine (d.s.p.) whose heir was his sister Maud who married John Lord Botetourt (d. 1324). In 1288 Botetourt was holding a land of Cam manor at a rent of 13s. 4d. which was reduced to 6s. 8d. a year. Woodmancote passed from Botetourt to Robert de Swynburne (d. 1326). It was held by his widow at her death in 1341 and was then purchased from his grandson and heir Thomas by Thomas (III) Lord Berkeley: Ellis; *CIPM* ii, no. 56; vi, no. 693; Sanders, *English Baronies*, 11; *GEC* ii. 233–5; BCM SB 22 (cf. below, p. 560); *CFR* 1369–77, 365.

[3] Ellis; Smyth, i. 54–5.

[4] Smyth, i. 55; *St Augustine's Cartulary*, no. 68.

[5] Smyth, i. 45; below, 250.

[6] Smyth, i. 46, below, p. 442, A2/17/19 [SC 61], mentioning his son and heir Henry, who evidently died before his father.

[7] Smyth, i. 47. The Roger de Berkeley who in 1196–7 paid 60 marks to marry Hawise, widow of John de Somery and sister and heir of Gervase Paynel, was Roger de Berkeley of Dursley, not Roger FitzNicholas as Smyth assumes: *GEC* xii (1), 110; Smyth, i. 46. See also below, p. 293.

[8] Below, p. 535; Smyth, i. 50–1.

[9] Smyth, i. 52; Ellis.

[10] Smyth, i. 52; Sanders, *English Baronies*, 55.

[11] Ellis; Smyth, i. 52.

occurs once as Paynel.[1] Maurice was born *c.* 1186 and came of age in 1207, succeeding to half of the Paynel barony of Hooton Pagnell in Yorkshire and Lincolnshire as well as his father's lands.[2] He married, first, Maud, daughter and heir of Henry Doyly (d. 1232) of Hook Norton (Oxon.) and, secondly, Margaret, sister of William Earl Marshal and widow of Ralph de Somery (d. 1210), but he died without issue in 1230.[3] His half-sister Eve, usually called de Gurney as the heir of her mother Hawise de Gurney, seems to have been married three times, to Thomas de Tilly, Roger de Peauton and Thomas son of William FitzJohn of Harptree (Som.).[4] In 1213–14 she recovered the manor of Farrington (Som.) in dower against William FitzJohn but she died before her half-brother, leaving a son Robert, evidently by Thomas son of William FitzJohn, since he inherited the manors of Harptree and Farrington.[5] Robert de Gurney succeeded his uncle Maurice de Gaunt in 1230.[6] Robert married Hawise de Longchamp and is recorded as holding 21 fees in Somerset and Gloucester in 1262–3.[7] He was succeeded in 1270 by his son and heir Anselm de Gurney, who had two sons.[8] Anselm granted the manors of Englishcombe, Harptree and Farrington to the younger, Thomas, who took service with his cousin Thomas (II) Lord Berkeley, as did his son and grandson, the latter gaining notoriety as the regicide Thomas de Gurney.[9] Anselm's elder son John (d. 1290) left an only daughter Elizabeth, who married John Lord Ap Adam.[10]

Maurice (I) de Berkeley (1170–90)

FitzHarding's heir, his eldest son Maurice, inherited the manors of Portbury and Bedminster (Som.), Bray (Devon) and Acton (Glos.), and a much depleted Berkeley Herness. Shortly after his father's death, he obtained a confirmation from Henry II of the grant of Berkeley and in Oct. 1189, after the succession of Richard I, he obtained another confirmation for 1,000 marks.[11] He bought the manors of Foxcote, Purton, Hanham and 'Hampton' (Glos.), the two latter of which he then enfeoffed to tenants, and founded two hospitals within Berkeley Herness.[12] He died in June 1190 leaving Alice as his

[1] Ellis.

[2] Ibid.; *GEC* x. 320; Sanders, *English Baronies*, 55, says that Maurice came of age in 1205.

[3] Ellis; Smyth, i. 52; *GEC* x. 319–20, xii (1), 110; Sanders, *English Baronies*, 54, 113. Maud died without issue in the lifetime of her father in 1219. Maurice founded the hospital of St. Mark in Bristol, endowing it with the manor of Pawlett (Som.) and other land: *Cartulary of St. Mark's Hospital, Bristol*, ed. C. D. Ross (Bristol Record Society, xxi, 1959), pp. xii–xiii, xxvii.

[4] Ellis; Smyth, i. 52. Smyth assumed that she had a husband surnamed Gurney.

[5] Smyth, i. 52.

[6] Smyth, i. 52. The Paynel lands were inherited by Andrew Lutterel, a distant cousin of Maurice's mother Avice Paynel de Gaunt: Sanders, *English Baronies*, 55. Sanders calls this Gurney barony that of 'Beverston' (including the lordship's other manors of Elberton and King's Weston), possibly because there was a castle at Beverston which Maurice de Gaunt built or substantially repaired without royal licence, for which he was pardoned shortly before his death: Sanders, *English Baronies*, 14; Smyth, iii. 101. Robert inherited the two Gurney manors of Barrow and Englishcombe and the FitzJohn manors of Farrington and Harptree, as well as the eight manors granted by FitzHarding to his son Robert.

[7] Smyth, i. 53.

[8] Ibid.

[9] *CPR* 1338–40, 368. The regicide left four sons, Thomas, John, George and the well-known Matthew de Gurney (d. 1406), who all died without issue.

[10] Smyth, i. 53–4; *GEC* i. 179–81. It was from their son, Thomas ap Adam, that Thomas (III) Lord Berkeley and his brother bought back the manors of Beverston, King's Weston, Elberton and Over in 1330.

[11] Smyth, i. 64–5, 76.

[12] Ibid. 69, 77; below, pp. 429, 524. 'Hampton' may be Rockhampton.

widow.[1] She bought several holdings, some of which she granted to her younger sons, and 'lyved till extreame old age'.[2] They had six sons and a daughter but, mercifully, except for the necessary continuance of the line, they were not as prolific as Maurice's siblings. The daughter Maud was married to Elias (III) Giffard (d. 1190) and had two sons, the elder, Elias (IV) (d. 1248), being the father of John Lord Giffard of Brimpsfield (d. 1299). The younger, Osbert (d. 1237), was granted the reversion of the manor of Foxcote (Glos.) by his uncle Thomas (I) Lord Berkeley in 1227 and was the father of another Osbert, who was prominent in the troubles of Henry III's reign.[3]

The six sons were Robert and Thomas, successively lords of Berkeley, and Richard, Henry, Maurice and William.[4] Henry appears only as witnessing several family charters and presumably died without issue.[5] More is known of the remaining three, principally through grants of lands to them, many of them made under certain conditions and being early examples of entails. William, the youngest, was granted by his father half the manor of Gossington, in the Herness, and the manor of Portbury, but in 1195–6 he exchanged Portbury with his brother Robert (II) Lord Berkeley for the other half of Gossington.[6] The terms of the exchange were that if William died before his brother, without issue by his wife, the Gossington moiety would revert to Robert, and *vice versa* regarding Portbury. William was married but seems to have died without issue.[7] Maurice, the fifth son, was granted two holdings in Berkeley and Gossington by his uncle Roger Berkeley of Dursley and two more, in Hinton and Cam, by his father.[8] On his marriage, his brother Robert (II) granted the manor of Foxcote to him and his issue, the manor to revert to Robert and his heirs if there was no issue, and he died, without issue, before Robert.[9] The third son, Richard, appears only as witness to a couple of charters, but in 1220–1 a son of his was granted by Thomas (I) the land in Gossington which had reverted after the death of William, the grant being made to 'Robert son of Richard, my nephew,' on the condition that it would revert if Robert died without issue.[10] Robert witnessed several charters for his

---

[1] Smyth, i. 65.

[2] Ibid. 73–4; below, pp. 123, 225, 283, 439–40.

[3] Smyth, i. 76; *GEC* v 639, 649-53. Osbert had originally been granted the Devon manor of Bray but agreed to exchange it for Foxcote after the death of Robert's widow Lucy de Berkeley, who was holding in dower: below, p. 421.

[4] Their respective ages are indicated in a charter concerning St. Augustine's Abbey and Longbridge Priory (both family foundations) witnessed by all of them except Thomas, in the order Robert, Richard, Henry, Maurice and William: below, p. 565. Since Thomas succeeded Robert he was older than Richard, who was the only one of the six, other than Thomas, to have issue.

[5] Below, pp. 123, 180, 225, 283, 442, 439–40, 565. Smyth, i. 75, says that Henry and Richard went to Scotland with William the Lion when the Scottish king was released but that is highly unlikely.

[6] Below, p. 276; Smyth, i. 74; iii. 200–1.

[7] Smyth, i. 75, says nothing of any descendants, although elsewhere, iii. 201, he offers a descent which he describes as suspect. The reversion of Portbury to Robert (II), and Thomas (I)'s grant to his nephew of the land in Gossington which William had held, seem to be conclusive evidence that William died without issue: below, p. 276.

[8] Smyth, i. 74; below, p. 293.

[9] Smyth, i. 100; below, 525. Smyth, i. 74, says that Maurice had a son Thomas to whom he made over his lands in Hinton and Cam, and that Thomas died without issue at the end of Henry III's reign when the lands reverted to 'Thomas Lord Berkeley', but Maurice certainly died without issue (cf. Smyth, i. 100) before his brother Robert, for Foxcote was held in dower by Robert's widow Lucy and by his will he devised to St. Augustine's Abbey lands which he had bought in Cam and Foxcote, and which the abbey later granted to his brother Robert: below, pp. 421, 525; *GEC* v. 650 n.

[10] Below, pp. 246, 276, 550. This Robert fitz Richard was not the knight of the same name who granted lands to the church of St. Michael on Steep Holme before 1209 (below, pp. 523, 533–4) and left a daughter and heir Agacia who married John de Keu.

uncle Thomas and had three children: Sir Robert de Kingston (d.s.p. 1275), Alice and Letuaria.[1]

Robert (II) de Berkeley (1190–1220)

Robert, Maurice (I)'s eldest son, was brought up at the court of Henry II, testimony to his father's close relations with that monarch.[2] He paid a relief of £1,000, at £200 down and the rest at £80 a year, although in 1195–6 he was pardoned 500 marks for his good service in war, and he obtained confirmations of the grant of the lordship from Richard I in Sept. 1190 (two months after his father's death), again in Nov. 1198 after the 'loss' of the Great Seal, and a third in April 1199 from the new monarch John for 60 marks.[3] He founded the hospital of St. Katherine in Bristol and, having recovered Portbury from his brother in 1195–6, he acquired another large holding there by exchange for lands of equal quantity in the lordship at Woodford. He also bought more land in Somerset at Chatley and Tellisford.[4] In July 1204 he was granted Herbert de Moreville's half of Portbury manor (which was in the king's hands because Moreville was a Norman) to hold during the king's pleasure rendering the profits to the Exchequer.[5] He was constable of Bristol Castle between 1202 and 1204, a justice itinerant in 1208 and a witness in 1207–8 to royal charters, but soon afterwards he lost the royal favour and in 1211 his castle and lands were seized, to be restored only after a fine of 2,000 marks and a further 100 marks to have a fair trial by his peers for his life, a total debt of £1,400.[6] Although partially restored to royal favour, he joined the baronial revolt and during John's vigorous counter-attack Berkeley Castle was siezed and placed under a royal castellan by June 1216.[7]

In this dire crisis it seems that Robert's brother Thomas took steps to secure the inheritance to himself. Thomas was Robert's heir presumptive as after some years Robert's marriage to Juliana, daughter of Robert de Ponte de l'Arche and niece of William Marshal, earl of Pembroke, was still childless.[8] Thomas obtained the support of Pembroke by agreeing to marry another of his orphaned nieces, Joan, daughter of Ralph de Somery (d. 1210), and in return Pembroke was to arrange for the king to take Thomas's homage and restore to him his brother's barony and lands, to discharge him of a debt of 210 marks which Robert owed to the earl of Salisbury, to have Berkeley Castle delivered to him, and to arrange for him to 'be freed of' the king's justiciar (presumably Peter des Roches) and

---

[1] Below, pp. 37, 91, 160–1, 192, 277, 283. Sir Robert de Kingston also held land in Kingston, a hamlet within the manor of Slimbridge, and his lands were later acquired from Letuaria's son Robert de Dounton by John de Acton for his younger son Odo: below, p. 278. Part, at least, of Alice's portion was bought by Maurice (II) Lord Berkeley: below, p. 277.

[2] Smyth, i. 82.

[3] Below, p. 3; Smyth, i. 82–3. These fresh confirmations from successive monarchs are testimony to the relatively precarious tenure of the lordship in the early days.

[4] Below, pp. 522, 528, 532–3; Smyth, i. 74, 89, 100. This holding in Woodford was repurchased by Thomas (III) in 1329: Smyth, i. 326.

[5] The Berkeley portion of Portbury, and the new holding there, were held of the Morevilles: below, p. 528.

[6] The Pipe Roll for 1212–13 records the settlement with Robert and that he had repaid £250 already, now paid another £200 and was pardoned £50 by the king, leaving a debt remaining of £900. This £900 stayed on the books until 1218–19 when he agreed to repay it at £100 a year and was finally cleared in 1230–1: Smyth, i. 90–2; GEC ii. 126.

[7] Smyth, i. 91–2, 94–5.

[8] Ibid. 97–8. William de Ponte de l'Arche, probably Juliana's brother, witnessed charters of Robert and his brother Thomas (I): below, pp. 264, 421, 498, 521.

of William Briwerre.[1] In the event these arrangements were nullified as Robert was eventually pardoned and finally came to terms in Feb. 1217 and for a fine of 1,450 marks was restored to his lands but not to the Castle. Juliana died in Nov. 1217 and he immediately hurried into marriage with Lucy, said to be a niece of William Longespée, earl of Salisbury (illegitimate son of Henry II), but he died in May 1220, still childless. His haste may suggest nothing more than a natural desire for an heir of his own body, but it might also suggest that he had been offended by Thomas's actions in 1216–17. Certainly, he left Thomas with a heavy burden of debt and several other troublesome legacies of the civil war. Shortly after Robert's death Lucy married Hugh son of Hugh de Gurney, and she died in 1234, having held Bedminster, Wotton, Slimbridge and other manors in dower.[2]

Thomas (I) de Berkeley (1220–43)

Robert's brother Thomas had some difficulty in succeeding to the lordship. When the sheriff of Gloucestershire went to Berkeley Castle to take it into the king's hands on Robert's death, the earl of Salisbury, who had been granted custody of it, refused to hand it over without an express order by the king and council on the grounds that his niece Lucy was with child.[3] Thomas enlisted the aid of his wife's cousin, the earl of Pembroke, who wrote to the justiciar Hubert de Burgh asking for justice for Thomas, and on 9 Aug. 1220 Thomas did homage.[4] He did not have seisin of the Castle until 1224 and in the interim he was paying the wages of the royal keepers from his debts to the king.[5] The spectre of debt hung over Thomas for the rest of his life. In 1224 he came to an arrangement with the Exchequer to repay the debts of himself and his late brother at £80 a year,[6] and as well as the enormous sums remaining on the royal books from Robert's troubles, Lucy survived Robert for 14 years, holding her dower lands; the inflation of 1180–1220 can only have added to Thomas's problems. Nevertheless, before 1230 he recovered the three Somerset hundreds from his cousin Maurice de Gaunt.[7]

Thomas's entanglement with William Briwerre (d. 1226), which arose from his agreement to marry one of Briwerre's daughters, was resolved, probably in 1221, when Thomas granted to Briwerre the marriage of his son and heir Maurice, on condition that he would be married to the daughter of Richard FitzRoy and Rose of Dover. Richard was an illegitimate son of King John and Rose was the daughter and heir of Robert de Dover (d. 1205) and a granddaughter of Briwerre; she brought the barony of Chilham to FitzRoy.[8] It was also agreed that Briwerre would acquit Thomas of 200 marks which he owed to the king, and that Thomas would make over to Briwerre his manors of Portbury and Arlingham for a term of 15 years. On Briwerre's death, if not before, Rose of Dover took possession of the two manors and she was ejected from Arlingham in Dec. 1236, a proceeding which she disputed on technical grounds.[9]

Joan de Somery does not seem to have brought any lands to Thomas but she gave him six sons and two daughters, Margaret and Isabel. Isabel held land in the manor of Ham, and

---

[1] *Curia Regis Rolls*, xi, no. 50; *GEC* xii (1). 111. Thomas's marriage to Joan de Somery, usually regarded as having occurred in 1220, is said by Smyth, i. 117, to have been in 1217. Their son and heir was of sufficient age by 1221 to be the subject of a marriage agreement.

[2] Smyth, i. 96–8, 106, 108 n.; *GEC* ii. 126.

[3] Smyth, i. 106, 108 n.

[4] Ibid. 107, 108 n.; *GEC* ii. 126; xii (1), 111.

[5] Smyth, i. 107.

[6] Ibid. 107, 116, 126.

[7] Below, p. 521.

[8] Sanders, *English Baronies*, 111–12.

[9] *Curia Regis Rolls*, xvi, no. 148B.

died probably shortly before 1307, apparently unmarried.[1] Thomas gave to Margaret half the manor of Uley on her marriage with Sir John FitzMatthew (d. 1261), by whom she was the mother of Matthew FitzJohn (d.s.p. 1309) and Joan (d. 1295). That Joan married Walter (d.s.p. 1301), son and heir apparent of John Lord Beke (d. 1303).[2] Margaret married secondly Sir Anselm Basset (d. 1280) in 1265 and was still living in 1287.[3] Basset held land in Somerset and Gloucestershire, and bought lands in Cam and Uley from Margaret's brothers Richard and William.[4]

The younger sons of Thomas (I) were Thomas, Robert, Henry, William and Richard, of whom three died young and all died without legitimate issue. Thomas was granted the Devon manor of Bray, to him and his heirs, and lands at Symond's Hall in the lordship by his father, bought more lands in Symond's Hall from his cousin Elias de Combe, but died without issue between 1243 and 1247 when such lands as he had not granted to Kingswood Abbey reverted to his brother Maurice.[5] After Thomas's death, his brother Robert sued the abbey with seven suits in 1247–8 for lands in Berkeley and Symond's Hall as heir of his brother but was fined for making a false claim since he was not the eldest brother.[6] Nothing else is known of Robert and he presumably died without issue soon after. The fourth son, Henry, was granted lands within the lordship at Billow, Wotton and Cam by his father, and by his mother a messuage and virgate in Bradley, to him and his issue with reversion to his brother Richard and his issue.[7] He also died without issue. The remaining two sons, Richard and William, lived longer. Richard presumably inherited the Bradley holding on Henry's death and he acquired other lands within the lordship, in Nibley from his mother, and in Uley, Huntingford and Wick by purchase.[8] In 1268–9 he initiated a suit against a substantial free tenant of the lordship, Robert de Stone, for a half-virgate in Cam, and some time between 1265 and 1280 he granted a holding in Cam to his sister Margaret and Anselm Basset.[9] In 1271–2 he stood as surety for his brother William, and in March 1271 he witnessed a Berkshire charter of his uncle Sir Roger de Somery (d. 1273).[10] The date of his death and possible issue are unknown.

The last son, William, was granted a holding in Bradley and two holdings amounting to 2½ virgates in Cam by his father, and the manor house at Bradley and two other holdings there, in tail, by his mother, and in 1262 he acquired a large holding in Uley which he later

---

[1] Below, pp. 162, 172, 198–9, 400.

[2] Below, pp. 357–8; GEC iii. 182–4; Smyth, iii. 182–4, 186–8. Joan had her mother's manor of Uley which Walter Beke is recorded as holding of Thomas (II) Lord Berkeley in 1284–5. On her death without issue it reverted to her brother Matthew. Uley should have passed on Matthew's death in 1309 to Margaret's issue by Anselm Basset or to Thomas (II) de Berkeley, but in 1287 Matthew had granted the reversion of all his lands (including that of Uley) to the king and queen. Uley was granted to Walter de Gloucestre (d. 1311) and was bought from his son and heir by Maurice de Berkeley of Stoke Giffard.

[3] GEC iii. 182–4; Smyth, i. 121, does not record her first marriage.

[4] Smyth, iii. 132, 184.

[5] Below, pp. 297–8; Smyth, i. 117, 119, 123, iii. 316. In 1250–1 Maurice was impleaded by William de Foured for ½ hide in East Bray, a suit which was decided in Maurice's favour after a trial by battle: Smyth, i. 133. East Bray does not appear later in Berkeley hands.

[6] Smyth, i. 119. Given his mother Joan's predilection for granting lands to her younger sons, not only in tail but also with specific remainders, it is possible that these lands were under an entail which was violated by the grant to the abbey.

[7] Smyth, i. 119; iii. 81.

[8] Ibid. i. 120.

[9] Below, p. 354; Smyth, i. 121. His seal shows a shield of arms, the arms being a chevron with a label of five points.

[10] Smyth, i. 120; Cat. Anct. D. iii, D306.

sold to Anselm Basset and Margaret.[1] He followed his eldest brother into the king's service: he was with Henry III in Gascony in 1254–5 as a king's yeoman and by 1261 was a knight, in the interim receiving several marks of royal favour. In 1271–2, having caused a serious breach of the peace, he promised before the king to join the Hospitallers or Templars and leave the kingdom, a promise for which his brother Richard was one of the pledges.[2] By Oct. 1256 William had married Avice de Blackford, heir of four Devon manors and the widow of Robert de Blackford (d. 1253), by whom she had had a son John. In 1261 William alienated three of her manors to Ralph de Gorges, intending to deprive young John de Blackford of his inheritance. Avice and William were both dead by June 1272 when her son was acknowledged as her heir, and William seems to have had no legitimate issue.[3] His nephew, Thomas (II), was able to recover some of the lands which William had sold, on the grounds of the entails created by William's mother Joan.[4]

On the death of Thomas (I) in 1243 Berkeley and the Somerset lands (Portbury, Bedminster and the three hundreds) passed to his eldest son and heir, Maurice (II).[5] Thomas's widow Joan lived almost as long as Maurice; her dower was settled around 1246 and she had the manors of Wotton, Cam, Coaley, Hurst, Alkington and Hinton.[6] In 1247–8 her lands were valued at £200 a year which, if this was an underestimate as may be assumed, shows that the Berkeley estate was then worth over £600 a year.[7] She lived until 1276, surviving her husband by 33 years, but was active on her family's behalf, buying lands which she granted in tail to her younger sons Henry, Richard and William, obtaining grants of free warren in her dower manors of Cam and Wotton, and obtaining a grant of a market and fair at Wotton, in which manor she created a borough in 1253.[8]

Maurice (II) de Berkeley (1243–81)

Thomas (I) had conducted a relatively successful holding operation for the family, and his heir started the family's recovery through his close connection with Henry III, receiving several marks of royal favour.[9] Maurice was with the king for Christmas at Windsor and did his homage there on 24 Dec. 1243.[10] This favour may perhaps be attributed at least partly to Maurice's marriage to the king's niece Isabel.[11] According to Smyth, Maurice and Isabel were married and had issue by 1240. Isabel's marriage portion was the Essex manor of Great Wenden, which was worth around £45 a year, and in 1262 Maurice was granted free warren and a market and fair there.[12]

---

[1] Below, pp. 349, 358; Smyth, i. 120; iii. 109, 140, 181, 184.

[2] *CCR* 1253–4, 247; 1254–6, 396; 1256–9, 227; 1259–61, 308, 381, 401–2, 499; 1264–8, 515–16; *CPR* 1247–58, 330, 343, 395, 481, 503–4; 1258–66, 619; 1266–72, 298, 499; *CLibR* 1251–60, 349. Smyth, i. 120; iii. 173–7, incorrectly assigns this William's activities to William de Berkeley of Dursley, who was born in 1269 and died in 1300.

[3] Smyth, i. 120; *CIPM* i, nos. 262, 799. In 1290, during a law-suit initiated by Thomas (II) for the recovery of lands in Bradley granted by Joan to her son William under an entail, Sir William was said to have died without issue, and there is no mention of his heirs in the inquisition *post mortem* of 1272. He had a son Maurice de Camme who was presumably illegitimate but was granted some lands by his father and lived until 1301 or later: below, pp. 163–4, 182, 269, 347, 855.

[4] Smyth, iii. 109–10.

[5] Ibid. i. 122–3.

[6] Below, p. 13; Smyth, i. 117, 127.

[7] Smyth, i. 117, 122–3. A value of £212 12s. 11d. was given to the lordship in her late husband's inquisition *post mortem*.

[8] Below, pp. 13, 348–9, 354, 865; Smyth, i. 119; *CChR* 1226–57, 401.

[9] Smyth, i. 116, 126.

[10] Ibid. 126.

[11] Above, p. xxvii; *GEC* ii. 127; Smyth, i. 145–6.

[12] *CChR* 1257–1300, 43.

Maurice's association with the court culminated in March 1261 when he was retained to be of the king's household with a fee of 40 marks a year and the usual robes.[1] After the battle of Lewes in May 1264 Maurice suffered from his loyalty to the king by the loss of his lands, but Henry, although under the control of the victorious Montfortian council, continued to look after his niece.[2] After the battle of Evesham restored the *status quo* in Aug. 1265, payment of Maurice's annual fee was resumed in October and the livery of robes in May of the following year.[3] The royal favour seems to have continued when Edward I succeeded his father. Maurice's heir Thomas (II) took a crusading vow (adopting the ten crosses in his arms as a result), most probably at the parliament at Northampton in June 1268 along with the Lord Edward and numerous others.[4] In 1280 Maurice was granted free warren in his demesne lands of Berkeley Herness and Portbury, and he and his son Thomas were granted respectively four bucks and two bucks.[5]

Maurice's financial position was weakened by his mother's longevity and, although his wife's manor of Wenden extended the estate outside the counties of Gloucestershire and Somerset for the first time, he bought no new manors.[6] His efforts were concentrated instead on the small-scale development of his inherited manors, making small acquisitions and exchanges.[7] He was the first of the Berkeley lords to evince that manifestation of the 'high farming' of the period.

Maurice (II) had four sons, Thomas, Maurice, Robert and Simon, and a daughter Maud who 'lived long', bought land in Nibley and died without issue.[8] Maurice the son was active with his father in the troubles of 1264–5 but is reported to have been killed in a tournament in 1279, two years before his father's death.[9] Simon was destined for the church and was presented to Slimbridge church by his father in 1270 when he was still under-age.[10] In 1275 their father granted half the manor of Arlingham, a detached portion of Berkeley hundred, to Robert and Simon jointly. Simon was dead by 1281, when one William was parson of Slimbridge,[11] and Robert, and the cadet branch which he founded, retained the moiety of Arlingham. Robert married Elizabeth, probably a daughter of Sir John de Acton and Margaret, daughter and coheir of John de Aller, and seems to have had with her part of her

---

[1] *CCR* 1259–61, 392–3; *CPR* 1258–66, 147; *CLibR* 1260–7, 31, 60, 94.

[2] Two months after the battle the king restored Wenden to Isabel and in August granted her two Kent manors, for the sustenance of herself and her children: *CCR* 1261–4, 353–4, 390.

[3] Smyth, i. 139; *CCR* 1264–8, 193; *CLibR* 1260–7, 182.

[4] Smyth, i. 219. Thomas does not seem to have actually joined the crusade: B. Beebe, 'The English Baronage and the Crusade of 1270', *BIHR* xlviii (1975), 143–8.

[5] *CChR* 1257–1300, 233; *CCR* 1279–88, 25.

[6] In 1246 he arranged with the Exchequer to pay his debts at £40 a year, being pardoned £24 because of his recent service in Wales; in 1253 he again had to borrow money, 60 marks from the king, to equip himself for the campaign in Gascony, and was pardoned another 50 marks of his debts: *CChR* 1257–1300, 127, 133.

[7] For his similar activities in Wenden, see below, pp. 424–5.

[8] Below, pp. 353–4.

[9] Smyth, i. 147–8. Smyth says that Maurice was the eldest son, but circumstantial evidence points strongly to Thomas being the eldest: he was married in 1267 to the sister of Robert de Ferrers, earl of Derby, was holding the important manor of Bedminster by 1276, and was named after his grandfather, as was customary, while Maurice was named after his father (customary for the second son), was apparently unmarried and did not hold any of the family lands.

[10] *Reg. Giffard*, 44.

[11] PRO CP25/1/75/30 no. 20; Smyth, i. 150.

mother's inheritance in Somerset.[1] He had two sons, John and Robert, and died *c*. 1300.[2] John was in the wardship of his uncle Thomas (II) Lord Berkeley and died in 1320 leaving four daughters, Elizabeth, Felicia (or Leticia), Thomasia and Margaret. Thomasia had died without issue by 1332.[3] Elizabeth married James de Wilton and then Walter de Thornhill, in 1355 settling her lands on herself and Walter and their issue with reversion to James and Joan, her children by her former husband.[4] Leticia married John Westmancote, and Margaret married Richard de Aston, who died without issue, and then John atte Yate; the inheritance was divided between the Thornhills, Westmancotes and Yates.[5] Robert de Berkeley's younger son Robert had from his father holdings at Billow and Clingre in Cam, and he acquired other lands within the Herness and in Wiltshire.[6] He died in 1315–16, leaving a daughter Isabel, who married Hugh de Bisley, and a son and heir Thomas.[7] Thomas died between 1340 and 1343; his five year old son John was in the wardship of Thomas (III) Lord Berkeley and died in 1348, his heir being his sister Margaret, who married Ralph Trye.[8]

The first period of the estate's history was a quiet one. Mainly, it seems, because of the political background the lords' marriages before that of Maurice (II) brought no lands to the estate. Similarly, few lands were purchased and such new manors as were bought were often sub-enfeoffed. After the cadet branches descended from FitzHarding's sons Robert and Nicholas, no more were established until that descended from Maurice (II)'s son Robert of Arlingham. Younger sons, who were numerous but not prolific, were endowed with holdings from within the lordship, most of which reverted to the lordship on the childless deaths of the cadets, and some which had been granted to religious houses were repurchased by the lords. The lordship of Maurice (II) pointed to the future with the acquisition of lands outside Gloucestershire and Somerset through his wife, the beginning of an intense concentration on developing the potential of existing manors, and the dispersal of lands to cadet branches.

Second Period: *c*. 1280–1417

Until c. 1280 the shape of the Berkeley estate had changed little but thereafter it was composed of two elements, the original patrimony or core, around which the acquisition and dispersal of the other lands, the second element, ebbed and flowed. The patrimony, which remained with the family (with one major exception) throughout the period, lay in two blocks of land. The smaller consisted of the large manors of Portbury and Bedminster with the small hundreds of Portbury, Bedminster and Hartcliff, in the north-eastern corner of Somerset, immediately west and south of Bristol, and a quantity of rents from the city

---

[1] In Feb. 1289 Margaret de Acton settled a rent of 10*s.* and appurtenances in Blackford (Som.) on Robert and Elizabeth and their issue, with remainder to herself and her heirs. John, son and heir of Robert and Elizabeth, held quarter parts of the manors of Wanstrow and Stathe (Som.) which were part of the same inheritance: PRO CP25/1/197/12; *Somerset Fines, 1196–1307*, 265, 273–4.

[2] Smyth, iii. 59.

[3] *GIPM* v. 30; *CPR* 1330–4, 240.

[4] PRO CP25/1/199/24 no. 42, 77/66 no. 252; *Feud Aids* iv. 354, 359; *Somerset Fines, 1307–99*, 183; *CIPM* xiv, no. 10, p. 9; below, p. 97.

[5] *CPR* 1330–4, 240; *CIPM* xii, no. 116; xiv, no. 10, p. 9; Smyth, iii. 59; below, pp. 95–6.

[6] PRO SC6/1148/12; Smyth, i. 149; iii. 350; below, pp. 65, 81; *CCR* 1323–7, 98; *CIM* ii, nos. 277, 764.

[7] Smyth, i. 149; below, pp. 66, 476.

[8] BCM GAR 125–7 (cf. below, A1/24/136); Smyth, i. 149.

itself, which had been acquired by Robert FitzHarding before 1140.[1] The Bristol suburb of Redcliffe Street, on the southern bank of the Avon, had grown up on the land of Bedminster manor.[2] That block provided an income of *c.* £200 a year in the 14th century. The larger block was the lordship of Berkeley, which was far more important in terms both of income and of the status and influence it provided. Although FitzHarding had granted some manors, principally detached portions, to St. Augustine's Abbey and to members of his family, and although some lands continued to be held of the Berkeleys of Dursley, who held Dursley in chief, it was a source of extraordinary strength. It included two boroughs, Wotton-under-Edge and Berkeley, and by 1281 was divided, somewhat arbitrarily, into nine manors, Ham (the largest and closest to the castle, which included the previously distinct manor of Appleridge), Wotton under Edge, Symond's Hall, Cam, Coaley, Hinton, Hurst, Slimbridge and Alkington; each manor incorporated several vills and hamlets. The manors formed the hundred of Berkeley, which was held by the family, and the hundred was entirely contained within a five-mile radius of Berkeley Castle at its centre. In the 14th century the lordship, including the hundred, was worth *c.* £800 a year. During the Mortimer régime Thomas (III) de Berkeley obtained the privilege of return of writs, which enlarged the family's control within this compact and rich territorial unit.[3] Although, between them, the two portions of the patrimony may have provided as little as £800 a year in 1281, by 1321 the income from them had risen to around £975, and by 1389 it had risen still more to £1,050. The value which Thomas (III) placed on the core lands, as the patrimony, was marked when, *c.* 1349, he settled the lordship of Berkeley and the manor and hundred of Portbury on himself for life with remainder to his son and heir Maurice in tail male, so that the lands should not be alienated or partitioned between coheirs.[4] Bedminster had already been settled in jointure and tail general on the marriage of Maurice (III) in 1289 and was therefore detached from the rest of the patrimony in 1417 when, on the death of Thomas (IV), it passed to his daughter Elizabeth, countess of Warwick.

Thomas (II) (1281–1321) and Maurice (III) de Berkeley (1321–6)

Thomas (II) inherited from his father a good position in court circles, which he fostered and improved by years of faithful service to Edward I as a councillor, military commander and ambassador. On the king's death in 1307 Thomas was probably well over sixty and, although he continued to serve the new king for a few more years and lived on until 1321, it was his son and heir, Maurice, who increasingly took up the more active role. Maurice was given around half the inheritance by his father in 1301 when he was about thirty and started his career as a military commander in the Scottish campaigns of the end of Edward I's reign. From 1308 he was summoned to parliament along with his father, and he was appointed to a series of important positions, warden of Berwick-upon-Tweed 1315–16, justiciar of Wales 1316–17 and seneschal of Gascony in Feb. 1320 (an office which he appears not to have taken up). He was a leader of the rebels in the Despenser war of 1321 and, having succeeded his father in Nov. 1321, surrendered to the king in Feb. 1322 and spent the rest of his life imprisoned in Wallingford Castle. He died in May 1326, a few months before the coup led by Isabella and Mortimer. The period 1281–1321 was one of intense activity in the estate, the 'high farming' era which generated an astonishing number of charters that now survive in the archive. The wives of Thomas (II), Maurice (III) and

---

[1] *CIPM* ii, no. 407; PRO SC6/1148/2, 8. The rents from Bristol amounted to £6 14*s.*, during the forfeiture, £5 16*s.* 4*d.* between 1350 and 1356, and £6 12*s.* 6*d.* between 1361 and 1364: BCM GAR 417–18 (cf. below, p. 443).

[2] *CIPM* ii, no. 407; *GIPM* iv. 118 . Redcliffe Street provided £16 in rents in 1281.

[3] PRO SC8/157/7832.

[4] Below, pp. 4–5; *Somerset Fines, 1307–99*, 21; Smyth, i. 364; PRO C136/58 no.1; C135/199 no. 9.

Thomas (III) brought lands to their husbands which expanded their interests outside Gloucestershire and northern Somerset, but the lords themselves were actively engaged in developing and increasing the estate by purchase, both of small holdings within the patrimony manors and of new manors.

This very deliberate and positive policy of land acquisition began with the making of small additions whenever possible to the manors of the patrimony, sometimes as small as a fraction of a single acre. Major purchases with the same end in view were the acquisitions of the small manor of Bradley within the lordship manor of Wotton in 1292, the manor of Henry de Middleton at Portbury in 1299 and the manor of Frampton on Severn in 1303, which was immediately leased at a rent of £14 13*s*. 4*d*. to be paid to the lordship manor of Hurst.[1] Thomas also acquired holdings in Bradley and Arlingham through successful litigation in 1290.[2] His efforts were directed particularly at the acquisition of rents, however, and it is clear that he had a preference for that form of revenue. The process gradually grew in scale. After *c*. 1300 Thomas and Maurice began to expand their territorial ambitions and to acquire whole manors. During the 1310s Thomas bought substantial holdings at Leckhampton and Hartpury north of Berkeley hundred besides one called Planches within the lordship manor of Cam, and Maurice the manors of Upton St. Leonards and King's Weston (Glos.), and Kingston Seymour and Portishead, along with a number of smaller holdings at Winterhead, Barton, Winscombe, Ashton, Cheddar and Tickenham, in northern Somerset.[3] Each was concentrating principally on areas local to their separate households: Thomas, from Berkeley, on central and northern Gloucestershire and Maurice, from Portbury, on northern Somerset. Maurice's wife's lands in northern Somerset gave him an added interest in that area, and her other lands in Wiltshire gave him a secondary focus, resulting in the acquisition of another holding at her manor of Brigmerston.[4] The last major addition to the estate was the manor of Awre, opposite Berkeley on the other side of the Severn, with its appurtenant advowson and hundred of Bledisloe, which was acquired in two halves. The first was granted to Maurice by his lord Aymer de Valence in 1308, and the second was settled on Thomas (III) by Roger Mortimer in marriage with his daughter in 1319.[5] Thomas (II) also bought lands in the area to add to the manor in 1308 and 1317, and their acquisition seems to have prompted Maurice to buy another holding on the west bank of the Severn, at Beachley, in 1317–18.[6]

Other lands were acquired but held only temporarily. The manor of Sopworth (Wilts.), worth around £12 a year, was granted to Maurice (III), for life, by Aymer de Valence in 1308,[7] and the manors of King's Stanley (Glos.) and Great Rollright (Oxon.) were granted to Thomas and Maurice respectively in 1314 and 1316 by Edward II.[8] King's Stanley was the subject of a dispute with John Lord Giffard of Brimpsfield, to whom it had passed by 1316, and Great Rollright was also held only briefly. Maurice also leased for a term of years thirds of the manors of Olveston and Berwick in Henbury from Roger, son and heir of

---

[1] PRO CP25/1/75/36 no. 156; Smyth, i. 189; PRO CP25/1/75/39 no. 250, 40 no. 265; below, pp. 458–60.

[2] Smyth, i. 193, iii. 110; *Cal. Doc. Irel.* 1293–1301, 686 (where Wick is not Wick in Ireland, as implied); below, p. 92.

[3] BCM SB 10 f. 31; below, pp. 300, 475–6, 496–8, 525; PRO CP25/1/198/18 no. 46; *CPR* 1327–30, 269; *Rot. Parl.* ii. 399; Smyth, i. 274; *CIPM* viii, no. 678. The holdings at Winterhead, Barton and Winscombe were settled on Maurice, his wife Eve and their younger son Maurice.

[4] *Rot. Parl.* i. 396; PRO C137/23 no. 39.

[5] BCM GAR 255 (cf. below, A1/51/50); *CPR* 1327–30, 269; *Feud. Aids*, ii. 264, 273; *Genealogist*, NS xxxv (1919), 96.

[6] Below, pp. 431, 437, 457; Smyth, i. 327.

[7] BCM GAR 255, GAR 319 (cf. below, A1/51/50, A2/97/1).

[8] Below, pp. 487, 510; *Feud. Aids*, ii. 266; Smyth, i. 274; *CIPM* viii, no. 678.

the Berkeley retainer Sir Peter Crok (d. 1308 × 1316), which may have been worth c. £7 a year.[1]

Between 1270 and 1319 the estate benefited from the marriage portions of the wives of successive lords, the only time at which this was a factor since earlier marriages had been dictated by politics, and the landed portion was replaced by the cash portion during the 14th century. The manors of the marriage portions expanded the estate beyond the confines of Gloucestershire and northern Somerset for the first time, although these too were only temporary additions as they were used to endow younger sons. The first major addition of the kind had been Isabel Fitzroy's, which had not, as might have been expected, been used to provide for the younger son, Robert (of Arlingham). In 1267 Thomas had married Joan de Ferrers, sister of the Robert who was dispossessed of his earldom of Derby by the Lord Edward. By her he had four sons, Maurice (III), Thomas, John and James (who joined the church), and two daughters, Margaret and Isabel.[2] Joan died in 1309 and Thomas did not remarry.[3] She brought him the manors of Coston (Leics.) and Eynesbury (Hunts.).[4] In 1289 the heir Maurice (III) married Eve, daughter of Eudo de la Zouche and Milicent de Montalt, and she brought the manors of Brigmerston and Milston (Wilts.) and holdings at Edingworth and Milverton and a rent of £10 from Bridgwater (Som.).[5] The two Ferrers manors cannot be evaluated but the Zouche lands and rent were worth almost £50 a year.[6] Maurice and Eve had five sons, Thomas (III), Maurice and John, and Eudo and Peter who joined the church, and two daughters, Milicent and Isabel.[7] Eve died in 1314 and about three years later Maurice married Isabel, daughter of Gilbert de Clare, earl of Gloucester. She brought him a rent of £8 from Speenhamland (Berks.), the manors of Burford and Shipton-under-Wychwood (Oxon.), and the manor of Stanley Pontlarge and holdings at Falfield and Ampney Crucis (Glos.) but most of them were held by Isabel for life only and benefited Maurice only between the marriage and the forfeiture in 1322.[8] She survived him and lived until 1338.

Maurice was probably aged around nineteen when he married Eva la Zouche in 1289 and his father Thomas granted the manor of Bedminster to the couple.[9] In 1301 Thomas handed over another portion of the inheritance to his heir, granting him the other Somerset manor of Portbury, and around half the lordship in return for a rent of £120 and Maurice's obligation to pay annuities totalling £54 to his brothers and sister, to keep up payment of the annuities and maintenance agreements already promised to those who had sold land to Thomas, and

[1] PRO SC6/1145/15, 1147/12.

[2] Margaret married first Thomas FitzMaurice of Ireland, whose marriage her father had bought in 1284 and by whom she was the mother of the first earl of Desmond, and then Reginald Russell; Isabel became a nun: *CCR* 1279–88, 252, 264, 265, 300, 301, 365; *CFR* 1272–1307, 199, 208, 425–6; *CPR* 1307–13, 383; *VCH Som.* ii. 150; *GEC* iv. 234–7. James became bishop of Exeter after the murder of Bishop Stapledon during Queen Isabella's coup in 1326; James was elected on 5 Dec. 1326 but died on 21 or 24 June 1327.

[3] Smyth, i. 207.

[4] Ibid. 205–6; *CIPM* i, nos. 732, 776; ii, no. 423, pp. 297, 310.

[5] Below, pp. 538–9; PRO SC6/1148/15; Smyth, i. 244.

[6] *CCR* 1288–96, 46. The two Wilts. manors were worth £30 a year, and Milverton £7–8: below, p. 527.

[7] Milicent married John Lord Mautravers (d. 1364) *c.* 1314 and Isabel married Robert Lord Clifford (d. 1344) in 1328. Eudo died in his brother's household at Bradley in Aug. 1328 and Peter in 1341.

[8] *CIM* ii, no. 681, 950; *CFR* 1319–27, 96, 124, 175, 181; *CCR* 1323–7, 219; 1327–30, 46; *CIPM* v, no. 316; PRO CP40/269/41 dorse; *Feud. Aids*, ii. 270. The arrangements which Isabel's father made for his second marriage cut her out of the Clare inheritance.

[9] Smyth, i. 244.

other burdens on the estate such as rents to chantries.[1] From this time on, therefore, a large part of the estate was administered from the household which Maurice set up at Portbury. The division of the Berkeley patrimony into two blocks made a natural choice of lands for the adult heir: Bedminster manor was granted to Thomas (II) before he succeeded his father and to Maurice (III) and Maurice (IV) on their marriages.[2] When Maurice's eldest son and heir, Thomas (III), reached adulthood and married Margaret daughter of Roger Mortimer of Wigmore in 1319, his grandfather was still alive and the couple were established with the manor of Awre, both the Mortimer and Berkeley moieties being settled on them.[3]

Thomas (II) had two other lay sons to establish, Thomas and John, and Maurice (III) also two, Maurice and John. Both generations were dealt with in much the same way, the elder of each pair having his mother's marriage portion, with some additional lands within Gloucestershire which had been acquired, and the younger more haphazardly with lands which had been acquired. Thomas (II)'s sons also married heiresses. Thomas was granted Coston (Leics.) and Eynesbury (Hunts.) some time before 1300 and later, in the 1310s, the manor of Wick in Arlingham, a holding at Hartpury and a rent of 10 marks from the Arlingham fisheries (Glos.).[4] He married first Margery, daughter and heir of Sir Robert de Bray of Wollaston (Northants.), by whom he had a daughter Katherine, and secondly Isabel, daughter and heir of Sir John Hamelyn of Wymondham (Leics.).[5] He died in 1346 leaving Katherine to inherit Wollaston and a son John by his second wife who inherited Coston, Eynesbury, Wymondham and the lands in Gloucestershire.[6] This cadet branch in Leicestershire was still going strong in the 16th century. Thomas's brother John had an annuity of £20 before 1301 and was also granted a small manor at Bradley (in Wotton) and sundry other new small holdings around the hundred.[7] He married Hawise, daughter and heir of Thomas de Timworth (d. c. 1290) of Bratton Clovelly (Devon). In Nov. 1311 Bratton Clovelly was settled on Hawise's mother Lucy for life, with reversion to Hawise and her issue, along with the manor of Bradford-on-Tone and substantial holdings at Hoccombe near Milverton, which Lucy had acquired.[8] Two years later they were settled again on Lucy for life, with reversion to John de Berkeley and his wife Hawise and the issue of Hawise. Lucy had died by March 1316 when John was holding Bratton Clovelly, but both John and Hawise were dead without issue by Sept. 1317 when Kingswood Abbey drew up a charter promising religious benefits for their souls in recognition of their substantial grants of land to the abbey.[9]

In the next generation, Maurice (III)'s second son, Maurice of Stoke Gifffard, was granted the manor of Bradley (bought by his grandfather), before 1321, and the reversions of his mother's lands in Somerset and Wiltshire and of Kingston Seymour (bought by his

---

[1] Below, p. 14.

[2] In a similar fashion, Wotton, the secondary centre of the Berkeley block, was set aside for the use of widows, being held by Thomas (I)'s widow Joan in the mid 13th century, by Maurice (III)'s widow Isabel and by Thomas (III)'s widow Katherine in the 14th century. Maurice (IV)'s widow did not hold it because Katherine was still alive at Maurice (IV)'s death.

[3] *Genealogist*, NS xxxv (1919), 96; below, p. 432; PRO SC6/1148/12.

[4] Smyth, i. 209; below, pp. 92–3, 476; BCM SB 10 f. 351. The charter recording the grant of Coston and Eynesbury (SB 10 f. 351) is undated but was witnessed by Thomas (II)'s brother Sir Robert (d. 1300–1).

[5] *VCH Northants*. iv. 58; below, p. 93.

[6] *CIPM* viii, no. 630; below, p. 93.

[7] Below, pp. 14, 93; BCM GAR 256 (cf. below, A1/51/51); Smyth, i. 214.

[8] Below, p. 93; BCM SB 10 ff. 26–7; *Proc. Som. Arch. & Nat. Hist. Soc.* xxviii (1882), 174, 177, 178, 192–5, assumes incorrectly that the husband of Hawise de Timworth was John de Berkeley of Dursley. Lucy married secondly Simon de Meriet.

[9] Smyth, i. 215; iii. 317.

father), lands worth around £60 a year.[1] He bought three more manors in Gloucestershire, King's Weston and Elberton in 1330 and Uley by 1340.[2] He was retained by the king as a banneret in 1330 and received generous grants in fee of forfeited land, worth probably around £300 a year, but his son and heir was deprived of them when their earlier holders were restored to favour.[3] He married by 1330 Margery de Vere who was probably a daughter of Alphonse de Vere (d. 1328) and sister of John, who succeeded his uncle Robert as earl of Oxford in 1331.[4] They had three sons, Thomas, Maurice and Edward, and two daughters, Emma and Isabel. Isabel was still alive and apparently unmarried in 1400, and Emma married Thomas, son and heir apparent of Sir John de la Ryvere of Tormarton.[5] Maurice married Joan, daughter and heir of William Hereward of Devon, and had died by 1371 when Sir John de Wylington quitclaimed his interest in the wardship of Maurice's son and heir, another Maurice (IV).[6] The young heir had evidently died without issue by 1400.[7] The third son Edward married Joan, daughter and heir of Cecilia de Hickling of Suffolk but died without issue in 1380.[8] Maurice of Stoke Giffard's eldest son Thomas was thirteen at his father's death in 1347. He married Katherine, daughter of John de Botetourt, in 1355 and died in 1361 leaving a son Maurice, born in late 1358, as his heir.[9] This Maurice proved his age in 1380 and died in 1400, his heir being a posthumous son, another Maurice, who was coheir to the Botetourt inheritance in 1420.[10] Maurice (III)'s third son, John, had by 1322 been granted the manor of King's Weston and holdings at Leckhampton, Cam (*Planches*) and Awre and Blakeney (Glos.), which had been bought by his father and grandfather and were worth *c.* £30 a year.[11] He died, apparently without issue, in 1336.

Thomas (II) died in July 1321 and the estate was taken into the king's hands following his son's surrender in Feb. 1322. During the previous forty years the estate had been enlarged by the landed portions of their wives and the acquisition of several new manors and other holdings. Their territorial horizons had been expanded by marriage into Huntingdonshire, Leicestershire, Oxfordshire and Wiltshire, and by royal grant into Oxfordshire, although the purchasing policy was directed primarily at strengthening the patrimony and the immediately adjacent areas of Gloucestershire and north Somerset. All the lands brought as marriage portions, and most of those which had been purchased, had been granted to younger sons, but the manors of Awre, Portishead and Upton St. Leonards, worth *c.* £34 a year, and holdings at Ashton, Cheddar, Tickenham and Beachley, had been added to the inheritance of Thomas (III),[12] while the lands worth £30 a year granted to his younger brother reverted to him on John's death in 1336, having been granted in tail male. Most of

[1] Below, pp. 501, 540; PRO SC6/1148/12, 15; *CIM* ii, no. 919; Smyth, iii. 148.

[2] *CPR* 1327–30, 507; PRO CP25/1/77/57 no. 40, 65 no. 230; *Reg. Bransford*, 274; Smyth, iii. 186–8. The three manors were valued at almost £90 a year in 1400: *CIPM* xviii, no. 409.

[3] *CMR* nos. 2270 (iii), 2271 (i); *CPR* 1327–30, 530, 1330–4, 145.

[4] *CPL* ii. 368.

[5] *GIPM* vi. 224; PRO CP25/1/77/66 no. 267. Sir John was succeeded by his son Henry: Saul *Knights and Esquires*, 228.

[6] Below, p. 574.

[7] *GIPM* vi. 224.

[8] *CFR* 1337–47, 417; *CCR* 1349–54, 421; 1369–74, 340; *CPR* 1374–7, 437; *CIPM* xv, no. 310.

[9] *CPR* 1354–8, 257; *CCR* 1360–4, 226, 235, 237; *CFR* 1356–68, 198; *CIPM* xi, no. 10; Smyth, i. 257.

[10] *CCR* 1377–81, 288–9; 1419–22, 87; 1422–9, 39; *CFR* 1399–1405, 81; 1405–13, 79; *CPR* 1399–1401, 431–2; Smyth, i. 259.

[11] Below, pp. 169, 300, 498; BCM GAR 122 (cf. below, A1/24/131); PRO SC12/36/11 m. 8; SC6/1147/12, 1148/12.

[12] PRO SC6/1148/12; BCM GMR 17 (cf. below, A4/2/28).

the two lords' efforts, however, had been directed at making the numerous small additions to the manors of the patrimony, and the greatly increased value of those manors was Thomas (III)'s main benefit from the careers of his father and grandfather.

Thomas (III) (1326–61) and Maurice (IV) de Berkeley (1361–8)

The estate was officially restored to Maurice's heir, Thomas (III), in Jan. 1327. His relationship with Mortimer thrust the family to the forefront of national politics, especially with the imprisonment and death of Edward II at Berkeley Castle in 1327, and ensured that the family received a number of benefits during Mortimer's régime. When, in 1330, the political tide turned Thomas faced a parliamentary trial for the death of Edward III's father. He was finally cleared in 1337 but spent the 1330s under a cloud. He was restored to royal favour in the 1340s and briefly took up a prominent position again, before relapsing into obscurity in old age, devoting himself to domestic pursuits and the acquisition of land. His marriage with Margaret Mortimer brought him three sons, Maurice (IV), Thomas and Roger, and a daughter Joan.[1] Margaret died in 1337 and ten years later Thomas married again, to Katherine, daughter of Sir John de Clevedon and widow of Sir Peter le Veel, who gave him another four sons, another Thomas, another Maurice, Edmund and John. Despite this plethora of younger sons, only one, the youngest, survived Thomas.

Like his grandfather, Maurice (IV) enjoyed most of his active career before becoming lord. Born probably around 1320, in 1338 he was married to Elizabeth, daughter of the younger Despenser, and by her had three sons, Thomas (IV), Maurice and James, and three daughters. Elizabeth survived him and remarried, to the Somerset knight Sir Maurice Wyth, dying in 1389. In the early 1340s Maurice had been crusading in Spain, and was then retained before 1347 by the Black Prince, whom he accompanied on the Poitiers campaign of 1355–7. He was wounded and captured at Poitiers and, after three years in captivity in France, was eventually released in 1360, having paid around half his ransom of £2,000 and made arrangements to pay the remainder. His wound appears to have made him an invalid for the rest of his life and he cut no figure in either national or local politics while lord. His early death in 1368 can probably be attributed to the same cause, and his heir was the sixteen-year-old Thomas.

The forty years between 1280 and 1320 had been notable for the unusual quantity of land purchased (by no means all of which had been earmarked for younger sons, provision for whom was most often the reason for magnates to buy land), but Thomas (III) far exceeded his father and grandfather in this respect. Purchase was, however, the only means by which the estate was changed permanently, since marriage portions by then were paid in cash rather than in land (although Thomas's second wife did bring with her a large quantity of land which she held for life). Thomas's stepmother was still alive when he was restored to the estate in 1327, so he did not immediately hold the entire inheritance. She held the manor and hundred of Portbury (and the manor of Kingston Seymour settled on Thomas's brother) in jointure and was granted as dower the manor and borough of Wotton, the manor of Symond's Hall and rents of £63 from Cam and Coaley and £23 6s. 8d. from Bedminster.[2] In 1329 she released Portbury manor and hundred to Thomas (presumably in return for an annuity) and died in 1338.[3]

---

[1] Joan was married in 1337 to Thomas, son and heir of John de Haudlo (d. 1347) and Maud Burnell, and secondly, following the death of her young husband, to Reginald (later Lord) Cobham in 1342.

[2] *CIM* ii, no. 919; Smyth, i. 245; below, p. 14; BCM GAR 424 (cf. below, A4/2/8).

[3] Smyth, i. 245. She was still alive in June 1337 despite the assertion in *VCH Berks*. iv. 100 that she died on 7 July 1333: below, p. 458.

To a certain extent Thomas followed his grandfather's practice of acquiring small holdings to add to his existing manors. Some additions were more substantial, such as the sub-manor of Sages, worth £17 a year, within Slimbridge manor,[1] but to a far greater extent he concentrated on acquiring whole manors. He bought 14 new manors, in possession or reversion, and had a temporary interest (mostly through leases for life or for a term of years) in seven other manors. In 1330 he made his first major purchase, the manors of Beverston and Over (Glos.) and Barrow Gurney and a large holding at Tickenham (Som.), from Thomas ap Adam, and in 1332 the reversion of the manor of Syde (which fell in in 1339), also in Gloucestershire.[2] In 1339 he bought a moiety of Elston (Wilts.), and between 1342 and 1346 the manors of Woodmancote (Glos.), Clevelode (Worcs.) and a moiety of Cheddar (Som.) with the reversion of the other moiety.[3] In 1355 he acquired another six manors, buying those of Tockington (Glos.) and a moiety of Sock Dennis (Som.) with the reversion of the other moiety[4] and arranging a complicated marriage agreement with Sir Ralph de Middleney whereby the reversion of Middleney's inheritance of four manors and other associated holdings in Somerset was settled on Thomas's younger sons after his death.[5] All these 14 manors, with other holdings purchased by Thomas at Cricklade (Wilts.), 1350, Tickenham (Som.), 1330 and 1352, and Falfield, by 1337, Compton Greenfield, by 1340, Westonbirt, by 1344, Bentham, by 1346, Down Hatherley, by 1346, and Alveston (Glos.), were eventually inherited by Thomas's only surviving younger son, John.[6] John also had some lands which had been held by his uncle John and which had reverted to his father in 1336. Those which were most closely associated with the patrimony (in Cam and in Awre) were kept for Thomas's heir, but King's Weston and Leckhampton were included in the numerous entails made by Thomas for his younger sons.[7] The lands which passed to John were worth an absolute minimum of £300 a year.

Those fourteen manors and other smaller holdings were permanent acquisitions inherited by Thomas's sons Maurice or John, but Thomas also obtained a temporary interest in the Herefordshire manor of Burghill between 1327 and 1336,[8] and the Wiltshire manor of Sheldon between 1351 and 1363.[9] Furthermore, in 1347 his second wife brought him another nine manors which she held in jointure and dower from her first husband: Charfield, Tortworth, Hamfallow and Huntingford (Glos.), Ablington and Alton (Wilts.), Norton Fitzwarren (Soms.), Plympton (Devon) and 'Lariharn'. These were worth at least

---

[1] BCM GAR 247 (cf. below, A1/43/125).

[2] Below, pp. 148, 514; PRO CP25/1/77/62, no. 16, /69 no.347; Glos Record Office D1866/T18, T19; *Somerset Fines, 1307–99*, 238.

[3] *Wilts. Fines, 1327–77*, no. 199, below, pp. 338, 541; BCM GAR 30 (cf. below, A1/3/132); PRO CP25/1/199/24 no. 61; C135/156 no.12. For Woodmancote, *CPR 1340–3*, 443; BCM GAR 125 (cf. below, A1/24134); Smyth, i. 349; iii. 387–8, giving two conflicting accounts.

[4] Smyth, i. 330; J. Maclean, 'The Manor of Tockington', *TBGAS* xii (1887–8), 135–6; *GIPM* v. 309; below, p. 532.

[5] *Somerset Fines, 1347–99*, 28–9; *CIPM* xi, no. 517; PRO C136/38 no. 10; C139/35 no. 50.

[6] PRO C136/38 no. 10; C139/35 no. 50; CP25/1/77/56 no. 12, /67 no. 295; *Wilts. Fines, 1327–77*, no. 380; below, pp. 338, 458, 477, 488, 499, 533; Smyth, i. 328, 330, 350, *CCR 1360–4*, 236. Apart from the reference by Smyth there is no evidence that Alveston was held by Thomas (III), but it was held by John at his death.

[7] PRO C136/38 no. 10; C139/35 no. 50; CP25/1/77/66 no. 268, /69 no. 330; below, pp. 301, 477–8, 488, 499.

[8] Below, pp. 504–6.

[9] Below, pp. 542–3; and see discussion below.

£70 a year,[1] and they benefited Thomas until his death in 1361 but were eventually inherited by the heirs of Katherine's first husband.[2] The Veel connection also led Thomas to have an interest in the manor of Penleigh (Wilts.), which in 1350 was acquired by Thomas and Katherine jointly, with the reversion belonging to Katherine's children by Peter le Veel.[3]

Thomas's land dealings also involved some sales. The block purchase from ap Adam in 1330 had included the reversion of the manor of Monewden (Suff.), held for life by Isabel Hastings, and two years later Thomas sold it to Isabel.[4] In 1320 Thomas had bought a small holding at Childrey (Berks.) and acquired another reversionary holding there, which he sold to Nicholas de la Beche in 1338,[5] and in 1354 he sold the reversionary interest which he had acquired in the manor of Yewdon (Bucks.) to Thomas Doyly.[6] Finally there were the manors of Eastham and Eckington (Worcs.).[7] Eckington had been acquired from the Mortimers by 1333 but was sold in 1358, the timing suggesting strongly that it was parted with in order to help with the payment of Maurice (IV)'s ransom. In Eastham Thomas seems to have acquired an interest from one of his servants, Richard le Porter, in 1341 and supplemented it with rents in the area acquired from another servant, Roger de Eastham. The manor did not continue in Berkeley hands: it may have been sold like Eckington, the various interests may have been for life only, or the manor may have been given up to resolve a disputed title which also concerned Clevelode (which did stay in Berkeley hands).

As well as ensuring by settlements and entails tha the vast bulk of his acquisitions benefited his numerous younger sons, Thomas also had the patrimony to protect and his eldest son Maurice to establish. When in 1338 Maurice and Elizabeth were married, Thomas settled on them in jointure the lordship manor of Hurst (with its appurtenant rent from Frampton and a rent from the lordship manor of Cam), entailing it on their heirs male.[8] In 1349 Thomas settled the remaining portion of the lordship (8 manors, 2 boroughs, 2 advowsons, the castle and the hundred) and the manor of Upton St. Leonards, and in 1352 the manor and hundred of Portbury, on himself for life with reversion to Maurice and his male issue.[9] Before his death the entire estate had been entailed in tail male except for a few small holdings, and Bedminster and Awre (settled in tail general in 1289 and 1319 respectively). The year before his marriage Maurice was granted the Bristol block of the patrimony (Portbury, Bedminster and their hundreds), initially at an annual rent of 400 marks, which was gradually reduced and then given up altogether.[10] In 1342 he was granted the manor of Wenden and the £10 rent from Bridgwater and 10 years later the small holding

[1] Smyth, i. 346; iii. 210–12, 234–40, *Wilts. IPM*, 151; *CIPM* viii, no. 466; xvi, nos. 214–15; BCM GAR 126–34, GAR 422 (cf. below, A1/24/135–43, A3/16/1), GMR 3. Charfield, Tortworth, Ablington, Alton, Plympton and Hamfallow were together valued at about £70: *GIPM* v. 300–1; PRO C136/38 no. 10; BCM GAR 126–34. There are no available valuations for Huntingford, Norton Fitzwarren or 'Lariharn'.

[2] PRO C136/38 no. 10.

[3] *VCH Wilts.* viii. 159; *Wilts. Fines, 1327–77*, no. 376.

[4] Below, p. 539; *CPR 1327–30*, 507; *CCR 1330–3*, 424, 529.

[5] Below, p. 419; BCM SR 39 (cf. below, A4/2/7); *CMR* no. 872; *CCR 1337–9*, 522.

[6] *VCH Bucks.* iii. 49; below, p. 420.

[7] *VCH Worcs.* iv. 70, 187, 267; PRO CP25/1/260/23 no. 51; below, p. 545; BCM GAR 398–400 (cf. below, A2/98/6, A2/99/1–2).

[8] PRO C135/199 no. 9; C136/58 no. 1.

[9] Below, pp. 4–5.

[10] Smyth, i. 364, 365; cf. below, p. 529. Thomas (III) was holding Bedminster again 1356–60: BCM GAR 361 (cf. below, A2/67/24).

at Christon and Uphill close to his manor of Portbury.[1] After succeeding his father, he bought the reversion of the manors of Little Marshfield and Purton (Glos.) in 1366, and Little Marshfield was settled on his younger son James in tail male, Purton probably being intended for another son, who died young.[2] Maurice needed to buy lands for his younger sons since nearly all the lands inherited from his father were entailed.[3] In addition to the lands granted to him before he succeeded, he inherited holdings at Chicklade (Wilts.) and a manor at Yorkley (Glos.).[4] Thomas had created that manor by a number of small acquisitions along the west bank of the Severn, south of Awre, between 1330 and 1350.[5] Maurice also benefited from the additions to the patrimony manors made by his father and from the holdings in Cam and Awre which had reverted to Thomas on the death of his younger brother John in 1336. He never enjoyed the full benefit of his inheritance because his stepmother outlived him by several years and held in dower the manors of Cam, Wotton and Symond's Hall, the borough of Wotton and a third of the hundreds of Bedminster and Berkeley, in addition to jointure in the most valuable of her husband's acquisitions, the reversion belonging to her son John.[6]

The period from the restoration in 1327 to the death of Maurice (IV) in 1368 is notable not only for the huge additions made to the estate (manors and lands worth well over £300 a year, around a third of the value of the patrimony inherited by Thomas in 1327) but that they had all been achieved by purchase. Marriage had brought Thomas substantial lands but they were temporary interests only. His heir benefited little, but the manor at Yorkley and the small holdings at St. Chloe, Uphill and Chicklade passed to him and he added the manor at Purton, having also acquired Little Marshfield for his younger son.

Thomas (IV) de Berkeley (1368–1417)

Until the death of Maurice (IV) the family had benefited from a succession of adult heirs, most of the lords being over thirty when they inherited, but the estate was now in wardship for six years. Thomas's father-in-law, Warin Lord Lisle (d. 1382), obtained the wardship, which ended in Jan. 1374, but for some time after reaching his majority Thomas was further handicapped by the longevity of two dowagers, his mother and step-grandmother, who held over half his inheritance until their respective deaths in 1389 and 1385. Aged fourteen, he had married the seven-year-old Margaret, Lisle's only daughter, in 1367, and in 1381 she became her father's heir. In 1385 she produced her only child, a daughter Elizabeth, who was betrothed to Richard Beauchamp, son and heir of the earl of Warwick (d. 1401), six months after her mother's death in 1392. Being outside the court circle, Thomas suffered from Richard II's policy of bolstering the local positions of his favourites, and was an enthusiastic supporter of Bolingbroke's invasion in 1399. He was actively involved in the deposition of Richard II and for the next seven or eight years he played a prominent role on the national stage as councillor and admiral for Henry IV. After 1406, however, he retired into relative obscurity. He did not remarry after Margaret's death and on his own death in

---

[1] Smyth, i. 364, 365, 371; PRO C136/58 no. 1; C138/28 no. 50.

[2] Below, p. 481.

[3] The manor of Wenden (Essex), the manor of Yorkley (then known as Tutnalls and Purton), a holding in Iron Acton and Sages in Slimbridge (Glos.), and the rent from Bridgwater and the holding at Christon and Uphill (Som.) were the only unentailed lands available to Thomas (IV) when he wanted to raise cash through a mortgage in 1375: below, p. 482.

[4] Below, p. 485; BCM GAR 320, GMR 17 (cf. below, A2/37/19, A4/2/28); PRO C135/199 no. 9; C136/58 no. 1; Wilts. Fines, 1327–77, no. 379.

[5] Below, pp. 432, 471–3, 503; BCM GAR 326 (cf. below, A1/2/13); PRO C135/199 no. 9.

[6] PRO C136/38 no. 10. By April 1363 she had recovered against her son John (aged eleven) her dower of Syde manor and in holdings in Westonbirt, Down Hatherley, Leckhampton and Bentham: below, pp. 14, 488.

1417 the estate was divided between his daughter, who had the Lisle lands and some of the Berkeley lands, and his nephew James, who inherited the bulk of the Berkeley patrimony under the entail of the mid 14th century.

During the fifty-year lordship of Thomas (IV) purchase again played an important part in the development of the estate but the most significant change was the accession of the Lisle estate in 1382. During Maurice (IV)'s lordship the Berkeley estate had been divided by the assignment of dower to his father's widow and further division followed his death in 1368 since he too left a widow, Elizabeth. Elizabeth was granted Wenden (Essex), two-thirds of Portbury and Portishead and Uphill (Som.), the small holding at Chicklade (Wilts.), and the manors of Coaley, Upton and Awre, and the small holding at St. Chloe (Glos.) in dower, and already held Hurst (with a rent from Cam) in jointure.[1] Katherine's dower was worth £285 a year and Elizabeth's jointure and dower a further £335 a year, leaving lands worth £540 a year for the 16-year-old heir Thomas (IV).[2] The wardship of his lands was granted to his father-in-law for £400 a year.[3]

That Thomas felt purse-pinched in early adulthood is seen in his mortgage of the unentailed lands in 1375 to raise 400 marks and in an agreement with his step-grandmother Katherine in Jan. 1375 to cut and sell timber from the manor of Wotton.[4] His situation improved with the fortuitous death of his brother-in-law Gerard, Lisle's only son and heir, without issue between Jan. 1380 and Nov. 1381, when Lisle and Thomas came to an agreement by which Lisle allowed his daughter to inherit his estate.[5] Lisle died the following year and his estate, worth c. £600 a year, was duly joined to the Berkeleys'.[6] The Lisle estate consisted of numerous manors and other holdings scattered all over the south of England, but lying principally in two groups, the smaller one of seven manors in Devon and Cornwall, the larger based on seven Berkshire manors with four in Wiltshire, three in Oxfordshire, three in Northamptonshire and one each in Buckinghamshire and Middlesex.[7] His wife's inheritance widened Thomas's territorial horizons. Like his own, it did not all come to him immediately, since about half was held in dower and jointure by Lisle's widow Joan (d. 1392), and a further two manors in jointure by Gerard's widow Amy, but during the next 10 years his position gradually improved following the deaths of the various widows.

Not surprisingly, Thomas had bought no new lands before the various groups of dower lands came into his hands, although he did acquire temporarily two Gloucestershire manors and a borough from the widow of one of his late retainers in 1383.[8] Land-buying was largely a matter for consideration when lords had surplus cash in hand and Thomas had none to spare, certainly until 1382 and more probably until 1389 or 1392. Thereafter he held two inheritances and it would not have been surprising if he had then merely sat back to enjoy the profits: his wife died in 1392 leaving an only daughter, and there were no younger sons, provision for whom was the prime motive for land acquisition. It is all the more interesting, therefore, that Thomas did purchase a number of manors and lands after 1392. Some of them were connected with the Lisle inheritance, such as a large holding in Kingston Lisle, Fawler, Baulking and Uffington (Berks.), which he bought in 1397 and two years later leased at £5 a year, the manor of East Peek (Devon) and a moiety of Nethercott (Wilts.) bought in 1413, and a holding in Charlton, in Hungerford (Berks.) in

---

[1] PRO C136/58 no. 1.
[2] BCM GMR 17 (cf. below, A4/2/28).
[3] *CFR* 1356–69, 388.
[4] Below, p. 343.
[5] Below, p. 656; *GEC* viii. 39.
[6] PRO SC12/18/42 dorse.
[7] Below, pp. 575 sqq.
[8] BCM SR 67, GMR 17 (cf. below, A4/2/14, 28); *CPR* 1381–5, 228.

1414.[1] Other acquisitions were clearly connected with the Berkeley inheritance and included lands in Bancombe, in Charlton (Som.) in 1383, the Edingworth and Milverton holdings of his second cousin Maurice of Stoke Giffard before 1395, and a couple of advowsons, Chicklade in 1380 and St. Andrews, London (the parish in which most of his London holdings lay), in 1394.[2] In 1398 he acquired the reversion of the St. Amand manor of South Cerney and Cerney Wick (Glos.), and in 1399 holdings at Wraxall and Weston-in-Gordano in Portbury hundred (Som.);[3] and then in 1412 a holding at Horton and Yate (Glos.), another holding within Portbury hundred at Portishead and the manor of Cerney Wick (Glos.), in 1414 the manor of Shorncote (Wilts.) and in 1415 the manor of Tickenham, in Portbury hundred (Som.)[4] There were also acquisitions within Berkeley hundred, a number in Wotton manor in the vills of Bradley, Nibley and Wortley, two holdings in Arlingham, one in Ham, several in the boroughs of Wotton and Berkeley, as well as others elsewhere.[5] Most of those lands lay in three clear territorial areas, Portbury hundred, Berkeley hundred, and on the Gloucestershire–Wiltshire border. The focus on Portbury hundred is emphasised in his further acquiring the advowsons of Portishead and Walton-in-Gordano in 1412, and free warren in Walton- and Weston-in-Gordano, Portishead and Charlton in 1401, which can be compared with his obtaining a confirmation of the grant of free warren in Berkeley Herness and Portbury in 1413.[6] It therefore appears that the purchases of lands and rights were carefully chosen to suit the portion of the inheritance settled in tail male (Berkeley lordship and Portbury) and thus for the benefit of his nephew James. Thomas enfeoffed all these latter acquisitions (Shorncote, Chicklade and those in Gloucestershire, Somerset and London) to a group of trustees three weeks before his death and, although no instructions for their disposal are included in the grant, it was probably for the purpose of leaving them to James, through either an entail or a use.[7] Despite the enfeoffment, the jury at Thomas's inquisition *post mortem* returned that the lands were all held in fee simple and they were the subject of a long dispute with Thomas's daughter Elizabeth and her husband the earl of Warwick.[8]

The sale of Wenden in 1404 partly balanced Thomas's acquisitions. It was the only principal manor which had not been entailed, either in fee tail or tail male, and so the only one available when he needed to raise cash in a rush in order to loan £1,000 to the king. Although it had been part of the estate for 150 years it had long been the one anomaly in an otherwise concentrated estate, and its distance from the administrative centre had already led to its being farmed by 1389.

At Thomas (IV)'s death in 1417 the Berkeley estate, after following a pattern of recurrent growth and diminution over the previous 140 years, had reached a pinnacle. As well as the Berkeley patrimony itself, hugely increased in value since 1281, and a few other manors in Gloucestershire added to it, Thomas had held the Lisle estate and had bought a further four manors with numerous other small holdings. On his death, however, it broke apart. To his

---

[1] Below, pp. 590–1, 625, 629, 631–2, 634. Thomas also acquired a weekly market and three annual fairs at Penzance (where the Lisle manor of Alverton lay) in 1406: *CChR 1341–1417*, 430.

[2] Below, pp. 522, 524, 527, 530; BCM SB 10 f. 239 and v.

[3] Below, pp. 425, 451, 524, 536.

[4] Below, pp. 452, 544; PRO CP25/1/79/85 no. 57; *Somerset Fines, 1399–1461*, 47, CCR 1409–13, 334.

[5] PRO CP25/1/79/85 no. 46; Smyth, iii. 59, 61, 112, 213, 287; below, pp. 126, 192, 258, 305, 310–11, 314–16, 342, 348, 396. For Thomas (IV)'s purchases in general, Smyth, ii. 13–16.

[6] *CChR1341–1417*, 416; CCR 1409–13, 334; below, pp. 15, 519, 534.

[7] Below, p. 530. No instructions for their employment are mentioned in his will, which had been made in Feb. 1415.

[8] PRO C138/28 no. 50.

daughter went lands worth *c*. £725 a year, comprising the Lisle lands (£600 a year) and the manors of Awre and Bedminster with their hundreds (£125 a year). To his nephew went an estate worth *c*. £1,000 a year consisting of the lordship of Berkeley (with the manor of Upton) worth £825 a year, and Portbury manor and hundred worth £130 a year. In addition to the lands which he had from his uncle, James had his father's manor of Little Marshfield and the prospect of his mother's inheritance in Wales and the Marches. If the Berkeley inheritance had passed to him peacefully after his uncle's death, and if he had inherited all his mother's lands, James would have held land of greater value than any of his predecessors had done on succeeding their fathers.

Third Period: 1417–92

James (I) de Berkeley (1417–63)

James was the son of Thomas (IV)'s younger brother James who had married a Marcher heiress and died in 1405 fighting the Welsh under Glendower. He was eleven in 1405 and heir apparent to the substantial inheritance of his mother, Elizabeth Bluet: the two minor Marcher lordships of Raglan and Stradewy, and the manors of Thruxton (Herefs.) and Daglingworth (Glos.). Elizabeth was also the prospective heir on the death of Adam de Peasenhall to the ap Rees lands of the lordship of Talgarth and the manor of Shifnal (Salop.).[1] Her inheritance was worth at least 400 marks a year but in the event James inherited very little of it.[2] In 1408 Elizabeth and her third husband, Thomas ap Harry, sold Thruxton to Thomas's elder brother John, and in the following year, Peasenhall having granted them Talgarth, they settled the manor and 50 marks of rent on themselves and their issue with remainder to the right heirs of Elizabeth. They evidently had no issue, however, as, after her fourth marriage to William ap Thomas, Talgarth was resettled in 1420. In Aug. 1429 the lordship was granted to James de Berkeley and his heirs but that may have been part of a deal with ap Thomas, for in July 1425 James and his wife Isabel granted Raglan to ap Thomas for life and in 1430 ap Thomas bought Raglan outright for 1,000 marks, which seems to have included Stradewy. James also failed to get Shifnal, which was regarded as an escheat, the reversion being sold by Henry IV. James therefore inherited from his mother only Talgarth and Daglingworth.

James may have sold Raglan and Stradewy in order to fund his fight to retain his Berkeley inheritance against his cousin Elizabeth and her husband Richard earl of Warwick. There can be little doubt that Elizabeth's father Thomas fully recognized and approved his nephew as his heir male, despite allegations to the contrary. James and his brother Maurice were in their uncle's care at Berkeley from 1410 and Thomas twice sold James's marriage, specifically as his heir male, in 1410 to John St. John and in 1414 to Humphrey Stafford, and in 1412 St. John requested an exemplification of the entail of 1349 of the Berkeley estate.[3] Furthermore, Thomas's very specific policy of acquiring land centred on Berkeley and Portbury hundreds and his granting of all the lands which he had acquired to feoffees three weeks before his death strongly suggest that he was not only happy for the patrimony to pass to James but also intended to enhance it. James's troubles arose from the attempts of the Warwicks to claim as much of it as they could. An early attempt to claim the whole lordship of Berkeley on the grounds of a fee tail settlement in the time of Robert FitzHarding seems to have been dropped quickly.[4] They were rather more persistent and successful with two other ploys, first a claim to the manors of Wotton, Symond's Hall,

---

[1] For what follows, below, pp. 657 sqq.

[2] Below, A1/1/46 [GC 4129].

[3] Below, pp. 5, 563. According to Smyth, citing a manuscript of *c*. 17 Hen. VI (1438–9), Thomas twice sold the marriage of James, once for 1,000 marks and once for 1,200 marks: Smyth, ii. 79–80.

[4] Below, pp. 9–10.

Hinton, Cam and Coaley, on the grounds that they had been settled in tail general on the marriage of Maurice (II) Lord Berkeley to Isabel Fitzroy in the mid 13th century, and, secondly, claims to portions of some manors which they maintained had not been included in the 1349 entail, such as the rents from Iron Acton, which had been paid to Ham manor for over a century, and Sages, in Slimbridge, which had been bought by Thomas III in the mid 14th century.[1]

The Warwicks' determination was apparent immediately after Thomas (IV)'s death, which occurred when they were in Gloucestershire, staying either at the Castle or at Wotton, while James was in Dorset with his father-in-law Humphrey Stafford.[2] Thomas died on 13 July and James sued out a writ of *diem clausit extremum* two days later, but on 21 July the custody of the lands was granted to three of Warwick's retainers.[3] The inquisition *post mortem* at Gloucester at the end of September was adjourned because the evidence was disputed. On 22 Oct. Warwick sued out a *supersedeas* countermanding James's writ, and after some legal manoeuvring Warwick's writ was countermanded on 5 Nov., another inquisition was held and the jury found that James was heir, as Thomas's male heir, to the entailed lands and the countess was heir to the rest. James did fealty and had his homage respected on 1 Dec. but, handicapped by the desertion of some of his uncle's closest servants to the Warwicks, he was unable to sue livery, pay his relief and have proper possession until, on 1 Nov. 1420, he obtained the support of the duke of Gloucester by promising him the reversion of lands of his mother's inheritance to the value of 400 marks a year.[4] Recognition courts at all the lordship manors were held on 6 May 1421,[5] and James had licence to sue livery at Michaelmas 1421 and paid his relief of 100 marks. His belated succession was recognised by his first appearance on the Gloucestershire commissions of the peace on 2 Sept. and his first summons to parliament on 20 Oct.

On 1 Sept. 1422 James took the precaution of granting the Castle and the manors of Berkeley, Ham, Appleridge, Hinton, Hurst, Slimbridge, Cam, Coaley, Alkington, Upton St. Leonards, Wotton and Symond's Hall to a powerful group of feoffees consisting of Humphrey duke of Gloucester, John Mowbray, duke of Norfolk, John Holand, earl of Huntingdon, Thomas Stanley, Robert Wingfield and John Morgan.[6] The countess of Warwick died on 28 Dec. 1422, but the dispute continued. On 10 Sept. 1421 James and Warwick agreed, under bonds of 10,000 marks each, to submit the dispute to the arbitration (which was not to include the manors of Wotton, Portbury, Cerney and Shorncote) of the bishop of Worcester and the justice John Juyn, provided that the award was made before Christmas. The date was not met, and on 20 May 1423 they again entered into bonds for arbitration before midsummer, yet again for an award by 1 Nov., and once more for a partial award which was made on 24 Nov. 1424, with the promise of a final award before the following Michaelmas. That award, made on 6 Oct. 1425, declared that Warwick would hold for his life the manors of Wotton, Symond's Hall and Coaley and holdings in Frampton on Severn, Cromhall, Iron Acton, Kingscote and Minchinhampton (Glos.) and the

---

[1] The rent of 22 marks from Frampton on Severn which was paid to Hurst manor had specifically been mentioned in the 1338 settlement on Maurice (IV) and his wife.

[2] For what follows see, unless otherwise stated, Smyth, ii. 41–8, 57–76.

[3] The render was remitted on 12 June 1418: Smyth, ii. 41. A court was held at Alkington in the name of the Warwicks on 21 Sept. 1418: BCM GCR 1 (cf. below, A1/3/163). For the grant of the custody of Thomas's lands to John Harewell, John Barton and John Baysham on 21 July 1417: below, p. 562.

[4] Below, p. 10.

[5] BCM GRR 7 (cf. below, A4/2/30).

[6] Below, p. 6. The dukedom of Norfolk was in fact not revived until 1425.

hundreds of Hartcliff and Portbury and the manor of Portishead, Limeridge Wood, Weston-in-Gordano and lands in Christon and Uphill (Som.), while James would retain, to him and his male issue, the manors of Cam, Hinton and Slimbridge (Glos.).[1]

There the matter rested until the death of Warwick on 30 April 1439. His inquisition *post mortem*, held on 6 Sept., reopened the dispute by finding that he died holding, by the courtesy of England, the manors of Hinton, Cam, Coaley, Wotton and Symond's Hall, as Elizabeth's inheritance by entail from Maurice (II) (d. 1281) and his wife Isabel, and the manor of Slimbridge, as her inheritance from Maurice (I) (d. 1190) and his wife Alice, the manor having been granted to them in free marriage by her father. The findings were clearly faulty: James had retained possession of Cam, Hinton and Slimbridge and, under the award of 1425, Warwick had had only a life interest in Wotton, Symond's Hall, Coaley and the other lands. The countess Elizabeth's heirs were her three daughters, Margaret (d. 1467) wife of John Talbot, later earl of Shrewsbury (d. 1453), Eleanor (d. 1467) wife successively of Thomas, Lord Roos (d. 1430), Edmund Beaufort, duke of Somerset (d. 1455), and Walter Rokesley, and Elizabeth (d. 1480), wife of George Nevill, Lord Latimer (d. 1469). The dispute continued between James and the three sisters, the Talbots taking the lead. Margaret was Talbot's second wife and her heir was her son John, Talbot's fourth son, created Lord Lisle in 1444 and Viscount Lisle in 1451, who died with his father in 1453. After that, Margaret was fighting on behalf of her grandson Thomas Talbot (k. 1470).

James took possession of Wotton, Symond's Hall and Coaley after Warwick's death and held them peaceably for three years, but was dispossessed by the countess of Shrewsbury (John Talbot having been created earl of Shrewsbury on 20 May 1442), the three coheirs bringing an assize of novel disseisin against James for Cam, Hinton and Slimbridge, and James one against them for Wotton and Coaley. An unusual document illustrating the local effect of these disputes records that on 24 Feb. certain tenants of Coaley manor acknowledged that, having returned to James and paid their rents to him the previous Christmas, they would thereafter be true tenants to him and his heirs.[2] An arbitration of 5 April 1448 awarded Wotton, Symond's Hall and Coaley and all the other disputed lands mentioned in the arbitration of 1425 (except the 22 marks in Frampton on Severn and £10 rent from Sages in Slimbridge) to the three coheirs, and to James and his male issue Cam, Hinton, Slimbridge, Hurst and Portbury. The award was reaffirmed in July 1449, but James refused to give his assent. The dispute grew increasingly violent during the 1440s and culminated in 1451 when, having suborned some Berkeley servants, Lisle was let into Berkeley Castle, captured James and his sons and forced them to enter into bonds to abide by the latest award, i.e. that the coheirs would have Wotton, Symond's Hall and Coaley, and Berkeley hundred, and James would have Berkeley, Ham, Appleridge, Alkington, Hinton, Hurst, Slimbridge, Cam, Upton St. Leonards, the 22 marks rent in Frampton on Severn and Portbury.[3] Meanwhile, the countess of Shrewsbury had captured James's wife Isabel and imprisoned her in Gloucester Castle, where she died in Sept. 1452. James's sons James and Thomas accompanied Talbot to France in 1453 where at Chatillon in July Thomas was captured, and James killed, along with Talbot himself and his son John Lord Lisle.

James's marriage to Stafford's daughter was short-lived and childless. In 1423–4 James married Isabel, daughter of Thomas Mowbray, duke of Norfolk (d. 1399). She was the widow of Henry de Ferrers (d. by 1423), son and heir apparent of William Lord Ferrers of Groby (d. 1445), by whom she had an only daughter Elizabeth. Elizabeth married Sir Edward Grey (d. 1457), a younger son of Reginald Lord Grey of Ruthin: Edward became Lord Ferrers of Groby in her right and was a feoffee for James and William de Berkeley in

---

[1] Smyth, ii. 48; below, p. 10.
[2] Below, p. 176.
[3] Below, p. 11.

1447.[1] Their elder son John, Isabel's grandson, was killed at St. Albans in 1455 (his widow infamously marrying Edward IV), and their younger son Edward married Elizabeth, sister and heir of Thomas Talbot, Viscount Lisle (k. 1470), and was himself created Lord Lisle in 1475 and Viscount in 1483.

Isabel Mowbray brought to James the manors of Aspley, Alspath and Flecknoe (Warws.), which her brother had granted to her and Ferrers on their marriage in July 1416, and Marks and Buttsbury (Essex), which she had held in jointure with Ferrers.[2] She gave James four sons, William, James, Maurice and Thomas. Her elder brother Thomas was executed in 1405 but their brother John succeeded to the vast inheritance in 1413 and was restored to the dukedom in 1425, died in 1432 and was succeeded by his son John (VI) (d. 1461). Isabel's puissant brother John does not seem to have become involved in the dispute between the Berkeleys and the Warwicks and may have been handicapped by the fact that his wife Katherine was George Nevill's sister. After Isabel's death James married Joan Talbot, daughter of the first earl of Shrewsbury, reaching agreement with her brother the second earl in July 1457 that the earl would give 100 marks with his sister and redeem one bond of £1,000 from James to the king, and that James would make a jointure for Joan in £120 of land.[3] Joan survived James and married secondly Edmund Hungerford.

Talgarth and Daglingworth, along with a moiety of the manor of Brokenborough (Glos.), which James and Isabel had purchased, were settled on their younger sons in 1434–5, one moiety of Talgarth on James, the other moiety on Maurice, and Daglingworth and Brokenborough on Thomas, being available for the purpose because not held in tail male like the Berkeley patrimony. After James was killed at Chatillon in 1453 the manors were transferred between different sets of feoffees in a way that is confusing, but it is clear that the settlement of 1434–5 was not strictly adhered to: Daglingworth was included in settlements on the eldest son William and his wife in the 1470s, and Brokenborough was granted to Maurice and his wife Isabel. Little Marshfield was at some time granted to the youngest son Thomas but was also held by his brother Maurice by 1461. Maurice had married Isabel, daughter of Philip Mead, and after the death of her brother Richard and his children c. 1488 she inherited various lands in Gloucestershire and in Bedminster, Wraxall, Ashton and Tickenham (Som.). On William's death in 1492 Maurice was his heir, although he inherited very little in the first instance. Thomas, who was under nineteen when captured at Chatillon, was granted by his father the lands held in fee simple (presumably purchased) in Gloucestershire, some of which lay in Berkeley, Dursley and Hinton, and on 13 Dec. 1482 his brother William granted him an annuity of £19 for life.[4] On 18 March 1454 Humphrey duke of Buckingham appointed him receiver general of his lands in Gloucestershire, Wiltshire and Hampshire, at £5 a year with 2s. for each day spent travelling on his business. Thomas married Margaret, daughter and heir of Richard Guy of Minsterworth, by whom he had four sons and three daughters, and died in 1484.

James and Isabel also had three daughters.[5] Elizabeth, who had a portion of £200, married Thomas Burdet of Warwickshire, shortly before Nov. 1448. Isabel married William Trye of Hardwicke (Glos.) and in Aug. 1476 her brother William granted to the Tryes the rent of 40s. which they owed for the holding called Inwood in Cam until her portion of £200 be paid.[6] The third daughter, Alice, married Richard Arthur of Clapton (Som.).

---

[1] Below, p. 531.

[2] *GEC* v. 357–8.

[3] Below, pp. 562–3.

[4] Smyth, ii. 83–4.

[5] Ibid. 90–3.

[6] Trye was descended from Ralph Trye who married Margaret, granddaughter and eventually heir of Robert de Berkeley of Billow; cf. above, p. xxxi.

William Lord Berkeley (1463–92)

William was born *c.* 1426 and when aged thirteen joined the household of Henry Beaufort, bishop of Winchester, with whom he went to Calais in 1438–9. On 15 May 1440 his father granted the manor of Portbury to him and Nicholas Poyntz for a term of 40 years, and in 1447 William granted his estate in the manor to John Mowbray, duke of Norfolk (his cousin), Edward Grey (his brother-in-law), James Ormond and others.[1] Relations between William and his cousin Norfolk were evidently close: in 1448 Norfolk granted to William all his lands in Ireland to hold for life at a rent of a rose a year, and in Jan. 1453 appointed him supervisor of Gower and steward of Chepstow for life, with the customary fees and an additional annual rent of £20.[2] In sharp contrast, William seems not to have been on good terms with his father: on 20 Aug. 1460 they reached an agreement under ten headings, beginning 'First that the said Sir William should not henceforth greeve, vex nor trouble the said lord James his father, nor any of his servants, counsellors or tenants of any of his Lordship's manors in Gloucestershire, by lawe nor otherwise.'[3]

One of William's first acts on succeeding his father was to agree with James's widow Joan that she would receive an annuity of £100 in lieu of her dower and jointure but he soon renewed the dispute with Margaret countess of Shrewsbury, petitioning for the restoration of Wotton, Symond's Hall, Coaley, and the New Leaze and Sages in Slimbridge, and recounting the Talbots' assault on the castle in 1451 and its consequences. A flurry of bills and replies ensued, in one of which William accused the countess of having hired a man to kill him when he came to London to sue out his livery. Before the case came to issue, the countess died in June 1468 leaving her grandson Thomas Talbot, Viscount Lisle, as her heir to the manors of Wotton, Symond's Hall, a moiety of Arlingham, and various lands and rents in Arlingham, Cromhall, Alkington, Hurst, Dursley, Nibley, Sharncliffe, Kingscote, a sixth part of Iron Acton, lands in Horwood, Murcott and Gloucester, the manor of Wick in Arlingham, Sages Place and Sages Land in Slimbridge, and the 'hundred' of Wotton (formerly the hundred of Berkeley). Those lands had been allotted to Margaret in a division of the lands between the coheirs in Nov. 1466, her sister the duchess Eleanor having the manors of Coaley and Portishead, and her sister Elizabeth Nevill having Limeridge Wood in Portbury. Thomas Talbot's mother Joan, daughter and coheir of Thomas Cheddar,[4] died in the same year as his grandmother and, as he was then only nineteen, the two inheritances were granted to William Herbert, earl of Pembroke, the father of Thomas's wife Margaret. Thomas sued his livery on 14 July 1469 and had possession of his lands, which were valued at 1,873 marks 12*s.* 3*d.* (or £1,249 5*s.* 7*d.*), but on 20 March 1470 he and his followers met William, his brothers Maurice and Thomas, and their supporters in the skirmish at Nibley Green, where Thomas Talbot was killed. His widow Margaret brought an action against William for the death of her husband, and, on petitions by both parties, an agreement was reached in parliament on 6 Oct. 1472 that William and his heirs should have the manors of Wotton, Symond's Hall and the other Berkeley lands which Talbot had inherited from his grandmother, paying to the viscountess £100 a year for her life. Shortly afterwards she married Henry Bodrugan and she quietly received the annuity for many years. Talbot's heirs were his sisters Margaret and Elizabeth, and when Margaret died without issue in 1475 Elizabeth became sole heir: days after her sister's death, her husband Edward Grey was created Lord Lisle on 14 March 1475. Grey was William's nephew, being the son of William's half-sister, but he immediately renewed the dispute. An

---

[1] Below, p. 531.
[2] Below, p. 567; Smyth, ii. 138.
[3] Smyth, ii. 75–6.
[4] *GEC* viii. 57.

agreement was made on 25 Feb. 1482 that Wotton and Symond's Hall, a rent of 34*s.* 4*d.* in Nibley and Sharncliffe, a sixth of Iron Acton, New Leaze, the Warth and Sages in Slimbridge, Westmancotes in Arlingham, etc., should be settled on William and his male issue, William to give Edward and Elizabeth an annuity of £20 during the life of the Viscountess Margaret and after her death £100, but the agreement does not seem to have been enforced.

William's first known wife was Elizabeth, daughter of Reginald West, Lord de la Warr (d. 1450) by Margaret (d. 1433), daughter and heir of Robert Thorley.[1] Smyth says that they were married in 1466, but since William was then forty or more and Elizabeth at least 33, and since their childless marriage ended in divorce in 1467, they were probably married much earlier. William then married Joan Strangeways, daughter of Katherine duchess of Norfolk by her second husband Thomas Strangeways. Joan was the widow of Sir William Willoughby to whom she was married by July 1461 when her half-brother, John duke of Norfolk, granted them the reversion of six Yorkshire manors held for life by Katherine, for their lives. Willoughby had died by Aug. 1468 and in the November following she married William Lord Berkeley.[2] In June 1475 her nephew, John duke of Norfolk, granted to William and Joan the six Yorkshire manors, for the life of Joan, and his estate officials were instructed to accept them as occupiers. By Willoughby she had had two sons, Edward and Richard, and two daughters, Cecilia and Anne, and William was very generous to these stepchildren. In May 1480 he arranged with Richard Beauchamp, Lord St. Amand, for Anne Willoughby to marry Beauchamp's son and heir Sir John, and granted the couple his manor of Arlingham (Glos.) for their lives.[3] He also seems to have been involved in the mariage of Cecilia Willoughby to Edward Dudley, who succeeded his grandfather John Sutton, Lord Dudley, in 1487, for in Dec. 1480 William and Joan entered into an indenture to pay Edward 500 marks.[4] Edward Willoughby frequently acted as a feoffee for William, and William settled several manors from the Mowbray inheritance on Edward and Richard.[5] Joan gave William a son Thomas in 1470 and a daughter Katherine in 1474. Thomas was made a Knight of the Bath on 18 April 1475 (on the same occasion as the king's eldest son was made prince of Wales and his younger son duke of Norfolk), and in June contracts were made for his marriage to Mary, daughter of William Herbert, earl of Pembroke. In the same year the manor of Cam was settled on Katherine, but both Thomas and Katherine died shortly afterwards. Joan died in Feb. 1484 and in the summer of 1486 William married Anne, daughter of John Fiennes, Lord Dacre, but they had no issue. She outlived him, later married Sir Thomas Brandon and died in Sept. 1497.

William remained on close terms with his cousin John duke of Norfolk, and in 1467 John made a grant of timber at Haynes (Beds.) to William's creditors to void William's bond to them of 1,000 marks. William was named as John's coheir apparent in the grant, although John, while childless, was then only 23. John died in Jan. 1476, leaving an only daughter Anne, aged three. Edward IV moved immediately to secure the inheritance for his younger son Richard (born Aug. 1473) and on 28 May William Berkeley made over his title to the lands that he might inherit if Anne Mowbray died to Richard and his issue and the king, in

---

[1] Smyth, ii. 138–9.

[2] In Aug. 1468, as Willoughby's widow, Joan was granted an annuity of 100 marks from the tunnage and poundage of London: *CPR* 1467–77, 107.

[3] Below, p. 95.

[4] Below, p. 564.

[5] The reversion of Cherry Hinton (Cambs.) after the death of the duchess Elizabeth, Caludon (Warws.) in July 1488, and Kennett and Kentford (Cambs.) in Feb. 1488. Kennett and Kentford reverted to Henry Lord Berkeley in 1559–60 on the failure of the male issue of Edward and Richard Willoughby.

exchange for a release from his bonds to the Talbots.[1] Anne Mowbray died in Nov. 1481 but in Jan. 1483 an Act of Parliament vested the Norfolk inheritance in Richard for life, his heirs and the king's heirs, and Berkeley, who had been created Viscount Berkeley in April 1481, confirmed his renunciation of the inheritance.[2] The king's death in April 1483 nullified the agreement. Soon after Richard III's accession Berkeley was created earl of Nottingham[3] and the Mowbray inheritance was at last divided between the coheirs, Howard and Berkeley,[4] but in March 1484 Berkeley made an agreement with Richard and settled on the king a large proportion of the inheritance.[5] Again, the agreement was nullified by Richard's death at Bosworth on 22 Aug. 1485 and with Henry VII's accession William Berkeley again started with a clean sheet, being created Earl Marshal on 19 Feb. 1486.[6] According to Smyth, he had disapproved of the marriage contracted by his brother and heir presumptive, Maurice, and therefore determined to disinherit him. From Feb. 1486 he began to alienate his inheritance in good earnest, and this time included the lordship of Berkeley itself. In Feb. 1486 he granted to Sir William Stanley his portion of Bromfield and Yale[7], in the following August he settled the reversion of six Berkeley manors on Thomas Grey, marquess of Dorset, and in Feb. 1488 he settled those and another on the king, adding another three in June 1488. Also settled on the king were Gower and numerous other Mowbray manors (all those in Bedfordshire, Huntingdonshire, Leicestershire, Derbyshire, Hertfordshire and Cambridgeshire, the Brotherton manors in Susssex, and another ten in Surrey, Essex and Warwickshire). The Yorkshire and Lincolnshire lands, the manors in Buckinghamshire, and five other manors in Essex, Warwickshire, Sussex and Surrey were settled on Thomas Stanley, earl of Derby, two manors in Shropshire and Worcestershire on Humphrey Coningsby, three in Middlesex and Bedfordshire on Reginald Bray (including two also settled on the king), and four in Cambridgeshire and Warwickshire on his Willoughby stepsons (including two also settled on the king). That comprised his whole inheritance from the Mowbrays except for his eighth portion of Lewes which passed to his brother Maurice, despite an attempt to settle it on the king in 1490.[8] On 28 Jan. 1489 he was created marquess of Berkeley,[9] a title which he enjoyed for three years before his death in Feb. 1492. His brother Maurice, although 56 when William died, tackled the situation with vigour, and within seven years had recovered around fifty of the seventy Mowbray manors in England by challenging the legality of the alienations. Berkeley remained lost to the family, however, until the failure of the male issue of Henry VII with the death of Edward VI in 1553 restored it to Maurice's great-grandson Henry, born posthumously in 1534.

THE BERKELEY CASTLE MUNIMENTS

The catalogue relates to the medieval portion of the muniments in Berkeley Castle and includes all estate and administrative documents of a date up to the death of William marquess of Berkeley in 1492. Inevitably, the cut-off results in some artificiality in that the catalogue includes the medieval documents pertaining to estates which came to the

---

[1] Below, p. 685.
[2] Below, pp. 566–7, 685.
[3] Below, p. 567.
[4] For the division of the inheritance, below, pp. 678–9.
[5] Below, p. 685.
[6] Howard had been created duke of Norfolk and Earl Marshal in 1483 but had been killed at Bosworth and attainted.
[7] Below, p. 707.
[8] *VCH Suss.* vii. 5.
[9] Below, p. 567.

Berkeleys after that date while excluding the post-1492 documents belonging to estates which came to them earlier.[1]

The principal events after 1492 by which documents in the catalogue are presumed to have arrived in the Castle are the inheritance *c*. 1500 of lands from the Breouse family of Tetbury by Maurice Berkeley, the marriage in 1587 of Frances, daughter of Henry Lord Berkeley (d. 1613), to George Shirley, the marriage in 1596 of Sir Thomas Berkeley (d. 1611), Henry's son and heir apparent, to Elizabeth, only child of George Carey Lord Hunsdon (d. 1603), and the marriage in 1614 of Thomas and Elizabeth's son George Lord Berkeley (d. 1658) to Elizabeth, daughter and coheir of Sir Michael Stanhope of Sudbourne (d. 1621). The most significant purchase after 1492 which affects the archive is that of the bulk of the Blount inheritance in Gloucestershire in 1519–20.

The Berkeley family, through various vicissitudes, have remained in possession of the Castle from 1553 until the present day and as a consequence the Castle now contains one of the largest collections of medieval documents in private hands in the country. The catalogue describes some 5,500 documents, chiefly deeds, although there are several manorial account rolls (mostly for the manors of Berkeley hundred), and several court rolls, besides other administrative documents. For the historian, the most disappointing lack is that there are few documents concerned with household administration. In the history of scholarship the collection has the honourable distinction of having inspired John Smyth of Nibley in the early 17th century to write his history of the Berkeley family by using the original documents, an important break from the tradition of merely re-writing and updating earlier chronicles.

The importance of the collection was recognised early in modern times and at the end of the 19th century extensive work on the archive was begun by Edward Peacock and completed by Isaac Herbert Jeayes. Unfortunately, their methods cannot be approved by those aware of modern archival practice. Instead of attempting to preserve or reconstitute the bundles of deeds relating to the various estates they rearranged the whole archive in strictly chronological order, grouping the undated charters under (for instance) '*temp*. Hen. III' or 'late Edw. I'. Jeayes then extracted those items which he considered to be particularly important, chiefly those concerning royal or papal grants, and denominated them as Select Charters, relegating the vast bulk remaining to a General series, each series being separately numbered in sequence.[2] He later added the pre-1250 documents from the General series to the Select series, on the grounds that their early date qualified them, and so the General series starts with charter number GC 278*. Jeayes and Peacock paid less attention to the other documents, but Jeayes did select some of the account rolls, wills and other documents for his catalogue of the documents in the Select series.[3] Jeayes's references remain in use as shelf-marks, with SC for the Select series charters and GC for the General series charters. The present editor has extended the system to include account rolls (prefixed GAR), court rolls (GCR), rental rolls (GRR), and others (GMR).

EDITORIAL METHOD

Over the many centuries during which the muniments have been in the Castle the effects of damp, insects, rodents, pillage and deliberate mutilation and destruction, besides the

---

[1] Although the post-1492 documents have not been studied and consequently have not been used in any formal way in the construction of the catalogue, occasional references have been made in order to clarify certain points.

[2] Where he later found that he had to insert a document or documents into the series he added an asterisk or asterisks to the General series number.

[3] *Descriptive Catalogue of the Charters and Muniments in the possession of the Rt. Hon. Lord FitzHardinge at Berkeley Castle*, compiled by I. H. Jeayes (Bristol, 1892).

re-arrangement already mentioned, have so disorganised the documents that it is now impossible to reconstruct the original order in which they were created and stored. The present catalogue attempts a notional re-assembly by grouping the items according to the estates to which they relate, as is apparent from the list of contents (above, pages v–xiv). Rather more than half of the catalogue relates to the Berkeley estate, Part A, beginning with the manors in Berkeley hundred, for which there are relatively very large numbers of deeds. In that part, and in other parts of the catalogue where appropriate, deeds have been grouped where they appear to refer to the same piece of land, those for which there is evidence that they came into Berkeley hands being placed before the rest. In Parts B to K of the catalogue each estate is divided, where relevant, into the different inheritances of which it was composed, and the entries arising from each inheritance are arranged in alphabetical order of the counties, and within each county in alphabetical order of the manors or parishes, in which the property lay.

The present editor has assigned to each item a distinctive reference that indicates its position in the catalogue. The numbers assigned by Jeayes and the similar references now used as shelf-marks are also given, and a key below, pp. lxi–lxxxviii, relates those references to the sequential references used in the catalogue.

In the abstracts of deeds, place-names are usually given in the spelling of the manuscripts. Exceptions include the names of counties used to locate places, the names of places of residence (other than surnames) that occur in the statements of the parties to deeds or in witness-lists, and the names of the rivers Severn and Wye. The identifiable place-names occurring in notes of accounts and court rolls are similarly modernised. Persons' surnames are given in the abstracts in the spelling of the manuscripts except that descriptive surnames in Latin using common nouns (usually occupational terms) or adjectives are, where possible, translated; for relatively unusual surnames the Latin word may be given in brackets, in italic and in the nominative case or with a preposition. Latin and French forenames are translated into English where there is no problem: thus Matilda appears as Maud, Dionisia as Denise, but Amicia retains her Latin form rather than appearing as Amice, Amy, Amity or Aimée. Where French or English words and phrases that occur in documents that are mainly in Latin need to be distinguished they are either enclosed in quotation marks or are given in translation or modernised form with the original word or words in italic within brackets.

Illegible parts of documents are represented by an ellipsis (. . .). Editorial interpolations are in square brackets, with editorial comments in italic. The omission from an abstract of detail, typically listing titles of honour, offices or varieties of holding, is represented by '[etc.]'.

Work on the arrangement of the muniments is continuing and from time to time reveals documents that had hitherto been overlooked. For that reason, if for none other, the present catalogue should be seen as susceptible to amendment.

Additional research, chiefly in secondary sources, has been done only where necessary to establish the means by which certain documents reached the archive. The introductions to the several sections, and the references to secondary sources cited, are consequently uneven in their range.

PEDIGREES

1. Descendants of Harding son of Eadnoth

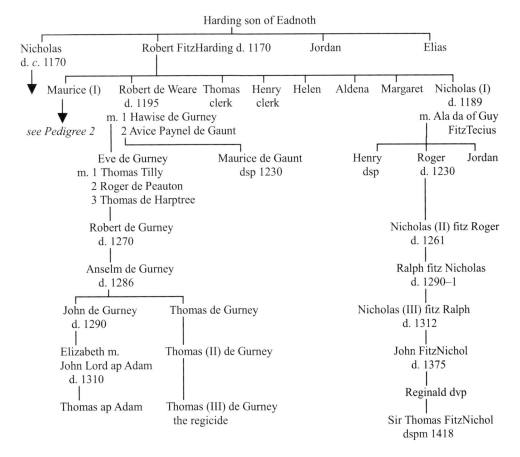

2. Berkeley: descendants of Maurice (I) de Berkeley

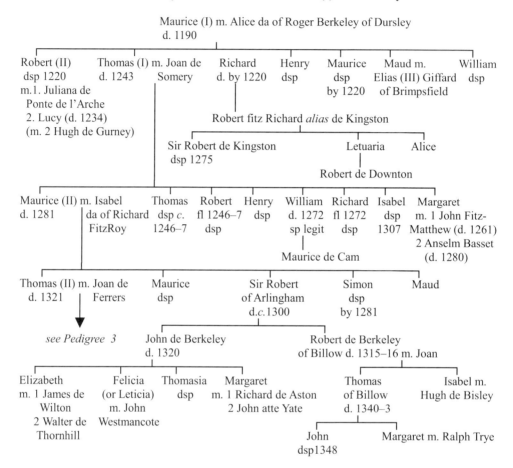

3. Berkeley: descendants of Thomas (II) de Berkeley

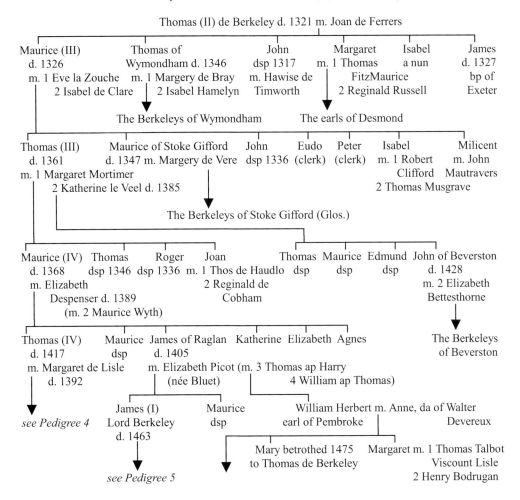

Thomas (II) de Berkeley d. 1321 m. Joan de Ferrers

Maurice (III)
d. 1326
m. 1 Eve la Zouche
2 Isabel de Clare

Thomas of
Wymondham d. 1346
m. 1 Margery de Bray
2 Isabel Hamelyn

The Berkeleys of Wymondham

John
dsp 1317
m. Hawise de
Timworth

Margaret
m. 1 Thomas
FitzMaurice
2 Reginald Russell

The earls of Desmond

Isabel
a nun

James
d. 1327
bp of
Exeter

Thomas (III)
d. 1361
m. 1 Margaret Mortimer
2 Katherine le Veel d. 1385

Maurice of Stoke Gifford
d. 1347 m. Margery de Vere

The Berkeleys of Stoke Gifford (Glos.)

John
dsp 1336

Eudo
(clerk)

Peter
(clerk)

Isabel
m. 1 Robert
Clifford
2 Thomas Musgrave

Milicent
m. John
Mautravers

Maurice (IV)
d. 1368
m. Elizabeth
Despenser d. 1389
(m. 2 Maurice Wyth)

Thomas
dsp 1346

Roger
dsp 1336

Joan
m. 1 Thos de Haudlo
2 Reginald de
Cobham

Thomas
dsp

Maurice
dsp

Edmund
dsp

John of Beverston
d. 1428
m. 2 Elizabeth
Bettesthorne

The Berkeleys
of Beverston

Thomas (IV)
d. 1417
m. Margaret de Lisle
d. 1392

see Pedigree 4

Maurice
dsp

James of Raglan
d. 1405
m. Elizabeth Picot (m. 3 Thomas ap Harry
(née Bluet)   4 William ap Thomas)

Katherine

Elizabeth

Agnes

James (I)
Lord Berkeley
d. 1463

see Pedigree 5

Maurice
dsp

William Herbert m. Anne, da of Walter
earl of Pembroke   Devereux

Mary betrothed 1475
to Thomas de Berkeley

Margaret m. 1 Thomas Talbot
Viscount Lisle
2 Henry Bodrugan

4. Berkeley: descendants of Thomas (IV) de Berkeley

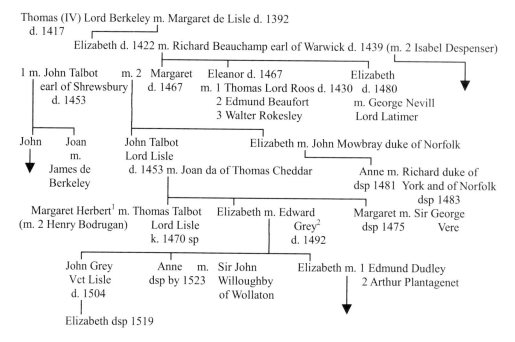

5. Berkeley: descendants of James (I) de Berkeley

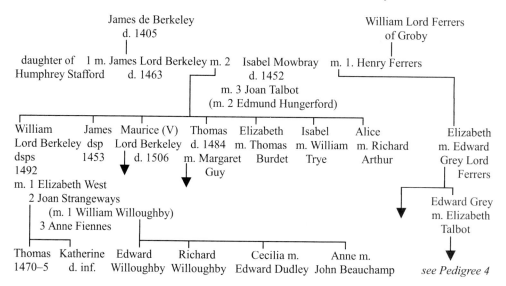

---

[1] Daughter of William Lord Herbert, earl of Pembroke, and Anne, sister of Walter Devereux, Lord Ferrers.

[2] Second son of Edward Grey, Lord Ferrers of Groby, 1475 Lord Lisle, 1483 Viscount Lisle.

6. Mowbray

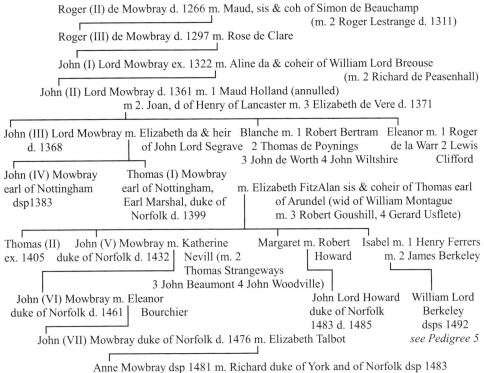

Roger (II) de Mowbray d. 1266 m. Maud, sis & coh of Simon de Beauchamp
(m. 2 Roger Lestrange d. 1311)

Roger (III) de Mowbray d. 1297 m. Rose de Clare

John (I) Lord Mowbray ex. 1322 m. Aline da & coheir of William Lord Breouse
(m. 2 Richard de Peasenhall)

John (II) Lord Mowbray d. 1361 m. 1 Maud Holland (annulled)
m 2. Joan, d of Henry of Lancaster m. 3 Elizabeth de Vere d. 1371

John (III) Lord Mowbray m. Elizabeth da & heir   Blanche m. 1 Robert Bertram   Eleanor m. 1 Roger
d. 1368   of John Lord Segrave   2 Thomas de Poynings   de la Warr 2 Lewis
                                            3 John de Worth 4 John Wiltshire   Clifford

John (IV) Mowbray   Thomas (I) Mowbray
earl of Nottingham   earl of Nottingham,
dsp1383   Earl Marshal, duke of   m. Elizabeth FitzAlan sis & coheir of Thomas earl
                  Norfolk d. 1399   of Arundel (wid of William Montague
                                            m. 3 Robert Goushill, 4 Gerard Usflete)

Thomas (II)   John (V) Mowbray m. Katherine   Margaret m. Robert   Isabel m. 1 Henry Ferrers
ex. 1405   duke of Norfolk d. 1432 │ Nevill (m. 2   Howard   m. 2 James Berkeley
                        Thomas Strangeways
                  3 John Beaumont 4 John Woodville)

John (VI) Mowbray m. Eleanor
duke of Norfolk d. 1461 │ Bourchier   John Lord Howard   William Lord
                                        duke of Norfolk   Berkeley
                                        1483 d. 1485   dsps 1492
John (VII) Mowbray duke of Norfolk d. 1476 m. Elizabeth Talbot   *see Pedigree 5*

Anne Mowbray dsp 1481 m. Richard duke of York and of Norfolk dsp 1483

7. Segrave

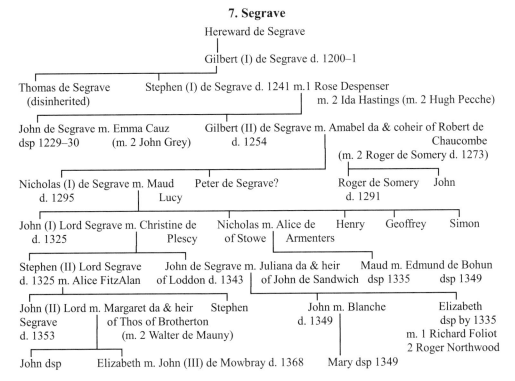

Hereward de Segrave

Gilbert (I) de Segrave d. 1200–1

Thomas de Segrave   Stephen (I) de Segrave d. 1241 m.1 Rose Despenser
(disinherited)   m. 2 Ida Hastings (m. 2 Hugh Pecche)

John de Segrave m. Emma Cauz   Gilbert (II) de Segrave m. Amabel da & coheir of Robert de
dsp 1229–30   (m. 2 John Grey)   d. 1254   Chaucombe
                                            (m. 2 Roger de Somery d. 1273)

Nicholas (I) de Segrave m. Maud   Peter de Segrave?   Roger de Somery   John
d. 1295   Lucy   d. 1291

John (I) Lord Segrave m. Christine de   Nicholas m. Alice de   Henry   Geoffrey   Simon
d. 1325   Plescy   of Stowe │ Armenters

Stephen (II) Lord Segrave   John de Segrave m. Juliana da & heir   Maud m. Edmund de Bohun
d. 1325 m. Alice FitzAlan   of Loddon d. 1343 │ of John de Sandwich dsp 1335   dsp 1349

John (II) Lord m. Margaret da & heir   Stephen   John m. Blanche   Elizabeth
Segrave   of Thos of Brotherton   d. 1349   dsp by 1335
d. 1353   (m. 2 Walter de Mauny)   m. 1 Richard Foliot
                                                        2 Roger Northwood

John dsp   Elizabeth m. John (III) de Mowbray d. 1368   Mary dsp 1349

8. Lovet of Rushton

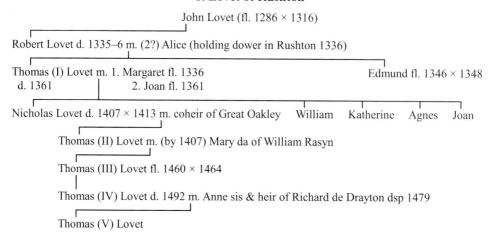

John Lovet (fl. 1286 × 1316)

Robert Lovet d. 1335–6 m. (2?) Alice (holding dower in Rushton 1336)

Thomas (I) Lovet m. 1. Margaret fl. 1336
d. 1361　　　　　2. Joan fl. 1361

Edmund fl. 1346 × 1348

Nicholas Lovet d. 1407 × 1413 m. coheir of Great Oakley　　William　Katherine　Agnes　Joan

Thomas (II) Lovet m. (by 1407) Mary da of William Rasyn

Thomas (III) Lovet fl. 1460 × 1464

Thomas (IV) Lovet d. 1492 m. Anne sis & heir of Richard de Drayton dsp 1479

Thomas (V) Lovet

9. Drayton

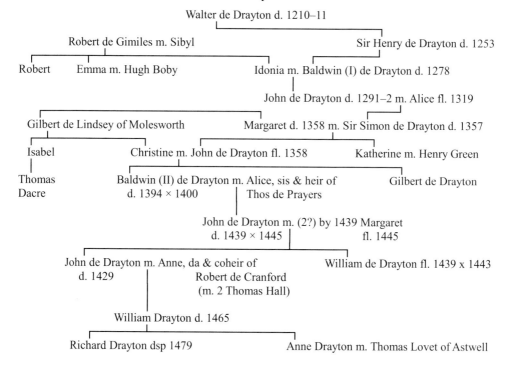

Walter de Drayton d. 1210–11

Robert de Gimiles m. Sibyl　　　　　　Sir Henry de Drayton d. 1253

Robert　　Emma m. Hugh Boby　　　　Idonia m. Baldwin (I) de Drayton d. 1278

John de Drayton d. 1291–2 m. Alice fl. 1319

Gilbert de Lindsey of Molesworth　　　Margaret d. 1358 m. Sir Simon de Drayton d. 1357

Isabel　　　Christine m. John de Drayton fl. 1358　　Katherine m. Henry Green

Thomas
Dacre　　　Baldwin (II) de Drayton m. Alice, sis & heir of　　Gilbert de Drayton
　　　　　　d. 1394 × 1400　　　Thos de Prayers

John de Drayton m. (2?) by 1439 Margaret
d. 1439 × 1445　　　　　　fl. 1445

John de Drayton m. Anne, da & coheir of　　　William de Drayton fl. 1439 x 1443
d. 1429　　　　Robert de Cranford
　　　　　　(m. 2 Thomas Hall)

William Drayton d. 1465

Richard Drayton dsp 1479　　　Anne Drayton m. Thomas Lovet of Astwell

10. Prayers

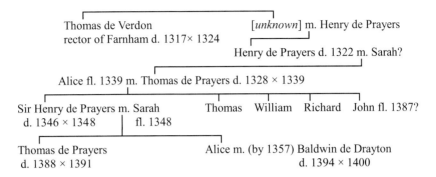

Thomas de Verdon
rector of Farnham d. 1317× 1324

[*unknown*] m. Henry de Prayers

Henry de Prayers d. 1322 m. Sarah?

Alice fl. 1339 m. Thomas de Prayers d. 1328 × 1339

Sir Henry de Prayers m. Sarah
d. 1346 × 1348 | fl. 1348

Thomas   William   Richard   John fl. 1387?

Thomas de Prayers
d. 1388 × 1391

Alice m. (by 1357) Baldwin de Drayton
d. 1394 × 1400

11. Cranford

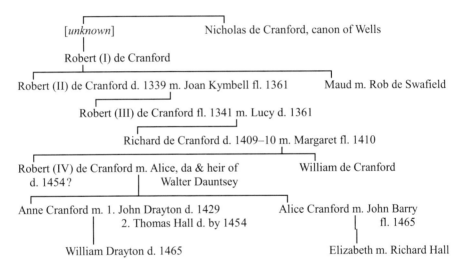

[*unknown*]

Nicholas de Cranford, canon of Wells

Robert (I) de Cranford

Robert (II) de Cranford d. 1339 m. Joan Kymbell fl. 1361

Maud m. Rob de Swafield

Robert (III) de Cranford fl. 1341 m. Lucy d. 1361

Richard de Cranford d. 1409–10 m. Margaret fl. 1410

Robert (IV) de Cranford m. Alice, da & heir of
d. 1454? | Walter Dauntsey

William de Cranford

Anne Cranford m. 1. John Drayton d. 1429
2. Thomas Hall d. by 1454

Alice Cranford m. John Barry
fl. 1465

William Drayton d. 1465

Elizabeth m. Richard Hall

12. Paris and Ivaus

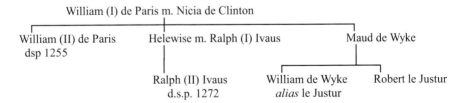

William (I) de Paris m. Nicia de Clinton

William (II) de Paris
dsp 1255

Helewise m. Ralph (I) Ivaus

Maud de Wyke

Ralph (II) Ivaus
d.s.p. 1272

William de Wyke
alias le Justur

Robert le Justur

13. Blount

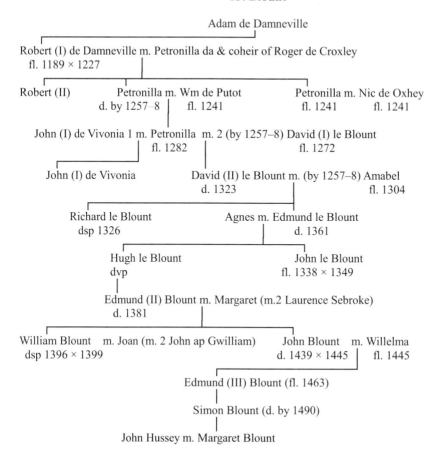

Adam de Damneville

Robert (I) de Damneville m. Petronilla da & coheir of Roger de Croxley
fl. 1189 × 1227

Robert (II)   Petronilla m. Wm de Putot   Petronilla m. Nic de Oxhey
    d. by 1257–8   fl. 1241   fl. 1241   fl. 1241

John (I) de Vivonia 1 m. Petronilla m. 2 (by 1257–8) David (I) le Blount
     fl. 1282   fl. 1272

John (I) de Vivonia   David (II) le Blount m. (by 1257–8) Amabel
     d. 1323   fl. 1304

Richard le Blount   Agnes m. Edmund le Blount
dsp 1326   d. 1361

Hugh le Blount   John le Blount
dvp   fl. 1338 × 1349

Edmund (II) Blount m. Margaret (m.2 Laurence Sebroke)
d. 1381

William Blount   m. Joan (m. 2 John ap Gwilliam)   John Blount   m. Willelma
dsp 1396 × 1399   d. 1439 × 1445   fl. 1445

Edmund (III) Blount (fl. 1463)

Simon Blount (d. by 1490)

John Hussey m. Margaret Blount

COLLATION OF SHELFMARKS WITH
THE REFERENCES USED IN THE CATALOGUE

GAR: General Account Rolls. GC: General Charters. GCR: General Court Rolls. GMR: General Miscellaneous Rolls. GRR: General Rental Rolls. GSUB: General Series Unbound Books. SB: Select Books. SC: Select Charters. SR: Select Rolls. Wills.

Document ref.	Catalogue ref.	Document ref.	Catalogue ref.	Document ref.	Catalogue ref.
GAR 1–20	A1/3/102–21	GAR 322	A1/36/66	GAR 422	A3/16/1
GAR 21–52	A1/3/123–54	GAR 323	A2/46/7	GAR 423	D7/9/1
GAR 55–88	A1/12/123–56	GAR 324–5	A2/49/3–4	GAR 424–5	A4/2/8–9
GAR 89–96	A1/14/60–7	GAR 326	A2/52/2	GAR 426	A2/36/11
GAR 97	A1/19/47	GAR 327–8	D2/1/2–3	GAR 427–8	D1/1/29–30
GAR 98–9	A1/14/68–9	GAR 329	C2/2/18	GAR 429	H1/6/1
GAR 100–18	A1/24/108–26	GAR 330–4	B1/1/85–9	GAR 430	D1/1/31
GAR 119–48	A1/24/128–57	GAR 335–6	D4/1/1–2	GAR 431	K1/4/1
GAR 149–52	A1/24/159–62	GAR 338	H3/7/2	GC 278*	D5/23/38
GAR 153–67	A1/36/27–41	GAR 339–40	D5/9/6–7	GC 279	see p. lxxxviii
GAR 168–9	A1/36/43–4	GAR 341	A2/4/1	GC 280	G4/1/1
GAR 170	A1/36/51	GAR 342	D7/2/1	GC 281	A1/24/51
GAR 171–6	A1/36/45–50	GAR 344	D7/4/1	GC 282	A1/24/52
GAR 177–81	A1/36/52–6	GAR 345–6	A2/6/24–5	GC 283	B1/3/2
GAR 182–9	A1/36/58–65	GAR 347–8	A2/53/16–17	GC 284	A1/27/10
GAR 190	A1/36/67	GAR 349	D5/36/1	GC 285	F1/1/17
GAR 191–204	A1/39/21–34	GAR 350–1	D6/1/6–7	GC 286	G4/10/1
GAR 207–19	A1/43/83–95	GAR 353	K4/10/1	GC 287	A1/12/161
GAR 220–7	A1/43/98–105	GAR 354–5	D3/2/1–2	GC 288–9	A1/3/29
GAR 228	A1/43/124	GAR 356–7	D5/74/21–2	GC 291	A1/5/7
GAR 229–46	A1/43/106–23	GAR 358–60	A2/65/8–10	GC 292	D5/82/3
GAR 247–51	A1/43/125–9	GAR 361	A2/67/24	GC 293	A1/4/6
GAR 252	A1/51/46	GAR 362–85	A2/75/6–29	GC 294–5	A1/3/55
GAR 253–7	A1/51/48–52	GAR 386	A3/14/1	GC 296	B1/5/1
GAR 258	A1/48/8	GAR 387	A3/14/2	GC 298	A2/37/3
GAR 259	A1/51/53	GAR 388	A2/77/20	GC 299	A1/57/4
GAR 260	A1/48/9	GAR 389	A2/81/3	GC 300	A2/37/4
GAR 261–3	A1/51/54–6	GAR 390	D7/6/1	GC 300*	A1/8/10
GAR 264	A1/48/10	GAR 391	D7/8/1	GC 301	A1/2/28
GAR 265–8	A1/51/57–60	GAR 392	D3/1/1	GC 302	B1/2/6
GAR 269	A1/48/11	GAR 395	G4/12/3	GC 303	A1/32/1
GAR 270	A1/51/61	GAR 396–7	A2/94/2–3	GC 304	B1/4/3
GAR 271	A1/51/47	GAR 398	A2/98/6	GC 305	A1/57/2
GAR 272–3	A1/51/62–3	GAR 399–400	A2/99/1–2	GC 306	A1/12/72
GAR 274–5	A1/51/65–6	GAR 401	D1/14/9	GC 307	B1/1/28
GAR 276	A1/51/64	GAR 402	D1/21/1	GC 308	B1/2/4
GAR 277	A1/51/67	GAR 403	D1/18/6	GC 309	D5/82/4
GAR 279–81	A1/50/111–13	GAR 404	D1/21/2	GC 310–11	B1/1/2
GAR 282	A1/13/25	GAR 405–8	A1/11/23–6	GC 312	G5/2/1
GAR 283–7	E1/1/54–8	GAR 409	A2/68/3	GC 313	D5/20/58
GAR 288–300	A2/18/1–13	GAR 410	A1/1/83	GC 314	G4/6/69
GAR 302–3	E1/5/1–2	GAR 411	A4/2/26	GC 315	A2/6/18
GAR 304	A2/28/1	GAR 412–14	A1/1/88–90	GC 316	A1/24/274
GAR 305–12	E1/7/5–12	GAR 415	A2/16/2	GC 317	A1/58/7
GAR 314–18	A2/35/16–20	GAR 416–18	A2/17/26–8	GC 318	A1/3/241
GAR 319	A2/97/1	GAR 419	A1/39/35	GC 319	B1/1/3
GAR 320	A2/37/19	GAR 420	D1/2/4	GC 320	B1/1/31
GAR 321	A2/41/4	GAR 421	D1/2/3	GC 321	A1/29/4

Document ref.	Catalogue ref.	Document ref.	Catalogue ref.	Document ref.	Catalogue ref.
GC 322	G4/6/74	GC 381	D5/20/56	GC 444	A2/67/28
GC 323	D5/52/4	GC 382	A1/10/3	GC 445	A1/2/30
GC 324	A1/2/24	GC 384	D5/41/10	GC 446	A2/6/15
GC 325	A1/43/2	GC 385	F1/1/14	GC 447	A1/32/15
GC 326	A1/2/13	GC 386	A1/31/44	GC 448	B1/1/29
GC 327	A1/3/225	GC 387	D5/84/1	GC 449	A1/32/5
GC 328	A2/13/1	GC 388	D5/41/2	GC 450	A1/12/76
GC 329	A1/43/76	GC 389	B1/4/2	GC 451	B6/3/33
GC 329*	E1/11/1	GC 390	A1/48/6	GC 452	A1/64/17
GC 330	A1/2/23	GC 391	A1/50/121	GC 453	A1/24/89
GC 331	A1/43/13	GC 392	D5/31/9	GC 454	A1/24/88
GC 332	A1/3/4	GC 393	D5/79/1	GC 455	A1/9/12
GC 333	A1/3/3	GC 394	A1/3/7	GC 456	B3/4/1
GC 334	D5/57/1	GC 395	G5/6/7	GC 457	A1/52/11
GC 335	E1/1/50	GC 397	D5/26/2	GC 458	A1/2/15
GC 336	A1/56/19	GC 398	G4/6/35	GC 459	A1/3/33
GC 337	A1/56/22	GC 399	D5/26/1	GC 460	A1/3/5
GC 338	A1/56/21	GC 400	A2/12/1	GC 461	G4/6/26
GC 339	A1/56/23	GC 401	A1/22/2	GC 462	A1/43/6
GC 340	A1/56/20	GC 402	F1/1/5	GC 463–4	B1/1/32
GC 341	D5/82/2	GC 403	A1/12/59	GC 465	A2/6/26
GC 342	A1/55/3	GC 404	D5/75/1	GC 466	E1/1/42
GC 343	E1/1/3	GC 406	B1/1/39	GC 467	B1/2/7
GC 344	D5/37/3	GC 407	D5/29/7	GC 468	A1/9/6
GC 345	B4/4/12	GC 408	K8/1/2	GC 469	G1/3/1
GC 346	A1/58/8	GC 409	G4/3/1	GC 470	D5/101/4
GC 347	F1/5/5	GC 410	B6/4/5	GC 471	B4/4/15
GC 348	A1/52/9	GC 411	A1/12/70	GC 471*	A5/6/1
GC 349	A1/12/162	GC 412	B5/8/1	GC 472	B1/4/12
GC 350	A1/66/2	GC 413	D5/45/1	GC 473	D5/81/15
GC 351	A1/3/57	GC 414	A1/19/53	GC 474	D5/5/1
GC 352	A1/11/16	GC 415	E1/1/49	GC 475	B1/1/43
GC 353–4	A1/3/30–1	GC 416	D5/19/1	GC 476	B1/1/42
GC 355	A1/3/26	GC 417	D5/44/1	GC 478	A1/6/2
GC 356	A1/3/21	GC 418	A2/6/21	GC 479	D5/74/24
GC 357	A1/46/1	GC 419	A2/39/1	GC 480	J2/4/1
GC 358	A1/51/10	GC 420	F1/5/31	GC 481	D5/81/23
GC 359	A1/3/49	GC 421	D5/41/11	GC 481*	A1/1/10
GC 360	A1/51/28	GC 422	A1/34/5	GC 482	D5/74/16
GC 361	A1/31/26	GC 423–4	D5/41/5–6	GC 483	D5/1/8
GC 362	A1/26/13	GC 425	A1/24/288	GC 484–5	D5/46/1–2
GC 363	A1/29/2	GC 426	A1/64/42	GC 486–7	G2/1/6
GC 364	A1/51/78	GC 427	A1/24/2	GC 488	G2/1/3
GC 365	A1/12/202	GC 428	D5/60/2	GC 489	A2/39/3
GC 367	A1/24/276	GC 428*	D5/60/1	GC 490	B7/3/2
GC 368	K4/15/1	GC 429–30	J1/6/2–3	GC 491	F1/1/11
GC 369	H1/1/1	GC 431	A3/12/1	GC 492	F1/4/12
GC 370	B1/1/49	GC 432	B1/1/69	GC 493	F1/4/11
GC 371	B3/2/7	GC 434	B1/1/94	GC 494	D5/47/2
GC 372	D5/31/8	GC 435	B6/3/7	GC 495	A1/1/9
GC 373	B1/3/6	GC 436	A1/57/6	GC 496	A1/31/4
GC 374	D5/23/19	GC 437	A1/32/12	GC 497	A1/35/1
GC 375	D5/23/11	GC 438	B6/3/54	GC 498	E1/9/1
GC 376	D5/23/24	GC 439	A1/65/25	GC 499	B3/5/6
GC 377	D5/58/2	GC 440	A1/3/233	GC 500	A1/8/17
GC 378	A1/2/27	GC 441	F1/4/13	GC 501–2	D5/15/13–14
GC 379	A1/59/18	GC 442	B6/3/56	GC 503–4	D5/74/1–2
GC 380	D5/20/57	GC 443	A1/24/278	GC 505	D5/15/6

Document ref.	Catalogue ref.	Document ref.	Catalogue ref.	Document ref.	Catalogue ref.
GC 506	D5/87/1	GC 564	A2/6/34	GC 624	B2/4/3
GC 507	A1/54/1	GC 565	A1/56/3	GC 625	A1/8/6
GC 508	A1/53/10	GC 566	F1/5/9	GC 626	A1/3/44
GC 509	D5/86/1	GC 567	A2/17/41	GC 627	J1/6/4
GC 510	A1/53/12	GC 568	A1/31/28	GC 628	F1/3/7
GC 511	A1/14/87	GC 569	D5/3/2	GC 629	A2/8/6
GC 512	A2/88/9	GC 570	A1/50/22	GC 630	D5/81/10
GC 513	A2/6/27	GC 571–2	A1/52/2	GC 631	A1/13/1
GC 514	B4/5/1	GC 573	A1/52/3	GC 632	A1/65/15
GC 515	B1/2/2	GC 574	D5/55/1	GC 633	A1/14/74
GC 516	A2/62/3	GC 575	A1/24/40	GC 634	A1/50/228
GC 517	A4/2/18	GC 576	B1/1/10	GC 635	J1/6/5
GC 518	A2/44/1	GC 577	A1/11/7	GC 636–7	A1/4/7
GC 519	B1/2/5	GC 578	D5/74/8	GC 638	B7/3/5
GC 520	A1/2/22	GC 579	G3/2/2	GC 639	B2/8/3
GC 521	A1/3/247	GC 580	G4/6/45	GC 640	A1/12/10
GC 522	A1/3/220	GC 581	K1/1/1	GC 641	J1/4/9
GC 523	A1/65/1	GC 582	A1/43/45	GC 642	A1/4/36
GC 524–5	A1/12/168–9	GC 583	C1/3/4	GC 643	A2/24/6
GC 526	F1/7/1	GC 584	K4/17/1	GC 644	A1/60/58
GC 527	A1/43/41	GC 585	A1/64/25	GC 645	D5/3/11
GC 528	A1/34/6	GC 586	A1/24/217	GC 646	D5/3/10
GC 529	B1/2/3	GC 587	A1/51/8	GC 647	D5/54/1
GC 530	A1/25/4	GC 588	A1/5/10	GC 648	D7/7/1
GC 531	D5/23/40	GC 589	A2/44/2	GC 649	D7/7/2
GC 532	B7/3/3	GC 590	A1/19/11	GC 650	D5/54/2
GC 533	A1/14/12	GC 591	A1/14/71	GC 651	D7/7/3
GC 534	A4/2/23	GC 592	A2/14/1	GC 652	A1/65/32
GC 535	B7/3/10	GC 593	A1/45/20	GC 653	A1/3/65
GC 536	A2/61/1	GC 594	B2/3/1	GC 654	D5/3/18
GC 537	A4/2/24	GC 595	D5/8/4	GC 655	A2/50/3
GC 538	A1/14/12	GC 596	A1/12/46	GC 656	D7/7/4
GC 539	A1/2/32	GC 597	A1/25/19	GC 657	A1/8/18
GC 540	G4/6/55	GC 598	A1/32/6	GC 658	B7/1/2
GC 541	B6/4/6	GC 599	D5/89/1	GC 659	B7/1/1
GC 542	A2/88/10	GC 600	D5/74/18	GC 660	B6/3/14
GC 543	D5/74/5	GC 601	A1/3/236	GC 661–2	A1/59/12–13
GC 544	J1/3/1	GC 602	A1/14/72	GC 663	D5/64/4
GC 545	A2/90/1	GC 603	A2/12/2	GC 664	B6/3/58
GC 545*	A2/90/2	GC 604	A1/34/21	GC 665	A2/24/40
GC 546	D5/92/2	GC 605	G5/6/10	GC 666	A1/64/31
GC 547	F1/2/6	GC 606	B1/2/8	GC 667	A1/64/35
GC 548	F1/2/5	GC 607	D5/48/1	GC 668	B6/3/41
GC 549	F1/5/29	GC 608	A1/3/248	GC 669	B6/3/27
GC 550	A1/48/4	GC 609	A1/35/11	GC 670	B6/3/5
GC 551	A1/12/203	GC 610	B1/3/3	GC 671	B1/1/44
GC 552	A1/34/16	GC 611–12	A1/59/10–11	GC 672–3	B6/1/3–4
GC 553	A1/9/8	GC 613	J1/4/7	GC 674	B1/1/19
GC 554	F1/5/21	GC 614	D5/49/4	GC 675	G4/6/64
GC 555	A1/3/50	GC 615	A1/65/6	GC 676	A1/27/2
GC 556	A1/3/237	GC 616	A1/3/94	GC 677	B1/4/13
GC 557	F1/2/1	GC 617	D5/48/2	GC 678	A1/34/20
GC 558	F1/2/13	GC 618	A1/36/8	GC 679	A1/6/16
GC 559	F1/2/9	GC 619	J1/4/8	GC 680	A1/3/56
GC 560	G4/6/34	GC 620	B1/1/45	GC 681	A1/3/2
GC 561	D5/4/1	GC 621	B1/2/9	GC 682	A1/43/64
GC 562	F1/2/8	GC 622	B7/3/4	GC 683	A1/29/3
GC 563	F1/2/7	GC 623	A2/77/5	GC 684	A1/43/5

Document ref.	Catalogue ref.	Document ref.	Catalogue ref.	Document ref.	Catalogue ref.
GC 685	A1/2/19	GC 743	D5/23/22	GC 801	A1/16/2
GC 686	A1/3/27	GC 744	A1/12/206	GC 802	A1/60/27
GC 687	A1/66/3	GC 745	D5/81/12	GC 803	A1/11/88
GC 688	A1/34/2	GC 746	D5/20/41	GC 804	D5/81/11
GC 689	A1/27/12	GC 747	D5/20/39	GC 805	D5/31/10
GC 690	A1/3/214	GC 748	A1/26/1	GC 806	E1/1/25
GC 691	A1/3/80	GC 749	G3/1/23	GC 807	A1/34/7
GC 692	A1/24/86	GC 750	B2/5/4	GC 808	D5/29/16
GC 693	A1/58/2	GC 751	A1/9/28	GC 809	B6/1/5
GC 694	A1/24/6	GC 752	G3/4/1	GC 810	A1/5/1
GC 695	A1/51/31	GC 753	A1/36/70	GC 811–12	A2/77/3
GC 696	F1/2/16	GC 754	D5/20/48	GC 813	G5/6/14
GC 697	D5/30/3	GC 755	A1/43/9	GC 814	A2/88/8
GC 698	D6/9/2	GC 756	A1/29/1	GC 815	A1/14/11
GC 699	A1/24/219	GC 757	E1/1/79	GC 816	A1/24/257
GC 700	A1/3/71	GC 758	F1/1/3	GC 817	D5/10/1
GC 701	A1/12/3	GC 759	A1/24/284	GC 819	D5/18/3
GC 702	A1/56/10	GC 760	A1/24/285	GC 820	A1/24/265
GC 703	C2/1/4	GC 761	A1/3/227	GC 821	K4/1/1
GC 704	C2/1/3	GC 762	A1/3/213	GC 822	A1/50/89
GC 705	A1/50/215	GC 763	A1/24/272	GC 823	A1/50/116
GC 706	F1/3/3	GC 764	A1/3/238	GC 824	A1/31/46
GC 707	D5/12/1	GC 765	D5/79/7	GC 825	A1/31/45
GC 708	A1/50/114	GC 766	D5/29/8	GC 826	A1/31/8
GC 709	B6/3/21	GC 767	A1/24/281	GC 827	B2/4/6
GC 710	A1/3/240	GC 768	J1/4/10	GC 828	A1/24/215
GC 711	A1/26/7	GC 769	B1/3/4	GC 829	D5/47/5
GC 712	A2/44/5	GC 770	D5/94/1	GC 830	B4/8/3
GC 713	A1/56/7	GC 771	G4/6/68	GC 831	D5/3/5
GC 714	A2/37/2	GC 772	A1/43/65	GC 832	D5/50/6
GC 715	A1/52/1	GC 773	D5/6/1	GC 833	B4/4/11
GC 716	A1/50/165	GC 774	A1/19/3	GC 834	A2/17/40
GC 717	A2/19/5	GC 775	D5/20/49	GC 835	B2/5/2
GC 718	A1/21/1	GC 776	A2/37/7	GC 836	B1/1/82
GC 719	A1/31/27	GC 777	A2/37/5	GC 837	A1/58/6
GC 720	A1/65/23	GC 778	A1/12/1	GC 838	A2/6/35
GC 721	A1/24/216	GC 779	A1/2/40	GC 839	A2/19/3
GC 722	A1/12/165	GC 780	A1/67/4	GC 840	B1/1/92
GC 723	D5/17/1	GC 781	G4/6/75	GC 841	A1/56/5
GC 724	D5/81/8	GC 782	B2/5/7	GC 842	A1/3/216
GC 725	A2/11/6	GC 783	A1/60/62	GC 843	A1/12/5
GC 726	A1/24/283	GC 784	A1/12/207	GC 844	A1/50/2
GC 727	C2/1/18	GC 785	A1/12/75	GC 845	A1/64/44
GC 728	A1/14/80	GC 786	A1/64/50	GC 846	D5/29/14
GC 729	A1/27/11	GC 787	F1/5/35	GC 847	A2/57/2
GC 730	A1/31/43	GC 788	A1/43/32	GC 848	A1/14/38
GC 731	A1/67/3	GC 789	D5/20/27	GC 849	A1/50/1
GC 732	A1/24/282	GC 790	D5/48/3	GC 850	A1/58/21
GC 733	G4/6/1	GC 791	D5/20/38	GC 851	A1/32/22
GC 734	D5/74/9	GC 792	B1/1/36	GC 852	A1/59/15
GC 735	A1/3/63	GC 793	B1/2/12	GC 853	A1/34/24
GC 736	A1/14/4	GC 794	E1/8/7	GC 854	D5/1/11
GC 737	A1/59/4	GC 795	B1/4/16	GC 855	A1/3/179
GC 738	B1/1/47	GC 796	D5/94/6	GC 856	A1/3/178
GC 739	D5/20/35	GC 797	D5/94/3	GC 857	A1/3/180
GC 740	A1/19/2	GC 798	A1/33/4	GC 858	A1/3/165
GC 741	D5/23/10	GC 799	A1/8/7	GC 859	A1/3/170
GC 742	D5/23/23	GC 800	B5/2/1	GC 860	A1/64/26

Document ref.	Catalogue ref.	Document ref.	Catalogue ref.	Document ref.	Catalogue ref.
GC 861	A1/65/13	GC 921	B6/3/40	GC 979	B2/5/12
GC 862	A1/64/43	GC 922	A1/3/242	GC 980	A1/11/78
GC 863	A1/33/2	GC 923	A1/3/73	GC 981	A1/12/218
GC 864	B1/1/17	GC 924	A2/30/1	GC 982	A1/12/170
GC 865	B1/1/27	GC 925	D5/20/60	GC 983	B1/1/91
GC 866	D5/74/17	GC 926	B6/6/1	GC 984	A1/24/287
GC 867	A1/11/76	GC 927	D5/52/3	GC 985	D5/15/7
GC 868	A1/24/64	GC 928	A1/43/3	GC 986	A1/3/212
GC 869	A1/24/67	GC 929	A2/19/14	GC 987	A1/3/13
GC 870	A1/24/85	GC 930	A1/6/1	GC 988	A1/4/35
GC 871	A1/24/68	GC 931	A1/2/25	GC 989	A1/12/79
GC 872–3	F1/1/8–9	GC 932	A1/34/27	GC 990	A1/65/17
GC 874	A1/35/6	GC 933	B2/5/11	GC 991	F1/1/15
GC 875	A1/3/89	GC 934	A1/6/6	GC 992	A1/3/181
GC 876	A1/6/10	GC 935	A1/3/215	GC 993	D7/7/5
GC 877	A1/9/13	GC 936	D5/20/28	GC 994	J1/4/1
GC 878	A1/43/30	GC 937	B1/4/18	GC 995	A1/24/87
GC 879	A1/3/176	GC 938	A1/34/26	GC 996	J1/6/6
GC 880	A1/3/175	GC 939	G4/6/18	GC 997–8	A1/7/1–2
GC 881	D5/97/2	GC 940	F1/5/23	GC 999	A1/43/47
GC 882	A1/65/14	GC 941	A1/12/219	GC 1000	A1/36/21
GC 883	A1/52/10	GC 942	A1/50/3	GC 1001	A1/3/22
GC 884	A2/17/7	GC 943	B6/3/39	GC 1002	A1/51/9
GC 885	D5/79/2	GC 944	B6/3/38	GC 1003	A1/43/46
GC 886	A1/43/8	GC 945	F1/1/16	GC 1003*	D5/69/1
GC 887	A1/50/218	GC 946	F1/5/10	GC 1004–5	A1/36/15–16
GC 888	F1/2/12	GC 947	G2/1/7	GC 1006	B6/3/13
GC 889	A1/12/209	GC 948	A1/12/208	GC 1007	B2/8/2
GC 890	A1/14/9	GC 949	F1/1/21	GC 1008	A1/14/40
GC 891	A1/14/7	GC 950	A2/39/4	GC 1009	A1/14/50
GC 892	A1/14/81	GC 951	A2/44/12	GC 1010	A1/14/30
GC 893	A1/14/84	GC 952	C2/2/20	GC 1011	D5/13/3
GC 894	A1/19/1	GC 953	A2/15/1	GC 1012	A1/36/22
GC 895	A1/59/9	GC 954	B2/5/5	GC 1013	A1/59/22
GC 896	A1/64/6	GC 955	F1/3/6	GC 1014	A1/9/29
GC 897	A2/19/29	GC 956	A1/64/49	GC 1015–16	A1/14/51
GC 898	A1/46/6	GC 957	A1/11/104	GC 1017	A1/19/8
GC 899	A2/24/29	GC 958	A1/14/1	GC 1018	A1/19/7
GC 900	D5/23/26	GC 959	A2/19/12	GC 1019	A1/36/9
GC 901	B6/3/11	GC 960	A1/3/217	GC 1019*	A1/1/75
GC 902	F1/2/10	GC 961	A1/34/23	GC 1019**	A1/1/75
GC 903	A2/6/31	GC 962	D5/41/9	GC 1020	A1/3/196
GC 904	G5/6/12	GC 963	D5/73/1	GC 1021	D5/3/12
GC 905	A1/43/68	GC 964	A1/60/81	GC 1022	A1/3/95
GC 906	D5/20/34	GC 965	A2/42/7	GC 1023	A1/5/11
GC 907	A1/64/48	GC 966	A2/31/1	GC 1024	A1/19/12
GC 908	A2/24/5	GC 967	K4/11/3	GC 1025	A2/44/10
GC 909	B7/3/1	GC 968	A2/19/30	GC 1026	A1/58/3
GC 910	G3/1/31	GC 969	A2/50/2	GC 1027	D5/1/10
GC 911	A2/19/15	GC 970	B6/3/53	GC 1028	D5/1/9
GC 912	D5/100/3	GC 971	A1/65/18	GC 1029	J2/4/2
GC 913	A1/12/7	GC 972	K3/2/2	GC 1030	A1/11/77
GC 914	A2/44/16	GC 973	D5/3/14	GC 1031	A1/31/14
GC 915	A1/64/21	GC 974	A1/64/54	GC 1032	A2/24/15
GC 916	A2/8/3	GC 975	A1/64/57	GC 1033	A1/24/55
GC 917–18	A1/3/194–5	GC 976	D5/47/4	GC 1034	B7/3/6
GC 919	A1/65/24	GC 977	D5/47/6	GC 1035	A1/4/9
GC 920	A1/9/27	GC 978	A2/44/11	GC 1036	J1/6/7

Document ref.	Catalogue ref.	Document ref.	Catalogue ref.	Document ref.	Catalogue ref.
GC 1037	J1/6/14	GC 1097	A1/24/73	GC 1159	A2/44/8
GC 1038	A1/2/37	GC 1098	D5/79/3	GC 1160	A1/58/9
GC 1039	A1/39/2	GC 1099	A1/12/93	GC 1161	D5/81/2
GC 1040	A1/24/211	GC 1100	A1/12/220	GC 1162	A1/64/24
GC 1041	B4/4/13	GC 1101	A1/4/15	GC 1163	A1/64/29
GC 1042	A1/59/23	GC 1102	A1/4/8	GC 1164	A1/64/27
GC 1043	A1/11/9	GC 1103	A1/4/12	GC 1165	A1/64/30
GC 1044	A2/23/1	GC 1104	A1/4/10	GC 1166	A1/50/217
GC 1045	A1/11/9	GC 1105	D5/92/4	GC 1167	A1/3/205
GC 1046	A2/23/2	GC 1106	A1/18/4	GC 1168	A1/3/166
GC 1047	D5/49/1	GC 1107	A1/4/18	GC 1169	A1/3/167
GC 1048	A1/44/3	GC 1108	A1/8/12	GC 1170	A1/3/169
GC 1049	A2/23/3	GC 1109	A1/50/128	GC 1171	A1/12/217
GC 1050	D5/63/1	GC 1110	G4/6/27	GC 1172	B6/3/26
GC 1051	A1/12/6	GC 1111	A1/4/13	GC 1173	B6/3/12
GC 1052	E1/7/2	GC 1112	D5/29/11	GC 1174	B6/3/8
GC 1053	J1/6/8	GC 1113	A1/19/28	GC 1175	B6/3/5
GC 1054	A2/11/7	GC 1114	A1/2/46	GC 1176	D5/50/4
GC 1055	A1/3/182	GC 1115	B7/1/3	GC 1177	B1/1/21
GC 1056	A1/12/60	GC 1116	A1/2/39	GC 1178	B1/1/20
GC 1057	D5/101/9	GC 1117	A1/56/16	GC 1179–80	B1/1/33
GC 1058	J1/6/10	GC 1118	A1/12/11	GC 1181	B1/2/1
GC 1059	E1/4/1	GC 1119	A1/59/24	GC 1182	G4/6/65
GC 1060	A1/24/229	GC 1120	A1/12/12	GC 1183	B4/1/1
GC 1061	A1/24/212	GC 1121	A1/6/15	GC 1184	D5/23/7
GC 1062	E1/1/7	GC 1122	B4/4/19	GC 1185	D5/23/5
GC 1063	D5/20/2	GC 1123	A1/31/33	GC 1186	A1/27/3
GC 1064	D5/20/1	GC 1124–5	A1/3/188–9	GC 1187–8	A1/31/9–10
GC 1065	A1/24/212	GC 1126	A2/24/16	GC 1189	B6/3/25
GC 1066	K4/14/1	GC 1127	F1/1/18	GC 1190	A1/51/23
GC 1067	J1/4/4	GC 1128	A1/43/16	GC 1191	D5/51/4
GC 1068	D5/101/7	GC 1129	A1/26/3	GC 1192	D5/23/35
GC 1069	A1/9/4	GC 1130	A1/43/17	GC 1193	D5/23/34
GC 1070	A2/23/4	GC 1131	A1/4/20	GC 1194	A1/12/200
GC 1071	D5/20/3	GC 1132–3	G3/1/32–3	GC 1195	F1/5/6
GC 1072	A2/44/9	GC 1134–6	A2/8/7–9	GC 1196	A1/52/8
GC 1073	B7/3/7	GC 1137	G3/3/1	GC 1197	A1/3/64
GC 1074	A1/24/3	GC 1138	A2/15/12	GC 1198	A1/11/33
GC 1075	A1/14/3	GC 1139	A1/8/19	GC 1199	A1/3/20
GC 1076–7	A1/24/71–2	GC 1140	D5/29/12	GC 1200	A1/1/70
GC 1078	A1/31/32	GC 1141	C2/1/10	GC 1201	A1/12/163
GC 1079	A1/14/41	GC 1142	A1/14/27	GC 1202	A5/3/4
GC 1080	A1/4/37	GC 1143	B2/8/4	GC 1203	A1/11/5
GC 1081	D5/63/2	GC 1144	A2/66/1	GC 1204	A1/2/29
GC 1082	G3/1/30	GC 1145	D1/5/1	GC 1205	A1/24/66
GC 1083	A1/20/3	GC 1146	B2/8/5	GC 1206	A1/11/6
GC 1084	A2/24/8	GC 1147	A1/64/8	GC 1207	A1/12/92
GC 1085	A1/17/1	GC 1148	A1/12/94	GC 1208	A1/59/8
GC 1086	A2/86/1	GC 1149	A1/51/2	GC 1209	A1/2/12
GC 1087–8	J1/6/9	GC 1150	A1/51/4	GC 1210	A1/32/3
GC 1089	C2/2/2	GC 1151	D5/20/5	GC 1211	A1/12/91
GC 1090	J2/5/1	GC 1152	A1/45/12	GC 1212	A1/32/4
GC 1091	A1/2/38	GC 1153	D5/74/4	GC 1213	A1/43/4
GC 1092	A1/20/4	GC 1154	A1/9/11	GC 1214	A1/14/77
GC 1093	A1/24/4	GC 1155	A1/2/11	GC 1215	A1/43/77
GC 1094	A1/12/19	GC 1156	A1/59/16	GC 1216	A1/3/33
GC 1095	A1/50/123	GC 1157	A1/59/14	GC 1217	A1/56/9
GC 1096	D5/29/15	GC 1158	B2/1/1	GC 1218	A1/56/8

Document ref.	Catalogue ref.	Document ref.	Catalogue ref.	Document ref.	Catalogue ref.
GC 1219	A1/14/46	GC 1280	G3/1/29	GC 1341	A2/24/28
GC 1220	A2/3/5	GC 1281	A2/44/1	GC 1342	A1/64/22
GC 1221	A1/48/1	GC 1282	G4/6/63	GC 1343	A1/24/220
GC 1222	A1/57/5	GC 1283	A1/3/70	GC 1344	A1/2/16
GC 1223	A4/2/19	GC 1284	B6/3/9	GC 1345	A1/30/1
GC 1224	A1/51/24	GC 1285	G4/6/76	GC 1346	A1/2/26
GC 1225	A1/14/39	GC 1286	C2/1/17	GC 1347	A1/2/33
GC 1226	A1/14/8	GC 1287	D5/15/2	GC 1348	A1/2/18
GC 1227	A1/14/26	GC 1288	A1/31/49	GC 1349	A1/2/17
GC 1228	A1/13/20	GC 1289	A1/12/160	GC 1350	B2/5/6
GC 1229	A1/31/30	GC 1290	A1/14/83	GC 1351	B2/5/9
GC 1230–1	A1/65/16	GC 1291	A1/14/82	GC 1352	B6/3/19
GC 1232	A1/56/15	GC 1292	A1/14/5	GC 1353–4	A1/3/206–7
GC 1233	A1/14/14	GC 1293	D5/20/30	GC 1355	A1/3/209
GC 1234	A1/24/189	GC 1294	D5/20/29	GC 1356	B6/3/17
GC 1235	A1/31/31	GC 1295	D5/20/43	GC 1357	A1/31/1
GC 1236	A1/19/37	GC 1296	D5/20/42	GC 1358	A1/31/3
GC 1237	A1/9/10	GC 1297	D5/20/44	GC 1359	A1/31/2
GC 1238	A1/56/11	GC 1298	D5/20/53	GC 1360	A1/31/48
GC 1239	A1/44/1	GC 1299	A2/67/7	GC 1361	A1/31/7
GC 1240	A2/67/15	GC 1300	B1/1/35	GC 1362	A1/31/6
GC 1241	A1/59/20	GC 1301	A1/58/13	GC 1363	G3/4/2
GC 1242	A1/46/2	GC 1302	A1/51/22	GC 1364	D5/20/51
GC 1243	A1/43/78	GC 1303–4	D5/23/16–17	GC 1365	A2/63/1
GC 1244	B6/3/15	GC 1305	A1/11/103	GC 1366	K4/5/1
GC 1245	A2/15/9	GC 1306	A2/24/22	GC 1367	A1/19/25
GC 1246–7	A2/21/3–4	GC 1307	A1/12/171	GC 1368	F1/1/1
GC 1248	B6/3/28	GC 1308	A1/19/56	GC 1369	F1/1/4
GC 1249	B6/3/30	GC 1309	A1/19/4	GC 1370	A2/19/13
GC 1250	C1/2/1	GC 1310	A1/43/152	GC 1371	B6/3/55
GC 1251	A1/67/5	GC 1311–12	A1/19/5–6	GC 1372	D5/74/10
GC 1252	F1/3/5	GC 1313	A1/19/16	GC 1373	K4/8/1
GC 1253	A2/44/7	GC 1314	A1/19/27	GC 1374	A1/3/69
GC 1254	D5/100/2	GC 1315	A1/19/50	GC 1375	D5/3/20
GC 1255	D5/74/7	GC 1316	D5/20/46	GC 1376	A1/12/51
GC 1256	A1/2/20	GC 1317	D5/23/18	GC 1377	D5/94/2
GC 1257	A1/36/71	GC 1318	G4/2/1	GC 1378	C2/1/1
GC 1258	D5/74/3	GC 1319	A1/59/6	GC 1379	D5/20/50
GC 1259	B6/3/20	GC 1320	A1/24/5	GC 1380	G4/6/67
GC 1260	D5/92/3	GC 1321	A1/59/7	GC 1381	A1/57/7
GC 1261	F1/2/18	GC 1322	A1/37/1	GC 1382	A1/3/246
GC 1262	A2/6/1	GC 1323	A1/59/1	GC 1383	A1/3/250
GC 1263	A2/53/6	GC 1324	A1/59/3	GC 1384	A1/12/158
GC 1264	A2/65/11	GC 1325	D5/20/25	GC 1385	A2/15/10
GC 1265	D5/39/1	GC 1326	D5/20/36	GC 1386	A1/12/166
GC 1266	D5/91/2	GC 1327	A1/12/164	GC 1387	A1/3/226
GC 1267	A1/2/21	GC 1328	A1/12/8	GC 1388	A2/24/39
GC 1268	A2/53/7	GC 1329	A1/32/2	GC 1389	B1/4/19
GC 1269–70	G4/6/13–14	GC 1330	A1/3/173	GC 1390	D5/20/55
GC 1271	A2/44/5	GC 1331	D5/3/9	GC 1391	D5/20/31
GC 1272	A2/44/4	GC 1332	D5/82/5	GC 1392	A1/3/1
GC 1273	F1/2/11	GC 1333	D5/23/21	GC 1393	A1/3/232
GC 1274	A1/14/22	GC 1334–5	A1/43/39–40	GC 1394	A1/24/225
GC 1275	A1/14/76	GC 1336	A1/43/42	GC 1395	A1/24/271
GC 1276	A1/25/9	GC 1337	H1/7/1	GC 1396	A1/12/77
GC 1277	A1/3/177	GC 1338	G2/1/5	GC 1397	A1/65/4
GC 1278	A1/25/8	GC 1339	F1/2/14	GC 1398	A1/65/27
GC 1279	A1/50/133	GC 1340	A1/43/7	GC 1399	A1/4/21

Document ref.	Catalogue ref.	Document ref.	Catalogue ref.	Document ref.	Catalogue ref.
GC 1400	A1/31/5	GC 1465	A1/24/256	GC 1525	A1/24/33
GC 1401	A1/8/16	GC 1466	A1/3/10	GC 1526	F1/5/8
GC 1402	A2/8/5	GC 1467	A1/3/8	GC 1527	F1/5/22
GC 1403	A1/26/15	GC 1468	A1/24/53	GC 1528	A1/50/119
GC 1404	A1/31/42	GC 1469	B1/1/40	GC 1529	A1/34/8
GC 1405–6	A1/9/25–6	GC 1470–1	A1/51/5–6	GC 1530	D5/64/5
GC 1407	B4/4/14	GC 1472	A2/37/8	GC 1531	K4/11/4
GC 1408	B6/3/32	GC 1473	A2/31/3	GC 1532	A1/22/5
GC 1409	F1/2/4	GC 1474	A2/37/9	GC 1533	A1/14/2
GC 1410	A1/14/75	GC 1475	A2/37/11	GC 1534	E1/1/80
GC 1411	B6/3/34	GC 1476	A2/37/6	GC 1535	D5/95/1
GC 1412	A1/3/184	GC 1477	A1/24/226	GC 1536	A2/33/1
GC 1413	D1/11/3	GC 1478	A1/3/224	GC 1537	A1/56/25
GC 1414	A2/6/22	GC 1479	A2/44/6	GC 1538	B6/3/24
GC 1415	A1/50/210	GC 1480	B2/5/8	GC 1539	B6/3/23
GC 1416	A2/15/7	GC 1481	A1/59/21	GC 1540	K4/11/2
GC 1417	A2/29/5	GC 1482	A1/3/6	GC 1541	D5/3/16
GC 1418	A1/24/280	GC 1483	A1/14/13	GC 1542	D5/7/1
GC 1419	B1/1/18	GC 1484	A1/12/214	GC 1543	D5/53/1
GC 1420	D5/41/3	GC 1485	A1/12/9	GC 1544	D5/24/1
GC 1421	D5/41/1	GC 1486	A2/88/3	GC 1545	A1/24/275
GC 1422	J2/4/3	GC 1487	A1/24/270	GC 1546	A1/24/1
GC 1423–4	A1/34/18–19	GC 1488	A1/64/51	GC 1547	A2/42/6
GC 1425	A1/3/23	GC 1489	A1/4/22	GC 1548	A1/50/220
GC 1426	B6/3/36	GC 1490	A1/24/279	GC 1549	A1/66/5
GC 1427	B1/4/4	GC 1491	F1/5/24	GC 1550	A1/66/4
GC 1428	B1/1/1	GC 1492	D5/5/2	GC 1551	G1/4/2
GC 1429	B6/9/1	GC 1493	A1/12/59	GC 1552	A1/14/73
GC 1430–1	B1/1/22	GC 1494	B2/5/3	GC 1553	D5/77/1
GC 1432	B6/6/3	GC 1495	A1/2/35	GC 1554	A1/61/17
GC 1433	B1/1/84	GC 1496	B1/1/38	GC 1555	A1/24/266
GC 1434	A1/16/1	GC 1497	A1/34/25	GC 1556	D5/25/3
GC 1435	A1/24/277	GC 1498	F1/2/3	GC 1557	D5/3/13
GC 1436	F1/2/15	GC 1499	F1/2/2	GC 1558	A1/24/218
GC 1437–8	A1/60/80	GC 1500	A1/12/4	GC 1559	A1/64/56
GC 1439	A1/12/74	GC 1501	E1/3/3	GC 1560	A1/37/4
GC 1440	A1/22/7	GC 1502	G4/6/36	GC 1561	A1/3/221
GC 1441	A1/43/34	GC 1503	B1/1/30	GC 1562	A1/3/45
GC 1442	D5/29/10	GC 1504	A1/12/204	GC 1563	J1/6/1
GC 1443–4	D5/29/5–6	GC 1505	B6/3/22	GC 1564–5	D5/3/3–4
GC 1445	A1/12/216	GC 1506	A1/6/7	GC 1566	A1/55/4
GC 1446	A1/40/1	GC 1507	A1/66/8	GC 1567	E1/1/6
GC 1447	A1/40/2	GC 1508	A2/67/27	GC 1568	A1/59/17
GC 1448	A1/40/3	GC 1509	D5/42/4	GC 1569	D5/42/1
GC 1449	A1/40/2	GC 1510	D5/41/12	GC 1570	K4/11/1
GC 1450	A1/43/35	GC 1511	A1/39/1	GC 1571	A2/36/2
GC 1451	A1/46/5	GC 1512–13	A1/12/212–13	GC 1572	D5/54/5
GC 1452–3	A1/45/18	GC 1514	B6/3/4	GC 1573	A1/43/63
GC 1454–5	A1/43/38	GC 1515	A1/12/211	GC 1574	A1/50/219
GC 1456	A1/58/4	GC 1516	D5/8/2	GC 1575	G5/1/1
GC 1457	A1/24/214	GC 1517	D5/8/1	GC 1576	A1/34/22
GC 1458	A1/24/213	GC 1518	A1/56/24	GC 1577	A1/3/228
GC 1459	D5/5/4	GC 1519	A1/19/49	GC 1578	A1/3/185
GC 1460	B1/4/20	GC 1520	D5/9/3	GC 1579	B6/3/37
GC 1461	C1/1/1	GC 1521	A2/39/5	GC 1580	B1/1/41
GC 1462	A1/2/14	GC 1522	A2/6/17	GC 1581	A1/24/187
GC 1463	B2/8/1	GC 1523	D5/31/5	GC 1582	D5/92/1
GC 1464	A2/98/3	GC 1524	A2/67/26	GC 1583	A1/24/221

Document ref.	Catalogue ref.	Document ref.	Catalogue ref.	Document ref.	Catalogue ref.
GC 1584	A1/56/4	GC 1642–3	A2/24/9	GC 1701	A1/60/59
GC 1585	A1/12/201	GC 1644	A1/12/95	GC 1702	A1/56/26
GC 1586	A1/9/7	GC 1645–6	A2/10/2	GC 1703–4	D5/66/1–2
GC 1587	A2/17/34	GC 1647	A1/3/174	GC 1705–6	G4/6/16–17
GC 1588	A1/3/251	GC 1648	A1/2/41	GC 1707–8	A1/12/99–100
GC 1589	A1/4/11	GC 1649	A5/10/5	GC 1709	B2/5/10
GC 1590	A2/6/19	GC 1650	A1/2/42	GC 1710	A2/50/5
GC 1591	G4/10/2	GC 1651	A1/4/24	GC 1711	A1/24/91
GC 1592	A1/49/15	GC 1652	A1/50/21	GC 1712	A1/51/33
GC 1593	A1/4/23	GC 1652*	A1/3/183	GC 1713	A2/24/23
GC 1594	A1/31/47	GC 1652**	A1/3/183	GC 1714	A1/12/101
GC 1595	G4/10/3	GC 1652***	A1/3/192	GC 1715	A1/31/35
GC 1596	A1/3/68	GC 1652****	A1/3/192	GC 1716	B3/3/1
GC 1597	A2/21/1	GC 1653	A1/6/11	GC 1717	A1/34/10
GC 1598	A1/12/73	GC 1654	G4/4/1	GC 1718	A2/24/17
GC 1599	A1/3/66	GC 1655	A1/65/19	GC 1719	H1/1/3
GC 1600	A1/43/14	GC 1656–7	A1/19/13–14	GC 1720	A1/31/36
GC 1601	G5/6/15	GC 1658–9	A1/39/8–9	GC 1721	A2/15/11
GC 1602	A1/24/286	GC 1660	D1/23/1	GC 1722	A1/24/14
GC 1603	A1/64/28	GC 1661	G3/1/53	GC 1723	A1/24/207
GC 1604	A1/31/12	GC 1662	B1/1/70	GC 1724	A1/4/38
GC 1605	A1/45/19	GC 1663	A2/44/13	GC 1725–6	A1/12/102–3
GC 1606	A1/3/32	GC 1664	A1/19/15	GC 1727	A1/3/82
GC 1607	A1/43/12	GC 1665	A1/12/96	GC 1728	A1/14/52
GC 1608	A1/60/82	GC 1666	A1/24/7	GC 1729	A1/24/206
GC 1609	A1/21/2	GC 1667	A1/3/15	GC 1730	A1/65/7
GC 1610	A1/12/167	GC 1668	D5/92/5	GC 1731	A2/24/10
GC 1611	F1/1/4	GC 1669	A1/51/32	GC 1732–3	A2/24/12
GC 1612	A1/3/51	GC 1670	A1/3/16	GC 1734	A1/64/58
GC 1613	F1/5/34	GC 1671	A1/5/12	GC 1735	A2/37/10
GC 1614	A1/33/5	GC 1672	A1/12/61	GC 1736–7	A1/12/62
GC 1615	A1/12/78	GC 1673	A1/12/97	GC 1738	A1/24/92
GC 1616	A1/12/23	GC 1674	A1/9/14	GC 1739	A1/67/6
GC 1617	A1/3/249	GC 1675	A1/12/98	GC 1740	A1/24/56
GC 1618	A1/12/205	GC 1676	A1/24/90	GC 1741	A1/12/63
GC 1619	A2/42/8	GC 1677	A1/31/34	GC 1742	A1/24/77
GC 1620	A1/33/3	GC 1678	A1/24/8	GC 1743	A1/50/164
GC 1621	B6/3/31	GC 1679	A1/9/15	GC 1744	A1/34/9
GC 1622	A1/64/55	GC 1680	A1/5/13	GC 1745	A1/19/41
GC 1623	A1/12/159	GC 1681	A2/10/3	GC 1746	A1/3/197
GC 1624	A1/60/71	GC 1682	A1/19/17	GC 1747	A1/16/3
GC 1625	A1/12/210	GC 1683	G4/6/61	GC 1748	A1/50/132
GC 1626	A1/50/124	GC 1684	C2/1/2	GC 1749–51	A1/19/31–3
GC 1627	F1/2/17	GC 1685	A1/19/18	GC 1752–3	A1/24/9–10
GC 1628	A1/43/15	GC 1686	A1/19/38	GC 1754	A1/24/93
GC 1629	A1/64/23	GC 1687	C2/1/7	GC 1755	A2/6/28
GC 1630	A1/43/10	GC 1688	A1/3/190	GC 1756	G3/1/24
GC 1631	G4/6/15	GC 1689	A1/2/43	GC 1757	A1/44/2
GC 1632	A1/12/2	GC 1690	A1/2/44	GC 1758	A1/24/15
GC 1633	A1/24/258	GC 1691	A1/3/46	GC 1759	A1/24/11
GC 1634	A1/6/3	GC 1692	E1/4/2	GC 1760	A1/9/9
GC 1635	G4/6/37	GC 1693	A1/19/39	GC 1761–2	A1/45/4
GC 1636	A1/12/41	GC 1694–5	A3/7/1–2	GC 1763	A1/24/13
GC 1637	A1/64/16	GC 1696	A1/36/10	GC 1764	A1/24/94
GC 1638	A1/4/19	GC 1697	A2/64/1	GC 1765	A1/31/15
GC 1639	D5/29/13	GC 1698	A2/50/4	GC 1766	A1/26/8
GC 1640	A1/26/4	GC 1699	A1/64/52	GC 1767	A1/9/16
GC 1641	A1/51/25	GC 1700	A1/6/17	GC 1768	B6/1/6

Document ref.	Catalogue ref.	Document ref.	Catalogue ref.	Document ref.	Catalogue ref.
GC 1769	A2/24/14	GC 1831	A1/12/64	GC 1893	C2/2/19
GC 1770	A2/24/13	GC 1832	A1/1/84	GC 1894	A1/26/6
GC 1771	A1/31/16	GC 1833	A1/3/97	GC 1895	B2/5/1
GC 1772	D5/101/5	GC 1834	A1/12/65	GC 1896	A1/12/21
GC 1773–5	A1/5/14–16	GC 1835	A1/3/84	GC 1897	A1/12/222
GC 1776	A1/2/47	GC 1836	A1/24/12	GC 1898	A1/19/42
GC 1777	B1/1/46	GC 1837	A1/24/290	GC 1899	A1/12/22
GC 1778	A1/3/17	GC 1838	A1/64/18	GC 1900	A1/62/4
GC 1779	B6/6/2	GC 1839	A1/31/15	GC 1901	A3/3/2
GC 1780	A1/24/289	GC 1840–1	A1/5/22–3	GC 1902	A1/12/24
GC 1781	A1/46/3	GC 1842–3	A1/3/14	GC 1903	A1/7/5
GC 1782	A1/31/37	GC 1844	A1/12/52	GC 1904	A1/12/67
GC 1783	A1/5/17	GC 1845	A1/14/35	GC 1905	A1/14/55
GC 1784	A1/64/9	GC 1846	A1/14/34	GC 1906	A1/31/39
GC 1785–6	A1/5/18–19	GC 1847	B4/4/15	GC 1907	A1/9/17
GC 1787	A1/14/53	GC 1848	G5/6/16	GC 1908	A1/24/20
GC 1788	A1/5/20	GC 1849	A2/24/24	GC 1909	D5/21/1
GC 1789	A1/19/34	GC 1850	G3/1/26	GC 1910	A1/24/96
GC 1790	A1/24/35	GC 1851	A1/12/13	GC 1911	G3/1/36
GC 1791	A1/2/45	GC 1852	G4/6/77	GC 1912	A2/32/1
GC 1792	D5/81/3	GC 1853	A1/5/24	GC 1913	D5/54/3
GC 1793	C2/1/8	GC 1854	A1/12/80	GC 1914	G3/1/37
GC 1794	D5/81/1	GC 1855	A1/12/18	GC 1915	A1/39/14
GC 1795	A1/24/16	GC 1856	A1/3/210	GC 1916	D5/74/6
GC 1796	B6/5/1	GC 1857	A1/31/38	GC 1917	A1/14/6
GC 1797	G3/1/25	GC 1858	A1/12/66	GC 1918	A1/31/18
GC 1798	A1/8/13	GC 1859	A1/3/211	GC 1919	A1/45/7
GC 1799	A1/3/83	GC 1860	A1/12/14	GC 1920	A2/32/2
GC 1800	G3/1/50	GC 1861–2	A1/12/104–5	GC 1921	A1/39/15
GC 1801	D5/81/4	GC 1863	A1/19/19	GC 1922	A2/32/3
GC 1802	A1/1/99	GC 1864	A1/19/20	GC 1923	D5/62/1
GC 1803	D5/81/5	GC 1865	A1/19/30	GC 1924	A1/18/2
GC 1804	G4/6/19	GC 1866	A1/16/4	GC 1925	A2/32/4
GC 1805	A1/29/5	GC 1867–8	A1/39/11–12	GC 1926	A1/19/43
GC 1806	A1/64/10	GC 1869	A1/14/54	GC 1927	A1/43/67
GC 1807	A1/2/6	GC 1870	A1/39/13	GC 1928	B4/4/16
GC 1808	A1/2/5	GC 1871	A1/3/243	GC 1929	A1/5/25
GC 1809	A1/2/4	GC 1872	C2/1/9	GC 1930	A1/3/218
GC 1810	A1/24/95	GC 1873	A1/19/21	GC 1931	A1/64/36
GC 1811	A1/2/3	GC 1874	A1/14/44	GC 1932	C2/1/12
GC 1812	A1/2/2	GC 1875	A1/46/9	GC 1933	A1/19/42
GC 1813	A1/32/16	GC 1876	A1/24/230	GC 1934	C2/1/11
GC 1814	A1/2/1	GC 1877	C2/2/6	GC 1935	A1/19/9
GC 1815	A1/50/4	GC 1878	A2/15/2	GC 1936–7	A1/3/219
GC 1816	A1/2/7	GC 1879	A1/12/53	GC 1938	A1/19/44
GC 1817	A1/36/17	GC 1880	A1/12/106	GC 1939	A1/50/223
GC 1818	A2/24/19	GC 1881	A1/12/20	GC 1940	D5/74/11
GC 1819	A1/3/96	GC 1882	A1/9/30	GC 1941	A2/17/42
GC 1820–1	A1/14/42–3	GC 1883	A1/26/5	GC 1942	A1/49/5
GC 1822	A1/19/35	GC 1884	K4/2/1	GC 1943–4	A1/24/25–6
GC 1823	A2/62/1	GC 1885	A2/67/8	GC 1945	A1/50/134
GC 1823*	G3/1/51	GC 1886	A1/31/17	GC 1946	A1/50/136
GC 1824	D5/81/6	GC 1887	D5/81/9	GC 1947	A1/50/206
GC 1825–6	A1/14/32	GC 1888	D5/81/16	GC 1948	A1/50/135
GC 1827	A1/5/21	GC 1889	A1/34/28	GC 1949	A1/64/37
GC 1828	A1/43/44	GC 1890	A1/12/221	GC 1950	G3/1/54
GC 1829	A1/43/43	GC 1891	A1/2/50	GC 1951	A1/24/194
GC 1830	G3/1/52	GC 1892	A1/65/8	GC 1952	A1/41/4

Document ref.	Catalogue ref.	Document ref.	Catalogue ref.	Document ref.	Catalogue ref.
GC 1953	A1/24/29	GC 2016	D5/71/2	GC 2077	A1/18/6
GC 1954–5	A1/65/20	GC 2017	A1/3/62	GC 2078	A1/60/91
GC 1956	A1/24/17	GC 2018	A1/3/229	GC 2079	A1/45/13
GC 1957	A1/24/97	GC 2019	A2/6/29	GC 2080	A1/62/6
GC 1958	A1/31/19	GC 2020	A1/45/1	GC 2081	A1/64/19
GC 1959	D5/8/5	GC 2021	A1/24/36	GC 2082	A1/3/34
GC 1960	A1/24/259	GC 2022	A1/24/19	GC 2083	D5/71/3
GC 1961	A1/64/38	GC 2023	A1/45/5	GC 2084	A1/3/52
GC 1962	A1/14/56	GC 2024	A1/45/3	GC 2085	A1/3/35
GC 1963	A1/65/11	GC 2025	A1/5/26	GC 2086	D5/15/11
GC 1964	A1/12/223	GC 2026	A1/6/12	GC 2087	A1/45/17
GC 1965	A1/43/49	GC 2027	A1/3/85	GC 2088	A1/3/53
GC 1966	A1/5/3	GC 2028	A1/12/25	GC 2089–90	D5/81/18–19
GC 1967	A1/5/2	GC 2029	A1/3/198	GC 2091	A1/7/3
GC 1968	A2/6/5	GC 2030	A1/3/75	GC 2092	A1/64/32
GC 1969	A1/12/81	GC 2031	A1/17/8	GC 2093	A1/64/33
GC 1970	A1/5/8	GC 2032	A1/12/26	GC 2094	A1/3/230
GC 1971	A2/40/1	GC 2033	A1/6/13	GC 2095	D5/15/12
GC 1972	A1/24/18	GC 2034	A2/48/2	GC 2096	A1/3/231
GC 1973–4	D5/15/9–10	GC 2035	A1/39/6	GC 2097	A1/36/11
GC 1975	C2/2/7	GC 2036	A1/45/6	GC 2098	A1/50/224
GC 1976	D5/1/12	GC 2037	D5/15/5	GC 2099	A2/22/1
GC 1977	A1/50/90	GC 2038	A1/39/17	GC 2100	A1/12/29
GC 1978	D5/93/1	GC 2039	A1/17/2	GC 2101	A2/61/2
GC 1979	A1/62/5	GC 2040–1	D5/101/11–12	GC 2102	A1/64/1
GC 1980	A1/11/10	GC 2042	B1/5/2	GC 2103	D5/85/1
GC 1981	A2/32/5	GC 2043	A1/12/27	GC 2104	A1/9/19
GC 1982	A1/43/50	GC 2044	A1/6/4	GC 2105–6	A1/12/30
GC 1983	A1/14/10	GC 2045	A1/14/15	GC 2107	A1/17/4
GC 1984	A1/12/54	GC 2046	A1/12/15	GC 2108	A1/64/2
GC 1985	A1/3/47	GC 2047	A1/9/18	GC 2109	A1/12/31
GC 1986	A1/36/23	GC 2048	A1/12/225	GC 2110	A1/64/3
GC 1987	A1/3/98	GC 2049	A1/14/16	GC 2111	A1/12/32
GC 1988	A1/7/6	GC 2050	A1/34/17	GC 2112	A1/12/55
GC 1989*	A1/19/42	GC 2051	D5/14/1	GC 2113	G4/6/21
GC 1989–90	D5/81/13–14	GC 2052	A1/3/76	GC 2114	A1/3/99
GC 1991–2	A1/4/39	GC 2053	A1/17/3	GC 2115	A2/88/11
GC 1993	D5/15/3	GC 2054	A1/4/25	GC 2116	A2/24/2
GC 1994	D5/38/2	GC 2055	D5/47/1	GC 2117	A1/9/1
GC 1995	D5/15/4	GC 2056	A2/48/3	GC 2118	A1/31/20
GC 1996	A1/65/5	GC 2057	A1/3/252	GC 2119	A1/9/2
GC 1997	A1/12/224	GC 2058	A1/8/1	GC 2120	A1/24/191
GC 1998	A1/12/107	GC 2059	A1/12/107	GC 2121	A1/64/34
GC 1999	A1/62/12	GC 2060	A1/21/3	GC 2122	A1/3/77
GC 2000	K10/1/5	GC 2061	B6/3/43	GC 2123	G4/8/1
GC 2001	A1/39/16	GC 2062	A1/45/8	GC 2124	A1/3/37
GC 2002	A2/48/1	GC 2063–4	A1/8/3–4	GC 2125	A1/64/4
GC 2003	G4/6/20	GC 2065	A1/8/2	GC 2126	A1/9/20
GC 2004	A1/31/50	GC 2066	A1/19/45	GC 2127	A1/3/38
GC 2005	A1/12/108	GC 2067	A1/65/9	GC 2128	A1/3/48
GC 2006	A1/41/1	GC 2068	D5/47/3	GC 2129	G5/6/17
GC 2007	A2/32/6	GC 2069	A1/3/9	GC 2130	A1/50/5
GC 2008	A1/3/11	GC 2070	A1/64/7	GC 2131	A1/64/5
GC 2009	A1/41/2	GC 2071	A1/3/199	GC 2132	A1/12/109
GC 2010	A1/3/58	GC 2072	D5/81/17	GC 2133	A1/24/78
GC 2011	A1/3/12	GC 2073–4	A1/5/27–8	GC 2134	A1/12/35
GC 2012–14	A1/3/59–61	GC 2075	A1/31/24	GC 2135–6	A1/43/79–80
GC 2015	D5/71/1	GC 2076	A1/17/6	GC 2137	A1/31/23

Document ref.	Catalogue ref.	Document ref.	Catalogue ref.	Document ref.	Catalogue ref.
GC 2138	A1/24/200	GC 2198	A1/6/5	GC 2265	A1/55/2
GC 2139	A1/12/36	GC 2199	A1/64/53	GC 2266	B7/2/1
GC 2140	G4/6/22	GC 2200	A1/3/25	GC 2267	B4/6/1
GC 2141	A1/12/37	GC 2201	A1/49/3	GC 2268	B7/2/2
GC 2142	A1/50/197	GC 2202	A1/8/9	GC 2269	G2/1/8
GC 2143	G3/1/27	GC 2203	G4/6/78	GC 2270	A1/25/5
GC 2144	A1/49/6	GC 2204	A1/24/37	GC 2271	D5/46/3
GC 2145	G4/6/28	GC 2205	A1/5/31	GC 2272	D5/71/4
GC 2146	A1/24/57	GC 2206	A1/9/21	GC 2273	A2/17/22
GC 2147	A1/12/226	GC 2207	B4/4/17	GC 2274	A1/3/78
GC 2148	A1/49/7	GC 2208	A2/46/2	GC 2275	A1/4/16
GC 2149	G4/5/1	GC 2209	A2/46/1	GC 2276	B4/2/1
GC 2150	A1/3/54	GC 2210	A2/75/1	GC 2277	A1/3/18
GC 2151	A1/31/21	GC 2211	A2/62/2	GC 2278	A1/12/111
GC 2152	A1/45/14	GC 2212	A1/6/8	GC 2279–80	B4/9/1–2
GC 2153–4	A1/50/166–7	GC 2213–14	A1/24/27	GC 2281	A1/62/14
GC 2155	A2/21/2	GC 2215	D5/81/24	GC 2282	A1/43/48
GC 2156	D5/79/8	GC 2216	A1/14/57	GC 2283	B6/3/44
GC 2157	A2/12/3	GC 2217	D5/1/13	GC 2284	A1/3/19
GC 2158	A1/3/186	GC 2218	A2/11/8	GC 2285	A1/3/41
GC 2159	A1/12/16	GC 2219	A1/2/51	GC 2286	G4/6/5
GC 2160	A1/12/39	GC 2220	A1/55/1	GC 2287	A1/43/21
GC 2161	A1/60/36	GC 2221–2	A1/14/17–18	GC 2288	B6/3/45
GC 2162	A2/45/1	GC 2223	D5/20/6	GC 2289	A1/12/45
GC 2163	A1/31/22	GC 2224	D5/20/7	GC 2290	A1/5/32
GC 2164	A1/5/29	GC 2225	D5/20/6	GC 2291	A1/14/20
GC 2165	A1/3/39	GC 2226–7	D5/20/13–14	GC 2292	A1/12/83
GC 2166	A2/15/4	GC 2228	D5/20/10	GC 2293	A2/10/4
GC 2167	A1/31/25	GC 2229–30	D5/20/11	GC 2294	A1/49/9
GC 2168	A1/5/30	GC 2231–2	D5/20/8–9	GC 2295	A2/48/4
GC 2169	A1/24/175	GC 2233	D5/20/12	GC 2296–7	A1/49/10–11
GC 2170	A1/3/187	GC 2234	A2/50/6	GC 2298	B6/4/3
GC 2171	A1/24/58	GC 2235	A2/75/2	GC 2299	A1/24/260
GC 2172–3	A1/12/43	GC 2236	A1/50/6	GC 2300	D2/2/1
GC 2174	A1/24/231	GC 2237	A1/14/36	GC 2301	A1/24/30
GC 2175	A1/64/59	GC 2238	A1/9/3	GC 2302	D5/13/4
GC 2176	A1/5/9	GC 2239	A1/58/12	GC 2303	A1/12/110
GC 2177	D1/17/1	GC 2240	A1/3/253	GC 2304	A1/12/84
GC 2178	D7/5/1	GC 2241–2	A1/14/19	GC 2305	A1/12/48
GC 2179	A1/3/40	GC 2243	A2/85/1	GC 2306	A1/12/49
GC 2180	A1/7/4	GC 2244–6	D5/79/4–6	GC 2307	A1/12/47
GC 2181	D5/74/19	GC 2247	A1/60/76	GC 2308	B6/3/46
GC 2182	G4/6/70	GC 2248–9	A1/43/18–19	GC 2309	B1/1/11
GC 2183	A1/12/42	GC 2250	A2/23/8	GC 2310	A1/39/10
GC 2184	A1/30/4	GC 2251	A1/43/20	GC 2311	B4/6/2
GC 2185	A1/17/9	GC 2252	A1/49/4	GC 2312	D5/4/2
GC 2186	G4/6/29	GC 2253	A1/46/4	GC 2313	B6/4/2
GC 2187	A1/17/5	GC 2254	B6/4/1	GC 2314–15	A1/12/33–4
GC 2188	A1/8/14	GC 2255	A1/14/28	GC 2316	B1/3/5
GC 2189	A1/24/98	GC 2256	A1/24/21	GC 2317	A1/43/154
GC 2190	B1/4/14	GC 2257	A1/58/22	GC 2318	B4/10/2
GC 2191	A1/49/2	GC 2258	A2/58/1	GC 2319	A1/65/30
GC 2192	A1/49/8	GC 2259	A1/24/201	GC 2320	A1/50/137
GC 2193	B1/4/15	GC 2260	A1/12/44	GC 2321	D5/13/2
GC 2194	A1/49/1	GC 2261	A2/75/3	GC 2322	A2/63/2
GC 2195	A1/3/24	GC 2262	A1/65/3	GC 2323	G4/13/3
GC 2196	A1/6/14	GC 2263	A1/12/82	GC 2324	A1/9/22
GC 2197	A1/3/36	GC 2264	A1/31/40	GC 2325	A1/5/33

Document ref.	Catalogue ref.	Document ref.	Catalogue ref.	Document ref.	Catalogue ref.
GC 2326	K4/7/1	GC 2391	A1/50/24	GC 2452	D5/81/21
GC 2327	G4/6/32	GC 2392	A1/3/201	GC 2453	A1/50/211
GC 2328–9	A1/24/268	GC 2393	A1/8/20	GC 2454	A1/60/93
GC 2330–1	A1/5/4–5	GC 2394	A1/68/1	GC 2455	D5/62/2
GC 2332	A1/50/207	GC 2395	D5/87/2	GC 2456	A2/89/1
GC 2333	A1/24/38	GC 2396	G4/6/71	GC 2457–8	A1/3/222–3
GC 2334	A1/5/6	GC 2397	A2/24/1	GC 2459	A1/64/60
GC 2335	D5/90/2	GC 2398	G4/6/72	GC 2460	A1/51/11
GC 2336	A1/2/31	GC 2399	A1/65/21	GC 2461	A1/38/1
GC 2337	A1/34/4	GC 2400	A1/62/7	GC 2462–4	A1/64/61–2
GC 2338	A1/12/40	GC 2401	G1/4/3	GC 2465	A2/30/2
GC 2339	A2/62/4	GC 2402	A1/3/42	GC 2466	A1/58/23
GC 2340–1	A1/64/40–1	GC 2403	B2/7/1	GC 2467	A1/24/31
GC 2342	A1/19/10	GC 2404	A1/62/8	GC 2468	A1/50/124
GC 2343	A1/14/37	GC 2405	G3/1/48	GC 2469	A1/43/36
GC 2344	D5/74/12	GC 2406	A1/24/209	GC 2470	B6/3/42
GC 2345	A1/24/22	GC 2407–8	K3/2/3–4	GC 2471	A1/3/193
GC 2346	C2/1/5	GC 2409	A1/12/227	GC 2472	B6/3/6
GC 2347	A2/1/1	GC 2410	G3/1/49	GC 2473	A1/24/205
GC 2348	G4/6/31	GC 2411	A1/24/202	GC 2474	A1/31/11
GC 2349	G4/6/30	GC 2412	A1/24/233	GC 2475	B1/2/11
GC 2350	A1/62/1	GC 2413	A1/3/203	GC 2476	D5/8/3
GC 2351	D5/74/13	GC 2414	A1/24/203	GC 2477	A2/31/4
GC 2352	A1/24/23	GC 2415	D5/89/2	GC 2478	A1/3/93
GC 2353	A1/45/15	GC 2416	B6/6/5	GC 2479	A1/52/4
GC 2354	A1/14/45	GC 2417	G4/6/56	GC 2480	A2/12/10
GC 2355	A1/31/51	GC 2418	A1/64/65	GC 2481	A1/3/81
GC 2356	A1/12/28	GC 2419	A1/24/39	GC 2482	A1/24/188
GC 2357	A1/24/79	GC 2420	D5/69/2	GC 2483	A1/60/119
GC 2358	A1/3/200	GC 2421	A1/24/34	GC 2484	A1/13/24
GC 2359	A1/12/112	GC 2422	A1/24/204	GC 2485	A1/29/6
GC 2360–1	G4/6/33	GC 2423	D5/81/20	GC 2486	A1/36/20
GC 2362	A1/4/3	GC 2424	G4/8/2	GC 2487	A1/8/8
GC 2363	B7/3/9	GC 2425	A1/9/31	GC 2488	A1/12/85
GC 2364	A2/15/13	GC 2426	A2/54/1	GC 2489	D5/68/1
GC 2365	D5/78/1	GC 2427	G4/6/62	GC 2490	E1/1/9
GC 2366	A2/21/5	GC 2428	A1/50/30	GC 2491	B6/3/29
GC 2367	A2/37/12	GC 2429	A1/24/227	GC 2492	A1/26/2
GC 2368	G2/1/18	GC 2430	A1/53/1	GC 2493	D5/49/3
GC 2369	B6/6/4	GC 2431	A2/11/9	GC 2494	A1/24/291
GC 2370	D5/16/1	GC 2432	A1/65/12	GC 2495	A1/50/216
GC 2371–2	A1/17/7	GC 2433–4	A1/53/2	GC 2496	A1/43/11
GC 2373	A1/64/39	GC 2435	G4/6/25	GC 2497	A2/11/3
GC 2374	D5/74/14	GC 2436–7	G4/6/23–4	GC 2498	A1/11/82
GC 2375	A1/3/254	GC 2438	A1/24/235	GC 2499	A2/67/9
GC 2376	A1/24/261	GC 2439	A1/11/105	GC 2500	E1/1/8
GC 2377	D5/79/9	GC 2440	A1/6/18	GC 2501	A1/67/7
GC 2378	A1/24/208	GC 2441	B1/1/55	GC 2502	D5/20/26
GC 2379–80	A1/61/4	GC 2442	B1/1/54	GC 2503	A1/65/29
GC 2381	A1/62/2	GC 2443	A1/60/92	GC 2504	A1/45/2
GC 2382	A1/50/29	GC 2444	A1/24/262	GC 2505	D5/15/8
GC 2383	A1/50/23	GC 2445	A2/36/1	GC 2506–7	A1/3/171–2
GC 2384	A1/50/122	GC 2446	A1/65/22	GC 2508	D5/3/8
GC 2385	A1/14/88	GC 2447	A1/62/15	GC 2509	B6/3/52
GC 2386	A2/19/7	GC 2448	A1/50/125	GC 2510	A1/31/13
GC 2387	A1/24/292	GC 2449	B1/1/56	GC 2511	A1/50/130
GC 2388	D5/23/30	GC 2450	G5/6/18	GC 2512	A2/6/20
GC 2389–90	D5/23/31	GC 2451	A1/50/126	GC 2513	B6/3/16

Document ref.	Catalogue ref.	Document ref.	Catalogue ref.	Document ref.	Catalogue ref.
GC 2514	A1/3/208	GC 2572	A1/26/10	GC 2635	G5/6/11
GC 2515	A1/11/80	GC 2573	A1/51/26	GC 2636	A1/24/267
GC 2516	A1/3/191	GC 2574	B5/9/7	GC 2636*	E1/1/46
GC 2517	D5/20/52	GC 2575	A1/60/2	GC 2637	B1/1/57
GC 2518	A1/66/10	GC 2576	A1/8/11	GC 2638	E1/4/4
GC 2519	A2/6/2	GC 2577	A1/3/168	GC 2639	A1/32/24
GC 2520	A1/65/28	GC 2578	A1/3/90	GC 2640	A1/11/106
GC 2521	A1/64/20	GC 2579	A2/32/9	GC 2641	A1/1/73
GC 2522	B1/4/17	GC 2580	A1/50/93	GC 2642	E1/1/44
GC 2523	G4/6/4	GC 2581	A1/50/50	GC 2643	C2/2/4
GC 2524	A1/46/10	GC 2582	A2/35/8	GC 2644	A1/62/9
GC 2525	A1/57/8	GC 2583	A1/60/121	GC 2645	C2/2/5
GC 2526	A1/50/221	GC 2584	A1/13/10	GC 2646	A2/81/1
GC 2527	A1/24/222	GC 2585	A1/39/3	GC 2647	A1/64/12
GC 2528	A1/12/17	GC 2586–7	A1/60/11–12	GC 2648	A1/50/139
GC 2529	A3/5/1	GC 2588	A1/50/10	GC 2649	D5/81/25
GC 2530	A1/65/2	GC 2589	A1/50/9	GC 2650	A2/36/3
GC 2531	A2/24/18	GC 2590–1	A1/58/10–11	GC 2651	A1/39/36
GC 2532	A2/24/11	GC 2592	A1/60/21	GC 2652	B1/4/5
GC 2533	A2/24/7	GC 2593	A1/60/5	GC 2653	A5/1/1
GC 2534	E1/1/29	GC 2594	A1/50/131	GC 2654	A2/53/8
GC 2535	A1/30/2	GC 2595	B6/3/18	GC 2655	A1/61/1
GC 2536	F1/5/26	GC 2596	A1/43/58	GC 2656	A1/62/10
GC 2537	A1/34/15	GC 2597	A2/44/17	GC 2657	D5/81/26
GC 2538	A1/19/26	GC 2598	A1/61/26	GC 2658	A1/50/140
GC 2539	A1/43/66	GC 2599	G2/1/2	GC 2659	G3/1/14
GC 2540	A1/3/74	GC 2600	A1/60/30	GC 2660	A1/66/11
GC 2541	A1/11/102	GC 2601	A1/60/35	GC 2661	D5/81/27
GC 2542	D5/13/1	GC 2602	A1/60/74	GC 2662	A2/53/9
GC 2543	A1/12/215	GC 2603	A1/60/6	GC 2663	G5/4/2
GC 2544	B6/3/3	GC 2604–5	A1/60/8–9	GC 2663*	D5/69/3
GC 2545	A1/53/11	GC 2606	A1/24/298	GC 2664	B4/8/6
GC 2546	A1/43/153	GC 2607	J1/2/1	GC 2665	A1/61/5
GC 2547	A1/11/89	GC 2608	A1/60/48	GC 2666	D5/62/3
GC 2548	F1/5/4	GC 2609–10	A1/12/183–4	GC 2667–8	A2/53/10–11
GC 2549	F1/5/11	GC 2611	A1/60/110	GC 2669–70	A2/53/13–14
GC 2550	G3/1/1	GC 2612	A1/60/46	GC 2671	A5/1/2
GC 2551	B6/4/7	GC 2613	A1/61/10	GC 2672	A2/12/4
GC 2552	A2/8/4	GC 2614	A3/10/1	GC 2673	A2/53/12
GC 2553	A1/14/21	GC 2615–16	E1/4/3	GC 2674	A1/56/28
GC 2554	D5/53/1	GC 2617	A1/4/4	GC 2675	G2/3/1
GC 2555	A1/60/57	GC 2618	E1/1/43	GC 2676	G4/6/38
GC 2556	A1/3/72	GC 2619	B1/1/59	GC 2677	G2/3/2
GC 2557	J1/4/6	GC 2620–1	A1/64/45–6	GC 2678	A1/24/173
GC 2558	A1/24/190	GC 2622–3	A1/64/63–4	GC 2679	D1/9/1
GC 2559	A1/59/19	GC 2624	A1/64/11	GC 2680	A1/24/293
GC 2560	A1/3/202	GC 2625	A1/24/236	GC 2681	A2/77/6
GC 2561	A1/50/222	GC 2626	A1/64/47	GC 2682	D5/53/7
GC 2562	E1/1/26	GC 2627	B1/1/60	GC 2683	A2/44/14
GC 2563	A1/65/26	GC 2628	A1/1/72	GC 2684	E1/8/1
GC 2564	A1/50/149	GC 2629	K4/12/1	GC 2685	A1/11/107
GC 2565	A1/24/59	GC 2630	A1/1/73	GC 2686	D5/53/3
GC 2566	A1/3/79	GC 2631	A1/50/127	GC 2687	A1/11/81
GC 2567	A1/36/7	GC 2632	D5/81/22	GC 2688	A4/2/21
GC 2568	A1/14/91	GC 2632*	A2/25/1	GC 2689	A1/50/212
GC 2569	A1/43/33	GC 2632**	A2/53/1	GC 2690	D4/4/1
GC 2570	A1/51/7	GC 2632***	A2/53/1	GC 2691	A1/31/52
GC 2571	A1/24/54	GC 2633–4	A2/53/2–3	GC 2692	A1/61/6

Document ref.	Catalogue ref.	Document ref.	Catalogue ref.	Document ref.	Catalogue ref.
GC 2693	A5/9/7	GC 2753	A1/60/55	GC 2814	D5/20/16
GC 2694	B7/3/11	GC 2754	G2/1/9	GC 2815	A1/9/32
GC 2695	A2/89/2	GC 2755	A1/61/7	GC 2816–17	A2/15/5–6
GC 2696	A1/60/25	GC 2755*	A2/13/2	GC 2818	A1/58/16
GC 2697	A1/60/24	GC 2756	A1/65/33	GC 2819	A1/62/11
GC 2698	A1/64/13	GC 2757	J1/2/2	GC 2820	A1/56/17
GC 2699–2700	A1/58/5	GC 2758	D1/1/2	GC 2821	A2/65/2
GC 2701	D1/19/1	GC 2759	A1/39/7	GC 2822	A1/61/13
GC 2702	B7/3/12	GC 2760	A2/17/12	GC 2823	D5/20/17
GC 2703	A1/14/89	GC 2761–2	D5/1/4–5	GC 2824	D1/18/1
GC 2704	B1/4/6	GC 2763–4	A1/61/23–4	GC 2825	A1/24/99
GC 2705	G5/6/19	GC 2765–6	A1/12/229	GC 2826	D1/18/2
GC 2706	B1/4/7	GC 2767	A2/65/1	GC 2827	D5/20/18
GC 2706*	A1/13/26	GC 2768	A1/60/20	GC 2828	B2/2/1
GC 2707	A1/13/27	GC 2769	A1/64/15	GC 2829	A1/50/16
GC 2708	A1/50/120	GC 2770	G2/1/10	GC 2830	A1/43/51
GC 2709	A1/61/2	GC 2771	G5/6/20	GC 2831–2	A1/43/52
GC 2710	A2/9/1	GC 2772	A2/12/6	GC 2833	A1/14/29
GC 2710*	A1/13/5	GC 2773	G2/1/11	GC 2834	A2/35/21
GC 2711	D5/92/6	GC 2774	A1/12/230	GC 2835	A1/12/172
GC 2712	A2/36/4	GC 2775	B6/2/1	GC 2836	D5/20/21
GC 2713	A1/12/228	GC 2776	E1/1/30	GC 2837	A1/41/3
GC 2714	G2/3/3	GC 2777	A1/52/12	GC 2838	D5/3/19
GC 2715	A1/3/255	GC 2778	A2/17/13	GC 2839	A1/50/138
GC 2716	A2/62/5	GC 2779	A1/51/12	GC 2840	A1/45/10
GC 2717	A2/24/20	GC 2780–1	A2/12/7–8	GC 2841	A1/24/42
GC 2718	A1/43/69	GC 2782	B1/4/21	GC 2842	B6/6/6
GC 2719	A2/64/2	GC 2783	A2/64/9	GC 2843	A1/24/43
GC 2720	A1/50/143	GC 2784	D1/6/1	GC 2844	A2/53/5
GC 2721	B7/2/3	GC 2785	A1/64/66	GC 2845	C2/1/6
GC 2722	G2/3/4	GC 2786	A1/61/21	GC 2846	E1/8/8
GC 2723	B7/3/13	GC 2787	B1/4/8	GC 2848	A2/25/2
GC 2724–5	B7/2/4	GC 2788	B5/5/1	GC 2849	A1/58/24
GC 2726	A2/6/3	GC 2789	B1/4/22	GC 2850	A2/59/1
GC 2727	A2/17/36	GC 2790	D5/1/6	GC 2851	B6/6/8
GC 2728	B1/1/24	GC 2791	A1/58/15	GC 2852	B6/6/7
GC 2729	A1/13/2	GC 2792	G5/6/23	GC 2853	A1/13/19
GC 2730	D5/69/4	GC 2793	A2/67/10	GC 2854	A1/13/9
GC 2731	A1/62/3	GC 2794	A1/45/9	GC 2855	A1/13/13
GC 2732	B7/2/5	GC 2795	A1/24/232	GC 2856	A1/13/17
GC 2733–4	D5/1/1–2	GC 2796	A2/12/9	GC 2857	A2/37/13
GC 2735	A1/61/20	GC 2797	D5/69/5	GC 2858	F1/5/36
GC 2736	A1/24/195	GC 2798	A1/50/225	GC 2859	A2/6/6
GC 2737	D5/1/3	GC 2799	A2/17/43	GC 2860	A5/10/9
GC 2738	A1/28/1	GC 2800	A1/23/1	GC 2861	D5/20/20
GC 2739	A1/65/31	GC 2801	A1/12/231	GC 2862	A2/16/1
GC 2740	D5/77/2	GC 2802	B1/4/9	GC 2863	A1/24/60
GC 2741–2	A1/60/65–6	GC 2803	D5/92/7	GC 2864	A2/65/12
GC 2743	A1/58/14	GC 2804	A1/50/117	GC 2865	A1/61/3
GC 2744	A2/12/5	GC 2805	A1/24/263	GC 2866	A1/61/18
GC 2745–6	A1/60/54	GC 2806	A1/13/12	GC 2867	A1/61/14
GC 2747	A1/64/14	GC 2807	A2/51/1	GC 2868	C2/2/21
GC 2748	A2/17/35	GC 2808	D5/33/3	GC 2869	D5/49/2
GC 2748*	A2/83/4	GC 2809	D5/71/5	GC 2870	D5/71/6
GC 2749	A2/62/6	GC 2810	B6/7/1	GC 2871	D5/98/1
GC 2750	A1/13/18	GC 2811	D5/20/19	GC 2872	A1/24/198
GC 2751	A1/24/234	GC 2812	D5/20/15	GC 2873	A2/35/22
GC 2752	B2/4/4	GC 2813	G5/6/21	GC 2874	A1/50/118

Document ref.	Catalogue ref.	Document ref.	Catalogue ref.	Document ref.	Catalogue ref.
GC 2875	C2/1/13	GC 2938	A2/6/13	GC 3003	G4/6/6
GC 2876	A2/22/2	GC 2939	A1/34/12	GC 3004	A1/50/145
GC 2877	A2/67/11	GC 2940	A2/37/14	GC 3005	A1/50/63
GC 2878	A2/17/1	GC 2941–2	A2/6/9–10	GC 3006–7	A1/58/17
GC 2878*	A2/77/18	GC 2943	A2/88/4	GC 3008	A1/12/235
GC 2879	A2/77/19	GC 2944	A2/92/1	GC 3009	D1/19/2
GC 2880	A1/24/197	GC 2945	A1/12/234	GC 3010	J1/4/2
GC 2881	A1/24/294	GC 2946	A1/51/16	GC 3011	B5/4/1
GC 2882	A2/6/7	GC 2947–9	A1/51/13–15	GC 3012	A1/60/14
GC 2883	A1/19/36	GC 2950	G3/1/2	GC 3013	A2/56/1
GC 2884	A1/24/24	GC 2951	A1/24/32	GC 3014	A1/14/90
GC 2885	K10/1/6	GC 2952	D5/53/5	GC 3015	A1/60/1
GC 2886	D5/88/1	GC 2953	D5/53/4	GC 3016	A1/60/15
GC 2887	D5/74/20	GC 2954	D5/53/6	GC 3017–18	A2/56/2–3
GC 2888	A1/11/79	GC 2955	B5/9/1	GC 3019	A1/31/53
GC 2889	A1/24/28	GC 2956	A1/12/233	GC 3020	A1/50/34
GC 2890	A1/1/105	GC 2957–8	E1/1/34–5	GC 3021	A1/50/37
GC 2891	A1/27/13	GC 2959	A1/60/75	GC 3022	A1/50/36
GC 2892–3	A1/24/196	GC 2960	A1/60/33	GC 3023	A1/50/42
GC 2894	A1/45/21	GC 2961	G3/1/3	GC 3024	A1/50/41
GC 2895–6	D5/8/6–7	GC 2962	A2/26/1	GC 3025–6	B5/4/2–3
GC 2897	A1/50/198	GC 2963	A1/39/37	GC 3027	A1/60/99
GC 2898–9	A1/50/31–2	GC 2964	A1/43/53	GC 3028	A1/50/141
GC 2900	A2/6/4	GC 2965	A1/3/244	GC 3029–30	A1/60/100–1
GC 2901	A1/50/33	GC 2966	A1/12/175	GC 3031	A1/60/4
GC 2902–3	A1/25/10–11	GC 2967	A1/3/43	GC 3032–3	A1/60/77–8
GC 2904	E1/1/31	GC 2968	A2/11/4	GC 3034	G5/6/22
GC 2905	A2/6/8	GC 2969	G2/4/1	GC 3035–6	A1/60/83
GC 2906	A1/24/199	GC 2970	A2/42/10	GC 3037	A1/60/84
GC 2907	A3/8/1	GC 2971	C2/1/14	GC 3038	A1/60/79
GC 2908	B2/6/1	GC 2972	A1/11/34	GC 3039	A1/60/3
GC 2909	A2/42/9	GC 2973	A1/60/56	GC 3040	A2/44/18
GC 2910	A1/32/7	GC 2974	A1/62/16	GC 3041	B4/4/4
GC 2911–12	E1/1/32–3	GC 2975	A2/6/11	GC 3042	A1/61/15
GC 2913	A3/6/1	GC 2976	D5/20/22	GC 3043	A1/60/17
GC 2914	A3/4/1	GC 2977	E1/1/36	GC 3044	E1/1/38
GC 2915	A1/50/226	GC 2978	A2/24/21	GC 3045	E1/1/37
GC 2916	B2/6/2	GC 2979	A1/43/70	GC 3046	A1/60/104
GC 2917	A2/65/3	GC 2980	D5/101/13	GC 3047	A1/12/177
GC 2918	A1/45/11	GC 2981	D5/46/4	GC 3048	A1/12/176
GC 2919	B2/6/3	GC 2982	A1/35/5	GC 3049	D1/18/4
GC 2920–1	A1/35/2–3	GC 2983	A2/6/12	GC 3049*	D1/1/9
GC 2922	J2/3/1	GC 2984	A1/53/4	GC 3050	D1/1/10
GC 2923	A1/32/8	GC 2985	A1/53/3	GC 3051	D5/1/17
GC 2924	A1/60/60	GC 2986	A1/24/296	GC 3052	B2/2/2
GC 2925	G3/1/34	GC 2987	A2/98/5	GC 3053	A1/60/38
GC 2926	A1/35/4	GC 2988	A1/50/13	GC 3054	A1/60/37
GC 2927	A1/32/9	GC 2989–90	A1/61/8–9	GC 3055	A1/60/115
GC 2928	A1/8/5	GC 2991	A1/61/11	GC 3056	A2/94/1
GC 2929	D7/1/1	GC 2992	A1/50/144	GC 3057	D5/1/14
GC 2930	A1/12/173	GC 2993–4	A1/60/13	GC 3058	A1/60/34
GC 2931	D5/78/2	GC 2995–6	A1/60/67–8	GC 3059	A1/50/142
GC 2932	A1/12/232	GC 2997	A2/20/1	GC 3060	A1/60/86
GC 2933	A1/12/174	GC 2998	B4/6/12	GC 3061	A2/41/1
GC 2934	D5/8/8	GC 2999	A1/61/12	GC 3062	D1/22/1
GC 2935	A1/24/295	GC 3000	D1/18/3	GC 3063	A2/93/2
GC 2936	D7/3/1	GC 3001	A1/53/5	GC 3064	A2/93/1
GC 2937	A2/6/14	GC 3002	A2/52/1	GC 3064*	A2/65/4

Document ref.	Catalogue ref.	Document ref.	Catalogue ref.	Document ref.	Catalogue ref.
GC 3064**	A2/93/5	GC 3129	B3/7/4	GC 3196–7	A1/50/14–15
GC 3064***	A1/13/6	GC 3130	B4/4/3	GC 3198	A1/60/44
GC 3065	A1/24/237	GC 3131	A1/50/43	GC 3199	G4/12/1
GC 3066–7	A1/60/18	GC 3132	A2/17/15	GC 3200	E1/8/4
GC 3068	A2/11/1	GC 3133	A2/48/5	GC 3201	A2/37/16
GC 3069	A1/60/51	GC 3134–7	A1/24/297	GC 3202–3	B6/3/47
GC 3070	A1/60/42	GC 3138	A1/50/35	GC 3204	A1/50/148
GC 3071	A1/24/238	GC 3139	A2/42/11	GC 3205	B3/2/8
GC 3072–4	A1/60/105–7	GC 3140	A1/50/38	GC 3206–7	A1/1/18
GC 3075	A2/93/3	GC 3141–2	A1/60/117	GC 3208	A1/1/14
GC 3076	A2/11/10	GC 3143	D5/23/2	GC 3209–10	A1/1/16–17
GC 3077–8	D5/23/1	GC 3144	G2/1/12	GC 3211	A1/1/15
GC 3079	A1/50/11	GC 3145	B1/1/23	GC 3212	A1/45/22
GC 3080	A2/60/1	GC 3146	A1/50/44	GC 3213	A1/60/94
GC 3081	A2/93/4	GC 3147	A1/24/228	GC 3214	A1/60/96
GC 3082	K4/6/1	GC 3148	B1/1/25	GC 3215	A1/60/95
GC 3083	A1/60/103	GC 3149	G5/6/2	GC 3216	E1/8/5
GC 3084	A1/60/102	GC 3150–1	A1/50/26–7	GC 3217	A1/11/109
GC 3085	D5/1/16	GC 3152	E1/1/51	GC 3218–19	A1/11/84–5
GC 3086	D5/1/15	GC 3153	A1/13/29	GC 3220	D1/1/12
GC 3087	D5/1/16	GC 3154	A2/34/1	GC 3221	A1/11/110
GC 3088	A1/60/19	GC 3155	A1/11/108	GC 3222	A2/35/6
GC 3089–90	A3/1/1–2	GC 3156	A2/92/3	GC 3223	A2/92/4
GC 3091	A1/25/20	GC 3157–8	C2/1/15–16	GC 3224	A1/1/20
GC 3092	A1/61/25	GC 3159	G5/5/1	GC 3225	A2/35/5
GC 3093	A1/15/1	GC 3160	A2/67/16	GC 3226–7	J1/6/12–13
GC 3094	A2/65/5	GC 3161	A1/12/236	GC 3228	A1/50/158
GC 3095	A1/60/22	GC 3162	B7/3/14	GC 3229	A1/50/91
GC 3096	D1/1/7	GC 3163	J1/4/5	GC 3230	A1/50/227
GC 3097	A1/60/23	GC 3164	A2/37/15	GC 3231–2	D1/1/13–14
GC 3098	A3/3/1	GC 3165	A1/50/169	GC 3233	D1/14/3
GC 3099	A3/2/1	GC 3166	A1/50/168	GC 3234	G4/6/46
GC 3100	A2/29/1	GC 3167	B6/3/2	GC 3235	D3/3/2
GC 3101	D5/1/18	GC 3168	A1/50/147	GC 3236	E1/1/39
GC 3102	A2/49/1	GC 3169	D5/77/3	GC 3237	D1/6/2
GC 3103	A2/41/2	GC 3170–1	A2/26/7–8	GC 3238*	D3/3/1
GC 3104	A1/49/12	GC 3172	G5/10/1	GC 3239	B4/8/4
GC 3105–6	A2/35/3–4	GC 3173	A1/50/150	GC 3239*	A2/77/9
GC 3107–8	A2/92/2	GC 3174–5	E1/10/1–2	GC 3240–2	A2/77/10–12
GC 3109	A2/2/1	GC 3176	A1/50/151	GC 3243	A2/29/10
GC 3110	A1/50/146	GC 3177	A1/60/52	GC 3244	B5/8/2
GC 3111	A1/13/28	GC 3178	A1/50/152	GC 3245	A2/35/7
GC 3112	E1/1/47	GC 3179	A2/67/17	GC 3246	A2/65/6
GC 3113	B1/4/23	GC 3179*	A2/83/1	GC 3247	B7/3/16
GC 3114	A2/77/8	GC 3180	G3/1/28	GC 3247*	B1/1/4
GC 3115	G5/6/24	GC 3181	G3/1/38	GC 3248	A1/60/89
GC 3116	A1/61/16	GC 3182	A1/65/10	GC 3249	A1/1/13
GC 3117	A1/61/19	GC 3183	E1/7/4	GC 3250	A1/1/80
GC 3118	A1/60/87	GC 3184	A1/50/154	GC 3251	A1/60/123
GC 3119	A1/50/25	GC 3185	A1/50/12	GC 3252	A2/25/3
GC 3120	A1/60/72	GC 3186	A1/50/155	GC 3253	D1/1/1
GC 3121	A1/24/100	GC 3187	A2/50/7	GC 3254	A1/13/4
GC 3122–3	A2/29/6–7	GC 3188	B1/1/58	GC 3255	A1/36/12
GC 3124–5	A1/50/129	GC 3189	A1/50/157	GC 3256	A1/39/18
GC 3125*	K4/3/1	GC 3190–2	A1/49/14	GC 3257	A2/27/1
GC 3126–7	B4/4/1–2	GC 3193	A2/64/3	GC 3258	A1/66/12
GC 3127*	A2/64/10	GC 3194	A2/49/2	GC 3259	A1/51/17
GC 3128	B4/4/5	GC 3195	B4/8/2		

Document ref.	Catalogue ref.	Document ref.	Catalogue ref.	Document ref.	Catalogue ref.
GC 3260	A1/13/11	GC 3317	A1/60/28	GC 3381	C2/2/8
GC 3261	A1/24/45	GC 3318	A2/19/32	GC 3382	D5/101/16
GC 3262	A1/19/40	GC 3319	A1/12/192	GC 3383	A1/50/45
GC 3263	A1/12/69	GC 3320	A2/81/2	GC 3384	G4/6/47
GC 3264	A1/24/101	GC 3321	A2/67/5	GC 3385	A1/14/33
GC 3265	A1/13/21	GC 3322	A1/60/63	GC 3386	A1/24/183
GC 3266	A2/15/8	GC 3323	A1/60/41	GC 3387	D5/96/1
GC 3267	A1/21/4	GC 3324	A1/60/50	GC 3388	A1/61/22
GC 3268	A1/9/23	GC 3325	A2/11/2	GC 3389–90	A1/27/14
GC 3269	A2/35/9	GC 3326	A1/12/237	GC 3391	A1/39/19
GC 3271	A2/2/2	GC 3327	A2/98/1	GC 3392	A1/50/209
GC 3272	A2/23/5	GC 3328	A2/45/2	GC 3393–4	A2/50/8–9
GC 3273	A1/12/50	GC 3329–30	A1/60/69–70	GC 3395	A1/12/238
GC 3274	A1/12/113	GC 3331	A1/33/6	GC 3396	A1/7/7
GC 3275	A1/36/24	GC 3332	G3/1/45	GC 3397	A1/50/28
GC 3276	A1/60/122	GC 3333	A1/22/4	GC 3398	B7/3/18
GC 3277	A2/35/1	GC 3334	A1/60/47	GC 3399	A1/13/16
GC 3278	A1/3/91	GC 3335	D5/42/2	GC 3400	A1/30/7
GC 3278	A2/98/2	GC 3336	B6/3/35	GC 3401	B3/8/1
GC 3279	A2/67/21	GC 3337	A1/60/45	GC 3402–3	D1/1/5–6
GC 3280	A1/13/23	GC 3338	A1/60/10	GC 3404	J1/4/3
GC 3281	A1/25/6	GC 3339	A1/24/301	GC 3405	A1/50/162
GC 3282	A1/13/14	GC 3340	G1/4/4	GC 3406	A1/11/28
GC 3283	A1/47/1	GC 3341	A1/60/55	GC 3407	A2/35/13
GC 3284	A2/53/4	GC 3342	A1/60/29	GC 3408	B4/8/5
GC 3285	A1/43/71	GC 3343	A1/60/32	GC 3409	A2/42/4
GC 3286	A2/53/15	GC 3344	A2/35/2	GC 3410	A1/12/178
GC 3287	A2/45/3	GC 3345	A1/60/90	GC 3411	A1/50/163
GC 3288	A1/24/44	GC 3346	A1/60/109	GC 3412	A1/13/8
GC 3289	A1/50/156	GC 3347–8	A2/37/17	GC 3413	G3/1/39
GC 3290	A1/60/64	GC 3349	A1/36/3	GC 3414	A1/33/7
GC 3291	A1/60/53	GC 3350	B1/1/53	GC 3415	A2/53/8
GC 3292	A1/50/8	GC 3351–2	A2/29/8–9	GC 3416	G2/2/1
GC 3293	A1/60/85	GC 3353	A1/3/245	GC 3417	D1/1/8
GC 3294	A1/60/88	GC 3354	A2/67/12	GC 3418	A1/56/29
GC 3295	A1/37/2	GC 3355	A2/29/3	GC 3419	J1/6/11
GC 3296	A1/58/18	GC 3356	A2/98/4	GC 3420–1	A1/50/74–5
GC 3297	A1/11/92	GC 3357–8	A2/35/10–11	GC 3422	A1/13/7
GC 3298	A2/11/5	GC 3359	B7/3/17	GC 3423	A1/13/8
GC 3299	A1/36/2	GC 3360	D6/8/1	GC 3424	J1/3/2
GC 3299*	D5/61/1	GC 3361	A1/50/160	GC 3425	A1/35/7
GC 3300	A1/36/1	GC 3362	B4/3/1	GC 3426	B7/3/19
GC 3301	A1/61/27	GC 3363	A1/53/6	GC 3427	A1/12/179
GC 3302	A1/60/61	GC 3364	A1/50/48	GC 3428	B7/3/20
GC 3303	A1/60/40	GC 3365	A1/14/31	GC 3429	A1/12/180
GC 3304	A1/60/39	GC 3367	A2/35/12	GC 3430	A5/1/3
GC 3305	A1/60/31	GC 3366	B4/2/3	GC 3431	A2/35/14
GC 3306	A1/60/49	GC 3368	B4/3/2	GC 3432	J1/7/2
GC 3307	A1/60/16	GC 3369	B5/4/4	GC 3433	A2/78/2
GC 3308	A1/50/7	GC 3370	A2/2/3	GC 3434	A2/78/1
GC 3309	A1/60/108	GC 3371	A1/19/22	GC 3435	A2/75/4
GC 3310	A2/29/4	GC 3372	A1/53/7	GC 3436–7	A1/12/181–2
GC 3311	B6/3/50	GC 3373	D5/13/5	GC 3438	B6/3/48
GC 3312	A1/62/19	GC 3374	A1/50/208	GC 3439	K10/1/7
GC 3313	A1/60/73	GC 3375–7	A2/95/1–3	GC 3440	A2/50/22
GC 3314	A1/60/26	GC 3378	D5/9/4	GC 3441	B5/8/3
GC 3315	A1/60/7	GC 3379	A2/46/3	GC 3442	B5/9/2
GC 3316	A1/50/153	GC 3380	A1/60/98	GC 3443	A1/12/87

Document ref.	Catalogue ref.	Document ref.	Catalogue ref.	Document ref.	Catalogue ref.
GC 3444	G3/1/17	GC 3507	A1/68/3	GC 3569	A1/62/18
GC 3445	A1/50/170	GC 3507*	G5/6/3	GC 3570	B5/6/1
GC 3446	A1/24/184	GC 3508–9	B3/9/1–2	GC 3571	A1/46/8
GC 3447	B7/3/21	GC 3510	A5/8/1	GC 3572	A1/52/13
GC 3448	A1/11/111	GC 3511	A1/11/32	GC 3573	A2/36/5
GC 3449	B7/3/27	GC 3512	A2/37/18	GC 3574	A2/46/4
GC 3450	A1/50/229	GC 3513	A2/10/1	GC 3575	E1/8/6
GC 3451	B6/3/49	GC 3514	A2/44/15	GC 3576	A2/36/7
GC 3452	K4/22/1	GC 3515	A1/13/3	GC 3577	A2/36/6
GC 3453	D5/47/9	GC 3516	A1/24/41	GC 3578–9	A2/36/8–9
GC 3454	A2/50/23	GC 3517	B1/1/5	GC 3580	B4/6/4
GC 3455	A1/50/46	GC 3518	A2/6/30	GC 3581	A1/43/57
GC 3456	J1/3/3	GC 3519	D5/24/2	GC 3582	A1/3/204
GC 3457	B7/3/22	GC 3520–1	A1/50/174–5	GC 3583–4	A1/50/39–40
GC 3458	G4/6/79	GC 3522	G5/6/3	GC 3585–6	A2/7/1
GC 3459	A1/50/230	GC 3523	A1/50/159	GC 3587	G3/1/40
GC 3460	B4/6/3	GC 3524	A2/38/1	GC 3588	G4/6/39
GC 3461	A1/50/199	GC 3525	H1/12/3	GC 3589	A1/11/93
GC 3462	A2/91/1	GC 3526	G3/1/19	GC 3590	A1/3/256
GC 3463	A1/50/231	GC 3527	A1/50/57	GC 3591	A1/50/180
GC 3464	A1/12/239	GC 3528	A5/8/2	GC 3592	B4/4/20
GC 3465	B6/3/51	GC 3529	B4/9/3	GC 3593	A2/30/3
GC 3466	A1/56/12	GC 3530	A1/24/299	GC 3594	A2/36/10
GC 3467	A3/17/1	GC 3531	B5/9/4	GC 3595	A1/24/300
GC 3468	A1/68/2	GC 3532	B5/9/3	GC 3596	A2/50/10
GC 3469	A1/50/49	GC 3533	K4/23/1	GC 3597	A1/24/224
GC 3470	A2/95/5	GC 3534–5	A1/65/34	GC 3598	B1/1/71
GC 3471	J1/3/4	GC 3536	A1/62/17	GC 3599	B1/1/61
GC 3472–3	A1/53/8–9	GC 3537	A1/62/13	GC 3600	A1/10/1
GC 3474	A2/64/4	GC 3537*	A1/50/92	GC 3601	G4/6/48
GC 3475	D1/6/3	GC 3538	A2/41/3	GC 3602	A2/50/19
GC 3476	G2/1/13	GC 3539	A1/50/17	GC 3603	A2/65/7
GC 3477	A2/20/2	GC 3540–1	A2/50/16–17	GC 3604	A2/42/5
GC 3478	A1/50/161	GC 3542	A1/24/176	GC 3605	A1/24/223
GC 3479	B2/2/3	GC 3543	A1/50/232	GC 3606	D5/77/4
GC 3480	A1/11/29	GC 3544	D1/7/1	GC 3607	G4/6/49
GC 3481	D1/1/4	GC 3545	A1/31/54	GC 3608	B1/1/6
GC 3482	B4/2/4	GC 3546	B4/7/1	GC 3609	A5/9/4
GC 3483	B4/2/5	GC 3547	A1/12/240	GC 3609*	A2/24/42
GC 3484	A1/56/13	GC 3548	A1/1/74	GC 3610	A1/50/201
GC 3485	B1/2/10	GC 3549–50	A1/12/185–6	GC 3611	A1/50/233
GC 3486	A1/11/83	GC 3551	B7/3/23	GC 3612	J1/3/7
GC 3487	G5/8/1	GC 3552	A1/12/187	GC 3613	A1/50/171
GC 3488	B6/7/2	GC 3553	A1/62/20	GC 3614	A2/64/7
GC 3489	A1/35/9	GC 3554–5	B7/3/25–6	GC 3615	A2/50/18
GC 3490	A1/35/8	GC 3556	D5/37/4	GC 3616	A1/50/58
GC 3491	D5/23/3	GC 3557	B5/1/1	GC 3617	A1/63/1
GC 3492–3	D1/11/1–2	GC 3558	A1/50/200	GC 3618	A1/12/188
GC 3494	A1/11/30	GC 3559	A2/24/41	GC 3619	G3/1/41
GC 3495	A1/35/10	GC 3560	A2/69/1	GC 3620–1	A1/50/64–5
GC 3496	G3/1/18	GC 3561	B7/3/28	GC 3622	A1/24/239
GC 3497–8	A1/35/12–13	GC 3562	K5/1/1	GC 3623	A1/50/59
GC 3499	A1/56/14	GC 3563	B1/1/13	GC 3624	A2/64/8
GC 3500–2	A2/67/18–20	GC 3564	A2/60/2	GC 3625	A1/24/242
GC 3503	C2/2/3	GC 3565	A1/43/55	GC 3626	A1/43/132
GC 3504	A1/43/142	GC 3566	B7/3/29	GC 3627	A1/24/243
GC 3505	A1/13/22	GC 3567	A2/60/3	GC 3628	A1/50/172
GC 3506	H1/12/2	GC 3568	B5/1/2	GC 3629	A1/50/66

Document ref.	Catalogue ref.	Document ref.	Catalogue ref.	Document ref.	Catalogue ref.
GC 3630	G4/6/40	GC 3693	B1/1/66	GC 3753*	B4/4/7
GC 3631	A5/10/7	GC 3694	A1/50/173	GC 3754	B1/4/11
GC 3632	A1/50/177	GC 3695	B1/1/68	GC 3754*	B5/7/1
GC 3633	A1/24/244	GC 3696–8	B1/1/62–4	GC 3755	A1/50/186
GC 3634	A1/50/47	GC 3699	G3/1/20	GC 3755*	B4/4/8
GC 3635	A1/11/35	GC 3700	A1/40/5	GC 3756	A1/45/23
GC 3636	A1/43/22	GC 3701	A1/11/53	GC 3757	A1/11/113
GC 3637	J1/1/1	GC 3702	B1/1/64	GC 3758	A1/24/246
GC 3638	A1/50/60	GC 3703	A1/12/243	GC 3759	A1/24/245
GC 3639	A1/11/47	GC 3704	A1/40/4	GC 3760	A2/50/13
GC 3640	A1/11/91	GC 3705	A2/36/14	GC 3761	G4/11/1
GC 3641	A1/12/241	GC 3706	E1/6/1	GC 3762	A2/88/6
GC 3642	J1/4/11	GC 3707	A1/67/9	GC 3763	A1/50/68
GC 3643	G4/5/2	GC 3708	A1/12/189	GC 3764	B4/4/9
GC 3644	B1/4/10	GC 3709	A1/24/185	GC 3765	A1/50/236
GC 3645	B6/10/1	GC 3710	G3/1/22	GC 3766	A2/70/1
GC 3646	A1/50/184	GC 3711	G3/1/21	GC 3767	A1/50/51
GC 3647	B3/2/1	GC 3712	A1/11/49	GC 3768	A5/1/7
GC 3649	B6/1/7	GC 3713	B4/4/18	GC 3769–70	A1/24/249
GC 3650	B3/5/1	GC 3714	A1/49/13	GC 3771	E1/1/48
GC 3651	B1/1/7	GC 3715	A2/29/2	GC 3773	A2/70/2
GC 3652	B6/1/8	GC 3716	B1/1/67	GC 3774	A1/34/29
GC 3653–4	B3/5/2–3	GC 3717	A1/43/54	GC 3776	A1/1/107
GC 3655	B2/6/4	GC 3718	B4/7/2	GC 3777–8	A1/11/41–2
GC 3656	B2/4/2	GC 3719	A1/43/23	GC 3779	K4/9/1
GC 3657	B3/5/4	GC 3720	A1/11/54	GC 3780	A1/67/10
GC 3658	B1/1/8	GC 3721	A1/11/40	GC 3781	A1/50/67
GC 3659	B3/5/5	GC 3722	G4/2/2	GC 3782	A1/58/20
GC 3660	A1/24/192	GC 3723	D4/4/2	GC 3783	A1/50/52
GC 3661	A2/50/20	GC 3724	A1/11/48	GC 3784	A1/25/21
GC 3662	A1/12/242	GC 3725	A1/12/195	GC 3785	A1/67/11
GC 3663	A1/50/234	GC 3726	A2/50/12	GC 3786	A2/24/34
GC 3664	A1/11/112	GC 3727	A1/11/55	GC 3787	G4/6/7
GC 3665–6	B6/3/1	GC 3728	A1/50/18	GC 3788–93	A2/19/17–22
GC 3667	A1/50/76	GC 3729	A1/11/57	GC 3794	A5/8/3
GC 3668	A1/11/12	GC 3730	A1/11/56	GC 3795	A1/35/14
GC 3669–70	A1/11/13	GC 3731	A1/50/187	GC 3796–7	A1/50/190–1
GC 3671	A1/36/25	GC 3732	E1/1/40	GC 3798	A1/22/8
GC 3672	A2/26/4	GC 3733	A1/11/94	GC 3799	A2/19/23
GC 3673	A1/43/134	GC 3734	A1/11/95	GC 3800	A1/12/244
GC 3676	A1/50/235	GC 3735	A1/12/190	GC 3801	K3/1/1
GC 3677	A2/36/12	GC 3736	A1/50/178	GC 3802	B2/4/5
GC 3678	G5/6/25	GC 3737	A2/88/5	GC 3803	A5/9/5
GC 3679	K10/1/2	GC 3738	B3/2/3	GC 3804	A1/11/114
GC 3680	K10/1/1	GC 3739	A1/50/176	GC 3805	G3/1/42
GC 3681	A2/67/1	GC 3740	A1/36/18	GC 3806	B4/6/5
GC 3681*	B6/8/1	GC 3741	A1/50/185	GC 3807	A1/24/240
GC 3682	B3/2/2	GC 3742	A2/60/4	GC 3808	A1/50/193
GC 3683	G4/6/50	GC 3743	B3/2/4	GC 3809–10	A2/24/35–6
GC 3684	A1/4/17	GC 3744	G5/6/26	GC 3810*	A1/14/58
GC 3685	A2/67/2	GC 3745–6	A1/50/19	GC 3811	A1/50/192
GC 3686	A2/96/1	GC 3747	B4/4/6	GC 3812	G2/1/19
GC 3687	A2/36/13	GC 3748	B3/6/1	GC 3813	D1/23/8
GC 3688	A1/11/51	GC 3750	A2/24/32	GC 3814	A1/50/53
GC 3689	A1/43/133	GC 3751	A2/17/23	GC 3815–16	H2/1/1–2
GC 3690	A1/12/243	GC 3752	A2/24/33	GC 3817	A1/50/237
GC 3691	A3/17/2	GC 3752*	A2/24/33	GC 3818	A1/11/43
GC 3692	A1/11/52	GC 3753	B4/4/7	GC 3819	D1/19/3

Document ref.	Catalogue ref.	Document ref.	Catalogue ref.	Document ref.	Catalogue ref.
GC 3820	B4/6/6	GC 3893	A2/19/8	GC 3960	E1/1/11
GC 3821	B5/8/4	GC 3894–5	A2/24/37	GC 3961	B7/3/24
GC 3823	A1/24/250	GC 3896–7	A2/24/38	GC 3962	B6/3/10
GC 3824	A1/12/114	GC 3898	A1/50/240	GC 3963	A1/11/94
GC 3825	A1/11/50	GC 3899	B2/6/5	GC 3964	E1/1/10
GC 3826	G3/1/47	GC 3900	A2/76/1	GC 3965	B4/4/10
GC 3827	D6/9/3	GC 3901	E1/1/16	GC 3966	A1/39/38
GC 3828	A1/50/238	GC 3902	A1/1/102	GC 3967	A1/60/97
GC 3829	D1/14/1	GC 3903	A1/43/25	GC 3968	G5/6/1
GC 3830	A1/12/245	GC 3904–6	A1/4/31–3	GC 3969	A1/50/98
GC 3831	B4/6/7	GC 3907	A1/50/188	GC 3970	A1/27/4
GC 3832	E1/1/81	GC 3908	A1/24/264	GC 3971	A1/50/99
GC 3833	A2/46/5	GC 3909	A1/12/246	GC 3972	A1/50/56
GC 3834–5	A1/4/26–7	GC 3910	E1/1/17	GC 3973	A5/8/4
GC 3835*	G1/5/1	GC 3911	E1/9/2	GC 3974	A1/24/302
GC 3836	A1/50/181	GC 3912–13	A1/51/18	GC 3974–5	G2/1/14–15
GC 3837	A1/4/28	GC 3914	B1/1/72	GC 3976	A1/1/100
GC 3838	A1/50/239	GC 3915	A1/50/94	GC 3977	A1/67/12
GC 3839	G5/9/1	GC 3916	E1/1/18	GC 3978	A1/11/31
GC 3840	A2/60/5	GC 3917	A1/57/9	GC 3979	A1/11/115
GC 3841	A1/35/15	GC 3918	A1/12/196	GC 3980–1	A2/96/2–3
GC 3842	A4/2/22	GC 3919	A1/50/95	GC 3982	A1/12/194
GC 3843–4	A1/35/16–17	GC 3920	A2/23/6	GC 3983	A1/12/193
GC 3845	A1/12/191	GC 3921	A1/24/102	GC 3984	B5/7/2
GC 3846	G1/6/3	GC 3922	A1/24/303	GC 3985	A2/24/3
GC 3847	D1/16/1	GC 3923	B1/1/74	GC 3986	A1/50/204
GC 3848	A1/50/69	GC 3924	A1/50/96	GC 3987–9	A1/51/19–21
GC 3849	A1/50/182	GC 3925	B1/1/73	GC 3989*	A2/83/2
GC 3850	A1/50/70	GC 3926–8	B1/1/75–7	GC 3990	A1/50/195
GC 3851	A1/50/194	GC 3929	A2/19/31	GC 3991	A1/50/100
GC 3852	A1/24/247	GC 3930	A1/43/27	GC 3992	A1/50/202
GC 3853	G2/4/2	GC 3931	A1/50/86	GC 3993	A1/50/196
GC 3854	B2/6/6	GC 3932	G5/3/1	GC 3994	A1/50/203
GC 3855	A1/50/54	GC 3933	A1/50/71	GC 3995	B5/7/3
GC 3856	A1/43/136	GC 3934	B4/6/8	GC 3996	A1/50/101
GC 3857	A1/50/55	GC 3935	B1/1/65	GC 3997	A2/83/3
GC 3858–9	G4/6/53	GC 3936	A1/4/34	GC 3998	G4/6/8
GC 3860–1	G4/13/1–2	GC 3937	A1/50/20	GC 3999	A1/50/189
GC 3862	A1/50/183	GC 3938	A1/50/97	GC 4000	J1/5/1
GC 3863–4	A1/4/29–30	GC 3939	A1/12/88	GC 4001	A2/17/10
GC 3865	A1/24/177	GC 3940	B4/6/9	GC 4002	A2/6/23
GC 3866–7	A1/36/4–5	GC 3941	A2/46/6	GC 4003–4	A2/19/24–5
GC 3868	A1/43/135	GC 3942	D3/4/1	GC 4005	A2/77/13
GC 3869	A1/24/248	GC 3943	A1/43/26	GC 4006–7	A1/43/137–8
GC 3870–2	G4/6/54	GC 3944	A2/19/9	GC 4008	A1/50/179
GC 3873	D1/19/4	GC 3946	A1/62/21	GC 4009	A1/24/241
GC 3875	A1/12/115	GC 3947	A1/43/24	GC 4010	A1/50/102
GC 3876	D1/19/5	GC 3948	A2/73/1	GC 4011	A1/11/36
GC 3877	A1/1/101	GC 3950	A1/50/61	GC 4012	K4/20/1
GC 3878	A1/36/6	GC 3951	A2/64/11	GC 4013	A1/63/4
GC 3879	G1/2/1	GC 3952	A2/73/2	GC 4014	A1/50/62
GC 3880–1	A1/50/84–5	GC 3953	A2/88/1	GC 4015	G4/9/1
GC 3882	A1/43/143	GC 3954	B1/1/78	GC 4016–17	A1/11/45–6
GC 3883–6	A1/63/2–3	GC 3955	A2/85/2	GC 4018	G4/6/51
GC 3887	A1/24/74	GC 3956	A2/17/9	GC 4019	G5/6/4
GC 3888	A1/50/205	GC 3957	B1/1/95	GC 4019*	A1/24/193
GC 3889–90	G3/1/4	GC 3958	A1/43/28	GC 4020	A1/50/72
GC 3891–2	G3/1/5–6	GC 3959	A1/14/23	GC 4021	E1/1/27

Document ref.	Catalogue ref.	Document ref.	Catalogue ref.	Document ref.	Catalogue ref.
GC 4022	A1/12/89	GC 4094	A1/63/7	GC 4162	A2/77/15
GC 4023	A1/50/73	GC 4095	H1/9/1	GC 4163	A1/24/179
GC 4024	A1/50/77	GC 4096–7	B4/6/10–11	GC 4164	D1/1/34
GC 4025	A1/50/103	GC 4098–9	A2/96/4–5	GC 4166–7	G2/1/16–17
GC 4026–7	A1/50/78–9	GC 4100–1	A1/11/58–9	GC 4168	A1/11/71
GC 4028	A2/17/24	GC 4102	A1/50/108	GC 4169	G4/13/4
GC 4029	A1/1/103	GC 4103	A2/67/23	GC 4170	K1/2/1
GC 4030	A1/24/75	GC 4104–5	D5/77/5–6	GC 4171	A2/26/9
GC 4032	E1/8/2	GC 4106	A1/19/46	GC 4172	G2/4/3
GC 4033	G4/6/41	GC 4107	A1/14/78	GC 4173	A1/52/5
GC 4034	C2/2/10	GC 4108–9	A1/3/257	GC 4173*	A1/43/72
GC 4035–7	A1/50/80–2	GC 4110	A1/50/109	GC 4174–5	A2/35/15
GC 4038	A2/19/26	GC 4111	J1/3/5	GC 4176	A5/8/5
GC 4039	A1/52/6	GC 4112	A5/10/10	GC 4177	A1/11/62
GC 4040	A1/50/104	GC 4114	A1/14/79	GC 4178	A1/43/149
GC 4041	A1/52/5	GC 4115–16	A1/43/140–1	GC 4179–80	D1/1/32–3
GC 4042	A2/19/27	GC 4117	A1/11/60	GC 4181	C2/2/17
GC 4043	A1/14/25	GC 4118	A1/11/116	GC 4182–3	D1/1/35–6
GC 4044	A2/24/4	GC 4119	A1/12/56	GC 4184–5	D1/1/38–9
GC 4045–6	A1/50/105–6	GC 4120–1	A1/12/57	GC 4186	D1/1/37
GC 4047	A5/1/4	GC 4122	A1/11/61	GC 4187	D1/1/40
GC 4048	A1/46/11	GC 4123	A1/31/55	GC 4188	A1/24/103
GC 4049	G4/6/42	GC 4124	D5/77/7	GC 4189–92	D1/1/41–4
GC 4050	A1/52/7	GC 4125–8	C2/2/11–14	GC 4193	D1/1/47
GC 4051–3	A1/24/251–3	GC 4129	A1/1/46	GC 4194	D1/1/46
GC 4054	A1/4/40	GC 4130	K4/4/1	GC 4195–7	D1/1/48–50
GC 4055	A1/50/87	GC 4131	A1/64/67	GC 4198	D7/1/2
GC 4056	A2/17/16	GC 4132	A1/32/25	GC 4199	D1/1/51
GC 4057–8	A2/8/10	GC 4133	K7/1/1	GC 4200	D1/1/45
GC 4059	A1/35/18	GC 4134–5	E1/1/20–1	GC 4201–2	D5/77/8–9
GC 4060–1	A2/76/2–3	GC 4135*	E1/1/22	GC 4203	A1/68/4
GC 4062	G4/6/43	GC 4136	A1/50/83	GC 4204	A1/27/6
GC 4063	A2/17/25	GC 4137	A1/1/26	GC 4205	A2/50/14
GC 4064	A1/12/90	GC 4138	K3/2/1	GC 4206	A1/12/116
GC 4065–6	A2/17/17–18	GC 4139	A1/36/19	GC 4207	A1/25/12
GC 4067	A1/24/46	GC 4140	G4/12/2	GC 4208–9	A2/43/1–2
GC 4068–9	A2/85/3–4	GC 4141	G4/6/44	GC 4210–12	G3/1/9–11
GC 4070	A2/67/22	GC 4141*	G3/1/15	GC 4214	A2/50/15
GC 4071	A1/27/5	GC 4142	A1/11/69	GC 4215	D5/77/10
GC 4072	A1/3/100	GC 4143	A1/39/4	GC 4216	A5/8/6
GC 4073–4	A1/63/5–6	GC 4144	A1/43/144	GC 4217	A1/3/101
GC 4075	A1/14/59	GC 4145	C1/2/2	GC 4218	A1/42/1
GC 4076	G5/6/27	GC 4146	A1/1/47	GC 4219	G1/7/1
GC 4077	K4/18/1	GC 4146*	A1/1/47	GC 4220	A1/27/8
GC 4078	A2/50/21	GC 4147	A2/42/1	GC 4221	A1/3/86
GC 4079	A1/11/90	GC 4148	A1/11/67	GC 4222–3	A1/43/59–60
GC 4080–1	B5/9/5–6	GC 4149	A1/11/117	GC 4224	A1/24/61
GC 4082	G3/1/7	GC 4150	A1/11/68	GC 4225–7	A1/11/63–4
GC 4083–4	B5/7/4–5	GC 4151	A1/43/147	GC 4228	A1/25/13
GC 4085	A1/24/47	GC 4152	G3/1/35	GC 4229–30	A1/43/146
GC 4086	A1/11/38	GC 4153	A2/42/2	GC 4231	A1/43/61
GC 4087	A1/11/37	GC 4154	A1/11/70	GC 4232	A1/24/254
GC 4088	A1/36/13	GC 4155	E1/3/4	GC 4233	A1/24/255
GC 4089	A1/4/1	GC 4156	D5/76/1	GC 4234	D5/78/3
GC 4090	A1/51/34	GC 4157	A1/43/148	GC 4235	A1/24/104
GC 4091	A1/50/107	GC 4158–9	A1/67/13–14	GC 4235*	G3/1/12
GC 4092	A5/1/5	GC 4160	A1/43/145	GC 4236	A1/43/81
GC 4093	A1/43/139	GC 4161	C2/2/15	GC 4237	A1/24/76

Document ref.	Catalogue ref.	Document ref.	Catalogue ref.	Document ref.	Catalogue ref.
GC 4238	A1/36/26	GC 4307	K3/3/1	GC 4373	A5/8/12
GC 4239–40	A1/11/65	GC 4308	A1/58/19	GC 4374	A2/60/6
GC 4241	D5/78/4	GC 4309	A1/11/74	GC 4375	D1/23/4
GC 4242	A1/27/7	GC 4310	A1/51/35	GC 4376	A1/24/269
GC 4243–4	A1/3/87–8	GC 4311	A1/8/15	GC 4377	A2/43/12
GC 4245	A1/12/117	GC 4312	A1/1/104	GC 4379–80	A2/43/13–14
GC 4246	A1/24/106	GC 4314	A1/4/2	GC 4381	A1/51/39
GC 4247	E1/9/3	GC 4316	G3/1/46	GC 4382	D1/1/18
GC 4248	G3/1/13	GC 4317	A1/11/75	GC 4383	A5/8/15
GC 4249	A5/4/2	GC 4318–21	A2/43/5–8	GC 4384	A1/1/31
GC 4250	A1/12/197	GC 4322	E1/1/28	GC 4385	A1/51/40
GC 4251	A1/11/66	GC 4323	A2/43/9	GC 4386	D1/3/1
GC 4252	A1/11/19	GC 4323*	K10/1/11	GC 4387	A1/1/68
GC 4253	K4/19/1	GC 4324	G5/6/6	GC 4388	A1/11/96
GC 4254	D3/4/2	GC 4325	A1/1/64	GC 4389	A2/43/15
GC 4255	A1/24/180	GC 4325*	H2/2/1	GC 4391	A1/32/26
GC 4256	A1/12/198	GC 4326	A1/10/2	GC 4392	A1/1/69
GC 4257	A1/25/14	GC 4327	A1/24/62	GC 4393	A5/8/13
GC 4258	D5/72/1	GC 4328	J1/6/15	GC 4394	A1/51/41
GC 4259	A2/77/16	GC 4329	G4/6/11	GC 4395	A1/51/36
GC 4260	A1/24/105	GC 4330	A1/1/65	GC 4396	A1/1/61
GC 4261	J2/2/1	GC 4331	A5/7/1	GC 4397	A5/5/8
GC 4262	H1/12/1	GC 4332	D1/1/17	GC 4398	A5/8/14
GC 4262*	H1/8/1	GC 4334	D1/18/5	GC 4399–4400	A5/8/16–17
GC 4263	A1/11/72	GC 4335	A1/1/66	GC 4401	A5/1/9
GC 4264–5	A1/25/15–16	GC 4337	A1/1/28	GC 4402	D1/1/19
GC 4266*	K10/1/4	GC 4338	J1/3/6	GC 4403	A5/7/3
GC 4267	A1/1/108	GC 4338**	A1/24/181	GC 4404	A1/1/32
GC 4268–9	A1/1/53–4	GC 4339	D2/1/1	GC 4404*	A1/51/37
GC 4270	A2/30/4	GC 4341	A5/8/8	GC 4405	D1/1/26
GC 4272	K2/1/1	GC 4342	D4/2/1	GC 4406	A5/8/18
GC 4273	A1/1/55	GC 4343	D1/1/20	GC 4407	A1/51/42
GC 4274	A1/1/82	GC 4344	A2/26/5	GC 4408–10	D1/1/21–3
GC 4275	A1/1/56	GC 4345	A2/88/2	GC 4411	A1/51/43
GC 4276	A2/43/3	GC 4346	A2/77/21	GC 4412–13	A1/1/33–4
GC 4277	K5/16/1	GC 4347	A1/1/78	GC 4415	D5/18/4
GC 4278	A2/43/4	GC 4348	A1/43/150	GC 4416	A1/51/44
GC 4279	D3/5/2	GC 4349	A5/8/9	GC 4417*	A1/11/20
GC 4280	H1/11/1	GC 4350	A5/7/2	GC 4418	G4/6/52
GC 4281	A1/11/118	GC 4351	D1/23/6	GC 4419	D1/14/4
GC 4282	G4/6/9	GC 4353	A2/77/17	GC 4420	A1/12/118
GC 4283–7	A1/63/8–12	GC 4354–5	A2/43/10–11	GC 4421	G4/6/12
GC 4289	A3/3/3	GC 4357	A2/87/1	GC 4421*	G4/6/12
GC 4290	A1/36/14	GC 4357*	A1/24/182	GC 4422	A5/8/19
GC 4291	K2/2/1	GC 4357**	H1/3/2	GC 4423	A1/11/21
GC 4292	G3/1/43	GC 4358	A1/56/18	GC 4424	A1/51/45
GC 4293	G3/1/44	GC 4359	A1/50/110	GC 4425	D1/1/24
GC 4294	E1/1/53	GC 4360	E1/1/12	GC 4426	A5/1/10
GC 4296	A1/39/5	GC 4361	A2/26/6	GC 4427	D5/83/2
GC 4297	A1/7/8	GC 4362	A1/43/82	GC 4427*	A1/1/62
GC 4298	G4/6/10	GC 4364	D5/51/7	GC 4428–30	A5/8/20–2
GC 4299–300	A1/32/18–19	GC 4365	A1/43/151	GC 4431	A1/24/63
GC 4301	A1/32/20	GC 4366	G1/6/2	GC 4432	A1/11/97
GC 4302	A1/11/73	GC 4367–8	D1/23/4	GC 4433–4	D1/1/27
GC 4303	G5/6/5	GC 4369	A1/1/29	GC 4435	A1/11/119
GC 4304	K1/3/1	GC 4370	A5/8/11	GC 4436	A2/42/3
GC 4305	D5/83/1	GC 4371	A1/1/30	GC 4437	A1/16/5
GC 4306	A5/8/7	GC 4372	A1/12/58	GC 4438	A1/24/184

Document ref.	Catalogue ref.	Document ref.	Catalogue ref.	Document ref.	Catalogue ref.
SC 61	A2/17/19	SC 121	A2/24/27	SC 181	B1/1/34
SC 62	D5/23/36	SC 122	D5/50/1	SC 182	D5/74/23
SC 63	B6/1/1	SC 123	D5/30/2	SC 183	E1/1/24
SC 64	A2/80/2	SC 124	D5/33/1	SC 184	D5/26/6
SC 65	B3/7/1	SC 125	A1/11/100	SC 185	F1/5/1
SC 66	A2/50/1	SC 126	F1/5/27	SC 186	A2/31/5
SC 67	G4/6/2	SC 127	F1/5/33	SC 187	D5/100/1
SC 68	A1/37/3	SC 128	D5/91/1	SC 188	D5/23/15
SC 69	A2/77/2	SC 129	D6/1/2	SC 189	A2/24/31
SC 70	H1/10/2	SC 130	D5/31/6	SC 190	A2/39/2
SC 71	A2/74/3	SC 131	D5/31/4	SC 191	B1/1/83
SC 72	D5/23/12	SC 132	D5/31/3	SC 192	A1/45/16
SC 73–4	A1/56/1–2	SC 133–4	D5/31/1–2	SC 193	A1/14/48
SC 75	A1/51/77	SC 135	D5/31/7	SC 194	B1/1/93
SC 76	G5/6/8	SC 136	D5/38/1	SC 195	D5/20/33
SC 77	D5/41/8	SC 137	D5/3/15	SC 196	B2/9/1
SC 78	D6/7/1	SC 138	D5/20/47	SC 197	D5/26/4
SC 79	A1/20/1	SC 139	A2/24/25	SC 198	B1/4/1
SC 80	see p. lxxxviii	SC 140	A1/24/50	SC 199	B1/1/81
SC 81	A2/74/4	SC 141	F1/5/15	SC 200	D5/47/8
SC 82	D1/13/1	SC 142	D5/50/2	SC 201	A2/24/30
SC 83	A2/80/1	SC 143	K8/1/1	SC 202	D5/23/14
SC 84	A2/71/3	SC 144	G5/6/13	SC 203	A2/88/7
SC 85–6	A2/71/1–2	SC 145	A1/19/52	SC 204	F1/5/25
SC 87	D5/97/1	SC 146	F1/5/17	SC 205	B1/1/51
SC 88	B3/7/2	SC 147	A2/67/13	SC 206	E1/1/78
SC 89	A2/3/3	SC 148	A2/5/1	SC 207	B6/4/4
SC 90	F1/4/1	SC 149	D5/23/37	SC 208	D5/94/5
SC 91	H1/2/1	SC 150	D5/29/1	SC 209	F1/3/2
SC 92	A1/25/17	SC 151	D5/9/1	SC 210	F1/4/4
SC 93	A1/27/1	SC 152–3	D5/29/2–3	SC 211	A1/24/49
SC 94	A2/26/10	SC 154	D5/9/2	SC 212	D5/50/3
SC 95	A2/67/6	SC 155	B6/1/2	SC 213	H1/4/1
SC 96	A5/3/10	SC 156	F1/4/2	SC 214	D5/23/20
SC 97	D5/43/3	SC 157	A1/1/113	SC 215	F1/4/5
SC 98	D6/4/1	SC 158	A1/1/112	SC 216	A1/57/3
SC 99	A1/19/51	SC 159	D5/26/3	SC 217	A2/72/1
SC 100	B3/7/3	SC 160	A1/24/48	SC 218	E1/1/2
SC 101	A2/68/2	SC 161A–B	A1/11/1–2	SC 219	D5/64/1
SC 102	D5/65/1	SC 162	A1/32/11	SC 220	D5/51/3
SC 103	D1/4/1	SC 163	A2/17/21	SC 221	E1/1/4
SC 104	A2/82/3	SC 164	A1/58/1	SC 222	D5/45/2
SC 105	E1/1/23	SC 165	A1/11/3	SC 223	D6/1/3
SC 106	F1/5/16	SC 166	A1/24/80	SC 224	D5/29/4
SC 107	D5/2/1	SC 167	A1/11/4	SC 225–6	D5/4/3–4
SC 108	D6/2/1	SC 168	A2/3/4	SC 227	D5/59/1
SC 109	D5/18/1	SC 169	A1/11/15	SC 228	D5/22/1
SC 110	A2/82/1	SC 170	A2/47/1	SC 229	A5/9/3
SC 111	H1/10/3	SC 171	D5/52/1	SC 230	F1/4/6
SC 112	A1/50/213	SC 172	D6/5/1	SC 231	D5/1/19
SC 113	B1/1/9	SC 173	D5/3/1	SC 232	G3/2/1
SC 114	G5/7/1	SC 174	G2/1/1	SC 233	A1/26/11
SC 115	D5/40/1	SC 175	D5/50/5	SC 234	A2/68/1
SC 116	D5/23/9	SC 176	A1/2/8	SC 235	D7/10/1
SC 117	D5/23/8	SC 177	D5/23/13	SC 236	D5/22/2
SC 118	A1/14/49	SC 178	D5/35/1	SC 237	A1/26/12
SC 119	D5/37/1	SC 179	A1/2/10	SC 238	F1/2/19
SC 120	A2/74/2	SC 180	A1/14/47	SC 239	D5/27/2

Document ref.	Catalogue ref.	Document ref.	Catalogue ref.	Document ref.	Catalogue ref.
SC 240	A1/11/14	SC 301	A1/48/5	SC 363	D5/20/45
SC 241	F1/5/12	SC 302	F1/1/12	SC 364	D5/3/7
SC 242–3	F1/5/14	SC 303	A1/25/3	SC 365	D5/23/25
SC 244	A1/66/1	SC 304–5	D5/34/1–2	SC 366	A1/50/115
SC 245	F1/5/13	SC 306	D5/20/59	SC 367	A1/26/9
SC 246	F1/1/6	SC 307	D5/20/54	SC 368	A1/2/9
SC 247	F1/5/32	SC 308	A1/24/210	SC 369	A2/57/1
SC 248	A1/48/3	SC 309	F1/1/20	SC 370	A1/66/7
SC 249	D6/3/1	SC 310	A2/24/26	SC 371	A2/37/1
SC 250	D5/23/6	SC 311	A1/34/11	SC 372	A2/19/28
SC 251	D5/52/2	SC 312	A1/24/82	SC 373	F1/1/2
SC 252	D5/91/3	SC 313	D5/23/29	SC 374	A1/22/6
SC 253	D5/54/4	SC 314–15	D5/23/27–8	SC 375	B1/1/79
SC 254	D5/94/4	SC 316	D5/50/7	SC 376	A2/77/4
SC 255	D6/1/1	SC 317	D1/15/1	SC 377	D5/56/1
SC 256	D5/17/2	SC 318	A1/2/34	SC 378	A1/50/214
SC 257	D5/67/1	SC 319	B1/1/52	SC 379	D5/51/5
SC 258	D5/23/33	SC 320	A1/30/6	SC 380	H3/1/1
SC 259	D5/37/2	SC 321	A1/22/3	SC 381	G4/6/3
SC 260	D5/51/6	SC 322	B1/1/50	SC 382	A1/14/86
SC 261	D5/40/2	SC 323	A2/6/1	SC 383	F1/1/7
SC 262	D5/28/1	SC 324	D5/82/1	SC 384	A2/15/3
SC 263	D5/25/1	SC 325	B1/1/80	SC 385	A1/18/1
SC 264	D5/3/6	SC 326	A1/25/7	SC 386	D6/9/1
SC 265	D5/25/2	SC 327	A1/25/2	SC 387	A1/24/69
SC 266	D5/58/1	SC 328	A1/34/13	SC 388	G4/6/66
SC 267	D5/15/1	SC 329	A1/3/239	SC 389	D5/20/23
SC 268	D5/64/2	SC 330	F1/5/28	SC 390	D5/20/32
SC 269	D5/19/2	SC 331	F1/3/1	SC 391	D5/20/37
SC 270	D5/27/3	SC 332	F1/1/13	SC 392	B1/1/37
SC 271	D5/94/7	SC 333	F1/4/8	SC 393	B6/3/57
SC 272	F1/4/9	SC 334	F1/4/3	SC 394	F1/1/19
SC 273	F1/5/2	SC 335	A1/48/2	SC 395	A2/31/2
SC 274	G5/6/9	SC 336	A1/34/14	SC 396	A1/11/87
SC 275	A1/3/28	SC 337	G4/6/73	SC 397	K4/13/1
SC 276	A1/43/31	SC 338	A1/9/24	SC 398	F1/5/20
SC 277	A1/51/29	SC 339	A1/20/2	SC 399	F1/5/19
SC 278	A1/3/92	SC 340	A1/51/79	SC 400	F1/5/18
SC 279	A1/43/75	SC 341	A2/6/32	SC 401	A1/66/9
SC 280	A1/1/98	SC 342	B5/3/1	SC 402	A2/19/2
SC 281	A1/26/14	SC 343	B1/1/16	SC 403	B1/3/7
SC 282	F1/4/14	SC 344	A1/51/30	SC 404	A1/56/27
SC 283–5	A1/24/65	SC 345	A1/4/5	SC 405	A1/12/38
SC 286	A1/43/37	SC 346	A1/67/2	SC 406	A1/56/6
SC 287	A1/32/14	SC 347	E1/1/41	SC 407	J1/7/1
SC 288	A1/24/81	SC 348	D5/23/39	SC 408	A1/31/41
SC 289	A1/32/13	SC 349	A1/14/85	SC 409	F1/3/4
SC 290	D5/74/15	SC 350	A1/11/17	SC 410	G5/4/1
SC 291	B1/3/1	SC 351–2	A1/24/83–4	SC 411	D5/20/24
SC 292	A2/6/33	SC 353	A2/6/16	SC 412	D5/26/5
SC 293	F1/5/3	SC 354	D5/81/7	SC 413	D5/29/9
SC 294	D5/65/2	SC 355	D5/20/40	SC 414	D5/33/2
SC 295	A2/67/14	SC 356–7	B3/2/5–6	SC 415	A1/30/3
SC 296	K4/21/2	SC 358	B1/1/48	SC 416	A2/80/3
SC 297	A1/12/71	SC 359	A1/19/55	SC 417	D5/19/3
SC 298	A1/11/101	SC 360	A1/19/54	SC 418	A1/4/14
SC 299	K4/21/1	SC 361	A1/59/5	SC 419	A1/66/6
SC 300	A1/3/67	SC 362	A1/59/2	SC 420	A2/17/33

Document ref.	Catalogue ref.	Document ref.	Catalogue ref.	Document ref.	Catalogue ref.
SC 421	D5/3/17	SC 478	D5/101/3	SC 543	A2/26/3
SC 422	A1/12/199	SC 479	A3/9/1	SC 544	A2/17/4
SC 423	D5/26/7	SC 480	A1/39/6	SC 545	A2/50/11
SC 424	A1/1/71	SC 481	B7/3/8	SC 546	A5/10/8
SC 425	H1/1/2	SC 482	A4/2/20	SC 547	A1/11/39
SC 426	D5/90/1	SC 483–4	A1/11/11	SC 548	B2/4/1
SC 427	A1/30/5	SC 485	E1/7/3	SC 549	A1/51/27
SC 428	E1/1/5	SC 486	A1/60/120	SC 550	A2/83/5
SC 429	G2/1/4	SC 487	D1/23/2	SC 551	A2/67/3
SC 430	A2/79/1	SC 488–9	A2/32/7–8	SC 552	A1/24/186
SC 431	F1/4/10	SC 490	D5/20/4	SC 553	A5/3/5
SC 432	A1/57/1	SC 491	B1/1/12	SC 554–5	A5/3/6
SC 433	F1/5/30	SC 492	A1/25/18	SC 556	K10/1/3
SC 434	A1/24/273	SC 493	A2/90/3	SC 557	E1/1/15
SC 435	F1/1/10	SC 494	A1/1/85	SC 558	E1/1/13
SC 436	A1/43/1	SC 495	A5/3/2	SC 559	B7/3/30
SC 437	D5/99/1	SC 496	D1/9/2	SC 560	A1/1/22
SC 438	A1/3/235	SC 497	D5/1/7	SC 561	A2/19/16
SC 439	A1/34/3	SC 498	D5/101/14	SC 562	A1/1/106
SC 440	F1/4/7	SC 499	D5/101/6	SC 563–4	A1/1/107
SC 441	F1/1/22	SC 500	A1/1/86	SC 565	G4/7/1
SC 442A	B1/1/14	SC 501	D1/23/7	SC 566	K10/1/8
SC 442B–C	B1/1/15	SC 502	D1/1/3	SC 567	E1/1/14
SC 443	A2/19/4	SC 503	A1/67/8	SC 568	A5/9/6
SC 444	D5/17/3	SC 504	A1/13/15	SC 569	A2/19/10
SC 445	A1/3/234	SC 505	A1/60/114	SC 570	A2/17/8
SC 446	D5/64/3	SC 506–7	A1/60/113	SC 571	H3/7/1
SC 447	B1/1/26	SC 508	A1/60/112	SC 572	G1/4/5
SC 448	A1/33/1	SC 509	A1/60/111	SC 573	A1/14/24
SC 449	F1/5/7	SC 510	A1/60/112	SC 574–5	A5/2/1–2
SC 450	A3/11/1	SC 511	D1/1/11	SC 576	A1/11/44
SC 451	A1/1/114	SC 512	A1/60/116	SC 577	A2/17/11
SC 452	K4/24/1	SC 513	A1/60/43	SC 578	A2/19/11
SC 453	B4/10/1	SC 514	A2/35/23	SC 579	A1/1/23
SC 454	A2/19/6	SC 515	A5/4/1	SC 580	A1/1/77
SC 455	A1/32/23	SC 516	A2/17/14	SC 581	A2/77/14
SC 456	A1/1/8	SC 517	A2/17/2	SC 582	A4/2/29
SC 457	A1/31/29	SC 518	A1/60/118	SC 583–4	A1/1/43–4
SC 458	A5/9/8	SC 519	D5/101/8	SC 585	A1/1/45
SC 459	A2/44/3	SC 520	A1/6/9	SC 586	C2/2/16
SC 460	A1/50/88	SC 521–2	A2/17/3	SC 587	G3/1/16
SC 461	A1/18/3	SC 523	A1/1/19	SC 588	E1/1/19
SC 462	C2/2/1	SC 524	A1/11/86	SC 589	A1/1/24
SC 463	A2/60/7	SC 525	A1/11/18	SC 590	G3/1/8
SC 464	A1/11/8	SC 526	B7/3/15	SC 591	A1/1/48
SC 465	D5/23/32	SC 527–8	A1/19/23–4	SC 592	E1/1/52
SC 466	G1/4/1	SC 529	A1/12/86	SC 593	A1/1/49
SC 467	A1/2/36	SC 530	A2/95/4	SC 594	A1/1/50
SC 468	A1/48/7	SC 531	C2/2/9	SC 595	K10/1/10
SC 469	D5/101/1	SC 532–3	A2/64/5–6	SC 596	D3/5/1
SC 470	A1/9/5	SC 534	A1/32/17	SC 597	A5/5/5
SC 471	A1/24/70	SC 535	G3/1/55	SC 598	D5/9/5
SC 472	D5/101/10	SC 536	A5/10/6	SC 599	A1/14/92
SC 473	D5/99/2	SC 537	A1/1/21	SC 600	A5/3/11
SC 474	F1/5/37	SC 538	A1/1/81	SC 601	A5/6/2
SC 475	A1/51/3	SC 539–40	A1/43/56	SC 602	A5/1/8
SC 476	D5/101/2	SC 541	A1/46/7	SC 603–4	A5/6/3–4
SC 477	A1/19/29	SC 542	A2/26/2	SC 605	A5/5/6

Document ref.	Catalogue ref.	Document ref.	Catalogue ref.	Document ref.	Catalogue ref.
SC 606	A5/6/5	SC 647	D1/2/1	SR 41	A1/3/122
SC 607	A5/5/7	SC 648–50	A1/1/39–41	SR 42	A1/24/127
SC 608	A1/1/57	SC 651	A1/1/12	SR 43	A1/36/42
SC 609–10	D1/1/15–16	SC 652	A5/3/12	SR 44	A1/43/96
SC 611	A1/27/9	SC 653	A5/5/4	SR 45–6	A1/43/97
SC 612	A1/24/107	SC 654	A5/3/13	SR 47	A1/36/57
SC 613	D5/11/1	SC 655	A1/1/63	SR 48	A1/24/158
SC 614	A1/1/27	SC 656–7	D7/1/3–4	SR 52	K10/1/9
SC 615–16	A1/1/58	SC 679	D7/1/5	SR 53	G4/12/4
SC 617	D6/6/1	SR 1	A1/2/48	SR 55	D5/101/15
SC 618–19	A2/17/37–8	SR 2	A1/12/119	SR 58–9	A4/1/1
SC 620	A5/8/10	SR 3	A1/51/73	SR 60–1	A4/1/2–3
SC 621	D5/23/4	SR 4	A1/12/120	SR 62	A4/1/5
SC 622	H1/3/1	SR 5	A1/43/130	SR 63	A4/1/4
SC 623	F1/7/3	SR 6–7	A1/3/160–1	SR 64	A4/1/6
SC 624	A1/1/59	SR 8–10	A1/3/159	SR 67	A4/2/14
SC 625	A5/10/11	SR 11	C1/3/1	SR 68	B4/3/3
SC 626	G1/6/1	SR 12	C1/3/2	SR 88	A5/2/3
SC 627	A1/1/87	SR 13	A1/14/70	SR 97	A5/10/3
SC 628	A1/1/11	SR 14	C1/3/3	SR 102	A5/10/1
SC 629	A1/51/38	SR 15–16	A1/24/171–2	SR 105	A5/10/2
SC 630	D1/23/5	SR 17	A1/2/49	SR 130	D1/23/9
SC 631	A2/43/16	SR 18	A1/43/131	SR 132	A1/24/174
SC 632	A1/1/67	SR 20–1	A1/51/74	SR 137	A1/1/60
SC 633	H1/5/1	SR 22	A1/51/75	SR 138	A1/1/109
SC 634	A1/18/5	SR 23	B1/1/90	SR 139–40	A5/10/4
SC 635	A5/10/12	SR 24	B1/1/96	SR 142	A1/12/157
SC 636	A1/1/79	SR 25	A2/55/1	SR 144	A3/15/1
SC 637	A5/5/1	SR 26	B3/1/1	SR 145	A1/1/42
SC 638	A5/6/6	SR 27–8	D1/6/4	SR 146	A1/1/76
SC 639	A5/5/9	SR 29	F1/6/1	SR 147	D1/1/56
SC 640	A5/5/2	SR 30	A1/12/122	SR 148–9	A1/1/51–2
SC 641	D1/1/28	SR 31	A2/72/2	SR 150	A2/42/12
SC 642	A5/6/7	SR 32	A2/77/7	SR 184	G4/6/57
SC 643	A5/5/3	SR 33	A2/88/12	Wills 1–11	K9/1/1–11
SC 644	A5/6/8	SR 36	A2/20/3	Wills 12–15	K9/1/13–16
SC 645	A5/1/6	SR 37	A2/23/7	Wills 16	K9/1/12
SC 646	A1/1/25	SR 39–40	A4/2/7	Wills17–19	K9/1/17–19

NOTE. The following documents are not included in the catalogue:

GC 279   illegible

SC 80   a fragment, with a seal, of a charter of King John, of which only a few words remain

Document references which are not included in the sequences above either relate to documents of a date later than 1492 or are unused, in several instances because other references have been substituted for them.

LIST OF COPIES OF THE MUNIMENTS
IN THIS CATALOGUE ON MICROFILM (MF)
AND MICROFICHE (BCF)
IN THE GLOUCESTERSHIRE RECORD OFFICE

The programme of filming is continuing, and further documents may have become available since the catalogue went to press. Enquiry should be made at the Gloucestershire Record Office.

General Account Rolls

GAR	1–99	MF 1400	GAR	158–243	MF 1406	GAR	327–434	MF 1418
GAR	100–157	MF 1403	GAR	244–326	MF 1416	GAR	428	BCF 245–246

General Charters

GC	201–640	MF 1337	GC 2166–2533	MF 1366	GC 4201–4560	MF 1375
GC	641–1000	MF 1346	GC 2534–2920	MF 1367	GC 4561–4908	MF 1380
GC	1001–1362	MF 1353	GC 2921–3335	MF 1368	GC 4909–5220	MF 1384
GC	1363–1750	MF 1354	GC 3336–3750	MF 1373		
GC	1743–2165	MF 1356	GC 3751–4200	MF 1374		

General Court Rolls

GCR 1–200 MF 1420   GCR 201–218 MF 1421

General Miscellaneous Rolls

GMR 1–47 MF 1421

General Rental Rolls

GRR 1–41 MF 1421

General Unbound Books

GSUB 82   BCF 488–489

Select Books

SB 1	MF 1166	SB 22 MF 1160	SB 75/1–3 BCF 15
SB 10	MF 1159	SB 24 MF 1158	
SB 18	MF 1158	SB 33 BCF 4–8	

Select Charters

SC	1–100	MF1290	SC 401–700 MF 1297
SC 101–400	MF 1293	SC 701–892 MF 1315

Select Rolls

SR	1–7	MF 1276	SR 64–85 MF 1279	SR 176–182 MF 1281
SR	8–38	MF 1277	SR 86–175 MF 1280	SR 184 MF 1281
SR	39–63	MF 1278		

Wills

Wills 1–26   MF 1158

CATALOGUE OF
MEDIEVAL MUNIMENTS AT
BERKELEY CASTLE

PART A
THE BERKELEY ESTATE

1: THE HUNDRED OF BERKELEY

The lordship of Berkeley, almost coterminous with the hundred and centred on the castle, was also known as the 'great manor', the liberty and the barony of Berkeley, or Berkeley Herness. Its acquisition by Robert FitzHarding marked the foundation of the baronial family of Berkeley. The Herness included some detached portions which, with others within it, were granted by FitzHarding to his younger sons and to St. Augustine's Abbey, his monastic foundation in Bristol. The abbey received the manors of Almondsbury, Ashleworth, Horfield and half of Cromhall, while his son Robert received Beverston, King's Weston and Elberton and his son Nicholas the manors of Hill and Nympsfield. The other half of Cromhall was also soon subinfeudated and Arlingham, another detached portion, was granted to Robert, a younger son of Maurice (II) Lord Berkeley (d. 1281), in 1275. Moreover, the parish and manor of Dursley, with those of Newington Bagpath and Ozleworth held of Dursley, remained with the original holders (thereafter known as the Berkeleys of Dursley) and were held directly of the king. The remainder, entailed by Thomas (III) Lord Berkeley in 1349, formed the lordship as it was held by all FitzHarding's descendants until it was settled on Henry VII and his male issue by William marquess of Berkeley (d. 1491). It included the manor and parish of Slimbridge, which was not originally a member of the Herness but was granted with the daughter of Roger de Berkeley of Dursley on her marriage to Maurice (I), FitzHarding's son and heir, and soon came to be considered as part of the Herness. William's brother and heir managed to recover most of the other lands which William had settled on the king but his descendants had to wait until 1553 and the end of the male line of Henry VII for the lordship to revert to them.

Structurally, the lordship was divided in several ways, into manors, vills, parishes and tithings, which appear to have been almost entirely discrete, causing much confusion. During the later middle ages the lordship was administered as nine large manors, Alkington, Cam, Coaley, Ham (with Appleridge), Hinton, Hurst, Symond's Hall, Slimbridge and Wotton-under-Edge (Wotton 'Forren' or 'Forinseca'), and two boroughs, Berkeley and Wotton-under-Edge (Wotton 'Intrinseca'), each manor incorporating several vills. The various holdings were not necessarily confined to one vill, or even one manor, and the number of surviving charters concerning the lordship makes for a certain amount of confusion. Some prominent tenants held land in several manors, but unless there is firm evidence that holdings in several vills formed an indivisible entity they are treated below vill by vill. The hundred was divided ecclesiastically into several parishes, those of Arlingham, Horfield, Cromhall, Almondsbury and Ashleworth being detached portions, and those of Berkeley, Wotton, Cam, Coaley, Slimbridge, Uley, King's Weston, Beverston, Dursley, Newington Bagpath and Ozleworth the main portion. Berkeley parish included the manors of Alkington, Appleridge, Hill, Ham, Hinton and Breadstone; Wotton parish included the vills of Nibley, Combe, Huntingford, Wortley, Bradley and Symond's Hall. Some parishes contained chapelries, Stone and Hill within Berkeley parish, Nibley and Symond's Hall within Wotton parish, Stinchcombe within Cam parish and Kingscote within Beverston parish.

THE LORDSHIP OF BERKELEY

THE LORDSHIP

Grant by Henry II to FitzHarding and his heir Maurice (I), with subsequent charters[1]

A1/1/1 [SC 1]   n.d. [c. 1150]

Henry duke of Normandy and Robert FitzHarding.

Henry has granted to Robert the manor of Betthone and £100 worth of land in the manor of Berkeley with all liberties and customs, to hold by the service of two mewed hawks, with an undertaking to build a castle at Berkeley.

Witnesses: Reginald earl of Cornwall, Robert de Dunstanvilla, Richard de Humez, constable, Manasser Biseth, steward, Warin son of Gerold the chamberlain, William son of Hamon, Philip de Columbers, the abbot of St. Augustine's, brother Adam his canon, Henry son of Robert, William Cumin, Jordan brother of Robert [*i.e.* FitzHarding], Jordan and David his [*i.e.* FitzHarding's] nephews, Richard de Hanum.

At: Bristol.

A1/1/2 [SC 2]   n.d. [c. 1153]

Henry duke of Normandy and Robert FitzHarding.

Henry has granted Berkelai and all of Berkelaihernesse to Robert, to hold by service of one knight or, if Robert or his heirs desire it, by 100s. a year; Robert has given Henry 500 marks.

Witnesses: The abbot of St. Augustine's, Bristol, Henry the treasurer, William Cumin, Roger earl of Hereford, Richard de Humez, constable, Manasser Biseth, steward, Robert de Saltemareis.

A1/1/3 [SC 3]   n.d. [c. 1153]

Henry duke of Normandy and Maurice son of Robert son of Harding.

Henry has granted the same to Maurice, to hold by the same service.

Witnesses: The abbot of St. Augustine's, Bristol, Henry the treasurer, William Cumin, Roger earl of Hereford, Richard de Humez constable, Manasser Biseth, steward, Robert de Saltemareis.

A1/1/4 [SC 6]   n.d. [1154]

King Henry II and Robert FitzHarding.

Grant by Henry, as king, of the same, to hold by service of five knights.

Witnesses: Richard [de Warwick] abbot of St. Augustine's, Bristol, Reginald earl of Cornwall, Roger earl of Hereford, Richard de Humez, constable, Manaser Biseth, steward, William son of Hamund, Warin son of Gerold, Robert de Saltemareis.

A1/1/5 [SC 7]   n.d. [1154]

King Henry II and Maurice son of Robert FitzHarding.

Grant by Henry, as king, of the same, to hold by service of five knights.

Witnesses: Richard [de Warwick] abbot of St. Augustine's, Reginald earl of Cornwall, Roger earl of Hereford, Richard de Humez, constable, Manaser Biseth, steward, William son of Hamund, Warin son of Gerold, Robert de Saltemareis.

A1/1/6 [SC 34]   30 Oct. 1 Ric. I [1189]

Eleanor queen of England and [Maurice] de Berchelay.

Eleanor has confirmed to Maurice Berckelay and all Berckelayhurnesse.

Witnesses: Reginald [FitzJocelin, bishop] of Bath, Hugh [de Nonant, bishop] of Chester, earl William of Salisbury, William Marshal, Ralph son of Godfrey, Geoffrey de Wanci.

---

[1] The first five charters are thought to be spurious: above, p. xxi. *Transcripts* of SC 1–2 and 7: Smyth, i. 22–5, 64–5; of SC 1–2: Jeayes, pp. 1–4. *Facsimiles*: *TBGAS* cix. 127–37.

A1/1/7 [SC 51]   18 Nov. 10 Ric. I [1198]
King Richard I and Robert son of Maurice de Berkelai.

The king has renewed his charter confirming to Robert the king's father's grant of Berkelai and Berkelai hernesse to Robert's grandfather Robert FitzHarding and earl Robert of Gloucester's grant of Bedministra, witnessed by Hugh [du Puiset] bishop of Durham, Hugh [de Nonant] bishop of Chester, Reginald [FitzJocelin] bishop of Bath, earl William de Mand[eville], John the marshal, Robert de Witefeld, Hugh Bardulf, Geoffrey son of Peter, Hugh Pantulf, Thomas Noel, and given, under the king's former seal, by the hand of William de Longchamps, chancellor, 27 Sept. 1 Ric. I [1189] at Browd.[1]

Witnesses: H. archdeacon of Canterbury, William the marshal, William de Aubinni, Robert Tregoz, Robert de Wanci, Walter de Ely, Gerard Prochard, Richard Revell, Warin son of Gerold, Saer de Quenci, Thomas Basset, Richard de Clifford.

At: Les Andelys (by the hand of Rocelin acting in place of the chancellor).

A1/1/8 [SC 456]   St. Matthias, 6 Edw. I [24 Feb. 1278]
Henry de Berkeley, lord of Dursley, and Sir Maurice de Berkeley.

Henry has quitclaimed to Maurice and his heirs the barony of Berkeley and the manor of Slymbbrugge .

Witnesses: Sir Godfrey Giffard, bishop of Worcester, Sir Reginald [de Ham] abbot of Gloucester, Sir John abbot of Bristol, Sir John Giffard, Sir John de Boun, Sir John de Acton, Sir Richard de Ripariis, Sir William Maunsel, knights, John de Clyfford, Nicholas de Aperleye, William de Mathine, Milo de Longetoft, Elias de Cumba, Peter de Stintescumbe.

At: Slimbridge.

A1/1/9 [GC 495]   n.d. [*c.* 1278]
Henry son of John de Berkeleye and Sir Maurice son of Thomas de Berkeleye.

Henry has quitclaimed to Maurice the whole manor of Berkeleye, with the hamlet of Wotton and the market and fair there, and all other hamlets and members of the said manor and barony; further, the manor of Slymbregg' . . .

Witnesses: Sir John Mautravers, Sir Ralph de Wylinton, . . . , Sir Geoffrey de Wroxhal, knights, Thomas de Rodeberewe, John Achard.

A1/1/10 [GC 481*]   Two weeks after St. John the Baptist, 6 Edw. I [8 July 1278]
Maurice de Berkel and Henry de Berkel.

Final concord concerning the manor of Berkel; Henry has acknowledged the right of Maurice, and has quitclaimed the manor to him, and Maurice has given him £200.

At: Westminster.

A1/1/11 [SC 628]   16 March 12 Edw. IV [1472]
King Edward IV and William Lord Berkeley.

The king has inspected his own letters patent of 1 March 11 Edw. IV, confirming to William the grants and confirmations of Berkeley and Berkeley Herness made by his ancestors Henry II, John and others.

At: Westminster.

A1/1/12 [SC 651]   15 Feb. 3 Hen. VII [1488]
King Henry VII and William [de Berkeley] Earl Marshal and of Nottingham.

The king has inspected the charters of his predecessors to Robert FitzHarding and his descendants concerning the castle and manor of Berkeley [etc.], and has confirmed them.

At: Westminster.

---

[1] *Transcript*: CChR iv. 178–9.

Entail by Thomas (III), 1349

Early versions (*see also below*, A1/1/80 [GC 3250], *for the separate entail of the castle*)

A1/1/13 [GC 3249]   n.d. [*c.* 1349]
William de Syde, Walter Goldemere, David de Milkesham [and John le Vyth?]; and Sir Thomas de Berkelee.

William, Walter, David [and John?] have granted to Thomas the manors of Camme, Coueleye, Slymbrugge [with the advowson] and Uptone Seint Leonard, with all the knights' fees and reversions; for Thomas's life, with reversion to Maurice de Berkelee his son and his male issue, the male issue of Thomas and Katherine his wife, and the right heirs of Thomas.

A1/1/14 [GC 3208]   n.d. [*c.* 1349]
Thomas de Berkel'; and William de Syde, Walter Goldemere, David de Milkesham and John le Vyth.

Thomas has granted to William, Walter, David and John the manor of Berkel' (except for the castle), the hundred of Berkel', the manors of Wottone (with the advowson), Symondeshale, Hamme, Appelrugge, Alkyntone, Hynetone, Camme, Couelee, Slymbrugge (with the advowson), and Upton Saint Leonard, with all appurtenances, knights' fees and reversions. *Witnesses*: Sir Thomas de Bradeston, Sir Edmund de Clyvedone, Sir John de Berkel', Sir Simon Basset, knights, John FitzNichol, William de Chiltenham.

A1/1/15 [GC 3211]   n.d. [*c.* 1349]
Thomas de Berkel' and John de Clyve.

Thomas has appointed John to receive seisin of the manor of Berkel' (except for the castle), the hundred of Berkel', the manors of Hamme, Appelrugge, Alkyntone, Hynetone, Wottone (with the advowson), Symondeshale, Camme, Couelee, Slymbrugge (with the advowson), and Upton Saint Leonard, with all appurtenances, knights' fees and reversions, which he had by grant of the said [*sic*] William [de Syde], Walter [Goldemere], David [de Milkesham] and John le Vyth.

A1/1/16 [GC 3209]   n.d. [*c.* 1349]
(1) Thomas de Berkel'; (2) William de Syde, Walter Goldemere, David de Milkesham and John le Vyth; (3) Roger de Estham and William Curteys.

William, Walter, David and John have appointed Roger and William to deliver seisin to Thomas of the manor of Berkel' (except for the castle), the hundred of Berkel', the manors of Wottone (with the advowson), Symondeshale, Hamme, Appelrugge, Alkyntone, Hynetone, Camme, Couelee, Slymbrugge (with the advowson), and Upton Saint Leonard, with all appurtenances, knights' fees and reversions.

A1/1/17 [GC 3210]   n.d. [*c.* 1349]
William de Syde, Walter Goldemere, David de Milkesham and John le Vyth; and Sir Thomas de Berkel'.

William, Walter, David and John have granted to Thomas the manor of Berkel' (except for the castle), the hundred of Berkel', the manors of Hamme, Appelrugge, Alkyntone, Hynetone, Wottone (with the advowson), and Symondeshale, with all appurtenaces, knights' fees and reversions, to Thomas for life, with remainder to Maurice de Berkel', his son, and his male issue, the male issue of Thomas and his wife Katherine, and the right heirs of Thomas.

A1/1/18 [GC 3206; *duplicate* GC 3207]   Fri. after St. Vincent, 22 Edw. III [23 Jan. 1349]
Thomas de Berkelee; and William de Syde, Walter Goldemere, Matthew vicar of Berkelee, David de Milkesham and John Wyth.

Thomas has enfeoffed William, Walter, Matthew, David and John of the castles and manors of Berkelee and Beverston, and the hundreds of Berkelee, Blideslowe, Bedministre, Portbur' and Hareclyve, and the manors of Wottone (with the advowson), Symondeshale,

Hamme, Appelrugge, Alkyntone, Hynetone, Camme, Coueleye, Slymbrugge (with the advowson), Aure (with the advowson), and Uptone Saint Leonard, with all the knights' fees and reversions pertaining to the said manors and castles, on condition that within 15 days after they receive seisin they re-enfeoff Thomas, to him for his life with remainder to Maurice de Berkelee, his son, and Maurice's male issue, the male issue of Thomas and Katherine his wife, and the right heirs of Thomas.

At: Berkeley.

Final version, subsequent confirmations and the breaking of the entail in 1485

A1/1/19 [SC 523]   10 Jan. 22 Edw. III [1349]

King Edward III and Thomas de Berkele.

The king has granted licence for Thomas to grant to William de Syde, Walter Goldmere and David de Milkesham the castle and manor of Berkele, the manors of Hamme, Appelrugge, Alkynton, Hyneton, Wotton, Simondeshale, Camme, Coueleye, Slymbrugge and Upton St. Leonards, the hundred of Berkeley, and the advowsons of the churches of Wotton and Slymbrugge, so that they may regrant them to him for life, with remainder to Maurice his son and the heirs male of his body, failing which the heirs male of the body of Thomas and Katherine his wife, failing which Thomas's right heirs.

At: Otford.

A1/1/20 [GC 3224]   Easter, 23 Edw. III [12 April 1349]

Thomas de Berkele; and William de Syde, Walter Goldmere and David de Milkesham.

Final concord concerning the castle of Berkele and the manors of Berkele, Hamme, Appelrugge, Alkyntone, Hynetone, Wottone, Simondeshale, Camme, Coueleye, Slymbrugge and Upton Sancti Leonardi, and the hundred of Berkele, and the advowsons of Wottone and Slymbrugge; Thomas has acknowledged the right of William, Walter and David by his gift, and they have granted the castle [etc.] to Thomas for his life, with remainder to Maurice de Berkele, son of Thomas, and his male issue, the male issue of Thomas and his wife Katherine, and the right heirs of Thomas.

At: Westminster.

A1/1/21 [SC 537]   . . . Nov. 35 Edw. III [1361]

King Edward III and Maurice de Berkeley.

The king has exemplified his charter of 1349 granting licence to Thomas de Berkeley, father of Maurice, to grant the castle and manor of Berkeley [etc.] to William de Syde, Walter Goldmere and David de Milkesham and for them to regrant it to Thomas for life, with remainder to Maurice his eldest son and the heirs male of his body [etc.].

At: Westminster.

A1/1/22 [SC 560]   16 Feb. 6 Ric. II [1383]

King Richard II and Thomas de Berkeley.

The king has inspected and confirmed to Thomas (i) the licence [*as above*, A1/1/19, SC 523]; (ii) the final concord [*as above*, A1/1/20, GC 3224]; (iii) the final concord of Trinity 26 Edw. III concerning the manor of Portbury whereby Thomas de Berkeley and Maurice his son have acknowledged the right of William de Syde and Walter Goldmere, and William and Walter granted the manor back to Maurice in tail.

At: Westminster.

A1/1/23 [SC 579]   29 Nov. 14 Hen. IV [1412]

King Henry IV and John St. John, knight.

The king, at John's request, has exemplified the final concord [*as above*, A1/1/20, GC 3224].

At: Westminster.

A1/1/24 [SC 589]   22 Oct. 5 Hen. VI [1426]
King Henry VI and James de Berkeley.

The king, at James's request, has exemplified the writ of livery of seisin of 35 Edw. III [1361] to Maurice de Berkeley on the death of his father Thomas, following the inquisition after Thomas's death, which showed that he held the castle of Berkeley and the manors of Berkeley, Ham [etc.], for life, with remainder to Maurice his son and the male heirs of his body.

At: Westminster.

A1/1/25 [SC 646]   24 April 2 Ric. III [1485]
William de Berkeley, earl of Nottingham; and Edward Willoughby, Robert Logge, clerk, John Fyssher and John Wythe.

The king has exemplified the recovery by Edward, Robert, John and John against the earl of the manors of Berkeley, Hamme, Appelrugge, [Alkington, Hinton], Camme, Hurste and Slimbrugge.

At: Westminster.

Various later settlements

Settlement by James Lord Berkeley, 1422 (recovered 1466)

A1/1/26 [GC 4137]   1 Sept. 1 Hen. VI [1422]
(1) James Berkeley, knight, lord of Berkeley; (2) Master John Tumbrell chaplain, and Adam Trehayron; (3) Humphrey duke of Gloucester, John [de Mowbray] duke of Norfolk, John [Holand] earl of Huntingdon, Thomas Stanley, knight, Robert Wynkefeld and John ap Philip Morgan.

James has appointed John and Adam to give seisin to Humphrey and the others of his castle of Berkeley, and also of his manors of Berkeley, Hompme, Appelrigge, Hyntone, Hurst, Slymbrugge, Camme, Alkintone, Uptone Sancti Leonardi, Wottone sub Egge, Cowley and Symondeshale (Glos.), with all the appurtenances.

A1/1/27 [SC 614]   1 May 6 Edw. IV [1466]
Thomas son and heir of Thomas late Lord Stanley; and William Stanley, John Haward, John Wynkefeld, knights, William Berkeley of Uley, Thomas Wynkefeld, William Langley and Maurice Berkeley, esquires.

Whereas James late Lord Berkeley, granted by his charter of 3 Sept. 1 Hen. VI [1422] to Humphrey duke of Gloucester, John [de Mowbray] duke of Norfolk, John [Holand] earl of Huntingdon, Robert Wynkfeld, John ap Philip Morgan and Thomas Lord Stanley the castle of Berkeley, the manors of Berkeley, Ham [etc.], to hold in trust, now Thomas grants the same to William and the others.

Witnesses: Thomas Whytynton, Thomas French, John Thorp, Maurice Denyse, John Poyntz.

A1/1/28 [GC 4337]   1 May 6 Edw. IV [1466]
(1) Thomas Stanley, knight, Lord Stanley, son and heir of Thomas Stanley, late Lord Stanley; (2) Thomas Campdene, chaplain, and Robert Grevile; (3) William Stanley, John Haward, John Wynkfeld, knights, Thomas Wynkfeld, William Berkeley of Uley, William Langley, Maurice Berkeley, esquires, and John Tuynow.

Thomas Stanley has appointed Thomas Campdene and Robert Grevile to deliver seisin of Berkeley Castle and the manors of Berkeley, Hampmme, Appulregge, Hynton, Hurst, Slymbrigge, Cam, Alkynton, Upton Sancti Leonardi, Wotton sub Egge, Cowley and Symondeshale (Glos.) to William and the others.

Settlements by William Lord Berkeley, including Arlingham, Daglingworth and Barbaste in Wickwar, 1472–7[1]

A1/1/29 [GC 4369]   18 July 12 Edw. IV [1472]

Thomas Berkeley, esquire, John atte Wode and Maurice Kyng; William Berkeley, Lord Berkeley, and Joan his wife.

Thomas, John and Maurice have demised to William and Joan theirs manors of Wottone sub Egge, Cowley, Symondeshale, Alkyngton, Hynton, Erlyngham and Daglyngworth (Glos.); for their lives.

Witnesses: Richard Beauchamp, knight, John Cassy, esquire, Thomas Whytyngton, Walter Skay, John Methelay.

At: Wotton.

A1/1/30 [GC 4371]   20 July 12 Edw. IV [1472]

(1) Thomas Berkeley, esquire, John atte Wode and Maurice Kyng; (2) John Alford; (3) William Berkeley, Lord Berkeley, and Joan his wife.

Thomas, John and Maurice have appointed John Alford to deliver seisin to William and Joan of their manors of Wottone sub Egge, Cowley, Symondeshale, Alkyngton, Hynton, Erlyngham and Daglyngworth (Glos.).

At: Wotton.

A1/1/31 [GC 4384]   14 June 14 Edw. IV [1475]

(1) Thomas Berkeley, esquire, John Attwode and Maurice Kyng; (2) Robert Grevyle and John Wylmot; (3) William Berkeley, knight, lord of Berkeley.

Thomas, John and Maurice have appointed Robert and John to deliver seisin to William of Berkeley Castle and the manors of Berkeley, Ham, Hynton, Hurst, Upton Sancti Leonardi, and the holding called Sagislond and a rent of 22 marks in Frampton super Sabrinam with Berkeley hundred; to hold as by their charter of enfeoffment.

A1/1/32 [GC 4404]   18 Feb. 15 Edw. IV [1476]

(1) William Berkeley, knight, Lord Berkeley, and Joan his wife; (2) John Alford and Thomas Tylar; (3) Thomas Berkeley, esquire, John at Wode and Maurice Kyng.

William and Joan have appointed John and Thomas to receive seisin from Thomas, John and Maurice of the manor of Cam, to hold for their lives.

A1/1/33 [GC 4412]   11 June 17 Edw. IV [1477]

William Berkeley, knight, lord of Berkeley, and Joan his wife; (2) Thomas Strangewysse the younger and Thomas Dorney; (3) Thomas Berkeley, esquire, Maurice Kynge and John Wode.

William and Joan have appointed Thomas and Thomas to receive seisin of the castle and lordship of Berkeley, the manors of Berkeley, Hamme, Appulerugge, Alkynton, Hynton, Hurste, Slymbrygge, Daglyngworth and Barbaste within the lordship of Wykewarr and a rent of 22 marks a year in Frompton super Sabrinam, as by the charter of Thomas, Maurice and John.

At: Daglingworth.

A1/1/34 [GC 4413]   11 June 17 Edw. IV [1477]

(1) Thomas Berkeley, esquire, Maurice Kynge and John Wode; (2) John Rogers and Oliver Russell; (3) William Berkeley, lord of Berkeley, knight, and Joan his wife.

Thomas, Maurice and John have appointed John and Oliver to deliver seisin of the castle and lordship of Berkeley, the manors of Berkeley, Hamme, Appulerugge, Alkynton,

---

[1] The settlements were possibly in order to create a jointure for Joan Strangeways, William's second wife, widow of Sir William Willoughby.

Hynton, Hurste, Slymbrygge, Daglyngworth and Barbaste within the lordship of Wykewarr and a rent of 22 marks a year in Frompton super Sabrinam, to William and Joan.
At: Daglingworth.

Settlement on Thomas Grey, marquess of Dorset, 1486
A1/1/35 [GC 4446]   8 Aug. 1 Hen. VII [1486]
Edward Willughby, Robert Logge, clerk, John Fissher, serjeant-at-law, and John Wyche, clerk; and Thomas [Rotherham] archbishop of York, John [de Vere] earl of Oxford, William [de Berkeley] earl of Nottingham and his wife Anne, and Richard FitzHugh, Lord FitzHugh, George FitzHugh, dean of the cathedral church of Lincoln, Thomas Fenys and Thomas Hoo.

Edward and the others have demised to the archbishop and the others their manors of Alkyngton and Camme (Glos.) and Portbury (Som.), which they lately recovered from the said earl of Nottingham in the court of Richard III; to them and the issue of the earl of Nottingham, with remainder to Thomas marquess of Dorset and his male issue, and the right heirs of the earl of Nottingham.

A1/1/36 [GC 4447]   9 Aug. 1 Hen. VII [1486]
William [de Berkeley] Earl Marshal and of Nottingham [etc.]; and Edward Willughby, esquire, Robert Logge and John Wyche, clerk.

William has granted to Edward, Robert and John, and their heirs and assigns, his manor of Cowley (Glos.); and has appointed Anthony Crakenthorp and John atte Wode to deliver seisin.

A1/1/37 [GC 4448; *duplicate* GC 4449]   10 Aug. 1 Hen. VII [1486]
Edward Willughby, Robert Logge, clerk, John Fissher serjeant-at-law, and John Wyche, clerk; and William Earl Marshal and of Nottingham [etc.].

Edward, Robert, John and John have demised to William the castle and manor of Berkeley and the manors of Hamme, Appulrugge and Hynton (Glos.), which they recently recovered from William by writ of right in the court of Richard III; to him and his issue, with remainder to Thomas marquess of Dorset and his male issue, and the right heirs of William; and they have appointed Anthony Crakenthorp and John atte Wode to deliver seisin.

A1/1/38 [GC 4450]   10 Aug. 1 Hen. VII [1486]
(1) William [de Berkeley] Earl Marshal [etc.]; (2) Maurice Kyng and Thomas Tyler; (3) Edward Willughby, Robert Logge, clerk, John Fissher serjeant-at-law and John Wyche, clerk.

William has appointed Maurice and Thomas to receive seisin from Edward, Robert, John and John of the castle and manor of Berkeley and the manors of Hamme, Appulrugge and Hynton (Glos.).

Settlement on King Henry VII in tail male, 1488
A1/1/39 [SC 648]   8 Feb. 3 Hen. VII [1488]
King Henry VII; and Edward Willoughby and Robert Logge.

The king has granted licence to Edward and Robert to grant to William [de Berkeley] Earl Marshal and of Nottingham the manor of Cowley (Glos.), to him and the heirs of his body, failing which, reversion to the king and the heirs male of his body, failing which to the earl's right heirs.
At: Westminster.

A1/1/40 [SC 649]   8 Feb. 3 Hen. VII [1488]
King Henry VII; and John Fisher, serjeant-at-law, Edward Willoughby, esquire, and Robert Logge, clerk.

The king has granted licence to John, Edward and Robert to grant to William [de Berkeley] Earl Marshal and of Nottingham the castle and manor of Berkeley and the manors of Hamme and Appulrugge, to him and the heirs of his body, with remainder to the king and the heirs male of his body, failing which to the earl's right heirs.
At: Westminster.

A1/1/41 [SC 650]   8 Feb. 3 Hen. VII [1488]
King Henry VII; and John Fisher, serjeant-at-law, and Robert Logge.

The king has granted licence to John and Robert to grant the manors of Slymbrugge and Hurst (Glos.) to William [de Berkeley] Earl Marshal and of Nottingham, James [Goldwell] bishop of Norwich, Christopher Willoughby, knight, Robert Willoughby, knight, Edward Willoughby, esquire, and Richard Willoughby, esquire, and the heirs of the body of the earl, failing which to the king and the heirs male of his body, failing which to the right heirs of the earl.
At: Westminster.

The Great Dispute of the 15th century
The following documents relate to the dispute between the heir male, James Lord Berkeley, and the heir general, Elizabeth, daughter of Thomas (IV) Lord Berkeley, wife of Richard Beauchamp, earl of Warwick, and mother of three daughters, Eleanor (who married Edmund Beaufort, earl of Dorset and duke of Somerset), Margaret (who married John Talbot, earl of Shrewsbury), and Elizabeth (who married George Lord Latimer).

A1/1/42 [SR 145]   n.d.
Result of an inquiry made at Miskin (*Meskyn*) in Wales about the dates of death and age of Despenser heirs, from Hugh (d. 23 Edw. III [1349]) to Thomas (d. 1 Hen. IV [1400]).[1]

A1/1/43 [SC 583]   n.d. [*c.* 1417]
At the request of Richard [Beauchamp] earl of Warwick (by William Sturmy, knight, John Harwell, Thomas Calston and John Baysham), Robert Russell, mayor of Bristol, David Duddebroke, sheriff, and others acknowledge the deposition made by John Bonjon, that, in the time of Henry IV, Thomas de Berkeley granted the castle and manor of Berkeley [etc.] and the manors and hundreds of Portbury and Bedminster [etc.] to Nicholas [Bubwith] bishop of Bath and Wells, Thomas Rede, John Bonjon and John Whitmore of Wotton under Egge.
At: Bristol.

A1/1/44 [SC 584]   9 June 6 Hen. V [1418]
Lionel Sebrook, esquire; and William Nicoll, mayor of Southampton, and others.

William and the others declare that Lionel came before them and swore on oath that, within 12 days after Christmas, 4 Hen. V [1416], at which time he was steward of the household to Thomas de Berkeley, when he and Thomas were in the chamber called the Wythedrawing Chambre in the manor of Wotton, Thomas showed him an old writing of a fee tail of the time of Robert FitzHarding concerning the castle and lordship of Berkeley.
At: Southampton.

A1/1/45 [SC 585]   15 June 6 Hen. V [1418]
King Henry V; and Richard Beauchamp, earl of Warwick, and Elizabeth his wife, daughter of Thomas late lord of Berkeley.

At the request of Richard and Elizabeth, the king has inspected the confirmation by King

---

[1] Cf. *GEC* iv. 271–81.

John to Robert son of Maurice of his father's grant to Robert FitzHarding of Berkeley and Berkeley Herness and of Bedminster manor.

Witnesses: John duke of Bedford, guardian of England.

At: Westminster.

A1/1/46 [GC 4129]   1 Nov. 8 Hen. V [1420]

James lord of Berkeley; and John Tirell esquire and Walter Shirington clerk.

Whereas James is bound to John and Walter in 10,000 marks payable at Easter, John and Walter have granted that if James pays to them 1,000 marks within 18 months of obtaining possession of the castle and lordship of Berkeley, and if he grants to Humphrey duke of Gloucester, his heirs and assigns the reversion after his (James's) death of lands and holdings in Wales (*Wallia*) and elsewhere to the value of 400 marks a year which lately were of the inheritance of James's mother, the bond will be void.

At: London.

A1/1/47 [GC 4146*; *copy* GC 4146]   6 Oct. 4 Hen. VI [1425]

Richard [Beauchamp] earl of Warwick and James de Berkeley, lord of Berkeley.

Following the arbitration by Philip [Morgan] bishop of Worcester and John Juyn, Richard and James have agreed that Richard shall hold, for his life, the manors of Wottone, Symondeshale and Cowley, and lands [etc.], in Framptone, Cromhale, Actone Ylger, Cyngescote and Mynchinhampton (Glos.), and in the hundreds of Harclyf and Portbury (Som.).

A1/1/48 [SC 591]   17 July 17 Hen. VI [1439]

King Henry VI and James de Berkeley.

At the request of James, the king has inspected the inquisition *post mortem* of Maurice de Berkeley held at Newport near Berkeley on Wednesday after the translation of St. Thomas, 42 Edw. III [11 July 1369].

At: Westminster.

A1/1/49 [SC 593]   14 Nov. 18 Hen. VI [1439]

King Henry VI; and Edmund [Beaufort] earl of Dorset[1] and Eleanor his wife, John Talbot, knight, and Margaret his wife, and George Lord Latymer and Elizabeth his wife.

At the request of Edmund, Eleanor, John, Margaret, George and Elizabeth, the king has exemplified the following records: (i) grant by Henry III to his brother Richard king of the Romans, of the custody of the lands and the marriage of Edmund the king's son, dated 12 Nov. 46 Hen. III [1261]; (ii) writ of Henry III to the sheriff of Kent to deliver to Isabel wife of Maurice de Berkeley the manors of Herietesham and Trottesclive, dated 10 Aug. 48 Hen. III [1264]; (iii) writ of Henry III to the sheriff of Gloucestershire to hold an inquisition *post mortem* after the death of Thomas de Berkeley, dated 21 Dec. 28 Hen. III 1243], and the inquisition; (iv) grant by Henry III to Maurice de Gant of the castle which he has built in his manor of Beverstone, dated 29 July 13 Hen. III [1229]; (v) pardon from Edward I to Thomas de Berkeley and Maurice his son of a fine of 1,000 marks for various transgressions judged before John Botetourte and his associates, in return for the free services of 10 men-at-arms in the forthcoming expedition to Scotland, dated Preston 2 July 34 Edw. I [1306].

At: Westminster.

A1/1/50 [SC 594]   21 Dec. 18 Hen. VI [1439]

King Henry VI; and Edmund [Beaufort] earl of Dorset and Eleanor his wife, John Lord Talbot and Margaret his wife, and George Lord Latymer and Elizabeth his wife.

At the request of Edmund, Eleanor, John, Margaret, George and Elizabeth, the king has inspected his writ to the escheator of Gloucestershire to make partition between Eleanor, Margaret and Elizabeth, daughters and coheirs of Elizabeth late countess of Warwick after

---

[1] Edmund was not formally created earl until Aug. 1441.

the death of their father Richard [Beauchamp], who held the lands by the courtesy of England. At: Westminster.

A1/1/51 [SR 148]   2 Nov. 19 Hen. VI [1440]
Inquisition *post mortem* for Glos. taken after the death of Richard Beauchamp, earl of Warwick.

A1/1/52 [SR 149]   5 April 26 Hen. VI [1448]
Decision of William Lord Ferrers, John Lord Beaumont, John Fortescue and John Yelverton, justices, arbitrators between Edmund [Beaufort] duke of Somerset and Eleanor his wife, John [Talbot] earl of Shrewsbury and Margaret his wife and George Nevill and Elizabeth his wife of the one part and James Berkeley of the other, concerning the lands of Thomas, late Lord Berkeley, in Glos. and Som.[1]

A1/1/53 [GC 4268]   1 July 27 Hen. VI [1449]
(1) John Beauchamp, knight, lord of Beauchamp, John Fortescu, chief justice, and William Yelverton, justice; (2) Edmund [Beaufort] duke of Somerset, and Eleanor his wife, John [Talbot] earl of Shrewsbury and Margaret his wife, and George lord of Latymer, knight, and Elizabeth his wife; (3) James Berkeley, lord of Berkeley, knight.
    Award by John Beauchamp, John and William, as arbitrators in the dispute between Edmund and the others on the one part and James Berkeley on the other part, concerning the lands [etc.] of Thomas late lord of Berkeley in Glos. and Som.

A1/1/54 [GC 4269]   1 Sept. 29 Hen. VI [1450]
John Tesyn of Awre (Glos.), yeoman, and Lady Margaret [Talbot], countess of Shrewsbury.
    John is bound to the countess in £12 2*s.* 4*d.* payable at Michaelmas.

A1/1/55 [GC 4273]   8 Oct. 30 Hen. VI [1451]
James lord of Berkeley, William Berkeley, knight, James Berkeley, Maurice Berkeley and Thomas Berkeley, esquires; and John [Talbot] earl of Shrewsbury and his wife Margaret, Edmund [Beaufort] duke of Somerset and his wife Eleanor and George Lord Latymere and his wife Elizabeth.
    James and the others have granted that they will assure to the earl and the others and the heirs of Margaret, Eleanor and Elizabeth, by fine or other method, the manors of Wotton, Symondeshale and Coueley, and all other lands and holdings awarded to the earl and the others at Surcetur by John Lord Beauchamp, William Lord Ferrers, John Fortescu, knight, and William Yelverton, and also the hundred of Berkeley with return of writs, and the earl and Margaret, on behalf of the others, will assure to James and his male issue the castle and manor of Berkeley, the manors of Hamme, Alkynton, Appulrugge, Hynton, Hurste, Slymbrugge, Camme, Upton Leonard, 22 marks in Frampton upon Severn (Glos.), and the manor of Portbury (Som.) and all the other lands awarded to James, and James, William, James, Maurice and Thomas bind themselves in £10,000 to perform these promises.

A1/1/56 [GC 4275]   5 Nov. 30 Hen. VI [1451]
[John Talbot] earl of Shewsbury and James Lord Berkeley.
    The earl has received from James £24 in part payment of 50 marks. [*In English.*] [A second acquittance attached is illegible.]

A1/1/57 [SC 608]   6 July 1 Edw. IV [1461]
King Edward IV and Margaret [Talbot] countess of Shrewsbury.
    The king has granted to Margaret the wardship and marriage of Thomas [Talbot] son and heir of John late Viscount Lisle.
At: Westminster.

---

[1] See Smyth, ii. 61–2.

A1/1/58 [SC 615; *duplicate* SC 616]   15 Nov. 6 Edw. IV [1466]
(1) Margaret [Talbot] countess of Shrewsbury; (2) Eleanor [Beaufort] duchess of Somerset;
(3) Elizabeth wife of George Nevill, Lord Latimer.

Tripartite indenture between Margaret, Eleanor and Elizabeth for the division of lands in
Glos. and Som., principally Wotton manor and borough, and Bedminster, and other
holdings, as the daughters and coheirs of Elizabeth [Beauchamp] late countess of Warwick.

A1/1/59 [SC 624]   6 April 10 Edw. IV [1470]
King Edward IV; and Elizabeth Talbot and Margaret Talbot, sisters and heirs of Thomas
Talbot, late Viscount Lisle.

The king has granted to Elizabeth and Margaret special livery of all the manors, lands,
holdings [etc.] which descended to them on the death of their brother .
At: Banbury.

A1/1/60 [SR 137]   [1470]
Contemporary copy of letters [etc.] which passed between Maurice Kyng and Thomas Holt
of the one part and William Lord Berkeley and Thomas Talbot, Viscount Lisle, of the other
shortly before the battle of Nibley, 1470. [*In English*.][1]

A1/1/61 [GC 4396]   1 May 15 Edw. IV [1475]
King Edward IV and William [Berkeley].

Exemplification of various documents concerned with the dispute between James Lord
Berkeley and his sons of the one part and Margaret [Talbot] countess of Shrewsbury and
her sisters of the other.

A1/1/62 [GC 4427*]   25 Feb. 21 Edw. IV [1482]
William Viscount Berkeley; and Edward Grey, knight, Lord Lisle, and Elizabeth his wife.

Whereas there have been disputes over the manors of Wotton Underegge and Simondesale
and the borough of Wotton, the advowson of Wotton, various rents and holdings in Nebley,
Sernecliff, Acton Ilger, Iren Acton, Horwode, Newlese and the Warth, Alderleigh,
Kyngiscott, Erlyngham, Roddesleighweer, Sagyslandis in Slymbrigge and the advowsons of
the chantries of St. John the Baptist, Wortley, and of St. Giles, Hilsley, it has been agreed,
after arbitration by Thomas [Grey] marquess of Dorset, that the lands should be settled on
William and his issue and William shall grant an annuity of £20 to Edward and Elizabeth and
the heirs of Elizabeth, until the death of Margaret [Talbot] Viscountess Lisle, when the
annuity shall cease. [*In English*.] Endorsed (in a 17th-century hand): *never tooke effect*.

A1/1/63 [SC 655]   14 Oct. 5 Hen. VII [1489]
The king has inspected the record of a commission of *oyer et terminer* brought by the three
daughters of Richard [Beauchamp] earl of Warwick and Elizabeth Berkeley and their
husbands, concerning the forcible entry of their manors of Wotton, Simondshall and Coaley
by James Lord Berkeley and his sons William, James, Maurice and Thomas; at Campden
on 4 Oct. 1451 and at Cirencester on 9 and 10 Dec. 1451.
At: Westminster.

> *Dower portions*
> *Joan Talbot, widow of James Lord Berkeley* (*d. 1463*), *who married secondly Edmund*
> *Hungerford*

A1/1/64 [GC 4325]   24 Jan. 3 Edw. IV [1464]
Joan Berkeley, Lady Berkeley, widow of the late James Berkeley, lord of Berkeley, knight,
and William lord of Berkeley, knight.

Joan has quitclaimed to William all the lands [etc.] which were of the said James in
England, and all her claim to dower.

---

[1] *Transcript of one letter*: Smyth, ii. 107.

A1/1/65 [GC 4330]   St. Mark, 5 Edw. IV [25 April 1465]
Joan widow of James Berkeley, knight, lord of Berkeley, and William lord of Berkeley, knight.

Joan has received from William £15 in part payment of an annuity of £40 for her life granted to her by William, viz. £5 for the Annunciation term of 4 Edw. IV and £10 for the Annunciation term last past.

A1/1/66 [GC 4335]   17 Feb. 5 Edw. IV [1466]
Joan, widow of James Berkeley, knight, lord of Berkeley, and William Berkeley, lord of Berkeley, knight.

Joan has received from William £10 for the . . . term of an annual rent of £40 for her life.

A1/1/67 [SC 632]   26 May 14 Edw. IV [1474]
Edmund Hungerford, esquire, and Joan his wife, late wife of James Lord Berkeley; and William Lord Berkeley, son and heir of James.

Whereas Joan quitclaimed to William all her late husband's lands in Glos. and elsewhere in her charter of 20 Sept. 7 Edw. IV [1467], Edmund now confirms the quitclaim and quitclaims the same to William Lord Berkeley, Thomas Berkeley, esquire, Maurice Kyng and John atte Wode, and will receive an annuity of £45 for life from Thomas, Maurice and John, by a mandate of William dated 26 Nov. 13 Edw. IV [1473].

A1/1/68 [GC 4387]   Morrow of Michaelmas, 14 Edw. IV [30 Sept. 1474]
Edmund Hungerford, esquire, and William Lord Barkeley.

Edmund has received from William £11 5s. in part payment of an annual rent of £45 paid to him and Lady Joan Barkeley his wife, widow of James lord of Barkeley, father of William, for the life of Joan.

A1/1/69 [GC 4392]   Morrow of Christmas, 14 Edw. IV [26 Dec. 1474]
Edmund Hungerford, esquire, and William Lord Barkeley.

Edmund has received from William £11 5s. in part payment of an annual rent of £45 paid to him and Lady Joan Barkeley his wife, widow of James lord of Barkeley, father of William, for the life of Joan.

Other dower portions

A1/1/70 [GC 1200]   n.d. [c. 1250?]
Maurice lord of Berkel' and Lady Joan de Berkel', his mother.

Maurice has granted to Joan, in dower, all the manor of Wotton' with appurtenances, with a third part of the land which Thomas de Berkel', Maurice's brother, held at Egge; also the manors of Camma, Coueleg', Hurste and Alcinton, with their appurtenances, as Lord Thomas de Berkel' his father held them, and the manor of Hiniton; and Joan has quitclaimed all the lands which she previously had in dower in all his other manors in the counties of Glos., Som., and Devon, saving to Joan the service of the lord of Cromhale.
Witnesses: Sir Robert de Gurnay, Roger de Lokinton, Maurice de Saltmarsh (*de salso marisco*), Richard de Cromhale, Robert de Hales, Maurice's steward, Jordan de Bradiford, Andrew de Bradestan, Peter de Wika, Nicholas le Rus.

A1/1/71 [SC 424]   2 Aug. 36 Hen. III [1252]
King Henry III and Joan de Berkeley.

The king has granted free warren in the manors of Wotton and Cam, which Joan holds in dower, and a weekly market and annual fair in Wotton, to Joan and, after her death, to Maurice her son and heir.
Witnesses: Geoffrey de Lezign', the king's brother, Peter de Sabaudia, Master William de Kilkenny, archdeacon of Coventry, Robert Walerand, Gilbert de Segrave, Elias de Rabayn,

Robert de Muscegros, E[lerius], abbot of Pershore, Robert le Norreys, Nicholas de Sancto Mauro, Roger de Lokinton.
At: Woodstock.

A1/1/72 [GC 2628]							3 May 1 Edw. III [1327]
Thomas lord of Berkel' and Isabel widow of his father Maurice de Berkel'.

Thomas has assigned to Isabel as her dower in the lands and holdings which were of Maurice in Glos. all the manor of Wottone and the market town of Wottone with the fair and market and all the lands and holdings in Symoundishale by Wottone, to hold for her life. [*In French.*]
At: Berkeley.

A1/1/73 [GC 2630; *duplicate* GC 2641]	Wed. before St. Barnabas, 1 Edw. III [8 June 1327]
Isabel widow of Sir Maurice de Berkele and Sir Thomas de Berkele, her dear son, son and heir of Maurice.

Whereas Thomas has granted to her the manors of Wotton and of Symondeshale, with the market town of Wottone, and a rent of £23 for her life from the manor of Bedemenystre for dower, Isabel has quitclaimed to Thomas all actions of dower. [*In French.*]
At: Wotton.

A1/1/74 [GC 3548]							18 Jan. 37 Edw. III [1364]
Lady Katherine de Berkele, lady of Wotton, and Sir Maurice lord of Berkele.

Katherine has received her dower in the fees appurtenant to the lordship of Berkele, viz. all the fees appurtenant to the manors of Wottone, Symondeshale and Camme, with the third part of the hundreds of Berkele, Portbury, Bedmenstre and Harclyve, viz. that she will take a third part of the profts at four annual terms, and the lady has granted that if the marriage of John her son is declared by law to be the right of the lord of Berkele, this indenture will be void. [*In French.*]
At: Berkeley.

Miscellaneous

A1/1/75 [GC 1019*; *duplicate* GC 1019**]			1 Aug. 29 Edw. I [1301]
Thomas de Berkeleye, lord of Berkeley, and Maurice de Berkel', his eldest son.

Thomas has leased to Maurice his manors of Wotton, Symond' and Hynetone (Glos.) and his manor of Portbur' (Som.), with all the appurtenances except the fisheries of Hyneton in the Severn and saving to Joan his wife the fisheries at Portbur' in the Severn; also his borough of Wotton with the fair and market, half of the fisheries which he had of the gift of Robert de Berk' his brother in Erlyngham, all the fines, perquisities, wardships, reliefs [etc.] from all his tenants of Camme, Couel' and Slymbr', after Whitsun next coming, for Thomas's life; also two beasts in the chase of Mukkelwode in the summer and four in the winter, and pasture for 50 goats, and 12 a. of meadow in the meadow of Perham in Hamme belonging to the manor of Wotton, with the woods of Camme and Couel', to hold all the above for Maurice's life, rent, during Thomas's life, £120 a year and £30 a year to James de Berk', Thomas's son, until James has prebends or other churches worth £40 a year, and if James dies before Thomas then the £30 to be paid to Thomas [etc.].
Witnesses: Sir John de Boutetourte, Sir John Abbadam, Sir Walter de Glouc', Sir John de Acton, Sir John Basset, Sir Edmund Basset, Sir Thomas de Gornay, Sir William de Wauton, knights, Robert de Bradeston, Robert de Berk', Robert de Budelescombe, Thomas de Beol', Thomas de Swonhungre.
At: Berkeley.

A1/1/76 [SR 146]					Sun. after St. James, 37 Edw. III [30 July 1363]
Copy of an inquisition taken at Gloucester of the knights' fees which pertain to the barony

of Berkeley, arranged under the following headings: Hinton, Slimbridge, Arlingham, Hame, Hurst, Portburye, Cam, Cowley, Arlingham.

A1/1/77 [SC 580]   20 Nov. 1 Hen. V [1413]
King Henry V and Thomas lord of Berkeley.

The king has inspected and confirmed to Thomas the charters of his predecessors viz. (i) of King Edward I to Maurice de Berkeley of free warren in all his demesne lands in Glos. and in the manor of Portbury (Som.), dated Westminster, 18 Nov. 8 Edw. I [1280]; (ii) of King Henry IV to Thomas de Berkeley of free warren in his demesne lands of Walton, Weston, Porteshed and Charlton near Wroxhale (Som.), dated Westminster, 24 Aug. 2 Hen. IV [1401].
At: Westminster.

A1/1/78 [GC 4347]   24 Nov. 7 Edw. IV [1467]
Maurice Berkeley, esquire, brother of William Lord Berkeley; and Thomas Berkeley, esquire, brother of William, and Richard Abadam, yeoman.

Whereas the said Lord Berkeley, Thomas and Richard are bound in 300 marks to Edmund Wardys to be paid at 20 marks a year for 15 years, and whereas Maurice is also bound by a bond of 22 Nov. in the aforesaid year to Thomas and Richard in 300 marks, Thomas and Richard grant that if William dies within the 15 years, before the sum of 300 marks is repaid, and Maurice has possession of the manor of Berkeley, Maurice will pay the residue of the said 300 marks to the said Edmund, and the bond of Maurice to Thomas and Richard will be void. [*In English.*]
At: Bristol.

A1/1/79 [SC 636]   1 Jan. 1477 [1478]
Arnulph Colyn, commissary general of John [Alcock], bishop of Worcester, and William Lord Berkeley.

Arnulph has received from William the sum of £4 for payment of Peter's Pence due from the manors of Berkeley and Wotton due to John [Carpenter], late bishop of Worcester.

THE CASTLE

A1/1/80 [GC 3250]   n.d. [*c.* 1349]
Walter Goldemere, David de Milkesham and John le Vyth; and Sir Thomas de Berkelee.

Walter, David and John have granted to Thomas their castle of Berkelee, for the life of Thomas, with reversion to Maurice de Berkelee his son and his male issue, the male issue of Thomas and Katherine his wife, and the right heirs of Thomas.
Witnesses: Sir Thomas de Bradeston, Sir Edmund de Clyvedone, Sir John de Berkelee, Sir Simon Basset, knights, John FitzNichol, William de Chiltenham.

A1/1/81 [SC 538]   25 May 1364
Twelve archbishops and bishops have granted forty days' indulgence to all who worship or make benefactions to the chapel of the Blessed Virgin Mary and St. John in the castle of Berkeley.[1]
At: Avignon.

A1/1/82 [GC 4274]   [20] Oct. 30 Hen. VI [1451]
John [Talbot] earl of Shrewsbury, Margaret his wife and John Talbot, Lord Lisle, their son; and James Lord Berkeley, William Berkeley, knight, James Berkeley, Maurice Berkeley and Thomas Berkeley esquires.

James, William, James, Maurice and Thomas have demised to John, Margaret and John the castle of [Berkeley] . . . for a term of two years, saving to James, and six people serving him, reasonable living and easements, . . .

A1/1/83 [GAR 410] Castle gardener's account   39–41 Edw. III [1365–7]

[1] *Transcript*: Jeayes, pp. 170–2.

THE HUNDRED
The Liberty

Charters

A1/1/84 [GC 1832]   Thurs. after St. Peter and St. Paul, 4 Edw. II [1 July 1311]
Thomas de Berkelee, lord of Berkeley; and Robert atte Moere and Leticia his wife.

Whereas Robert and Leticia were bound by an indenture between them and Thomas to come to the two lawdays of Berkelee hundred every year for a virgate of land which they hold of Thomas in Hurste, for life, at a rent of 40*s.* a year, Thomas has remitted to them the said two suits for a rent of 12*d.* a year, for their lives.
Witnesses: Nicholas de Beoleye, Walter de Gosyntone, Richard de Estmed, William le Boteler, Richard Baat.
At: Berkeley.

A1/1/85 [SC 494]   8 June 4 Edw. III [1330]
King Edward III and Thomas de Berkeley.

The king has inspected the charters of his predecessors Henry II, Richard I and John to Robert FitzHarding and his successors concerning Berkeley honour and has confirmed them; and has granted further that Thomas should have the liberty of return of writs within the hundred of Berkeley.
Witnesses: H[enry Burghersh], bishop of Lincoln, chancellor, R[oger Northburgh], bishop of Coventry and Lichfield, John de Eltham, earl of Cornwall, Henry earl of Lancaster, John de Warenna, earl of Surrey, Oliver de Ingham, John Mautravers, steward of the royal household.
At: Woodstock.

A1/1/86 [SC 500]   Thurs. after St. Peter in chains, 11 Edw. III [7 Aug. 1337]
Thomas lord of Berkeley and John [Snow] abbot of St. Augustine's, Bristol.

Thomas has granted to the abbey that they may keep the stray animals taken by their bailiffs on their demesne lands within the hundred of Berkeley.
At: Berkeley.

A1/1/87 [SC 627]   1 March 11 Edw. IV [1472]
King Edward IV and William Lord Berkeley.

At William's request, the king has exemplified the inspeximus by Edward III of all the grants made by his ancestors, Henry II, Richard I [etc.] to successive Lords Berkeley, and of Edward III's grant to Thomas de Berkeley of the liberty of return of writs within Berkeley hundred, the exemplification being necessary because the inspeximus by Edward III has been accidentally lost.
At: Westminster.

Bailiffs' accounts

A1/1/88 [GAR 412]	11–12 Edw. III [1337–8]
A1/1/89 [GAR 413]	19–20 Edw. III [1345–6]
A1/1/90 [GAR 414]	46–7 Edw. III [1372–3]

Court rolls

A1/1/91 [GCR 3]	11 Oct. 5 Hen. V [1417]
A1/1/92 [GCR 369]	8 Nov. 5 Hen. [1417] to 10 Feb. 8 Hen. V [1421]
A1/1/93 [GCR 4]	30 Hen. VI [1451–2]
A1/1/94 [GCR 5]	37 Hen. VI [1458–9]
A1/1/95 [GCR 6]	1–2 Edw. IV [1461–2]
A1/1/96 [GCR 7]	2–3 Edw. IV [1462–3]

A1/1/97 [GSUB 82] Draft court book for the hundred of Berkeley and the honour manors with Arlingham, Oct. 19 Edw. IV to April 1 Edw. V [1479–83], and one court each for Oldland, 2 Oct. 20 Edw. IV [1480], and Newport, 17 Dec. 22 Edw. IV [1482].

The region

Berkeley

A1/1/98 [SC 280]   n.d. [1220 × 1243]
Hugh Gule and Thomas lord of Berkeley.

Hugh has sold and quitclaimed to Thomas all the rights which he might have through Hugh Gule his father in lands, rents, and services in Berkeleyhernesse, for which Thomas gave him 3½ marks.
Witnesses: Sir Ignatius de Cliftun, Geoffrey de Lawertune, Henry de Berkeley, William de Essetun, Thomas de Rodeberwe, Adam Coby, John Sewacre, Alfred le Sipward, Maurice de Bevintun, Maurice de Stanes, Peter de Wika, William son of Robert.

A1/1/99 [GC 1802]   Mon. after St. Gregory, 4 Edw. II [15 March 1311]
Robert de Berkelee and Sir Thomas de Berkelee.

Robert has quitclaimed to Thomas common in enclosures and encroachments (*purpresturis*) made by Thomas in Mikkelwod, Wolfaresfeld, Hethfelde and all other places within the hundred of Berkelee.
Witnesses: Sir Maurice de Berkelee, Sir John Lovel of Snorscombe, Sir William de Wauton, knights, Richard de Rodeny, John Boteler, John Chaumpeneys, Robert de Butlescombe.
At: Berkeley.

A1/1/100 [GC 3976]   20 June 1 Hen. IV [1400]
Thomas Berkleye, lord of Berkeley; and Philip Watertone and Cecilia his wife.

Thomas has granted to Philip and Cecilia, for the good service of Philip, all the lands, holdings [etc.] that were of Robert Poyns within the lordship of Berkleye; for their lives, at the old rent.
Witnesses: Thomas FitzNycol, John Rolves, Richard Egton, Thomas Wyth, Thomas Staverton.

The Walbrook holding

A1/1/101 [GC 3877]   Sun. before St. Simon and St. Jude, 17 Ric. II [26 Oct. 1393]
John Walbroke of Berkeley; and Ralph Coke, John Toneswelle, Nicholas Hugones and John Byl.

John has granted to Ralph, John, Nicholas and John, and their heirs and assigns, all his lands and holdings within the hundred of Berkele.
Witnesses: Richard Egetone, Richard Gylmyn, Thomas Lucas, Thomas Upyntone, Richard Smyth.
At: Berkeley.

A1/1/102 [GC 3902]   Sun. before St. Nicholas, 19 Ric. II [5 Dec. 1395]
Ralph Coke, John Tounsewell, Nicholas Hugons and John Byl; and John Rolvys, John Camme, parson of Brean, and Thomas Brystowe chaplain.

Ralph, John, Nicholas and John have granted to John, John and Thomas, and their heirs and assigns, all the lands and holdings which they had by grant of John Walbroke within the hundred of Berkeley.
Witnesses: Richard Egtone, John Egtone the younger, Thomas Lucas, Richard Gylmyn, Richard Smyth.
At: Berkeley.

Other

A1/1/103 [GC 4029]   Thurs. the feast of All Saints, 10 Hen. IV [1 Nov. 1408]
John Coby the younger, son and heir of the late John Coby of Berkeley; and Walter Toyt of

Breadstone and John Hugonys of Berkeley.

John Coby has granted to Walter and John Hugonys, and their heirs and assigns, all his lands and holdings within the hundred of Berkeley.

Witnesses: Richard Ektone, John Floure, John Beltone, Nicholas Kyng, William Brokenbourgh.

A1/1/104 [GC 4312]   20 April 1 Edw. IV [1461]
Isabel Derlynge of Bristol, widow, daughter and heir of William Scot, late burgess of Bristol; and William Russell, *alias* Gwyllam Russel, of the same, merchant, and Margery his wife, Isabel's daughter.

Isabel has granted to William and Margery, and their heirs and assigns, all her lands, holdings [etc.] in the lordship of Berkeley in Glos.

Witnesses: Robert Ricardes, Richard Clayvyle, Thomas Payne, Richard Lee, Thomas Berkeley.

THE PARISH

Chantries in the parish church

St. Mary's

A1/1/105 [GC 2890]   1 Dec. 11 Edw. III [1337]
Thomas lord of Berkelee, and Sir Thomas ate Welle, chaplain of the Virgin Mary in Berkeley church.

Whereas Thomas ate Welle and his predecessors have held of Thomas de Berkelee and his ancestors 2 messuages in Berkelee and 8 a. of land in Hamme for a rent of 6*s.* 6*d.* a year, Thomas de Berkelee wills and grants that Thomas ate Welle and his successors shall have the said rent for celebrating on the anniversaries of Sir Maurice his father for his soul [on the feast of St. Petronilla, 31 May] and his late wife Margaret [5 May], and for himself after his death.

At: Berkeley.

St. Andrew's

A1/1/106 [SC 562]   16 June 7 Ric. II [1384]
King Richard II and Lady Katherine widow of Thomas de Berkeley.

The king has granted to Katherine licence to grant certain messuages and lands in Berkeley, Ham, Alkington and elsewhere to the chaplain of St. Andrew's altar in the parish church of Berkeley to celebrate divine service for her soul and those of her mother and father.

At: Westminster.

A1/1/107 [SC 563; *duplicates* SC 564 *and* GC 3776]   30 June 8 Ric. II [1384]
Thomas de Berkeley, lord of Berkeley, and Katherine widow of Thomas de Berkeley.

Thomas has confirmed and granted licence to Katherine for her grant to support a chaplain at the altar of St. Andrew in the parish church of Berkeley of lands in Berkeley, Ham, Alkington and elsewhere.

Other

A1/1/108 [GC 4267]   21 March 27 Hen. VI [1449]
William Hoper *alias* Wattys of Chipping Sodbury (Glos.) and Edith his wife; and John Thorp of Wanswell and Margaret his wife.

William and Edith, daughter and heir of John Shippard, late of Berkeley, have granted to John and Margaret, and John's heirs and assigns, all their lands, holdings [etc.] in Berkeley parish.

Witnesses: John Hervy, Richard Clavyle, John Payn.

A1/1/109 [SR 138]   [late 15th cent.]
Extracts from the registers of the bishops of Worcester concerning the admission of rectors
[etc.] to the parish churches of Slimbridge [1207–1475] and Berkeley [1287–1460], and
various chantries, with copies of documents relating to Longbridge hospital near Berkeley.

THE ADVOWSONS

A1/1/110 [SC 14]   n.d. [1164 × 1170]
Robert FitzHarding and St. Augustine's Abbey, Bristol.
    Robert has confirmed to the abbey his grant of the churches of Berkeley Herness, viz.
Berkeley, Wotton, Beverston, Ashelworth and Almondsbury, with their chapels, lands and
liberties.[1]
Witnesses: Henry dean of Mortain, Maurice his brother, Gerinus parson of Wotton,
Geoffrey the chaplain, Nigel son of Arthur, Reginald parson of Cam, W. de Saltemareis,
Adam his brother, Elias son of Harding, Richard the scribe (*scriptor*), Alan de Bedmenistra.

A1/1/111 [SC 17]   n.d. [1164 × 1170]
R[oger de Gloucester], bishop of Worcester, and St. Augustine's Abbey, Bristol.
    The bishop has confirmed to the abbey the grant to them of the churches of Berkeley
Herness, viz. Berkeley, Wotton, Beverston, Almondsbury, Ashelworth and Cromhall.
Witnesses: Matthew the archdeacon, Clement prior of Llanthony, Randolf Gansel, Nicholas
the dean, Augustine the chaplain, Daniel the chaplain.

A1/1/112 [SC 158]   n.d. [*c.* 1218]
William [de Blois], bishop of Worcester, and St. Augustine's Abbey, Bristol.
    William has confirmed the grant by his predecessor Roger to the abbey of the churches of
Berkelehernesse, viz. Berkeley, Wotton, Beverstone, Almondesbury, Ashelworth and
Cromhall, witnessed by Matthew the archdeacon, Clement prior of Llanthony, Ralph
Gansel, Nicholas the dean, Augustine the chaplain, Daniel the chaplain.
Witnesses: Ralph canon of Oseney, Warin the chaplain, Master Godfrey, Master William de
Tuneb', William son of Godfrey, Master Hugh de Porwico, John de Draitun.

A1/1/113 [SC 157]   n.d. [*c.* 1218]
William [de Blois], bishop of Worcester, and St. Augustine's Abbey, Bristol.
    The bishop has taken the canons under his protection and has granted to them the
revenues of the churches of Berkeley, Almodesbury, Wutton and Esselesworth for their use
and support.
Witnesses: Ralph canon of Oseney, Warin the chaplain, Master Godfrey, Master William de
Tuneb', William son of Godfrey, Master Hugh de Portwico, John the clerk of Draitun.

A1/1/114 [SC 451]   n.d. [1276 × 1286]
Henry de Berkeley, lord of Dursley, and Abbot J[ohn de Marina] of St. Augustine's Abbey,
Bristol.
    Henry has quitclaimed to the abbey all the lands, churches, advowsons [etc.], which they
hold in Berkeley and Berkeleishurnes.
Witnesses: Sir Bartholomew de Sulby, Sir Alexander Dando, knights, Philip de Doghton,
William Golofre, Robert de la Stone.

ACTON (IN HAM)

Mentioned as a separate vill in the Quo Warranto proceedings of 1287, Acton (*Egeton*) was
part of Ham manor although portions lay within Hinton manor. It was closely associated
with neighbouring Halmore and, indeed, Smyth regarded the two places as being one. It is
now represented by Acton Hall, in Hamfallow.

---

[1] *Transcript*: Smyth, iii. 87; Jeayes, pp. 9–10; *St Augustine's Cartulary*, no. 67.

BERKELEY INTERESTS
Grants in Halmore, April 1311[1]

A1/2/1 [GC 1814]   1 April 4 Edw. II [1311]
Thomas de Berkelee, lord of Berkeley; and Reginald le White and Isabel his wife.

Thomas has granted to Reginald and Isabel 2 a. and a fardel of land at Halmare between his land and the road from the Severn to Wottone in Homme; to hold enclosed, to them and their issue, rent 3s. a year.

Witnesses: Thomas de Stone, John Capel, John Wayfer, Robert de Stanford, Matthew Hatholf.

At: Berkeley.

A1/2/2 [GC 1812]   1 April 4 Edw. II [1311]
Thomas de Berkelee, lord of Berkeley; and Thomas le Large and Maud his wife.

Thomas has granted to Thomas and Maud 2½ a. 20 perches of land at Halmare beside the road from the Severn to Wottone in Homme; to hold enclosed, to them and their issue, rent 3s. 6d. a year.

Witnesses: Thomas de Stone, John Capel, John de Swonhongre, Robert de Stanford, Matthew Hatholf.

At: Berkeley.

A1/2/3 [GC 1811]   1 April 4 Edw. II [1311]
Thomas de Berkelee, lord of Berkeley; and Walter in the Herne and Juliana his wife.

Thomas has granted to Walter and Juliana a fardel and 12 perches of land at Halmare between his land and the road from the Severn to Wottone in Homme; to hold enclosed, to them and their issue, rent 4d. a year.

Witnesses: Robert de Bradestone, Thomas de Stone, John Capel, John de Swonhongre, Robert de Stanford, Matthew Hatholf, John le Frig.

At: Berkeley.

A1/2/4 [GC 1809]   1 April 4 Edw. II [1311]
Thomas de Berkelee, lord of Berkeley; and Matthew Hatholf and Juliana his wife.

Thomas has granted to Matthew and Juliana 1 a. 30 perches of land at Halmare in Homme, by the road from the Severn to Wottone; to hold enclosed, to them and their issue, rent 2s. a year.

Witnesses: Thomas de Stone, John de Swonhongre, John Wayfer, Robert de Stanford, Robert Wyhtteladde.

At: Berkeley.

A1/2/5 [GC 1808]   1 April 4 Edw. II [1311]
Thomas de Berkelee, lord of Berkeley; and Adam Doucesone of Hinton and Isabel his wife.

Thomas has granted to Adam and Isabel ½ a. 13 perches of land at Halmare in Homme; to hold enclosed, to them and their issue, rent 9d. a year.

Witnesses: Thomas de Stone, John de Swonhongre, John Wayfer, Robert de Stanford, Matthew Hatholf.

At: Berkeley.

A1/2/6 [GC 1807]   1 April 4 Edw. II [1311]
Thomas de Berkelee, lord of Berkeley; and Reginald atten Abbeye and Amicia his wife.

Thomas has granted to Reginald and Amicia ½ a. 16 perches of land at Halmare in Homme; to hold enclosed, to them and their issue, rent 9d. a year.

---

[1] All the rents were paid to Ham manor under the heading *Egeton*.

Witnesses: Robert de Bradeston, Thomas de Stone, John Wayfer, Robert de Stanford, Matthew Hatholf.
At: Berkeley.

A1/2/7 [GC 1816]   6 April 4 Edw. II [1311]
Thomas de Berkelee, lord of Berkeley, and Walter Doucesone of Hinton.

Thomas has granted to Walter 2 a. 30 perches of land at Halmare in Homme; to hold enclosed, to him and his issue, rent 2*s.* 8*d.* a year.
Witnesses: Robert de Bradestone, Thomas de Stone, John Wayfer, Robert de Stanford, Matthew Hatholf.
At: Berkeley.

Exchange of 2 virgates for a wood

A1/2/8 [SC 176]   n.d. [early Hen. III]
Robert de Berkelai and Isillia daughter of Alexander de Egintun.

Robert has granted to Isillia 2 virgates of land in Hinetun called Kingesgerde and Husland in exchange for the wood called Garstin and Aldredesmare.
Witnesses: Henry de Coueleg, Bernard de Cramal, Richard de Cromhal, Bernard de Stanes, Bernard de Brothestan, Eustace de Camm, Maurice son of Nigel, Gilbert de Ege[tun], Hugh de Camm, Richard de Bradel, Oliver de Berkeley.

A1/2/9 [SC 368]   n.d. [early Hen. III]
Isillia daughter of Alexander de Ekinton and Robert de Berkele.

Isillia has granted to Robert certain lands in Hineton in exchange for 2 virgates there.
Witnesses: . . . Bernard de Cromhale, . . . , Bernard de Stanes, Bernard de Brodestan, Eustace de Camme, Maurice son of Nigel, Gilbert de Egetun, Hugh de Camme, Richard de Bradele, Oliver de Berkele, Elias de . . .

A1/2/10 [SC 179]   n.d. [early Hen. III]
William son of Elias de Saltmarsh (*de salso marisco*) and Sir Robert de Berkeley.

William, with the consent of Maud his wife, has confirmed to Robert the land and wood which Isillia daughter of Alexander de Eggintuna, his grandmother, gave in exchange to Robert for 2 virgates of land in Eggetuna belonging to Hinton manor.
Witnesses: Henry Swan, Elias the chaplain, Sir Roger, John Wolf (*Lupus*), Bernard de Brothestan, Thomas de Tiringeham, Bernard de Stanes, Bernard de Cromhale, Maurice son of Nigel, John de Eggetuna, Maurice de Bevingtuna.

Wysecroft

A1/2/11 [GC 1155]   n.d. [late Hen. III]
Reginald at the well (*ad fontem*) and Sir Maurice de Berkel.

Reginald has granted to Maurice a croft of land called Wikecroft in the vill of Egetun, to hold of Reginald, rent 1*d.* a year, and Maurice has given him 2 marks.
Witnesses: Bartholomew de Olepenn, Walter de Egetun, William de Egetun, Robert de Bradestone, Robert ate Bur', Richard de Stanford.

A1/2/12 [GC 1209]   n.d. [late Hen. III]
Maurice de Berkeley and Richard de Wenden.

Maurice has granted to Richard and his issue a croft of land in the vill of Egetun called Wysecroft, which he bought from Reginald at the well (*ad fontem*); rent a pair of gilt spurs a year.
Witnesses: Bartholomew de Olopenn', Walter de Egetun, William de Egetun, Robert de Bradeston, Richard de Stanford, Thomas Ravel, Richard Oufre, Michael the clerk.

Bran Wood

A1/2/13 [GC 326]   Sunday before Lent, 1270 [23 Feb. 1270]
Hildeburg widow of Thomas Mathias and Sir Maurice de Berkeley.

Hildeburg has confirmed to Maurice, her lord, the wood called la Barndewode, which
Maurice had by gift of Philip de Leycestre which once belonged to her free holding.
Witnesses: Sir William de Maunsel, Sir Robert de Kingestun, Sir Nicholas le Lou, knights,
Walter de Egetone, Richard de Stanford, Thomas de Swonhongre, Geoffrey Neel.

A1/2/14 [GC 1462]   n.d. [late Hen. III]
Isabel widow of Philip de Leycestre and Sir Maurice de Berkel'.

Isabel has granted [*sic*] to Maurice the wood called Barndewode, which Maurice had by
grant of Philip.
Witnesses: William de Matheme, Robert de Brathestone, John de Craweleye, Walter de
Egetune, Thomas de Swonhungre, Geoffrey Neel.

A1/2/15 [GC 458]   The Circumcision, 1273 [1 Jan. 1274]
Isabel widow of Philip de Leycestre and Sir Maurice de Berkel.

Isabel has quitclaimed to Maurice 30 a. of wood with appurtenances called la
Barndewode.
Witnesses: William de Matheme, Robert de Bratheston, Walter de Egeton, Thomas de
Swonhongre, Geoffrey Neel.

Hildeburg de Acton's holdings

The Stanford holding in Coliarescroft, Withiacre and Hethenacre
A1/2/16 [GC 1344]   n.d. [*temp*. Hen. III]
Hildeburg de Egeton and Richard de Stanford.

Hildeburg has granted to Richard 1 a. of meadow in Eghememore called Wythiacre; rent
a clove a year, and Richard has given her 3 marks.
Witnesses: Walter de Egeton, Thomas . . . Thomas de Asselesworth, Adam Hathulf, William
le Hert, William le Heyward, Richard le Duc.

A1/2/17 [GC 1349]   n.d. [*temp*. Hen. III]
Hildeburg de Egeton, widow, and Richard de Stanford.

Hildeburg has granted to Richard 5⅓ a. of land in Egeton, lying in the furlong called
Coliarescroft, beside the land of Robert de la Boure, her son, and 2 a. of meadow in
Egehememore, one called Withiacre and the other called Hethenacre; and he has given her
[10 marks].
Witnesses: Walter de Egeton, Robert de Bratheston, Thomas son of Thomas de Ahsselwrth,
. . .

A1/2/18 [GC 1348]   n.d. [*temp*. Hen. III]
Hildeburg de Egeton, widow, and Richard de Stanford and Juliana his wife.

Hildeburg has granted to Richard and Juliana 5⅓ a. of land in Egeton in the furlong
called Coliarescroft, beside the land of Robert de la Boure, her son, and up to the river
called Barunesbroc; also 2 a. of meadow in Egehememore, one called Wythyacre and the
other called Hethenacre; rent a rose a year, and they have given her 10 marks.
Witnesses: Walter de Egeton, Robert de Bradeston, Thomas son of Thomas Ahsselwrth,
Adam Hathulf, Geoffrey Neel.

A1/2/19 [GC 685]   n.d. [late Hen. III]
Maurice de Berkel and Richard de Stanford.

Maurice has confirmed to Richard 5⅓ a. of land in Egeton in the furlong called
Coliarescroft and 2 a. of meadow in Egehememore, one called la Withiacre and one called

la Hethenacre, which Richard had by grant of Hildeburg widow of Thomas Mathias, to hold of Hildeburg and her heirs.

Witnesses: Sir Richard de Berkel, Maurice's brother, Sir Thomas de Berkel, Maurice's son, Sir Nicholas le Lou, knights, Walter de Egeton, Robert de Brotheston, Thomas son of Thomas de Aysselworth, Adam Hathulf, Walter Sely.

A1/2/20 [GC 1256]   n.d. [late Hen. III]

Robert de la Boure and Richard de Stanford.

Robert has confirmed to Richard the 5⅓ a. of land in Egeton, which he had by grant of Hildeburg Robert's mother, in the furlong called Coliarescrofte, also 2 a. of meadow in Egehememor called Wythiacre and Hethenacre.

Witnesses: Walter de Egeton, Robert de Bratheston, Thomas son of Thomas de Aysshelworth, John de Crauleyg, William son of William le Hert, Walter Sely.

A1/2/21 [GC 1267]   n.d. [*c*. Nov. 1285]

Philip de la Bure of Acton and Sir Thomas de Berkel', his lord.

Philip has granted to Thomas the rents and services of William de Egeton, Robert le Witteladde and Richard de Stanford for lands in Egeton, and Thomas has given him 40*s*.

Witnesses: Robert de Bradeston, John de Crauleye, Thomas de Swonhungre, Thomas Aleyn, Robert Bastard, Adam Hathulf.

A1/2/22 [GC 520]   Thurs. before St. Andrew, 14 Edw. I [29 Nov. 1285]

Philip of the chamber (*de camera*) of Acton and Sir Thomas de Berkel.

Philip has assigned William de Egeton, Robert Witteladde and Richard de Stanford and all their heirs, to Thomas and his heirs.

At: Berkeley.

Other

A1/2/23 [GC 330]   Sat. the morrow of St. Edmund the king, 56 Hen. III [21 Nov. 1271]

Hildeburg widow of Thomas Mathias and Sir Maurice de Berkeley.

Hildeburg has granted to Maurice 2 a. of land in the furlong called Baronescroft in the vill of Egeton; Maurice has given her 20*s*. Endorsed: *Hyneton*.

Witnesses: Sir Robert de Kyngeston, Master Philip de Leycestre, Walter de Egeton, John de Crauleygh, Thomas de Beleygh, Geoffrey Neel, Robert de Egeton.

A1/2/24 [GC 324]   n.d. [*c*. 1270]

Hildeburg widow of Thomas Mathias and Sir Maurice de Berkeley.

Hildeburg has granted to Maurice, her lord, 1 a. of land and pasture in Egeton, between Muchel Elm and Little Elm, and between her pasture called Horslese and Maurice's wood called Barndewod.

Witnesses: Sir William Maunsel, Sir Nicholas Wolf (*Lupus*), Sir Robert de Kyngeston, knights, Philip de Douhgton, steward of Berkeley, Walter de Egeton, Geoffrey Neel.

A1/2/25 [GC 931]   n.d. [late Hen. III]

Hildeburg widow of Thomas Mathias and Sir Maurice de Berkel'.

Hildeburg has granted to Maurice the pasture next to Hewod called Lager, between Maurice's pasture which he had from her and the pasture of William de Egeton which he had from her.

Witnesses: John de Brothestan, John de Craul', Walter de Egeton, Geoffrey Neel, Adam Hathulf, Richard de Stanford, William son of Robert, Robert de Stan'.

Stillcroft, with other holdings in Berkeley borough

Land held of the Acton family

A1/2/26 [GC 1346]   n.d. [early Edw. I]
Walter de Egeton and Adam le Stille.

   Walter has confirmed to Adam the land in the vill of Egetone which Walter le Stille once held of John de Egeton, his father; to Adam and Margery his wife for their lives; further he grants that Adam, eldest son of Adam and Margery, should hold the land; to him and his issue, rent 4*s.* a year, and they have given him 5 marks in acknowledgement.
Witnesses: Bartholomew de Olepenne, Peter de Stintescumbe, Robert de Bradestone, Thomas de Beleye, Richard de Stanford, Thomas the serjeant (*serviens*).

A1/2/27 [GC 378]   n.d. [late Hen. III]
John de Egeton; and Adam le Still and Margery his wife.

   John has confirmed to Adam and Margery all the land in the vill of Egeton which Walter le Still once held of John his father; for their lives, rent 4*s.* a year; acknowledgement 2 marks. Endorsed: *Hynton.*
Witnesses: Andrew de Brothestan, Thomas Matthias, William son of Eustace, Richard le Frankelain, Robert Bret, Walter Frig, Adam de Cur', Adam the hayward (*messor*).

Garston

A1/2/28 [GC 301]   Eve of Whit-Sunday, 45 Hen. III [11 June 1261]
John de Egeton, son and heir of John de Egeton, and Sir Maurice de Berkeley.

   John has quitclaimed to Maurice la Garstone and Gorstruding. Endorsed: *Hyneton.*
Witnesses: Sir Maurice de Saltmarsh (*de salso marisco*), Peter de . . . , John de Brotheston, Nicholas de Craulegh, Adam Moton, William de Wyk, Thomas de Wyk, William son of Robert, John Sewaker, Robert le Herde.

A1/2/29 [GC 1204]   n.d. [late Hen. III]
Maurice de Berkel' and Peter de Wike.

   Maurice has granted to Peter all the land called Garstone and Gorstyrudinge, which contains 70 a.; rent 35*s.* a year, and Peter has given him 6 marks.
Witnesses: Sir Roger de Lokinton, Sir Maurice de Saltmarsh (*de salso marisco*), Sir Walter de Burgo, knights, Master Roger de Glouc', Maurice's steward, John de Egeton, Robert Bastard, Maurice de Stan', William son of Eustace, Thomas Mathyas, Adam Coby, John Sewaker, Alfred Skypward, Walter Sely, clerk.

A1/2/30 [GC 445]   n.d. [late Hen. III]
Peter de Wika and Adam le Stille of Acton.

   Peter has granted to Adam 8 a. of land in la Garston which lies next to the street from the heath (*bruera*) to Egenhamehull . . . 45*s.*
Witnesses: Master Philip de Leycestre, John de Egeton, John de Brotherton, Nicholas de Craulegh, Robert le Herde, Thomas Matthias, Walter Sely, clerk.

Passage from Adam le Stille to Thomas (II) de Berkeley

A1/2/31 [GC 2336]   n.d. [early Edw. I]
Adam le Stille and James de Berkeley, son of Sir Thomas de Berkeley.

   Adam has granted to James the messuage and land with a croft, garden [etc.] which he had by grant of Walter de Egeton, and which Adam le Stille his father formerly held, in Egetone, and an annual rent of 4*s.* from 8 a. of land in the furlong called Garstone which he had by grant of John de Wyke; rent 4*s.* a year to the said Walter and John and 1*d.* a year to John, and James has given Adam 30 marks.
Witnesses: Sir Richard de Vivar', Sir Roger de Lokintone, Sir Maurice de Saltmarsh (*de*

salso marisco), knights, Peter de Stintescumb, Elias de Cumbe, Robert de Coueley, Robert de Draychote.

A1/2/32 [GC 539]   St. Matthew, 16 Edw. I [21 Sept. 1288]
John de Egeton, son and heir of Walter de Egeton, and James de Berkele, son of Sir Thomas lord of Berkeley.

John has quitclaimed to James the messuage with crofts [etc.] which Adam le Stille once held of John in Egeton; James to pay him the rent of 4*s.* a year, and James has given him 2 marks.
Witnesses: Robert de Stone, Robert de Bradeston, Thomas de Swonhongre, Thomas de Boeleye, Thomas Aleyn, William Capel, John de Craule.
At: Berkeley.

A1/2/33 [GC 1347]   n.d. [*temp.* Edw. I]
John de Egeton and Sir Thomas lord of Berkeleya.

John has granted to Thomas the rent of 4*s.* from John Hues and the other rents and services from the said John and James de Berkel' for lands and holdings formerly of Adam Stille in Egeton; Thomas has given him 40*s.*
Witnesses: Robert de Bradeston, Thomas de Beleye, Thomas de Swonhungre, Robert Wyther, Richard de Wyk, Walter Moton, Robert Bastard, Adam Hatholf, William de Webbeleye, clerk.

A1/2/34 [SC 318]   n.d. [1262 × 1287]
Henry de Berkeley, lord of Dursley, and Bartholomew de Olepenne.

Henry has granted to Bartholomew, for his service, the rent of 10*s.* paid by William de Bernewood for the fulling mill in Dursley which William holds for life, and after William's death to hold the mill, to him and his heirs; rent a rose a year.
Witnesses: Miles de Langethot, Peter de Stintescumbe, Elias de Cumbe, Robert de Coueley, Robert de Olepenne, Robert Dosy.

A1/2/35 [GC 1495]   n.d. [1281 × 1300]
Bartholomew de Olepenne and James de Berkeley, son of Sir Thomas de Berkeley.

Bartholomew has granted to James a rent of 10*s.* which he had by grant of Sir Henry de Berkeley, in the town of Dersley, received from William de Bernewod for the fulling mill in the same town, held for life, and the reversion of the mill after the death of William, to hold of Henry; rent a rose a year, and James has given him 100*s.*
Witnesses: Sir Robert de Berkeley, Sir William de Aubeny, Sir Roger de Lokinton, Peter de Stintescumbe, Robert de Stone, Elias de Cumbe, William de Cumbe.

A1/2/36 [SC 467]   St. Nicholas, 31 Edw. I [6 Dec. 1302]
James de Berkelegh, rector of Chew; and John his brother and Hawise, John's wife.

James has granted to John and Hawise lands at Stylle in Egeton and Berkelegh, . . . of Clopton, and 2 a. of meadow in the meadow of Perham, which James had of the gift of . . . , and 2 a. of meadow in the meadow called Brodemed by the gift of . . . and 13*s.* 4*d.* rent . . . [of Bartho]lomew de Olepenne due from Thomas de Bernewode for a mill; to hold as in the charters of the gifts to himself.
Witnesses: . . . . Laudo, Robert son of Payn, Simon de Monte Acuto, John de Beauchamp (*de Bello Campo*), John Meriet, [William] de Wauton, Peter Crok, knights, Robert de Buttlescombe, Richard de Byselee.

A1/2/37 [GC 1038]   Thurs. the feast of St. Nicholas, 31 Edw. I [6 Dec. 1302]
(1) Thomas de Berkelegh, lord of Berkeley; (2) James his son; (3) John de Berkelegh, son of Thomas, and Hawise, John's wife.

Thomas has inspected and confirmed the charter of James to John and Hawise granting to them and their heirs all his lands and holdings in Berkelee, Egeton, Hamme, Camme, Hurste and Wotton.

Witnesses: Sir William Martyn, Sir Robert son of Payn, Sir Simon de Mountagu, Sir John de Beauchamp (*de Bello Campo*), Sir John de Meriet, Sir Henry de Glastingbury, Sir John Basset, Sir William de Wauton, Sir Thomas de Gornay, Sir John de Sancto Laudo, Sir Peter Crok, knights, Robert de Butlescombe, Richard de Byselee.

A1/2/38 [GC 1091]   Sun. the feast of St. Ambrose, 33 Edw. I [4 April 1305]
Isabel widow of John de Egetone and Sir Thomas de Berkelegh, her lord.

Isabel has quitclaimed to Thomas the rents and services of her dower, viz. one third of rents of 22*s.* 8*d.* from Richard le Sergant, Adam son of Duk, William le Freman, Reginald le White, Juliana Baderon, Thomas Lug and Robert Phelip, and also from John Huwes for the holding which was of Adam Stille in Hyneton and Egeton; Thomas has given her a certain sum of money.

Witnesses: Richard de Byselegh, Robert de Bradestone, Thomas de Beolegh, Thomas de Swonhongre, John de Alkelegh.

At: Berkeley.

A1/2/39 [GC 1116]   1 May 34 Edw. I [1306]
John de Berkel' and Sir Thomas de Berkel', his father.

Whereas Thomas gave John a rent of 18*s.* 8*d.* from tenants which he had by grant of John de Egeton, viz. from Richard le Serjant 5*s.* 8*d.*, Adam fiz Douze 4*s.*, William Freman 3*s.* 4*d.*, Reginald le Whyte 12*d.*, Juliana Baderon 22*d.*, Thomas le Lug 22*d.* and Robert Phelipes 12*d.*, John has quitclaimed the rent to Thomas, for 20 marks. [*In French.*]

Witnesses: Sir Nicholas de Kyngeston, Sir William de Wauton, Sir Peter Crok, knights, Robert de Bradeston, Robert de Berkel', Thomas de Beoleye, John de Swonhungre, Robert Wyther, Robert Bastard.

At: Berkeley.

Holding in Church Lane

A1/2/40 [GC 779]   n.d. [late 13th cent.]
Juliana called Maydose, daughter of William the baker (*pistor*) of Berkeley; and Walter le Cuppere and Alice his wife.

For a certain sum of money, Juliana has granted to Walter and Alice her holding in Berkeleya in the lane from the market to the church.

Witnesses: John Sewaker, Henry le Cuppere, John le Cuppere, Henry Gardin', John Bonserjant.

A1/2/41 [GC 1648]   Tues. the feast of St. Valentine, 1 Edw. II [13 Feb. 1308]
Alice widow of Walter le Cuppere and Sir Thomas de Berkelee, lord of Berkeley.

Alice has granted to Thomas her holding in the lane leading to the church of Berkelee, and Thomas has given her 4 marks and remitted to her the service which she owes for 3 a. of enclosed land beside the king's highway from Swonhongre to Berkelee, while she lives.

Witnesses: John Sewaker, John le Cuppere, Roger le Cuppere, Robert Averey, Henry le Gardener, John Kyllecote, William le Wylde.

A1/2/42 [GC 1650]   1 March 1 Edw. II [1308]
Thomas de Berkeleye, lord of Berkeley; and Hugh le Proute and Agnes his wife.

Thomas has granted to Hugh and Agnes the holding which he had by grant of Alice widow of Walter le Cuppere, in Berkeleye; to them and their issue, rent 8*s.* a year.

Witnesses: Henry le Gardener, John le Cuppere, Roger le Cuppere, William Iweyn, John Kyllecote.

At: Berkeley.

Exchange of Stillcroft for rents

A1/2/43 [GC 1689]   1 April 2 Edw. II [1309]
John de Berkelee, son of Sir Thomas de Berkelee, and Sir Thomas his father.

John, with the assent of Hawise his wife, has granted to Thomas his enclosure called Stillecrofte, containing land and meadow, beside the road to Folmoresbrugge, at Egetone in Hamme, in exchange for 8*s*. 2*d*. rent from Hugh le Proute for a holding in Berkelee and 8*d*. rent from John Sely for a plot next to the marketplace of Berkelee.

Witnesses: Robert de Bradestone, Robert de Berkelee, Thomas de Beolee, Thomas de Styntescombe, Robert Wither, Robert atte Cherche, Richard de Wike.
At: Berkeley.

A1/2/44 [GC 1690]   1 April 2 Edw. II [1309]
Sir Thomas de Berkelee, lord of Berkeley; and John de Berkelee his son and Hawise his wife.

Thomas has granted to John and Hawise a rent of 8*s*. from Hugh le Proute for the holding which he had by demise of Alice Cuppare, with the reversion of the holding if Hugh dies without issue, and a rent of 2*d*. from Hugh, and one of 8*d*. from John Sely, in exchange for an enclosure called Stillecrofte at Egetone in Hamme.

Witnesses: Robert de Bradestone, Robert de Berkelee, Thomas de Beolee, Thomas de Styntescombe, Robert Wither, Robert atte Cherche, Richard de Wike.
At: Berkeley.

A1/2/45 [GC 1791]   Tues. one week after the Purification, 4 Edw. II [9 Feb. 1311]
John de Berklee, son of Sir Thomas de Berkelee; and Walter le Breware and Constance his wife.

John has granted to Walter and Constance two crofts in Egetone near Hurste, called Homstillecroft and Luytelestillecroft; to them and their issue, rent 13*s*. 4*d*. a year.

Witnesses: Robert de Bradestone, Nicholas de Beoleye, Walter de Gosinton, William le Boteler, Richard Bat.
At: Berkeley.

Other

A1/2/46 [GC 1114]   St. George, 34 Edw. I [23 April 1306]
Thomas de Berkelee, lord of Berkeley, and St. Augustine's Abbey, Bristol.

Thomas has granted to the abbey, for the support of their church, all the lands and holdings in Egeton which escheated to him after the death of John de Egetone, until the full age of John son and heir of the said John. [*In French*.]
At: Berkeley.

A1/2/47 [GC 1776]   Sun. in All Saints, 4 Edw. II [1 Nov. 1310]
John de la Boure and Sir Thomas de Berkelee, his lord.

John has granted to Thomas the rents and services of Robert Phelipes, Matthew Hathulf and Walter Douce for three holdings in Egetone, and for this Thomas has quitclaimed to him the rents and services of Nicholas son and heir of Henry de la Boure.

Witnesses: Robert de Bradestone, Robert de Berkelee, Thomas de Stone, John Capel, Robert de Stanford, Nicholas Neel, William de Heort.
At: Berkeley.

ADMINISTRATIVE DOCUMENTS: CHARTER ROLLS

A1/2/48 [SR 1]   *temp*. Hen. II to Edw. III
Abstracts of charters concerning the vill of Acton, numbered in a contemporary hand to no. 61, the first seven missing.

A1/2/49 [SR 17]

A selection of abstracts from A1/2/48 [SR 1] above, nos. 23–53 but not continuous, further abbreviated, but without current holders and current values; top missing, large blank at bottom of last membrane.

OTHER TENANTS AND HOLDINGS

A1/2/50 [GC 1891]   St. Simon and St. Jude, 6 Edw. II [28 Oct. 1312]

John le Frigg of Acton and Agnes his wife; and John their son.

John and Agnes have granted to John 1 a. of land in the field called Egamehulle, rendering the customary services to the chief lord.

Witnesses: Thomas de Bradestone, Robert de Stanford, John Carbonel, William Heert, Matthew Hathulf, William of the corner (*de anglo*), John of the chamber.

At: Acton.

A1/2/51 [GC 2219]   12 March 11 Edw. II [1318]

Thomas de Bradestone; and John le Serjaunt and John his son.

Thomas has granted to John and John a rent of 5*s.* a year from Nicholas de Craweleye and Maud his wife for a messuage and 10 a. of land which they hold for their lives, in Egetone, with the reversion of the holding; to them and the issue of John le Serjaunt, rent 5*s.* a year.

Witnesses: John Capel, John de Swonhongre, John Wyth, Thomas de Craweleye, William Capel.

At: Breadstone.

ALKINGTON

Alkington was one of the larger manors of the lordship and incorporated the vills of Bainham, Newport, Swanley, Wick (including Goldswick and Dangervilles Wick) and Woodford, as well as a large part of Michaelwood Chase. Newport (*Novus Burgus*) appears to have been created in the mid 13th century, at the same time as Wotton borough, in an attempt to take advantage of a site on the main Gloucester to Bristol road, a site which explains why the fairs obtained by Thomas (III) in 1347 were to be held there rather than elsewhere. It should not be confused with the new town of Berkeley itself.

BERKELEY ACQUISITIONS
Exchanges with Walter le Grip

A1/3/1 [GC 1392]   n.d. [late Hen. III]

Walter le Grip of Newport and Maurice de Berkel'.

Walter has granted to Maurice the land between the land of William de Cumbe and the land of Robert Brun, and 1 a. lying in the field called Ryeme; Maurice has given him 20*s.*

Witnesses: Bartholomew de Olepenn, William de Cumbe, Robert Brun, Walter de Egeton, Richard Alfred, Thomas Kavel, John Sewaker.

A1/3/2 [GC 681]   n.d. [*c.* 1273]

Sir Maurice de Berkel and Walter le Grip.

Maurice has granted to Walter 8 a. of land which William le Fowel' once held, of which 2 a. lie at the bridge called Ryamesbrugge in the west part of the road to Mukelewode called la Hommes, 4 a. in the croft called Esneworth and 2 a. in the field of Nattuk; rent 2*s.* a year; and in return Walter has granted to Maurice all his meadow in the field called Hamstalle, and his croft, and the meadow in Wayemore.

Witnesses: William de Matheme, Robert de Bratheston, William de Angervill, John de Craweleye, Adam Motun.

A1/3/3 [GC 333]   The Purification, 56 Hen. III [2 Feb. 1272]
Sir Maurice de Berkeley and Walter le Grip.

Maurice has granted to Walter 1¾ a. of land in the furlong called Longecroft and one grove in Dersleye containing 1 a. and ¹/₆ a. next to Smalemed, in exchange for land in Hamstalle containing 2½ a. and ¹/₁₂ a. lying next to Maurice's land with ¼ a. and 16 perches at the head of the land which was of Robert Marescall.

Witnesses: Robert de Bratheston, Walter de Egeton, John de Crawelegh, Thomas de Swonhongre, Geoffrey Neel.

Marshall holding in Longelond in Hamstall, and meadow in Parham

A1/3/4 [GC 332]   Sun. after the Purification, 56 Hen. III [7 Feb. 1272]
Robert Marescall of Newport and Sir Maurice de Berkeley.

Robert has granted to Maurice 1¾ a. and 3 perches of land in the field of Hamstalle lying in the furlong called Longelond next to the land which Maurice had from Walter le Grip in an exchange, with all the land which Alice his mother had in the same furlong in dower; Maurice has given Robert 40*s.*

Witnesses: John le Breth, Adam Motun, Robert de Bratheston, John de Crawelegh, Walter de Egetune, Thomas de Swonhongre, Geoffrey Neel, William son of Robert, Walter Sely.

A1/3/5 [GC 460]   Whit-Sunday, 1274 [20 May]
Robert the marshal (*marescallus*) of Newport and Sir Maurice de Berkel'.

Robert has leased to Maurice the meadow in the east part of the meadow called Ryamesmed, for a term of 12 years, and Maurice has given him 20*s.*

Witnesses: William de Matheme, Adam Motun, Nicholas de Wodeforde, William Herieth, William de Angervill.

A1/3/6 [GC 1482]   n.d. [late Hen. III]
Robert Marescall of Newport and Sir Maurice de Berkel'.

Robert has granted to Maurice the land which his [Robert's] mother held in dower, until the end of the term agreed between them.

Witnesses: Sir William Maunsel, . . . de Kyngeston, William de Mathem', Robert de Brothestone, Walter de Egeton.

Lorridge holding in the Actrees

A1/3/7 [GC 394]   n.d. [late Hen. III]
Henry son of John de Lorewynge and Walter his brother.

Henry has granted to Walter 1 a. of land at Habemede, to hold as in the charter of Thomas Martin of Stintescumbe, and ½ a. in the field called Aketre, to hold as in the charter of Adam de Lorewynge, Henry's brother.

Witnesses: Peter de Stintescumbe, Robert de Stone, Nicholas de Wodeford, Thomas de Stintescumbe, Henry de Bathem'.

A1/3/8 [GC 1467]   n.d. [*temp.* Edw. I]
Walter de Lorewenge and John de Lorewenge his brother.

Walter has granted to John ½ a. of land in the field called Aketre, to hold as in the charter of Henry de Lorewenge his brother; rent ½*d.* a year.

Witnesses: Henry de Ba', Nicholas de Wodeford, . . . de Metesdone, William de Kyneltre, Adam de Lorewenge, . . .

A1/3/9 [GC 2069]   n.d. [early 14th cent.]
John de Lorewenge and Richard de Lorewenge his brother.

John has granted to Richard, his heirs and assigns ½ a. of land in the field called Aketre, to hold as in the charter to Walter de Lorewenge, John's brother; rent ½*d.* a year, and Richard has given John 1 mark.

Witnesses: Thomas de Swonhungre, Henry de Ba, Nicholas de Wodeford, William de Metesdone, Walter the weaver (*textor*), William de Brockoure, Adam de Lorewenge, William de Kyneltre.

A1/3/10 [GC 1466]   n.d. [*temp.* Edw. I]
Henry son of John de Lorewynge and Richard his brother.

   Henry has granted to Richard 1 a. of land in the furlong called Habynghulle, beside the land of Juliana de Lorewynge, Henry's sister, as in the charter of Adam de Lorewynge, Henry's brother, rent to Adam 4*d.* a year; also ½ a. in the field called Aketre, rent to Adam ½*d.* a year.
Witnesses: Peter de Stintescumbe, Robert de Stone, Nicholas de Wodeford, Thomas de Stintescumbe, Henry de Bathon'.

A1/3/11 [GC 2008]   1 Feb. 8 Edw. II [1315]
John Page of Berkeley and Richard de Lorewynge.

   John has quitclaimed to Richard and his heirs the land which Richard holds in the field called Aketre in Alkyntone.
Witnesses: John le Cuppere, Henry le Gardener, William de Kyneltre, Roger Archer, William Gryp.
At: Berkeley.

A1/3/12 [GC 2011]   2 Feb. 8 Edw. II [1315]
Richard de Lorewynge and Sir Thomas de Berkeleye, lord of Berkeley.

   Richard has granted to Thomas and his heirs a rent of 6*d.* from 1 a. of land in the field called Aketre, in the manor of Alkyntone.
Witnesses: William de Kyneltre, Roger Archer, William Gryp, John le Cuppere, Robert Averai, John Sewaker, Edward de Fromelode.
At: Berkeley.

Wor holding of land in Stretley

A1/3/13 [GC 987]   n.d. [early 14th cent.]
William le Wor; and William son of William de Burgo and Mabel his wife.

   William has granted to William and Mabel all his land with the dower third which the said William son of William de Burgo released to his [William le Wor's] mother in the field called Stretley; rent ½*d.* to the chief lord of the fee, and they have given him 40*s.*
Witnesses: William de Burgo, Thomas de Swonhungre, Richard de Avene, Warin son of William, Robert of the church, Walter Motun, Adam le Frend.

A1/3/14 [GC 1842; *another version* GC 1843, *in French*]   Sun. after St. Luke, 5 Edw. II
                                                                        [24 Oct. 1311]
William le Bourg of Nibley and Sir Thomas de Berkelee, lord of Berkeley.

   William has granted to Thomas 4 a. and 22 perches of land in the field called Stretleye, near the wood of Mikkelwod, which he had by grant of William le Wor, in Alkyntone.
Witnesses: Thomas de Stone, Richard de Avene, Maurice de Beoleye, Warin son of William, Richard de Wyke, Geoffrey Moton, William Gold.
At: Berkeley.

Walbrook holding in Baynham

A1/3/15 [GC 1667]   Sun. the feast of St. Michael, 2 Edw. II [29 Sept. 1308]
Nicholas Person of Woodford and Sir Thomas de Berkelee, his lord.

   Nicholas has granted to Thomas 6 a. and 9 perches of land which he had by grant of Roger de Walebrok, in Alkynton.
Witnesses: Robert de Berkeley, Robert de Bradestone, Thomas de Beoleye, Thomas de Styntescombe, Robert de Butlescombe, Robert Wyther.
At: Berkeley.

A1/3/16 [GC 1670]   Fri. the feast of All Saints, 2 Edw. II [1 Nov. 1308]
Thomas de Berkeley, lord of Berkeley; and Ralph Walebrok and Joan his wife.

Thomas has granted to Ralph and Joan 1 a. 45 perches of land in the field called Bayenham, which he had by grant of Nicholas Person of Wodeford, in Alkynton; to them and their issue, rent 2s. 6d. a year.

Witnesses: Roger de la Garstone, Richard de Avene, Robert Wyther, John Purlewent, Nicholas the clerk, John le Cuppere, Henry le Gardyner.

At: Berkeley.

Noble land: croft, rent and reversion

A1/3/17 [GC 1778]   Sun. the feast of All Saints, 4 Edw. II [1 Nov. 1310]
Richard le Noble and John de Seham.

Richard has granted to John 1 a. of land in Richard's croft at Alkyntone beside the path from Alkyntone to Berkelee.

Witnesses: Robert de Berkelee, Thomas de Stone, John Capel, John With, John le Cuppere, Henry le Gardener, William de Kyneltre.

At: Berkeley.

A1/3/18 [GC 2277]   St. Philip and St. James, 12 Edw. II [1 May 1319]
John de Seham; and William aten Abbeye of Berkeley and Eve his wife.

John has leased to William and Eve 1 a. of land in the manor of Alkyntone; for their lives, rent [2]s. a year.

Witnesses: John le Serjaunt, Walter Sewaker, William Kyneltre, Adam de Mettesdone, Geoffrey Motun.

At: Alkington.

A1/3/19 [GC 2284]   1 Aug. 13 Edw. II [1319]
John de Seham and Sir Thomas de Berkeleye, lord of Berkeley.

John has granted to Thomas, his heirs and assigns a rent of 2s. a year from William atten Abbeye and Eve his wife for 1 a. of land which they hold for life of John, with the reversion of the land after their deaths, in the manor of Alkyntone.

Witnesses: Richard de Avene, John le Serjaunt, John Wyth, Thomas de Craweleye, John le Cuppere, William de Kyneltre, William le Gryp.

At: Berkeley.

Hurd holdings

Land in Hamstall, exchanged for meadow in Matford

A1/3/20 [GC 1199]   n.d. [late Hen. III]
John de Berkel' and Robert le Herde.

John has granted to Robert all the land above Hamstalle which Osbert Creht held of John, next to the land of Sir Maurice de Berkel'; rent 1d. a year.

Witnesses: Sir Maurice de Saltmarsh (*de salso marisco*), Sir Walter de Burgh, knights, Master Roger Glouc', steward of Berkeley, Peter de Wyke, Richard de Wyke, Henry Marescall, Nicholas de Carswell, Walter Sely, clerk.

A1/3/21 [GC 356]   n.d. [late Hen. III]
Sir Maurice de Berkeley and Roger le Herde.

Maurice has granted to Roger the meadow which William Cnotte once held of Maurice in the meadow of Matford in villeinage, in exchange for land above Hamstalle, viz. the land which Robert le Herde, father of the said Roger, had by gift of John de Berkeley, and Robert will render to Maurice 16d. a year.

Witnesses: Walter de Egetun, John de Crawelegh, Thomas de Swonhongre, Geoffrey Neel, William Capel, Robert de Stane.

A1/3/22 [GC 1001]   Sun. before Michaelmas, 28 Edw. I [25 Sept. 1300]
Thomas de Berkel', lord of Berkeley, and Roger le Herde.

Thomas has inspected and confirmed the charter of his father, Maurice de Berkel', granting to Roger the meadow which William Cnotte once held of Maurice in the meadow of Mathforde in villeinage, in exchange for land above Hamstalle, viz. all the land which Robert le Herde, father of Roger, had by grant of John de Berkel'; Roger to hold the meadow from Maurice at a rent of 6d. a year. Witnesses to Maurice's charter: Walter de Egeton, . . . de Crauleye, Thomas de Swanhongre, Geoffrey Neel, William Capel, Robert de Stone.

Witnesses: Robert de Bradeston, Thomas de Swonhungre, Thomas de Beoleye, Robert Wyther, William . . . , William le Gold.
At: Berkeley.

Land in the Actrees and Blackpool

A1/3/23 [GC 1425]   n.d. [1301 × 1317]
Adam le Hurde of Alkington; and Sir John de Berkelegh, son of Sir Thomas de Berkelegh, and Hawise his wife.

Adam has granted to John and Hawise 6¼ a. of land and 2 a. of meadow, of which 3 a. of land lie at Aketre, and 3¼ a. of land and 2 a. of meadow at Blakepole, in Alkynton; rent 12d. a year to the chief lord of the fee.

Witnesses: John de Saltmarsh (*de salso marisco*), Robert de Bradeston, Robert de Berkeleye, Thomas de Beoleye, Thomas de Styntescombe.

A1/3/24 [GC 2195]   1 Oct. 11 Edw. II [1317]
Adam le Hurde and Sir Thomas de Berkeleye, lord of Berkeley.

Adam has quitclaimed to Thomas 2 qr. of wheat and 2 qr. of beans a year, in which Sir John de Berkeleye, son of the said Thomas, and the Lady Hawise his wife were bound to him for his life.

Witnesses: John de la Hay, Nicholas Daungervile, William le Gryp, William de Kyneltre, William Cut.
At: Berkeley.

A1/3/25 [GC 2200]   31 Oct. 11 Edw. II [1317]
Thomas de Berkeleye, lord of Berkeley; and Mary le Clere of Tortworth and Walter her son.

Thomas has granted to Mary and Walter the croft called Blakepoleshomme, between Thomas's wood of Mickelwode and Aveneclive within the manor of Alkyntone; to them and Walter's issue, rent 13s. 4d. a year.

Witnesses: John de Saltmarsh (*de salso marisco*), Richard de Avene, Richard de Wyke, William le Golde, Philip the smith of Woodford.
At: Berkeley.

Land in Alkington exchanged for land in Hamstall

A1/3/26 [GC 355]   n.d. [late Hen. III]
Maurice de Berkeley and Robert le Herde.

Maurice has granted to Robert a plot of land in Alcinton between the land of the said Robert and the road to Maurice's park, which contains at the northern head 7 perches and at the southern head ½ perch, and in length 14 perches, in exchange for certain land above Hamstall.

Witnesses: Sir Nicholas Wolf (*Lupus*), Maurice's steward, Maurice de Stane, Peter de Wyk, John de Berkeley, William son of Robert, Walter Sely.

A1/3/27 [GC 686]   n.d. [late Hen. III]
Maurice de Berk' and Robert le Herde.

Maurice has granted to Robert a certain plot of land in Alkinton between the land of Robert and the road to Maurice's park, 7 perches at the north head, ½ perch at the south head and 14 perches long, in exchange for land above Homstall to the north of Maurice's park, 2 perches and 3 ft. at the west head, 2½ perches at the east head and 10 perches long.
Witnesses: Sir Nicholas Wolf (*Lupus*), Maurice's steward, Maurice de Stan, Peter de Wyk, John de Berk', William son of Robert, Walter Sely.

Other Berkeley grants

A1/3/28 [SC 275]   n.d. [1220 × 1243]
Thomas de Berkele and Robert son of William Hurde.

Thomas has confirmed to Robert a half-virgate in Alquinton which William his father held from Robert, Thomas's brother; rent 10*s.* a year, for which Robert gave to Thomas 20*s.* in acknowledgement.
Witnesses: Peter de Stintescumbe, Thomas de Tyringham, John de Eggeton, Robert de Planche, Elias the butler (*pincerna*), Elias de Bevinton, Alexander de London, Arnulf the clerk.

A1/3/29 [GC 288; *duplicate* GC 289]   Fourth Sunday in Lent, A.D. 1257 [18 March 1258]
Sir Maurice de Berkeley and Robert le Herde.

Maurice has granted to Robert a ditch with the watercourse of Dover', between Maurice's pasture called Oxenlese and Coulese and the land of Robert, the ditch extending from the road called Smalestret above Maurice's land of la Wurthy, with the easements; rent 6*d.* a year.
Witnesses: Sir Maurice de Saltmarsh (*de salso marisco*), Peter de Wik, Nicholas de Craulegh, Adam Moton, John Sewaker, Walter Sely.

A1/3/30 [GC 353]   n.d. [late Hen. III]
Maurice lord of Berkeley and Robert le Herde.

Maurice has granted to Robert ½ a. of land in the street before Robert's gate in Alcinton, between Strorcroft and Robert's assart; rent 1*d.*; Robert has given Maurice ½ mark.
Witnesses: Sir Maurice de Saltmarsh (*de salso marisco*), Sir Roger de Lokinton, Sir Walter de Burgo, knights, Andrew de Brothestan, John de Egeton, John de Wodeford, Robert Bastard, Walter Sely, clerk.

A1/3/31 [GC 354]   n.d. [late Hen. III]
Maurice lord of Berkeley and Robert [le Herde].

Maurice has granted to Robert the land called Leygh which Thedulf le Herde once held, in exchange for the meadow which Robert had in Monemede, and further a croft called Redeclyve at the meadow called Couwerelese . . .
Witnesses: Sir . . . , Sir Maurice de Saltmarsh (*de salso marisco*), Sir Walter de Burgo, knights, Master Roger de Gloucestre, steward of Berkeley, Peter de Wyk, Maurice de Stane.

A1/3/32 [GC 1606]   n.d. [late Hen. III]
Maurice de Berkel' and Robert le Herde.

Maurice has granted to Robert 8¼ a. of land in Maurice's Hehtfeld, beside the road from Mukelewode to Berkel'; rent 4*s.* 1½*d.* a year, and Robert has given him 7*s.* 8*d.*
Witnesses: Maurice de Saltmarsh (*de salso marisco*), Peter de . . . , John Sewaker, . . . Walter Sely, clerk.

A1/3/33 [GC 1216; *duplicate* GC 459]   The Purification, 1273 [2 Feb. 1274]
Maurice de Berkel' and Roger le Herde.

Maurice has granted to Roger all the land called Shorteacre in the field of Bainham, which Richard Imeke formerly held in villeinage, and for this Roger has granted to Maurice a croft of land lying between the field called Hamstall and the land called Kentwineshul, extending to the land called Holecroft above the meadow of Monemed.
Witnesses: William de Matheme, Adam Motun, William de Wyke, Walter de Egetun, John de Crawelegh.

A1/3/34 [GC 2082]   20 Feb. 9 Edw. II [1316]
Thomas de Berkeleye, lord of Berkeley, and Adam le Herde.

Thomas has granted to Adam 7 perches of land with the house built on it at Neweport, beside the road which runs through the middle of Neweport from Wodeford to la Hethfelde, in Alkyntone; to hold enclosed, to him and his issue, with remainder to William son of Richard le Deyarre, and his issue, rent 12*d.* a year.
Witnesses: John Capel, Walter Sewaker, Roger Archer, William de Kyneltre, William le Gryp.
At: Berkeley.

A1/3/35 [GC 2085]   6 March 9 Edw. II [1316]
(1) Thomas de Berkeleye; (2) Edith Pothering, widow of Richard Pothering; (3) Adam le Hoerde.

Thomas has inspected two charters of Edith, one granting to Adam, his heirs and assigns her holding in Neweport between the road and the furlong called la Leye, in Alkyntone; witnessed by Richard de Avene, William le Golde, William de Kyneltre, Ralph Walebrok, Maurice Bernard, William le Gryp and John de Cleyhongre, dated at Neweport Sunday before St. Vincent, 9 Edw. II [18 Jan. 1316], the second granting to Adam, his heirs and assigns all the land which she had by grant of William Warderobe of Wodeforde in the field called Ryhame, with the meadow adjacent, for a certain sum of money, witnessed by Richard de Avene, Geoffrey Moton, William le Golde, William le Gryp, John de Lorewynge, Richard de Lorewynge, and John Bonserjant, dated at Neweport Tuesday the feast of St. Julian, bishop and confessor, 9 Edw. II [27 Jan. 1316]; and Thomas has confirmed the charters, for which Adam, for himself and his heirs, has granted to Thomas a rent of 4*d.* a year.
Witnesses: John Capel, John le Serjaunt, John Wyth, William le Gryp, William de Kyneltre.
At: Berkeley.

A1/3/36 [GC 2197]   10 Oct. 11 Edw. II [1317]
Adam le Hurde and Sir Thomas de Berkeleye, lord of Berkeley.

Adam has granted to Thomas, his heirs and assigns the messuage with a garden, curtilage and two crofts in Alkyntone which Ailric Pothering formerly held and Adam had by grant of Roger le Hurde his father.
Witnesses: Richard de Avene, Roger de la Garstone, John Capel, John le Serjaunt, Nicholas Daungerville, William le Gryp, William de Kyneltre.
At: Berkeley.

Passage from Maud le Wood, née Hurd, to Thomas (II) Lord Berkeley
A1/3/37 [GC 2124]   20 Oct. 10 Edw. II [1316]
William atte Wode and Maud his wife; and Sir Thomas de Berkeleye, lord of Berkeley.

At Thomas's suit and expense, William and Maud will sell, in the king's court at Hilary next coming, to Sir Thomas and his heirs, all the lands and holdings which they have of the inheritance of Maud in Alkyntone; and after the fine has been levied, Thomas will enfeoff them in houses in St. Michael Street in Berkeleye to the value of 10*s.* a year, for their lives, and will provide them each with a robe a year at Christmas of coloured cloth, and 4 qr. each of wheat, beans and oats [etc.], and has paid them £4, and will support their son William in his household for life, and will marry their daughter Alice to the son and heir of Richard Bat or another free man of an equally good holding. [*In French.*]

Witnesses: John le Serjant, John Capel, John Wyth, John de la Hay, William de Kyneltre, William Purlewent, Nicholas Daungervile.

At: Berkeley.

A1/3/38 [GC 2127]   1 Nov. 10 Edw. II [1316]

William atte Wode of Alkington and his wife Maud, and Sir Thomas de Berkeleye, lord of Berkeley.

William and Maud have granted to Thomas, his heirs and assigns all their lands, holdings, rents [etc.] in Alkyntone, with the reversion of the dower which Adam Moton and Joan la Hoerde his wife hold, after the death of Joan.

Witnesses: John Capel, John le Serjant, John de la Hay, John Wyth, William de Kyneltre, William Gryp, Adam le Hurde.

At: Berkeley.

A1/3/39 [GC 2165]   1 May 10 Edw. I [1317]

Thomas de Berkeleye, lord of Berkeley; and John le Vygnur of Berkeley and Agnes his wife.

Thomas has leased to John and Agnes all his land in the furlong called Joelesaketre beside John's land and the road from Neweport to Berkeleye called le Churchewey, which he had by grant of William atte Wode, in Alkyntone; to them and their issue, rent to the chapel of Mary in Berkeleye 6*d.* a year (being the customary rent from the holding) and to Thomas 8*d.* a year.

Witnesses: John Capel, John Wyth, Thomas de Craweleye, John le Cuppere, Edward de Fromelode, William de Kyneltre, William le Gryp.

At: Berkeley.

A1/3/40 [GC 2179]   Tues. after St. Barnabas, 10 Edw. II [14 June 1317]

Thomas de Berkeleye, lord of Berkeley, and Thomas Page.

Thomas de Berkeley has leased to Thomas Page his meadow in Matforde beside the watercourse of Matforde, which he had by grant of William atte Wode and Maud la Hurde his wife, in Alkyntone; to him and his issue, rent 6*s.* a year.

Witnesses: John Capel, Walter Sewaker, Roger Archer, William le Gold, William le Gryp.

At: Berkeley.

A1/3/41 [GC 2285]   St. Laurence the martyr, 13 Edw. II [10 Aug. 1319]

Adam Moton and Joan his wife; and Sir Thomas de Berkeleye, lord of Berkeley.

Adam and Joan have leased to Thomas, his heirs and assigns 4½ a. 3½ perches of land and garden in an enclosure which they hold at Alkyntone of the dower of Joan after the death of Walter le Hurde, formerly her husband, and 1 a. of land in an enclosure with a rent of 20*d.* from a cottage built in the said acre from Isabel Dolat and her sister Edith by the lease of Joan and Richard le Deyare, formerly her husband; for Joan's life, and for this Thomas is bound to Adam and Joan in 3 qr. of wheat a year from the manor of Alkyntone for Joan's life by way of exchange for the land, and Thomas has leased to them a messuage with a garden and curtilage which Nicholas le Daye previously had by grant of John le Fytheler at Neweport in Alkyntone; for their lives, rent 2*s.* 6*d.* a year to Thomas and 18*d.* a year to Nicholas.

Witnesses: Richard de Avene, John de Sautemareis, John Capel, John le Serjaunt, John de la Hay, John Wyth, Thomas de Craweleye.

At: Berkeley.

Wood holding in Oldbury

A1/3/42 [GC 2402]   St. George, 16 Edw. II [23 April 1323]
William ate Wode of Woodford; and William ate Wode his son and Christine his wife.

William the elder has granted to William the younger and Christine, and their heirs and assigns, 10 selions and one fore-earth of land in the manor of Alkyntone, in the furlong called Oldebur'.
Witnesses: John de Saltmarsh (*de salso marisco*), Walter Sewaker, John ate Hay, William Golde, William Kyneltre, Peter Dauwes, Adam de Mettesdone.
At: Woodford.

A1/3/43 [GC 2967]   Tues. after the Purification, 4 Edw. III [6 Feb. 1330]
William atte Wode and Sir Thomas lord of Berkeleye.

William has granted to Thomas 2 a. of land containing 10 selions in Alkyntone, lying in the furlong called Oldebury, which he had by grant of his father William.
Witnesses: Peter de Styntescombe, John de Milkesham, Robert de Coueleye, John Capel, John de Eggetone.
At: Berkeley.

Tilly holding in Alkington, Dangervilles Wick and Stone

A1/3/44 [GC 626]   Sun. after the Purification, 25 Edw. I [3 Feb. 1297]
Sir Thomas de Berkel and Adam Tilly.

Thomas is bound to Adam to sustain him for life in food and drink, as the other grooms, and one robe, as the other grooms, and 2*s.* a year from the receiver of Berkele for shoes and linen cloth, and Adam will stay with the retinue (*familia*) wherever it goes; for which Adam has granted to Thomas all his lands and holdings in Wyk de Angervile, Alkynton and Stane.
Witnesses: Sir Robert de Berkel', Sir Robert le Veel, knights, Robert de Stone, Robert de Bradestone, Peter de Stintescumb, William de Burgo, Nicholas de Wodeford.

A1/3/45 [GC 1562]   n.d. [1281 × 1300]
Adam Tilly and Sir Thomas de Berkel', his lord.

Adam has granted to Thomas all his lands and holdings in Wyke Dangervile, Alkyngton and Stone. Attached is a list of Adam's lands, with the rents which he paid to the lord of Berkeley, and of his own tenants and the rents which they paid to him.
Witnesses: Sir Robert de Berkel', Sir Robert le Veel, knights, Robert de Stone, Robert de Bradestone, Peter de Stintescumbe, William de Burgo, Nicholas de Wodeford.

A1/3/46 [GC 1691]   8 April 2 Edw. II [1309]
Thomas de Berkelee, lord of Berkeley; and Richard le Turnor and Amicia his wife.

Thomas has granted to Richard and Amicia his croft at Swanleye in Alkynton, which Nicholas atte Slo previously held in villeinage, with the reversion of a messuage and house at Stone held for life by the three sisters, Annunciata, Joan and Juliana, daughters of Maud daughter of Agatha de Stone, by grant of Adam Tilli of Wyke; to them and their issue, rent 5*s.* a year to the manors of Hamme and Alkynton. Endorsed: *Memorandum that of the rent of five shillings, twelve pence is paid to Hamme manor and four shillings to Alkynton.*
Witnesses: Roger de la Garstone, Thomas de Stone, Nicholas the clerk, Richard Broun, William le Golde, Philip the smith, William Cut.
At: Berkeley.

A1/3/47 [GC 1985]   20 July 8 Edw. II [1314]
Maud widow of Adam Tilly and Sir Thomas de Berkelee, lord of Berkeley.

Maud has quitclaimed to Thomas 1 qr. of beans a year from the manor of Alkyntone, for her dower in the lands and holdings which Thomas acquired from Adam.

Witnesses: Richard de Avene, Geoffrey Moton, William le Gold, William de Kyneltre, Adam Dangervylle.
At: Berkeley.

A1/3/48 [GC 2128]   3 Nov. 10 Edw. II [1316]
Thomas de Berkeleye, lord of Berkeley, and John de Froucestre.

Thomas has granted to John the messuage with a curtilage, garden and 10 a. of enclosed land, of the holding formerly of Adam Tylli, which Richard de Longeberewe previously held of Thomas, at Wyke in Alkyntone; to him and his issue, rent 6*s.* 8*d.* a year, with permission to improve the land from the green way in Mickelwode, so long as wagons and carts still have free passage.
Witnesses: Richard de Avene, Warin son of William, Geoffrey Moton, William le Golde, Nicholas Daungervile.
At: Berkeley.

Joel holding

A1/3/49 [GC 359]   n.d. [1220 × 1243]
Thomas de Berkeleia and Hugh son of Joel.

Thomas has granted to Hugh 14½ a. of land in Ackevrue called Edelmesgarste lying between the land of Walter Stut and the ditch (*rinum*) called Cronham next to the land of Maurice son of Nigel which William le Hurde holds of Maurice; rent 3*s.* 7½*d.*, acknowledgement ½ mark. Endorsed: *Alkynton*.
Witnesses: Adam son of Nigel, Simon de Olepenne, Robert son of Richard, Richard de Couelegh, Maurice son of Nigel, Maurice de Bevintun, Maurice de Stanes, William Cobi, Walter Sewaker, Adam the clerk.

A1/3/50 [GC 555]   n.d. [late Hen. III]
Henry Johel, son of Hugh Johel, and Sir Maurice lord of Berkel'.

Henry has granted to Maurice all the land which he held of Maurice in the manors of Hamme and Alcrinton, and also the holding which Edith his mother holds in dower.
Witnesses: Sir Maurice de Saltmarsh (*de salso marisco*), Sir Roger de Lokinton, Andrew de Brothestan, John de Egeton, Peter de Wyke, Adam Coby, John Sewaker, Robert le Herde.

Pothering holding

A1/3/51 [GC 1612]   n.d. [*temp.* Edw. I]
Alice de Haggeleye, widow, and Margery de Haggeleye, unmarried woman; and William Pothering and Edith his wife.

Alice and Margery have granted to William and Edith ½ a. of meadow in Matford, beside the river-bank above the field called Oldebur'; rent ½*d.* a year and William and Edith have given them a certain sum of money.
Witnesses: Walter Moton, Robert Grip, William de Kineltre, William le Masun, Maurice Bernard.

A1/3/52 [GC 2084]   1 March 9 Edw. II [1316]
Henry son and heir of Walter Jordan of Kingscote and Edith Pothering of Newport.

Henry has quitclaimed to Edith, her heirs and assigns ½ a. of meadow in Matforde, extending to the river of Matforde above the field called Oldebur', which Edith held for life and which after her death ought to descend to Henry.
Witnesses: John Capel, Walter Sewaker, Roger Archer, William de Kyneltre, William le Gryp.
At: Newport.

A1/3/53 [GC 2088]   20 March 9 Edw. II [1316]
Thomas de Berkeleye, lord of Berkeley, and John de la Hay.

    Thomas has granted to John 1 a. of meadow in Matforde which he had by grant of Edith Pothering, in Alkyntone; to him and his issue, rent a rose a year.
Witnesses: John de Saltmarsh (*de salso marisco*), Richard de Avene, John Capel, Walter Sewaker, Roger Archer, William Golde, William le Gryp.
At: Berkeley.

A1/3/54 [GC 2150]   Mon. after the Purification, 10 Edw. II [7 Feb. 1317]
Alice de Hageleye and Margaret de Hageleye, sisters; and John de la Hay.

    Alice and Margaret have quitclaimed to John, his heirs and assigns a rent of 1*d.* a year from 1 a. of meadow in Matforde.
Witnesses: John Capel, John le Serjaunt, Walter Sewaker, Roger le Archer, Philip the smith, William Cut, Richard le Tornor.
At: Wick.

Lands acquired by Maurice (II) Lord Berkeley by exchange

A1/3/55 [GC 294; *duplicate* GC 295]   43 Hen. III [1258–9]
Maurice de Berkeley and Philip son of Reginald Thedulf.

    Philip has granted to Maurice all the land called Buristude and Buryal with all his meadow of Monmede and a messuage which John Thedulf his brother held, in exchange for $8^3/_8$ a. in Aketre which Maurice has granted him.
Witnesses: Sir Maurice de Saltmarsh (*de salso marisco*), William de Mathem, Peter de Wik, Robert de Wik, Ralph de Angervile, Adam Moton, Robert le Herde, Walter Sely, clerk.

A1/3/56 [GC 680]   n.d. [late Hen. III]
Maurice de Berk' and Nicholas Flambard.

    Maurice has granted to Nicholas 1 selion of land which Robert Portar once held, in exchange for 2 selions and a side-piece (*coster*) of land.
Witnesses: Robert Wyth', Walter de Wyk, Richard de Sancta Brigida, William de Tonnay, William the clerk.

A1/3/57 [GC 351]   n.d. [*temp.* Hen. III]
Maurice de Berkeley and John de Berkeley.

    Maurice has granted to John all his grove of Vilethe with 1 selion of land, and a meadow which Richard de Kineltre held of him near the ditch where the hedge of Maurice's park of Oclee was, in exchange for all that meadow which John had in the meadow of Monmed and all his grove between mid-stream of Doverle and the ditch where the park hedge was.
Witnesses: Maurice de Stane, Henry Marescall, Ralph de Angervill, Robert Caudel, Robert le Herde, Walter Sely.

Rents for land in the Actrees, acquired Feb. 1315

A1/3/58 [GC 2010]   2 Feb. 8 Edw. II [1315]
William atten Abbeie of Berkeley and Sir Thomas de Berkeleye, lord of Berkeley.

    William has granted to Thomas and his heirs a rent of 6*d.* from 1½ a. of land in the field called Aketre, in the manor of Alkyntone.
Witnesses: Henry le Gardener, John le Cuppere, Edward de Fromelode, John Sewaker, William de Kyneltre, Roger Archer, William le Gryp.
At: Berkeley.

A1/3/59 [GC 2012]   2 Feb. 8 Edw. II [1315]
Nicholas the miller and Sir Thomas de Berkeleye, lord of Berkeley.

    Nicholas has granted to Thomas and his heirs a rent of 8*d.* from 1½ a. of land in the field called Aketre, in the manor of Alkyntone.

Witnesses: William de Kyneltre, Roger Archer, William Gryp, Henry le Gardener, John le Cuppere, John Sewaker, Robert Averai.

At: Berkeley.

A1/3/60 [GC 2013]   2 Feb. 8 Edw. II [1315]

William de Kyneltre and Sir Thomas de Berkeleye, lord of Berkeley.

William has granted to Thomas and his heirs a rent of 4*d.* from 1 a. of land in the field called Aketre, in the manor of Alkyntone.

Witnesses: John le Cuppere, Henry le Gardener, John Sewaker, Edward de Fromelode, Roger Archer, William le Gryp, Richard de Lorewynge.

At: Berkeley.

A1/3/61 [GC 2014]   2 Feb. 8 Edw. II [1315]

William le Frig and Sir Thomas de Berkeleye, lord of Berkeley.

William has granted to Thomas and his heirs a rent of 6*d.* from 1 a. of land in the field called Aketre, in the manor of Alkyntone.

Witnesses: Henry le Gardener, John le Cuppere, John Sewaker, Edward de Fromelode, Robert Averai, Roger Archer, William Gryp.

At: Berkeley.

A1/3/62 [GC 2017]   3 Feb. 8 Edw. II [1315]

John de Lorewynge and Sir Thomas de Berkeleye, lord of Berkeley.

John has granted to Thomas and his heirs a rent of 12*d.* from 2 a. of land in the field called Aketre, in the manor of Alkyntone.

Witnesses: Henry le Gardener, John le Cuppere, Robert Averay, John Sewaker, Roger Archer, William de Kyneltre, William Gryp.

At: Berkeley.

Other acquisitions

In Matford

A1/3/63 [GC 735]   n.d. [late Hen. III]

Hugh Clerk and Sir Maurice lord of Berkel', his lord.

Hugh has granted to Maurice ½ a. of meadow in Matford between the meadow which was of John de Wodeford and the meadow which Adam the weaver (*textor*) of Swanleygh now holds; Maurice has given him 10*s.*

Witnesses: Sir Roger de Lokinton, Sir Nicholas Wolf (*Lupus*), steward of Berkeley, Sir Maurice de Saltmarsh (*de salso marisco*), knights, Maurice de Stan, Henry Marsh (*Marescus*) of Newport, Robert le Bastard, William Eustache, John de Egeton, Robert le Herde, Walter Sely, clerk.

A1/3/64 [GC 1197]   n.d. [late Hen. III]

John de Berkel' and Sir Maurice de Berkel', his lord.

John has granted to Maurice his meadow in Matford, and Maurice has given him 20*s.*

Witnesses: Peter de Wyke, Richard de Wyke, Robert Bastard, Maurice de Stan', William Eustace, William son of Robert, Robert le Herde, Walter Sely, clerk.

A1/3/65 [GC 653]   7 May 27 Edw. I [1299]

Agnes widow of Robert de Stone and Sir Thomas de Berkeleye.

Agnes has quitclaimed to Thomas, her lord, one third of 2 a. of meadow in Matford of her dower; Thomas has given her 1 qr. of wheat, for her urgent business.

Witnesses: Sir Walter vicar of Berkeley, Richard de Avene, Walter Motoun, William le Golde, Walter le Webbe.

At: Berkeley.

A1/3/66 [GC 1599]   n.d. [early 14th cent.]
John de Yweleye and Sir Thomas de Berkeleye, lord of Berkeley.

John has granted to Thomas the rent of 4s. a year from John de Oulepenne for the holding which John called le Lorimer formerly held in Oulepenne; further, he has granted to Thomas all his meadow in Mathforde, in exchange for 1 a. of meadow at Coueleye which James Cotel formerly held in the meadow called Mormede.
Witnesses: William de Wautone, knight, Robert de Bradestone, Thomas de Beoleye, William le Wariner, Robert de Draycote.

Other

A1/3/67 [SC 300]   n.d. [c. 1248]
Abbot William [Long] of St. Augustine's and Sir Maurice de Berkeley.

The abbot has quitclaimed to Maurice 1 virgate of land in the heath (*brueria*), which Maurice has given to Master Philip de Leycestria, reserving to the abbey right of way across it for the carriage of hay and corn in the proper seasons, and a tithe of the fruits of the land.
Witnesses: Sir Roger de Lokinton, Sir Maurice de Saltmarsh (*de salso marisco*), Sir Walter de Burgo, knights, Andrew de Bradestan, John de Eggeton, Thomas Mathias, Robert Bastard, Robert le Herde, Adam Coby, John Sewaker.

A1/3/68 [GC 1596]   n.d. [late Hen. III]
William de Wyke and Sir Maurice de Berkel'.

William has granted to Maurice 6 a. of land and $^1/_8$ a. of meadow in Vyleth, beside the meadow which Lady Joan de Berk', his mother, holds in dower; Maurice has given him 50s.
Witnesses: Sir Richard de Wygorn, Sir Maurice de Saltmarsh (*de salso marisco*), knights, Peter de Wyke, Robert de Wyke, Thomas de Wyke, Adam Moton, Nicholas de Craul', Robert le Herde.

A1/3/69 [GC 1374]   n.d. [late Hen. III]
William le Fryg and Sir Maurice de Berkel', his lord.

William has granted to Maurice his assart next to Appelrugge to the east, and for this Maurice has granted to him in exchange certain lands in his manor of Alcinton which Peter de Wike formerly held, 11½ a. and 3 perches.
Witnesses: Sir Maurice de Saltmarsh (*de salso marisco*), Peter de Wike, John Sewaker, Robert le Herde, John de Egeton, Walter Sely, clerk.

A1/3/70 [GC 1283]   n.d. [*temp.* Edw. I]
Roger Chudele of Stinchcombe and Sir Thomas de Berkel'.

Roger has granted to Thomas all the lands which he had with Juliana his wife, which he bought from William de Wyke, viz. all the land which lies in the field called Wynneleye and all the land in the field called Oppeleye.
Witnesses: Peter de Styntescumb, Elias de Cumbe, William de Cumbe, William de Burgo, Robert de Stane, Robert de Bradestane, Thomas Aleyn.

A1/3/71 [GC 700]   n.d. [*temp.* Edw. I]
Ralph Bolecot of Lydney and Agnes le Wayte his wife; and Sir Thomas de Berkeley.

Ralph and Agnes have granted to Thomas the croft which they had in Alkinton next to the great street between Kineltre and Alkinton; and Thomas has given them 4 marks.
Witnesses: Bartholomew de Olepenn, Elias de Cumbe, Robert de Bratheston, Robert de Stone, Thomas Aleyn.

A1/3/72 [GC 2556]   n.d. [*temp.* Edw. I]
Richard le Sopere and Sir Thomas de Berkeleye, lord of Berkeley.

Richard has granted to Thomas a plot of his garden extending towards the meadow called

Joeleshom; Thomas has given him a certain sum of money.
Witnesses: John le Cuppere, Henry le Gardener, Walter le Cuppere, Philip Coby, Roger le Cuppere, Edward de Fremelode, Adam Pynel.

A1/3/73 [GC 923]   n.d. [late 13th cent.]
Alice daughter of William Herieth of Newport, widow, and Sir Thomas de Berkel', her lord.

Alice has granted to Thomas, for a certain sum of money, 2½ a. of land in Kingesfilethe, and ¼ a. in Baynham, next to the land of her sister Isabel.
Witnesses: Robert de Stan', William Capel, Richard de Wyke, Walter Moton, William de Kineltre.

A1/3/74 [GC 2540]   n.d. [*temp.* Edw. II]
John Page of Berkeley and Sir Thomas de Berkeleye, lord of Berkeley.

John has granted to Thomas a rent of 1*d.* a year from Philip Broun for the lands and holdings of John in Alkyntone.
Witnesses: Thomas de Bradeston, Thomas de Boeleye, Peter de Styntescombe, Henry le Gardener, John Sewaker.

A1/3/75 [GC 2030]   1 April 8 Edw. II [1315]
Richard Noblepas and Sir Thomas de Berkeleye, lord of Berkeley.

Richard has granted to Thomas a rent of 6*d.* a year from his lands and holdings in Berk' and Alkyntone.
Witnesses: John Capel, John le Serjant, William de Kyneltre, Henry le Gardyner, Roger le Cuppere.
At: Berkeley.

A1/3/76 [GC 2052]   Sat. after the decollation of St. John the Baptist, 9 Edw. II [30 Aug. 1315]
Robert de Berkeleye and Sir Thomas de Berkeleye, lord of Berkeley.

Robert has quitclaimed to Thomas his right in a rent of 4*s.* a year which he had by grant of Nicholas Person of Alkyntone, with the reversion of the messuage and land which Eve [Belethan] holds for life. [*In French.*]
Witnesses: Sir John Mautravers the son, Sir William de Wautone, knights, John le fiz Nichol, Thomas de Bradeston, Walter Sewaker.
At: Berkeley.

A1/3/77 [GC 2122]   Wed. the feast of Michaelmas, 10 Edw. II [29 Sept. 1316]
John Willy of Berkeley and Sir Thomas de Berkeleye, lord of Berkeley.

John has granted to Thomas his croft of land at Alkyntone.
Witnesses: John Capel, John le Serjant, Walter Sewaker, John Wyth, John le Cuppere, William de Kyneltre, William le Gryp.
At: Berkeley.

A1/3/78 [GC 2274]   10 April 12 Edw. II [1319]
Walter Sewaker and Sir Thomas de Berkeleye, lord of Berkeley.

Walter has granted to Thomas, his heirs and assigns a rent of 12*d.* a year from Alice le Mortymer and Walter son of Simon le Yonge of Cleyhongre, for a parcel of land which Alice and Walter hold of Walter [Sewaker] for their lives, with the reversion of the land, which lies in the field called Ryaham, extending above Cokschawestrete in Alkyntone.
Witnesses: Richard de Avene, Roger de la Garstone, John de Sautemareis, John Capel, John de la Hay, John de Lorewinge, Geoffrey Moton.
At: Berkeley.

A1/3/79 [GC 2566]   n.d. [early Edw. III]
William de Wautone, knight, and Sir Thomas lord of Berkelegh, his lord.

William has granted to Thomas the reversion of the manor of Alkintone with all the appurtenances, and that the said manor which, ought to revert to William and his heirs after the death of Joan widow of John de Wautone, will remain to the said Thomas.
Witnesses: Edmund de Lyons, William de Chiltenham, John Capel, John de Egetone, John de Clyve.

BERKELEY GRANTS

In the heath and Heathfield

A1/3/80 [GC 691]   n.d. [*temp.* Edw. I]
Sir Thomas de Berkel and Walter de Stanton.

Thomas has . . . [confirmed?] . . . to Walter his pasture rights for 9 oxen, 6 cows, . . . , 2 sheep, 5 sows . . . and their offspring in the heath (*bruera*) outside Berkel, after three weeks when the hay is made . . .

A1/3/81 [GC 2481]   n.d. [early 14th cent.]
Thomas de Berkeley, lord of Berkeley, and William de Kyneltre.

Thomas has granted to William ½ a. 57 perches of land above the heath (*brueria*) called Hethfelde opposite his house, and 13 perches of land beside the holding of William Carpentar, in Alkyntone; to hold enclosed, rent 14*d.* a year.
Witnesses: Robert de Bradeston, Robert de Berk', Thomas de Beoleye, Thomas de Styntescombe, Richard de Avene, Walter Moton, William Gold.

A1/3/82 [GC 1727]   1 April 3 Edw. II [1310]
Thomas de Berkelee, lord of Berkeley, and Adam son of Walter Doucesone of Hinton.

Thomas has granted to Adam ½ a. of land above the heath in Alkynton, to hold enclosed; to him and his issue, rent 10*d.* a year.
Witnesses: Robert de Berkeley, Robert de Bradestone, Thomas de Beolee, Richard de Avene, William de Kyneltre.
At: Berkeley.

A1/3/83 [GC 1799]   1 March 4 Edw. II [1311]
Thomas de Berklee, lord of Berkeley, and Walter de Kyneltret.

Thomas has granted to Walter 10½ a. 28 perches of land above the heath (*bruer'*) in Alkyntone; to hold enclosed, to himself and his issue or his brother Robert de Kyneltret and his issue, rent 13*s.* 4*d.* a year.
Witnesses: Richard de Avene, Thomas de Stone, John Capel, John With, Adam de Mettesdone, William de Kyneltret, William le Grip.
At: Berkeley.

A1/3/84 [GC 1835]   Tues. the feast of St. Margaret the virgin, 5 Edw. II [20 July 1311]
Thomas de Berkelee, lord of Berkeley; and John de Bocovere and his wife.

Thomas has granted to John and his wife 4½ a. 12 perches of land above the heath (*bruer'*) between Lorewyngeswode and the road from Neuport to Cuckebiesachsches in Alkyntone; to hold enclosed, to them and their issue, rent 6*s.* 8*d.* a year.
Witnesses: Robert de Bradestone, Thomas de Stone, Richard de Avene, Maurice de Beoleie, William de Kyneltreo.
At: Berkeley.

A1/3/85 [GC 2027]   1 April 8 Edw. II [1315]
Thomas de Berkeleye, lord of Berkeley; and Walter Alford, his carter, and Cecilia his wife.

Thomas has granted to Walter and Cecilia 1½ a. 18 perches of land above the heath

(*bruera*), in Alkyntone; to hold enclosed, to them and their issue, rent 18*d.* a year.
Witnesses: Thomas de Bradeston, Richard de Avene, John Capel, Walter Sewaker, William de Kyneltre.
At: Berkeley.

In Culverfield and Heathfield

A1/3/86 [GC 4221] Wed. after St. Hilary, 20 Hen. VI [17 Jan. 1442]
James lord of Berkeley, knight; and William Wynchecombe and Alice his wife.

James has leased to William and Alice a pasture in the manor of Alkyngton, which William Broun lately held, viz. Colverfeld and Hurdefeld, containing 89 a.; for their lives, rent £7 6*s.* 8*d.* a year.
At: Berkeley.

A1/3/87 [GC 4243] 12 Jan. 23 Hen. VI [1445]
James Berkeley, lord of Berkeley, knight, and his beloved servant Gilbert Johnson.

James has granted to Gilbert, for his good service, an annual rent of 40*s.* from the manor of Alkynton, viz. from the pasture called Colverfelde; for his life.
At: Berkeley Castle.

A1/3/88 [GC 4244] 12 Jan. 23 Hen. VI [1445]
James Berkeley, lord of Berkeley, knight, and his beloved servant William Maye.

James has granted to William, for his good service, an annual rent of 40*s.* from the manor of Alkynton, viz. from the pasture called Colverfelde; for his life.
At: Berkeley Castle.

Leases of villein land

A1/3/89 [GC 875] n.d. [mid 14th cent.]
Thomas lord of Berkelee; and William le Clerk and Agnes his wife and William their son.

Thomas has leased to William, Agnes and William a messuage and a half-virgate of land, which Agnes widow of Nicholas le Swon previously held of him in villeinage in Alkynton; for their lives, rent 33*s.* 4*d.* a year and heriot after any deaths and suit to the lawdays of Berkeley hundred.
Witnesses: John de Egeton, Robert Groundy, Robert Motun, John Purlewent, John Bastard.

A1/3/90 [GC 2578] n.d. [mid 14th cent.]
Thomas lord of Berkelee; and Walter le Bonde and Edith his wife.

Thomas has leased to Walter and Edith a messuage and 7 a. of land, which William Toyt previously held in villeinage in Alkyntone; for their lives, rent 10*s.* a year.
Witnesses: John Serjant the elder, John de Milkesham, Stephen Kyneltres, John ate Boure, Henry de Eketone, John [Purlewent].

A1/3/91 [GC 3270] n.d. [mid 14th cent.]
Thomas lord of Berkelee; and William le Maltmon, Edith his wife and Maurice their son.

Thomas has leased to William, Edith and Maurice the messuage and quarter-virgate of land [*ferendellum*] which Thomas Daunt previously held in villeinage in Alkyntone; for their lives, rent 13*s.* 4*d.* a year, and 4*d.* and 1 bu. of oats for the maintenance of the woodward of Mikkelwode.
Witnesses: Stephen Kyneltreo, Richard Aleyn, John Purlewent, John Bastard, John atte Boure.

Other grants

A1/3/92 [SC 278] n.d. [1220 × 1243]
Thomas de Berkeley and Robert son of William the cowherd (*vaccarius*).

Thomas has granted to Robert 2 a. of land with a messuage, which Alric Pithering held, in Alcrinton; rent 12*d.* a year, and Robert has given him an acknowledgement of 1 mark.
Witnesses: Ralph de Redlega, Henry de Berkeley, William de Berkeley, Walter de Angrevill, Walter Stut, John de Wike, John de Wudeford, Maurice de Stanes.

A1/3/93 [GC 2478] n.d. [late Hen. III]
Maurice de Berkel'; and Margaret and Alice, daughters of William the mason (*cementar'*) of Newport.

Maurice has granted to Margaret and Alice all the land [etc.] which William formerly held of him, except 1 a. of land in the field called Ryhamme, in exchange; rent 12*s.* a year.
Witnesses: Sir Robert de Kyngeston, knight, William de Matheme, Adam Motun, Thomas de Wyke, William de Wyke, Roger le Herde, William . . .

A1/3/94 [GC 616] Sat. after the translation of St. Thomas [of Canterbury], 24 Edw. I
[14 July 1296]
Sir Thomas de Berkel'; and Richard de Avene and Margaret his wife.

Thomas has leased to Richard and Margaret all his arable land lying in the field called Baynham in four furlongs containing 33 a. and 1 a. of meadow in the meadow called Filethemed; rent 30*s.* a year.
Witnesses: Sir Robert de Berkel' knight, Robert de Stanes, Robert de Bradeston, Peter de Stintescumbe, William de Burgo, Nicholas de Wodeforde, Walter Moutun.
At: Berkeley.

A1/3/95 [GC 1022] Sun. after Michaelmas, 29 Edw. I [1 Oct. 1301]
Sir Thomas de Berkeleye, lord of Berkeley; and Mary le Clere of Tortworth and Walter her son.

Thomas has granted to Mary and Walter 1 a. of land lying between the wood of Mickelwode and the rhine called Avene; rent 12*d.* a year.
Witnesses: Robert de Bradeston, Thomas le Serjant, Robert de Stanford, Nicholas de Wodeford, Philip the smith of Woodford, William le Gold, William de Webbel, clerk.
At: Berkeley.

A1/3/96 [GC 1819] 20 April 4 Edw. II [1311]
Thomas de Berkelee, lord of Berkeley, and Nicholas Dangerville.

Thomas has granted to Nicholas 4 a. 20 perches of land at la Goldende in Alkyntone, with licence to improve the said land from Thomas's marlpit in Sandrugge, called Wylotesmarlput; to hold enclosed, to him and his issue, rent 4*s.* a year.
Witnesses: Thomas de Stone, Maurice de Beoleie, Walter Sewaker, William le Golde, Roger Archer.
At: Berkeley.

A1/3/97 [GC 1833] Wed. after St. Paul, 4 Edw. II [7 July 1311]
Thomas de Berkelee, lord of Berkeley, and Thomas the miller (*molendinar'*).

Thomas de Berkelee has granted to Thomas the miller 1 a. and a fardell of land in two parcels near Mabeliecroyce in Alkyntone; to hold enclosed, to him and his issue, rent 20*d.* a year.
Witnesses: Richard de Avene, John With, John le Cuppere, Henry le Gardener, William de Kyneltret.
At: Berkeley.

A1/3/98 [GC 1987] 1 Aug. 8 Edw. II [1314]
Thomas de Berkelee, lord of Berkeley; and William atten Abbeye and Eve his wife.

Thomas has granted to William and Eve his croft at Alkyntone, and a rent of 12*d.* a year from Agnes, widow of Walter Walebrok, for a cottage and curtilage beside the said croft,

which she holds for life, with the reversion after her death, with licence to improve the land from Thomas's marlpit in the field called Riham, the which croft, cottage and curtilage Thomas had by grant of Richard Noblepas; to them and their issue, rent 9*s.* a year.
Witnesses: John le Cuppere, Henry le Gardener, Roger le Cuppere, Geoffrey Moton, William de Kyneltre.
At: Berkeley.

A1/3/99 [GC 2114]   Tues. the feast of St. Margaret [the virgin], 10 Edw. II [20 July 1316]
Thomas de Berkeleye, lord of Berkeley, and William le Gryp.

Thomas has leased to William a croft and a grove adjacent called la Conynger with an enclosed meadow called Brokmede lying next to the grove, all of which John de Coueleye previously held and contains in total 2½ a. 1 rood of land; also 3 selions and 4 gores of land in the field called Tounmannehamstal and a horsepond in the street of Neweport, in Alkyntone; to him and his issue, rent 9*s.* a year.
Witnesses: Richard de Avene, Peter de Styntescoumbe, Walter Sewaker, John Wyth, Roger Archer, William le Golde, William de Kyneltre.
At: Berkeley.

A1/3/100 [GC 4072]   1 Aug. 13 Hen. IV [1412]
Thomas Berkeley, lord of Berkeley; and Robert Botiller and Maud his wife.

Thomas has leased to Robert and Maud two cottages with an apple-tree and curtilage in the manor of Alkynton, which Thomas Cutte and Robert Dosy held; for their lives, rent 7*s.* 2*d.* a year.
At: Berkeley.

A1/3/101 [GC 4217]   Mon. before St. Martin, 19 Hen. VI [7 Nov. 1440]
James Berkeley, lord of Berkeley, knight, and John Grevel, esquire.

James has granted to John, for his good and laudable service, a pasture in the manor of Alkyngton called Cowemore and Hurdham, and an annual rent of £4 6*s.* 8*d.* from the same manor; for his life.
At: Berkeley.

BERKELEY ADMINISTRATIVE DOCUMENTS
Account Rolls

A1/3/102 [GAR 1]	14–15 Edw. I [1286–7]
A1/3/103 [GAR 2]	15–16 Edw. I [1287–8]
A1/3/104 [GAR 3]	17–18 Edw. I [1289–90]
A1/3/105 [GAR 4]	20–1 Edw. I [1292–3]
A1/3/106 [GAR 5]	21–2 Edw. I [1293–4]
A1/3/107 [GAR 6]	24–5 Edw. I [1296–7]
A1/3/108 [GAR 7]	25–6 Edw. I [1297–8]
A1/3/109 [GAR 8]	26–7 Edw. I [1298–9]
A1/3/110 [GAR 9]	27–8 Edw. I [1299–1300]
A1/3/111 [GAR 10]	30–1 Edw. I [1302–3]
A1/3/112 [GAR 11]	1–2 Edw. II [1307–8]
A1/3/113 [GAR 12]	3–4 Edw. II [1309–10]
A1/3/114 [GAR 13]	5–6 Edw. II [1311–12]
A1/3/115 [GAR 14]	6–7 Edw. II [1312–13]
A1/3/116 [GAR 15]	10–11 Edw. II [1316–17]
A1/3/117 [GAR 16]	15–16 Edw. II [1321–2]

A1/3/118 [GAR 17]	17–18 Edw. II [1323–4]
A1/3/119 [GAR 18]	4. . . [March?] to Michaelmas [1324]
A1/3/120 [GAR 19], draft	18–19 Edw. II [1324–5]
A1/3/121 [GAR 20]	18–19 Edw. II [1324–5]
A1/3/122 [SR 41]	20 Edw. II – 1 Edw. III [1326–7]
A1/3/123 [GAR 21]	2–3 Edw. III [1328–9]
A1/3/124 [GAR 22], scribal error in heading	6–7 Edw. III [1332–3]
A1/3/125 [GAR 23]	7–8 Edw. III [1333–4]
A1/3/126 [GAR 24]	9–10 Edw. III [1335–6]
A1/3/127 [GAR 25]	11–12 Edw. III [1337–8]
A1/3/128 [GAR 26]	13–14 Edw. III [1339–40]
A1/3/129 [GAR 27]	16–17 Edw. III [1342–3]
A1/3/130 [GAR 28]	17–18 Edw. III [1343–4]
A1/3/131 [GAR 29]	Michaelmas to 8 Dec. 19 Edw. III [1345]
A1/3/132 [GAR 30]	8 Dec. 19 Edw. III to Michaelmas 20 Edw. III [1345–6]
A1/3/133 [GAR 31]	20–1 Edw. III [1346–7]
A1/3/134 [GAR 32]	21–2 Edw. III [1347–8]
A1/3/135 [GAR 33]	22–3 Edw. III [1348–9]
A1/3/136 [GAR 34]	23–4 Edw. III [1349–50]
A1/3/137 [GAR 35]	Michaelmas 24 to 8 June 25 Edw. III [1350–1]
A1/3/138 [GAR 36]	8 June to Michaelmas 25 Edw. III [1351]
A1/3/139 [GAR 37]	25–6 Edw. III [1351–2]
A1/3/140 [GAR 38]	26–7 Edw. III [1352–3]
A1/3/141 [GAR 39]	27–8 Edw. III [1353–4]
A1/3/142 [GAR 40]	28–9 Edw. III [1354–5]
A1/3/143 [GAR 41]	29–30 Edw. III [1355–6]
A1/3/144 [GAR 42]	30–1 Edw. III [1356–7]
A1/3/145 [GAR 43]	31–2 Edw. III [1357–8]
A1/3/146 [GAR 44]	32–3 Edw. III [1358–9]
A1/3/147 [GAR 45]	33–4 Edw. III [1359–60]
A1/3/148 [GAR 46]	40–1 Edw. III [1366–7]
A1/3/149 [GAR 47]	7–8 Ric. II [1383–4]
A1/3/150 [GAR 48]	8–9 Ric. II [1384–5]
A1/3/151 [GAR 49]	9–10 Ric. II [1385–6]
A1/3/152 [GAR 50]	10–11 Ric. II [1386–7]
A1/3/153 [GAR 51]	11–12 Ric. II [1387–8]
A1/3/154 [GAR 52]	12–13 Ric. II [1388–9]

Rentals

A1/3/155 [GRR 1] Rental of demesne	n.d. [late 14th cent.]
A1/3/156 [GRR 2]	1 Ric. II [1378]

Unfinished late 15th-century copy. [GRR 4 is the bottom half of the same.]

A1/3/157 [GRR 3]	n.d. [*temp.* Hen. IV]
A1/3/158 [GRR 5]	Feb. 2 Hen. VI [1424]

Charter rolls

A1/3/159 [SR 8, SR 9, SR 10]

Parts of a roll of abstracts of charters concerning the manor of Alkington. The abstracts are numbered: SR 8 starts *c.* no. 50 and continues to no. 134, ending in the middle of an entry; SR 10 runs from no. 162 to no. 184, and SR 9 contains nos. 167–70 (the numbers later crossed out) and 185–257, after which there is a large blank portion.

A1/3/160 [SR 6]   Hen. III to Edw. I

Abstracts of charters concerning the manor of Alkington, probably drawn from A1/3/159 [SR 8–10] above, but further abbreviated and a selection only. The abstracts are numbered 1–4, 6–8, 12, 19–24, 26–33, 37–8, 41, 44, 46, 48, 51, 176, 205–6, 209–10, 225, 227–8, 233, 234–5, 237, 239, 14–16, 18, 38 [repeated, the same as earlier], 64, 150, 161; on the dorse, 172, 168–170, 172, 191, 196, 217, 251, and two unnumbered. The abstracts show current valuations and holders, and later entries are in a different hand.

A1/3/161 [SR 7]

A fair copy of A1/3/160 [SR 6] above, some entries from which it omits.

Other administrative documents

A1/3/162 [GMR 14]   n.d. [*c.* 1325]

Customs and services of virgaters, half-virgaters and quarter-virgaters.

A1/3/163 [GCR 1]   21 Sept. 6 Hen. V [1418]

Court of Richard [Beauchamp] earl of Warwick and Elizabeth his wife.

A1/3/164 [GCR 2]   29 March 7 Hen. V [1419]

THE GOLD HOLDING

The tenant William le Gold built up a substantial holding within Alkington manor, with holdings in several vills in the later 13th century and the early 14th. Some of these he granted to Thomas (II) Lord Berkeley, and the rest seems to have been settled on his sister Edith and her husband William Theyn and their son Henry and his issue.

Dangerville holdings in Wick and Dangervilles Wick

Grants by William Dangerville and his daughter Juliana

A1/3/165 [GC 858]   n.d. [late 13th cent.]

William de Angervill and William le Gold.

William de Angervill has granted to William le Gold 3 a. of arable land in the croft called Puricroft in the vill of Wike and 1¼ a. of meadow; rent 2*d.* a year and William le Gold has given him 48*s.*

Witnesses: Peter de Stintescumb, Robert de Brothestan, Thomas the serjeant (*serviens*), William de Mathine, Walter Motun, Nicholas de Wodeford, Thomas le Archer.

A1/3/166 [GC 1168]   n.d. [*temp.* Edw. I]

William de Angervill and William le Gold.

William de Angervill has granted to William le Gold a parcel in the vill of Wike lying in Holecroft between William de Angervill's croft called Thornhull and William le Gold's croft which he had by grant of Hugh de Angervill, William's brother; rent 1*d.* a year for an obit for Ralph de Angervill his father, for the lives of William [le Gold] and Christine his wife, and they have given him 2 marks.

Witnesses: Sir Robert le Veel, Sir Maurice de Saltmarsh (*de salso marisco*), knights, Robert de Ston', Peter de Stintescombe, Robert de Brothestan, William de Mathine, Walter Motun, Walter de Stintescombe, clerk.

A1/3/167 [GC 1169]   n.d. [*temp.* Edw. I]
William de Angervill and William le Gold.

William de Angervill has granted to William le Gold a croft called Holecroft in the vill of Wyke and 1½ a. of meadow lying between the said croft and the furlong called Longebreche; rent 3*d.* a year, and William le Gold has given him 3 marks and 12*d.*
Witnesses: Peter de Stintescumbe, Robert de Brotheston, Thomas de Boleg', Reginald de Gosinton, Robert de Stone, Nicholas de Wodeford, William de Mathine, Walter Motun, Robert de Wik, Reginald son of Reginald Edwine, William le Frend, Walter le Frend, Walter the clerk.

A1/3/168 [GC 2577]   n.d. [late 13th cent.]
William de Aungervile of Wyke and Juliana his daughter.

William has granted to Juliana rents of 6*s.* 7*d.*, viz. from William de Burgo 2*s.*, from Hugh Aungervyld 2*s.* 6*d.*, from William Golde 7*d.*, from Richard Aungervyle 5*d.* and from Adam son of Adam the miller (*molendinar'*) 13*d.*; rent to the chief lord 5*s.* 1*d.* a year.
Witnesses: William de Burgo, Robert Draycote, Robert Dosy, William Frend, Reginald Draysid, William de Matheus, Walter Motoun.

A1/3/169 [GC 1170]   n.d. [*temp.* Edw. I]
Juliana daughter of William de Aungerwyle, unmarried woman; and William le Gold and Christine his wife.

Juliana has quitclaimed to William and Christine the annual rent of 7*d.* which they owe for the lands and meadow which William had by grant of William her father in Longebreche, Piricroft and Holecroft; and they shall now owe a rent of 2*d.* a year, viz. 1*d.*. for the souls of Ralph de Aungerwyle and his wife and of William de Aungerwyle and his wife and 1*d.* for the souls of the same, in Berkel' church; they have given her 5*s.*
Witnesses: Peter de Styntescumbe, Robert de Bradeston, Thomas de Boeleye, Thomas de Swonhangre, Nicholas de Wodeford, Henry de Batonia, John the clerk.

A1/3/170 [GC 859]   n.d. [late 13th cent.]
Juliana daughter of William de Aungerwyle, unmarried woman, and William Gold.

Juliana has quitclaimed to William an annual rent of 7*d.* which he rendered to her for the land which she had by grant of William her father in Longebreche in the vill of Wyke, and for the land and meadow in Puricroft, and for the land of the gift of her father in Holecroft, rendering 1*d.* a year in Berkeley church for the souls of Ralph de Aungerwyle and his wife and of William de Aungerwyle and his wife; and he has given her 5*s.*
Witnesses: Peter de Stintescumbe, Robert de Brodestan, Thomas de Beleye, Thomas de Swonhungre, Nicholas de Wodeford, Henry de Batonia, John the clerk of Hill (*Hull*).

A1/3/171 [GC 2506]   n.d. [*c.* 1300]
Juliana daughter of William Dangervile, unmarried woman; and William le Gold and Christine his wife.

Juliana has granted to William and Christine all the rents in Dangervileswike which she had by grant of her father; rent to the chief lord 5*s.* 1*d.* a year.
Witnesses: Robert de Bradeston, Thomas le Serjant, William de Burgo, Richard de Avene, William de Webbeleye, clerk.

A1/3/172 [GC 2507]   n.d. [*c.* 1300]
Juliana daughter of William Dangervile, unmarried woman; and William le Gold and Christine his wife.

Juliana has granted to William and Christine a croft between Thornhulle and Pynnokesrudyngge and a plot of land with a peartree at its head in the vill of Wyke, and also the rents and services of William de Burgo, Hugh Dangervyle, the said William le

Gold, Richard Dangervyle and Adam son of Adam the miller (*molendinar'*), all of which she had by grant of her father.

Witnesses: Robert de Bradeston, Thomas le Serjant, William de Burgo, Richard de Avene, William de Webbeleye, clerk.

A1/3/173 [GC 1330]   n.d. [*temp.* Edw. I]
Juliana Dangervile; and William le Gold and Christine his wife.

Juliana has quitclaimed to William and Christine the land which they had by grant of William Dangervile, between the land of Robert de Stone and Dolerudinge, extending to the land of the said Robert above Marlput.

Witnesses: Nicholas de Wodeford, Walter the weaver (*textor*), Adam Godinow, Richard Long, William de Kyneltre, Henry the clerk.

A1/3/174 [GC 1647]   St. Wulfstan, 1 Edw. II [19 Jan. 1308]
Walter Daungervyle; and William le Gold and Christine his wife.

Walter has quitclaimed to William and Christine the lands, holdings [etc.] which they had from Juliana Daungervyle.

Witnesses: Richard de Avene, Richard de Wyke, Walter Moton, John le Macon, Adam Daungervyle.

At: Wick.

Grant by Hugh Dangerville of a croft and house, etc., in Dangervilles Wick

A1/3/175 [GC 880]   n.d. [late 13th cent.]
Hugh de Angervill and William le Gold.

Hugh has granted to William the croft in Wike between the garden of William de Angervill his brother and the croft called Breche; rent 1*d.* a year, and William has given him 4½ marks.

Witnesses: William de Mathine, William de Burgo, Walter de Egeton, Robert de Brothestan, John de Craul', Adam Motun, William de Wik.

A1/3/176 [GC 879]   n.d. [late 13th cent.]
Hugh de Angervill, son of Ralph de Angervill, and William le Gold.

Hugh has granted to William the house with a garden, curtilage [etc.] in the vill of Wike which he had by the grant of Ralph his father; rent 23*d.* a year, and William has given him 3 marks, and 12*d.* to Alice his wife, daughter of Richard Buchard, and 3*d.* to Richard their son.

Witnesses: Peter de Stintescumb, William de Mathine, William de Burgo, Robert de Brothestan, John de Craul', Robert de Wyke, Adam Motun, William de Wike, Walter de Stintescumb, clerk.

Grant by Thomas Dangerville of Mabeliecroft in Wick

A1/3/177 [GC 1277]   n.d. [late Hen. III]
William de Canvill and Thomas de Angervill.

William has granted to Thomas a croft in the vill of Wike called Mabeliecroft; rent a rose a year, and Thomas has granted to William in exchange all his land in the furlong called Hemestret, as appears in his charter.

Witnesses: Peter de Stintescum, William de Wike, Adam Motun, Richard de Grava, Richard of the church, Thomas de Wike.

A1/3/178 [GC 856]   n.d. [late 13th cent.]
Thomas de Angervill and William le Gold.

Thomas has granted to William a croft in the vill of Wike called Mabeliecroft, lying between the land of Thomas's father Ralph de Angerville called Newerudinge and the land

which Everard Mundegune once held; rent a rose a year, and William has given him 16*s*., and to Joan his wife a falcon.
Witnesses: Peter de Stintescumb, William de Mathine, Adam Motun, William de Wike, William de Angervill, Robert de Wike, William le Frend, Walter le Frend, Reginald son of Reginald Edwine.

Grant by Walter Dangerville of land in la Redefelde of Wick
A1/3/179 [GC 855]   n.d. [late 13th cent.]
William son of William de Angervile and Walter his elder brother.

William has granted to Walter, for a certain sum of money, 1 a. of land in la Redefelde of Wyke, which he had by grant of Nicholas de Haggeleye in the manor of Alkinton; rent 1*d.* a year for a mass for the soul of Margery who was the wife of William de Angervile.
Witnesses: Nicholas de Wodeford, Walter de Bathon, Walter de Tresham, Walter the weaver (*textor*).

A1/3/180 [GC 857]   n.d. [late 13th cent.]
Walter de Angerwile and William le Gold.

Walter has granted to William, for a certain sum of money, 1 a. of land above Vexhul in the Redefeld of Wyke, viz. that which he had by grant of William his brother; rent 1*d.* a year for a mass for the soul of Margery who was the wife of William de Angerwile.
Witnesses: Nicholas de Wodeford, Walter Walter Motun [*sic*], Walter de Tresham, John the clerk of Hill (*Hull*).

Herieth holdings in Alkington and Newport
William Herieth died evidently leaving four daughters, Maud, Alice, Joan and Isabel, and his holding was divided between them. Maud later died without issue and her portion passed to her sisters. William le Gold seems to have concentrated on the portions of Joan, who married Walter le Webbe, and of Alice, who married Thomas Flambard and William Ruggeweye *alias* Clerk.

Joan's portion
A1/3/181 [GC 992]   Wed. the feast of St. Hilary, 28 Edw. I [13 Jan. 1300]
Walter called le Webbe of Swanley; and William le Gold and Christine his wife.

Walter, with the assent of his wife Joan, has granted to William and Christine 7 selions of land in the field called Ryham, for their lives, and after their deaths to William le Theym and Edith his wife.
Witnesses: Richard de Avene, Walter Moton, Adam de Angervile, John called le Mason, William de Webbel', clerk.
At: Wick.

A1/3/182 [GC 1055]   Sat. the feast of St. Benedict, 32 Edw. I [24 March 1304]
Walter le Webbe and Joan his wife; and William le Gold and Christine his wife.

Walter and Joan have granted to William and Christine all their land in the field of Riham, which Joan inherited after the death of her father William Herieth and which William had by grant of Nicholas de Wodeford, and 1 selion in Baynham which she inherited after the death of her sister Maud, and all the land which she inherited after the death of Maud which Maud had by grant of Nicholas; William and Christine have given Walter and Joan a certain sum of money.
Witnesses: Thomas le Serjant, Walter Moton, Philip the smith of Woodford, William de Kyneltre le Mason, Richard le Erl, Walter the clerk.
At: Wick.

A1/3/183 [GC 1652*; *counterpart* GC 1652**]   Two weeks after Easter, 1 Edw. II
[28 April 1308]
William Gold and Christine his wife; and Walter le Webbe and Joan his wife.

Final concord concerning 8 a. of land with meadow in Alkynton by Berkelee; Walter and Joan have acknowledged the right of William and Christine, by their gift, and William and Christine have given them 10 marks.
At: Westminster.

A1/3/184 [GC 1412]   n.d. [*temp.* Edw. I]
Joan Heriet; and William Golde and Christine his wife.

Joan has granted to William and Christine all the land and meadow in Kinecroft and all the land in Baynham which she had after the death of Maud her sister, rendering the customary services to the chief lord of the fee.
Witnesses: Richard de Avene, Walter Moton, William de Keneltre, John Mason, Walter Dolling, Maurice Bernard.

A1/3/185 [GC 1578]   n.d. [*temp.* Edw. I]
Walter le Webbe and Joan Herieth his wife; and William Golde and Christine his wife.

Walter and Joan have granted to William and Christine all their land with meadow in Kinecrofte, with the meadow in Nupsetemede, in the manor of Alkinton, which they had after the death of William Herieth; William and Christine have given them a certain sum of money.
Witnesses: Nicholas de Wodeford, Richard de Avene, Walter Moton, John Mason, Walter Dolling, Thomas ate Hulle, Henry Grout.

Alice's portion: *part acquired through John Pynel*
A1/3/186 [GC 2158]   Mon. before the Annunciation, 10 Edw. II [21 March 1317]
John son of Henry Pynel; and William le Golde, Christine his wife and Henry le Theyn.

John has granted to William, Christine and Henry, and Henry's heirs and assigns, all his lands and holdings at la Neweport within the manor of Alkyntone, which Thomas Flambard, Alice his wife, and Agnes Heryeth formerly held.
Witnesses: Richard de Avene, William Kyneltre, Adam Daungervyle, Geoffrey Motun, John le Masun.
At: Berkeley.

A1/3/187 [GC 2170]   Mon. before Ascension, 10 Edw. II [9 May 1317]
John son of Henry Pynel; and William le Golde and Christine his wife.

John has quitclaimed to William and Christine, and William's heirs, all the lands and holdings in Neuport within the manor of Alkyntone which were of Thomas Flambard, Alice his wife and Agnes Herieth.
Witnesses: Walter Sewaker, William de Kyneltre, Adam Daungervyle, Geoffrey Moton, John le Mason.
At: Berkeley.

Alice's portion: *part acquired directly by William and Christine le Gold*
A1/3/188 [GC 1124]   Translation of St. Wulfstan, 34 Edw. I [7 June 1306]
William Clerk and Alice Herieth his wife; and William le Gold.

William and Alice have granted to William their messuage with a garden, curtilage and adjacent land in Neuport, with their part of a house, garden, curtilage and land of a croft within an enclosure in Neuport, which William Morvyle holds, and a plot [*cell*] lying in Hamstal between the land of Joan Herieth and Isabel Herieth, which Alice his wife inherited on the death of Maud her sister.

Witnesses: Robert de Berkeleye, Robert de Bradeston, Richard de Avene, Walter Moton, Richard le Erl, William de Kyneltre.
At: Newport.

A1/3/189 [GC 1125]   Translation of St. Wulfstan, 34 Edw. I [7 June 1306]
William Clerk and Alice Herieth his wife; and William le Gold.

William and Alice have granted to William their messuage with a garden, curtilage and adjacent land in Neuport by Berkeleye.
Witnesses: Robert de Berkeleye, Robert de Bradeston, Richard de Avene, Walter Moton, Richard le Erl, Walter Clerk.
At: Newport.

A1/3/190 [GC 1688]   Easter Day, 2 Edw. II [30 March 1309]
William de Ruggeweye, clerk, and Alice Herieth his wife; and William le Gold and Christine his wife.

William and Alice have quitclaimed to William and Christine all the lands which they have granted to them, viz. a croft called la Hedfelde in the manor of Alkyntone.
Witnesses: Adam Daungervyle, John le Macon, Geoffrey Moton, Elias le Feror, William de Kyneltre.
At: Wick.

A1/3/191 [GC 2516]   n.d. [*c.* 1300]
Alice Flamberd, widow of Thomas Flamberd; and William Golde and Christine his wife.

Alice has granted to William and Christine, and William's heirs and assigns, all the land with meadow in Kynecroft, with the meadow in Nupsedemede, which she inherited after the death of William Herieth her father, in the manor of Alkyntone; they have given her a certain sum of money.
Witnesses: Nicholas de Wodevorde, Robert atte Schurche, Richard de Avene, Walter Motun, John le Mason.

A1/3/192 [GC 1652***; *counterpart* GC 1652****]   Two weeks after Easter, 1 Edw. II
[28 April 1308]
William Gold and Christine his wife; and William le Clerk and Alice his wife.

Final concord concerning 8 a. of land with meadow in Alkynton by Berkelee; William and Alice have acknowledged the right of William and Christine, by their gift, and William and Christine have given them 10 marks.
At: Westminster.

Hagley holdings

The sisters Alice and Margery Hagley occur in several charters of Alkington manor and were evidently the ultimate heirs of the Hagley holdings.

Walter, Nicholas and Richard de Hagley

A1/3/193 [GC 2471]   n.d. [late 13th cent.]
William de Aungervile and Walter de Hageley.

William has granted to Walter, for his service, a croft in the vill of Wike called Lutlerudigge, beside Proubroc, between the land of Walter and of Walter's sister Cecilia; rent 12*d.* a year, and Walter has given him 1 mark.
Witnesses: Henry de Batonia, Robert de Stane, Nicholas de Wodeford, Thomas le Archer, Robert Caudel, Robert Brun.

A1/3/194 [GC 917]   n.d. [late 13th cent.]
Nicholas de Hagel', son of Walter de Hagel', and William le Gold.

Nicholas has granted to William a messuage with a croft, curtilage, garden [etc.] which

Maud de Caldewell formerly held in the vill of Wyke; rent 1*d.* a year and William has given him 34*s.*

Witnesses: William de Mathine, William de Burgo, Henry de Batonia, William de Angervill, Adam Motun, William de Wik, Thomas de Angervill, Walter de Stintescumb, clerk.

A1/3/195 [GC 918]   n.d. [late 13th cent.]
Nicholas de Hagel' and William le Gold.

Nicholas has granted to William the messuage, with a croft, garden, curtilage [etc.] which William Dyn and his wife Maud formerly held in the vill of Wyke; to William and his wife Christine for their lives, rent 1*d.* a year, and they have given him 34*s.*

Witnesses: Peter de Stintescumbe, Robert de Brothestan, Nicholas de Wodeford, William de Mathine, Walter Motun, John de Craul', Thomas le Masun, Henry de Batona.

A1/3/196 [GC 1020]   Sun. after the Exaltation of Holy Cross, 29 Edw. I [17 Sept. 1301]
(1) Richard de Haggeleye, chaplain; (2) Robert de Bradestone; (3) William le Gold and Christine his wife.

Richard has appointed Robert to give seisin to William and Cristine of Richard's holding in Dangervile Wike which he inherited from Nicholas his father. [*In French.*]
At: Hereford.

Alice and Margery de Hagley

A1/3/197 [GC 1746]   [Nativity of] St. John the Baptist, 3 Edw. II [24 June 1310]
Margery de Haggeley, unmarried woman; and William le Gold and Christine his wife.

Margery has granted to William and Christine, and after their deaths to Henry le Theyn, his [William's] nephew, of Ayston, 2 selions of land in le Redefelde in Dangervileswyke; for a certain sum of money.

Witnesses: Richard de Avene, Adam Dangervile, John le Machon, Richard Dollyng, Adam le Frend.
At: Dangervilles Wick.

A1/3/198 [GC 2029]   1 April 8 Edw. II [1315]
Alice de Haggeleye; and William le Gold and Christine his wife.

Alice has granted to William and Christine, and William's heirs, the reversion of ½ a. of land which Edith widow of Richard Pothering holds for life, in the field called Redefeld in Alkyntone.

Witnesses: Robert de Berk', Richard de Avene, Adam Daungervyle, William de Kyneltre, Adam de Metesdone.
At: Berkeley.

A1/3/199 [GC 2071]   Sun. before Epiphany, 9 Edw. II [4 Jan. 1316]
Margery de Hageleye; and William le Gold and Christine his wife.

Margery has granted to William and Christine, and William's heirs, the reversion of ½ a. of land called le Medaker, which Edith wife of Richard Pothering holds for life, in the field called Redefeld in Alkyntone.

Witnesses: Richard de Avene, Geoffrey Moton, Adam Daungervyle, William de Kyneltre, Adam Mettesdone.
At: Berkeley.

A1/3/200 [GC 2358]   Mon. after Holy Trinity, 15 Edw. II [7 June 1321]
John de Froucestre, son of Thomas de Coueleye, and Margery de Haggeleye; and William le Gold, Christine his wife and Henry le Theyn.

John and Margery have quitclaimed to William, Christine and Henry, and Henry's heirs,

the lands, holdings, rents [etc.] of the inheritance of Margery within the hundred of Berkeleye.
Witnesses: Richard de Avene, Adam Daungervyle, John le Masun, Walter Belamy, Adam le Frend.
At: Dangervilles Wick.

A1/3/201 [GC 2392]   Tues. after St. Lucy, 16 Edw. II [14 Dec. 1322]
Alice de Haggeleye, John de Froucestre and Margery his wife; and William le Gold, Christine his wife and Henry le Theyn.

   Alice, John and Margery have quitclaimed to William, Christine and Henry, and Henry's heirs, all the lands which they had by their enfeoffment in the hundred of Berkeleye.
Witnesses: Adam Daungervile, John le Masun, Walter Belamy, Thomas le Wor, Adam le Frend.
At: Dangervilles Wick.

Other holdings

   Tilly holding
A1/3/202 [GC 2560]   n.d. [late 13th cent.]
Adam Tilly; and William de Golde and Christine his wife.

   Adam has granted to William and Christine, and William's heirs and assigns, a messuage with a garden and curtilage and a croft in the vill of Dangervileswyke, lying between le Longebreche and Bimieleyestrete; rent 1*d.* a year, and William has given him 20*s.*
Witnesses: Peter de Stintescumbe, Walter Motun, Thomas le Masun, Nicholas de Wodeforde, Walter the weaver (*textor*), Richard le Veysi, William de Kyneltre.

A1/3/203 [GC 2413]   Wed. the feast of St. Andrew, 17 Edw. II [30 Nov. 1323]
William le Gold and Christine his wife; and Eve le Veysy, daughter of Richard le Veysy.

   William and Christine have granted to Eve, for her life, two thirds of a messuage and two thirds of a curtilage in Wyke, in the manor of Alkyntone, which Adam Tilly formerly held; rent 21*d.* a year while William and Christine live, and after their deaths, if she survives them, two masses for their souls in the parish church of Berkeleye in the presence of the Holy Cross, and 1*d.* a year.
Witnesses: Adam Dangervyle, Richard Dollyng, Richard Gold, John Machun, Robert ate Hulle.
At: Wick.

A1/3/204 [GC 3582]   Thurs. the feast of Corpus Christi, 40 Edw. III [4 June 1366]
Richard le Theyn, son and heir of Henry le Theyn of Ashton by Bristol; and Thomas le Wor and Maud his wife and John le Bonde and Edith his wife.

   Richard has leased to Thomas, Maud, John and Edith a croft called Tyllyscroft in Wyke Daungervyle beside the road called Bymeleystret and 1 a. of land in Redefeld; for their lives, rent 18*d.* a year, and 1*d.* a year to the lord of Berkele in Richard's name.
Witnesses: John le Serjaunt, Thomas Skay, John de Swanle, Richard Aleyn, William Gryp.
At: Alkington.

   Cornbreche
A1/3/205 [GC 1167]   n.d. [*temp.* Edw. I]
Ralph de Angervill and Hugh his son.

   Ralph has granted to Hugh a croft in the vill of Wike called Cornbreche; rent 6*d.* a year.
Witnesses: William de Canvill, Adam Motun, Richard de Grava, William de Wike, Thomas de Angervill, Richard de Angervill, William le Wor.

A1/3/206 [GC 1353]   n.d. [*temp.* Edw. I]

John, son and heir of Robert the smith of Nibley; and William le Gold and Christine his wife.

John has granted to William and Christine his croft in Wyka called Cornbreche, beside the croft of Richard le Gold called Breche; rent 6*d.* a year, and they have given him 5 marks.

Witnesses: William de Burgo, Warin son of William, Walter Motun, Reginald Draysid, Michael le Hunte.

A1/3/207 [GC 1354]   n.d. [*temp.* Edw. I]

John, son and heir of Robert the smith of Nibley; and William le Gold and Christine his wife.

John has granted to William and Christine his croft in Wyka, beside the croft of Richard le Gold; rent 6*d.* a year, and they have given him 5 marks.

Witnesses: William de Burgo, Warin son of William, Walter Motun, Thomas le Masun, Reginald Draysid.

A1/3/208 [GC 2514]   n.d. [late 13th cent.]

John son and heir of Robert the smith of Nibley; and William Golde and Christine his wife.

John has granted to William and Christine, and their heirs and assigns, his croft in Wyka; rent 6*d.* a year, and they have given him 5 marks.

Witnesses: William de Burgo, Walter Motun, Warin son of William, Thomas le Masun, Reginald Draysid, Walter le Frend, Thomas le Wor.

A1/3/209 [GC 1355]   n.d. [*temp.* Edw. I]

John son of Robert the smith of Sharncliffe (*Cernclive*) and William le Golde.

John has quitclaimed to William a croft called Cornbreche, and William has given him 5 marks.

Witnesses: Peter de Stintescom', William de Mathine, Walter Motun, Nicholas de Wodeford, Thomas le Archer, Thomas le Masun, Adam de Bursewell.

Tounmoune hamstall

A1/3/210 [GC 1856]   Thurs. in Epiphany, 5 Edw. II [6 Jan. 1312]

Philip Coby and Sir Thomas de Berkelee, lord of Berkeley.

Philip has quitclaimed to Thomas 2 a. of land in the field called Tounmounehamestal in Alkyntone, which he recovered by writ of right in the hundred of Berkelee.

Witnesses: Thomas de Stone, Richard de Avene, John Capel, Walter Sewaker, John With, Geoffrey Moton.

At: Berkeley.

A1/3/211 [GC 1859]   Tues. after Epiphany, 5 Edw. II [11 Jan. 1312]

Thomas de Berkelee, lord of Berkeley; and William le Gold and Christine his wife.

Thomas has granted to William and Christine ½ a. 8 perches of land in Tounmounehamestal, which he had by grant of Philip Coby, in Alkyntone; rent 6*d.* a year.

Witnesses: Thomas de Stone, Richard de Avene, Geoffrey Moton, Walter Sewaker, William de Kyneltreo.

At: Berkeley.

The Grout holding

A1/3/212 [GC 986]   n.d. [*early 14th cent.*]

Martin de Wodeford and Henry le Grout.

Martin has granted to Henry 1 a. of land in the field called Radelye, which he had by grant of Nicholas de Wodeford, between the land of Nicholas and the land called Spitelaker; rent a rose at St. John the Baptist if required, and Henry has given him 1 mark.

Witnesses: Thomas Alein, John de Crawleg, Walter Moton, Walter the weaver (*textor*), William de Bockoure, William Mason, John Wonsum.

A1/3/213 [GC 762]　　　　　　　　　　　　　　　　　n.d. [late 13th cent.]
Henry Grout; and William Gold and Christine his wife.

　　Henry has granted to William and Christine 1 a. of land in the field called Redclyff, which he had by grant from Martin de Wodeford, next to the land called Spitelaker; rent a rose a year, and they have given him 10*s*.
Witnesses: Walter Moton, Walter the weaver (*textor*), Richard Veise, Maurice the mason (*cementar'*), William de Kyneltre, Adam Tilly, Nicholas the clerk.

Other holdings

A1/3/214 [GC 690]　　　　　　　　　　　　　　　　　n.d. [late Hen. III]
Maurice de Berkel' and William le Gold.

　　Maurice has granted to William a forge (*fabrica*) in the vill of Wike next to William's house, measuring 3½ by 2½ perches.
Witnesses: Sir William Mansel, Peter de Stintescumbe, William de Burgo, William de Methine, William de Wike, Adam Moton, Nicholas de Wodeford, William de Angervile.

A1/3/215 [GC 935]　　　　　　　　　　　　　　　　　n.d. [late 13th cent.]
Walter Motun, son of Adam Motun, and William le Gold.

　　Walter has granted to William 1½ a. of land in the field called Redefeld in the furlong called Mulelond; rent a clove a year.
Witnesses: Peter de Stintescumbe, William de Mathine, William de Burgo, Robert de Brothestan, Thomas de Boleyg, William de Angervill, Robert de Wik, Walter de Stintescumbe, clerk.

A1/3/216 [GC 842]　　　　　　　　　　　　　　　　　n.d. [late Hen. III]
Nicholas de Wodeford and William le Gold of Wick.

　　Nicholas has granted to William 1 a. of land in the field of Ryham in the furlong called Blakelond, and William has given him 9*s*.
Witnesses: Sir Maurice de Saltmarsh (*de salso marisco*), knight, Walter de Egeton, Robert de Brothestan, Thomas de Boleye, William de Egeton, John de Craul', Robert de Stan'.

A1/3/217 [GC 960]　　　　　　　　　　　　　　　　　n.d. [early 14th cent.]
John de Sautemareys of Woodford; and William le Gold and Christine his wife.

　　John has granted to William and Christine all his land in the field called Redefeld; to hold of the chief lord of the fee, rent a rose a year.
Witnesses: Robert de Berkelee, Robert de Bradestone, Thomas de Beoleye, Richard de Avene, Walter Moton.

The Golds' successors

Berkeley

A1/3/218 [GC 1930]　　　　　　　　　　　　　　20 June 6 Edw. II [1313]
William le Golde and Sir Thomas de Berkelee, lord of Berkeley.

　　William has granted to Thomas a messuage at Dangervylleswike of the holding formerly Hageleie, with a curtilage and garden, and 21 a. of land and 1 a. 50 perches of meadow, in the crofts called Hageleiesrudyngge, le Hongynggerudyngge, Lutleruddyngge, and Hageleiesoverrudyngge, the fields called Riham and Hamstal, and the enclosures called Herietescroft and Kynecroft.
Witnesses: Thomas de Stone, Thomas de Bradestone, Richard de Avene, John Capel, Walter Sewaker, Geoffrey Moton, William de Kyneltreo.
At: Berkeley.

A1/3/219 [GC 1936; *duplicate* GC 1937]   1 Aug. 7 Edw. II [1313]
Thomas de Berkelee, lord of Berkeley; and William le Golde and Christine his wife.

Thomas has leased to William and Christine a messuage at Daungervileswike of the holding formerly Haggeleye, with a curtilage and garden, and 21 a. of land and 1 a. 50 perches of meadow, as in William's charter of enfeoffment to Thomas, in Alkyntone; for their lives, rent 2*s.* 10*d.* a year.
Witnesses: Richard de Avene, John Capel, Maurice de Beyleye, Walter Sewaker, Geoffrey Moton.
At: Berkeley.

The Theyns

A1/3/220 [GC 522]   Morrow of St. John the Baptist, 14 Edw. I [25 June 1286]
William Theyn, son of William Theyn of Ashton, and Edith his wife; and Christine Golde wife of William Golde of Wike.

William and Edith are bound to Christine in an annual rent of 8 marks in pension while she lives, after the death of William her husband if she outlives him; if they fail, she may distrain on all their lands in Glos. and Som., in the hundreds of Berkeley and Harcliff.
Endorsed: *Alkynton.*
Witnesses: Peter de Stintescumbe, William de Burgo, Thomas le Serjant, Thomas Aleyn, Robert de Bradestone, Thomas de Buleye, Nicholas de Wodeford, Warin son of William, Roger Coby, Henry le Grout, clerk.
At: Wike.

A1/3/221 [GC 1561]   n.d. [*temp.* Edw. I]
Edith widow of William Theyn and Christine wife of William Golde, Edith's brother.

Edith has quitclaimed to Christine a messuage and 20 a. of land and 8 a. of meadow which William holds for life in Berkeleye and Nubbeleye, for her life after William's death.
Witnesses: Robert de Bradestone, Robert de Berkeleye, Thomas de Beoleye, Thomas de Swonhongre, Richard de Avene, Walter Moton, Robert of the church, John le Skay, John le Machon.

A1/3/222 [GC 2457]   Tues. after Whit-Sunday, 19 Edw. II [13 May 1326]
Edith widow of William le Theyn of Ashton; and William le Gold and Christine his wife.

Edith is bound to William and Christine to pay to them, for their lives, 8 marks a year, as appears more fully in a writing, for all lands, holdings [etc.] within the hundred of Berkeleye, as in the same fine.
At: Ashton.

A1/3/223 [GC 2458]   Tues. after Whit-Sunday, 19 Edw. II [13 May 1326]
Edith widow of William le Theyn of Ashton in Somerset; and William le Gold and Christine his wife.

Edith is bound to William and Christine to pay to them, for their lives, 8 marks a year, viz. 2 marks at each of the terms of Christmas, Easter, the Nativity of St. John the Baptist and Michaelmas.
At: Ashton.

OTHER INTERESTS

Holding of Walter le Nevou alias Walter de Tresham

A1/3/224 [GC 1478]   n.d. [early Edw. I]
Robert son of Henry Mareschalle and Robert son of William de Gosintune.

Robert Mareschalle has granted to Robert de Gosintune a messuage with a garden and ditch in the town of Newport (*Novus Burgus*), viz. that which William de Hersefeld sometime held of his father Henry; rent 2*s*. 6*d*. a year, and Robert de Gosintune has given him 2½ marks in acknowledgement.

Witnesses: Sir Robert de Kingeston, Peter de Wyke, William de Camvile, Robert de Stanes, Adam Mutun, William Heriit, Walter Grip.

A1/3/225 [GC 327]   St. Philip and St. James [1 May] 1271
Robert Marescall of Newport and Sir Maurice de Berkeley.

Robert has granted to Maurice, his lord, the rent of 2*s*. 6*d*. which William de Gosinton pays him for a holding which William holds of Robert in the second town of Newport (*Novus Burgus*).

Witnesses: Sir William Maunsel, Sir Nicholas Wolf (*Lupus*), knights, Philip de Doughton, steward of Berkeley, Philip de Leycestre, John de Craule.

A1/3/226 [GC 1387]   n.d. [*temp.* Edw. I]
Robert de Gosinton and Walter le Nevou.

For a certain sum of money, Robert has granted to Walter all his holding in Neuport, beside the holding formerly of William Herieth, to hold of the lord of Berkel'; rent 2*s*. 6*d*. a year.

Witnesses: Thomas Alein, Walter Moton, Walter the weaver (*textor*), Richard Erl, William Pothering, William le Masun.

A1/3/227 [GC 761]   n.d. [late 13th cent.]
Agnes widow of Robert son of William de Gosinton and Walter de Tresham.

Agnes has quitclaimed to Walter her dower rights in a messuage in Neuport which Walter had by grant of Robert her late husband.

Witnesses: Richard de Avene, Walter Moton, Robert Grip, Maurice Bernard, William Pothering, Ralph Walebroc.

A1/3/228 [GC 1577]   n.d. [*temp.* Edw. I]
Walter le Webbe and Walter le Nevou.

Walter le Webbe has granted to Walter le Nevou, for a certain sum of money, 1 a. of land in the field called Hawe and 1 a. in the field called Brerilonde, to hold of the lord of Berkel'; rent ½*d*. a year.

Witnesses: Thomas Alein, Walter Moton, Richard Erl, William Pothering, Maurice Bernard, Thomas Flambard.

A1/3/229 [GC 2018]   4 Feb. 8 Edw. II [1315]
John the souter (*sutor*) of Newport and John de Coueleye.

John the souter has granted to John de Coueleye his messuage in Neuport with a garden and curtilage, and 2 a. of land, one in Hamstal at Pokewelle and the other in Brerilonde, and all his land in the field called Hawe beside the park of Okleye, which Alice his wife inherited after the death of Walter de Tresham, in Alkyntone; for life, rent a rose a year and after a term of 8 years from Michaelmas following, 20*s*. a year.

Witnesses: Elias le Feror, William Grip, William de Kyneltre, Richard Pothering, Maurice Bernard.
At: Berkeley.

A1/3/230 [GC 2094]   Sun. before St. George, 9 Edw. II [18 April 1316]
John the souter (*sutor*) of Newport and John de Coueleye.

John the souter, with the assent of Alice his wife, has quitclaimed to John de Coueleye, his heirs and assigns the reversion of 1 a. of land which he previously held for a term, in Hamstal at Pokewelle in Alkyntone.

Witnesses: Elias le Feror, William de Kyneltre, John de Cleyhungre, Maurice Bernard, William le Grip.
At: Berkeley.

A1/3/231 [GC 2096]   Mon. the Invention of Holy Cross, 9 Edw. II [3 May 1316]
Edith daughter and heir of John the souter (*sutor*) of Newport and Alice his wife, unmarried woman, and John de Coueleye.

Edith has quitclaimed to John, his heirs and assigns 1 a. of land in Hamstal at Pokewelle in Alkyntone.
Witnesses: William le Gold, William de Kyneltre, Elias le Feror, Ralph Walebrok, William Grip.
At: Berkeley.

Kingswood Abbey holdings

Walter le Grip's grant
A1/3/232 [GC 1393]   n.d. [late Hen. III]
Walter le Griph and Kingswood Abbey.

Walter has granted to the abbey, for the support of the iron fabric, all the meadow he had in Matford within the manor of Berkel'.
Witnesses: Roger de Lokynton, William de Mathine, William de Burgo, William Capel, Nicholas de Wodeford, Henry de Baton', Roger le Herde.

A1/3/233 [GC 440]   n.d. [late Hen. III or Edw. I]
Maud widow of Walter le Griph and Kingswood Abbey.

Maud has quitclaimed to the abbey her dower rights in the meadow at Matford in the manor of Berkeley which Walter granted to the abbey.
Witnesses: Thomas de Beol', William de Burg, William Capel, Nicholas de Wodeford, Henry de Baton.

A1/3/234 [SC 445]   n.d. [late Hen. III]
Robert the marshal (*marescallus*) of Newport and Kingswood Abbey.

Robert has quitclaimed to the abbey, for the support of the iron fabric, that meadow which he sold to Walter le Gryip in Mathford within the manor of Berkeley.
Witnesses: Roger de Lokynton, William de Mathine, William de Burgo, William Capel, Nicholas de Wodeforde, Henry de Batonia, Roger le Hurde.

A1/3/235 [SC 438]   n.d. [late Hen. III]
Maurice de Berkeley and Kingswood Abbey.

Maurice has granted to the abbey free entry into a certain meadow containing 1 a. which the abbey was given by Walter le Grip for the support of the iron fabric of the abbey.

Other
A1/3/236 [GC 601]   7 March 22 Edw. I [1294]
Sir Thomas de Berkel and brother Alexander, keeper of the fabric of Kingswood Abbey.

Memorandum of the accounting between Thomas and Alexander for the work done for the fabric through brother Alexander by Thomas in Glos. and Som., so that they are equal; also the same day Thomas granted to brother Alexander licence to enter and hold 4 a. of land for a term of 9 years, and ½ a. of meadow for 10 years, which he had from Walter le Webbe in the manor of Alkinton.
At: Berkeley Castle.

A1/3/237 [GC 556]   n.d. [late Hen. III]
Kingswood Abbey and John Palmere.

The abbot and convent have granted to John the land in Newport lying between Knightelande and the plot and *lanceat* [lance-shaped plot?], with the lower head above the land of Roger Nattock and the upper head above the abbey's land, which William le Mon' held, a croft opposite the house of William de Radeford, and 2 a. of land in Stanhemfelde; rent 3s. 6d. a year.

Witnesses: Ralph de Angervile, Henry the marshal (*marescallus*), John de Berkeley, John de Wodeford, Maurice de Stanes, Osbert de Kineltre.

Hurd holdings

Robert le Hurd's holding

A1/3/238 [GC 764]   n.d. [early Hen. III]
Alice de Hamme and Robert le Herde.

Alice has granted to Robert all the land, meadow and appurtenances which Robert once held in the manor of Alclinton of Adam son of Nigel and of Robert her father; rent 4*s.* a year.
Witnesses: John de Egeton, Nicholas Rufus, Adam Cobi, Maurice de Bevintun, John de Wodeford, Maurice de Stan, Robert the forester.

A1/3/239 [SC 329]   n.d. [*temp.* Hen. III]
Walter de Burch and Robert le Herde.

Walter has granted to Robert the lands which Robert formerly held of Adam son of Nigel and of Robert his brother, in Alchinton, lying next to the land which he holds of Sir Thomas de Berkeley; rent 4*s.* a year and the royal service which pertains to 8 a.; Robert has paid an acknowledgement of 40*s.*
Witnesses: Sir William de Clifford, Henry de Berkeley, John de Egintun, Nicholas the red (*ruffus*), Adam Cobi, John de Wyk, Maurice de Bevinton, . . . de Wodeford, Henry de . . .

Other Hurd holdings

A1/3/240 [GC 710]   n.d. [late Hen. III]
Alexander de la Burigate and Robert le Herde.

Alexander has granted to Robert 1 a. of land containing 10 selions with a fore-earth; rent a root of ginger a year, and Robert has given him 11*s.*
Witnesses: Sir Nicholas Wolf (*Lupus*), steward of Berkeley, Sir Maurice de Saltmarsh (*de salso marisco*), Peter de Wike, John Sewaker, Henry Mar', Adam Motun, Thomas Cavel, Thomas son of Alan, William the palmer (*palmerius*).

A1/3/241 [GC 318]   Decollation of St. John the Baptist, 53 Hen. III [29 Aug. 1269]
Helen daughter of Robert le Herde and Roger le Herde.

Helen has quitclaimed to Roger 1 a. of land with buildings upon it.
At: Woodford.

A1/3/242 [GC 922]   n.d. [late 13th cent.]
Joan widow of Roger le Herd of Alkington and Adam her son.

Joan has granted to Adam 8¼ a. of land and meadow which she had from Sir Maurice lord of Berkel, as in his charter to her; to hold of the lord of Berkeley at 12*d.* a year.
Witnesses: Robert de Stan', Robert Wyther, Thomas Alein, William Pothering, Robert Grip.

A1/3/243 [GC 1871]   Sun. the feast of St. Gregory, 5 Edw. II [12 March 1312]
William le Herde of Alkington and Maud his wife; and Adam le Herde.

William and Maud have leased to Adam all their land in the croft called Herdehedfeld, beside the road from Berkel' to Kyneltre; to hold from the Michaelmas following for 6 years, and he has given them a certain sum of money.
Witnesses: William Golde, William de Kyneltre, Adam de Mettesdone, Richard Pothering, Ralph Walebroc.
At: Alkington.

Alice le Panyter

A1/3/244 [GC 2965]   Sat. the feast of St. Edmund the king, 13 Edw. III [20 Nov. 1339]
Robert son and heir of Geoffrey Moton; and Richard le Panyter of Berkeley and Alice his wife.

Robert has leased to Richard and Alice 16 selions of land in Hedfeldecrofte in Alkyntone; for their lives, rent 13½d. a year.
Witnesses: Robert Groundy, Robert Prikke, Stephen de Kyneltre, William ate Herne, Henry le Eyr.
At: Alkington.

A1/3/245 [GC 3353]   n.d. [mid 14th cent.]
Walter atte Welle of Cornwell and Alice wife of Richard le Panyter of Berkeley.

Walter has granted to Alice, her heirs and assigns all his land in Alkyntone which he had by grant of the said Richard.
Witnesses: Stephen de Kyneltre, Richard Aleyn, William ate Herne, John Sley, Nicholas Skot.

Other holdings

A1/3/246 [GC 1382]   n.d. [late Hen. III]
Adam Cobi and William the tailor (*cissor*).

Adam has granted to William a croft in the manor of Alkuinton which Arnold de Berkel', clerk, gave to him in exchange; rent 1 lb. of cumin a year, and William has given him 4½ marks.
Witnesses: Peter de Wyke, Nicholas de Crauleygh, John de Brotheston, John Sewaker, Thomas son of Alan, Adam Mutun, William de Wike, Thomas de Wyke, Ralph de Angervill, Walter Sely, clerk.

A1/3/247 [GC 521]   The Purification, 14 Edw. I [2 Feb. 1286]
William Cole of Berkeley; and Richard Erl and Agnes his wife.

William has granted to Richard and Agnes 1 a. of land in Juelesaket, to them and their heirs, for 6s. 8d. Endorsed: *Alkynton*.
Witnesses: Thomas Aleyn, Walter Schipward, Roger Tannar', Walter le Herde, John Marescal, Richard le Savener.

A1/3/248 [GC 608]   Easter 23 Edw. I [3 April 1295]
William de Cumbe of Wortley and William le Wor of Wike.

William de Cumbe has leased to William le Wor a croft with meadow called Bredeleyze for a term of 20 years, and all the meadow lying in Wineleyze, except le Sondput, for 30 years.
Witnesses: Walter de Schaldefeld, William le Born, Peter Stintescumbe, Walter Motun, Nicholas de Grove, Michael le Hunt', John Schausi.

A1/3/249 [GC 1617]   n.d. [*temp.* Edw. I]
Walter de Lorewinge; and William de Modibroc and Helen his wife.

Walter has granted to William and Helen all his land in the furlong called Aketre; to hold of Thomas son of Adam de Lorewinge, rent ½d. a year to Thomas and royal service as in the manor of Hamme; William and Helen have given Walter 20s.
Witnesses: Thomas Alein, William de Mettesdon, Adam Godmon, Walter Moton, William de Kineltre, William de Bechoure, Richard le Savoner.

A1/3/250 [GC 1383]   n.d. [*temp.* Edw. I]
Adam Godimon of Matson; and Isabel and Isillia his daughters.

Adam has granted to Isabel and Isillia all his land in the field called Riham, which he had

by grant of Thomas de Wyke and Thomas had in exchange from William de Wyke for land at Nibbeley; to them and their issue, rent 2*d*. a year.
Witnesses: Thomas Aleyn, Adam de Lorewinge, William de Mettesdon, William de Kineltre, Osbert de Kineltre, Richard le Savoner.

A1/3/251 [GC 1588]   n.d. [*temp.* Edw. I]
William le Wor of Wick and Thomas son of Ralph de Angervile.

   William has granted to Thomas a curtilage by Thomas's house; rent 1*d*. a year, and Thomas has given him 5*s*.
Witnesses: Walter Moton, Philip de la Holte, William Golde, Adam de Angervile, Richard le Sopere.

A1/3/252 [GC 2057]   Wed. after Michaelmas, 9 Edw. II [1 Oct. 1315]
William ate Wode of Alkington and Maud his wife; and William de Kyneltre, Juliana his wife and Stephen and Robert their sons.

   William and Maud have leased to William, Juliana, Stephen and Robert a parcel of land in the field called Echedone in Alkyntone near Musardeswode; for their lives, rent for 32 years, 4¾*d*., and after that term 5*s*. a year; William de Kyneltre has given them 24*s*.
Witnesses: Richard de Avene, William le Gold, Adam Daungervyle, Geoffrey Moton, Adam Mettesdone, Ralph Walebrok, William le Grip.
At: Alkington.

A1/3/253 [GC 2240]   Thurs. before St. John Baptist, 11 Edw. II [22 June 1318]
Joan widow of Walter le Webbe of Newport and Agnes widow of John le Vygnur of Berkeley.

   Joan has quitclaimed to Agnes a parcel of land in the field called Redeleye beside Rihamesbrok.
Witnesses: William le Gold, William de Kyneltre, Maurice Bernard, Ralph Walebrok, Adam le Herde.
At: Newport.

A1/3/254 [GC 2375]   Sat. before St. George, 15 Edw. II [17 April 1322]
Adam le Muleward of Woodford by Berkeley, son and heir of the late Hugh le Muleward of the same; and Peter Dauwes of Stone, Agnes his first wife and William their son.

   Adam has granted to Peter, Agnes and William and the heirs and assigns of William, for a certain sum of money, a croft of land in Alkyntone within the manor of Berkelee, beside the road from Thornbury to Gloucester (*Gloucestrea*).
Witnesses: Walter Sewaker, William Cut, Walter le Toyt, Henry Broun, Nicholas le Clerk of Pedington, Philip Gybbes, Roger le Archir.
At: Woodford.

A1/3/255 [GC 2715]   St. Nicholas, 4 Edw. III [6 Dec. 1330]
(1) William Bernard of Newport; (2) Adam Moton; (3) John Imeke of Newport and Alice his wife.

   William has appointed Adam his attorney to give seisin to John and Alice of ½ a. of meadow in Matford.
At: Newport.

A1/3/256 [GC 3590]   Wed. before St. Gregory, 41 Edw. III [10 March 1367]
William Modebroke of Berkeley and John Walebroke of the same.

   William has granted to John, his heirs and assigns 2½ a. of land, of which 1 a. lies in the field called Aketreo by le Hethefeld and 3 selions containing 1½ a. lie in the field called Aketreo by Berkelee.
Witnesses: John Coby, John Byl, Nicholas Schipward, Nicholas Sopere, Richard Scryveyn.
At: Berkeley.

A1/3/257 [GC 4108; *duplicate* GC 4109]   6 Jan. 4 Hen. V [1417]
John Dangervyle of Wick and Thomas Dangervyle his son.

John has leased to Thomas a croft called Longrudyng beside the headland called
Swynborne, extending above Lytulswynborne; for his life, rent 12*d.* a year.
Witnesses: Thomas Serch, John Maltman, Robert Boteler, John Bruward, Richard Jones.
At: Wick.

ALKINGTON: DANGERVILLES WICK

BERKELEY INTERESTS

Sparkes and Worthyswick

A1/4/1 [GC 4089]   Mon. after Easter, 1 Hen. V [24 April 1413]
Thomas Berkeleye, lord of Berkeley; and John Evike, Margaret Evike his wife and Thomas
Evike their son.

Thomas has leased to John, Margaret and Thomas the holding with a dovecot at
Wyke Daungervile called Worthieswyke, which Juliana widow of Elias Sparke previously
held, and a messuage and half-virgate called Sparkys, which Juliana held for life, in
Alkyntone; for their lives, rent for Worthieswyke 21*s.* 4*d.* a year and for Sparkys holding
32*s.* a year.
Witnesses: John Coweley, John Serche, John Dorney.
At: Berkeley.

A1/4/2 [GC 4314]   10 July 1 Edw. IV [1461]
William Berkeley, son and heir of James Berkeley, lord of Berkeley; and John Duryard and
Joan his wife.

William has confirmed to John and Joan the grant to them by James of the reversion of
the holding at Daungerwykeswyk [*sic*] called Wortheswyke and the reversion of a
messuage and half-virgate called Sparkes after the death or surrender of John Juipke; for
their lives, rent for Wortheswyke 21*s.* 4*d.* a year and for Sparkes 32*s.* a year.
Witnesses: John Huchon, Thomas Clerk, John Boteler.
At: Alkington.

Other holdings

A1/4/3 [GC 2362]   1 July 14 Edw. II [1321]
Thomas de Berkelee, lord of Berkeley, and Edith widow of Thomas le Veel.

Thomas has leased to Edith a plot of land in the high street at Daungervileswyke to build
on, beside the road from Mickelwode to le Cleyputtes, in Alkyntone; to hold enclosed, to
her and her issue, rent a rose a year.
Witnesses: William le Golde, Nicholas Daungervile, Adam Daungervile, Robert Truyt,
William Cut.
At: Berkeley.

A1/4/4 [GC 2617]   Mon. the feast of St. Laurence [the martyr], 1 Edw. III [10 Aug. 1327]
William le Gold and Thomas de Berkelegh, lord of Berkeley.

William has granted to Thomas, his heirs and assigns a plot of land in Daungervyleswyke
and a plot opposite his house in Daungervyleswyke.
Witnesses: John le Serjaunt, John Capel, John de Swonhungre, Robert de Asshelworth,
William Gylemyn.
At: Berkeley.

BERKELEY (LATER BISLEY) HOLDING IN DANGERVILLES WICK AND BRADLEY

The holding was created by Robert de Berkeley of Billow, a younger son of Sir Robert of Arlingham (younger brother of Thomas (II) Lord Berkeley), and passed to his daughter Isabel who married Hugh Bisley. It was acquired by Thomas (IV) Lord Berkeley in 1390 from a later Hugh de Bisley.

Wor holding in Dangervilles Wick

The mill

A1/4/5 [SC 345]   n.d. [*temp.* Hen. III]
Robert de Blavens and Walter son of Holfi.

   Robert has granted to Walter the land with a mill which Alfred Cragg held on the day he died from Robert at Wikam, in free marriage with Levina daughter of Alfred; rent 20*s.* a year, to be paid at Briddesbroc, Robert's land in Essex, and the royal service which pertains to so much land in Berclehernesse; Walter has paid 5 marks to Robert and ½ mark to Rose his wife in acknowledgement.
Witnesses: Martin, John and Henry, chaplains, Simon de Olepenna, Maurice son of Nigel, Hugh de Bradele, Walter de Angervilla, Walter Stuoet, Arnold de Wika, William the hunter (*venator*), Adam Caud, Hugh de Cuhulla, Thomas son of Baldwin.

A1/4/6 [GC 293]   Michaelmas, 42 Hen. III [29 Sept. 1258]
John de Lorewinge and William le Wor.

   John has quitclaimed to William 1 virgate of land in the vill of Wike and a mill in the same place, which Walter le Wor, William's father, once held.
Witnesses: Peter de Stintescumbe, William de Wike, Adam Coby, Ralph de Angervile, Thomas de Wike.

A1/4/7 [GC 636; *duplicate* GC 637]   Thurs. after Epiphany, 26 Edw. I [9 Jan. 1298]
William le Wor and Richard de Avene.

   William has leased to Richard two thirds of a water-mill in Wyk in the manor of Berkeleye, with the reversion of the third which his mother Joan holds in dower; for Richard's life, rent 10*s.* a year after a term of 20 years; if Richard dies within the 20 years then it will remain with his heirs or assigns until the end of that term.
Witnesses: Walter Moton, Philip ate Holte, William le Gold, William Potheryng, William de Kyneltre, John le Mathom, William de Webbel', clerk.
At: Wyke.

A1/4/8 [GC 1102]   Sun. after St. Edmund the martyr, 34 Edw. I [21 Nov. 1305]
Joan widow of William le Wor the elder of Wick; and Robert de Berkleye, Joan his wife and Isabel their daughter.

   Joan has quitclaimed to Robert, Joan and Isabel her dower rights in the mill at Wik called Woresmulle, while they pay to her 4*s.* 8*d.* a year for her land in Wik.
Witnesses: Thomas de Buleie, Walter Moton, William Gold, John Mason, Walter Dollyng.
At: Wick.

Grossmead

A1/4/9 [GC 1035]   Michaelmas, 30 Edw. I [29 Sept. 1302]
William le Wor and Richard de Wyke.

   William has leased to Richard all his meadow called Grosmed next to his land called Rakebourne, with the dower when it falls in, for a term of 15 years, for a certain sum of money.
Witnesses: Richard de Avene, Walter Moton, William le Gold, Adam Daungervile, William de Webbeleye, clerk.
At: Nibley.

A1/4/10 [GC 1104]   Mon. the feast of St. Nicholas, 34 Edw. I [6 Dec. 1305]
Richard de Wyke and Robert de Berkelee.

Richard has quitclaimed to Robert the meadow called Grosemede between the grove which Robert had from William le Wor and the land called Rakebourne, which meadow he has leased from William for 15 years.
Witnesses: Robert de Bradeston, Thomas de Beoleye, Thomas de Stintescombe, Thomas de Swonhongre, John de Swonhongre.
At: Berkeley.

Other lands

A1/4/11 [GC 1589]   n.d. [early 14th cent.]
William le Wor; and Robert de Berkeleie, Joan his wife and Isabel their daughter.

William has granted to Robert, Joan and Isabel the land called Honggingecrofte lying between the land called Hulcrofte and the rhine called Doverle in Wike, to hold of the chief lord for the customary services.
Witnesses: Robert de Bradestone, Stephen Draicote, Thomas de Buleie, Walter Moton, William Golde, Adam Dangervile, John Mason.

A1/4/12 [GC 1103]   Sun. after St. Edmund the martyr, 34 Edw. I [21 Nov. 1305]
Robert de Berkeleie, Joan his wife and Isabel their daughter; and William le Wor.

Robert, Joan and Isabel have leased to William, for his life, the hall with the chamber and the old garden and the curtilage above the river extending above Mulecroft in Wik, which they had by grant of William, also the easements of the bakery and freedom from toll (*tolfre*) in the mill at Wik for his demesne corn; rent a rose a year.
Witnesses: Robert de Bradestone, Thomas de Buleie, Walter Moton, William Gold, Adam Dangervile.
At: Wick.

A1/4/13 [GC 1111]   Thurs. before Easter, 34 Edw. I [31 March 1306]
Joan le Wor; and Robert de Berkeleye, Joan his wife and Isabel their daughter.

Joan has granted to Robert, Joan and Isabel a messuage with a curtilage and croft in Wyke Dangervil, the croft lying between Rakeborne and the road; they have given her a certain sum of money.
Witnesses: Robert de Bradestone, Thomas de Beoleye, Walter Moton, Robert de la Churche, Warin son of William, Philip chaplain of Breadstone.
At: Wick.

The entire holding

A1/4/14 [SC 418]   n.d. [*temp.* Hen. III]
William son of William and Elias de Cumbe.

William has granted to Elias the rent of 20*s.* due from William le Wor for land and a mill which he holds at Wike, together with the services of William and his heirs, viz. in wardships, reliefs, escheats [etc.]; rent a clove a year and Elias has given him 18 marks and 10*s.*
Witnesses: William de Berkelay, Peter de Stintescumbe, Laurence de Alcrugge, Michael le Venur, Richard of the abbey (*de monasterio*), William de Wike, Bartholomew de Olepenna.

A1/4/15 [GC 1101]   Fri. before St. Denis, 33 Edw. I [8 Oct. 1305]
William le Woer; and Robert de Berkeleye, Joan his wife and Isabel their daughter.

William has granted to Robert, Joan and Isabel, for a certain sum of money, all his holding in Wyke Dangervile in the parish of Berkeleye.
Witnesses: Robert de Bradestone, Thomas de Boeleye, Thomas de Stintescumbe, Walter le Borouh, Richard de Avene, Walter Motoun, John le Duck.
At: Dangervilles Wick.

A1/4/16 [GC 2275]   Sun. before St. Mark the evangelist, 12 Edw. II [22 April 1319]
Thomas son and heir of Robert de Berkeleye; and Hugh de Byseleye and Isabel his wife, Thomas's sister.

Thomas has quitclaimed to Hugh and Isabel the holding with houses [etc.] which William le Wor granted to the said Robert his father, Joan his wife and Isabel their daughter, and the heirs of Robert, in Wyke Dangervile; to them and their issue.
Witnesses: Thomas de Berkeleye the elder, knight, Maurice de Berkeleye, John de Olepenne, John de Coueleye, John le Duk, Robert atte Yate of Dursley, John de Swanhungre, Stephen de Draycote.

A1/4/17 [GC 3684]   Thurs. before Michaelmas, 49 Edw. III [27 Sept. 1375]
Elias de Berlegh and Laurence Ivet of Bradley; and Hugh de Byseleye.

Elias and Laurence have granted to Hugh, his heirs and assigns a rent of 20*s.* a year from all the lands and holdings which William le Wor formerly held of William son of William in Daungervyle Wyke, and which William son of William granted to Elias de Combe, ancestor of the said Elias, and which descended to him by inheritance.
Witnesses: John Clyfforde, Robert Cherletone, John Sergeaunt, John atte Jate, John Joye.
At: Wotton.

Other grants to the Berkeleys in Alkington

A1/4/18 [GC 1107]   Tues. before St. Wulfstan, 34 Edw. I [18 Jan. 1306]
Richard le Sopere of Berkeley; and Robert de Berkleie, Joan his wife and Isabel their daughter.

Richard, with the consent of his wife Denise, has granted to Robert, Joan and Isabel all his land in Wika called 'inhock', next to the road from Stintescombe to Wik; for this Robert has granted to him all the land in Backscroft next to Kyneltre.
Witnesses: Robert de Bradeston, Thomas de Buleie, Robert Wither, Richard de Avene, Walter Moton, William Gold, Adam Dangervile.
At: Wick.

A1/4/19 [GC 1638]   Morrow of St. George, 34 Edw. I [24 April 1306]
Joan widow of Thomas de Angervill; and Robert de Berkeley, Joan his wife and Isabel their daughter.

Joan has quitclaimed to Robert, Joan and Isabel a messuage, curtilage and croft in Wyke Aungervile which Robert had by her demise and of which she was enfeoffed with Thomas, by William le Frend of Nybbeleg'.
Witnesses: Robert de Bradestone, Thomas de Beoleg', Walter Motoun, Robert de la Churche, Warin son of William, Philip chaplain of Breadstone.
At: Berkeley.

A1/4/20 [GC 1131]   Tues. after St. Denis, 34 Edw. I [11 Oct. 1306]
Walter Moton; and Robert de Berkeleye, Joan his wife and Isabel their daughter.

Walter has granted to Robert, Joan and Isabel, and Robert's heirs, for a certain sum of money, all the land in la Cleyvelde called Stonyeacre, next to the river of Overle.
Witnesses: Warin son of William, Robert de la Churiche, Richard de Wike of Nibley, John le Duck, Adam Daungervile, John le Masun, Walter Dolling.
At: Dangervilles Wick.

A1/4/21 [GC 1399]   n.d. [early 14th cent.]
Alice de Hageleye; and Robert de Berkeley, Joan his wife and Isabel their daughter.

Alice has granted to Robert, Joan and Isabel 1 a. of land in Wyke Aungervile in the field called Cleyfeld in the furlong called Pressals atte Purie, viz. that which she inherited after the death of her sister Margery; to them and the heirs of Robert, and he has given her 20*s.*

Witnesses: Thomas de Styntescumbe, Warin son of William, Walter de Gosyngton, Walter Motoun, Adam de Aungervile.

A1/4/22 [GC 1489] n.d. [early 14th cent.]
Walter Moton of Wick; and Robert de Berkeleye, Joan his wife and Isabel their daughter.

Walter has granted to Robert, Joan and Isabel 1 a. of land in Cleyfeld called Muleaker, extending to the river called Douverle in Wik.
Witnesses: Robert de Bradestone, Thomas de Buleie, Richard de Avene, Walter Moton, Richard le Veise, Nicholas of the vine (*de vinea*), Adam Dangervile.

A1/4/23 [GC 1593] n.d. [early 14th cent.]
Richard de Wike of Nibley; and Robert de Berkeleie, Joan his wife and Isabel their daughter.

Richard has granted to Robert, Joan and Isabel all his land and meadow in the field called Brodelye, to hold of the chief lord.
Witnesses: Robert de Bradeston, Robert Wither, Thomas de Buleie, Warin son of William, Robert of the church, Richard de Avene, Walter Moton, William Golde.

A1/4/24 [GC 1651] The Annunciation, 1 Edw. II [25 March 1308]
Sir Thomas de Berkelee, lord of Berkeley; and Robert de Berkelee of Billow, Joan his wife and Thomas their son.

Thomas has granted to Robert, Joan and Thomas, for their lives, pasture in his wood of Mikelwode for 44 goats, of which 4 are to be male and 40 female, and if they have only 33, then 3 male and 30 female, and if only 22, then 2 male and 20 female; and Thomas will have half of those born, he to have first choice, they to have the second, he to have the third, they to have the fourth, and so on, and the half remaining to Robert, Joan and Thomas will stay in the said pasture with their mothers until weaned and then to be removed so the numbers do not exceed the agreement.
Witnesses: Robert de Bradestone, Thomas de Styntescumbe, Thomas de Bole, Henry de Camme, Stephen de Draycote, Richard de Avene, Walter Motoun, Walter Hathemare.
At: Berkeley.

A1/4/25 [GC 2054] 3 Sept. 9 Edw. II [1315]
Robert de Berkeleye; and Walter Gylot, Richard Bat, Henry Waleweyn, William le Notyare, Nicholas Topyn, Richard Housty, Thomas atte Hulle, William son of William Snyte, William son of John Biyondebrok, William Gosedeye and Robert le Crockare.

Robert has released and quitclaimed his suit and action which he had started by writ of trespass in the king's court against Walter and the others for encroaching on his ditch at Wyke in Alkyntone. [*In French*.]
Witnesses: Thomas de Bradeston, Henry de Camme, Stephen de Draycote, John le Serjant, Walter Sewaker.
At: Berkeley.

Passage from Bisley, through feoffees

A1/4/26 [GC 3834] Mon. after St. Thomas the martyr, 13 Ric. II [3 Jan. 1390]
Hugh de Byseley; and Henry Waryner of Charfield and John de Stanshawe.

Hugh has granted to Henry and John, and their heirs and assigns, all the lands, holdings, rents [etc.] which he had in Bradeley and Wyke Daungerville within the hundred of Berkeley.
Witnesses: Sir John de Berkley, knight, Ralph Waleys, John Smalkombe, Roger Pyngel, Richard Panter.
At: Dangervilles Wick.

A1/4/27 [GC 3835]　　　　　Mon. after St. Thomas the martyr, 13 Ric. II [3 Jan. 1390]
(1) Hugh de Bysel'; (2) John Clastyngburi; (3) Henry Waryner of Charfield and John Stanshawe.

Hugh has appointed John to give seisin to Henry and John of all his lands [etc.] in Bradeley and Wyke Daungervyll.
At: Bisley.

A1/4/28 [GC 3837]　　　　　19 April 13 Ric. II [1390]
Hugh de Bislee and John de Stanshawe.

Hugh has quitclaimed to John all the lands [etc.] which John and Henry Waryner recently had by his grant in Daungervyleswyke and Bradelee.
Witnesses: William Smalecombe, Thomas Skey, Richard Phelpes.

A1/4/29 [GC 3863]　　　　　25 Jan. 15 Ric. II [1392]
John de Stanschawe; and William Smalcombe and William his son.

John has granted to William and William, and their heirs and assigns, all his lands, holdings, rents [etc.] in Bradeleye and Wyke Daungerville which he had by grant of Hugh Bisleye within the hundred of Berkeleye.
Witnesses: John de Berkeleye, Thomas FitzNichol, knights, Ralph Waleys, Edmund Forde, John Coueleye.
At: Dangervilles Wick.

A1/4/30 [GC 3864]　　　　　25 Jan. 15 Ric. II [1392]
(1) John de Stanschawe; (2) Thomas Stanschawe, John Wyntur, chaplain, John Dybes and John Bonde of Dangervilles Wick; (3) William Smalcombe the elder and William his son.

John has appointed Thomas, John, John and John to give seisin to William and William of all his lands, rents [etc.] in Bradeleye and Wyke Daungerville.
At: Dangervilles Wick.

A1/4/31 [GC 3904]　　　　　24 Feb. 19 Ric. II [1396]
William Smalcombe the elder; and John Camme, chaplain, and Thomas de Bristowe chaplain.

William has granted to John and Thomas, and their heirs and assigns, all the lands, holdings [etc.] that he had in Bradeley and Wyke Daungerville by grant of John de Stanschawe within the hundred of Berkeleye.
Witnesses: Edmund Basset, John atte Yate, John Skay, Laurence Juet, John Daungerville.
At: Wotton.

A1/4/32 [GC 3905]　　　　　24 Feb. 19 Ric. II [1396]
(1) William Smalcombe; (2) William his son; (3) John Camme and Thomas de Bristowe, chaplains.

William the elder has appointed William the younger to give seisin to John and Thomas of all the lands in Wyke Daungervill and Bradeleye that he had by grant of John Stanshawe.

A1/4/33 [GC 3906]　　　　　25 Feb. 19 Ric. II [1396]
William Smalcombe the younger; and John Camme chaplain and Thomas de Bristowe chaplain.

William has quitclaimed to John and Thomas the lands which he and his father, William Smalcombe, had by grant of John Stanschawe in Bradeley and Wyke Daungerville.
Witnesses: Edmund Basset, John atte Yate, John Skay, Laurence Juet, John Daungerville.
At: Wotton.

A1/4/34 [GC 3936]   4 Dec. 21 Ric. II [1397]
John Camme and Thomas de Bristowe, chaplains; and John Harsefeld.

John and Thomas have granted to John Harsefeld, for his good services to Sir Thomas lord of Berkley, all the lands, holdings, rents and reversions in Bradeley and Wykedayngervill which they had by grant of William Smalcombe the elder; for his life, for the customary services, with remainder after his death to the said Sir Thomas, his heirs and assigns.
Witnesses: Edmund Basset, John Skey, Laurence Berley, John Archer, Richard Ectone.
At: Wotton.

OTHER INTERESTS

Wor holding in Ragburn

A1/4/35 [GC 988]   n.d. [early 14th cent.]
William le Wor of Wick and Thomas son of Ralph de Angervile.

William has granted to Thomas 1 a. of land in Rakeboine; rent 1*d.* a year.
Witnesses: Walter Moton, Philip de la Holte, William Gold, Adam Dangervile, Richard le Sopere.

A1/4/36 [GC 642]   St. Gregory, 26 Edw. I [12 March 1298]
Thomas le Wor and Joan his wife; and Richard de Wyke and Denise his wife.

Thomas and Joan have leased to Richard and Denise all their land in Rakeborne for the life of Joan, who holds it in dower after the death of William le Wor of Wick.
Witnesses: Robert de Stone, Robert de Bradeston, Walter Moton, Philip de la Hote, Richard le Sopere, clerk.

A1/4/37 [GC 1080]   Christmas Day, 33 Edw. I [25 Dec. 1304]
William Vore and Maurice de Boleye.

William has granted to Maurice his headland called Rakeborne; for William's life, rent a rose a year.
Witnesses: Robert de Berkel', Robert de Bradestone, Thomas de Stintescumbe, Thomas de Boleye, Thomas Serjant, Warin de Nalbeleye, Thomas le Veel, Henry de la Hulle.
At: Billow.

Other holdings

A1/4/38 [GC 1724]   Wed. the feast of the Annunciation, 3 Edw. II [25 March 1310]
Richard de Wyke of Nibley; and Nicholas le White of Arlingham and Alice his wife.

Richard has leased to Nicholas and Alice a messuage at Daungervyleswyke with a house, garden, curtilage and croft containing 4 a., beside the king's highway at le Cleyputtes, also 1 a. of land in the field called Redefelde, for their lives, rent 9*s.* a year. Endorsed: *Borrowed of Wm. Basset 19 Oct. 1606.*
Witnesses: Adam le Frend, William le Frend, William le Gold, Adam Dangervyle, John Dorneye.
At: Dangervilles Wick.

A1/4/39 [GC 1991; *duplicate* GC 1992]   Sat. the feast of St. Bartholomew, 8 Edw. I
                                                                          [24 Aug. 1314]
William ate Wode of Alkington; and John called Ferthyng and Sibyl his wife.

William, with the assent of Maud his wife, has leased to John and Sibyl a holding with a garden and croft in Daungervyleswyke in Alkyntone; for their lives, rent 20*d.* a year.
Witnesses: Richard de Avene, William le Gold, William de Kyneltre, Geoffrey Moton, John le Mason.
At: Dangervilles Wick.

A1/4/40 [GC 4054]   Thurs. before St. Martin, 12 Hen. IV [6 Nov. 1410]
John Bower; and William Nyweman and Margaret his wife.

John has leased to William, Margaret and their eldest son all the land that Roger Jobyn previously held of John in Wyke Angervyle, and an annual rent of 18*d.* from John Bonde for a croft and 1 a. of land held of John for life; for their lives, rent 30*s.* a year.
Witnesses: John Maltmon, Thomas Serch, Maurice Cole, Robert Dosy, Robert Botyler.
At: Wick.

ALKINGTON: MICHAEL WOOD

Michael Wood was originally the *micele* (*mucele*, *muchele*) *wode*, the Great Wood, of which a remnant still exists, now reduced to the indignity of giving its name to a motorway service station.

SANDRIDGE

A1/5/1 [GC 810]   n.d. [late Hen. III]
Maurice de Saltmarsh (*de salso marisco*) and Sir Maurice de Berk' his lord.

Maurice de Saltmarsh has quitclaimed to Maurice de Berkeley, for himself and for all his men of Wodewodeford [*sic*], common in the wood of Sondrugg, and in the road 2 perches wide between his land and the land of Simon de Wodeford leading from the said wood to the road of Swanleygh, so that Maurice de Berkeley may enclose the wood.
Witnesses: Sir Warin de Raleygh, Sir Henry de Berk', Sir William Maunsel, knights, William de Mathem, Maurice de Stan', Peter de Wyk, Robert le Veel, Robert Bastard, John Sewaker, Adam Coby, John de Egeton, Thomas Mathyas.

A1/5/2 [GC 1967]   20 Feb. 7 Edw. II [1314]
Thomas de Berkelee, lord of Berkeley; and Thomas Robat and Alice his wife.

Thomas has granted to Thomas and Alice 4 a. of land at Sondrugge, beside the road from Swanleye to Sondrugge, in Alkyntone; to hold enclosed, to them and their issue, rent 6*s.* a year.
Witnesses: Thomas de Stone, John Capel, Walter Sewaker, Maurice de Beoleye, William le Gold.
At: Berkeley.

A1/5/3 [GC 1966]   20 Feb. 7 Edw. II [1314]
Thomas de Berkelee, lord of Berkeley; and Walter Robat and Eve his wife.

Thomas has granted to Walter and Eve 1 a. of land at Sondrugge, beside the road from Swanleye to Sondrugge, in Alkyntone; to hold enclosed, to them and their issue, rent 18*d.* a year.
Witnesses: Thomas de Stone, John Capel, Walter Sewaker, Maurice de Beoleye, William le Gold.
At: Berkeley.

BERKELEY ACQUISITIONS

Cof rent

A1/5/4 [GC 2330]   Sun. after St. Martin, 14 Edw. II [16 Nov. 1320]
Simon de Fromelode and John de Stanforde.

Simon has quitclaimed to John a rent of 4*s.* a year from the land and holding which Richard Cof holds at Mickelwode in Alkyntone.
Witnesses: Walter de Nasse, William Gamages, Richard de Haydone, John le Whyte, John de la Boxe.
At: Framilode.

A1/5/5 [GC 2331]   Sun. after St. Clement, 14 Edw. II [23 Nov. 1320]
Simon de Fromelode and Sir Thomas de Berkeleye, lord of Berkeley.

Simon has quitclaimed to Thomas a rent of 4s. a year from the land and holding which
Richard Cof holds at Mickelwode in Alkyntone.
Witnesses: Walter de Nasse, William Gamages, Richard de Haydone, Thomas de Bradeston,
John de la Boxe, John le Serjaunt, John le Whyte of Awre.
At: Framilode.

A1/5/6 [GC 2334]   Sun. after St. Nicholas, 14 Edw. II [7 Dec. 1320]
John de Stanforde and Sir Thomas de Berkeleye, lord of Berkeley.

John has quitclaimed to Thomas a rent of 4s. a year from the land and holding which
Richard Cof holds at Mickelwode in Alkyntone.
Witnesses: Walter de Nasse, William de Gamage, Thomas de Bradeston, John le Serjaunt,
John le Whyte of Awre, Richard de Haydone, Richard Cadel, William Holt, John de
Haydone.
At: Westbury.

Miscellaneous acquisitions

A1/5/7 [GC 291]   Trinity, 42 Hen. III [19 May 1258]
Sir Maurice de Berkeley and Sir Maurice de Saltmarsh (*de salso marisco*).

Maurice de Berkeley has given to Maurice de Saltmarsh 20s. for part of the wood of
Mukelwod which Maurice Saltmarsh held of him at a rent of 21d. a year.
Witnesses: Master William de Mathem, Peter de Wik, Ralph de Angervile, Maurice de
Stane, Thomas the serjeant (*serviens*), John de Egeton, William Sely, clerk.

A1/5/8 [GC 1970]   20 March 7 Edw. II [1314]
William Leonard and Sir Thomas de Berkelee, lord of Berkeley.

William has quitclaimed to Thomas a plot of land at Mikkelwode, with the buildings on
it, which he and Nicholas his brother had by grant of Thomas.
Witnesses: Richard de Avene, Maurice de Beoleye, John Capel, Walter Sewaker, Robert
Archer.
At: Berkeley.

A1/5/9 [GC 2176]   1 June 10 Edw. II [1317]
Thomas de Berkeleye, lord of Berkeley, and John de Seham.

Whereas Thomas enfeoffed John of 21 a. 18 perches of land at Mickelwode in
Alkyntone, John has rendered the holding to Thomas and quitclaimed it to him.
Witnesses: Thomas de Bradeston, Peter de Styntescombe, John Capel, John de la Hay,
Walter Sewaker, Nicholas Daungervile, William le Gold.
At: Berkeley.

BERKELEY GRANTS

A1/5/10 [GC 588]   Nativity of St. John the Baptist, 20 Edw. I [24 June 1292]
Sir Thomas de Berkele; and William Golde of Dangervilles Wick next to Michaelwood and
Christine his wife.

Thomas has leased to William and Cristine, for their lives, pasture for 40 goats in his
wood of Mikelwode; they have given him 40s.
Witnesses: Robert de Stone, Robert de Bradeston, Thomas Aleyn, Thomas de Swonhungre,
John de Craule, Richard de Wenden.

A1/5/11 [GC 1023]   Sun. after Michaelmas, 29 Edw. I [1 Oct. 1301]
Sir Thomas de Berkeleye, lord of Berkeley; and Adam de Derswelle and Agnes his wife.

Thomas has granted to Adam and Agnes 2 a. of land lying between the wood of
Mickelwode and the meadow of Nicholas de Wodeford, to them and their heirs, with

common rights in Mickelwode as much as pertains to the holding; rent 2*s.* a year.
Witnesses: Thomas le Serjaunt, Nicholas de Wodeford, Walter Moton, William le Gold, Philip the smith of Woodford.
At: Berkeley.

A1/5/12 [GC 1671]   Mon. the feast of St. Martin, 2 Edw. II [11 Nov. 1308]
Thomas de Berkelee, lord of Berkeley; and William le Deveysche [*sic; endorsed* Devenyche] and Alice his wife.
    Thomas has granted to William and Alice 1 a. 30 perches of land in Mikkelwode with appurtenances in Wodeford in Alkynton; to hold enclosed, to them and their issue, rent 20*d.* a year.
Witnesses: Richard de Avene, William le Golde, Richard le Erle, William Elys, Philip the smith.
At: Berkeley.

A1/5/13 [GC 1680]   Sun. the feast of the Purification, 2 Edw. II [2 Feb. 1309]
Thomas de Berkeley, lord of Berkeley, and Philip the butcher (*carnifex*).
    Thomas has granted to Philip 1 a. of land in Mykkylwode in Alkynton; to hold enclosed, to him and his issue, rent 20*d.* a year.
Witnesses: Robert de Bradestone, Robert de Berkeley, Thomas de Beoleye, Robert Wither, William le Golde.
At: Berkeley.

A1/5/14 [GC 1773]   Wed. the feast of St. Simon and St. Jude, 4 Edw. II [28 Oct. 1310]
Thomas de Berkelee, lord of Berkeley; and Nicholas le Proute and Isolda his wife.
    Thomas has granted to Nicholas and Isolda 1 a. 32 perches of land at Mikkelwode, between Sondrugge to the south and Swanleie to the north, in Alkyntone; to hold enclosed, to them and their issue, rent 18*d.* a year.
Witnesses: Thomas de Stone, John Capel, Walter Sewaker, William Gold, William Cut.
At: Berkeley.

A1/5/15 [GC 1774]   Wed. the feast of St. Simon and St. Jude, 4 Edw. II [28 Oct. 1310]
Thomas de Berkelee, lord of Berkeley; and Thomas Robet and Alice his wife.
    Thomas has granted to Thomas and Alice 2 a. 3 perches at Mikkelwode between Swanleye to the north and the land of Richard the miller (*molend'*) to the south, in Alkyntone; to hold enclosed, to them and their issue, rent 3*s.* a year.
Witnesses: Thomas de Stone, John Capel, Walter Sewaker, William Gold, Philip the smith.
At: Berkeley.

A1/5/16 [GC 1775]   Sat. the eve of All Saints, 4 Edw. II [30 Oct. 1310]
Thomas de Berkelee, lord of Berkeley; and Walter Robet and Eve his wife.
    Thomas has granted to Walter and Eve 1½ a. of land at Mikkelwode in Alkyntone, between the lands of Thomas Robet to the south and Swanleye to the north; to hold enclosed, to them and their issue, rent 2*s.* 3*d.* a year.
Witnesses: Thomas de Stone, John Capel, Walter Sewaker, William Gold, William Cut.
At: Berkeley.

A1/5/17 [GC 1783]   Epiphany, 4 Edw. II [6 Jan. 1311]
Thomas de Berkelee, lord of Berkeley; and Maurice de Beoleye, his kinsman, and Cecilia his wife.
    Thomas has granted to Maurice and Cecilia 50½ a. of land in Harehul beside Mikkelwode, with common in Mikkelwode, in Alkyntone; to them and their issue, to hold enclosed, rent 50*s.* a year.
Witnesses: Sir John de Berkelee, Sir William de Wauton, Sir Nicholas de Kynggestone,

knights, William de Colewith, Robert de Bradestone, Thomas de Stone, Peter de Styntescombe, Richard de Avene, Walter Sewaker.
At: Berkeley.

A1/5/18 [GC 1785]   1 Feb. 4 Edw. II [1311]
Thomas de Berkelee, lord of Berkeley; and Philip Gleche and Amicia his wife.

Thomas has granted to Philip and Amicia 5 a. of land in Mikkelwode between the road next to Sautemareisrudyngge, leading from Wodeforde to Hunteneforde, and the road below Sandrugge leading to la Goldende, with licence to improve the land from Thomas's marlpit beside the croft of Reginald atte Tote, and with common in Mikkelwode; to hold enclosed, to them and their issue, rent 7s. 6d. a year.
Witnesses: John Sautemareis, Thomas de Stone, John Capel, Walter Sewaker, Roger Archer.
At: Berkeley.

A1/5/19 [GC 1786]   1 Feb. 4 Edw. II [1311]
Thomas de Berkelee, lord of Berkeley; and William Cut and Alice his wife.

Thomas has granted to William and Alice 2 a. of land in Mikkelwode between the road next to Sautemareisrudyngge, leading from Wodeforde to Hunteneforde, and the road below Sandrugge leading to la Goldende, with licence to improve the land from Thomas's marlpit beside the croft of Reginald atte Tote, and with common in Mikkelwode; to hold enclosed, to them and their issue, rent 3s. a year.
Witnesses: John Sautemareis, Thomas de Stone, John Capel, Walter Sewaker, Roger Archer.
At: Berkeley.

A1/5/20 [GC 1788]   1 Feb. 4 Edw. II [1311]
Thomas de Berkelee, lord of Berkeley; and Richard le Tornor and Amicia his wife.

Thomas has granted to Richard and Amicia 5 a. of land in Mikkelwode between the road next to Sautemareisrudyngge, leading from Wodeforde to Hunteneforde, and the road below Sandrugge leading to la Goldende, with licence to improve the land from Thomas's marlpit beside the croft of Reginald atte Tote, and with common in Mikkelwode; to hold enclosed, to them and their issue, rent 7s. 6d. a year.
Witnesses: John Sautemareis, Thomas de Stone, John Capel, Walter Sewaker, Roger Archer.
At: Berkeley.

A1/5/21 [GC 1827]   1 June 4 Edw. II [1311]
Thomas de Berkeleye, lord of Berkeley; and Richard Redhod and Edith his wife.

Thomas has granted to Richard and Edith 1 a. of land in Thomas's wood of Mikelwode in Alkyntone; to hold enclosed, to them and their issue, rent 18d. a year.
Witnesses: Thomas de Stone, Richard de Avene, Maurice de Beolee, Walter Sewaker, William Golde.
At: Berkeley.

A1/5/22 [GC 1840]   Wed. a week after Michaelmas, 5 Edw. II [6 Oct. 1311]
Thomas de Berkelee, lord of Berkeley; and Stephen Reymond and Edith his wife.

Thomas has granted to Stephen and Edith 1½ a. of land in Mikkelwode beside the road from Hunteneford to Wodeford, with common in Mikkelwode, in Alkyntone; to hold enclosed, to them and their issue, rent 2s. 3d. a year.
Witnesses: Thomas de Stone, Richard de Avene, Maurice de Beoleie, Walter Sewaker, William Gold.
At: Berkeley.

A1/5/23 [GC 1841]   Wed. a week after Michaelmas, 5 Edw. II [6 Oct. 1311]
Thomas de Berkelee, lord of Berkeley; and William de Durswelle and Mary his wife.

Thomas has granted to William and Mary 1½ a. 13½ perches of land beside the road from Wodeford to Hunteneford, with common in Mikkelwod, in Alkyntone; to hold enclosed, to them and their issue, rent 2s. 4d. a year.
Witnesses: Thomas de Stone, Maurice de Beoleie, Richard de Avene, Walter Sewaker, William Gold.
At: Berkeley.

A1/5/24 [GC 1853]   Epiphany, 5 Edw. II [6 Jan. 1312]
Thomas de Berkelee, lord of Berkeley; and Mary Clere of Tortworth and Walter her son.

Thomas has granted to Mary and Walter 1½ a. 13½ perches of land beside Mikkelwode, between the land of Richard Redhod and the road from Wodeford to Hunteneford, with common in Mikkelwod, in Alkyntone; to hold enclosed, to them and Walter's issue, rent 2s. 4d. a year.
Witnesses: Thomas de Stone, Maurice de Beoleie, Richard de Avene, Walter Sewaker, William Gold.
At: Berkeley.

A1/5/25 [GC 1929]   20 June 6 Edw. II [1313]
Thomas de Berkelee, lord of Berkeley; and Nicholas le Proute and Isolda his wife.

Thomas has granted to Nicholas and Isolda 2 a. 5 perches of land at Mikkelwode between the headland called Lutlewikesworthy and Sondrugge, in Alkyntone; to hold enclosed, to them and their issue, rent 3s. 4d. a year.
Witnesses: Thomas de Stone, Richard de Avene, John Capel, Maurice de Beoleye, Walter Sewaker.
At: Berkeley.

A1/5/26 [GC 2025]   1 April 8 Edw. II [1315]
Thomas de Berkeleye, lord of Berkeley; and Nicholas Dangervile and Sibyl his wife.

Thomas has granted to Nicholas and Sibyl 2½ a. 37 perches of land at la Goldende beside Mikkelwode, in Alkyntone, with licence to improve the land from Thomas's marlpit in Sondrugge called Wylotesmarlpot; to hold enclosed, to them and their issue, rent 2s. 6d. a year.
Witnesses: Robert de Avene, Maurice de Boeleye, Walter Sewaker, William Golde, Roger Archer.
At: Berkeley.

A1/5/27 [GC 2073]   12 Jan. 9 Edw. II [1316]
Thomas de Berkeleye, lord of Berkeley, and William Kene.

Thomas has granted to William 1 a., 1 fardel and 21 perches of land with a cottage at Mickelwode, by the road from Wodeford to Hunteneford and the road to Sondrugge, and 1 a. of land at Mickelwode, by the road to Sondrugge, in Alkyntone, with common of pasture in Mickelwode; to hold enclosed, to him and his issue, rent 5s. 6d. a year.
Witnesses: Walter Sewaker, John de la Hay, Roger Archer, William Golde, William Cut.
At: Berkeley.

A1/5/28 [GC 2074]   12 Jan. 9 Edw. II [1316]
Thomas de Berkeleye, lord of Berkeley; and Robert Truyt and Maud his wife.

Thomas has granted to Robert and Maud 1 a., 1 fardel and 21 perches of land with a cottage at Mickelwode, by the road from Wodeford to Hunteneford and the road to Sondrugge, in Alkyntone, with common of pasture in Mickelwode; to hold enclosed, to them and their issue, rent 4s. a year.

Witnesses: Maurice de Beoleye, Walter Sewaker, John de la Hay, Roger Archer, William Golde.
At: Berkeley.

A1/5/29 [GC 2164]   1 May 10 Edw. II [1317]
Thomas de Berkeleye, lord of Berkeley, and Roger Wyrloke.
    Thomas has leased to Roger 1¾ a. of land at Mickelwode in two parcels, which Richard Redhod previously held of Thomas, in Alkyntone, with common of pasture in Mickelwode; to hold enclosed, to him and his issue, rent 2*s*. 6*d*. a year.
Witnesses: John Capel, John de la Hay, Walter Sewaker, Nicholas Daungervile, William le Golde.
At: Berkeley.

A1/5/30 [GC 2168]   6 May 10 Edw. II [1317]
Thomas de Berkeleye, lord of Berkeley; and Elias Wyrloke and Agnes his wife.
    Thomas has granted to Elias and Agnes 4 a. 5 perches of land at Mickelwode, of which the 5 perches lie beside the watercourse to the Smythesmulle, in Alkyntone, with common of pasture in Mickelwode; to hold enclosed, to them and their issue, rent 3*s*. 4*d*. a year, with licence to improve the land from the green places in the street of Hunteneforde, so long as wagons and carts still have free passage.
Witnesses: John de la Hay, Walter Sewaker, Nicholas Daungervile, William Cut, Robert Truyt.
At: Berkeley.

A1/5/31 [GC 2205]   Sun. after St. Katherine, 11 Edw. II [27 Nov. 1317]
Thomas de Berkeleye, lord of Berkeley; and Robert Truyt and Maud his wife.
    Thomas has leased to Robert and Maud 4 a. of land at Mickelwode between the road from Wodeforde to Hunteneforde by Sautemareisruydinge and the road to la Goldende below Sondrugge, with licence to improve the land from Thomas's marlpit by the croft of Reginald atte Tote, and with common of pasture in Mickelwode, the which land John le Kyng of Boritone previously held of Thomas, in Alkyntone; to hold enclosed, to them and their issue, rent 6*s*. a year.
Witnesses: John de Sautemareis, John Capel, John de la Hay, Walter Sewaker, Nicholas Daungervile.
At: Berkeley.

A1/5/32 [GC 2290]   4 Nov. 13 Edw. II [1319]
Thomas de Berkeleye, lord of Berkeley, and Robert son of Walter le Brid.
    Thomas has leased to Robert 6 perches of land at Wodeforde by his holding and ½ a. 2 perches of land at Mickelwode, in Alkyntone, with common of pasture in Mickelwode; to hold enclosed, to him and his issue, rent 14½*d*. a year.
Witnesses: Richard de Avene, John de la Hay, Nicholas Daungervile, William Cut, Robert Truyt.
At: Berkeley.

A1/5/33 [GC 2325]   20 Oct. 14 Edw. II [1320]
Thomas de Berkeleye, lord of Berkeley; and John de la Hay and Margaret his wife.
    Thomas has granted to John and Margaret 64 a. 12 perches of land at Wodeforde and Mickelwode, lying in various parcels, and 1 a. of meadow in Matforde, with common of pasture in Mickelwode; to hold the land enclosed, to them and John's issue, rent 24*s*. 6*d*. a year for their lives, and 64*s*. a year after their deaths.
Witnesses: John son of Nicholas, John de Saltmarsh (*de salso marisco*), Richard de Avene, Walter Sewaker, John Capel.
At: Berkeley.

ALKINGTON: NEWPORT

Newport was the new town (*novus burgus*) of Alkington founded on the main road between Gloucester and Bristol.

BERKELEY ACQUISITIONS
Marshall holdings

A1/6/1 [GC 930]   n.d. [late Hen. III]
Robert Marescall of Newport and Sir Maurice de Berkel'.

Robert has granted to Maurice the croft at the new town called Bancroft, and the messuage which Beatrice widow of William Maresc' held in dower, with the road beside the said holding.

Witnesses: Sir William Mansel, Sir Robert de Kyngeston, knights, William de Mathem, Walter de Egeton, Robert de Brothestan, William de Wyke, William Capel, Robert de Stan', Robert Caudel.

A1/6/2 [GC 478]   Sun. before St. Luke, 5 Edw. I [17 Oct. 1277]
Alice widow of Henry Marescall of Newport and Sir Maurice de Berkel'.

Alice has quitclaimed to Maurice land which she had in dower in the field next to the bridge of Riham, for her life, and Maurice has granted to her for that term a garden which he has at farm from Robert Marescall her son in the said vill of the new town.

Witnesses: William de Mathine, Adam Motun, William de Wik, William de Angervill, Walter Grip.

A1/6/3 [GC 1634]   n.d. [1281 × 1300]
Robert son and heir of Henry Marescall of Newport and Sir Thomas de Berkeley.

Robert has granted to Thomas his right and claim in all the lands and holdings which . . . his mother holds in dower in the town of Neweport, in the manor of Alkinton, so that after her death they will revert to Thomas; Thomas has given him 4 marks.

Witnesses: Sir Robert de Berkeley, Sir Roger de Lokynton, Sir Maurice de Saltmarsh (*de salso marisco*), knights, Bartholomew de Olepenne, Peter de Stintescombe, Robert de Stone, Robert de Bradestone.

Woodford holding

A1/6/4 [GC 2044]   16 May 8 Edw. II [1315]
Agnes de Wodeforde, widow, and Sir Thomas de Berkeleye, lord of Berkeley.

Agnes has granted to Thomas, his heirs and assigns two messuages with gardens and curtilages beside the road through the middle of Neweport from Wodeford to la Hethfelde, at Neweport in Alkyntone.[1]

Witnesses: Peter de Styntescombe, Maurice de Boeleye, Richard de Avene, John Capel, William de Kyneltre, Roger Archer, William le Gryp.

At: Berkeley.

A1/6/5 [GC 2198]   16 Oct. 11 Edw. II [1317]
Thomas de Berkeleye, lord of Berkeley; and Adam le Hurde and Maud his wife.

Thomas has granted to Adam and Maud his holding with the house built on it at Neueport which he previously had by grant of Agnes de Wodeforde, in Alkyntone; for their lives, rent 3s. a year.

Witnesses: Richard de Avene, Geoffrey Moton, William le Gryp, William Kyneltre, Maurice Bernard.

At: Berkeley.

---

[1] The road from Heathfield to Woodford is the main Gloucester–Bristol road.

Miscellaneous acquisitions

A1/6/6 [GC 934]   n.d. [late Hen. III]
Adam the miller and Sir Maurice de Berkel'.

Adam has quitclaimed to Maurice his mill of the new town, which Maurice has bought, and Maurice has given him 100*s*.
Witnesses: Sir Maurice de Saltmarsh (*de salso marisco*), William de Mathem, Peter de Wik, Nicholas de Craul', John de Bratheston, John Sewaker, Adam Coby, Thomas the serjeant (*serviens*), Robert le Herde, Walter Sely, clerk.

A1/6/7 [GC 1506]   11 Edw. I [1283]
Nicholas Pedulf of Newport and Sir Thomas de Berkeley.

Nicholas has granted to Thomas the holding which he had beside the mill of the new town (*novus burgus*) within the manor of Alkintone, in exchange for the messuage, croft, garden [etc.] which Edward de Alkinton formerly held in the same town (*villa*).
Witnesses: Bartholomew de Olepenne, Peter de Stintescumbe, Elias de Cumbe, Robert de Brathestone, Robert de Stone, Richard de Stanford, Thomas Alayn.

A1/6/8 [GC 2212]   Mon. the feast of St. Stephen, 11 Edw. II [26 Dec. 1317]
John son of Richard le Serjant and Sir Maurice de Berkeleye, son of Sir Thomas de Berkeleye.

John has granted to Maurice and his heirs a rent of 2*s*. a year at Neuport in Alkyntone, from the holding held for their lives by Maurice Bernard, Agnes his wife and Richard their son, with the reversion of the holding after their deaths.
Witnesses: Sir John Mautravers, Sir William de Wauton, knights, Richard de Avene, John de la Hay, John Capel, Thomas de Wyke, William le Golde.
At: Berkeley.

A1/6/9 [SC 520]   2 Dec. 21 Edw. III [1347]
King Edward III and Thomas de Berkeley.

The king has granted to Thomas licence to hold two fairs a year at Newport, near Berkeley, viz. the eve, day and morrow of the translation of St. Thomas, and the eve, day and morrow of St. Maurice.
Witnesses: J[ohn Stratford], archbishop of Canterbury, R[alph Stratford], bishop of London, W[illiam Edington], bishop of Winchester, . . . , William de Bohun, earl of Northampton, Richard [FitzAlan], earl of Arundel, . . . Thomas Wake of Liddel, Master John de Offord, our chancellor, Richard Talbot, steward of the household.
At: Westminster.

GRANTS

A1/6/10 [GC 876]   n.d. [late 13th cent.]
Thomas de Berkelegh, lord of Berkeley, and John Bonsergant.

Thomas has granted to John half of the house next to the holding of Walter de Tresham, which was previously of Thomas of the hall (*de aula*) in Nyeuport within the manor of Alkynton, with half of the curtilage and croft, to John and Helen his wife; for their lives, rent 5*s*. a year. [*In French*.]
Witnesses: Robert le Erl, Richard de Avene, Walter Moton, Richard Pothering, Walter Syngare, William Gryp, William Fischar.

A1/6/11 [GC 1653]   1 May 1 Edw. II [1308]
Thomas de Berkele, lord of Berkeley, and William son of Reginald Becke.

Thomas has granted to William a plot of land for buildings, beside the house of John Bonsergaunt in Neuweport in the manor of Alkinton; to him and his issue, rent 2*d*. a year.

Witnesses: Robert de Bradestone, Robert de Berkele, Thomas de Beleye, Walter Motoun, Richard le Erl.
At: Berkeley.

A1/6/12 [GC 2026]   1 April 8 Edw. II [1315]
Thomas de Berkeleye, lord of Berkeley, and Roger le Cuppere.

Thomas has granted to Roger 3 perches of land at Neuport between his holding and the road, in Alkyntone; to hold enclosed, to him and his issue, rent 2*d.* a year.
Witnesses: Thomas de Bradeston, John Capel, Walter Sewaker, William Gold, Roger Archer.
At: Berkeley.

A1/6/13 [GC 2033]   20 April 8 Edw. II [1315]
Thomas de Berkeleye, lord of Berkeley; and John le Pottare and Alice daughter of Richard le Erl.

Thomas has granted to John and Alice 7 perches of land at Neweport beside the street leading through the middle of Neweport from Wodeforde to la Hethfelde, in Alkyntone; to hold enclosed, to them and their issue, rent 4*d.* a year.
Witnesses: Maurice de Boeleye, John Capel, William Golde, Roger Archer, William de Kineltre.
At: Berkeley.

A1/6/14 [GC 2196]   10 Oct. 11 Edw. II [1317]
Thomas de Berkeleye, lord of Berkeley, and William son of Reginald Becke.

Thomas has granted to William the cottage with a curtilage at Neweport which Roger Becke his brother previously held of Thomas, in Alkyntone; to him and his issue, rent 16*d.* a year.
Witnesses: Richard de Avene, John de la Hay, Nicholas Daungervile, William de Kyneltre, William le Gryp, William le Golde, Maurice Bernard.
At: Berkeley.

MISCELLANEOUS

A1/6/15 [GC 1121]   Mon. after St. Augustine, 34 Edw. I [30 May 1306]
Maurice Bernard of Newport and Richard his son.

Maurice has granted to Richard 5 selions of arable land in the furlong called Cherechehull, next to the road called Chirechewey; for Richard's life, rent ½*d.* a year.
Witnesses: Richard Pothering, Richard le Eorl, Alan Marescall, Philip called the monk (*monachus*), William le Heorde, Ralph de Wallibrok, William de Kineltre.
At: Newport.

A1/6/16 [GC 679]   n.d. [*temp.* Edw. I]
John de Berkel' and Thomas de Wike.

John has granted to Thomas a messuage lying between the house of Henry Marescall and the house of Adam le Herde in the vill of Nuweburke, which John Cole formerly held; rent 2*d.* a year, and Thomas has paid 2 marks in acknowledgement.
Witnesses: Sir Henry de Wike, William Caunvile, Adam Mutun, Robert le Herde, Henry the marshal (*marescallus*), John the smith.

A1/6/17 [GC 1700]   St. Barnabas, 2 Edw. II [11 June 1309]
Richard le Erl of Newport and Isabel his daughter.

Richard has granted to Isabel a messuage in Neuport with half of a curtilage, also two crofts of land called Pokewelle and 1½ a. of land in the field called Ryham; to her and her issue, rent to the chief lord 3*s.* a year.

Witnesses: Richard de Avene, William le Gold, Geoffrey Moton, Richard Pothering, Alan Marescall, Ralph Walebrok, Maurice Bernard.
At: Newport.

A1/6/18 [GC 2440]　　　　　　St. John before the Latin Gate, 18 Edw. II [6 May 1325]
William de Kyneltre; and Thomas Robat of Woodford and Alice his wife, daughter of Jordan Harald of Newport.

William has granted to Thomas and Alice a plot of land in Neuport; rent 1*d.* a year to the chief lord of the fee.
Witnesses: John ate Hay, Peter de Stone, William Golde, Adam Daungervyle, William Cott', Adam de Mettesdone, Adam Moton.
At: Newport.

ALKINGTON: SWANLEY

THE WEBBE HOLDING

A1/7/1 [GC 997]　　　　Sun. before the Exaltation of Holy Cross, 28 Edw. I [11 Sept. 1300]
Sir Thomas lord of Berkeleye and Walter called le Webbe of Swanley.

Walter has enfeoffed Thomas in all his holding in Swanleye within the manor of Alkynton, and in return Thomas will sustain Walter in food and clothing for his life, as the officers in his household, one robe each year better than those of the grooms and provender with the officers if he remains with the household, and if elsewhere 1 qr. of corn every ten weeks, being half wheat and half beans, and his robe as before.
Witnesses: Robert de Bradeston, Thomas de Beoleye, Robert Wyther, Richard le Erel, Walter de Tresham.
At: Berkeley.

A1/7/2 [GC 998]　　　　Sun. after the Exaltation of Holy Cross, 28 Edw. I [18 Sept. 1300]
Walter called le Webbe of Swanley and Sir Thomas de Berkeleya, his lord.

Walter has granted to Thomas his messuage at Swanleye and 3 crofts, 7 a. of land and ½ a. of meadow in Matford and the reversion of ¼ a. held by William le Mason for life, in Alkynton.
Witnesses: Robert de Bradeston, Thomas de Beoleye, Richard de Avene, Walter Moton, Richard le Erel.
At: Berkeley.

A1/7/3 [GC 2091]　　　　　　　　　　　　　　　　1 April 9 Edw. II [1316]
Thomas de Berkeleye, lord of Berkeley, and Elias le Ferour.

Thomas has granted to Elias a messuage at Swanleye and 3 crofts containing 7 a. of land, and ¼ a. of land in the furlong called Brerilond, and ½ a. of meadow in Matford, all of which he had by grant of Walter le Webbe, also 1 a. of land in the furlong called Joeleslond and a croft called Kenecroft containing 5 a., in Alkyntone; to him and his issue, rent 10*s.* a year.
Witnesses: Richard de Avene, Peter de Styntescombe, Maurice de Boleye, John le Serjant, Walter Sewaker, Roger Archer, William le Golde.
At: Berkeley.

A1/7/4 [GC 2180]　　　Thurs. the eve of the nativity of St. John the Baptist, 10 Edw. II
[23 June 1317]
Joan widow of Walter le Webbe of Swanley and Sir Thomas de Berkeleye, lord of Berkeley.

Joan, with the assent of William le Webbe, her son and heir, has quitclaimed to Thomas the lands and holdings which Elias le Ferour holds by lease of Thomas at Swanleye, and also 1½ a. of land in the croft called Radefordeshul which Adam ate Slo holds in villeinage by lease of Thomas, in Alkyntone.

Witnesses: Richard de Avene, John de la Hay, Walter Sewaker, Nicholas Daungervile, Roger Archer, William le Gryp, William de Kyneltre.

At: Berkeley.

THE ARCHER HOLDING

A1/7/5 [GC 1903]   Sun. before St. Peter in cathedra, 6 Edw. II [18 Feb. 1313]
Nicholas son of William Warderobe of Woodford and Roger le Archer.

Nicholas has granted to Roger a rent of 2*s*. from John le Welysche and Isabel his wife and Agnes their daughter, for their lives, for the holding with a house, garden, curtilage and croft in Swanleye, with the reversion of the holding, and a parcel of land in le Rudyng, in Alkyntone.

Witnesses: Walter Sewaker, John Capel, Philip the smith of Woodford, William Cut, Richard le Tornor, Elias le Feror, Walter de Wodeford, clerk.

At: Swanley.

A1/7/6 [GC 1988]   4 Aug. 8 Edw. II [1314]
Roger Archer; and John le Welsche of Kingworthy, Isabel his wife and Agnes their eldest daughter.

Roger has granted to John, Isabel and Agnes his messuage with a curtilage and croft at Swanleye and 1 a. of land in the furlong called la Rudyngge, beside the wood of Mikkelwode, in Alkyntone; for their lives, rent 4*s*. a year.

Witnesses: Walter Sewaker, Elias le Ferrour, Philip the smith, William Cut, Richard le Turnour.

At: Berkeley.

A1/7/7 [GC 3396]   Translation of St. Thomas the martyr, 26 Edw. III [7 July 1352]
(1) Sir Maurice de Berkele, knight; (2) Sir Walter de Tudenham, rector of Cam; (3) John Larcher.

Maurice has appointed Walter to receive seisin of a messuage and 9 a. of land in Wodeworde [*sic*] and Swanlegh', and also of all the lands and holdings which John had in Wodeforde and Swanlegh within the manor of Alkyntone and which John granted to Maurice.

At: Berkeley.

OTHER

A1/7/8 [GC 4297]   St. Andrew, 37 Hen. VI [30 Nov. 1458]
Thomas Ferour of Swanley in Berkeley parish (Glos.), and his master (*magister*) William Berkeley, knight, son and heir of Sir James lord of Berkeley.

Thomas has granted to William all his lands, holdings, and goods in Swanley.

Witnesses: John Thorp of Wanswell, John Swanley, John Ekton of Pedington, William Teysaunt of Woodford, Thomas Dawnervyle of Wyke.

At: Berkeley.

ALKINGTON: WICK

Wick is now represented by Lower Wick (Lowerwick Farm), Middle Wick (Middlewick Farm) and Upper Wick (Wick House Farm). The Dangervilles and Golds gave their names to Dangervilles Wick (no present-day equivalent) and Gold Wick (now Goldwick Farm).

BERKELEY ACQUISITIONS
The Veysy holding

A1/8/1 [GC 2058]　　　　　　　　　　　　　　　6 Oct. 9 Edw. II [1315]

Richard le Veysy and Sir Thomas de Berkeleye, lord of Berkeley.

Richard has rendered and quitclaimed to Thomas a messuage with a garden, curtilage, mill and 1 fardel of land, which he previously had by grant of Sir Maurice de Berkeleye, and the site of the fulling mill, with a garden and croft called Walkaresheyes, which he previously had by grant of Robert de Stone, at Wyke in Alkyntone.

Witnesses: Richard de Avene, Maurice de Boeleye, John Capel, John de la Hay, William Golde.

At: Berkeley.

A1/8/2 [GC 2065]　　　　　　　　　　　　　　20 Nov. 9 Edw. II [1315]

Thomas de Berkeleye, lord of Berkeley, and Robert de Berkeleye, his nephew.

Thomas has granted to Robert a croft called Walkarescroft, formerly of Richard Lenveysee by demise of Robert de Stone, between the water called Doverle and the road from the house of Richard de Avene to the bridge called Wykesbrugge, at Wyke in Alkyntone; to him and his issue, rent 20*d.* a year; and if, in the future, any part of the croft is dissolved or removed by flooding of the Doverle, then Robert and his heirs have licence to plant willows or other trees, or carry out other work to consolidate the land, without impediment.

Witnesses: Peter de Styntescombe, Richard de Avene, Maurice de Boeleye, Warin son of William, William le Golde.

At: Berkeley.

A1/8/3 [GC 2063]　　　　　　　　　　　　　　20 Nov. 9 Edw. II [1315]

Thomas de Berkeleye, lord of Berkeley; and Nicholas Daungervile and Sibyl his wife.

Thomas has granted to Nicholas and Sibyl two parcels of land called Walkaresheyes, of which one lies between the road at Wykebrugge to the east and the water called Doverle to the west, extending to the said water to the north, above the croft formerly of William de Burgo, and the other lying between the said water and the said croft, extending above the field called le Redefeld, with a plot called la Mulestede and the stream of the Doverle pertaining to the plot, at Wyke in Alkyntone; to them and their issue, rent 11*d.* a year, and they must not divert or restrain the course of the water to the damage of the croft which Robert de Berkeleye had by grant of Thomas.

Witnesses: Richard de Avene, Maurice de Boeleye, John Capel, Adam Daungervile, William le Golde.

At: Berkeley.

A1/8/4 [GC 2064]　　　　　　　　　　　　　　20 Nov. 9 Edw. II [1315]

Thomas de Berkeleye, lord of Berkeley; and Maurice de Boeleye and Cecilia his wife.

Thomas has granted to Maurice and Cecilia the meadow with an alder grove (*alnet'*) called Knottemede, formerly of Richard Lenveisee, in Alkyntone, lying enclosed between the house of Richard and the field called Redefeld, and between the old stream and the rhine beside the millpond formerly of Richard; to hold enclosed, to them and Maurice's issue, with free access, rent 3*s.* 3*d.* a year.

Witnesses: Peter de Styntescombe, Richard de Avene, Robert of the church, Richard de Wyke, John Capel, William le Golde, Adam Daungervyle.

At: Berkeley.

A1/8/5 [GC 2928]   Sun. after St. Lucy, 12 Edw. III [20 Dec. 1338]
Thomas de Berkele, lord of Berkeley, and Thomas le Whor.

Thomas de Berkele has granted to Thomas le Whor the meadow called . . . and the [alder grove] adjacent which Richard le Veysi formerly held, in Alkyntone, enclosed, between the old stream and the rhine by the millpond; for life, rent 6s. 8d. a year.
At: Berkeley.

The Pynel holding

A1/8/6 [GC 625]   n.d. [c. 2 Feb. 1297]
Henry Pynel of Gossington; and Walter Moton and Scolastica his mother.

Henry has leased to Walter and Scolastica all the lands and holdings in the vill of Wyke which he had by grant of William de Wyk, viz. a house and garden, 1 a. in Baynham and a croft called Sephousecroft, for 4 years beginning at the Purification 25 Edw. I; rent 14s. a year.
Witnesses: Richard de Avene, Nicholas de Wodeforde, Philip de la Holte, William le Gold, William le Wor.

A1/8/7 [GC 799]   n.d. [early 14th cent.]
Henry Pynel of Gossington and Sir Thomas de Berkeleye, his lord.

Henry has granted to Thomas his house, garden, curtilage [etc.] and 1 a. of land in Baynham, and a croft called Schephousecroft in Wyk and Styntescoumbe, and an annual rent of 2d. from the field of Ryham, and an annual rent of a clove for 1 a. of meadow in Honyleye and 1½ a. of land in Baynham; and Thomas has given him 10 marks and 1 qr. of wheat.
Witnesses: Robert de Bradeston, Robert de Berkeleye, Thomas de Beoleye, Richard de Avene, Warin son of William, Robert of the church, Walter Motun.

A1/8/8 [GC 2487]   n.d. [early 14th cent.]
Thomas de Berkeleya, lord of Berkeley, and Walter Moton of Wyke.

Thomas has granted to Walter, his heirs and assigns two gardens, 1 a. of land in Bainham and a croft called Schephousecroft in the manor of Alkyntone; rent 14s. a year and, for his life, for the improvement of all his lands of Wyke, licence to dig turves and marl from the streets and paths, for two casks of cider which he has given to Thomas.
Witnesses: Robert de Bradestone, Thomas de Swonhungre, Richard de Avene, Richard de Wyke, Nicholas de Wodeford.

A1/8/9 [GC 2202]   7 Nov. 11 Edw. II [1317]
Christine Pynel and Sir Thomas de Berkeleye.

Christine has quitclaimed to Thomas, for a certain sum of money, her dower claim in one third of the lands which Thomas had by grant of Henry Pynel, late her husband, at Wyke in Alkyntone.
Witnesses: Richard de Avene, Geoffrey Moton, William le Golde, Nicholas Daungervile, William Cut.
At: Berkeley.

Miscellaneous acquisitions

A1/8/10 [GC 300*]   Morrow of Ascension, 45 Hen. III [3 June 1261]
William [Caumvile] and Maurice de Berkeley.

Final concord concerning customs and services which Maurice demands of William for his free holding which he holds of Maurice in Wyk, viz. 1 carucate of land, for which Maurice demands suit at his court of Berkeley every three weeks; Maurice has quitclaimed to William, and in return William has quitclaimed to Maurice all damages for Maurice's unjust distraint on the holding. Endorsed: *fine of William de Caumvile*.
At: Bristol.

A1/8/11 [GC 2576]   n.d. [1281 × 1300]
William de Angervile and Sir Thomas de Berkel'.

William has granted to Thomas his claim to the lands held of Thomas in the vill of Wike in the manor of Alkinton; Thomas has given him 20 marks.

Witnesses: Sir Robert de Berkeley, Sir William Daubeny, Sir Roger de Lokinton, Peter de Stintescumbe, Robert de Brathestone, Robert de Stone.

A1/8/12 [GC 1108]   16 Feb. 34 Edw. I [1306]
Thomas le Veyse, son of Richard le Veyse, and Sir Thomas de Berkeleye, his lord.

Thomas le Veyse has quitclaimed to Thomas de Berkeleye a messuage with a garden and enclosure which was of William de Angervyle, with 2 virgates of land which were of the same William, with the appurtenant meadow, pasture [etc.] at Wyke in Alkington.

Witnesses: Richard de Wyke, Walter Motun, Thomas de Swonhungre, Thomas de Lorewynge, William le Golde.

At: Berkeley.

A1/8/13 [GC 1798]   1 March 4 Edw. II [1311]
Thomas de Berklee, lord of Berkeley; and Richard de Avene and Margaret his wife.

Thomas has granted to Richard and Margaret 4½ a. 7 perches of land at Wike between the road from Berkelee to Wottone and the road from Wike to Stokenestrete, in Alkyntone; to hold enclosed, to them and their issue, rent 2s. 6½d. a year.

Witnesses: Robert de Bradestone, Thomas de Stone, Maurice de Beoleie, Richard de Wike, John Capel, Adam de Mettesdone, William de Kyneltret.

At: Berkeley.

A1/8/14 [GC 2188]   4 Aug. 11 Edw. II [1317]
Thomas de Berkeleye, lord of Berkeley, and Gilbert Jolif.

Thomas has granted to Gilbert 1 a. of land at Wyke in an enclosure which he had by grant of William atte Wode and Maud his wife, and also a plot of land called le Pundfolde containing 8 perches, in Alkyntone; to hold enclosed, to him and his issue, rent 16d. a year.

Witnesses: Richard de Avene, John de la Hay, Geoffrey Moton, Nicholas Daungervile, William le Golde.

At: Berkeley.

A1/8/15 [GC 4311]   16 April 1 Edw. IV [1461]
William Berkeley, knight, son and heir of James lord of Berkeley, and Thomas Daungerville the younger.

William has leased to Thomas the messuage with a curtilage and enclosure which John Baily previously held in Goldeswyke in Berkeley hundred; for his life, rent 5s. 10d. a year.

Witnesses: John Dosy, Thomas Cole, John Somerford.

At: Goldwick.

MISCELLANEOUS

A1/8/16 [GC 1401]   n.d. [late Hen. III]
Walter de Hagel' and William son of Ralph de Stane.

Walter has granted to William a rent of 2s. a year from the holding which Elias the skinner (*peletarius*) held of Walter, in the vill of Wyke, and William has given him 20s. as acknowledgement.

Witnesses: Sir Nicholas vicar of Berkeley, Peter de Wike, John de Brothestan, John de Egetun, Thomas the serjeant (*serviens*), Robert Bastard, Henry de Batonia, Robert Caudel, Walter de Stintescumbe, clerk.

A1/8/17 [GC 500]   St. Barnabas, 9 Edw. I [11 June 1281]
Alice de Hageleie and Margaret de Hageleie, her sister.

   Alice has granted to Margaret the garden in Wik called . . .
Witnesses: Richard de . . . , William Gold, Adam Angervill, Geoffrey Motun, John Mason.
At: Wike.

A1/8/18 [GC 657]   Wed. after the Exaltation of Holy Cross, 27 Edw. I [16 Sept. 1299]
William le Wor and Richard de Avene.

   William has leased to Richard 2 a. of his land in Wynleye between the stream called
Doverle and the road called Rodestret; for his life.
Witnesses: Walter Moton, William Gold, Walter Dallyng, John le Mason, William de
Webbeleye, clerk.
At: Wick.

A1/8/19 [GC 1139]   St. Nicholas, 35 Edw. I [6 Dec. 1306]
Nicholas Person of Woodford; and Elias de Tydryntone and Eve his wife.

   Nicholas has granted to Elias and Eve his house in Wyk with a garden and curtilage and
the adjacent croft containing 1 a. of land, and ¼ a. of land, which he had by grant of Isabel
Caudel; for their lives, rent 4*s.* a year.
Witnesses: Robert de Berkeleye, Richard de Avene, Walter Moton, William Gold, William
de Kyneltre, Walter the clerk.
At: Wick.

A1/8/20 [GC 2393]   Tues. the feast of St. Thomas the apostle, 16 Edw. II [21 Dec. 1322]
John de Lorwinch, son of Thomas de Lorwinch, and Roger son of Nicholas Seymor of
Paganhill.

   John has granted to Roger all his lands and holdings in Wyke by Berkeleye, with all his
goods and chattels there, with the reversion of the holding held for life by John Abbod in
Wyke, for which the rent is a rose a year.
Witnesses: John de Swonhangre, John le Serjant, Richard de Harsefeld, John . . . , William
Gilemyn, William Ithenard, Richard son of Richard the clerk of Paganhill.
At: Wick.

ALKINGTON: WOODFORD
BERKELEY ACQUISITIONS
The Person holding

A1/9/1 [GC 2117]   20 Aug. 10 Edw. II [1316]
Nicholas Person of Woodford and Sir Thomas de Berkeleye, his lord.

   Nicholas has rendered and quitclaimed to Thomas and his heirs his land by the road from
Wodeford to Matford, in Alkyntone.
Witnesses: John Capel, Walter Sewaker, Roger Archer, Philip the smith of Woodford,
William Cut.
At: Berkeley.

A1/9/2 [GC 2119]   Tues. the feast of St. Bartholomew, 10 Edw. II [24 Aug. 1316]
Thomas de Berkeleye, lord of Berkeley, and Philip son of Gilbert Clerk of Woodford.

   Thomas has leased to Philip the plot of land by the road from Wodeford to Matforde
which Nicholas Person previously held of Thomas, in Alkyntone; to hold enclosed, to him
and his issue, rent 8*d.* a year.
Witnesses: Walter Sewaker, Roger Archer, William le Golde, John the smith of Woodford,
William Cut.
At: Berkeley.

A1/9/3 [GC 2238]   8 June 11 Edw. II [1318]
Thomas de Berkeleye, lord of Berkeley; and Robert Truyt and Maud his wife.

Thomas has leased to Robert and Maud the plot of land beside their holding in the high street at Wodeford, which Nicholas Person previously held of Thomas, containing 35 perches of land, in Alkyntone; to hold enclosed, to them and their issue, rent 10*d.* a year.
Witnesses: John de la Hay, Nicholas Daungervile, William le Golde, Philip the smith of Woodford, William Cut.
At: Berkeley.

The Wanswell holding

A1/9/4 [GC 1069]   Wed. the feast of the nativity of St. John the Baptist, 32 Edw. I
                                                                        [24 June 1304]
Henry de Weneswell and Sir Maurice de Berkeley, eldest son of Sir Thomas de Berkeley.

Henry has granted to Maurice his messuage, which John de Coueleye formerly held, at Wodeford in Alkinton, and Maurice has given him 2 marks; further, Henry has quitclaimed to Maurice the crofts called Rudingge and Homcroft at Wodeford in Alkinton, which Maurice had by grant of Isabel, Henry's mother.
Witnesses: Sir Nicholas son of Ralph, Sir Nicholas de Kynkestone, Sir William de Wauton, knights, Robert de Bittlestone, Robert de Bradestone, Robert Wither, Nicholas de Pedinton.
At: Berkeley.

A1/9/5 [SC 470]   Sun. after St. Margaret the virgin, 32 Edw. I [26 July 1304]
Maurice de Berkeley, son of lord Thomas de Berkeley, and Henry de Wayneswelle.

Maurice has granted to Henry a messuage and croft called Homcroft, which John de Couelee sometime held, and a croft called Rudyng, at Wodeford in Alkynton, which messuage and croft he had by the gift of Henry, and the other croft by the gift of Isabel, Henry's mother; to Henry and his issue, rent 20*s.* a year.
Witnesses: Nicholas de Kyngeston, William de Wauton, knights, Robert de Bradeston, Robert Wyther, John de Saltmarsh (*de salso marisco*), Walter Moton, Richard Broun.
At: Berkeley.

From Gilbert Clerk

A1/9/6 [GC 468]   Whit-Sunday, 4 Edw. I [24 May 1276]
Gilbert son of Hugh Clerk and Sir Maurice de Berkel'.

Gilbert has leased to Maurice 3 a. of arable land in the vill of Wodeford and a croft called Whetcroft as a pledge for 40*s.* in which he is bound to Maurice for wheat which he bought from him, for a term beginning at Michaelmas 4 Edw. I; and Gilbert will repay 1 mark a year, and if he defaults at any of the terms the land stays with Maurice.
Witnesses: Bartholomew de Olepenn, Peter de Stintescumbe, Elias de Cumbe, Thomas de Beuleye, Richard de Wenden, William le Serjaunt, Michael de Wenden, clerk.

A1/9/7 [GC 1586]   n.d. [late Edw. I]
Gilbert called the clerk of Woodford and Sir Thomas de Berkelee, lord of Berkeley.

Gilbert has granted to Thomas a rent of 2*d.* a year from 6 a. of land in the croft called Honilond, between Thystelham and Matford in Wodeford within the manor of Alkynton.
Witnesses: Robert de Bradeston, Robert de Berkelee, Thomas de Beolee, Thomas de Styntescombe, Robert Wyth', Nicholas the clerk, William Golde.

Miscellaneous acquisitions

A1/9/8 [GC 553]   n.d. [early Edw. I]
William le Golde and Sir Thomas de Berkeleye.

William has quitclaimed to Thomas 2 a. of land next to 'la farre ock' in the manor of Alkinton, which he bought from Ralph Symond.

Witnesses: Peter de Stintescumbe, William de Burgo, Robert de Stone, Robert de Bradeston, Nicholas de Wodeford, Robert Bastard, Nicholas Iwein.

A1/9/9 [GC 1760]   Tues. after the Assumption, 4 Edw. II [18 Aug. 1310]
William Sokye of Berkeley and Sir Maurice de Berkelee.

William has rendered and quitclaimed to Maurice a messuage and two crofts of land, which he held of Maurice at Wodeford in Alkynton near Berkeleye.
Witnesses: Nicholas de Kyngeston, William de Wauton, knights, Robert de Bradeston, . . . John de Saltmarsh (*de salsomarisco*), Robert Wyther.
At: Portbury.

BERKELEY GRANTS

A1/9/10 [GC 1237]   n.d. [*temp*. Edw. I]
Thomas de Berkel, lord of Berkeley, and Walter Robard.

Thomas has granted to Walter a plot of land in the high street of Wodeford, next to the holding of Thomas Roberd, in Alkyntone; to Walter and Alice his wife and their issue, rent 4*d.* a year.
Witnesses: Richard de Avene, Richard de Wyke, William Gold, John le Mason, William Kyneltre, William Northlone.

A1/9/11 [GC 1154]   Nativity of St. John the Baptist, 35 Edw. I [24 June 1307]
Thomas de Berkel', lord of Berkeley, and Thomas Robard.

Thomas de Berkel' has granted to Thomas Robard a plot of land in the high street of Wodeford, lying next to the king's highway, in Alkyntone; to Thomas Robard and Alice his wife and their issue, rent 4*d.* a year.
Witnesses: Richard de Avene, Walter Motoun, William Gold, John le Mason, Alexander the clerk, William Cutel.
At: Berkeley.

A1/9/12 [GC 455]   Fri. in Michaelmas, 1 Edw. I [29 Sept. 1307]
Thomas de Berkeleye, lord of Berkeley; and Philip the butcher (*carnifex*) of Woodford and Agnes his wife.

Thomas has granted to Philip and Agnes 1 perch of land at Wodeford; to them and their issue, rent 1*d.* a year.
Witnesses: Richard de Avene, Thomas de Beoleye, Robert of the church, Philip the smith of Woodford, William Cut.
At: Berkeley.

A1/9/13 [GC 877]   Mon. the feast of St. Martin, 2 Edw. II [11 Nov. 1308]
Thomas de Berkeley, lord of Berkeley; and Thomas Robet and Alice his wife.

Thomas has granted to Thomas and Alice a plot of land next to the road at la Fayrok, containing 40 perches of land, at Wodeford in Alkynton; to hold enclosed, to them and their issue, rent 5*d.* a year.
Witnesses: Richard de Aven, William Gold, John le Mason, William Cut, Richard le Erl.

A1/9/14 [GC 1674]   1 Feb. 2 Edw. II [1309]
Thomas de Berkelee, lord of Berkeley, and Gilbert Jolif.

Thomas has granted to Gilbert a plot of land at Wodeford, containing 42 perches, in Alkyntone; to hold enclosed, rent 6*d.* a year.
Witnesses: Thomas de Stone, Maurice de Beoleye, Richard de Avene, Walter Sewaker, Roger Archer.
At: Berkeley.

A1/9/15 [GC 1679]　　　　　　　　Sun. the feast of the Purification, 2 Edw. II [2 Feb. 1309]
Thomas de Berkeleye, lord of Berkeley; and William Cut of Woodford and Alice his wife.

Thomas has granted to William and Alice ½ a. of land in Wodeford in Alkyntone; to them and their issue, rent 10*d.* a year.
Witnesses: Richard de Avene, Geoffrey Motoun, William Golde, Philip the smith of Woodford, Richard Erl, William ate Wode.
At: Berkeley.

A1/9/16 [GC 1767]　　　　　　　　Tues. in Michaelmas, 4 Edw. II [29 Sept. 1310]
Thomas de Berkelee, lord of Berkeley; and Walter Corbet and Joan his wife.

Thomas has granted to Walter and Joan 1 a. 8 perches of land at Wodeford in Alkyntone; to hold enclosed, to them and their issue, rent 12*d.* a year while Walter lives and afterwards 18*d.* a year.
Witnesses: Thomas de Stone, Maurice de Beoleie, Richard de Avene, Walter Sewaker, William Gold.
At: Berkeley.

A1/9/17 [GC 1907]　　　　　　　　　　　　　　10 March 6 Edw. II [1313]
Thomas de Berkelee, lord of Berkeley; and William atte Wode and William his son.

Thomas has granted to William and William ½ a. 10 perches of land at Wodeford in Alkyntone; to hold enclosed, to them and their issue, rent 8*d.* a year.
Witnesses: Richard de Avene, Maurice de Beoleye, John Capel, Walter Sewaker, Nicholas Iweyn.
At: Berkeley.

A1/9/18 [GC 2047]　　　　　　　　　　　　　　　1 June 8 Edw. II [1315]
Thomas de Berkeleye, lord of Berkeley; and Walter Corbet and Joan atte Wode.

Thomas has leased to Walter and Joan ½ a. of land in the high street at Wodeford, beside the road called la Portlone, in Alkyntone; to hold enclosed, to them and Walter's issue, rent 6*d.* a year.
Witnesses: John Capel, John de la Hay, Walter Sewaker, William le Golde, William Cut.
At: Berkeley.

A1/9/19 [GC 2104]　　　　　　　　　　　　　　　10 June 9 Edw. II [1316]
Thomas de Berkeleye, lord of Berkeley; and Walter Corbet and Joan his wife.

Thomas has leased to Walter and Joan 1 a. 27 perches of land in the high street at Wodeforde, lying in the triangular enclosure between three roads, viz. one called la Portlone leading from Neweport to the mill of John de Sautemaries, one from the house of John de Sautemaries to Northruydinge, and the third from Wodefordeshulle to Mickelwode, in Alkyntone; to hold enclosed, to them and their issue, rent while Walter lives 12*d.* a year, and after his death 18*d.* a year.
Witnesses: John Capel, John de la Hay, Walter Sewaker, William le Golde, William Cut.
At: Berkeley.

A1/9/20 [GC 2126]　　　　　　　　　　　　　　　1 Nov. 10 Edw. II [1316]
Thomas de Berkeleye, lord of Berkeley, and William Knyte.

Thomas has granted to William 1½ a. of land in the high street of Wodeforde next to his park of Oclee, between the gates of the park and the enclosure of Denise atte Fayrok', which John de Bademyntone, clerk, previously held of Thomas, in Alkyntone; to hold enclosed, to him and his issue, rent 2*s.* 6*d.* a year.
Witnesses: John de la Hay, John de Seham, Nicholas Daungervile, Roger Archer, William le Golde, William le Gryp, William de Kyneltre.
At: Berkeley.

A1/9/21 [GC 2206]   6 Dec. 11 Edw. II [1317]

Thomas de Berkeleye, lord of Berkeley; and Walter le Toyt and Joan his wife.

Thomas has leased to Walter and Joan a croft of land at Wodeforde called Coueleyesclive, with improvement from the pit [i.e. marlpit] called Coueleiesput, and with free access to the croft by a lane called Fithelelone, which Nicholas Person previously held of Thomas, and has also leased to them a plot of land to dig and remove and improve the croft, with free access for wagons and carts, beyond the meadow of Matforde, in Alkyntone; to them and their issue, rent 6s. and 6 capons a year.

Witnesses: Walter Sewaker, Nicholas Daungervile, Philip the smith of Woodford, William Cut, Robert Truyt.

At: Berkeley.

A1/9/22 [GC 2324]   1 Sept. 14 Edw. II [1320]

Thomas de Berkeleye, lord of Berkeley; and Walter le Toyt and Joan his wife.

Thomas has leased to Walter and Joan a plot of land at Wodeforde, 4 by 3 perches, and a croft called Schorteclive between the field called Oldebur' and the meadow of Matforde, in Alkyntone, with licence to improve the croft from the pit [i.e. marlpit] called Coueleyesput; to them and the issue of Walter, rent 2s. 6d. a year.

Witnesses: John de la Hay, Walter Sewaker, Philip the smith, William Cut, Robert Truyt.

At: Berkeley.

A1/9/23 [GC 3268]   n.d. [mid 14th cent.]

Thomas lord of Berkelee; and Walter Kene, Cecilia his wife and Thomas their son.

Thomas has leased to Walter, Cecilia and Thomas a messuage with a curtilage, garden and a quarter-virgate of land, which William le Bakare called Bovestret previously held of Thomas in villeinage in Wodeforde within the manor of Alkyntone, the holding being called Puryarestenement; for their lives, rent 13s. 4d. a year.

Witnesses: John Capel, John le Serjaunt the younger, John Purlewent, Stephen de Kyneltre, Richard Aleyn.

OTHER HOLDINGS

The Harold holding

A1/9/24 [SC 338]   n.d. [*temp.* Hen. III]

John de Wodeford and Robert Haraut.

John has granted to Robert the land in Wodeford which lies between the land which Herebert sometime held of Sir Thomas de Berkeley and the land which John Black (*Niger*) once held of the said John; rent 2d. a year and the royal service which pertains to 2 a. in that vill; for which Robert has given him 1 mark in acknowledgement.

Witnesses: Sir Henry de Berkele, Sir Richard de Cromhal, Maurice de Saltmarsh (*de salso marisco*), Maurice de Stanes, Robert le Herde, William de Stanes son of the clerk, Walter Seli.

A1/9/25 [GC 1405]   n.d. [late Hen. III]

Walter Harald, son and heir of Robert Harald, and Roger le Herde.

Walter has granted to Roger all his land in the vill of Wodeford, beside the land of Nicholas de Wodeford, extending to the croft called Brodeleye, as in the charter of John de Wodeford to Robert his father; rent to Nicholas de Wodeford 2d. a year, and Roger has given Walter 4½ marks.

Witnesses: Nicholas de Wodeford, William de Angervile, William Heriith, Adam Motun, Robert the marshal (*marescallus*), Gilbert son of Hugh, Walter le Grip, Hugh de Pedentone.

A1/9/26 [GC 1406]   n.d. [late Hen. III]
Walter Harald and Roger le Herde.

Walter has granted to Roger all his land in the vill of Wodeford, except the land which Emma Harald his mother held in the same vill in dower; rent to Nicholas de Wodeford 2*d.* a year, and Roger has given him 3½ marks.

Witnesses: Nicholas de Wodeford, William de Angervile, William Heriith, Adam Motun, Robert the marshal (*marescallus*), Gilbert son of Hugh Clerk, Hugh de Pedentone.

A1/9/27 [GC 920]   n.d. [late 13th cent.]
Walter Harald, son of Robert Harald, and Roger le Herde.

Walter has granted to Roger all his land in the vill of Wodeford except the land which Emma Harald, his mother, held in dower; rent 1*d.* a year to Nicholas de Wodeford and Roger has given him 3½ marks.

Witnesses: Nicholas de Wodeford, William de Angervile, William Heriik, Adam Moton, Robert the marshal (*marescallus*), Gilbert son of the clerk, Hugh de Pedenton.

Gleche holding

A1/9/28 [GC 751]   n.d. [late 13th cent.]
Henry son of Stephen the smith of Tortworth and Philip le Gleche of Woodford.

Henry has granted to Philip a plot of his holding in Wodeford, which he had by enfeoffment of Philip the smith his brother, between his croft and the king's highway; rent to Philip the smith a rose a year.

Witnesses: Nicholas de Wodeford, Philip the smith, Walter le Webbe, Richard Broun, William de Webbeleye, clerk.

A1/9/29 [GC 1014]   Sun. before the nativity of St. John Baptist, 29 Edw. I [18 June 1301]
Henry son of Stephen the smith of Tortworth; and Philip le Gleche of Woodford and Anynye his wife.

Henry has granted to Philip and Anynye a plot of his holding in Wodeford next to the road; rent a clove a year to the chief lord of the fee.

Witnesses: Nicholas de Wodeford, Nicholas de Pedinton, Walter Moton, Richard Broun, William de Webbeley, clerk.
At: Woodford.

Miscellaneous

A1/9/30 [GC 1882]   1 June 5 Edw. II [1312]
Richard son of Alexander the clerk of Woodford and John son of Adam le Kyng.

Richard has quitclaimed to John 40 perches of land with a cottage built thereon, in the high street of Wodeford opposite the house of the said Alexander.

Witnesses: Walter Sewaker, Philip the smith, William Cut, Richard le Tornour, Richard Broun.
At: Woodford.

A1/9/31 [GC 2425]   Fri. the feast of St. Margaret the virgin, 18 Edw. II [20 July 1324]
Juliana ate Wode of Woodford, widow; and Walter Corbat of Woodford and Joan his wife.

Juliana has granted to Walter and Joan and their heirs her holding, land and meadow, which she inherited after the death of William ate Wode, her brother, in Wodeforde in the manor of Alkyntone.

Witnesses: John ate Hay, Nicholas of the vine (*de vynea*), Robert de Asschelworth, William Cott', William Kyneltre, Walter le Toyt, Robert Daungervyle.
At: Woodford.

A1/9/32 [GC 2815]   1 April 9 Edw. III [1335]
Joan atte Wode of Woodford, widow, and Walter Saunderus of Woodford.

Joan has granted to Walter, his heirs and assigns her holding in Wodeforde within the manor of Alkyntone.

Witnesses: William Cut, Nicholas atte Hay, John le Tornor, John Scewakur, Nicholas Broun.
At: Woodford.

APPLERIDGE

The manor had nearly lost its separate identity by 1280, being administered with Ham as one of the many vills to comprise that large manor. From 1350 most of the demesne was enclosed within New Park, which was created by Thomas (III) Lord Berkeley (d. 1361), but the leases of 1368 and 1464 show that it was still officially regarded as a separate unit within Ham. The rent was reduced to 60s. a year in 1387–8.[1]

THE BERKELEY MANOR

A1/10/1 [GC 3600]   Mon. 2 Oct. 42 Edw. III [1368]
Sir Warin del Isle[2] and John Tysun.

Warin has leased at farm to John the manor of Appelrugge, to hold until the full age of Thomas son and heir of Maurice last lord of Berkele; rent £4 a year.
At: Berkeley.

A1/10/2 [GC 4326]   20 April 4 Edw. IV [1464]
William Berkeley, lord of Berkeley, knight; and John Corbet and Edith his wife.

William has leased to John and Edith the site of his manor of Appulrugge with the land and pasture adjacent, which Katherine Corbett, John's mother, previously held, in the lordship of Hamme (Glos.); for their lives, rent 60s. a year.

ROBERT THE FORESTER'S HOLDING

A1/10/3 [GC 382]   n.d. [late Hen. III]
Robert the forester (*forestarius*) and Walter Franceis.

Robert has granted to Walter the assart between the land of Walter de Parhame and Appelrugge and between the house of Walter de Perhame and the pasture of Sir William de Stanes; rent 4s. a year; acknowledgement 2 marks.

Witnesses: Sir Nicholas son of Roger, Sir William de Stanes, Nicholas de Bassingtone, Maurice de Bevintun, Maurice de Stanes, Jordan chaplain of Hill, Walter the steward (*senescallus*), William de Hulla, Alexander de Londoniis.

ARLINGHAM

Arlingham was a detached portion of Berkeley Herness and, although generous grants were made to St. Augustine's Abbey, a large manor was retained by the main line of the family until 1275 when half of it was granted by Maurice (II) (d. 1281) to his two younger sons Robert and Simon. The estate was soon divided between three daughters and coheirs of Robert's son John de Berkeley, and the manor lost its coherence. It was not included in the entail of the Herness made by Thomas (III) in 1349, but a number of holdings were hotly disputed between the heirs male and the heirs general in the 15th century. Subsequent purchases increased the family's interest there in the 15th century.

---

[1] BCM GAR 150 (cf. below, A1/24/160). For the rent in 1442, below, A1/24/61 [GC 4224].
[2] Warin Lord Lisle (d. 1382) was the father-in-law of Thomas (IV) Lord Berkeley; Thomas was only fifteen when his father died in 1368 and Warin bought the wardship at £400 a year.

BERKELEY ACQUISITIONS
Elias de Bristol

A1/11/1 [SC 161A]   n.d. [before 1220]

Robert de Berkelay and Elias son of Durand, canon of Hereford.

Robert has granted to Elias a virgate called Wodegerd which Roger of the wood (*de bosco*) held, a quarter-virgate which Brichthredul held, a pasture called Inhechinge lying between Fulemore and the road to the court of Arlingham, a croft called Winescroft which lies between Robert's wood of Arlingham and the land of William de Frethorne, and a meadow in Pulsham which lies between the meadow of Margaret de Linch and the vill of Arlingham; rent 2*s.* a year.[1]

Witnesses: Sir Adam son of Nigel, Oliver de Berkelay, Simon de Olepenna, Richard de Couelega, Peter de Stintescumbe, Robert de Albamara, Reginald de Gosintun, John de Eggentun, Elias de Buvill, Hugh, Robert Bertram, Robert son of Guy.

A1/11/2 [SC 161B]   n.d. [1216 × 1220]

Robert de Berkelay and Elias son of Durand, canon of Hereford.

Robert has granted to Elias 1 virgate of land in his manor of Arlingham, viz. the half-virgate which John son of Abraham held and the half-virgate which John the hayward (*messarius*) held. Rent the same as he owes for the other land which he holds of Robert in the same vill, viz. 2*s.* a year and Elias has given him two palfreys in acknowledgement.[2]

Witnesses: Sir David abbot of St. Augustine's, Bristol, Henry de Berkeley, Oliver de Berkeley, Simon de Olepenn, Richard de Coueleg, Adam son of Nigel, Bernard de Stanes, John de Eggentun, Maurice son of Nigel, Elias de Slimbruge.

A1/11/3 [SC 165]   n.d. [*c.* 1220]

Thomas de Berkele and Elias son of Durand, canon of Hereford.

Thomas has confirmed to Elias the grant of his brother Robert in Arlingham, to hold by the same services, viz. 2*s.* a year and whatever pertains to 1¼ virgate; Elias has paid 5 marks for the confirmation.

Witnesses: Richard de Couele, Elias de Buvill, Robert son of Guy, Robert Bertram, Hugh de Wike, Gilbert del Ling, Walter the parson's man, Hugh the baker (*pistor*), Ernulf son of Richard de Neweham.

A1/11/4 [SC 167]   n.d. [*c.* 1220]

Thomas de Berkel' and Elias de Bristoll, canon of Hereford.

Thomas has granted to Elias liberty to keep six oxen and one cow in his pastures of Arlingham.[3]

Witnesses: Robert son of Richard, Maurice son of Nigel, Henry de Berkeley, Arnulf the clerk, Ralph de Stanes, Elias de Buvill, Hugh de Wike.

Wick Court[4]

A1/11/5 [GC 1203]   n.d. [before 1255]

Maurice lord of Berkel' and Peter de Wike.

Maurice has granted to Peter in exchange, 13 a. of meadow in Maurice's manor of Hamme, for 13 a. of arable land in the vill of Erlingham.

Witnesses: Sir William de Alba Marle, Sir Ralph Musard, John de Eketon, Thomas Mathias, Andrew de Bradestan, Adam Nel, Nicholas de Craule, Adam Flambard, William son of Robert.

---

[1] *Transcript*: *St Augustine's Cartulary*, no. 142.
[2] *Transcript*: ibid. no. 141.
[3] *Transcript*: ibid. no. 163.
[4] See also below, A2/23/1 [GC 1044].

A1/11/6 [GC 1206]   n.d. [late Hen. III]
Maurice de Berkel' and Peter de Wike.

Maurice has granted to Peter all his land in Walamegarstone, and all the land called
Oldefryhtgorste, all the land called Stapelling, and all the meadow and pasture lying
between the water of Bradiflete and the meadow which Robert son of Isilia de Swanleygh
holds of Maurice; rent 20*d.* a year, and for this Peter has given to Maurice a quitclaim of all
his land of Wyke with all the appurtenances and fisheries.
Witnesses: Sir Maurice de Saltmarsh (*de salso marisco*), Maurice de Stan', John de Egeton,
Thomas the serjeant (*serviens*), Adam Coby, John Sewaker, Robert Bastard, John de
Brothestone, Nicholas de Craul', Walter Sely.

A1/11/7 [GC 577]   Mon. before St. Margaret the virgin, 18 Edw. I [17 July 1290]
Sir Thomas de Berkeleye; and Master Richard de Clifford and William de Clifford, bishop
of Emly.

Whereas Thomas has impleaded William and Richard in the king's court for a messuage
and 1 carucate of land in Erlyngham as his right and inheritance, their friends have agreed a
compromise, viz. that William and Richard have acknowledged the right of Thomas and
rendered it to him, and Thomas has granted that they should hold it for their lives from the
following Michaelmas, to revert to Thomas after their deaths, and until Michaelmas to be in
the hands of Master Thomas de Sudynton.
Witnesses: Sir Robert son of Payn, Sir Robert de Berkeleye, Sir William de Bereford, Sir
John de Clifford, knights, Master Thomas de Sudynton, Ralph Baron, William de Burgh,
Robert de Bradeston, Walter de Wyk, John de Bergh.
At: Westminster.

A1/11/8 [SC 464]   n.d. [*c.* 1290]
Thomas son of Maurice de Berkeleye; and William [de Clifford], bishop of Emly, and
Master Richard de Clifford.

Thomas has granted to William and Richard, for their lives, a messuage and 1 carucate of
land at Wyk in Erlyngham, which they previously rendered to him in the king's court as his
right and inheritance; rent 8*d.* a year and suit to his hundred court.
Witnesses: Robert son of Payn, Robert de Berkeleye, John de Clifford, knights, Master
Thomas de Sudinton, Bartholomew de Ulpenn, Robert de Stannes, Simon de Fremelade,
John Wyz, Walter de Wyk, John de Berewe.

A1/11/9 [GC 1045; *duplicate* GC 1043] Sun. a week after Easter, 31 Edw. I [14 April 1303]
Thomas de Berkelee, lord of Berkeley; and Richard de Clyfford, Sarah his wife and
Richard their eldest son.

Thomas has granted to Richard, Sarah and Richard his manor of Wyke by Erlyngham,
and the fishery which was of John de Boevyle called Berewater in the Severn; to them for
their lives, rent 1*d.* a year and the royal service for one twentieth of a knight's fee.
Witnesses: Sir Hugh de Veer, Sir Robert son of Payn, Sir John Abadam, Sir Walter de
Glouc', Sir Thomas de Gardinis, Sir Thomas le Boteler, Sir John Lovel of Snorscomb, Sir
John Basset, Sir Peter Crok, knights, Robert de Bradestone, Robert de Bettlescombe,
Richard de Byselee, Thomas de Styntescombe.
At: Berkeley.

A1/11/10 [GC 1980]   1 June 7 Edw. II [1314]
Sir Thomas son of Sir Thomas de Berkeleye; and Sir Reginald Russel and Margaret his wife.[1]

Thomas has leased to Reginald and Margaret, for their lives, his holding at Wyke on
Severn; rent 10 marks a year, beginning at Michaelmas 8 Edw. II [1314].
Witnesses: Sir William de Wauton, Sir Nicholas de Kyngeston, Sir William Maunsel, knights,

[1] Margaret was the grantor's sister.

John de Berkeleye, lord of Arlingham, Thomas de Stone, Robert de Berkel', William Clifford.
At: Berkeley.

A1/11/11 [SC 483; *duplicate* SC 484]   Mon. after St. Barnabas, 11 Edw. II [12 June 1318]
Thomas de Berkeley, lord of Berkeley; and Thomas de Berkeley, his son, and Isabel his [the son's] wife.

Thomas has granted to Thomas and Isabel (i) a rent of 10 marks a year from the fishery which he had by demise from Robert his brother, in Erlyngham, by the hand of the fisherman there, (ii) the manor of Wyke near Erlyngham, with the fishery there once of John de Beyvyle called Berewater in the Severn; (iii) a holding at Morecote and Hardpirie which he had by demise from Richard de Biseleye and William Durant; all in exchange for a rent which he had previously granted to Thomas; to them and Thomas's male issue; rent a lamprey due on the last day of May.
Witnesses: Maurice, the grantor's son, William de Wautone, Nicholas de Kyngestone, Thomas le Botiler, knights, William Colewych, Walter de Nasse, William Gamage, Thomas de Berkeley, Thomas de Bradeston.
At: Wymondham.

A1/11/12 [GC 3668]   Fri. after St. Denis, 48 Edw. III [13 Oct. 1374]
Geoffrey de Segrave and William Tournour of Wymondham; and John de Berkele, knight, and Elizabeth his wife.

Geoffrey and William have leased to John and Elizabeth all the lands, holdings [etc.] in Morcote in the parish of Hardpiry, Erlyngham and Erlyngham Wyke which they had by grant of the said John; to them and their issue, with remainder to John's issue, to Elizabeth wife of John de Seyton, knight, sister of John de Berkele, and her issue, and to Thomas de Berkelee, lord of Berkeley, his heirs and assigns.
Witnesses: Robert de Miltone, Walter Hewet, William Schef of Arlingham, John Hayward of the same, Thomas Byslee of Gloucester, William Hyeberere.
At: Arlingham.

A1/11/13 [GC 3669; *duplicate* GC 3670]   Sat. before St. Luke, 48 Edw. III [14 Oct. 1374]
(1) Thomas de Berkelee, lord of Berkeley; (2) Geoffrey de Segrave and William Tournour of Wymondham; (3) John de Berkele, knight, and Elizabeth his wife.

Confirmation by Thomas of the lease by Geoffrey and William to John and Elizabeth of all the lands, holdings [etc.] in Morcote in the parish of Hardpiry, Erlyngham and Erlyngham Wyke which they had by grant of the said John; to them and their issue, with remainder to John's issue, to Elizabeth wife of John de Seyton, knight, sister of John de Berkele, and her issue, and to Thomas de Berkelee, lord of Berkeley, his heirs and assigns.
Witnesses: John de Clyfford, William Modbrok of Berkeley, Richard de Myltoun, Walter Huwett, William Scheff of Arlingham, John Heyward of the same, Thomas Byslee of Gloucester, William Heyberere of the same.
At: Berkeley.

MISCELLANEOUS BERKELEY DOCUMENTS
A1/11/14 [SC 240]   One week after St. Augustine in May [26 May] 1236
Sir Thomas de Berkeley and St. Augustine's Abbey.

Settlement of suit between them concerning the tithes of pannage, fisheries and mills, and concerning the manor of Arlingham, the land of Bray, the land of Lorewinge, and rights of way, viz. that Thomas shall pay the tithes and the abbot shall give Thomas quittance for Arlingham, Bray and Lorewinge.[1]
Witnesses: Master Hubert, official of the bishop of Worcester, Sir William Putot, Sir Ralph de Wileton, Roger de Andeure, rector of Cam, Sir Henry de Berkele, Sir William de

---

[1] *Transcript*: *St Augustine's Cartulary*, no. 159.

Berkeley, Maurice son of Maurice de Berkeley, Maurice de Sautemareis, Roger de Sokerwik, Reginald de Camma.
At: Gloucester.

A1/11/15 [SC 169]   n.d. [early Hen. III]
Thomas de Berkeley and Drusiana daughter of Robert Bertram.

Thomas has granted to Drusiana all the land which Dolfin and James his son held in Woldrop; rent 10s. 8d. a year.
Witnesses: Richard de Kouele, Peter de Stintescumbe, Elias de Buvill, Hugh de Wike, Gilbert de Linche, Arnulf the clerk.

A1/11/16 [GC 352]   n.d. [*temp.* Hen. III]
Maurice de Berkeley and Robert son of Guy.

Maurice has confirmed to Robert 3 selions of land in the field of Southfeld in exchange for 5 selions of land above Glasclyve.
Witnesses: Peter de Wyke, Gilbert de Lynch, Richard de Sancta Brigida, Walter de Fromilod, William le Ward, Robert le Herde, Walter Sely, clerk.

A1/11/17 [SC 350]   n.d. [*temp.* Hen. III]
Maurice de Berkeley and Gilbert de Lynch.

Maurice has granted to Gilbert 4 selions of land lying in Westmarisco and in Newelond, in exchange for 2 selions of land in Glasmarisco.
Witnesses: Peter de Wyke, Richard de Wyke, Robert son of Guy, Richard de Sancta Brigida, Walter de Fremelod, Walter Sely.

A1/11/18 [SC 525]   St. Katherine, 23 Edw. III [25 Nov. 1349]
Maurice de Berkeley, son of Lord Thomas de Berkeley, and the hospital of the Holy Trinity near Longbridge in Berkeley.

Maurice has granted to the hospital all the lands, holdings, rents and appurtenances which he acquired from Richard le Ferour, brother and heir of Walter le Ferour, in Erlingham and elsewhere in Berkeley hundred, in order that they should keep the anniversaries of Walter and Margery his wife in the church of Erlingham and the anniversary of Sir Henry de Welynton in the chapel of Longbridge.
Witnesses: Walter Wyth, John Clifford, John Serjaunt the younger, John the clerk, Robert Groundi.
At: Berkeley.

A1/11/19 [GC 4252]   4 May 24 Hen. VI [1446]
Extract from the roll of the court of John [Talbot], earl of Shrewbury and Lord Talbot, and Margaret his wife, eldest daughter of Richard Beauchamp, late earl of Warwick, Edmund [Beaufort], marquess of Dorset, and Eleanor his wife, Warwick's second daughter, and George Lord Latemer and Elizabeth his wife, Warwick's third daughter.

Half of the pasture in the enclosure called Godescroft with 3 selions of land above Umbley, late of William Bowne, was leased to Richard Smalewell; to hold to him, his wife and son, for their lives, rent 3s. a year, and he paid a fine of 6s. 8d. and did fealty to the lords: sealed by John Edward, steward.
At: Arlingham.

A1/11/20 [GC 4417*]   7 April 18 Edw. IV [1478]
Robert Danyell and the lord [William Berkeley].

Extract from court roll: Robert came and took of the lord the reversion of a parcel of land in Erlyngham called le Rudyng and a parcel of water in the Severn called Erlewodiswatir, after the death of Thomas Danyell his father; to Robert and Thomas his son, for their lives, at the previous rent, fine 13s.

A1/11/21 [GC 4423]   1 Aug. 20 Edw. IV [1480]

Thomas Berkeley, esquire, Maurice Kyng and John at Wode; and Richard Beauchamp, bishop of Salisbury, Richard Beauchamp, knight, son and heir apparent of Lady Seyntmound, Thomas Mongomery and John Forster, clerk.

Thomas, Maurice and John have demised to Richard and the others the manor of Erlyngham (Glos.); for the life of John Beauchamp, knight, son and heir apparent of Richard Lord Beauchamp, knight, and Anne Wylloughby, daughter of Joan Lady Berkeley, as by the indenture between William Berkeley, knight, Lord Berkeley, and Richard Beauchamp, Lord Beauchamp, dated 15 May 20 Edw. IV [1480]; and Thomas, Maurice and John have appointed Thomas Tyler and Thomas Dorney to deliver seisin to Richard and the others.

Witnesses: William Trye, esquire, Thomas Whytyngton, Thomas Hanley, Thomas Morgan, Thomas Frensche.

A1/11/22 [GC 4473]   26 March 6 Hen. VII [1491]

Richard Clyffe and Sir John Beauchamp, knight.

Extract from court roll: Richard came and gave to John a fine of 13*s*. 4*d*. for entry to a messuage with appurtenances in Erlyngham, which Thomas Clyffe his father held; to Richard and his wife and son, for their lives, at the previous rent.

BERKELEY ADMINISTRATIVE DOCUMENTS
Accounts of the fishery man (piscator)

A1/11/23 [GAR 405]	3–4 Edw. II [1309–10]
A1/11/24 [GAR 406]	5–6 Edw. II [1311–12]
A1/11/25 [GAR 407]	6–7 Edw. II [1312–13]

Rent-collector's account

A1/11/26 [GAR 408]   18–19 & 19–20 Hen. VI [1439–41]

Rental

A1/11/27 [GRR 23]   n.d. [mid 15th cent.]

Account for the earl of Warwick during the minority of the heir to the Yates' portion.

BERKELEY OF ARLINGHAM DOCUMENTS

John de Berkeley, son and heir of Sir Robert de Berkeley (d. *c.* 1300), left four daughters of whom three married and had issue. Elizabeth married James de Wilton and Walter Thornhull and had issue by each, Leticia married John Westmancote, and Margaret married John atte Yate. According to Smyth, Thomas (IV) Lord Berkeley (d. 1417) acquired the Westmancotes' portion of the manor, which passed to his daughter Elizabeth Beauchamp and her three daughters.

The Westmancotes' portion

The weirs

A1/11/28 [GC 3406]   Mon. the morrow of Michaelmas, 27 Edw. III [30 Sept. 1353]

William Westmecote of Arlingham and William Bakere of Arlingham.

William Westmecote has granted to William Bakere, his heirs and assigns two weirs, with the fisheries and other appurtenances, within the lordship of Erlyngham, called Rodleyeswere and Garnewere.

Witnesses: Walter Jakemannes, Richard le Frere, John Jannes, Robert de Milton, Walter Hywet.

At: Arlingham.

A1/11/29 [GC 3480]   Sun. before St. Laurence the martyr, 33 Edw. III [4 Aug. 1359]

William de Westmoncote, son and heir of Leticia daughter and coheir of John de Berkeleye of Arlingham, and William le Baker of Arlingham.

William de Westmoncote has granted to William le Baker, his heirs and assigns all his fisheries in the Severn within the lordship of Erlyngham at the weirs of Rodleye and Garne, viz. one third of the fisheries of one quarter of the said weirs, and one third of a fishery called Reek in the same water.

Witnesses: Walter With, Robert de Middeltone, Richard le Stiward, John de Clifford, Richard de Longeneye, Roger de Reom, clerk.

At: Arlingham.

A1/11/30 [GC 3494]   Fri. before Michaelmas, 33 Edw. III [27 Sept. 1359]
William de Westmoncote, son and heir of Leticia daughter and coheir of John de Berkeleye of Arlingham, and William le Bakere of Arlingham.

Whereas William le Bakere is bound to William de Westmoncote in an annual rent of 4 marks, William de Westmoncote has granted that if William pays to the lord of Berkelee and his heirs 4 marks a year, for the farm of one third of the fisheries of one quarter of the weirs of Garne and Rodleye, the bond will be void. [*In French.*]

Witnesses: Walter With, Robert de Middeltone, Richard le Stiward, John de Clifford, Richard de Longeneye, Roger de Reom, clerk.

At: Arlingham.

A1/11/31 [GC 3978]   Sun. after the Assumption [*year erased, c.* Aug. 1359]
William de Westmonkote, son of John de Westmonkote and heir of Leticia daughter and coheir of John de Berkeley, late lord of Arlingham, and William le Bakare of Arlingham.

William de Westmonkote has granted to William le Bakare, his heirs and assigns the holding which John le Ridere formerly held of William in Erlyngham.

Witnesses: Edmund de Brokenberwe, Randolph Waleis, Richard Styward, Walter Huwett, John Janys.

At: Arlingham.

Miscellaneous

A1/11/32 [GC 3511]   Sun. after St. Martin, 34 Edw. III [15 Nov. 1360]
William de Westmoncote, lord of Arlingham, and Walter Huwetth of the same.

William has granted to Walter, his heirs and assigns a parcel of a curtilage in Herlyngham; rent 4*d.* a year.

Witnesses: Walter Wyth, Walter Jakenons, Philip le Heyward, Richard the cook (*coccus*), Thomas Bolgarstone.

At: Arlingham.

Various

A1/11/33 [GC 1198]   n.d. [1305 × 1320]
John de Berkeleye, lord of Arlingham, and William Pride of Arlingham.

John has granted to William, for a certain sum of money, a plot of land in the vill of Erlyngham next to the holding of John Mey; to him and his issue, rent 5*s.* a year.

Witnesses: Richard de Wyk, William de Clyfford, Walter Wyth, Elias . . . , John Mei, John de Symondeshale, Adam Flambard, . . . , Richard de la Wode, . . . Richard Wyth.

A1/11/34 [GC 2972]   Whit-Sunday, 14 Edw. III [4 June 1340]
James de Wyltone and Elizabeth his wife; and Joan daughter of William Top of Arlingham and Robert and Juliana her children.

James and Elizabeth have leased to Joan and Robert and Juliana, the son and daughter of Robert le Taylour and the said Joan, the plot of land in Erlyngham in the curtilage by the churchyard, between the curtilage of John de Westmoncote and the messuage formerly of the said William; for their lives, rent 2*s.* a year.

Witnesses: Richard de Clifford, Walter With, William Janes, Richard le Henye, Walter de Middeltone.

At: Arlingham.

ARLINGHAM CHURCH
The Huet curtilage

A1/11/35 [GC 3635]   Morrow of St. Simon and St. Jude, 45 Edw. III [29 Oct. 1371]
Walter Huet of Arlingham and John de Thornhulle.

Walter has granted to John, his heirs and assigns a curtilage.
Witnesses: Robert de Middeltone, William Scheof, John Heyward.
At: Arlingham.

A1/11/36 [GC 4011]   2 May 6 Hen. IV [1405]
John Thornhull of Arlingham; and Walter Frere, Robert Benteley and John Webbe of the same, proctors of the church of St. Mary.

John has granted to Walter, Robert and John, and their heirs and assigns, a parcel of the curtilage which he formerly acquired from Walter Huet in Erlyngham.
Witnesses: John Yate, John Westmoncote, Robert Mechelgros, William Hayward, Richard Miltone.
At: Arlingham.

A selion in Mangrove

A1/11/37 [GC 4087]   Sat. before St. Luke, 1 Hen. V [14 Oct. 1413]
Joan Pury, widow of Richard Pury of Mitcheldean; and Richard Longneye and John Webbe of Arlingham, proctors of the church of St. Mary.

Joan has granted to Richard and John a selion of land in Erlyngham in the field called Mangrove in le Middelforlong.
Witnesses: John Yate, William Westmoncote, Richard Miltone, Robert Muchulgros, William Hayward.
At: Arlingham.

A1/11/38 [GC 4086]   Sat. before St. Luke, 1 Hen. V [14 Oct. 1413]
(1) Joan Pury, widow of Richard Pury of Mitchelean; (2) William Hulot of Arlingham; (3) Richard Longneye and John Webbe of Arlingham, proctors of the church of St. Mary.

Joan has appointed William to deliver seisin to Richard and John of a selion of land in Erlyngham in the field called Mangrove in le Middelforlong.
At: Arlingham.

Various

A1/11/39 [SC 547]   Fri. the morrow of St. Katherine, 46 Edw. III [26 Nov. 1372]
John de Yate, Reginald the vicar, William de Erlyngham, and others and all the parishioners of Arlingham; and Nicholas Wyshongre, mason, of Gloucester.

Indenture made between the parishioners on the one part and Nicholas on the other concerning the building of a bell-tower to Arlingham church.
Witnesses: Sir Robert rector of Fretherne, Thomas Cadul, . . .
At: Arlingham.

A1/11/40 [GC 3721]   Sun. after All Saints, 1 Ric. II [8 Nov. 1377]
John Yate of Arlingham; and Nicholas Webbe and Robert Taylour, proctors of the church of St. Mary of Arlingham.

John has granted to Nicholas and Robert 7 selions of land in Erlyngham in the field called Northfeld, beside the land called Twelacre.
Witnesses: John Westmancote, John Hayward, Richard Cokkus, John Boulgastone, John Cordy.
At: Arlingham.

A1/11/41 [GC 3777]   Fri. after All Saints, 8 Ric. II [4 Nov. 1384]
Walter Huet of Arlingham; and John Yate, John Heyward, Robert Taylour and Nicholas Webbe.

Walter has granted to John, John, Robert and Nicholas, and their heirs and assigns, an annual rent of 2*s.* in Erlyngham from the holding of Thomas atte Walle and an annual rent of 4*d.* from a selion of land held of Joan Pouke in Neethetone.
Witnesses: John Westmoncote, John Bulgastone, Richard Cokkes, Walter Jakemon, Walter Frere.
At: Arlingham.

A1/11/42 [GC 3778]   Sat. after All Saints, 8 Ric. II [5 Nov. 1384]
Walter Huet of Arlingham; and John Yate, John Heyward, Robert Taylour and Nicholas Webbe.

Walter has granted to John, John, Robert and Nicholas, and their heirs and assigns, an annual rent of 12*d.* in Erlyngham from Walter Russel.
Witnesses: John Westmancote, Richard Cokkes, Walter Frere, William Scheof, Walter Jakemon.
At: Arlingham.

A1/11/43 [GC 3818]   Mon. after St. Laurence, 11 Ric. II [12 Aug. 1387]
John Yate, John Westmancote, John Heyward, Robert Bayly, John Bulgarstone, Richard Cokkes, William Scheoff and Walter Frere; and John Webbe, Alice his wife and Robert, Joan and Katherine their children.

John Yate and the others, with the assent of the community of the vill of Erlyngham, have leased to John, Alice, Robert, Joan and Katherine a messuage with a curtilage, which Richard Smyth formerly held in Erlyngham, called St. Mary's house; for their lives, rent to the proctors of St. Mary 4*s.* a year.
Witnesses: Ralph Wych, Richard Miltone, Philip Alayn, Walter Hyteman, Walter Jakeman.
At: Arlingham.

A1/11/44 [SC 576]   Sat. . . . , 7 Hen. IV [1405–6]
Richard Milton; and William Kentes. . . , vicar of Arlingham, and Richard de Teukesbury.

Richard has bound himself in 60 . . . [pounds?] to replace the first bell of Arlingham if it should ring out of tune with the second bell.
At: Gloucester.

A1/11/45 [GC 4016]   Eve of St. Andrew, 7 Hen. IV [29 Nov. 1405]
Robert Benteley and John Webbe, proctors of the church of St. Mary of Arlingham; and William Hulot, Katherine his wife and Robert their son.

Robert and John have leased to William, Katherine and Robert a toft of land in Erlyngham called Cuperescroft; for their lives, rent 5*d.* a year.
Witnesses: John Yate, John Westmoncote, Robert Mechelgros, William Hayward, Richard Miltone.
At: Arlingham.

A1/11/46 [GC 4017]   Eve of St. Andrew, 7 Hen. IV [29 Nov. 1405]
Robert Benteley and John Webbe, proctors of the church of St. Mary of Arlingham; and John Wylkynnes, Katherine his wife and John their son.

Robert and John have leased to John, Katherine and John a curtilage which was of William Fekkenam next to the curtilage called Cecelyhey, with a selion of land in the croft called Stuwardescroft; for their lives, rent 16*d.* a year.
Witnesses: John Yate, John Westmoncote, Robert Mechelgros, William Hayward, Richard Miltone.
At: Arlingham.

THE HEYDON HOLDING

Acquisition of the Bayly holding

Styward holdings: three selions

A1/11/47 [GC 3639]   Holy Trinity, 46 Edw. III [23 May 1372]
Richard Styward of Arlingham; and Robert Baylyf of Arlingham and Margaret his wife.

Richard has granted to Robert and Margaret, and Robert's heirs and assigns, 3 selions of land in Erlyngham in the south field, extending to the sea wall of the Severn [*murum Sabrine*].
Witnesses: Robert de Middeltone, Walter Huet, William Scheof, John Heyward, John de . . .
At: Arlingham.

A1/11/48 [GC 3724]   22 May 1 Ric. II [1378]
Robert Baylyf of Arlingham; and James Clyfford of Frampton, John Kedford of Newland [*nova terra*], Nicholas Hook of Ruardean and William Rolmies of Arlingham.

Robert has granted to James, John, Nicholas and William, and their heirs and assigns, 3 selions of land in Erlyngham in the south field beside the sea wall of the Severn [*murum Sabrine*].
Witnesses: John ate Yate, Walter Huet, John Hayward, William Schef, John Bolgarestone.
At: Arlingham.

Other Styward holdings

A1/11/49 [GC 3712]   Tues. before St. Augustine, 51 Edw. III [19 May 1377]
Agnes widow of Richard Styward of Arlingham and Robert Baylyf of Arlingham.

Agnes has quitclaimed to Robert her dower rights in the lands and holdings which Robert had by grant of Richard in Erlyngham.
Witnesses: John Yate, John Westmonkote, William Scheof, Philip Heyward, Walter Jakemonds.
At: Arlingham.

A1/11/50 [GC 3825]   Thurs. after St. James, 12 Ric. II [30 July 1388]
Robert Schouthern of Newent, John Kymhot and Thomas Clerk of Taynton; and Robert Bayly of Arlingham.

Robert, John and Thomas have quitclaimed to Robert, his heirs and assigns a selion of land in Erlyngham, which Robert acquired from Richard Steward in Erlyngham.
Witnesses: John Yate, John Westmoncote, John Hayward, Richard Cokkus, Richard Miltone.
At: Arlingham.

Jakemon holding

A1/11/51 [GC 3688]   Mon. after St. Thomas the martyr, 49 Edw. III [9 July 1375]
Walter Jakemones of Arlingham; and Robert Baylyf and Margaret his wife.

Walter has granted to Robert and Margaret, and Robert's heirs and assigns, 2 selions of land and a parcel of meadow in Erlyngham; rent to the chief lord 20*d.* a year.
Witnesses: John de Yate, John Westmankote, John Heyward, William Scheof, Richard Cokkes.
At: Arlingham.

A1/11/52 [GC 3692]   20 March 50 Edw. III [1376]
Walter Jakemon of Arlingham and Robert Baylyf of Arlingham.

Walter has granted to Robert, his heirs and assigns two messuages with curtilages and a selion of land in Erlyngham.
Witnesses: John de Yate, John Westmankote, John Heyward, Walter Huot, John Bulgastone.
At: Arlingham.

A1/11/53 [GC 3701]   Sun. after St. Lucy, 50 Edw. III [14 Dec. 1376]
Robert Baylyf of Arlingham; and William Rolves and Agnes his wife, Robert's daughter.

Robert has granted to William and Agnes and their issue two messuages and two curtilages and a selion of land in Erlyngham, which he had by grant of Walter Jakemon.
Witnesses: John Yate, John Westmonkote, Walter Huet, John Heyward, John Bulgastone.
At: Arlingham.

A1/11/54 [GC 3720]   Wed. after St. Denis, 1 Ric. II [14 Oct. 1377]
Robert Baylyf of Arlingham and William Rolves; and James Clifford of Frampton, Richard Leoward, John Ketforde, Nicholas Hoke and Walter Huet.

Robert and William have granted to James, Richard, John, Nicholas and Walter, and their heirs and assigns, all their lands [etc.] which were of Walter Jakemones in Erlyngham.
Witnesses: John Yate, John Westmancote, Thomas Thornhulle, John Heyward, John Bulgastone.
At: Arlingham.

A1/11/55 [GC 3727]   Mon. the feast of St. Thomas the apostle, 1 Ric. II [21 Dec. 1377]
Katherine daughter and heir of William Jakemon of Arlingham and Walter Jakemon of Arlingham, her uncle.

Katherine has quitclaimed to Walter all the lands and holdings in Erlyngham which were of Walter Jakemon the elder, father of Walter and grandfather of Katherine.
Witnesses: John Yate of Arlingham, John Westmonkote, Thomas Voxhongre, John Voxhongre of Rowde, John atte Venne.
At: Arlingham.

A1/11/56 [GC 3730]   Tues. before St. Mark the evangelist, 2 Ric. II [19 April 1379]
Roger Bernard of Rowde (Wilts.) and Katherine his wife; and Robert Baillyf of Arlingham (Glos.).

Roger and Katherine have granted to Robert, his heirs and assigns 2 messuages, 11 selions of land and 2 a. of meadow and pasture in Erlyngham; and Roger and Katherine are bound in £20 if Robert is disturbed in seisin by them or their heirs.
Witnesses: John atte Yate, John Westmecote, John Hayward of Arlingham, Henry Foxhangre, Thomas Foxhangre, Thomas Snappe of Rowde.
At: Rowde.

A1/11/57 [GC 3729]   Sun. before St. Mark the evangelist, 2 Ric. II [24 April 1379]
Walter Jakemon of Arlingham and Robert Baylyf of Arlingham.

Walter has quitclaimed to Robert two messuages, which were of Walter Jakemon his father, and 11 selions of land and 2 a. of meadow and pasture in Erlyngham, as in the charter of Katherine, daughter and heir of William Jakemon his brother.
Witnesses: John Yate, John Westmoncote, John Heyward, William Scheof, John Bulgastone.
At: Arlingham.

Settlements of 1414 and 1419

A1/11/58 [GC 4100]   Mon. after St. Andrew, 2 Hen. V [3 Dec. 1414]
Robert Bayly of Arlingham; and Sir John Hayward, chaplain, Thomas Staure of Newnham and Robert Bayly of Bristol, shoemaker.

Robert has granted to John, Thomas and Robert, and their heirs and assigns, all his lands and holdings in Erlyngham.
Witnesses: Richard Miltone, Robert Mochulgros, Michael ap Ythel, Richard Longneye, John Wylkyns.
At: Arlingham.

A1/11/59 [GC 4101]   Mon. after St. Andrew, 2 Hen. V [3 Dec. 1414]
Robert Bayly of Arlingham; and Sir John Hayward, chaplain, Thomas Staure of Newnham and Robert Bayly of Bristol, shoemaker.

Robert has granted to John, Thomas and Robert, and their heirs and assigns, all his goods and chattels within the lordship of Erlyngham.

Witnesses: Richard Miltone, Robert Mochulgros, Michael ap Ythel, Richard Longneye, John Wylkyns.

At: Arlingham.

A1/11/60 [GC 4117]   Fri. the feast of the translation of St. Thomas the martyr, 7 Hen. V
[7 July 1419]
Sir John Hayward, vicar of Arlingham, Thomas Staure of Newenham and Robert Bailly of Bristol, shoemaker; and Robert Bailly of Arlingham.

John, Thomas and Robert have granted to Robert Bailly of Arlingham, his heirs and assigns all their lands, holdings [etc.] within the lordship of Erlyngham, which they had by grant of the said Robert.

Witnesses: John Yate, Robert Mochulgros, Richard Miltone, William Hayward, John Aleyn.

At: Arlingham.

A1/11/61 [GC 4122]   Sat. the morrow of Michaelmas, 7 Hen. V [30 Sept. 1419]
Robert Bailly of Arlingham; and John Hayward vicar of Arlingham and Thomas Staure of Newnham.

Robert has granted to John and Thomas, and their heirs and assigns, all his lands, holdings [etc.] within the lordship of Erlyngham.

Witnesses: Richard Miltone, William Hayward, John Aleyn, John Lovell, William Howlot.

At: Arlingham.

Passage from Bayly to Heydon

A1/11/62 [GC 4177]   Michaelmas, 13 Hen. VI [29 Sept. 1434]
Robert Bayly of Arlingham and William Heydon of the same.

Robert has granted to William, his heirs and assigns 1 selion of land in the field called Hulles above Reydone and 4 perches of meadow in Pulsamesmede.

Witnesses: Robert Cordy, William Walle, Richard Robartes, Richard Bolley.

At: Arlingham.

A1/11/63 [GC 4225; *duplicate* GC 4226] Fri. before St. Gregory 20 Hen. VI [9 March 1442]
Robert Bayle of Arlingham and William Heydon of Arlingham.

Whereas Robert granted to William, his heirs and assigns all his lands and holdings [etc.] in Erlyngham, by charter dated at Erlyngham the Friday before St. Gregory, 20 Hen. VI, William has granted that if Robert pays to him, at Michaelmas A.D. 1444, 12 marks, the charter will be void.

At: Arlingham.

A1/11/64 [GC 4227]   14 March 20 Hen. VI [1442]
Robert Bayly of Arlingham (Glos.), husbandman, and William Heydon.

Robert is bound to William in 40*s.* payable at the Purification [2 Feb.] next; on the condition [*entered on the dorse*] that if Robert sells all his lands and holdings in Erlingham William will have first refusal.

A1/11/65 [GC 4239; *duplicate* GC 4240]   31 May 22 Hen. VI [1444]
Robert Bayle of Arlingham and William Heydon of Arlingham.

Whereas Robert granted to William all his lands, holdings [etc.] in Erlyngham, William

has granted that if Robert pays to him, at Michaelmas A.D. 1445, 20 marks, the charter will be void.
At: Arlingham.

A1/11/66 [GC 4251]   The Annunciation, 24 Hen. VI [25 March 1446]
Robert Bayly of Arlingham and William Heydun of the same.
    Robert has quitclaimed to William a messuage with a curtilage, rent, wood [etc.] which was of Robert in Erlyngham.
Witnesses: Robert Cordy, Richard Robars, Robert Hulet, William Rogers, William Frere.
At: Arlingham.

Acquisition of Milton holdings

A selion in le Burysonde

A1/11/67 [GC 4148]   Mon. before St. Andrew, 4 Hen. VI [26 Nov. 1425]
Richard Milton of Arlingham and William Heydon of the same.
    Richard has granted to William, his heirs and assigns a selion of land there, in le Burysonde.
Witnesses: Robert Mochulgros, William Hayward, John Forthey, Richard Longney, Robert Cordy.
At: Arlingham.

A1/11/68 [GC 4150]   Mon., Christmas Eve, 4 Hen. VI [24 Dec. 1425]
Walter Janes of Arlingham and William Heydon of Arlingham.
    Walter has quitclaimed to William a selion of land in le Burysounde.
Witnesses: Robert Mochulgros, William Hayward, Richard Milton, Richard Longneye, John Bolley.
At: Arlingham.

Other

A1/11/69 [GC 4142]   Sun. after St. Calixtus, 3 Hen. VI [15 Oct. 1424]
Richard Milton of Arlingham and William Haydon of the same.
    Richard has granted to William, his heirs and assigns 5 selions of land in the same vill, in the furlong called Polsamysforlong.
Witnesses: John Yate, Robert Mochulgros, William Hayward, Richard Longneye, John Forthey.
At: Arlingham.

A1/11/70 [GC 4154]   Wed. [*sic*] the feast of the nativity of St. Mary, 6 Hen. VI
                                                                    [8 Sept. 1427]
Richard Milton of Arlingham and William Heydon of the same.
    Richard has granted to William 5 selions of land within the lordship of Erlyngham.
Witnesses: Robert Mochulgros, William Hayward, Richard Walle, John Bolley, Robert Hoog.
At: Arlingham.

Other holdings acquired

A1/11/71 [GC 4168]   Mon. after the Purification, 8 Hen. VI [6 Feb. 1430]
Richard Bailly of Arlingham and William Heydon of the same.
    Richard has granted to William, his heirs and assigns 1 selion of land in Glasmersch.
Witnesses: Thomas Ocle, William Heyward, Robert Mochulgro, John Bolley, Philip ap Ythel.
At: Arlingham.

A1/11/72 [GC 4263]   St. George, 26 Hen. VI [23 April 1448]
Robert Fyppus of Bristol and William Heydon of Arlingham.
   Robert has quitclaimed to William 4 selions of land.
Witnesses: William Yate, Richard Robartus, Robert Cordy, William Walle, Richard Bolley.
At: Arlingham.

Settlement, 1460

A1/11/73 [GC 4302]   St. George, 38 Hen. VI [23 April 1460]
William Haydon of Arlingham; and Sir John Frere, chaplain, Thomas Boxe of Awre and
Richard Frere.
   William has granted to John, Thomas and Richard, and their heirs and assigns, all the
lands, holdings [etc.] that he had by grant of Robert Bayly in Erlyngham, except those held
of Flaxley Abbey and St. Augustine's Abbey, Bristol.
Witnesses: Sir Roger vicar of Arlingham, William Yate, esquire, Richard Roberdes, William
Walle, Thomas Hyches.
At: Arlingham.

A1/11/74 [GC 4309]   10 March 1 Edw. IV [1461]
 Sir John Frere, chaplain, of Arlingham, Thomas Box of Awre and Richard Frere of
Arlingham; and William Rogers, John Robertus, Richard Bolley, William Horne, Roger
Frere of Slowwe (*le Slo*) and John Horne.
   John, Thomas and Richard have granted to William, John, Richard, William, Roger and
John . . . lands, holdings [etc.] which they had by grant of William Heydun in the lordship
of Erlyngham.
Witnesses: William Yate, esquire, Roger Londe, vicar, Richard Robertus, William Wall,
John Mede, of Arlingham.
At: Arlingham.

A1/11/75 [GC 4317]   St. Barnabas, 2 Edw. IV [11 June 1462]
William Rogers of Arlingham, John Robertus, Richard Bolley, William Horne, Roger Frere
and John Horne of the same; and William Frere the elder of the same.
   William, John, Richard, William, Roger and John have leased to William Frere and his
issue all the lands, holdings [etc.] that they had by grant of Sir John Frere, chaplain,
Thomas Box and Richard Frere within the lordship of Erlyngham; for a term of 70 years,
rent to the chief lord 2*s.* a year, and to William, John, Richard, William, Roger and John
20*s.* a year.
Witnesses: William Yate, esquire, Richard Robertus, William Wall, John Mede, John Cordy.
At: Arlingham.

OTHER HOLDINGS
The Goose rent

A1/11/76 [GC 867]   n.d. [late 13th cent.]
Maud de la Beorewe, widow of John de la Beorewe, and Isabel her daughter.
   Maud has granted to Isabel a rent of 10*s.* within the manor of Erlyngham from the
holding of John le Gos, to her and her issue, and to revert to Maud and her heirs if Isabel
dies without issue.
Witnesses: Simon de Fromilod, Walter de Wyke, Richard de Wyke, William de Clyfford,
Robert Leoward, Richard de la Wode of Arlingham, John le Frankelayn of the same.

A1/11/77 [GC 1030]   Fri. the feast of the Purification, 30 Edw. I [2 Feb. 1302]
Alice de Salle, widow of Walter de Salle, and Isabel daughter of Maud de la Berwe.

Alice has quitclaimed to Isabel an annual rent of 10*s.*, which Maud gave to Isabel, from John le Gos in the vill of Erlyngham.
Witnesses: Richard de Salle, Walter de Wyke, Gilbert de Frethorn, Richard de Wyke, Richard de la Wode, John de Symundeshale, John le Frankeleyn.
At: Saul.

The Flambard holding

A1/11/78 [GC 980]   n.d. [early 14th cent.]
Denise la Venur of Arlingham; and Adam Flambard and Margery his wife.

Denise has granted to Adam and Margery 2 selions and one fore-earth of arable land in Erlyngham, the selions lying in the marsh below Berdone and the fore-earth in le Northfeld, also all her meadow in Cornforlong of the meadow of the said Westmerchs and half the meadow of Amicia de Grymenhulle in the same furlong of the same meadow which she inherited after the death of Amicia; Adam and Margery have given Denise 20*s.*
Witnesses: Walter de Wyke, Walter Wyth, Richard de Wyke, Richard Wyth, Richard de la Wode, Walter de Middeltone, John le Frankeleyn, clerk.

A1/11/79 [GC 2888]   Sun. after St. Martin, 11 Edw. III [16 Nov. 1337]
Thomas son of William le Spencer of Arlingham and Margery widow of Adam Flamberd of Arlingham.

Thomas has leased to Margery half of a messuage, curtilage and meadow which were of Adam in the vill of Erlyngham and which he had by grant of Alice daughter and heir of Adam; for her life, rent ¼*d.* a year.
Witnesses: Richard de Clifford, John le Hayward, Walter Janes, John With, Walter de Middeltone.
At: Arlingham.

The Smith holding

A1/11/80 [GC 2515]   n.d. [*temp.* Edw. II]
Richard the smith, son and heir of Adam the smith of Arlingham, and Richard the smith of the same.

Richard son of Adam has quitclaimed to Richard the lands and holdings which he had by his grant and sale in the vill of Erlyngham, with the reversion of the lands held in dower by Lucy widow of the late Adam the smith.
Witnesses: William le Styward, John le Hayward, Robert Jordan, Richard With, Robert le Hayward, Walter Leuward, Walter de Middeltone.

A1/11/81 [GC 2687]   Thurs. after St. Dunstan, 3 Edw. III [25 May 1329]
Richard le Smith of Arlingham and John son of William Pride of the same.

Richard has granted to John, his heirs and assigns, for a certain sum of money, an annual rent of ½*d.* from a curtilage and half a selion above la Hullus beside the land which Lucy le Smith holds in dower, from Lucy while she lives, and the reversion of the holding after her death.
Witnesses: John le Heyward, Robert Jordan, Richard With, John le Frere, William Dun, John Bridie, Walter de Middeltone.
At: Arlingham.

The Lypiatt holding

A1/11/82 [GC 2498]   n.d. [*temp.* Edw. II]
Edith Brongare; and Gilbert atte Lepeyate and Agnes his wife, Edith's daughter.

Edith has granted to Gilbert and Agnes 4 selions of land in the fields of Erlyngham, one in the field of Westmeish', one in la Southfelde, and two above the hill in the east part of

Berdone; to them and their issue, rent 4*d.* a year and, while Edith lives, half the crop growing in the selion in Westmersh, ploughing, sowing, hoeing, harvesting and carting half the crop to her house in Erlyngham at their expense.
Witnesses: Walter Wyth, Walter de Middeltone, Elias le Ferour, Robert Geffrei, Richard Wyth, Robert le Hayward, John le Frankelein, clerk.

A1/11/83 [GC 3486]   Sun. in the Invention of Holy Cross, 23 Edw. III [3 May 1349]
William son of Gilbert ate Leopeyate; and Gilbert his father, and Agnes, Gilbert's wife and William's mother.

   William has leased to Gilbert and Agnes 4 selions and a fore-earth of land in Erlingham; for their lives, rent ¼*d.* a year.
Witnesses: Walter With, . . . ate Berewe, Richard Styward, Walter Middeltone, Walter Ferour.
At: Arlingham.

Holdings of Richard and Robert Hayward

A1/11/84 [GC 3218]   Wed. the feast of the Annunciation, 23 Edw. III [25 March 1349]
John son of Robert le Hayward of Arlingham; and Richard le Hayward and Robert le Hayward, his brothers.
   John has granted to Richard and Robert, and their heirs, 18 selions of land in Erlyngham.
Witnesses: Walter Wyth, Richard le Stiward, Walter Jakemones, Robert de Myddeltone, John Janus.
At: Arlingham.

A1/11/85 [GC 3219]   Mon. after the Annunciation, 23 Edw. III [30 March 1349]
Richard son of Robert le Hayward of Arlingham and Robert le Hayward, his brother; and Walter Wyth, Walter Jakemones, John Janes, Robert de Middeltone, William son of Walter de Middeltone and Richard le Styward of Arlingham.
   Richard and Robert have granted to Walter and the others a rent of 5*s.* a year from lands which they had by grant of John son of Robert le Hayward, in Erlyngham. [*In French.*]
Witnesses: Walter de Symondeshale, Hugh de la Wode, Walter Jordan, Richard Cordy, Richard le Frere.
At: Arlingham.

A1/11/86 [SC 524]   Tues. after [the Annunciation], 23 Edw. III [31 March 1349?]
Walter Wyth, Walter Jakemones, John Janes, Robert de Middeltone, William son of Walter de Middleton and Richard le Styward of Arlingham; and Richard son of Robert le Hayward and Robert le Hayward, his brother.
   Walter and the others have acquitted Richard and Robert le Hayward of a rent of 15*s.* which they owe for land in Erlyngham, on condition that Richard and Robert distribute every Friday before Easter 4*s.* worth of white bread to the poor of Erlyngham and give 2 candles, containing 4 lb. of wax, for the lights in the chancel of the church at the elevation of the Host.
Witnesses: Richard de Clifford, . . . , Walter de Symondeshale, Walter le Ferour, Walter de Middeltone.
At: Arlingham.

The Pride or Baker holding

A1/11/87 [SC 396]   n.d. [*c.* 1360]
John Pride, son of John Pryde of Arlingham, and William le Baker.
   John has granted to William a messuage and selion of land extending to Ladyorchard, and 3 selions in the fields of Arlingham at Glasmersch, Polland and Waterusloudwyth.

Witnesses: Walter Wyth, Walter Jakemonns, Richard Stywarde, Thomas Bolgastone, John le Heywarde.

A1/11/88 [GC 803]   n.d. [*c.* 1360]
John Pride, son of John Pride of Arlingham, and William le Baker of the same.

   John has granted to William a messuage with 1 selion of land and a curtilage, and 3 selions of land in Erlingham, one between the land called Polland and the land called Waterislouwyth, to hold of the chief lord of the fee.
Witnesses: Walter Wyth, Walter Jakemon, Richard Stiward, Thomas Bolgarstone, John le Heyward. [*Early 15th-cent. copy.*]

A1/11/89 [GC 2547]   n.d. [*c.* 1360]
John Pride, son of John Pride of Arlingham, and William le Baker of the same.

   John has granted to William, his heirs and assigns all his lands and holdings at Erlingham with the reversions and all other appurtenances.
Witnesses: Walter Wyth, Walter Jakemones, Richard Stiwarde, . . . Wolgaston, John le Heywarde. [*15th-cent. copy.*]

A1/11/90 [GC 4079]   n.d. [*c.* 1360]
John son of John Pride of Arlingham, and William le Bakere of the same.

   John has granted to William a cottage with a curtilage.
Witnesses: Walter Wyth, Walter Jakemanns, Richard Stiward, Robert de Midlintone, John Janus. [*15th-cent. copy.*]

The Styward curtilage

A1/11/91 [GC 3640]   Sun. after St. Augustine, 46 Edw. III [30 May 1372]
Richard Styward of Arlingham; and William Fekkenham of the same and Margery his wife.

   Richard has granted to William and Margery, and William's heirs and assigns, a curtilage in Erlyngham.
Witnesses: Robert de Middeltone, Richard Clifford, William Scheof, John Heyward, Walter Jakemones.
At: Arlingham.

A1/11/92 [GC 3297]   Mon. the morrow of St. Hilary, 49 Edw. III [14 Jan. 1375]
William Feckenham of Arlingham; and Robert Baylyf, John Heyward, Walter Frere, Richard Cokkes, Hugh atte Wode and Walter Symondeshale.

   William has granted to Robert, John, Walter, Richard, Hugh and Walter, and their heirs and assigns, the curtilage which he had by grant of Richard Styward in Erlyngham.
Witnesses: John de Yate, John Westmoncote, Walter Jakemones, William Scheof, Thomas Peynte.
At: Arlingham.

The Arlingham or Frampton holding

A1/11/93 [GC 3589]   Fri. after St. Scholastica, 41 Edw. III [12 Feb. 1367]
Robert Hobbynes of Arlingham and William de Erlyngham.

   Robert has granted to William, his heirs and assigns 1 selion of land in the furlong [*stadium*] called Westwal; rent a rose a year.
Witnesses: William Dorylot, John Cordy, Gerald Adames, Richard Kokkes, Walter Frere.
At: Arlingham.

A1/11/94 [GC 3733; *duplicate* GC 3963]   Sat. before St. Edmund the king, 3 Ric. II
                                                                        [19 Nov. 1379]
William Erlyngham, burgess of Bristol, and John Fromptone of Arlingham.

   William has granted to John, his heirs and assigns all his lands and holdings in

Erlyngham, which he acquired from John Ridare, William Westmoncote, Robert [Hobbekyne] and John Pride.

Witnesses: John atte Yate, John Westmoncote, John Hayward, Richard Cockes, Thomas Cadul, John Rolkestone, Thomas Peyntour, John Thornehulle.

At: Llanthony by Gloucester.

A1/11/95 [GC 3734]   Sat. before St. Edmund the king, 3 Ric. II [19 Nov. 1379]

(1) William Erlyngham, burgess of Bristol; (2) John Hayward of Arlingham; (3) John Fromptone of Arlingham.

William has appointed John Hayward to give seisin to John Fromptone of all his lands and holdings in Erlyngham, which he acquired from John Ridare, William Westmoncote, Robert . . . and John Pride.

At: Llanthony by Gloucester.

The Pyke holding

A1/11/96 [GC 4388]   Fri. after St. Luke, 14 Edw. IV [28 Oct. 1474]

Richard Baldewyn of Grove and Walter Ketteford of Arlingham; and Sir Walter Longeney, chaplain, and John Roberts of Arlingham.

Richard and Walter have quitclaimed to Walter and John all the lands [etc.] in Erlyngham (Glos.) which they had by grant of Thomas Pyke of Wantage.

At: Wantage.

A1/11/97 [GC 4432]   Christmas Day, 22 Edw. IV [25 Dec. 1482]

Sir Walter Longeney, vicar of Arlingham, and John Rols of the same; and Walter Knyth of the same, Margaret his wife and Roger their son.

Walter and John have leased to Walter, Margaret and Roger a holding in Harlyngham which Walter Ketteford previously held; for their lives, rent 13s. 4d. a year.

Witnesses: Sir Walter Cordy, John Longney, John Horne.

At: Arlingham.

The Burysonde plot

A1/11/98 [GC 4454]   10 July 2 Hen. VII [1487]

John Frere, vicar of Portbury, John Frampton of Painswick, Nicholas Myll of Oxlinch (*Hockyslynge*) and Roger Aleyn of Eastington; and Richard Yate, gentleman, Walter Longeney, vicar of Arlingham, Walter Cordy, clerk, and John Horne.

John, John, Nicholas and Roger have granted to Richard, Walter, Walter and John, and their heirs and assigns, a vacant plot in le Burysonde in Erlyngham (Glos.), which they had by grant of William Wall, 5 by 3 perches; rent to the chief lord a red rose a year.

Witnesses: John Roberdys, William Cordy the elder, John Rollys, Henry Frere, Richard Sowth.

At: Arlingham.

A1/11/99 [GC 4455]   10 [July] 2 Hen. VII [1487]

(1) John Frere, vicar of Portbury, John Frampton of Painswick, Nicholas Myll of Oxlinch (*Hockyslynge*) and Roger Aleyn of Eastington; (2) Roger Cordy and John Evans; (3) Richard Yate, gentleman, Walter Longeney, vicar of Arlingham, Walter Cordy, clerk, and John Horne.

John, John, Nicholas and Roger have appointed Roger and John to give seisin to Richard, Walter, Walter and John, and their heirs and assigns, of a vacant plot in le Burysonde in Erlyngham (Glos.).

At: Arlingham.

Miscellaneous

A1/11/100 [SC 125]   n.d. [early 13th cent.]
John of the wood (*de bosco*) and John the chaplain, son of William Lefward.

John of the wood has granted to John the chaplain a selion of land in the field of Clunmarisco next to the ditch of Wurthin; rent a pair of white gloves a year at Easter. John the chaplain has given to John of the wood 15*s*., to Alice his wife 6*d*. and to John his heir 6*d*.

Witnesses: Elias de Beovilla, Hugh de Wika, Gilbert de Lincha, Roger de Camma, John de Dreicote, William parson of Erlingham, now dean, William the chaplain.

A1/11/101 [SC 298]   Nativity of St. John the Baptist [24 June] A.D. 1248
Roger de Cantilupo and Robert Bruning.

Roger has granted to Robert two putts in the Severn at a place called Monerewe, lying between the putts of Peter de Wike and the putts of Stephen de Holeweie; rent 1*d*. a year, and Robert has given him ½ mark.

Witnesses: William dean of Arlingham, Peter de Wika, Gilbert de Linch Richard de Sancta Brigida, Robert Guys (*Guidonis*), William Lefward, Adam Bertram.

A1/11/102 [GC 2541]   n.d. [late Hen. III]
Richard Pancevoth, lord of Hasfield, and St. Augustine's Abbey, Bristol.

Richard has quitclaimed to the abbey the land called la Berewe and 12 a. of meadow.

Witnesses: Sir Maurice de Berkel', Sir Maurice de Saltmarsh (*de salso marisco*), knights, Reginald de Acle, Henry Haket, Robert de Ledene, John de Paris, William de Morcote, John de Gyrumvile, Richard Toky.

A1/11/103 [GC 1305]   n.d. [*temp*. Edw. I]
Robert Cordi of Arlingham and Agnes his daughter.

Robert has leased to Agnes 3 selions of land in Erlyngham, one lying in Revelond, one in Westmersch and one at Cobelworthestret; for her life, paying to the church of Erlyngham, for the souls of Robert and Edith his wife, 4*d*. a year to the collector of works and 4*d*. a year to the collector of masses.

Witnesses: Richard de Clifford, Walter With, Richard le Styward, Walter son of John de Middeltone, Walter de Middeltone.

A1/11/104 [GC 957]   n.d. [early 14th cent.]
Richard de Sancta Brigida and John de la Brugge of Arlingham.

Richard has granted to John 3 selions of land within the manor of Erlyngham, two next to the ditch called Bardonus Deyc and one against la Berue; rent a clove a year, and John has given him 16*s*.

Witnesses: Robert Wid, John Wid, Walter de Wiche, Robert Lenard, Richard of the wood (*de bosco*), William Chadul, Richard le Frere.

A1/11/105 [GC 2439]   Fri. the morrow of St. Guthlac, 18 Edw. II [12 April 1325]
Ralph son of Thomas le Baker of Edgeworth (*Eggesworth*); and John Corneys and Alesia and Alice his sisters.

Ralph has quitclaimed to John, Alesia and Alice 2 a. of land in the vill of Erlyngham, as is more fully described in the charter of Richard le Baker his grandfather.

Witnesses: Richard de Clifford, Walter de Middultone, John le Hayward, John le Frankeleyn, John Frer'.

At: Arlingham.

A1/11/106 [GC 2640]   Easter Sunday, 1 Edw. III [12 April 1327]
Walter son of Robert Geoffrey of Arlingham and Maud his sister; and Robert their father.

Walter and Maud have leased to Robert the messuage, garden, and curtilage which they

had by grant of Robert in Middeltone in the vill of Erlingham, and also 6 selions of land, of which three lie in the territory called Glasemersch, two in the marsh of la Reye and one in Walforlong of Glasemersch, and 3 selions in the territory of Westmersch; for his life, rent 2*d.* a year.
Witnesses: Robert Jordan, John le Hayward, John le Frere, William Jones, Walter de Middeltone.
At: Arlingham.

A1/11/107 [GC 2685]　　　　　　　　　Sun. after Michaelmas, 3 Edw. III [1 Oct. 1329]
William Dun of Arlingham and Walter son of John de Middeltone of the same.
　　William has granted to Walter, his heirs and assigns, for £10, the messuage with a garden, curtilage, land, meadow [etc.] which John ate Slo formerly held in Erlingham, which William had by grant of John de la Beruwe; rent to the chief lord 4*s.* 5½*d.* a year.
Witnesses: Robert Jordan, Robert le Hayward, Richard With, John le Frere, Walter Janes, John le Taylur, John Bride, Richard son of John le Hayward, Walter de Middeltone.
At: Arlingham.

A1/11/108 [GC 3155]　　　　　　　Thurs. the feast of St. Andrew, 20 Edw. III [30 Nov. 1346]
John son of Robert Geffrey and John son of John Warde.
　　John Geffrey has granted to John Warde 1 selion of land in the territory of Erlingham in the furlong called Omberleye, and John Warde has granted to John Geffrey 1 selion of land above the sand-pit (*sablum*) in the vill of Erlingham.
Witnesses: Walter With, John le Heyward, John With, Richard le Stiward, Walter Janes, Richard Jones, Richard the clerk.
At: Arlingham.

A1/11/109 [GC 3217]　　　　　　　　Fri. after St. Gregory, 23 Edw. III [13 March 1349]
Walter de Middiltone the younger and Margaret daughter of John Geffrey of Arlingham.
　　Walter has granted to Margaret all the lands and holdings which he had in Erlyngham by grant of the said John; to her and her issue, with remainder to Isabel, John's daughter and Margaret's sister, and her issue, and John's right heirs.
Witnesses: Walter With, Richard le Styward, Walter Jakemones, Walter Jordan, Richard Cordi.
At: Arlingham.

A1/11/110 [GC 3221]　　　　　　　　Wed. after St. Ambrose, 23 Edw. III [8 April 1349]
Walter Wyth of Arlingham, lord of the Barrow, and Walter son of John de Middeltone of Arlingham.
　　Walter Wyth has quitclaimed to Walter de Middeltone a messuage, garden, land [etc.], which Walter de Middeltone previously held of Maud de la Berwe in Erlyngham, saving to Walter Wyth and his heirs an annual rent of 4*s.* 5½*d.*
Witnesses: Richard le Styward, Robert de Middeltone, Richard le Heyward, Walter de Symondeshale, Walter de Middeltone.
At: Arlingham.

A1/11/111 [GC 3448]　　　　　　　Mon. before Holy Trinity, 30 Edw. III [13 June 1356]
Walter Jakemonns of Arlingham and Sir William vicar of Arlingham.
　　Walter has granted to William, his heirs and assigns a messuage in Erlyngham, a messuage and curtilage in the same vill, 11 selions of land in the same parish and 2 a. of meadow in Westmersch.
Witnesses: John atte Yate, William Westmoncote, Robert Midlintone, Walter Huet, Richard Styward.
At: Arlingham.

A1/11/112 [GC 3664]   Fri. the feast of St. Wulfstan, 48 Edw. III [19 Jan. 1375]
Sir Roger vicar of Arlingham and Robert Taylour; and Cecilia Scott and John her son.

Roger and Robert have granted to Cecilia and John, and John's issue, all the lands and holdings in Erlyngham which they had by grant of John Schowe, Cecilia's husband and John's father; with remainder to Robert Bayly, John Heyward, John Bulgastone, Walter Jakemones, Richard Kokkes, Walter Frere and Walter Symondeshale, and their heirs and assigns.
Witnesses: John Yate, John Westmonkote, Robert Middeltone, Walter Huet, Thomas Peyntour.
At: Arlingham.

A1/11/113 [GC 3757]   Thurs. after Epiphany, 6 Ric. II [8 Jan. 1383]
Margery Pernel of Arlingham and Robert Benteley, mercer.

Margery has leased to Robert, for the term of her life, her messuage with a curtilage in Erlyngham; rent 3*s*. 4*d*. a year.
Witnesses: John Yate, John Westmancote, John Heyward, Robert Baylyf, Walter Jakemon.
At: Arlingham.

A1/11/114 [GC 3804]   Tues. the morrow of St. Barnabas, 9 Ric. II [12 June 1386]
Walter Pride of Arlingham; and Robert Bayly and Walter Hykemon.

Walter has granted to Robert and Walter, and their heirs and assigns, all his lands, holdings [etc.] which were of William Ganes in Erlyngham.
Witnesses: John Yate, John Westmancote, John Heyward, Walter Jakemon, William Scheof.
At: Arlingham.

A1/11/115 [GC 3979]   The Exaltation of Holy Cross, 1 Hen. IV [14 Sept. 1400]
Thomas Smyth, son and heir of Richard Smyth of Arlingham; and William Hayward and Robert Bentteley.

Thomas has granted to William and Robert, and their heirs and assigns, 1 selion of land in the field called Glasemersch.
Witnesses: John Yate, John Westmoncote, William Partrygge, Walter Frere, Richard Miltone.
At: Arlingham.

A1/11/116 [GC 4118]   Mon. after the translation of St. Thomas the martyr, 7 Hen. V
                                                        [10 July 1419]
Robert Bailly of Arlingham and Walter Fekenham of the same.

Robert has granted to Walter, his heirs and assigns 3 selions of land in various fields in Erlyngham.
Witnesses: John Yate, Robert Mochulgros, Richard Miltone, William Hayward, John Aleyn.
At: Arlingham.

A1/11/117 [GC 4149]   Mon., Christmas Eve, 4 Hen. VI [24 Dec. 1425]
Walter Janes of Arlingham and John Hopkyns *alias* Nichol of Malmesbury.

Walter has granted to John, his heirs and assigns 7 selions of land in Erlyngham.
Witnesses: Robert Mochulgros, Richard Miltone, William Hayward, Richard Longney, John Bolley.
At: Arlingham.

A1/11/118 [GC 4281]   12 Jan. 32 Hen. VI [1454]
John Cassy and William Notyngham, the king's commissioners; and the vill of Arlingham.

Receipt for the payment of the fifteenth and tenth, from Erlyngham, 60*s*.; under the seals of John and William.

A1/11/119 [GC 4435]   St. Gregory, 23 Edw. IV [12 March 1483]
John Fekeman of Newent; and John Horne, Richard Sowth and Walter Knyth.

John has granted to John, Richard and Walter 5 selions of land in Erlyngham.
Witnesses: John Longeney, John Wilkyns, John Frere, John Rolvis, Robert Bown.
At: Arlingham.

BERKELEY BOROUGH

The borough evolved at the Castle gate from the market mentioned in Domesday Book, but it was never a very significant commercial centre. A new town of Berkeley was created in the mid 13th century, along with the new towns at Newport and Wotton; there was also, distinct from the borough, a 'vill' of Berkeley which formed part of Ham manor.

BERKELEY ACQUISITIONS
The Maydose shop

A1/12/1 [GC 778]   n.d. [late 13th cent.]
Eve Maidosa, widow of William the baker (*pistor*) of Berkeley, and Henry son of Ralph le Gardiner of Berkeley.

Eve has granted to Henry a shop in the new town of Berkel', between the holding of Robert the smith and the street from la Boregate to the chapel of St. Radegund, and next to the road from Berkeley market to the bridge called Locfastebruge; rent 4 horseshoes a year, and Henry has given her 30*s*.
Witnesses: Thomas Alein, Walter Shipward, John Sewaker, John Bonserjant, Henry Cuppere, William Cuppere, Roger Tannare, Henry Grout.

A1/12/2 [GC 1632]   n.d. [*temp.* Edw. I]
Henry called Gardiner' of Berkeley and Sir Thomas de Berkel' his lord.

Henry has granted to Thomas a messuage in the new town of Berkel' which he had by grant of Eve called Maydose, next to the lane [*venella*] leading to the chapel of St. Radegund; Thomas has given him a certain sum of money.
Witnesses: Walter Schipward, Thomas Aleyn, John Sewaker, John Bonserjant, John Marescall, Henry le Cuppere, Richard le Savoner.

The Wood holding

A1/12/3 [GC 701]   n.d. [late 13th cent.]
John of the wood (*de bosco*) and Richard called Olyver.

John has granted to Richard the messuage with a curtilage which he inherited next to churchyard of Berkeley church, which was of Nicholas vicar of Berkeley his uncle, with all appurtenances except a house next to the road from the churchyard to the market of Berkeleye; rendering to the chief lord of the fee the customary services, viz. 3*s*. a year and suit to borough court of Berkeleye, and Richard has given him 100*s*.
Witnesses: Robert de Stanes, William Capel, Richard de Wyke, John Sewaker, Walter le C . . .

A1/12/4 [GC 1500]   n.d. [*temp.* Edw. I]
Richard Oliver and Sir Thomas de Berkel', his lord.

Richard has granted to Thomas the messuage with a curtilage beside the churchyard of Berkeleye which he bought from John of the wood (*de bosco*).
Witnesses: Robert de Stone, Robert de Wyther, Thomas de Swonhungre, John Sewaker, John Bonserjant, Henry le Coppere, Henry le Gardiner.

The Woodland holding

A1/12/5 [GC 843]   n.d. [late 13th cent.]
John de la Wodelonde and Sir Thomas de Berkeley, lord of Berkeley.

John has quitclaimed to Thomas a cottage in the town of Berkeley, next to the churchyard.

Witnesses: John Sewaker, John le Cuppere, Henry le Gardiner, Richard le Cuppere, Philip Coby.

A1/12/6 [GC 1051]   Sat. before St. Kenelm, 31 Edw. I [13 July 1303]
Maud widow of John de la Wodelond and Sir Thomas de Berkel', lord of Berkeley.

Maud has quitclaimed to Thomas her dower rights in all the lands which Thomas had by grant from John.

Witnesses: Robert de Bradestone, Robert de Berkel', Thomas de Beoleye, Thomas de Stintescombe, Robert de Buttelescomb, Robert Wyther, Richard de Wyk, John de Swonhungre, Richard Sone.

At: Berkeley.

The Gossard holding

A1/12/7 [GC 913]   n.d. [late 13th cent.]
Alice called Goshurde of Berkeley and William de Modibroc.

Alice has granted to William a messuage in the borough of Berkel'; to him and Helen his wife, rent 2*d.* a year to the lord of Berkeley, and they have given her 10*s.*

Witnesses: John Sewaker, reeve, Thomas Alein, John Bonserjant, Walter Schipward, Henry le Cuppere, Walter le Cuppere, Richard le Savoner.

A1/12/8 [GC 1328]   n.d. [late Hen. III]
Aldith la Cuppere of Berkeley and William Gosherde, her son.

Aldith has granted to William the rent of 1*d.* a year from William de Modibroc for a house.

Witnesses: Walter Shipward, John Sewaker, John Marscall, Henry Cuppere, William the smith.

A1/12/9 [GC 1485]   n.d. [*temp.* Edw. I]
William de Modibrok and Helen his wife; and Sir Thomas de Berkeleye.

William and Helen have quitclaimed to Thomas the messuage with a curtilage in the borough of Berkel' which they had by grant of William le Gosherde, Aldith le Gosherde and Alice le Gosherde.

Witnesses: Sir Walter vicar of Berkeley, Robert de Stone, Robert de Bradestone, Walter le Cuppere, John Sewaker, John le Cuppere, Nicholas de Pedynton, clerk.

A1/12/10 [GC 640]   Morrow of the Purification, 26 Edw. I [3 Feb. 1298]
Sir Thomas de Berkeley; and William de Modibrok and Helen his wife.

Thomas has granted to William and Helen the wardship and marriage of Eve, daughter and heir of Roger de Modibrok, also that they should have 1 a. of land which they had from Henry le Grout and 1 a. from Richard Averey and the garden from Richard le Marescal and a plot in Berkeley borough which they bought from Adam Hanekyn, and freedom from market tolls in Berkeley for their lives, and materials to build a house; and in return William and Helen have quitclaimed to Thomas a messuage and curtilage in Berkeley borough which they had from William le Gosherde, Aldyth le Gosherde and Alice le Gosherde.

Witnesses: Robert de Stone, Robert de Bradestone, John de Egeton, Richard Averey, Walter le Cuppere, John le Cuppere, Nicholas the clerk.

The Veel holding

A1/12/11 [GC 1118]   Thurs. in Ascension, 34 Edw. I [12 May 1306]
Thomas le Veel and Sir Thomas de Berkelee, lord of Berkeley.

Thomas le Veel has quitclaimed to Thomas de Berkelee, for a certain sum of money, two messuages and plots in the town of Berkelee which he had by grant of Sir Maurice de Berkelee, father of Thomas.
Witnesses: Henry le Gardener, John le Cuppere, Walter le Cuppere, John Sewaker, William le Wylde, John Kyllecote, Roger le Cuppere.
At: Berkeley.

A1/12/12 [GC 1120]   22 May 34 Edw. I [1306]
Thomas de Berkel', lord of Berkeley, and William Iweyn.

Thomas has granted to William a plot in the town of Berkel', which Thomas le Veel previously held by grant of Maurice de Berkel', Thomas's father, and which he remitted to Thomas; to William and his issue, rent 4*s.* a year.
Witnesses: Henry le Gardener, John le Cuppere, Roger le Cuppere, Walter le Cuppere, John de Killecote.
At: Berkeley.

The Coby house

A1/12/13 [GC 1851]   Tues. the feast of St. Thomas the apostle, 5 Edw. II [21 Dec. 1311]
Thomas de Berkelee, lord of Berkeley, and Leticia Schipward.

Thomas has granted to Leticia three bays of a house [*spacia domus*] with a curtilage near the holding of John Sely, which he had by grant of Philip Coby, between Thomas's garden and the road, in Berkelee; to her and her issue, rent to Philip Coby while he lives 6*s.* a year and after his death to Thomas and his heirs.
Witnesses: John le Cuppere, Henry le Gardener, Roger le Cuppere, John le Schipward, Robert le Schipward.
At: Berkeley.

A1/12/14 [GC 1860]   1 Feb. 5 Edw. II [1312]
Thomas de Berkelee, lord of Berkeley; and Thomas Alayn and Isabel his wife.

Thomas de Berkelee has granted to Thomas Alayn and Isabel two bays of a house [*spacia domus*] with a curtilage which he had by grant of Philip Coby in Berkelee; to them and their issue, rent 4*s.* a year to Philip Coby while he lives, and after his death to Thomas de Berkelee and his heirs.
Witnesses: John le Cuppere, Henry le Gardener, Roger le Cuppere, John Sewaker, John Schippard.
At: Berkeley.

A1/12/15 [GC 2046]   1 June 8 Edw. II [1315]
Thomas de Berkeleye, lord of Berkeley; and Margaret Aylwyne and Alice her daughter.

Thomas has leased to Margaret and Alice two bays of a house [*spacia domus*] which he had by grant of Philip Coby in the borough of Berkeleye; for their lives, rent to Philip Coby while he lives 4*s.* a year, and after his death to Thomas; with liberty, for their lives, to buy and sell in the port and marketplace of the borough.
Witnesses: John le Cuppere, Henry le Gardener, Roger le Cuppere, Robert Groundy, Henry de Kyllecote.
At: Berkeley.

A1/12/16 [GC 2159]   The Annunciation, 10 Edw. II [25 March 1317]
Thomas de Berckel' lord of Berkeley; and John son of Philip Cobi of Berkeley and John son of Nicholas Cobi.

Thomas has granted to John and John a bay [*spaciam*] of the house which he had by grant of the said Philip in Berckel', with the adjacent curtilage; for their lives, rent 2*s.* a year.
Witnesses: John le Coppere, Henry le Gardiner, Robert Groundi, Roger le Coppere, William Bodde.
At: Berkeley.

The Mason holding in Longbridge Street

A1/12/17 [GC 2528]   n.d. [early 14th cent.]
Thomas le Mason of Stone and Robert Nottestoke of Stone.

Thomas has granted to Robert, his heirs and assigns his holding in the borough of Berkelee in Longebruggestrete.
Witnesses: John le Cuppere, Roger le Cuppere, Henry le Gardiner, John le Schipward, Walter Snyte, Richard Broun, Walter de Sotheraye.
At: Berkeley.

A1/12/18 [GC 1855]   Thurs. in Epiphany, 5 Edw. II [6 Jan. 1312]
Robert Nottestok of Stone and Sir Thomas de Berkelee, lord of Berkeley.

Robert has granted to Thomas his holding in the borough of Berkelee in Longebruggestrete, which he had by grant of Thomas le Mason of Stone, next to the holding formerly of Walter de Gloucestre.
Witnesses: Thomas de Stone, John Capel, John le Cuppere, Henry le Gardener, Roger le Cuppere, John Sewaker, Edward de Fromelode.
At: Berkeley.

The Waleys holding in Castle Street

A1/12/19 [GC 1094]   Sun. after Easter, 33 Edw. I [25 April 1305]
William le Waleys of Wotton; and John le Coppere of Berkeley and Maud his wife.

William has granted to John and Maud his holding in Berckel', which he had by grant of William Brayn, son and heir of William le Belmon, in the street before the castle, to them and John's heirs; rent 12*d.* a year to the chief lord of the fee, and they have given him a certain sum of money.
Witnesses: Nicholas de Stowe, constable, Walter Sewaker, Henry le Gardiner, Roger le Coppere, Philip Coby, Richard Noblepas, Davi Page [*sic*], Robert Swele, William Purlewent, clerk.
At: Berkeley.

A1/12/20 [GC 1881]   1 June 5 Edw. II [1312]
John le Cuppere and Sir Thomas de Berkelee, lord of Berkeley.

John has granted to Thomas the plot which he had by grant of William le Waleys in the borough of Berkelee.
Witnesses: Henry le Gardener, John Sewoker, Roger le Cuppere, Edward de Fomelode, Adam Pynel.
At: Berkeley.

The Kilcott shop

A1/12/21 [GC 1896]   Wed. after St. Hilary, 6 Edw. II [17 Jan. 1313]
Henry de Killecote and Sir Thomas de Berkelee, his lord.

Henry has granted to Thomas his shop, which he had by grant of John de Killecote, his father, in the borough of Berkelee.
Witnesses: John le Cuppere, Henry le Gardener, John Sewaker, Roger le Cuppere, John le Schippard.
At: Berkeley.

A1/12/22 [GC 1899]   1 Feb. 6 Edw. II [1313]
Thomas de Berk', lord of Berkeley, and Robert Groundy.

Thomas has granted to Robert the shop which he had by grant of Henry de Killecote in the borough of Berk'; rent 6*d.* a year.
Witnesses: John le Cuppere, John Sewaker, Henry le Gardynder, Roger le Cuppere, David Page, Hugh le Proute, John le Schipward.
At: Berkeley.

The Lipsey holding in Church Street

A1/12/23 [GC 1616]   n.d. [*temp.* Edw. I]
Isabel Lipsi of Berkeley and Sir Thomas de Berkel', her lord.

Isabel has granted to Thomas her holding in Berkel' in the street from the church to the marketplace; Thomas has given her 1 mark.
Witnesses: Walter Schipward, reeve of the borough, Richard Averey, John Sewaker, John Bonserjant, Henry Cuppere.

A1/12/24 [GC 1902]   10 Feb. 6 Edw. II [1313]
Thomas de Berkelee, lord of Berkeley; and William le Fox, Juliana his wife, Walter their son and Mary his wife.

Thomas has granted to William, Juliana, Walter and Mary the holding which Isabel Lipsy held of Thomas, between Thomas's garden and the road from the church to the marketplace in the borough of Berkelee; to them and the issue of Walter and Mary, rent 2*s.* a year while William and Juliana live, and thereafter 3*s.* a year.
Witnesses: John le Cuppere, Henry le Gardener, John Sewaker, Roger le Cuppere, John le Schippard.
At: Berkeley.

The Glover shop

A1/12/25 [GC 2028]   1 April 8 Edw. II [1315]
Agnes le Glovare, widow, and Thomas de Berkeleye, lord of Berkeley.

Agnes has granted to Thomas, his heirs and assigns, for a certain sum of money, her portion of a shop in the borough of Berkeleye.
Witnesses: John le Cuppere, Henry le Gardyner, John Sewaker, John Judde, William Bodde.
At: Berkeley.

A1/12/26 [GC 2032]   20 April 8 Edw. II [1315]
Thomas de Berkeleye, lord of Berkeley, and Thomas called le Muleward.

Thomas de Berkeleye has granted to Thomas le Muleward, his heirs and assigns the half of a shop which he had by grant of Agnes le Glovare in the borough of Berkeleye; rent, 2*s.* a year.
Witnesses: Henry le Gardener, John le Cuppere, John Sewaker, Edward de Fromelode, Roger le Cuppere.
At: Berkeley.

The Berton holding in Marybrook Street

A1/12/27 [GC 2043]   16 May 8 Edw. II [1315]
Richard de Salle and Sir Thomas de Berkeleye, lord of Berkeley.

Richard has granted to Thomas his right and claim to a messuage and curtilage in Berkeleye which he had by grant of William de Bertone and his wife Denise by a fine of Easter 8 Edw. II.
Witnesses: John le Cuppere, Henry le Gardener, Roger le Cuppere, Robert Groundy, Henry de Kyllecote.
At: Berkeley.

A1/12/28 [GC 2356]   1 June 14 Edw. II [1321]
Thomas de Berkelee, lord of Berkeley, and Richard son of Robert Phelipes of Wanswell.

Thomas has granted to Richard the messuage and curtilage in Modybrok Street which he
had by grant of William de Bertone and his wife Denise in the borough of Berkelee; for life,
rent a rose a year.
Witnesses: John le Serjaunt, John Capel, John de la Hay, John le Cuppere, Henry le
Gardener.
At: Berkeley.

The Wood rent

A1/12/29 [GC 2100]   1 June 9 Edw. II [1316]
William atte Wode of Alkington and Sir Thomas de Berkeleye, his lord.

William has rendered and quitclaimed to Thomas, his heirs and assigns a rent of 7*d.* for a
house in St. Michael Street beside the churchyard in the borough of Berkeleye.
Witnesses: Thomas de Bradeston, John Capel, John le Serjant, John Wyth, John le Cuppere,
Henry le Gardener, John Sewaker.
At: Berkeley.

A1/12/30 [GC 2105; *duplicate* GC 2106]   Sun. after St. Barnabas, 9 Edw. II [13 June 1316]
(1) William atte Wode of Alkington; (2) his wife Maud le Herde; (3) Sir Thomas de
Berkeleye.

Whereas William enfeoffed Thomas of a rent of 6*d.* a year in the borough of Berkeleye
from a house in St. Michael Street for 6*s.* which Thomas gave him, and Maud his wife
quitclaimed the rent to Thomas, William grants that, if she survives him, his executors will
give her the 6*s.* [*In French.*]
Witnesses: John Capel, John le Serjant, John Wyth, John Sewaker, Henry le Gardener.
At: Berkeley.

The Soper holding

A burgage in Longbridge Street

A1/12/31 [GC 2109]   Thurs. the nativity of St. John the Baptist, 9 Edw. II [24 June 1316]
Denise widow of Richard le Sopere and Robert her son.

Denise has rendered to Robert the burgage opposite the court of St. Augustine's Abbey,
Bristol, beside the road from Longebrugge to the marketplace of Berkeleye, in Berkeleye.
Witnesses: Henry le Gardener, Roger le Cuppere, Nicholas Daungervile, John Martin,
Henry de Kyllecote.
At: Berkeley.

A1/12/32 [GC 2111]   1 July 9 Edw. II [1316]
Robert son and heir of the late Richard le Sopere and Sir Thomas de Berkeleye, lord of
Berkeley.

Robert has granted to Thomas, his heirs and assigns his burgage opposite the court of St.
Augustine's Abbey, Bristol, beside the road from Longebrugge to the marketplace of
Berkeleye, in Berkeleye.
Witnesses: John le Cuppere, Henry le Gardener, John Sewaker, Edward de Fromelode,
Roger le Cuppere, Henry de Kyllecote, Thomas Page.
At: Berkeley.

The widow's holding in Longbridge Street

A1/12/33 [GC 2314]   4 May 13 Edw. II [1320]
Denise widow of Richard le Sopere and Sir Thomas de Berkeleye, lord of Berkeley.

Denise has granted to Thomas all her holding with a garden, curtilage and appurtenances in Langebrugge Street for her life, in the borough of Berkeleye.

Witnesses: John le Cuppere, Henry le Gardener, John Sewaker, John Judde, Robert Groundi, Robert le Schipward, Henry de Kyllecote.

At: Berkeley.

A1/12/34 [GC 2315]   10 May 13 Edw. II [1320]

Robert son and heir of Denise le Sopere and Sir Thomas de Berkeleye, lord of Berkeley.

Robert has quitclaimed to Thomas the lands which Thomas has in Langebrugge Street by the grant of Denise his mother, which she has for life, in the borough of Berkeleye.

Witnesses: John le Cuppere, Edward de Fromelode, John Sewaker, Henry le Gardener, John Judde, Robert Groundi, Robert le Schipward.

At: Berkeley.

The Cook half-burgage

A1/12/35 [GC 2134]   1 Dec. 10 Edw. II [1316]

Philip the cook (*cocus*) and Joan his daughter and heir.

Philip has quitclaimed to Joan the half-burgage which he held for life by the law of England in the borough of Berkeleye, opposite the house of William le Fox.

Witnesses: Henry le Gardener, John le Cuppere, Roger le Cuppere, Henry de Kyllecote, Thomas Page.

At: Berkeley.

A1/12/36 [GC 2139]   6 Dec. 10 Edw. II [1316]

Joan daughter and heir of Philip the cook (*cocus*), unmarried woman, and Sir Thomas de Berkeleye, lord of Berkeley.

Joan has granted to Thomas, his heirs and assigns her half-burgage opposite the holding formerly of William le Fox, which she inherited after the death of her mother Margery Hodelyne, in the borough of Berkeleye.

Witnesses: John le Cuppere, Henry le Gardener, John Judde, Roger le Cuppere, Adam Pynel.

At: Berkeley.

A1/12/37 [GC 2141]   Tues. the feast of St. Thomas the apostle, 10 Edw. II [21 Dec. 1316]

Thomas de Berkeleye, lord of Berkeley; and William de Aure and Alice his wife.

Thomas has granted to William and Alice the half-burgage opposite the holding formerly of William le Fox which he had by grant of Joan daughter and heir of Philip the cook (*cocus*), in the borough of Berkeleye; to them and their issue, rent 18*d.* a year, with liberty to buy and sell in the marketplace and port of Berkeleye; if they die without issue, the holding will remain to Alice daughter of the said Alice for life, the rent being the same.

Witnesses: Henry le Gardener, John le Cuppere, John Judde, Robert Groundi, Roger le Cuppere, Robert Schipward, Henry de Kyllecote.

At: Berkeley.

The Sheppard holding

A1/12/38 [SC 405]   n.d. [*temp.* Edw. I]

Walter le Schipward and Sir Thomas de Berkeley.

Walter has granted to Thomas a curtilage in the borough of Berkeley, which extends from the king's road to the said Thomas's garden.

Witnesses: Richard Averey, John Sewaker, Walter le Cuppere, Henry Cuppere, Henry Grout, Richard le Sopere, Nicholas the clerk.

A1/12/39 [GC 2160]   The Annunciation, 10 Edw. II [25 March 1317]
Leticia le Schipward of Berkeley, widow, and Thomas de Berckel', lord of Berkeley.

Leticia has quitclaimed to Thomas, his heirs and assigns her dower in the holding which
Thomas had by grant of Walter le Schipward, her husband, in the borough of Berckel'.
Witnesses: John le Coppere, Henry le Gardiner, Richard de Kylmescote, clerk, Robert
Groundi, Roger le Coppere, John Jodde, William Iweyn.
At: Berkeley.

A1/12/40 [GC 2338]   6 Jan. 14 Edw. II [1321]
Leticia le Schipward, widow, and Sir Thomas de Berklee, lord of Berkeley.

Leticia has quitclaimed to Thomas, for a certain sum of money, her dower rights in the
holding, rent and reversions which Thomas had by grant of Walter le Schipward, late her
husband, in the borough of Berkeleye.
Witnesses: John le Cuppere, Henry le Gardener, John Judde, Edward de Fromelode, Roger
le Cuppere, Robert Groundi, Adam Pynel.
At: Berkeley.

The Woolbeater holding

A1/12/41 [GC 1636]   n.d. [*c.* July 1317]
Eve la Wolbetere of Berkeley and Sir Thomas de Berkel'.

Eve has granted to Thomas her messuage in the town of Berkel', in St. Michael Street,
next to her burgage; rent ½*d.* a year, and he has given her ½ mark.
Witnesses: Gilbert the baker (*pistor*), Walter Schipward, Thomas Alain, John Bonserjant,
Henry Cuppere, Richard le Savoner.

A1/12/42 [GC 2183]   Thurs. [*sic*] the morrow of the translation of St. Thomas the martyr,
                                                       11 Edw. II [8 July 1317]
(1) Eve la Wolbetar' of Berkeley; (2) Richard le Savoner of Berkeley; (3) Sir Thomas de
Berkel'; (4) Robert de Stone.

Eve has appointed Richard her attorney to give seisin to Thomas in a holding in Berkel'
and also to Robert in lands and holdings in the vill of Stane.
At: Berkeley.

The Bodde holding in Marybrook Street

A1/12/43 [GC 2172; *duplicate* GC 2173]   23 May 10 Edw. II [1317]
William Bodde; and John son of Richard le Serjant and John his son by Eleanor late his
wife.

William has granted to John and John the holding which he inherited after the death of
Thomas Bodde his father in the borough of Berkeleye, with a parcel of land which he had
by grant of Richard le Marescal in the borough; for their lives, rendering to the chief lord
the customary rent.
Witnesses: John le Cuppere, Richard de Culmescote, Edward de Fromelode, John Sewaker,
John Judde, Roger le Cuppere, Adam Pynel.
At: Berkeley.

A1/12/44 [GC 2260]   6 Dec. 12 Edw. II [1318]
William Bodde and Sir Thomas de Berkeleye, lord of Berkeley.

William has granted to Thomas all the rents and services of John le Serjaunt and his son
John for all the holdings which they hold of William for their lives in the borough of Berkeleye,
in the street called Modybrokestret, with the reversion of the holdings after their deaths.
Witnesses: Edward de Fromelode, John Sewaker, John le Cuppere, Henry le Gardener,
Roger le Cuppere, John Judde, Adam Pynel.
At: Berkeley.

A1/12/45 [GC 2289]   Thurs. in All Saints, 13 Edw. II [1 Nov. 1319]
John son of Richard le Serjaunt and Sir Thomas de Berkeleye, lord of Berkeley.

John has granted to Thomas, his heirs and assigns his holding in Modibrok Street which he previously had for the lives of himself and of John his son, of William Bodde, in the borough of Berkeleye; for the lives of himself and his son.
Witnesses: John Capel, John Wyth, John le Cuppere, Henry le Gardener, Roger le Cuppere.
At: Berkeley.

The FitzRobert holding in Longbridge Street

A1/12/46 [GC 596]   St. Margaret the virgin, 21 Edw. I [20 July 1293]
Maurice son of William called FitzRobert of Bevington and Isabel his daughter.

Maurice has granted to Isabel a messuage in the town of Berkel' in Longebrigge Street; rent a rose to him, and 6d. to the hospital of Holy Trinity, Longbridge.
Witnesses: John Sewaker, John Bonserjaunt, Roger the tanner (*tannarius*), William le Wilde, Walter le swineherd (*porcarius*), Richard le Sawuner, John the clerk of Hill.
At: Hill.

A1/12/47 [GC 2307]   20 March 13 Edw. II [1320]
Isabel daughter of Maurice son of William son of Robert and Sir Thomas de Berkeleye, lord of Berkeley.

Isabel has granted to Thomas, his heirs and assigns her messuage in Longebrugge Street beside the messuage formerly of Walter le Swan and the road from Longebrugge to the marketplace of Berkeleye, in the borough of Berkeleye.
Witnesses: John le Cuppere, Henry le Gardener, Robert Groundy, Roger le Cuppere, Hugh le Proute, Henry de Kyllecote, Robert le Schipward.
At: Berkeley.

The Wick holding in Church Street

A1/12/48 [GC 2305]   Sun. after St. Gregory, 13 Edw. II [16 March 1320]
Nicholas de Wyke and Sir Thomas de Berkeleye, lord of Berkeley.

Nicholas has granted to Thomas, his heirs and assigns the house opposite the house of Henry le Gardener beside the road from the marketplace to the church, in the borough of Berkeleye; rent 12d. a year to the lamp of the Blessed Virgin in Berkeleye and 12d. a year to the lamp of St. Anne of Berkeleye.
Witnesses: John le Cuppere, Henry le Gardener, Roger le Cuppere, Hugh le Proute, Henry de Kyllecote.
At: Berkeley.

A1/12/49 [GC 2306]   20 March 13 Edw. II [1320]
Thomas de Berkeleye, lord of Berkeley; and Walter de Charefelde and Joan his wife.

Thomas has leased to Walter and Joan the house opposite the house of Henry le Gardener, beside the road from the marketplace to the church, which Nicholas de Wyke previously held, in the borough of Berkeleye; to them and their issue, rent 2s. a year, and 12d. a year to the lamp of the Blessed Virgin and 12d. a year to the lamp of St. Anne.
Witnesses: John le Cuppere, Henry le Gardener, Roger le Cuppere, Hugh le Prout, Henry de Kyllecote.
At: Berkeley.

A1/12/50 [GC 3273]   n.d. [mid 14th cent.]
Thomas lord of Berkelee; and William le Saltare, Juliana his wife and John their son.

Thomas has leased to William, Juliana and John a messuage formerly of Walter de Charefelde in Berkelee; for their lives, at the customary rent.
Witnesses: Thomas Payn, William Modebrok, John Bil, John Coby, Thomas Goldhoppe.

Holdings of William le Gardener

Burgage

A1/12/51 [GC 1376]   n.d. [*temp*. Edw. I]
William le Gardiner of Berkeley and Sir Thomas de Berkeleye, his lord.

William has quitclaimed to Thomas the burgage which he had by grant of William Pridy in the new town of Berkeleye, which was formerly of William Sencler.
Witnesses: John le Coppere, Henry le Gardiner, Walter le Coppere, Robert Auveray, Philip Coby, Richard Noblepas, Nicholas the clerk.

A1/12/52 [GC 1844]   Tues. the feast of St. Andrew, 5 Edw. II [30 Nov. 1311]
Thomas de Berkelee, lord of Berkeley; and Ralph de Kyngestone and Sibyl his wife.

Thomas has granted to Ralph and Sibyl the house with a curtilage which he had by grant of William le Gardener, beside the road from Homme to the marketplace of Berkelee, in the borough of Berkelee; to them and their issue, rent 8*s.* a year.
Witnesses: John le Coppere, Henry le Gardener, John Sewaker, John Schipward, Edward de Fromelode.
At: Berkeley.

Other

A1/12/53 [GC 1879]   Mon. the morrow of Trinity Sunday, 5 Edw. II [22 May 1312]
John del Oke, prior of St. Bartholomew's Hospital, Gloucester, and Sir Thomas de Berkelee, lord of Berkeley.

The hospital has granted to Thomas, for a certain sum of money, a rent of 2*s.* in the town of Berkelee from the holding in which William le Gardiner lives.
Witnesses: John le Cuppere, Henry le Gardener, John Sewaker, Roger le Cuppere, Edward de Fromelode, John Schippard, Adam Pinel.
At: Gloucester.

A1/12/54 [GC 1984]   1 July 7 Edw. II [1314]
Thomas de Berkelee, lord of Berkeley; and John Page and Mary his wife.

Thomas has granted to John and Mary a rent of 12*d.* a year from Maud widow of William le Gardener, for a messuage with a curtilage, with the reversion of the holding after Maud's death, in Berkelee; to them and their issue, rent 12*d.* a year while Maud lives and 6*s.* a year thereafter.
Witnesses: John le Cuppere, Henry le Gardener, John Sewaker, Roger le Cuppere, John Schippard.
At: Berkeley.

A1/12/55 [GC 2112]   5 July 9 Edw. II [1316]
William called le Gardener and Maud his wife;[1] and Sir Thomas de Berkeleye, lord of Berkeley.

William and Maud have rendered to Thomas and his heirs the house in St. Michael Street which John de Coueleye previously held in Berkeleye.
Witnesses: John le Cuppere, Henry le Gardener, Roger le Cuppere, Adam Pynel, Thomas Page.
At: Berkeley.

The Packer holding in Church Street

A1/12/56 [GC 4119]   10 Aug. 7 Hen. V [1419]
John Shypward, son and heir of David Shypward of Berkeley, and Walter James *alias* Packere.

---

[1] The dates of this and the preceding deed, where Maud is said to be William's widow, are clear. It is most likely that two men each called William le Gardener married a Maud.

John has granted to Walter, his heirs and assigns a holding with a curtilage in the street leading to the church.

Witnesses: Richard Gilbert, bailiff of Berkeley, David Chapman, Richard Scot, Thomas BonJohn, John Taylour, John Flowre, Hugh Dyere.

At: Berkeley.

A1/12/57 [GC 4120; *duplicate* GC 4121]   24 Sept. 7 Hen. V [1419]

Walter Packere of Berkeley; and Thomas Packere, Joan his wife and their eldest child, male or female.

Walter has leased to Thomas and Joan and their eldest child his holding in the street called Churchestrete; for their lives, rent 10*s.* a year.

Witnesses: Richard Gilbert, David Chapman, Richard Scot, John Floure, Walter Hoopere.

At: Berkeley.

A1/12/58 [GC 4372]   1 Nov. 12 Edw. IV [1472]

Richard James, son and heir of Walter James *alias* Packer, of Berkeley (Glos.), and Maurice Berkeley, brother of William Lord Berkeley.

Richard has granted to Maurice, his heirs and assigns his holding with a curtilage in Berkeley in the street called Churchstrete.

Witnesses: Thomas Berkeley, esquire, William Barbour, John Haydon.

At: Berkeley.

Holdings of John de Berkeley (*d. 1317*)

The Noblepas holding (*rents of Abbewelle, Vox and Miller*)

A1/12/59 [GC 1493; *duplicate* GC 403]   n.d. [late Edw. I]

Richard Noble of Berkeley; and John de Abbewelle, Alice his wife and John their son.

Richard has granted to John, Alice and John the house with a curtilage which Margaret de Newham formerly held of Richard in the new town of Berk'; for their lives, rent 2*s.* a year.

Witnesses: John Coppere, Walter Coppere, Richard Serjant, Nicholas the miller (*molend'*), William Fox, Richard Coppere, William de Modebrok, Henry Gardin'.

A1/12/60 [GC 1056]   St. Fabian and St. Sebastian, 32 Edw. I [20 Jan. 1304]

Richard called Noblepas of Berkeley; and Walter le Vox, Joan his wife and Thomas their son.

Richard has granted to Walter, Joan and Thomas a messuage with a curtilage in the town of Berckel' between the holdings of John Sley and John de Abbewelle, for their lives, rent 2*s.* a year.

Witnesses: John le Coppere, Walter le Coppere, Richard le Coppere, William le Vox, Nicholas the miller (*molendinarius*), Henry le Gardin', William Purlewent, clerk.

At: Berkeley.

A1/12/61 [GC 1672]   St. Nicholas, 2 Edw. II [6 Dec. 1308]

Richard Noblepas of Berkeley; and John called the miller (*molendinar'*) of Berkeley and his wife Joan.

Richard has granted to John and Joan a plot of land beside Richard's holding in the town of Berckel'; to them and Joan's issue, rent 12*d.* a year, and they have given him a certain sum of money.

Witnesses: John le Coppere, Henry le Gardin', William Bodde, John le Vyngnur, Roger le Cuppere, John Sley, John Page.

At: Berkeley.

A1/12/62 [GC 1736; *duplicate* GC 1737]   22 May 3 Edw. II [1310]
Richard le Noble of Berkeley; and Sir John de Berkelee and Hawise his wife.

Richard has granted to John and Hawise a rent of 4*s.* from two holdings which Walter le Fox and John de Abbewelle hold of Richard for their lives in the high street of the borough of Berkelee, with the reversion of the holdings; to John and Hawise for their lives, rent a rose a year.

Witnesses: John le Cuppere, Roger le Cuppere, Henry le Garden', John Sewaker, Edward de Fromilode, John le Schipward, John the miller (*molend'*).
At: Berkeley.

A1/12/63 [GC 1741]   27 May 3 Edw. II [1310]
(1) Richard le Noble; (2) Sir John de Berkelee and Hawise his wife; (3) Walter le Fox and John de Abbewelle.

Richard notifies his tenants Walter and John of his grant to John and Hawise of their rents of 4*s.*
At: Berkeley.

A1/12/64 [GC 1831] Sun. after the nativity of St. John the Baptist, 4 Edw. II [27 June 1311]
Richard Noblepas of Berkeley; and Sir John de Berkelee and Hawise his wife.

Richard has granted to John and Hawise and John's heirs a rent of 4*s.* from two holdings of Walter le Fox and John de Abbewelle for their lives, with the reversion of the holdings; and also a rent of 12*d.* from the holding of John the miller (*molendinar'*) of Berkeley and Joan his wife, to John and Hawise and their issue, with the reversion of the holding if it happens, in the high street of Berkelee.

Witnesses: Robert de Bradestone, Robert de Berkelee, Nicholas de Beolee, John le Cuppere, Henry le Gardyner, Roger le Cuppere, John Sewaker, John Schipward.
At: Berkeley.

A1/12/65 [GC 1834]   15 July 5 Edw. II [1311]
John de Berkeleye; and Thomas Page of Berkeley and Maud his wife, daughter of William le Smyth.

John, with the assent of Hawise his wife, has granted to Thomas and Maud and their issue the holding which John de Abbewelle held in Berkeleye in the high street; rent 4*s.* a year.

Witnesses: John le Cuppere, Henry le Gardyner, Roger le Cuppere, John Schipward, Richard Noblepas.
At: Berkeley.

The Swele holding in St. Michael Street

A1/12/66 [GC 1858]   Fri. the morrow of Epiphany, 5 Edw. II [7 Jan. 1312]
Robert Swele; and Sir John de Berkelee and Hawise his wife.

Robert has granted to John and Hawise his house with a curtilage beside the street of St. Michael and the churchyard, in the borough of Berkelee; to them and John's heirs.

Witnesses: Thomas de Stone, John Capel, John le Cuppere, Henry le Gardener, John Sewaker, Roger le Cuppere, Edward de Fromelode.
At: Berkeley.

A1/12/67 [GC 1904]   1 March 6 Edw. II [1313]
John de Berkelee, son of Sir Thomas de Berkelee, and Sir Thomas, his said father.

John has granted to Thomas, his lord and father, all his house beside St. Michael Street, which he had by grant of Robert Swele, in the borough of Berkelee.

Witnesses: John le Cuppere, Henry le Gardener, John Sewaker, Roger le Cuppere, John le Viegnour, John le Schippard, Edward de Fromelode.
At: Berkeley.

Other Berkeley acquisitions and grants

A1/12/68 [SC 53] n.d. [1190 × 1200]

Alice de Berk' and William her son.

Alice has granted to William her burgage in Berkeley which she bought from Philip Heirun.

Witnesses: Hugh the little (*parvus*), Philip de Berkeley, Henry de Berkeley, Master Peter de Paris, Reginald the chaplain, Richard the chaplain, Walter the white (*albus*), William de Morton, Reginald the clerk.

A1/12/69 [GC 3263] n.d. [*c.* 1190 × 1220]

Robert de Berkel', son of Maurice de Berkel', and the brothers of the hospital of Jerusalem.

Robert, for the souls of himself, his wife, his father and his mother, has granted to the hospital the burgage in Berkeleya which was of Ailwyne the despenser, and a meadow by Longebrugge at Berkeleie.

Witnesses: Walter and Herbert chaplains, Roger de Berkeleia, Philip his brother, uncles of Robert, Adam son of Nigel, Bernard de Stanes, Maurice son of Nigel, Robert the bastard, Hugh de Saltmarsh (*de salso marisco*), Simon de Olepenne. [*14th-cent. copy.*]

A1/12/70 [GC 411] n.d. [1220 × 1241]

Eustace the butler (*pincerna*) of Berkeley and Sir Thomas de Berkeley.

Eustace has granted to Thomas all his land in the town of Berkel with the houses built on it and all other appurtenances; rent 1*d.* a year, and Thomas has given him 33*s.* and a furred green overtunic.

Witnesses: Ralph de Radlega, steward, Henry the chaplain (*capellan'*), Elias the butler (*pincerna*), Robert de Chandos, John Sewaker, Robert the merchant (*mercator*), Gilbert the cordwainer (*corviser*), Ford Tesse, Arnulf the clerk.

A1/12/71 [SC 297] A.D. 1248 [1248–9]

Abbot William [Long] of St. Augustine's Abbey, Bristol, and Sir Maurice de Berkeley.

The abbot and convent have quitclaimed to Maurice the messuage with appurtenances which Henry the chaplain held of them in Berkeley.

Witnesses: Roger de Lokinton, Maurice de Saltmarsh (*de salso marisco*), Richard de Cromhal, Walter de Burgo, Andrew de Bradestan, Ralph de Angervill, Maurice de Stanes, Peter de Wike, Richard de Wike.

A1/12/72 [GC 306] Eve of Holy Trinity [26 May] A.D. 1263

Maurice de Berkeley and Robert de Egethon.

Maurice has quitclaimed to Robert 2*s.* of the 4*s.* rent which Robert renders for his holding of Abbewell, in return for 2*s.* rent granted and quitclaimed by Robert to Maurice, which Robert received from the burgage held of him [Maurice] by Elias le Beltunc in the new town of Berkeley.

Witnesses: Peter de Wyk, Thomas the serjeant (*serviens*), John de Badelton, John de Craulegh, Geoffrey Carbunel.

A1/12/73 [GC 1598] n.d. [late Hen. III]

John Wyteye, son of Adam Wyteye, and Sir Maurice de Berkel'.

John has granted to Maurice his holding in the old town of Berkel', and Maurice has given him 20*s.*

Witnesses: Thomas son of Alan, Thomas Cavel, John Bonserjaunt, Richard Averey, Henry le Grut, Robert Chaumpeneys, Walter Sely.

A1/12/74 [GC 1439] n.d. [late Hen. III]
Juliana daughter of Amicia, widow, and Sir Maurice de Berkel'.

Juliana has granted to Maurice her burgage in the new town of Berkel' opposite the street to the castle, between the burgage of William Page and the street from Locfastebrugge to the house of Richard Averey; he has given her 10s.
Witnesses: Roger de Lokinton, Thomas de Swonhongre, Walter de Egeton, Thomas Cavel, William Page, Thomas son of Alan, Henry le Grut, John Bonserjaunt, William le Cuppere, Walter Sely.

A1/12/75 [GC 785] n.d. [late Hen. III]
Adam de Monemowe and Sir Maurice lord of Berk'.

Adam has quitclaimed to Maurice a certain boundary (*divisa*) between his holding and the land of Maurice, extending from Castle Street above the ditch which runs above the town of Berk' towards the Severn.
Witnesses: Simon de Edinton, vicar, William de Mathine, Peter son of Warin, John Sewaker, John Bonserjant, William le Cuppere, William the tailor (*cissor*).

A1/12/76 [GC 450] Sun. after St. John before the Latin Gate, 1 Edw. I [7 May 1273]
Maud widow of Alexander the souter (*sutor*) of Wotton and Sir Thomas de Berkeley, lord of Berkeley.

Maud has quitclaimed to Thomas the holding which John the skinner (*pelliparius*) held in the borough of Berkeleye.
Witnesses: John le Cuppere, Henry le Gardiner, Roger le Cuppere, John Jodde, William Bodde, John de Kyllecote, Hugh le Proute.
At: Berkeley.

A1/12/77 [GC 1396] n.d. [1281 × 1300]
Henry son of Henry Grout of Berkeley and Sir Thomas de Berkel', his lord.

Henry has granted to Thomas a half-burgage in the new town of Berkel' which he had by grant of John Carbonel, son and heir of Geoffrey le Sergant of Pochampton, beside the road from the churchyard to the market; rent 12d. a year, and Thomas has given him 16s.
Witnesses: Sir Robert de Berkel', Robert de Bradeston, William Capele, Thomas Aleyn, Walter Sypward, John Bonsergant, Henry Cuppere.

A1/12/78 [GC 1615] n.d. [early Edw. I]
John, burgess of Bristol, son and heir of Adam called the smith of Berkeley, and Sir Thomas de Berkel', his lord.

John has granted to Thomas all his holding, which he inherited after the death of his father Adam, next to the marketplace of Berkel'; rent a rose a year, and Thomas has given him 48s.
Witnesses: Sir Simon vicar of Berkeley, Sir Roger de Lokinton, Robert de Stan', Thomas de Swonhungre, Thomas Aleyn, Walter Schipward, John Bonserjant, Richard le Savoner.

A1/12/79 [GC 989] n.d. [early 14th cent.]
William le Wylde and Sir Thomas de Berkeleye, lord of Berkeley.

William has granted to Thomas, for a certain sum of money, a curtilage with appurtenances between William's holding and Thomas's garden. Endorsed: *Berkeleye*.
Witnesses: Henry le Gardener, John Sewaker, Roger le Cuppere, Philip Coby, John le Cuppere, William Bodde, John Paye.

A1/12/80 [GC 1854] Thurs. in Epiphany, 5 Edw. II [6 Jan. 1312]
Richard Noblepas and Sir Thomas de Berkelee, lord of Berkeley.

Richard has granted to Thomas, for a certain sum of money, a rent of 2s. from all his houses, lands and holdings within and outside the borough of Berkelee.

Witnesses: John le Cuppere, Henry le Gardener, Roger le Cuppere, John Sewaker, Robert Averay, John le Vignour, Edward de Fromelode.

At: Berkeley.

A1/12/81 [GC 1969]   20 March 7 Edw. II [1314]

John le Cuppere, son and heir of the late Robert le Cuppere, and Sir Thomas de Berkelee, his lord.

John has granted to Thomas, his heirs and assigns a rent of 6*d.* from Maud le Cuppere, his mother, for her life, for a messuage with a curtilage, with the reversion of the holding after her death, in the borough of Berkelee.

Witnesses: John le Cuppere, Henry le Gardener, John Sewaker, Roger le Cuppere, John le Schippard.

At: Berkeley.

A1/12/82 [GC 2263]   Mon. the feast of St. Vincent, 12 Edw. II [22 Jan. 1319]

Juliana widow of William Pridi of Berkeley and Sir Thomas de Berkeleye, her lord.

Juliana has quitclaimed to Thomas, his heirs and assigns her dower rights in a burgage which Maud Scorri holds in the borough of Berkeleye.

Witnesses: John le Cuppere, John Sewaker, John Jodde, Robert Groundy, Roger le Cuppere, Adam Pynel, John Page.

At: Berkeley.

A1/12/83 [GC 2292]   1 Dec. 13 Edw. II [1319]

Robert Groundy and Sir Thomas de Berkeleye, lord of Berkeley.

Robert has granted to Thomas a rent of 4*s.* a year from all his lands and holdings in the borough of Berkeleye and elsewhere within the hundred of Berkeleye.

Witnesses: John le Cuppere, Henry le Gardener, Edward de Fromelode, John Sewaker, Roger le Cuppere, Henry de Kyllecote, Robert le Schipward.

At: Berkeley.

A1/12/84 [GC 2304]   1 March 13 Edw. II [1320]

William called le Swon of Berkeley, and Thomas de Berkeleye, lord of Berkeley.

William has granted to Thomas, his heirs and assigns his holding in the borough of Berkeleye, in Langebrugge Street.

Witnesses: John le Cuppere, Henry le Gardener, Robert Groundy, Roger le Cuppere, Henry de Kyllecote, Thomas Page, Thomas Alayn.

At: Berkeley.

A1/12/85 [GC 2488]   n.d. [early 14th cent.]

Margery widow of John de Kilekote and Helen de Camme, sisters and widows; and Maurice de Berkel'.

Margery and Helen have granted to Maurice their burgage in the town of Berkel', beside the bridge to Hamme; he has given them 40*s.*

Witnesses: William de Burgo, Thomas de Bemleye, John Bonserjaunt, John Grewike, Robert Pinel, Robert Eule.

A1/12/86 [SC 529]   Sun. before St. Luke, 25 Edw. III [16 Oct. 1351]

Maurice de Berkeley, son and heir of Thomas de Berkeley, and the hospital of Holy Trinity, of Longbridge by Berkeley.

Maurice has granted to the hospital the holding in Berkeley which Richard le Panter sometime held, and the hospital will distribute every year on the anniversaries of Richard and Alice his wife 2*s.* in bread to the poor.

Witnesses: William Modebroc, John Wil, Thomas Goldhoppe, Walter le Coppare, John Coby.

At: Berkeley.

A1/12/87 [GC 3443]   4 March 30 Edw. III [1356]
John de Fromelode and Sir Thomas lord of Berkelee, his lord.

  John has quitclaimed to Thomas the holding which Edward Wyllyes sometime held in Berkelee.
Witnesses: William Modebroke, Thomas Payn, John Byl, Thomas Goldhoppe, David Schepward.
At: Berkeley.

A1/12/88 [GC 3939]   St. Laurence, 21 Ric. II [2 Feb. 1398]
William Swele, son and heir of John Swele of Berkeley, and Thomas Berkeleye, lord of Berkeley.

  William has granted to Thomas, his heirs and assigns his holding in Berkeleye.
Witnesses: William Smalcombe the elder, John Roules, John at Yate, Thomas Lucas, Richard Ecton.
At: Berkeley.

A1/12/89 [GC 4022]   Mon. after Epiphany, 9 Hen. IV [9 Jan. 1408]
John Coby, son of Philip Coby of Berkeley, and Thomas Berkeley, lord of Berkeley.

  John has quitclaimed to Thomas a burgage in the town of Berkeley.
Witnesses: Thomas Stauntone, Richard Eggetone, John Schipward, Thomas Wyth, John Byl.
At: Berkeley.

A1/12/90 [GC 4064]   St. Bartholomew, 12 Hen. IV [24 Aug. 1411]
Thomas Teysaunt, son and heir of Roger atte Wyche of Berkeley, and Thomas de Berkeley, lord of Berkeley.

  Thomas Teysaunt has quitclaimed to Thomas de Berkeley an annual rent of 3*s.* from a messuage with a curtilage in the town of Berkeley.
Witnesses: Edmund Basset, Thomas Staunton, Richard Ectone, Thomas Kendale, John Archer.
At: Berkeley.

BERKELEY GRANTS

A1/12/91 [GC 1211]   n.d. [late Hen. III]
Maurice de Berkel' and John le Gaunter.

  Maurice has granted to John a half-burgage next to the road from the market of Berkel' borough to Modibrok; rent 8*d.* a year, and John has given him ½ mark.
Witnesses: Peter de Wike, Adam Coby, John Sewaker, Thomas son of Alan, William le Palmar, William the smith, Adam Mare, Nigel de Staniteford, William le Cuppar, Walter Sely.

A1/12/92 [GC 1207]   n.d. [late Hen. III]
Maurice lord of Berkeley; and Thomas Aleyn (*Alani*) and Alice his wife.

  Maurice has granted to Thomas and Alice a messuage with a garden, curtilage and croft in the town of Berkel' which he had by gift of Nicholas Sely of Strogoil, which were formerly of Adam Cobi, between the king's highway from Longebrugge to Swonhunger and the road from Locfastebrugg to the house of Richard Averey; to them and their issue, rent 12*s.* a year, and they have given him a tun of wine.
Witnesses: Sir Roger de Lokinton, Sir Maurice de Saltmarsh (*de salso marisco*), knights, William de Burgo, Robert de Stanes, Thomas de Buleye, John de Crauleye, Richard Averey, John Sewaker.

A1/12/93 [GC 1099]   Sun. in the decollation of St. John the Baptist, 33 Edw. I
[29 Aug. 1305]

Thomas de Berkelee, lord of Berkeley; and John Glaysin and Alice his wife.

Thomas has granted to John and Alice one third of the messuage and curtilage between the churchyard of Berkelee, viz. from the bell next to the gate, towards the house of William le Fox, being the middle part of the messuage; to them and their issue, rent 2s. a year; with licence to buy and sell in the market of Berkelee and privileges as the burgesses.

Witnesses: John le Cuppere, Walter le Cuppere, Henry le Gardin', Roger le Cuppere, John de Kyllecot.

At: Berkeley.

A1/12/94 [GC 1148]   18 May 35 Edw. I [1307]

Thomas de Berkelegh, lord of Berkeley, and Thomas de Carswelle.

Thomas de Berkelegh has granted to Thomas de Carswelle the house between the holding of William Fox to the east and that of John Willy and the market to the west, in the borough of Berkelee; rent 4s. a year.

Witnesses: John le Cuppere, Walter le Cuppere, Henry le Gardener, Roger le Cuppere, William Fox.

At: Berkeley.

A1/12/95 [GC 1644]   Wed. the feast of St. Nicholas, 1 Edw. II [6 Dec. 1307]

Thomas de Berkeleye, lord of Berkeley; and William Iweyn and Sibyl his wife.

Thomas has granted to William and Sibyl a plot with a house built on it in the high street of Berkeleye, opposite the house of Sir Walter vicar of Berkeley; to them and their issue, rent 5s. a year.

Witnesses: John le Cuppere, Henry le Gardener, Roger le Cuppere, John Page, John Kyllecote.

At: Berkeley.

A1/12/96 [GC 1665]   Wed. the eve of the Assumption, 2 Edw. II [14 Aug. 1308]

Thomas de Berkelegh', lord of Berkeley, and John Burgeys, tailor.

Thomas has granted to John a cottage with a curtilage in the borough of Berkelegh'; to him and his issue, rent 3s. a year.

Witnesses: Henry le Gardener, John le Cuppere, William Iweyn, Roger le Cuppere, John Page.

At: Berkeley.

A1/12/97 [GC 1673]   Fri. the feast of St. Nicholas, 2 Edw. II [6 Dec. 1308]

Thomas de Berkelee, lord of Berkeley, and Thomas de Carswelle.

Thomas de Berkelee has granted to Thomas de Carswelle a plot of land in his marketplace of Berkel'; rent 2s. a year.

Witnesses: John le Cuppere, Roger le Cuppere, Henry le Gardiner, Sely le Cuppere, William le Fox.

At: Berkeley.

A1/12/98 [GC 1675]   Sun. the feast of the Purification, 2 Edw. II [2 Feb. 1309]

Thomas de Berkelee, lord of Berkeley, and John Swele.

Thomas has granted to John the cottage with a curtilage which Constance Godesbern previously held in the borough of Berkelee; to him and his issue, rent 5s. a year, with liberty to buy and sell merchandise in the port or marketplace of the borough.

Witnesses: John le Cuppere, Henry le Gardiner, Roger le Cuppere, John le Sipward, William Iweyn.

At: Berkeley.

A1/12/99 [GC 1707]   Fri. the feast of St. Peter in chains, 3 Edw. II [1 Aug. 1309]
Thomas de Berkelee, lord of Berkeley; and John Sely and Tangester his wife.

   Thomas has granted to John and Tangester a plot of land containing 13 perches of land
beside the plot formerly held by John de Berkelee, his son, in the new marketplace of
Berkelee, in the borough of Berkelee; to them and their issue, rent 16*d.* a year.
Witnesses: John le Cuppere, Henry le Gardener, Roger le Cuppere, William Budde, William
Iweyn.
At: Berkeley.

A1/12/100 [GC 1708]   Fri. the feast of St. Peter in chains, 3 Edw. II [1 Aug. 1309]
Thomas de Berkelee, lord of Berkeley; and John Rom and Sibyl his wife.

   Thomas has granted to John and Sibyl a shop below 'la yldehalle', beside the new
marketplace of Berkelee; to them and their issue, rent 4*s.* a year.
Witnesses: John le Cuppere, Henry le Gardener, John Sewaker, Roger le Cuppere, William
Budde.
At: Berkeley.

A1/12/101 [GC 1714]   Sun. the feast of St. Andrew, 3 Edw. II [30 Nov. 1309]
Thomas de Berkelee, lord of Berkeley; and John le Vignur and Agnes his wife.

   Thomas has granted to John and Agnes a building plot 30 by 20 ft. in the borough of
Berkelee; to them and their issue, rent 12*d.* a year and for each brewing brewed and sold
3*d.* for 'tolbarellis' [i.e. a duty on beer].
Witnesses: John le Cuppere, Roger le Cuppere, Henry le Gardener, Richard Noblepas, John
de Kyllecot.
At: Berkeley.

A1/12/102 [GC 1725]   1 April 3 Edw. II [1310]
Thomas de Berkelee, lord of Berkeley, and William le Knyght of Awre.

   Thomas has granted to William the messuage with a curtilage between the holdings of
John le Cuppere and Isabel de Asscheleworth in the borough of Berkelee; to him and his
issue, rent 4*s.* a year.
Witnesses: John le Cuppere, Henry le Gardener, John Sewaker, Roger le Cuppere, John le
Sypward.
At: Berkeley.

A1/12/103 [GC 1726]   1 April 3 Edw. II [1310]
Thomas de Berkelee, lord of Berkeley, and David Page.

   Thomas has granted to David a shop below 'la yeldhalle' next to the holding of John
Sely, and a small curtilage in the new marketplace of Berkelee appurtenant to the said shop.
Witnesses: John le Cuppere, Henry le Gardener, John Sewaker, Roger le Cuppere, John le
Sypward.
At: Berkeley.

A1/12/104 [GC 1861]   1 Feb. 5 Edw. II [1312]
Thomas de Berkelee, lord of Berkeley; and Richard Noblepas and Isabel his wife.

   Thomas has granted to Richard and Isabel his cottage, saving to Alice widow of Henry
Pynel as much of the cottage as she previously held of Thomas at a rent of 12*d.* a year for
her life; to them and their issue, rent 2*s.* a year for the life of Alice, and 3*s.* a year thereafter.
Witnesses: John le Cuppere, Henry le Gardener, Roger le Cuppere, John Sewaker, John
Schippard.
At: Berkeley.

A1/12/105 [GC 1862]   1 Feb. 5 Edw. II [1312]
Thomas de Berkelee, lord of Berkeley; and Adam Pynel and Juliana his wife.

Thomas has granted to Adam and Juliana the shop below la Boothhalle with a curtilage, in Berkelee; to them and their issue, rent 2*s*. a year.
Witnesses: John le Cuppere, Henry le Gardener, Roger le Cuppere, John Schippard, William Iweyn.
At: Berkeley.

A1/12/106 [GC 1880]   Wed. after St. Augustine, 5 Edw. II [31 May 1312]
Thomas de Berkel', lord of Berkeley; and Ralph de Kingestone and Sibyl his wife.

Thomas has granted to Ralph and Sibyl the plot beside their house which Walter Alewy formerly held in Berkelegh; to them and their issue, rent 12*d*. a year.
Witnesses: John le Cuppere, Henry le Gardyner, Roger le Cuppere, Adam Pynel, John Page.
At: Berkeley.

A1/12/107 [GC 1998; *duplicate* 2059]   10 Oct. 8 Edw. II [1314]
Thomas de Berkeleye, lord of Berkeley, and Thomas Page.

Thomas de Berkeleye has granted to Thomas Page the curtilage which he had by grant of Richard Noblepas between the ditch of the churchyard of Berkel' and the holding of John Sley, in the borough of Berkeleye; to Thomas Page and his issue, rent 2*s*. a year.
Witnesses: John le Cuppere, Henry le Gardener, Roger le Cuppere, John Sley, Adam Pynel.
At: Berkeley.

A1/12/108 [GC 2005]   6 Jan. 8 Edw. II [1315]
Thomas de Berkeleye, lord of Berkeley; and Robert de Stanbrugge and Margery his wife.

Thomas has granted to Robert and Margery a cottage with a curtilage in the borough of Berkeleye; to them and their issue, rent 2*s*. a year.
Witnesses: John le Cuppere, Henry le Gardener, Roger le Cuppere, John Sewaker, Edward de Fromelode.
At: Berkeley.

A1/12/109 [GC 2132]   1 Dec. 10 Edw. II [1316]
Thomas de Berkeleye, lord of Berkeley; and William ate Wode and Maud his wife.

Thomas has granted to William and Maud 3 houses built to the east of the burgage formerly of Sir Nicholas the chaplain, and a rent of 3*s*. from Walter vicar of Berkeley for the croft which Walter holds of Thomas for life, with the reversion of the croft, in the borough of Berkeleye; for their lives, rent 2*s*. a year, and with liberty to buy and sell in the marketplace or port of the borough.
Witnesses: John le Cuppere, Henry le Gardener, John Sewaker, Roger le Cuppere, Henry de Kyllecote.
At: Berkeley.

A1/12/110 [GC 2303]   1 March 13 Edw. II [1320]
Thomas de Berkeleye, lord of Berkeley, and William called le Swon of Berkeley.

Thomas has granted to William two bays [*spacia*] of his long house opposite la Canoneburi, in the borough of Berkeleye; to him and his issue, rent 2*s*. a year.

Witnesses: John le Cuppere, Henry le Gardener, John Judde, Robert le Schipward, Henry de Kyllecote.
At: Berkeley.

A1/12/111 [GC 2278]   6 May 13 Edw. II [1320]
Thomas de Berkeleye, lord of Berkeley, and John the miller (*molendinar'*) of Berkeley.

Thomas has granted to John a curtilage plot containing 10 perches of land in the borough of Berkeleye; to him and his issue, rent a rose a year.
Witnesses: John le Cuppere, Henry le Gardener, Adam Pynel, Roger le Cuppere, John Swele.
At: Berkeley.

A1/12/112 [GC 2359]   20 June 14 Edw. II [1321]
Thomas de Berkelee, lord of Berkeley; and Richard Noblepas and Juliana his daughter.

Thomas has granted to Richard and Juliana the cottage in St. Michael Street beside Richard's house, and 19 perches of curtilage beside the same street, between the cottage and the churchyard of Berkelee, in the borough of Berkelee; to them and Juliana's issue, rent 5*s.* a year.
Witnesses: John le Cuppere, Roger le Cuppere, Adam Pynel, John Swele, Ralph de Kyngestone.
At: Berkeley.

A1/12/113 [GC 3274]   n.d. [mid 14th cent.]
Thomas lord of Berkelee; and David le Shipward, Sibyl his wife and Isabel their daughter.

Thomas has leased to David, Sibyl and Isabel 5 cottages which Thomas Hathoulf and William Andreus held in Modebrokestret in Berkelee; for their lives, rent 5*s.* a year.
Witnesses: Thomas Payn, William Modebrok, John Byl, John Coby, Thomas Golthoppe.

A1/12/114 [GC 3824]   Sun. before St. Margaret the virgin, 12 Ric. II [19 July 1388]
Thomas de Berkeleye, lord of Berkeley; and Peter Grene, Juliana his wife and Margaret their daughter.

Thomas has leased to Peter, Juliana and Margaret the holding with a curtilage, between the holdings of John Walbrok and Walter Coppare, which William Syde and his wife Alice formerly held of Thomas in Berkeleye, except for a chamber which Alice Syde holds for life; for their lives, rent the same as William.
At: Berkeley.

A1/12/115 [GC 3875]   Wed. after the translation of St. Thomas the martyr, 17 Ric. II
                                                            [9 July 1393]
Thomas de Berkeleye, lord of Berkeley; and William Heynes and Helen his wife.

Thomas has leased to William and Helen the holding between the holdings of William Hert and Margaret Copener; for their lives, rent 4*s.* a year payable at the terms usual in the borough of Berkele.
At: Berkeley.

A1/12/116 [GC 4206]   St. George, 15 Hen. VI [23 April 1437]
Thomas Clyfford, Joan his wife and Richard her son; and James Berkeley, knight, lord of Berkeley.

Whereas, on the Monday after the nativity of the Virgin Mary, 2 Hen. VI [14 Sept. 1423], Thomas and Joan came to the full court and in the presence of the steward showed a certain charter of Sir Thomas de Berkeley, late lord of Berkeley, granting to Joan for her life 2 messuages in the town of Berkeley for a vacant plot there, the rent for her life being 9*s.* a year, James has confirmed the grant to Thomas, Joan and Richard, for their lives, and has granted licence to build a chamber there.
At: Berkeley.

A1/12/117 [GC 4245]   3 Feb. 23 Hen. VI [1445]
James Berkeley, lord of Berkeley, knight; and Geoffrey Caston and Agnes his wife.

James has leased to Geoffrey, Agnes and their eldest son a messuage in the borough of
Berkeley, with a curtilage and garden, in the street called Saltarestrete, which John Smarte
lately held; for their lives, rent 9s. a year.
Witnesses: John Dyer, Thomas Clifford, Richard Lee.
At: Berkeley.

A1/12/118 [GC 4420]   Nativity of St. Mary, 18 Edw. IV [8 Sept. 1478]
Master John Anstill, vicar of Berkeley, Robert Ricardys and John Ecton; and Richard
Thorpp and Margery his wife.

John, Robert and John have granted to Richard and Margery a holding in Berkeley in the
high street; to them and their issue, with remainder to the right heirs of John Thorpp,
Richard's father.
At: Berkeley.

ADMINISTRATIVE DOCUMENTS
Charter rolls

A1/12/119 [SR 2]   Ric. I to Hen. V
Abstracts of charters concerning the borough of Berkeley, numbered in a contemporary
hand 17–31, 44–8, 94, 117–18, 132, 148–9, 154, 52, and on the dorse 96, 164, 10–11, 52,
133, 135–6; in another hand is entered the current tenant of each holding and the current
rent.

A1/12/120 [SR 4]   Ric. I to Hen. V
Fair copy of A1/12/120 [SR 2], missing nos. 22, 25, 29, 94, 148, 52, 96 and 164, adding
no. 7 between nos. 149 and 154, and incorporating the current tenant and rent.

A1/12/121 [GMR 29]   n.d. [mid 15th cent.]
As A1/12/120 [SR 4], but entries not numbered.

A1/12/122 [SR 30]
Copies of three deeds concerning the liberties of the burgesses of Berkeley borough:
(i) by Thomas de Berkeley of common of pasture [etc.] [*c.* 20 Hen. III, 1235–6];[1]
(ii) by Maurice de Berkeley freeing the burgesses from payment of tallage, at their request,
Hilary 46 Hen. III [13 Jan. 1262];
(iii) by Maurice de Berkeley granting the burgesses freedom from suit to the hundred court
and confirming their liberties as under Thomas his father [early Edw. I].

Borough account rolls

A1/12/123 [GAR 55]	14–15 Edw. I [1286–7]
A1/12/124 [GAR 56]	17–18 Edw. I [1289–90]
A1/12/125 [GAR 57]	21–2 Edw. I [1293–4]
A1/12/126 [GAR 58]	27–8 Edw. I [1299–1300]
A1/12/127 [GAR 59]	2–3 Edw. II [1308–9]
A1/12/128 [GAR 60]	3–4 Edw. II [1309–10]
A1/12/129 [GAR 61]	5–6 Edw. II [1311–12]
A1/12/130 [GAR 62]	6–7 Edw. II [1312–13]
A1/12/131 [GAR 63]	3 March 17 Edw. II to Michaelmas 18 Edw. II [1324]
A1/12/132 [GAR 64]	18–19 Edw. II [1324–5]
A1/12/133 [GAR 65]	19–20 Edw. II [1325–6]

[1] See Smyth, iii. 84.

A1/12/134 [GAR 66]	20 Edw. II to 1 Edw. III [1326–7]
A1/12/135 [GAR 67]	7–8 Edw. III [1333–4]
A1/12/136 [GAR 68]	8–9 Edw. III [1334–5]
Scribal error in heading.	
A1/12/137 [GAR 69]	9–10 Edw. III [1335–6]
A1/12/138 [GAR 70]	12–13 Edw. III [1338–9]
A1/12/139 [GAR 71]	17–18 Edw. III [1343–4]
A1/12/140 [GAR 72]	18–19 Edw. III [1344–5]
Scribal error in heading.	
A1/12/141 [GAR 73]	19–20 Edw. III [1345–6]
A1/12/142 [GAR 74]	30–4 Edw. III [1356–60]
Four rolls attached at head.	
A1/12/143 [GAR 75]	Michaelmas 41 Edw. III to 8 June 42 Edw. III [1367–8]
A1/12/144 [GAR 76]	46–7 Edw. III [1372–3]
A1/12/145 [GAR 77]	47 Edw. III to 7 Ric. II [1373–83]
Ten rolls attached at head.	
A1/12/146 [GAR 78]	7–13 Ric. II [1383–9]
Six rolls attached at head.	
A1/12/147 [GAR 79]	4–5 Hen. VI [1425–6]
A1/12/148 [GAR 80]	6 Hen. VI [1427–8]
A1/12/149 [GAR 81]	17–18 Hen. VI [1438–9]
A1/12/150 [GAR 82]	31–2 Hen. VI [1452–3]
A1/12/151 [GAR 83]	36–7 Hen. VI [1457–8]
A1/12/152 [GAR 84]	37–8 Hen. VI [1458–9]
A1/12/153 [GAR 85]	39 Hen. VI to 1 Edw. IV [1460–1]
A1/12/154 [GAR 86]	3–4 Edw. IV [1463–4]
A1/12/155 [GAR 87]	12–13 Edw. IV [1472–3]
A1/12/156 [GAR 88]	13–14 Edw. IV [1473–4]

Miscellaneous

A1/12/157 [SR 142]   After Epiphany 20 Edw. II [1327]
Acknowledgements made by the burgesses of Berkeley for their holdings in the borough [to Thomas (III) Lord Berkeley on his succeeding to his inheritance], with descriptions of the holdings and their rents.

OTHER TENANTS AND HOLDINGS
The Kingswood Abbey holding

A1/12/158 [GC 1384]   n.d. [late Hen. III]
William son of Bernard Godrich and Walter son of Reginald Chesmongare.

William has granted to Walter a part of his land in the old town of Berkel', opposite the house of Alfred le Skipward; rent 6d. a year, and Walter has given him 3s. as acknowledgement.

Witnesses: Adam Coby, John Sewaker, Alfred Skipward, Hugh Johel, Hugh le Wayte, William Cuppere, Walter the clerk.

A1/12/159 [GC 1623]   n.d. [late Edw. I]
Edith la Chesmongare and Thomas Kavel.

Edith has granted to Thomas one third of a burgage in Berkel' beside the street which leads from the house of Richard le Shipward towards the bridge called Lokvastebrugge; rent a rose a year, and he has given her 5*s.*

Witnesses: Richard le Shipward, John Sewaker, Roger the miller (*molendinar'*), William le Palmer, John Bonserjaunt, Thomas Alein, Robert Chaumpeneis.

A1/12/160 [GC 1289]   n.d. [*temp.* Edw. I]

Thomas Cavel and Richard son of Alfred le Shipward.

Thomas has granted to Richard all his holding in the old town of Berkeley, which he had by grant of William Goddrich and Edith daughter of Walter le Chesmongare, held of Kingswood Abbey.

Witnesses: John Sewaker, John Bonserjaunt, William le Cuppere, Henry le Grut, William the tailor (*cissor*), Robert Chaumpeneys, Henry le Cuppere.

A1/12/161 [GC 287]   Mon. the morrow of Holy Trinity [4 June] A.D. 1257

William Goddriht and Thomas Cavel.

William has granted to Thomas all his holding in the town of Berkele, which he held of Kingswood Abbey, opposite the house of Alfred le Skipward; to hold of the monks at 12*d.* a year; Thomas has given him 8*s.*

Witnesses: Adam Coby, John Sewaker, Thomas son of Alan, Alfred Mariner, William le Paumer, William the smith, Peter de Wik, Thomas the serjeant (*serviens*), Nicholas de Crauleygh, Walter Sely, clerk.

A1/12/162 [GC 349]   n.d. [*temp.* Hen. III]

Maurice de Berkeley and Kingswood Abbey.

Maurice has granted to the abbey, for the fabric of the house, in alms, a rent of 12*d.* a year from the house which Ralph the gardener (*gardinarius*) held in the town of Berkeley, towards the bridge to the castle, in exchange for a rent of 12*d.* which the monks had from the house which Walter Sely held in the same town.

Witnesses: Peter de Stintescumbe, Robert de Stone, Ralph de Camme, Robert de Dreycot, Maurice de Camme, John de Crawle, Robert de Bradeston.

A1/12/163 [GC 1201]   n.d. [late Hen. III]

Maurice de Berkel' and Kingswood Abbey.

Maurice has granted to the abbey annual rents of 24*s.*, viz. 20*s.* from a half-virgate, 5 a. and 1 selion of land which Thomas de Aslesworth formerly held of the monks in the vill of Hamme, 2*s.* from the messuage which Richard son of Alfred formerly held in the town of Berkel', 12*d.* from the messuage which Thomas Cavel formerly held in the same town, and 12*d.* from the messuage which Walter Sely held before the castle gate in the same town; also 1 a. of meadow in the meadow of Perham which was formerly of John de Crauleg', for the support of the fabric of the abbey.

Witnesses: Sir Robert le Veel, Sir William Mansel, Sir Nicholas le Lou, Sir Robert de Kyngestun, Sir Warin de Raleg', knights, Philip de Du'ctun', Maurice's steward, William son of Robert, Walter de Eggetun, John de Crauleg', Geoffrey Neel, Robert Bastard.

The Cupper (later Gossard) holding

A1/12/164 [GC 1327]   n.d. [late Hen. III]

Aldith la Cuppere of Berkeley and Alice Gosherde her daughter.

Aldith has granted to Alice the plot in the town of Berk', with the house on it and with 1 selion in the curtilage, lying between Aldith's house and the house of Maud Gosherde; rent 2*d.* a year to the chief lord of Berk'.

Witnesses: Walter Shipward, reeve of Berkeley, John Sewaker, John Bonserjant, William Cuppere, Henry Cuppere, Roger the tanner (*tannar'*).

A1/12/165 [GC 722]   n.d. [*temp.* Edw. I]
Aldith le Cuppere of Berkeley and William Gosherde, her son.

Aldith has granted to William a house with a plot 10 by 30 ft., between her house and the road from the market to Longgebr', and 1 selion in the curtilage; rent to chief lord of Berkeley 2*d.* a year.

Witnesses: Walter Shipward, reeve of Berkeley, Roger Coby, John Sewaker, Gilbert the baker (*pistor*), William Cuppere, Henry Cuppere, Roger the tanner (*tannar'*), William Palmar.

A1/12/166 [GC 1386]   n.d. [*temp.* Edw. I]
William le Gosherde of Berkeley and William son of Walter de Shiptone.

William le Gosherde has granted to William de Shiptone a plot of land with the house built on it in the old town of Berk', with 1 selion in the curtilage; rent a rose a year and 2*d.* a year to the chief lord of Berk', and William de Shiptone has given him 8*s.*

Witnesses: Walter Shipward, John Sewaker, John Bonserjant, Henry Cuppere, Gilbert the baker (*pistor*), Roger the tanner (*tann'*), William Palmar, clerk.

A1/12/167 [GC 1610]   n.d. [*temp.* Edw. I]
Aldith le Cuppare of Berkeley; and William son of Maud le Glovare and Helen his wife.

Aldith has granted to William and Helen the plot of her chamber to the west of her house, towards the marketplace of Berk', measuring 28 by 28 ft.; rent 1*d.* a year, and they have given her 5*s.* 6*d.*

Witnesses: Thomas Alein, Walter Shipward, John Bonserjant, Henry Cuppere.

The Parker stall

A1/12/168 [GC 524]   15 Edw. I [1286–7]
Roger Choby; and Walter le Parkere and Juliana his wife.

Following a suit of novel disseisin at Gloucester, in 15 Edw. I, before the justices between Walter and Juliana and Roger and Richard Noblepas about a stall in the town of Berkele opposite the marketplace, which Anger the merchant (*mercator*) formerly held, Roger has quitclaimed the stall to Walter and his wife.

Witnesses: William de Burgo, Robert de Stone, Thomas de Swonhonger, John Sewaker, Thomas Aleyn, John Bonserjaunt.

A1/12/169 [GC 525]   15 Edw. I [1286–7]
Richard Noblepas; and Walter le Parkere and his wife Juliana.

Quitclaim by Richard (similar to A1/12/168 [GC 524] above).

Witnesses: William de Burgo, Robert de Stone, Thomas de Swonhonger, John Sewaker, Thomas Aleyn, John Bonserjaunt.

The Waleys holding

A1/12/170 [GC 982]   n.d. [early 14th cent.]
Richard son and heir of John Waleys of Berkeley and Robert de Coston.

Richard has quitclaimed to Robert, for a certain sum of money, a messuage with a curtilage in the new town of Berkel' which Adam the miller (*molendinar'*) and Helen his wife held of him for life, and also a messuage and a curtilage which Edith Halemo and Edith and Maud her daughters hold for 30 years; rent 2 lb. of wax a year for the lamp of Holy Cross in Berkeley church.

Witnesses: John le Cuppere, reeve, John Sewaker, Henry le Cuppere, Walter le Cuppere, Richard le Noble.

A1/12/171 [GC 1307]   n.d. [*temp*. Edw. I]
Robert de Costone and John le Boriton, miller of Ham.

Robert has granted to John the holding which he had by grant of Richard le Waleys in the town of Berck'; rent 2 lb. of wax a year for the lamp of Holy Cross of Berkeley, and John has given him a certain sum of money.
Witnesses: Walter Sewaker, John le Coppere, Richard le Coppere, Walter le Coppere, Richard Noblepas, Henry le Gardin', William Purlewent, clerk.

The Miller holding

A1/12/172 [GC 2835]   St. Thomas the apostle, 9 Edw. III [21 Dec. 1335]
John son of John the miller (*molen'*) of Berkeley and John Sley of Berkeley.

John the miller has leased to John Sley, for 30*s*., a messuage in Berckel' for a term of 3 years.
Witnesses: Robert Groundi, John le Coppere, William Jodde, Nicholas le Vyngnur, Walter le Coppere, John Walebroke.
At: Berkeley.

A1/12/173 [GC 2930]   Thurs. the feast of St. Silvester, 12 Edw. III [31 Dec. 1338]
John the miller (*molendinar'*) of Berkeley and John Sley.

John the miller has granted to John Sley, his heirs and assigns his holding in the borough of Berkel'.
Witnesses: Robert Groundy, John le Cuppare, Robert le Schipward, John le Schipward, John de Fromelode.
At: Berkeley.

A1/12/174 [GC 2933]   Sun. after Epiphany, 12 Edw. III [10 Jan. 1339]
Helen daughter of John the miller (*molendinar'*) and John Sley of Berkeley.

Helen has quitclaimed to John a messuage with a plot of land in the borough of Berkel'.
Witnesses: Robert Groundy, Edward de Fromelode, John Sewaker, John Schipward, John de Fromelode.
At: Berkeley.

A1/12/175 [GC 2966][1]   Sun. after Epiphany, 13 Edw. III [9 Jan. 1340]
Helen daughter of John the miller (*molendinar'*) and John Sley of Berkeley.

Helen has quitclaimed to John a messuage with a plot of land in the borough of Berkel'.
Witnesses: Robert Groundy, Edward de Fromelode, John Sewaker, John Schipward, John de Fromelode.
At: Berkeley.

The Gardener holding

A1/12/176 [GC 3048]   10 March 17 Edw. III [1343]
Robert son of Robert le Gardiner of Dursley; and Henry de Modybrok of Berkeley and Edania his wife.

Robert has quitclaimed to Henry and Edania a house in Berkeleye with a curtilage.
Witnesses: Robert Groundy, John Cuppare, John le Webbe, John Schipward, John Bil.
At: Berkeley.

A1/12/177 [GC 3047]   10 March 17 Edw. III [1343]
Robert son of Robert le Gardiner of Dursley; and Henry de Modybrok of Berkeley and Edania his wife.

---

[1] The only significant difference between this deed and that immediately above is in the regnal year. There may have been a clerical error.

Whereas Henry and Edania had by grant of Robert a house in Berkeleye with a curtilage, if they are impleaded by Robert, his wife, or by anyone in his name because of the lack of a warranty they will have 100*s.* from his goods.

Witnesses: Robert Groundy, John Cuppare, John le Webbe, John Schipward, John Bil.

At: Berkeley.

Richard Groundy's holding

A1/12/178 [GC 3410]   Sun. after the Annunciation, 28 Edw. III [30 March 1354]

Geoffrey Martyn of Bristol; and William Modbrok and Walter Coppare of Berkeley.

Geoffrey has leased to William and Walter the holding which Thomas Bode, Rose Brewer and John Vynour hold of him in the town of Berkel', and his meadow in Holemede, which holding and meadow he had by extent made on a statute merchant bond against Richard Groundi.

Witnesses: Thomas Payn, John Bill, Thomas Goldhoppere, Nicholas Schepherd, John Vynour.

At: Berkeley.

A1/12/179 [GC 3427]   Sun. after the translation of St. Thomas of Canterbury, 29 Edw. III
[12 July 1355]

Walter Coppare of Berkeley and William Westone of Berkeley.

Walter has leased to William his purparty of the land and meadow which he had with William Modebrok of Berkeley by lease of Geoffrey Martyn of Bristoll, and which Geoffrey had by an extent made on a statute merchant bond against Richard Groundy.

Witnesses: John Serjant, John Capel, Thomas Payn, John Byl, Thomas Goldehoppe, John Vynor.

At: Berkeley.

A1/12/180 [GC 3429]   Sun. after the translation of St. Thomas of Canterbury, 29 Edw. III
[12 July 1355]

William Modebroke of Berkeley; and William le Tannare and Alice his wife.

William has leased to William and Alice his purparty of the land and meadow which he had with Walter Coppare of Berkeley by lease of Geoffrey Martyn of Bristoll, and which Geoffrey had by an extent made on a statute merchant bond against Richard Groundy.

Witnesses: John Serjant, John Capel, Thomas Payn, John Bil, Thomas Goldehoppe, John Vynor.

At: Berkeley.

A1/12/181 [GC 3436]   Thurs. after Michaelmas, 29 Edw. III [1 Oct. 1355]

William Tannare of Berkeley; and Robert Shypward of Berkeley and Joan his wife.

William has leased to Robert and Joan his purparty which he had by grant of William Modebroke of two holdings which Thomas Bodde and Rose Bruere held in the borough of Berkele; for the life of Richard Groundy of Berkeley, rent 6*s.* a year.

Witnesses: John Serjant, John Capel, Thomas Payn, John Byl, Thomas Goldhoppe.

At: Berkeley.

A1/12/182 [GC 3437]   Thurs. after Michaelmas, 29 Edw. III [1 Oct. 1355]

William Westone of Berkeley; and Robert Shypward of Berkeley and Joan his wife.

William has leased to Robert and Joan his purparty which he had by grant of Walter Coppare of Berkeley, and which Walter and William Modebroke of Berkeley had by grant of Geoffrey Martyn of Bristoll; for the life of Richard Groundy of Berkeley.

Witnesses: John Serjant, John Capel, Thomas Payn, John Byl, Thomas Goldhoppe.

At: Berkeley.

The Scott holding

A1/12/183 [GC 2609]   n.d. [mid 14th cent.]
Nicholas le Skot of Newport and William le Muleward of Ham, his brother.

   Nicholas has granted to William a house with a curtilage in Berkeleye.
Witnesses: Robert Groundy, John Sewaker, John Schipward, Richard Aleyn, Henry Judde, John le Webbe, Adam Purlewent, clerk.

A1/12/184 [GC 2610]   n.d. [mid 14th cent.]
(1) Nicholas le Skot; (2) Robert Groundy and Adam Purlewent; (3) William le Muleward of Ham, Nicholas's brother.

   Nicholas has appointed Robert and Adam his attorneys to give seisin to William of a house and curtilage in Berkel'.
Witnesses: John Sewaker, Richard Aleyn, Henry le Heir, William Grip, Henry Judde.

The Sewaker rent

A1/12/185 [GC 3549]   Mon. before Easter, 38 Edw. III [18 March 1364]
Walter Brayn, chaplain; and David vicar of Berkeley, John Sergeant, John Aleyn of Hill, John Gare, John Coby, John Bil, Nicholas Schepward, Richard Scriveyn and Nicholas Sopare.

   Walter has surrendered to David and the others ¼d. rent from Helen daughter of John Sewaker of Berkeley for a messuage and curtilage which she holds for life by demise of her father, with the reversion of the holdings, which rent and reversion the said David and the others granted to him for his life.
Witnesses: Walter Holdelond, John Wolpenne, Henry de Eketone, William Purlewent, John Borford, clerk.
At: Berkeley.

A1/12/186 [GC 3550]   Tues. after Easter, 38 Edw. III [26 March 1364]
David vicar of Berkeley, John Sergeant, John Aleyn of Hill, John Gare, John Coby, John Bil, Nicholas Schepward, Richard Scriveyn and Nicholas Sopare; and Thomas Aleyn and Thomas his son.

   David and the others have granted to Thomas and Thomas ¼d. rent from Helen daughter of John Sewaker of Berkeley for a messuage and curtilage which she holds for life by demise of her father; for their lives, rent ¼d. while Helen lives and after her death 18d. a year.
Witnesses: Walter Holdelond, John Wolpenne, Henry de Eketone, William Purlewent, John Borford, clerk.
At: Berkeley.

A1/12/187 [GC 3552]   Sun. one week after Easter, 38 Edw. III [31 March 1364]
David vicar of Berkeley, John Sergeant, John Aleyn of Hill, John Gare, John Coby, John Bil, Nicholas Schepward, Richard Scriveyn and Nicholas Sopare; and Sir Walter Brayn of Dillwe, chaplain.

   David and the others have granted to Walter the rent of ¼d. from Helen daughter of John Sewaker of Berkeley, while she lives, and after her death of 18d. a year from Thomas Aleyn and Thomas his son for a messuage and curtilage.
Witnesses: Walter Holdelond, John Wolpenne, Henry de Eketone, William Purlewent, John Borford, clerk.
At: Berkeley.

The Sewaker holding

A1/12/188 [GC 3618]   Mon. after St. Peter and St. Paul, 44 Edw. III [1 July 1370]
Thomas son of the late Thomas Sewaker of Berkeley and Thomas Golthoppe, his uncle.

Thomas Sewaker has granted to Thomas Golthoppe, his heirs and assigns his holding in Berkelee abutting on the road to the holding of St. Mary's chapel.
Witnesses: William Modibroke, John Coby, John Byl, Nicholas Schippard, John Scherare.
At: Berkeley.

A1/12/189 [GC 3708]   Mon. in Easter week, 51 Edw. III [23 March 1377]
Thomas Golthoppe of Berkeley; and Sir Richard Balle, chaplain, and Ralph Coke of Monmouth.

Thomas has granted to Richard and Ralph, their heirs and assigns his holding in Berkel'.
Witnesses: John Sergeant of Stone, William Smalcombe, William Modybroke, Nicholas Schippard, Thomas Lucas.
At: Berkeley.

A1/12/190 [GC 3735]   Mon. after St. Andrew, 3 Ric. II [5 Dec. 1379]
Ralph Cok and Richard Balle, chaplain; and John Dreu and Joan his wife.

Ralph and Richard have leased to John and Joan their holding in Berkelee, which they acquired from Thomas Goldhoppe; for the lives of John and Joan, rent 6s. a year.
Witnesses: William Modybroke, Nicholas Schippard, Thomas Lucas.
At: Berkeley.

The Cook enfeoffment

The Malger holding

A1/12/191 [GC 3845]   Fri. the feast of St. Hilary, 14 Ric. II [13 Jan. 1391]
Robert Malger, son and heir of Rose Lokyntone, daughter and heir of John Lokyntone of Berkeley; and Ralph Cok of Monmouth, Richard Balle and John Barbour chaplains.

Robert has granted to Ralph, Richard and John, and their heirs and assigns, his holding with a curtilage in Berkele, between the holdings of Edith Swonhongre on each side.
Witnesses: John Clerk, Richard Smyth, Thomas Lucas, William Wayte, Richard Scot the elder.
At: Berkeley.

A1/12/192 [GC 3319]   n.d. [late 14th cent.]
Robert Malg', son and heir of Rose Lokyntone, daughter and heir of John Lokyntone; and Ralph Cok of Monmouth, Richard Balle and John Barbour, chaplains.

Robert has quitclaimed to Ralph, Richard and John his holding with a curtilage in Berkeley.
Witnesses: Thomas Lucas, John Clere, William Packar, Richard Scot the younger, John Swonhungre the younger.

The Bill holding

A1/12/193 [GC 3983]   Tues. after St. Hilary, 2 Hen. IV [18 Jan. 1401]
Richard Byl, son and heir of the late John Byl of Berkeley, and William Oteclyf, chaplain.

Richard has granted to William, his heirs and assigns the messuage with a curtilage in Berkeley between the holdings of Adam ate Wyche and Robert Hervy.
Witnesses: Thomas Lucas, John Egetone, John Stanleye, Richard Toukere, William Packere.
At: Berkeley.

A1/12/194 [GC 3982]   Tues. after St. Hilary, 2 Hen. IV [18 Jan. 1401]
(1) William Oteclyf, chaplain; (2) William Smart, chaplain; (3) Richard Byl, son and heir of
the late John Byl.

William Oteclyf has appointed William Smart to receive seisin of a messuage with a
curtilage in Berkeley, which he had by grant of Richard.

At: Berkeley.

Other

A1/12/195 [GC 3725]   Wed. 16 June 1 Ric. III [1378]
William le Muleward of Ham; and John Clerk and John Byl of Berkeley.

William has granted to John and John, and their heirs and assigns, a house with a
curtilage in Berkele.

Witnesses: John Sergeaunte of Stone, Ralph Waleys, William Smalcombe, William
Modybroke, William Scot, Thomas Uptone, William Hert.

At: Berkeley.

The combined holding

A1/12/196 [GC 3918]   4 March 20 Ric. II [1397]
John Clerk, John Bylle and Richard Scotte; and John Wedyngton, John Camme, William
Ottecleffe, clerk, and Thomas de Kendale.

John, John and Richard have granted to John, John, William and Thomas, and their heirs
and assigns, all the lands, holdings [etc.] within the hundred of Berkeley that they had by
grant of Ralph Kooc, John Barbour, Richard Balle, William le Mulward of Hamme,
Thomas Goldhoppe and Robert Malger of Berkeley.

Witnesses: John Rolves, William Smalcombe the elder, John Harcher, Richard Ectone, John
Ectone.

At: Berkeley.

The Doly holding

A1/12/197 [GC 4250]   26 Aug. 23 Hen. VI [1445]
William Doly, burgess of Bristol, and Katherine widow of John Wylkyns of Berkeley.

William has leased to Katherine parcels of the burgage and curtilage which John and
Katherine lately held in Berkeley, viz. a hall called Blackehalle, a cellar to the east of the
hall, a solar above the cellar, a house called le Norcery alehouse, half of the curtilage of the
said burgage and half the fruits of the trees there, with free access to water, the latrine and
other necessaries; for her life, rent 8*d.* a year.

Witnesses: Thomas Clifford, John Dyer, Richard Lee.

At: Berkelcy.

A1/12/198 [GC 4256]   30 March 25 Hen. VI [1447]
John Doly, burgess of Bristol; and Katherine widow of John Wylkyns of Berkeley, Thomas
her son, John Kyng, baker, Agnes his wife and John their son.

John has leased to Katherine, Thomas, John, Agnes and John, certain parcels of the
burgage and curtilage which John and Katherine lately held in Berkeley, viz. a hall called
Blackehalle, a cellar to the east of the hall, a solar above the cellar, a house called le
Norcery alehouse and a solar above it and half of the curtilage of the said burgage, with free
access to the latrine and to water for baking and brewing, viz. to the well [*fons*] and the
pool [*stagnum*] called Juddeswell; for their lives, rent 8*d.* a year.

Witnesses: Thomas Clifford, Richard Lee, Thomas Nelme.

At: Berkeley.

Miscellaneous

A1/12/199 [SC 422]   n.d. [*temp.* Hen. III]

Robert Zarnes of Berkeley and John Schiphard.

Robert has granted to John, in free marriage with Agnes his daughter, two burgages lying between that of Longbridge Priory and that of Richard Ferour and extending from Langebryggestrete to the lands of St. Augustine's; to them and their male issue, rent 2*s.* a year to the hospital of St. John, Clerkenwell.

Witnesses: John de Kingestone, knight, John de Aune, William Mettesdone, Eudo de Haucton, William Cuylire, Alan Marchald, William de Charfeld, Walter [de Charfeld] his son.

A1/12/200 [GC 1194]   n.d. [late Hen. III]

Arn[old] of Berkeley, clerk, founder [*fundator*] of the hospital of Holy Trinity, Longbridge, and the brothers of the hospital; and Gilbert the baker (*pistor*).

Arnold and the hospital have granted to Gilbert the burgage in the town of Berkel' next to the road from Locfastebrugge to the house of Alfred le Shipward, which they had by gift of Peter de Wyka; to him and his heirs, rent 4*s.* a year; and he has given them 2 marks.

Witnesses: Sir N. vicar of Berkeley, Adam Coby, Peter de Wik, John Sewaker, Thomas Cavel, Thomas Alein, William Cole, John Bonserjant, Walter Sely, clerk.

A1/12/201 [GC 1585]   n.d. [late Hen. III]

Nicholas de Wodeford and Henry le Cuppere.

Nicholas has granted to Henry the burgage in the new town of Berkel' beside the holding which Isabel le Cuppere holds of Sir Maurice de Berkel', and beside the road from la Locfastebrugge to la Boreghyate; to hold of the chief lord of Berkel', and Henry has given him 38*s.* 8*d.*

Witnesses: Thomas Cavel, John Sewaker, Walter Sely, William le Cuppere, Henry le Grut, Robert Champeneys, William the tailor (*cissor*).

A1/12/202 [GC 365]   n.d. [late Hen. III]

St. Augustine's Abbey, Bristol, and Robert le Hurde.

William [Long] the abbot and the convent have granted to Robert the burgage which William le Chamberlen held in Berkeley between the churchyard and the land which was of Richard de Lokinton, and 1 a. of land outside Berkeley, extending from Cronham to la Grave; rent 1 lb. of pepper a year, entry fine 1 mark.

Witnesses: Sir Henry and Sir William de Berkeley, knights, John de Egeton, Adam Coby, . . .

A1/12/203 [GC 551]   n.d. [late Hen. III]

Elias the clerk, son of Ralph the cook (*cocus*) of Berkeley, and Roger the weaver (*textor*).

Elias has granted to Roger the land, with the buildings on it, opposite the land of Arnulf de Berkeley, clerk, in the new town of Berkel', which Hugh the clerk formerly held of him; to hold the said burgage [*sic*] by a rent of 12*d.* a year to the chief lord of Berkeley and the customs of the borough of Berkeley which pertain to the same town; Roger has given Elias 15*s.* 6*d.*

Witnesses: John Sewaker, reeve of Berkeley, Adam Coby, Alfred Mariner, Peter de Wyk, Thomas son of Alan, William the smith, Adam the smith, Thomas Cavel, Robert de Sancto Claro, William le Cuppere, William Furst, Walter Sely, clerk.

A1/12/204 [GC 1504]   n.d. [late Hen. III]
Walter the parmenter, son and heir of Hugh the parmenter, and Roger the miller (*molend*').

Walter has granted to Roger his land in the town of Berkel', in the street to the house of Alfred le Mariner, except the land which William the tailor (*cissor*) held of Walter; rent to St. Augustine's Abbey, Bristol, 12*d.* a year, and to Kingswood Abbey, 2*s.* a year, and Roger has given him 6 marks.
Witnesses: John Sewaker, Peter de Wyk', Adam Coby, Thomas Cavel, Thomas son of Alan, Thomas the serjeant (*serviens*), William Palm', John Bonserjaunt, Walter Sely.

A1/12/205 [GC 1618]   n.d. [late Hen. III]
Roger the miller (*molend*') of Berkeley and Richard son of Alfred de Berkel'.

Roger has granted to Richard 1 a. of land in the old town of Berkel'; rent a rose a year, and 12*d.* a year to St. Augustine's Abbey, Bristol, and Richard has given Roger 2 marks.
Witnesses: Sir Maurice de Saltmarsh (*de salsomarisco*), William son of Robert, Peter de Wyke, John de Egeton, Thomas the serjeant (*serviens*), Thomas Aleyn, William Palmar', John Bonserjant.

A1/12/206 [GC 744]   n.d. [late Hen. III]
Gunnilda widow of Thomas le Dobler and Robert Pynel.

Gunnilda has granted to Robert her holding in the new town of Berkel', except the holding which Robert the arbalester (*balistarius*) held of her; rent 8*d.* a year to the chief lord of Berkeley, and Robert has given her 20*s.*
Witnesses: Peter de Wik, Adam Coby, John Sewaker, Thomas son of Alan, William Cule, Thomas Cavel, Walter Sely, clerk.

A1/12/207 [GC 784]   n.d. [late 13th cent.]
Roger le Meleward of Berkeley and Walter le Shipward of Berkeley.

Roger has granted to Walter, in free marriage with his daughter Maud, one quarter of a burgage in the town of Berk', rent 12*d.* a year, and also all the holding which he had by grant of St. Augustine's Abbey.
Witnesses: William le Cupper, John Bonserjant, Thomas . . . , Thomas Aleyn, Henry Grout.

A1/12/208 [GC 948]   n.d. [late 13th cent.]
David Page of Berkeley; and John le Cuppere and Juliana his wife.

David has granted to John and Juliana, for a certain sum of money, his house with a curtilage and the appurtenances of a burgage, which he had by grant of Sir Thomas de Berkel'; to hold of the lord of Berkele by a rent of 2*s.* a year.
Witnesses: Thomas Alein, Walter Schipward, reeve, John Bonserjant, Henry le Cuppere, Walter le Cuppere, Richard le Noble, Richard le Savoner, clerk.

A1/12/209 [GC 889]   n.d. [late 13th cent.]
Adam the carter (*caretarius*) of Woodlands (*la Wodelonde*) and Richard son of Robert the merchant.

Adam has granted to Richard the holding in the town of Berk' opposite the house of St. Augustine's Abbey, between the road to Longebrugg and the garden of the lord of Berkeley; rent to chief lord of Berkeley 1 lb. of cumin a year.
Witnesses: Sir Nicholas vicar of Berkeley, Robert Marescall, reeve, William Palmar', Thomas Cavel, John Sewaker, Thomas son of Alan, Simon de Long, Reginald de Long.

A1/12/210 [GC 1625]   n.d. [*temp.* Edw. I]
Margery daughter of John Waleys of Berkeley and John son of William le Cuppere of Berkeley.

Margery has granted to John her half-burgage in Berkel'; to hold of the lord of Berkel', rent 6*d.* a year, and he has given her 20*s.*
Witnesses: Walter Schipward, John Sewaker, John Bonserjant, Henry le Cuppere, Walter le Cuppere, William le Wilde, Richard le Savoner.

A1/12/211 [GC 1515]   n.d. [*temp.* Edw. I]
Gilbert le Pistor of Berkeley and Thomas de Lude, clerk.

Gilbert has granted to Thomas his burgage in Berkel', beside the burgage of Robert Cole, to hold of the hospital of Langebrugge; rent of 4*s.* a year, and Thomas has given him 60*s.*
Witnesses: Walter le Schipward, reeve, Thomas Aleyn, John Sewaker, John Bonserjant, Henry Cuppere, Richard le Savoner, clerk.

A1/12/212 [GC 1512]   n.d. [*temp.* Edw. I]
Maud daughter of Robert Pynel of Berkeley and William Pridy.

Maud has granted to William a burgage in the new town of Berk'; to hold of the chief lord at a rent 12*d.* a year, and William has given her 20*s.*
Witnesses: Thomas Alein, Thomas le Serjant, John Sewaker, John Bonserjant, Walter Shipward, Henry Cuppere, Henry Grout.

A1/12/213 [GC 1513]   n.d. [*temp.* Edw. I]
Robert Pinel and Richard le Noble.

Robert has granted to Richard a burgage in the town of Berkel'; to hold of the chief lord at a rent of 8*d.* a year, and Richard has given Robert 3 marks.
Witnesses: Bartholomew de Olepenne the elder, John Wyth, Thomas Kavel, John Sewaker, Thomas Aleyn, William le Cuppere.

A1/12/214 [GC 1484]   n.d. [*temp.* Edw. I]
Joan daughter of the late Roger called the miller (*molendinar'*) of Berkeley, unmarried woman; and Walter Schipward of Berkeley and Maud his wife.

Joan has granted to Walter and Maud the half-burgage which was formerly of Juliana Ernes and which she inherited after the death of Roger her father; to them and their issue, and they have given her 20*s.* and their part of the half-burgage which was of Eve Daniel.
Witnesses: Gilbert the baker (*pistor*), Robert Pinel, John Bonsergant, Henry le Cuppere, William le Cuppere, Richard le Savoner.

A1/12/215 [GC 2543]   n.d. [*temp.* Edw. I]
Adam son and heir of Robert Pinel and William called Pridi.

Adam has granted . . . to William his burgage in the new town of Berkel' . . . rent . . . 12*d.* a year.
Witnesses: . . . reeve, Thomas Alain, John . . . Cuppere, Richard . . . le Savoner, clerk.

A1/12/216 [GC 1445]   n.d. [*temp.* Edw. I]
John de Kilcote and Margery his wife; and John the smith and Edith his wife.

John and Margery have granted to John and Edith their burgage in the town of Berk', extending from the corner of the castle towards Locvastebrugge; for the lives of John and Edith and the life of one of their children, rent 3*s.* 4*d.* a year, and they have given John and Margery 6*s.*
Witnesses: Thomas Kavel, John Bonserjant, William le Cuppere, Walter le Grip, Walter le Gardiner.

A1/12/217 [GC 1171]   n.d. [*temp.* Edw. I]
Robert Ang'[ervill] and Juliana his sister.

Robert has quitclaimed to Juliana a certain shop in the town of Berk', viz. in the corner called la Horeyete.

Witnesses: William le Cuppare, John Bonserjant, Henry le Grut, William the tailor (*cissor*), Walter le Vinnur, Walter the teaseler (*cardinar'*), Robert Pinel.

A1/12/218 [GC 981]   n.d. [early 14th cent.]
Robert le Vingnur of Berkeley; and Hervidus de Sancto Edmundo and Juliana his wife.

Robert has granted to Hervidus and Juliana the holding in the old town of Berkel' which he inherited after the death of his mother Maud in the east part of the marketplace next to the great street; rent to the chief lord of Berkeley 4*d.* a year and the customs of the said borough of Berkel', and they have given Robert 10*s.*

Witnesses: John Sewaker, John Bonserjant, Thomas Aleyn, Gilbert the baker (*pistor*), Robert Pinel, William le Cuppere, Richard le Savoner.

A1/12/219 [GC 941]   n.d. [early 14th cent.]
Richard Noblepas and John the miller (*molendinarius*) of Berkeley.

Richard has granted to John a plot of land next to his holding, 20 by 29 ft., in the borough of Berkelee.

Witnesses: John Coppere, Henry Gardiner, John Sewaker, Roger Cuppere, Edward de Fromelode, John le Vynor, John de Fromelod.

A1/12/220 [GC 1100]   Michaelmas, 33 Edw. I [29 Sept. 1305]
Robert Averay of Berkeley; and Edward de Fromylode, Edith his wife and John their son.

Robert has granted to Edward, Edith and John a plot of land lying between Edward's holding and the holding of Thomas le Hopere; for their lives, rent 2*s.* a year, and they have given him a certain sum of money.

Witnesses: Walter Sewaker, John de Swonhungre, John le Coppere, John le Wynur, Thomas the miller (*molend'*), William Purlewent, clerk.

At: Berkeley.

A1/12/221 [GC 1890]   Sat. the feast of St. Dunstan, 6 Edw. II [21 Oct. 1312]
Walter Symond, chaplain, and Robert le Schoyare of Berkeley.

Walter, of his good will and special grace, has granted to Robert that if Robert pays him £8, with his expenses, he will transfer to Robert a holding in the borough of Berkelee, with a charter.

Witnesses: John le Cuppere, John Sewaker, Henry le Gardyner, Roger le Cuppere, Robert Groundy.

At: Berkeley.

A1/12/222 [GC 1897]   Fri. after St. Hilary, 6 Edw. II [19 Jan. 1313]
Henry Pridy, son of Margery de Morevyle, and William Page.

Henry has quitclaimed to William the lands and holdings which William and Juliana his wife had by his grant, for their lives, in and near the town of Berkeleye.

Witnesses: John de Alkleye, John de Brokeneberwe, William Waleys, Richard Peschall, Elias de Fylton, Josce de Reymun', John le Cuppere, John Wyth, John de la Chyrche.

At: Bristol.

A1/12/223 [GC 1964]   Wed. before the Purification, 7 Edw. II [30 Jan. 1314]
Robert son and heir of John le Schoyare of Berkeley and Walter de Lokyntone.

Robert has granted to Walter, his heirs and assigns his half-burgage in Berk' and a plot of land beside Walter's holding. [*15th-cent. copy.*]

Witnesses: John le Cuppere, John Sewaker, Roger le Cuppere, Robert Groundy, Hugh le Proute.
At: Berkeley.

A1/12/224 [GC 1997]   Mon. after St. Francis, [8] Edw. II [7 Oct. 1314]
[Alice le Cuppere] and [John de Seham]
[Alice] . . . . of Robert . . . . has quitclaimed to [John de] Seham for John's life . . . messuage in the borough of Berkel' . . . . Endorsed: *from Alice le Cuppere to John de Seham.*
Witnesses: Henry le Gardener, John le . . . , Edward F[romelode], . . .

A1/12/225 [GC 2048]   St. John the Baptist, 8 Edw. II [24 June 1315]
John ate Elme of Berkeley and Robert le Gardiner of Berkeley.
     John has granted to Robert, his heirs and assigns a plot of land 24 by 3 ft. in Berckel' between their houses.
Witnesses: John le Cuppere, Henry le Gardiner, Robert Groundy, John Jodde, Hugh le Proute.
At: Berkeley.

A1/12/226 [GC 2147]   The Purification, 10 Edw. II [2 Feb. 1317]
William Bodde of Berkeley and Isabel daughter of Agnes le Glovare of Berkeley.
     William has granted to Isabel, her heirs and assigns the holding in Berckel' which he had by grant of the said Agnes, beside the road from Modybroc to the marketplace of Berckel'.
Witnesses: John le Coppere, Henry le Gardiner, John Jodde, John le Vyngnur, Roger le Coppere, Robert Groundy, Hugh le Proute.
At: Berkeley.

A1/12/227 [GC 2409]   St. James, 17 Edw. II [25 July 1323]
Juliana daughter of Roger le Webbe of Berkeley; and Hervey and Henry her sons.
     Juliana has quitclaimed to Hervey and Henry her holding in Berckel'.
Witnesses: Henry le Gardiner, Robert Groundy, John Judde, William Iweyn, Thomas Page, John Sewaker, Adam Pynel.
At: Berkeley.

A1/12/228 [GC 2713]   Mon. before St. Luke, 4 Edw. III [22 Oct. 1330]
John Noblepas of Berkeley; and William ate Wode of Berkeley and Christine his wife.
     John has granted to William and Christine, and their heirs and assigns, a cottage in Berckel'.
Witnesses: Robert Groundy, William Judde, Adam Pynel, Henry de Modybrok, Nicholas Daungervyle, Robert le Schypward.
At: Berkeley.

A1/12/229 [GC 2765; *duplicate* GC 2766]   Wed. after St. Valentine, 7 Edw. III [17 Feb. 1333]
Thomas Swele; and John le Hoppare and Sibyl his sister.
     Thomas has leased to John and Sibyl his holding in Berkel'; for their lives, rent a rose a year.
Witnesses: Robert Groundy, John le Gardiner, William Jodde, Nicholas le Vynor, John de Fromelode.
At: Berkeley.

A1/12/230 [GC 2774]   St. Wulfstan, 7 Edw. III [19 Jan. 1334]
John son of John the miller (*molend'*) of Ham and Adam son of William Purlewent of Ham.
     John has granted to Adam, his heirs and assigns an annual rent of 1½d. from the holding which Adam Potu', John Scley and Juliana his wife hold for their lives in Berkeleye; with the reversion of the holding.

Witnesses: John le Gardyner, Robert Groundy, William Judde, Henry de Modybrok, John le Schypward, William le Vygnor, Robert le Schypward.
At: Berkeley.

A1/12/231 [GC 2801]   Nativity of St. Mary, 8 Edw. III [8 Sept. 1334]
Nicholas son of Alan Schott of Ham and John de Leytrintone.
   Nicholas has granted to John, his heirs and assigns his messuage in Berckeleye with a curtilage, which he had by grant of Alan his father.
Witnesses: John le Gardiner, Robert Groundi, William Jodde, Edward de Fromylode, Adam Pynel, Robert le Schypward, John Swele.
At: Berkeley.

A1/12/232 [GC 2932]   Sun. after the Circumcision, 12 Edw. III [3 Jan. 1339]
John son and heir of Richard Noblepas of Berkeley and John Sley of Berkeley.
   John Noblepas has quitclaimed to John Sley a messuage with a plot of land in the borough of Berkel'.
Witnesses: Robert Groundy, Edward de Fromelode, John le Webbe, Alexander de Baa, Henry Swele, John Schipward, John de Fromelode.
At: Berkeley.

A1/12/233 [GC 2956]   Thurs. the feast of the nativity of St. John the Baptist, 13 Edw. III
                                                                        [24 June 1339]
John de Seham; and Thomas Aleyn of Hill and Katherine his daughter.
   John has quitclaimed to Thomas and Katherine half of the holding which he has in Berkeleye next to the holding of John le Cook called Gamelef.
Witnesses: John de Milkesham, John de Egetone, John Purlewent, John de Lorewynge, John le Cuppere, Robert Grundi, John de Fromelode, Robert Prycke, John Gamelef.
At: Berkeley.

A1/12/234 [GC 2945]   Thurs. before St. Philip and St. James, 14 Edw. III [27 April 1340]
John le Bil of Berkeley and Roger ate Wyth of Berkeley.
   John has granted to Roger, his heirs and assigns a rent of 3*s.* from a messuage and curtilage which Roger previously had in Berkel'.
Witnesses: Robert Groundy, Robert Prikke, John Schipward, John Payn, John Gomylef.
At: Berkeley.

A1/12/235 [GC 3008]   Sun. the feast of St. Katherine, 15 Edw. III [25 Nov. 1341]
Henry le Cuppere, son of John le Cuppere, and Richard le Paneter.
   Henry has quitclaimed to Richard an annual rent of 3*s.* 7*d.* from a half-burgage in the town of Berkel'.
Witnesses: Robert Groundi, John le Cuppere, John Bil, John le Webbe, Richard Faukener.
At: Wotton.

A1/12/236 [GC 3161]   14 May 21 Edw. III [1347]
Robert le Schipward of Berkeley; and William le Gosherde and Margaret his wife, Robert's daughter.
   Robert has leased to William and Margaret a cottage with a curtilage in Berkeleye; for their lives, rent 3*d.* a year.
Witnesses: Robert Groundy, John Sewaker, John Schipward, John Gamelef, Adam Purlewent, clerk.
At: Berkeley.

A1/12/237 [GC 3326]   n.d. [mid 14th cent.]
Richard le Paniter of Berkeley and Sir Thomas atte Welle, chaplain.

   Richard has granted to Thomas his holding by the road from the marketplace of Berkelee
to Hamme.
Witnesses: Robert Groundy, John Sewaker, John le Webbe, Henry de Modebroke, John Bil.

A1/12/238 [GC 3395]   Sun. after St. John the Baptist, 26 Edw. III [30 June 1352]
Robert le Gardiner and David le Schipward.

   Robert has granted to David, his heirs and assigns his holding beside the road to the
church of Berkel'.
Witnesses: William de Modybrok, Thomas Goldhoppere, John le Webbe, Thomas Payn,
John le Byl, Nicholas le Schipward, John de Fromelode.
At: Berkeley.

A1/12/239 [GC 3464]   Trinity Sunday, 31 Edw. III [4 June 1357]
Juliana le Fryg of Berkeley; and John Walbroke of the same and Maud his wife.

   Juliana has granted to John and Maud, and John's heirs and assigns, two cottages with a
curtilage in Niwestret in Berkeleye.
Witnesses: William Modebroke, Thomas Payn, Walter Rogers, William le Tannare, John
Byl.
At: Berkeley.

A1/12/240 [GC 3547]   St. Lucy, 37 Edw. III [13 Dec. 1363]
William Modebroke of Berkeley and Nicholas Soper of Berkeley.

   William has granted to Nicholas, his heirs and asigns two plots in Berkele and an annual
rent of 8*s.* from the holding of John Walstiles.
Witnesses: Richard Groundy, John Coby, John Byle, Thomas Goldtop, Nicholas Sepward,
Thomas Lucas.
At: Berkeley.

A1/12/241 [GC 3641]   Mon. after the nativity of St. John the Baptist, 46 Edw. III
                                                                      [28 June 1372]
Juliana Saltere of Berkeley the elder, widow; and Richard Aleyn, Joan his wife and John,
Richard's son.

   Juliana has quitclaimed to Richard, Joan and John a holding in Berkel'.
At: Berkeley.

A1/12/242 [GC 3662]   Sun. before St. Thomas the apostle, 47 Edw. III [18 Dec. 1373]
Nicholas Sopere of Berkeley; and John Gamel and Sibyl his wife.

   Nicholas has leased to John and Sibyl a burgage with a house and garden adjacent in the
borough of Berkelee, with access to the spring and mill; for their lives, rent 10*s.* a year.
Witnesses: William Modybroke, Nicholas Schippard, Thomas Lucas, John Walbroke, John
Byl, clerk.
At: Berkeley.

A1/12/243 [GC 3690; *duplicate* GC 3703]   Sat. before the conversion of St. Paul,
                                                            50 Edw. III [24 Jan. 1377]
John Lokyntone of Berkeley; and John Swonhongre and Edith his wife.

   John has granted to John and Edith a cottage with a curtilage in Berkel'; to them and their
issue, rent 4*d.* a year.
Witnesses: William Modybroke, Thomas Lucas, Nicholas Schippard, Walter Cuppere, John
Gamel.
At: Berkeley.

A1/12/244 [GC 3800] St. Gregory, 9 Ric. II [12 March 1386]
Robert Warde and Margaret Warde; and Richard Ferour.

Robert and Margaret have leased to Richard their holding in Berkeleye between the holdings of Robert Balstake and Nicholas Schipward, except for a chamber with a chimney and a stable; for a term of 6 years, rent 6s. 8d. a year.
Witnesses: Nicholas Schipward, John Hopare, Peter Hamys, John Bakare.
At: Berkeley.

A1/12/245 [GC 3830] Thurs. in Ascension, 12 Ric. II [27 May 1389]
Richard Gylmyn; and John son of Robert Egetone and Joan his wife, Richard's daughter.

Richard has granted to John and Joan and their issue his newly constructed messuage in Berkele beside the house [*mansum*] of the vicar of Berkele; rent 6s. a year during Richard's life and 5s. a year to his heirs, and saving to Richard and Edith his wife a chamber at the head of the messuage and a stable for one horse.
Witnesses: John Sergeaunt of Stone, Ralph Waleys, John Egetone, Nicholas Schippere, Robert Mede.
At: Berkeley.

A1/12/246 [GC 3909] St. Mark the evangelist, 19 Ric. II [25 April 1396]
John Coby, son and heir of Philip Coby of Berkeley; and John Egetone, son of Robert Egeton, and Joan his wife.

John Coby has leased to John Egetone and Joan a holding with a garden called Schoyaresplace in Berkeley in the street called Saltaresende; for their lives and a term of 110 years, rent 4s. a year.
Witnesses: Thomas Lucas, Richard Sompterman, John Clerk, John Sebari, William Brokenberwe, William Packere, William ate Berwe.
At: Berkeley.

BEVERSTON

Beverston was a portion of Berkeley Herness granted by FitzHarding to his younger son Robert 'of Weare'. It passed from Robert to the Gurneys and then to the ap Adams, from whom it was bought by Thomas (III) de Berkeley in 1330, along with Over (in Almondsbury, Glos.) and Barrow Gurney (Som.). In 1352 it was entailed on Thomas and his second wife Katherine and their male isue and consequently passed to Thomas's younger son John 'of Beverston'.

THE AP ADAM MANOR

A1/13/1 [GC 631] Two weeks after Trinity, 25 Edw. I [23 June 1297]
John Abadam and Elizabeth his wife; and John de Knovyll.

Copy of final concord concerning the manors of Piryton, Radewyke, Northwyke and Beverston and the advowsons of Beverston church and the priory of Bilewyk (Glos.), the manors of Estharpetr' and Barwe and the advowson of the priory of Munchunbarwe (Som.), the manor and advowson of Cernecote (Wilts.), and the manor of Hamptonet (Sussex); John and Elizabeth have acknowledged the right of John de Knovyll, who has granted the manors and advowsons back to John and Elizabeth and their issue, with remainder to Elizabeth's right heirs.
At: Westminster.

A1/13/2 [GC 2729] Mon. before St. Giles, 3 Edw. III [28 Aug. 1329]
Thomas ap Adam, lord of Beverston, and Hugh de Gurnay, son of Hugh de Gurnay.

Thomas has quitclaimed to Hugh a rent of 10s. a year and suit to Thomas's court of Beverstan, which Hugh owes for his life for the land and holding formerly of Simon le Kyng in Beverstan. *Cancelled.*

Witnesses: Sir John de Inge, Thomas de Gurnay the younger, John de Avenynge, Robert de Salle, Robert le Taillour.
At: Beverston.

A1/13/3 [GC 3515]   n.d. [*c*. 1330]
Thomas ap Adam and Sir Thomas lord of Berkelee.
    Thomas ap Adam has granted to Thomas de Berkelee, his heirs and assigns his manor of Barwe (Som.) and his manor of Beverston (Glos.).
Witnesses: Sir William de Wautone, Sir Richard de la Ryvere, knights, William de Gamages, John Sergeaunt, John de Clyve.

A1/13/4 [GC 3254]   n.d. [*c*. 1330]
Thomas ap Adam, and Sir Thomas lord of Berkelee.
    Thomas ap Adam has granted to Thomas de Berkelee, his heirs and assigns his manors of Barewe (Som.) and Beverston (Glos.) and all the lordship, rents [etc.] which he has in the said counties.
Witnesses: Sir William de Wautone, Sir Richard de la Ryvere, knights, William de Gamages, John Sergeaunt, John de Clyve.

A1/13/5 [GC 2710*]   Three weeks after Michaelmas, 4 Edw. III [20 Oct. 1330]
Thomas de Berkeleye and Margaret his wife, by John de Chiltenham; and Thomas Apadam.
    Final concord concerning the castle of Beverstone and the manors of Beverstone and Ovre (Glos.), and the manor of Barewe (Som.); Thomas de Berkeleye has acknowledged the right of Thomas ap Adam by his gift, and Thomas ap Adam has granted the castle and manors to Thomas and Margaret and the heirs of Thomas. [GC 2710** *15th-cent. copy.*]
At: Westminster.

A1/13/6 [GC 3064***]   Two weeks after Hilary, 18 Edw. III [27 Jan. 1344]
Thomas son of Maurice de Berkele, knight; and Elias de Aylbrighton and Joan his wife.
    Final concord (made two weeks after Michaelmas 17 Edw. III [29 Sept. 1343]) concerning the manors of Beverston and Ovre; Elias and Joan have acknowledged the right of Thomas, and have quitclaimed for them and the heirs of Joan, and will warrant his right; Thomas has given them £100.
At: Westminster.

A1/13/7 [GC 3422]   Two weeks after Easter, 28 Edw. III [27 April 1354]
 Sir Thomas de Berkeleye the elder and Katherine his wife; and Walter Goldmere and John de Clyve.
    Final concord (made two weeks after Hilary [27 Jan.] the same year) concerning the castle and manor of Beverstone; Thomas has acknowledged the right of Walter and John by his gift, and they have granted the castle and manor to Thomas and Katherine and their male issue, with remainder to the right heirs of Thomas.
At: Westminster.

A1/13/8 [GC 3412; *duplicate* GC 3423]   n.d. [*c*. April 1354]
Maurice son and heir of Sir Thomas de Berkeleye, lord of Berkeley; and Sir Thomas and Katherine his wife.
    Maurice has ratified and confirmed the agreement made at Westminster at Hilary 28 Edw. III and afterwards recorded at Easter 28 Edw. III between Thomas de Berkeleye the elder and Katherine his wife, and Walter Goldemere and John de Clyve, concerning the castle and manor of Beverstone, whereby Thomas acknowledged the right of Walter and John by his gift and they granted the castle and manor to Thomas and Katherine and their male issue, with remainder to the right heirs of Thomas.

LEASES AND ADMINISTRATIVE DOCUMENTS

The Acton holding

The Broke lease

A1/13/9 [GC 2854]   Fri. the feast of All Saints, 10 Edw. III [1 Nov. 1336]
Thomas lord of Berkeley; and Simon son of Robert ate Broke of Beverston and Amicia his wife.

Thomas has leased to Simon and Amicia one third of the enclosure which Richard de Acton lately granted to Thomas and 24 a. of land of the holding which was of the said Richard, viz. 12 a. in Westefeld and 12 a. in Estfeld; for their lives, rent 13*s.* 4*d.* a year.
Witnesses: Robert le Hayward, John Smart, Robert le Taylour, Robert Burgeloun, Walter le Skay.
At: Beverston.

A1/13/10 [GC 2584]   n.d. [1330 × 1361]
Thomas lord of Berkeleye; and Giles Meynel and Alice his first wife.

Thomas has leased to Giles and Alice all the lands and holdings which John Athelard previously held of Thomas in Beverston; for their lives, rent 20*s.* a year.
Witnesses: Robert le Haiward, Robert Burgoloun, Robert le Tailour.

A1/13/11 [GC 3260]   n.d. [mid 14th cent.]
Thomas lord of Berkelee; and Simon ate Broke, Alice his wife and Robert their son.

Thomas has leased to Simon, Alice and Robert all the lands and holdings which Guy Maynel previously held in Beverston; for their lives, rent 26*s.* 8*d.* a year.
Witnesses: Sir Thomas [de Besforde] parson of Beverston, Philip Smart, Thomas Hayward, Simon Braynford, Robert Borgelon.

A1/13/12 [GC 2806]   Wed. in Holy Innocents, 8 Edw. III [28 Dec. 1334]
Thomas lord of Berkel' and Simon atte Broke.

Thomas has granted to Simon the reversion of a messuage and 1 virgate of land in Beverston, which Robert atte Broke, his father, holds of Thomas for his [Robert's] life; for Simon's life, for the same services as Robert rendered.
At: Portbury.

A1/13/13 [GC 2855]   Fri. in All Saints, 10 Edw. III [1 Nov. 1336]
Thomas lord of Berkeleye; and Simon son of Robert ate Broke and Amicia his wife.

Thomas has leased to Simon and Amicia the holding which William aten Orcharde sometime held of Thomas in villeinage in Beverston for their lives, rent 13*s.* 4*d.* a year.
Witnesses: Robert le Hayward, Philip Smart, Robert le Taillour, Robert Bergylon, Walter le Skay.
At: Beverston.

A1/13/14 [GC 3282]   n.d. [mid 14th cent.]
Thomas lord of Berkele; and William White and Edith his wife.

Thomas has leased to William and Edith a messuage and 1 virgate of land, viz. half of the holding which Simon atte Broke previously held in Beverston; for their lives, rent 13*s.* [4*d.*] a year.
Witnesses: Thomas le Haiward, Simon Braynford, Simon Hickes, Philip Smart, . . .

The Estham lease

A1/13/15 [SC 504]   Monday in Whitsun week, 14 Edw. III [29 May 1340]
Thomas de Berkeley, lord of Berkeley; and Roger de Estham and Agnes de Bedehampton.

Thomas has granted to Roger and Agnes, for their lives, all the land in Beverstone which he had from Richard de Acton which remains after his grants to Philip Smart and Simon ate

Broke, and the land called Haywardeslond in Beverstone; rent a rose a year.
Witnesses: John de Clyve, Robert le Hayward, of Beverstone, Philip Smart, Robert Burgylon, Robert le Taillour.
At: Berkeley.

A1/13/16 [GC 3399]   Sun. after St. Simon and St. Jude, 26 Edw. III [4 Nov. 1352]
Thomas lord of Berkelee and Matthew son of Sir John de Clyvedone.

   Thomas has leased to Matthew a messuage and 1 virgate of land, which Maud Boxwell sometime held in Beverston, and the reversion of all the lands and holdings which Roger de Estham holds of Thomas for life in the said vill; for his life, rent 20*s.* a year.
At: Wotton.

   The Smart lease

A1/13/17 [GC 2856]   Fri. the feast of All Saints, 10 Edw. III [1 Nov. 1336]
Thomas de Berkeleye, lord of Berkeley; and Philip Smart of Beverston and John his son.

   Thomas has leased to Philip and John one third of the enclosure which Thomas had by grant of Richard Dacton in the same vill of Beverston, and also 24 a. of land of the holding which was Richard's, viz. 12 a. in Westfeld and 12 a. in Estfeld; for their lives, rent 13*s.* 4*d.* a year.
Witnesses: Robert le Heyward, Simon atte Broke, Robert le Taillor, Robert Borgeloun, Walter Skay.
At: Beverston.

The Hayward holding

A1/13/18 [GC 2750]   8 June 6 Edw. III [1332]
Robert le Hayward of Beverston and Sir Thomas lord of Berkelee.

   Robert has quitclaimed to Thomas a pasture in the park of Beverstan which he formerly had for life by grant of Sir Thomas Appadam.
Witnesses: John de Avenyng, Thomas Testard, Robert le Taillour, Philip Smart, Robert Borgeloun.
At: Beverston.

A1/13/19 [GC 2853]   Fri. the feast of All Saints, 10 Edw. III [1 Nov. 1336]
Thomas de Berkeleye, lord of Berkeley; and Robert le Hayward of Beverston and Agnes his wife.

   Thomas has leased to Robert and Agnes a plot of land outside his enclosure; to hold enclosed, for their lives, rent 4*d.* a year.
Witnesses: Philip Smart, Simon ate Broke, Robert le Taillor, Robert Borgelon, Walter Skay.
At: Beverston.

A1/13/20 [GC 1228]   n.d. [*c.* 1335]
Thomas lord of Berkelee; and Thomas le Hayward and Agnes his wife.

   Thomas has granted to Thomas and Agnes two messuages and two half-virgates of land which Robert le Hayward, Thomas's father, previously held in Beverston, and also a messuage and 1 virgate which Thomas Testard formerly held in the same vill; for their lives, rent 23*s.* 4*d.* a year.
Witnesses: Roger de Estham, Roger Duynysch, John Smart, Robert Burgulon, Simon le Wlonke.

The Hicks holding

A1/13/21 [GC 3265]   n.d. [mid 14th cent.]
Thomas lord of Berkelee; and Simon Hickes and Alice his wife.

   Thomas has leased to Simon and Alice a messuage and 1 virgate of land which Robert le

Taillour recently held of Thomas in Beverston, also a messuage and 10 a. of land which Maud Hickes previously held, and half of a messuage and half-virgate of land which Thomas Salemon previously held; for their lives, rent 22s. 8d. a year, viz. 13s. 4d. for the messuage and virgate, 2s. 8d. for the messuage and 10 a., and 6s. 8d. for the half messuage and half-virgate.

Witnesses: Simon ate Broke, Philip Smart, Simon Braynford, Thomas Haiward, Thomas Brid.

A1/13/22 [GC 3505]   10 May 34 Edw. III [1360]

Thomas lord of Berkele; and John [. . .]uewyne and Amicia his wife.

Thomas has leased to John and Amicia a messuage and half-virgate of land, which Simon Hickes previously held in Beverston; for their lives, at the customary rent.

Witnesses: Thomas le Haiward, Simon Braynforde, Simon ate Broke, William Smart, Geoffrey Saleman.

At: Beverston.

Other holdings

A1/13/23 [GC 3280]   n.d. [mid 14th cent.]

Thomas lord of Berkelee and Peter Tudemersh.

Thomas has leased to Peter a messuage and 1 virgate of land, which John Palmare formerly held of Thomas in Beverston; for life, rent a rose a year.

A1/13/24 [GC 2484]   n.d. [1330 × 1361]

Thomas lord of Berkelee; and Richard Ernyte and Joan his wife.

Thomas has granted to Richard and Joan a messuage and half-virgate of land, which Robert Testard previously held in Beverston, also a half-virgate, which Christina Romayn previously held in Beverston, and a cottage and curtilage, which John Blissete previously held of Thomas in villeinage in Beverston; for their lives, rent 15s. 8d. a year, viz. 6s. 8d. for the messuage and half-virgate, 7s. for the half-virgate and 2s. for the cottage and curtilage, and the service to his court as the other tenants.

Witnesses: Simon atte Broke, Simon Braynforde, Thomas Ord, Simon Hickes, William Smart.

Account Roll

A1/13/25 [GAR 282]   7–8 Edw. III [1333–4]

OTHER DOCUMENTS
The constableship of the castle

A1/13/26 [GC 2706*]   23 June 4 Edw. III [1330]

William Thurmund and Sir Thomas lord of Berkeleye.

William has quitclaimed to Thomas the office of constable of the castle of Beverston, and of bailiff and overseer of the manor of Beverston, which offices he had by grant of Sir Thomas ap Adam, late lord of Beverston, and also 6 quarters . . . wheat and . . . shillings and 4d., and a furred robe, and hay . . .

Witnesses: Peter de Styntescombe, John de Milkesham, John de Clyve, [John] Wynth, William Capel.

At: Berkeley.

A1/13/27 [GC 2707]   28 July 4 Edw. III [1330]

Robert Pratard and Sir Thomas lord of Berkeleye.

Robert has quitclaimed to Thomas the office of constable of the castle of Beverston, and also 6½ qr. of wheat and 17s. 4d., and a furred robe price 20s., and hay [etc.] and a chamber

below the gate of the said castle, which is paid annually for the said office, and which he had by grant of Sir Thomas ap Adam for his [Robert's] life.
Witnesses: Peter de Styntescombe, John de Milkesham, John de Clyve, John Wyth, William Capel.
At: Berkeley.

Miscellaneous

A1/13/28 [GC 3111]   12 Jan. 18 Edw. III [1345]
John de la Ryvere, knight, lord of Tormarton, and Sir Thomas lord of Berkelee, his lord.

   John is bound to Thomas in 1,500 sheep which he has bought for a sum of money which John has received, to be delivered to Thomas's manor of Beverstone a fortnight after Easter next. [*In French.*]
At: Wotton under Edge.

A1/13/29 [GC 3153]   Fri. after All Saints, 20 Edw. III [3 Nov. 1346]
Clemence Baret and Sir Thomas lord of Berkelee.

   Clemence has surrendered to Thomas the cottage and land which she held of Thomas for her life in Beverstone.
At: Berkeley.

CAM

BERKELEY ACQUISITIONS
House at Woodend

A1/14/1 [GC 958]   n.d. [late Edw. I]
Robert de Saltmarsh (*de salso marisco*); and William Lillebourne of Cam and Lucy his wife.

   Robert has granted to William and Lucy a messuage and curtilage at la Wodende in Camme, which Walter Bouetoun formerly held of Robert, also a croft of arable land between the said house and Robert's croft called le Rudinge; to hold of the chief lord of the fee at a rent of a red rose a year if required, and William and Lucy have given Robert 44*s*.
Witnesses: Robert de Bradeston, Thomas de Beoleye, Henry de Camme, Walter Hathemere, Thomas in the Wodende, Robert Passelewe, Reginald the cook (*coquus*).

A1/14/2 [GC 1533]   n.d. [late Edw. I]
John de Saltmarsh (*de salso marisco*); and William Lyllebourn and Lucy his wife.

   John has quitclaimed to William and Lucy a house and curtilage at le Wodehend in Camme and a croft.
Witnesses: Robert de Bradeston, Robert de Berkeleye, Thomas de Boeleye, Henry de Camme, Thomas de Styntescumbe.

A1/14/3 [GC 1075]   Sun. the feast of St. Luke, 32 Edw. I [18 Oct. 1304]
William de Lyllebourne and Lucy his wife; and Sir Thomas de Berkelegh.

   William and Lucy have granted to Thomas two cottages and the enclosure lying between the grove of Thomas ate Wodende and their enclosure called Sautemareyscroft at le Wodende in Camme; Thomas has given them 5 marks.
Witnesses: Robert de Bradestone, Robert de Berkelegh, Thomas de Beolee, Thomas de Styntescombe, Henry de Camme, Robert de Coulegh, Stephen de Draycote, Walter Hathemare, Robert Passelewe.
At: Berkeley.

Cook holdings

Passelewe rent and reversion

A1/14/4 [GC 736]   n.d. [late 13th cent.]

Reginald called the cook of Cam; and Robert Passelewe and Eve his wife of the same vill.

Reginald has granted to Robert and Eve 1 a. of land in the field called Southfeld between the land which Richard son of Ralph held of the lord of Berkeley and the land which Nicholas de Estmed once held in villeinage of the lord of Berkeley, and between Grosleye and the road from Estmed to Dursleye; for their lives, rent 1*d.* a year, and Robert and Eve have given him 13*s.* and 2 bu. of wheat.

Witnesses: Maurice de Camme, Robert de Draycote, Henry de Camme, Richard de Salle, Thomas de la Wodende.

A1/14/5 [GC 1292]   n.d. [*temp.* Edw. I]

Reginald called the cook of Cam; and Robert Passelewe and Eve his first wife.

Reginald has granted to Robert and Eve 1 a. of land in the field called Dunfeld between the land of Sir Thomas de Berkel' which Reginald le Wodeward formerly held in villeinage and the land of Sir Thomas which Isabel de Estmed and Richard Schaterel formerly held in villeinage; for their lives, rent 1*d.* a year, and they have given him 1 mark.

Witnesses: Maurice de Camme, Robert de Dreycote, Henry de Camme, Walter Hathemare, Thomas de la Wodende.

A1/14/6 [GC 1917]   1 May 6 Edw. II [1313]

Reginald called the cook of Cam and Sir Thomas de Berkelee, lord of Berkeley.

Reginald has granted to Thomas a rent of 2*d.* a year from Robert Passelewe and his wife Eve for 2 a. of land in the fields called Southfeld and Dunfeld, held for their lives, with the reversion of the said 2 a., in Camme.

Witnesses: Thomas de Bradestone, Robert de Gosintone, Nicholas de Beoleie, John de Couelee, Stephen de Draycote, Walter Hathemare, Richard de Astmed.

At: Berkeley.

Garden etc.

A1/14/7 [GC 891]   n.d. [early 14th cent.]

Reginald the cook of Cam and Sir Thomas de Berkelee, his lord.

Reginald has granted to Thomas a plot of his garden . . . 14 by 34 ft. . . . in the field called Southfeld at Schoggyngcombe; also . . . and 1¾ perches of land in the field called Mad. . ., for a certain sum of money.

Witnesses: [Robert] de Bradeston, Robert de Berkelee, Thomas de Beolee, Thomas de Styntescombe, Henry de Camme, . . . , Robert de Couelee, Robert le Warner, Richard de Estmede.

A1/14/8 [GC 1226]   n.d. [*temp.* Edw. I]

Thomas de Berkelee, lord of Berkeley, and [Richard] . . .

Thomas has granted to [Richard] a plot of garden with the buildings which Thomas had by grant of . . . and 1 a. in the field called Southfeld at Schoggyngcombe, [which] . . . Wodeward held in villeinage and which he had by grant of same Reginald the cook with appurtenances in [Camme]; rent . . . , for his life.

Witnesses: Henry de Camme, Stephen de Draycote, Walter Hathemar, Richard de Estmed . . .

Other

A1/14/9 [GC 890]   n.d. [early 14th cent.]

Reginald called the cook of Cam and Sir Thomas de Berkeleye, his lord.

Reginald has granted to Thomas 4½ a. of land in Camme, 1 a. in the furlong called

Sokyngcombe, next to the king's highway to Dersleye, 1 a. in the furlong called Nethynge, 1 a. in the furlong called Fordleye, 3 selions in the furlong called Aylrychescroft next to the land of Sir John Basset, and 3 selions in the furlong below Moddemed; Thomas has given him 40s.

Witnesses: Thomas de Bradeston, Robert de Berkeleye, Thomas de Beoleye, Thomas de Styntescombe, Henry de Camme, R[obert] de Coueleye, Walter de Nasse, Stephen de Draycot, Walter Hathemar.

A1/14/10 [GC 1983]   20 June 7 Edw. II [1314]
Reginald the cook of Cam and Sir Thomas de Berkeleye, his lord.

Reginald has granted to Thomas, his heirs and assigns rents of ½d. and a rose from Richard in the Hale and John Chaumflour and Edith his wife for their lives, for 2 a. of land, with the reversion of the land, being 1 a. in the field called Doddenhawe and 1 a. in the field called Hidefeld, and also a plot of land, in Camme.

Witnesses: Henry de Camme, Stephen de Draycote, Walter Hathemare, Richard de Astmed, Robert Passelewe.
At: Berkeley.

The Coryate holding

A1/14/11 [GC 815]   n.d. [late 13th cent.]
Richard de Salle and Sir Thomas de Berkel'.

Richard has quitclaimed to Thomas a messuage and meadow in Camme which he had from Peter de Corefgate, son and heir of Walter de Corefgate.

Witnesses: Peter de Stintescumbe, Robert de Bradeston, Thomas de Beoleye, Maurice de Camme, Robert de Dreycot.

A1/14/12 [GC 533; *duplicate* GC 538]   Wed. after the translation of St. Benedict,
                                        16 Edw. I [14 July 1288]
Sir Thomas de Berkeley and Sir Robert de Berkeley, his brother.

Thomas has granted to Robert the holding which Richard de Salle and Walter de Corfgate held in the vill of Camme, and Robert has granted to Thomas his villein Walter le Palmer and his progeny and the land which he held of Robert in Coueley.

Witnesses: Sir Roger de Lokynton, knight, Robert de Stanes, Robert de Bradeston, Maurice de Camme, Walter de Wyke, Thomas de Swonhungre, Thomas de Boeley.
At: Berkeley.

Inwoods mead

A1/14/13 [GC 1483]   n.d. [1290 × 1300]
William de Mattesdon; and Robert de Berkeleye, younger son of Maurice de Berkel', and Joan his wife.

William has granted to Robert and Joan all his meadow in Inwodesmede, with free access to it; rent 1d. a year to the chief lord of the fee, and they have given him a certain sum of money.

Witnesses: Robert de Bradeston, Thomas de Beoleye, Maurice de Camme, Thomas de Stintescumbe, Henry de Camme, Richard de Milkesham, Walter Motun.

A1/14/14 [GC 1233]   n.d. [*temp.* Edw. I]
Thomas de Berkelee, lord of Berkeley; and Henry de la Hulle and Christine his wife.

Thomas has granted to Henry and Christine 1¾ a. and 7 perches of meadow in Inwodesmed, which he had by grant from Robert de Berkelee and which Robert previously had by grant of William de Mettesdone; for their lives, rent 6s. a year.

Witnesses: Robert de Berkelee, Robert de Bradeston, Thomas de Beoleye, Thomas de Swanhungre, Walter Motun.

Billow holdings

Rent and reversion of five acres in Hennegarstone and Apecroft

A1/14/15 [GC 2045]   20 May 8 Edw. II [1315]

Thomas de Boeleye and Sir Thomas de Berkeleye, lord of Berkeley.

Thomas de Boeleye has granted to Thomas de Berkeleye the rent of a root of ginger a year from Sir Philip de Bradestone, chaplain, for 5 a. of land which he holds for life, with the reversion of the land, being 13 selions in Hennegarstone and 2 a. in Apecroft at Teteshulle and a rent of ½*d.* a year from Richard Tharp for 1 a. of land in Hennegarstone which he holds for life, with the reversion of the land.

Witnesses: Sir John de Berkeleye, Sir William de Wauton, knights, John son of Nicholas, Thomas de Bradeston, John de Olepenne, Stephen de Draycote, John Capel.

At: Berkeley.

A1/14/16 [GC 2049]   1 July 8 Edw. II [1315]

Thomas de Berkeleye, lord of Berkeley; and Walter the hayward (*messor*) of Clingre and Juliana his wife.

Thomas has granted to Walter and Juliana 5 a. of land, of which 2 a. lie in the field called Teteshulle, 2½ a. in the field called Hennegarstone extending above Hennegarstonsbrok, and ½ a. in 2 selions, of which one lies in Middelfelde and the other in Southfelde, which he had by grant of Thomas de Boeleye, in Camme; to hold to them and their issue, rent 6*s.* a year.

Witnesses: Thomas de Bradeston, Henry de Camme, John de Coueleye, Stephen de Draycote, John le Duk.

At: Berkeley.

Spark mead

A1/14/17 [GC 2221]   3 April 11 Edw. II [1318]

Thomas de Boeleye and Sir Thomas de Berkeleye, lord of Berkeley.

Thomas de Boeleye has granted to Thomas de Berkeleye, his heirs and assigns all his meadow in the meadow called Sparcmede, beside the ditch called le Twedych.

Witnesses: Thomas de Bradeston, Walter de Nasse, Henry de Camme, Stephen de Draycote, Thomas le Spenser, Thomas de Craweleye, William le Botyler.

At: Billow.

A1/14/18 [GC 2222]   3 April 11 Edw. II [1318]

(1) Thomas de Boeleye; (2) Richard le Man; (3) Sir Thomas de Berkeleye, lord of Berkeley.

Thomas de Boeleye has appointed Richard his attorney to give seisin to Thomas de Berkeleye of the meadow in Sparcmede.

At: Billow.

The Valers holding

A1/14/19 [GC 2242; *duplicate* GC 2241]   Thurs. before the nativity of St. John the Baptist, 11 Edw. II [22 June 1318]

Thomas de Berkele, lord of Berkeley, and Margaret widow of Nicholas de Valers.

Thomas has granted to Margaret a rent of 30*s.* from a messuage and 1 virgate of land, which William de Astmede holds of Thomas in Camme; for her life, rent a rose a year; and for this and a certain sum of money Margaret has remitted to Thomas and his heirs all the lands, rents [etc.] which she has in Camme and Couele. Endorsed: *Borrowed of Wm Basset 19 Oct. 1606.*

Witnesses: Sir Walter de Gloucestre, Sir William de Wauton, knights, Thomas de Bradeston, Robert de Astone, John de Oulepenne, Robert le Waryner, Stephen de Draycote.

At: Berkeley.

A1/14/20 [GC 2291]   St. Martin, 13 Edw. II [11 Nov. 1319]
Margaret de Valers and Sir Thomas de Berkeleye, lord of Berkeley.

Margaret has granted to Thomas and his heirs all the lands and holdings [etc.] which she holds of Thomas, for iife, in Camme and Couele.

Witnesses: Sir Walter de Gloucestre, Sir William de Wautone, knights, Thomas de [Bra]denston, Robert de Astone, John de Oulepenne, Robert le Waryner, Stephen de Draycote.

At: Berkeley.

Coryates Place rent

A1/14/21 [GC 2553]   n.d. [early 14th cent.]
Richard called de Salle of Gloucestershire and Sir Robert de Wynton, clerk.

Richard has leased to Robert all his messuages in Camme with gardens, curtilages, a dovecot, watermill and 22 a. of land and 8*s*. rent and 1 a. of meadow called Coryotesmede; for his life and one year after his death, rent 39*s*. a year.

Witnesses: John de Oulepenne, Henry de Camme, Stephen de Draycote, Walter Hathemare, Peter de Styntescombe.

A1/14/22 [GC 1274]   n.d. [*temp.* Edw. I]
Henry de Camme the elder; and Henry his son and Lucy his wife, daughter of Adam Spilemon.

Henry has granted to Henry and Lucy, and their issue, the rent of 1*d*. a year from Ralph, son of Henry the elder, which he pays for a rent of 20*s*. 7*d*. which he holds for life, and the reversion of the rent of 20*s*. 7*d*. from William de Coregate and John de Hulmencot for holdings in Coueleye, and the rent of a rose a year from Isabel and Margaret daughters of Henry the elder, which they pay for a rent of 39*s*. from the holding of Richard de Salle in Camme, with the reversion of the said rent of 39*s*. after the deaths of Isabel and Margaret.

Witnesses: Stephen de Draycot, Richard de Salle, Walter Hathemare, John de Bradeford, Richard Balon, Robert Mayel, Stephen de Masyngdon.

A1/14/23 [GC 3959]   Trinity Sunday, 22 Ric. II [25 May 1399]
Walter Knyt and Elizabeth his wife; and Sir Thomas de Berkley, lord of Berkeley.

Walter and Elizabeth have granted to Thomas an annual rent of 39*s*. which they hold of Thomas for a holding in Camme called Coryetesplace; for his life, with remainder to the heirs of Walter and Elizabeth.

At: Cam.

A1/14/24 [SC 573]   20 June 1 Hen. IV [1400]
Thomas de Berkeley, lord of Berkeley; and John Wyntour and Katherine his wife.

Thomas has granted to John and Katherine, for the good service of John, for life, several holdings and curtilages in Berkeley and lands in the manor of Hamme, and they have surrendered to him a rent of 39*s*. a year due from a holding called Corietesplace in Camme.

Witnesses: Thomas FitzNicol, John Rolves, Richard Coton, Thomas Lucas.

At: Berkeley.

A1/14/25 [GC 4043]   Thurs. after St. Nicholas, 11 Hen. IV [12 Dec. 1409]
Walter Knight and Elizabeth his wife; and Henry Taylor and Joan his wife.

Walter and Elizabeth have granted to Henry and Joan a messuage and 72 a. of land, 4 a. of meadow, 13 a. of pasture and a rent of 8*s*., in Coaley and Cam, and the reversion on the death of Thomas Lord Berkeley of a rent of 19*s*. 6*d*. from a holding called Coryettysplace in Cam; rent 2*s*. to Walter and Elizabeth and the services due to the lord of the fee; if Henry and Joan die without heirs, reversion to Walter and Elizabeth. [*17th-cent. copy.*]

Witnesses: Henry Gossington, John Archer, William Langford, Richard Draycote, John Blanche.

Other acquisitions and grants

A1/14/26 [GC 1227]   n.d. [*temp.* Edw. I]
Sir Thomas de Berkeley and Walter de Corefgate of Cam.

Thomas and Walter have exchanged Walter's two crofts next to the bridge of Camme, viz. Roweley and Odicroft, and Thomas's 6 a. of land in Holemedfurlong.
Witnesses: Sir Roger de Lokinton, Peter de Stintescumbe, Miles de Langetot, Ralph de Camme, Robert de Coueley, Maurice de Camme, Robert de Dreychot.

A1/14/27 [GC 1142]   Tues. the eve of St. Thomas the apostle, 35 Edw. I [20 Dec. 1306]
Henry de Camme and Sir Thomas de Berkelee, lord of Berkeley.

Henry has quitclaimed to Thomas a ditch extending between Grovelondesweye and the land of Simon atte Yate and Walter Bacheler, Thomas's villeins, in Camme.
Witnesses: Robert de Berkelee, Robert de Bradeston, Thomas de Styntescombe, Stephen de Draycote, Walter Hathemare.
At: Berkeley.

A1/14/28 [GC 2255]   Sun. after St. Matthew, 12 Edw. II [24 Sept. 1318]
Peter de Styntescoumbe and Sir Thomas de Berkeleye, lord of Berkeley.

Peter has granted to Thomas, his heirs and assigns his meadow in the meadows called Hexteworth and Stynthememede, in Camme.
Witnesses: Sir William de Wautone, Sir John le Rous, Sir Thomas le Botyler, knights, John de Olepenne, Walter de Nasse, Thomas de Bradeston, John de Melkesham, John le Serjaunt, Walter Colewych.
At: Berkeley.

A1/14/29 [GC 2833]   16 Nov. 9 Edw. III [1335]
Thomas lord of Berkelee and Sir Simon Basset, knight.

Thomas has granted to Simon and his issue half of a dovecot in Camme which they had held jointly.
Witnesses: John de Milkesham, Peter de Styntescombe, Robert le Waryner.
At: Berkeley.

LEASES

Leases of villein land

Godknave half-virgate
A1/14/30 [GC 1010]   St. John before the Latin Gate, 29 Edw. I [6 May 1301]
Sir Thomas lord of Berkeley; and Gilbert Godknave of Cam and Leticia his wife.

Thomas has leased to Gilbert and Leticia the half-virgate which Walter Godknave previously held in the vill of Camme; for their lives, rent 20s. a year, their issue to remain in servile condition and the half-virgate to revert to Thomas on their deaths.
Witnesses: Robert de Berkeleye, Robert de Bradeston, Thomas de Beoleye, Henry de Camme, Richard de Estmead.

A1/14/31 [GC 3365]   16 May 25 Edw. III [1351]
Thomas de Berkelee, lord of Berkeley; and William de Tudenham, rector of Cam, and John Yondhalf.

Thomas has leased to William and John a messuage and half-virgate of land, which Leticia Godknave formerly held, and 1 a. of pasture, which Robert Wyther formerly held, in Camme; for their lives, rent 23s. a year and 12d. for the maintenance of the woodward and Peter's Pence.
Witnesses: Elias de Berlegh, John Dreycote, John de Milkesham, John ate Boure, Stephen Kyneltre.
At: Berkeley.

Heysogge half-virgate

A1/14/32 [GC 1825; *duplicate* GC 1826]   1 June 4 Edw. II [1311]
Thomas de Berkeleye, lord of Berkeley; and Maud Heysugge and Reginald her son and Agnes his wife, Thomas's villeins.

Thomas has granted to Maud, Reginald and Agnes the half-virgate which Maud previously held in villeinage in Camme; for their lives, rent 20s. a year, and they and their issue shall remain in servile condition.
Witnesses: Henry de Camme, Robert Warner, Stephen de Draycote, Walter Hathemare, Richard de Astmead.
At: Berkeley.

A1/14/33 [GC 3385]   Easter Day, 26 Edw. III [8 April 1352]
Thomas de Berkeleye, lord of Berkeley; and Henry Draycote, his first wife and Walter son of Robert Draycote.

Thomas has leased to Henry, his first wife and Walter a messuage and half-virgate of land which Agnes Heysougge previously held; for their lives, rent 21s. a year.
Witnesses: John Draycote, Robert de Coueleye, John Warner, Elias Berleye, Stephen Keneltre, William Astmed, John ate Boure.
At: Berkeley.

Bachelor half-virgate

A1/14/34 [GC 1846]   Tues. the feast of St. Andrew, 5 Edw. II [30 Nov. 1311]
Thomas de Berkelee, lord of Berkeley; and Robert Pride and Agnes his wife, Thomas's villeins.

Thomas has granted to Robert and Agnes the half-virgate which Walter le Bacheler previously held in villeinage in Camme; for their lives, rent 20s. a year, and they and their issue will remain in servile condition.
Witnesses: Henry de Camme, Robert Warner, Stephen de Draycote, Walter Hathemare, Richard de Astmed.
At: Berkeley.

A1/14/35 [GC 1845]   Tues. the feast of St. Andrew, 5 Edw. II [30 Nov. 1311]
Thomas de Berkelee, lord of Berkeley; and Robert Pride and Agnes his wife, Thomas's villeins.

Whereas Thomas has granted to Robert and Agnes the half-virgate which Walter le Bacheler previously held in villeinage in Camme, for their lives, he now grants that when they have a child the grant shall be extended for the child's life. [*In French*.]
Witnesses: Henry de Camme, Robert Warner, Stephen de Draycote, Walter Hathemare, Richard de Astmed.
At: Berkeley.

Atte Style half-virgate

A1/14/36 [GC 2237]   1 May 11 Edw. II [1318]
Thomas de Berkeleye, lord of Berkeley; and Robert atte Stile and Maud his wife.

Thomas has leased to Robert and Maud the half-virgate which Robert formerly held in villeinage in Camme; for their lives, rent 20s. a year, and they and their issue will remain in servile condition.
Witnesses: Henry de Camme, Robert le Warner, Stephen de Draycote, Walter Hathemare, Robert de Draycote.
At: Berkeley.

A1/14/37 [GC 2343]   7 March 14 Edw. II [1321]
Thomas de Berkelee, lord of Berkeley; and Robert atte Stile, Maud his wife and John their son.

Thomas has leased to Robert, Maud and John the half-virgate which Robert formerly held in villeinage in Camme; for their lives, rent 20s. a year, and they and their issue will remain in [servile] condition.

Witnesses: Henry de Camme, Robert le Warner, Stephen de Draycote, Walter Hathemare, Robert de Draycote.

At: Berkeley.

Other

A1/14/38 [GC 848] n.d. [late 13th cent.]

Sir Thomas lord of Berkel'; and Adam le Nuwemon of Cam and Helen his wife.

Thomas has leased to Adam and Helen the quarter-virgate of land which they previously held in villeinage in the vill of Camme, 1 a. of land in the furlong called Watcroft, and 3½ a. of land in the furlong called Dortribe; for their lives; rent 17s. 10d. a year.

Witnesses: Maurice de Camme, Henry de Camme, Robert de Dreycote, William Hathemere, Thomas de la Wodende, Robert Passelewe, Reginald the cook.

A1/14/39 [GC 1225] n.d. [*temp.* Edw. I]

Thomas lord of Berkeleye; and Joce de Anesty and Juliana de la Homme his wife.

Thomas has leased to Joce and Juliana the half-virgate with appurtenances which Juliana held of Thomas in villeinage in Camme; for their lives, rent 20s. a year, and they have given him 17 marks.

Witnesses: Robert de Bradestone, Thomas de Beleye, Maurice de Camme, Henry de Camme, Robert de Draycote, Walter Hathemere, Thomas de la Wodende.

A1/14/40 [GC 1008] St. Mark the evangelist, 29 Edw. I [25 April 1301]

Sir Thomas lord of Berkeley; and Richard atte Forde of Cam, Alice his wife and Richard their son.

Thomas has leased to Richard, Alice and Richard, the half-virgate which Richard previously held in villeinage in the vill of Camme; for their lives, rent 20s. a year, and their issue will remain in servile condition.

Witnesses: Robert de Berkeleye, Thomas de Beoleye, Robert de Draycote, Henry de Camme, Walter Hathemar.

A1/14/41 [GC 1079] Sun. the eve of St. Thomas the apostle, 33 Edw. I [20 Dec. 1304]

Thomas de Berkelee, lord of Berkeley; and Walter Azoutholf and Edith his wife.

Thomas has granted to Walter and Edith the holding and half-virgate of land which Richard Schatel formerly held of Thomas in villeinage in Camme, and 10 a. of land, of which 7 a. 54 perches lie in the furlong called Brystenelonde, 1¼ a. 23 perches in the furlong called Hengesthan, and 1¼ a. 8 perches in Tylesdene; to them and Walter's issue, rent 40s. a year.

Witnesses: Robert de Bradestone, Robert de Berkelee, Thomas de Beolee, Thomas de Styntescombe, Stephen de Draycote, Walter Hathemare, Robert Passelewe.

At: Berkeley.

A1/14/42 [GC 1820] 20 April 4 Edw. II [1311]

Thomas de Berkelee, lord of Berkeley; and John le Monk, Amicia his wife and William their son, Thomas's villeins.

Thomas has granted to John, Amicia and William, the quarter-virgate of land which John previously held in villeinage in Camme; for their lives, rent 10s. a year, and their issue will remain in servile condition.

Witnesses: Robert le Warner, Richard de Astmead, Walter Hathemare, Stephen de Draycote, William le Squier.

At: Berkeley.

A1/14/43 [GC 1821]   20 April 4 Edw. II [1311]
Thomas de Berkelee, lord of Berkeley; and Denise Stevenes, William her son and William's
wife, Thomas's villeins.

   Thomas has granted to Denise, William and his wife the virgate of land which Ralph
Stevenes previously held in villeinage in Camme, for their lives, rent 40s. a year, and their
issue will remain in servile condition.
Witnesses: Henry de Camme, Robert le Warner, Richard de Astmead, Walter Hathemare,
Stephen de Draycote.
At: Berkeley.

A1/14/44 [GC 1874]   3 April 5 Edw. II [1312]
Thomas de Berkelee, lord of Berkeley; and Walter Lucus and Maud his wife and Richard in
the Hale and Alice his wife, Thomas's villeins.

   Thomas has granted to Walter and Maud and Richard and Alice the half-virgate which
Walter and Maud previously held in villeinage in Camme; to them for their lives, rent 20s. a
year, and they and their issue will remain in servile condition.
Witnesses: Henry de Camme, Robert Warner, John de Couelee, Stephen de Draycote, Walter
Hathemare.
At: Berkeley.

A1/14/45 [GC 2354]   20 May 14 Edw. II [1321]
Thomas de Berkeleye, lord of Berkeley, and William Widie of Cam.

   Thomas has leased to William the half-virgate with a foreland and appurtenances which
Walter Wydie previously held of Thomas in villeinage in Camme; for his life, rent 20s. a
year for the half-virgate and the customary rent for the foreland.
Witnesses: Henry de Camme, Stephen de Draycote, Walter Hathemare, Thomas atte
Wodende, Robert de Draycote.
At: Berkeley.

Leases of other land

A1/14/46 [GC 1219]   n.d. [*temp.* Hen. III]
Thomas de Berkel' and William his eldest [*sic*] son.

   Thomas has granted to William all the land which Gilbert Stevene held in Thomas's
manor of Camme; rent 1d. a year.
Witnesses: Robert son of Richard, Peter de Stintescumbe, Richard de Couel, Thomas de
Tyringeham, John de Eggeton, Robert de Plaunche, Robert Couel, Elias the butler
(*pincerna*), Arnulf the clerk.

A1/14/47 [SC 180]   n.d. [*temp.* Hen. III]
Thomas de Berkelai and William de Berkelai, his son.

   Thomas has granted to William 1 virgate of land in the manor of Camme, which Walter le
Bel held; rent 4d. a year.
Witnesses: Elias Giffard, Nicholas son of Roger, Henry de Berkelai, Peter de Stintescumba,
Robert Bel, Thomas de Tiringham, John de Eggeton, Elias the butler (*pincerna*).

A1/14/48 [SC 193]   n.d. [*temp.* Hen. III]
Thomas de Berkele and Henry de Berkele, his son.

   Thomas has granted to Henry his assart [*rudigga*] of Buleia from his demesne of
Camma, extending from the highway to the bridge of Beleya; to hold by the services which
pertain to a half-virgate and 3d. a year.
Witnesses: Robert son of Richard, Richard de Cromhale, Peter de Stintescumbe, Richard de
Couele, Thomas de Tyringeham, John de Eggeton, Elias the butler (*pincerna*).

A1/14/49 [SC 118]   n.d. [*temp.* Hen. III]
Thomas de Berkeley and John de Gosinton.

Thomas has granted to John 2 a. of meadow and land which was held by Richard Salewine in Cam; rent 1*d.* a year at Easter.
Witnesses: Robert son of Richard, Peter de Stintescumbe, Richard de Couele, Simon de Holepenne, Elias the butler (*pincerna*), Elias de Bevinton, Arnulf the clerk.

A1/14/50 [GC 1009]   St. Mark the evangelist, 29 Edw. I [25 April 1301]
Thomas lord of Berkeley; and Walter Selyman of Cam and Maud his wife.

Thomas has leased to Walter and Maud the fardel of land in Camme which he previously held of Thomas for life; to them and their issue, rent ½ mark a year for their lives, and 6*d.* for 1½ a. of land enclosed next to le Holiewell, and after their deaths the rent of their issue 10*s.* 6*d.* a year.[1]
Witnesses: Robert de Berkel', Thomas de Swonhungre, Henry de Camme, Maurice de Camme, Walter Hathemere.
At: Berkeley.

A1/14/51 [GC 1015; *duplicate* GC 1016]   Fri. the feast of the nativity of St. John
                                                          the Baptist, 29 Edw. I [23 June 1301]
Thomas de Berkeleye, lord of Berkeley, and Walter de Hathemere.

Thomas has granted to Walter and his issue his furlong in Netherewyston of Camme, with 3 plots of pasture to enlarge his enclosure, another furlong in Oldebur' with 7 a. in the same furlong, and further all his land in Doddesgrave; to hold enclosed, rent 50*s.* a year, with licence to take soil from the roads of Camme and Coueleye to improve the land, provided that the passage of carts [etc.] is not impeded.
Witnesses: Robert de Bradestone, Robert de Berkeleye, Thomas de Beoleye, Thomas de Swonhungre, John de Egeton, Maurice de Camme, Robert de Draycote.
At: Berkeley.

A1/14/52 [GC 1728]   1 April 3 Edw. II [1310]
Thomas de Berkelee, lord of Berkeley, and Richard in the Hale the younger.

Thomas has granted to Richard 3½ a. 13 perches of land in Camme; for life, rent 4*s.* a year.
Witnesses: Robert de Berkeley, Robert de Bradestone, Henry de Camme, Stephen de Draycote, Walter Hathemare.
At: Berkeley.

A1/14/53 [GC 1787]   1 Feb. 4 Edw. II [1311]
Thomas de Berkelee, lord of Berkeley; and Walter le Hayward of Clingre and Juliana his wife.

Thomas has granted to Walter and Juliana 1 a. of land beside Inwodesgete, to hold enclosed; and 2 a. 3 perches of land in Wodelee; to them and their issue, rent 4*s.* 6*d.* a year.
Witnesses: Robert de Bradestone, Thomas de Beolce, Peter de Styntescombe, Henry de Camme, John de Bradeford, Robert le Warner, Walter Hathemare.
At: Berkeley.

A1/14/54 [GC 1869]   1 March 5 Edw. II [1312]
Thomas de Berkelee, lord of Berkeley, and Walter Hathemare.

Thomas has granted to Walter 3 a. 26 perches of land extending to the road above the meadow called Bourmede, saving to Thomas and his heirs a road through the said land; to him and his issue, rent 4*s.* a year.
Witnesses: Henry de Camme, Robert Warner, John de Couelee, Stephen de Draycote, Richard de Astmed.
At: Berkeley.

[1] *Transcript*: Smyth, iii. 129–30.

A1/14/55 [GC 1905]   1 March 6 Edw. II [1313]
Thomas de Berkelee, lord of Berkeley; and Robert Dary and Alice his wife.

Thomas has granted to Robert and Alice 3½ a. 1 rood of land between the castle field of Dursleye and the spring [*fons*] called le Schote; to hold enclosed, to them and their issue, rent 7*s*. 6*d*. a year.
Witnesses: Henry de Camme, Robert Warner, Nicholas de Beoleie, John atte Yete, William le Harpour.
At: Berkeley.

A1/14/56 [GC 1962]   1 Feb. 7 Edw. II [1314]
Thomas de Berkelee, lord of Berkeley, and John son of Alice atte Mulle of Cam.

Thomas has granted to John a rent of 5*s*. from the said Alice for the holding which she formerly held of Isabel de Berkelee, for her life, with the reversion of the holding after Alice's death, and also a plot of land in Camme; to him and his issue, rent 5*s*. a year during Alice's life and 13*s*. 4*d*. a year after her death.
Witnesses: Henry de Camme, Robert Warner, Stephen de Draycote, Walter Hathemare, Richard de Astmed.
At: Berkeley.

A1/14/57 [GC 2216]   20 Jan. 11 Edw. II [1318]
Thomas de Berkeleye, lord of Berkeley, and Walter Hoertes of Hinton.

Thomas has leased to Walter 1 a. of meadow in the meadow called Brademede, which William Doucesone previously held of Thomas, in Camme, with free access through Thomas's wood of la Redewode; to him and his issue, rent 4*s*. a year.
Witnesses: John le Serjaunt, Thomas de Craweleye, Thomas le Frig, Matthew Hatholf, Thomas atte Wode.
At: Berkeley.

A1/14/58 [GC 3810*]   Fri. after St. Denis, 10 Ric. II [12 Oct. 1386]
William atte Stile and the lord [Thomas de Berkeleye]

Extract from court roll: William came and took of the lord 2 messuages and 2 half-virgates of land, and also a cottage with a curtilage and a croft containing 1 a. of land, and 1 a. of land in Nethercame, and 1 a. of meadow in Charlmed, which was previously held for the life of Katherine late lady of Wottone as dower; to William and Alice his wife for their lives, rent for the 2 messuages and 2 half-virgates 40*s*. a year, for the cottage, curtilage and land 5*s*. a year, and for the meadow 4*s*. a year, and he gave to the lord for an entry fine 40*s*. and did fealty.
At: Cam.

A1/14/59 [GC 4075]   Mon. the feast of St. Stephen, 14 Hen. IV [26 Dec. 1412]
Thomas de Berkeley, lord of Berkeley; and Walter Bacheler and Alice his wife.

Thomas has leased to Walter and Alice a messuge and half-virgate of land and 4 a. of foreland in Eborlong; for their lives, at the previous rent.
Witnesses: Edmund Basset, William Smalcombe, William Longeforde.
At: Berkeley.

ADMINISTRATIVE DOCUMENTS
Account rolls

A1/14/60 [GAR 89] Cam and Coaley	24–5 Edw. I [1296–7]
A1/14/61 [GAR 90] Cam and Coaley	27–8 Edw. I [1299–1300]
A1/14/62 [GAR 91] Cam and Coaley	n.d. [*c*. 1300 × 1320]
A1/14/63 [GAR 92] Cam and Coaley	20 Edw. II to 1 Edw. III [1326–7]
A1/14/64 [GAR 93] Cam and Coaley	n.d. [1330s]

A1/14/65 [GAR 94] Cam and Coaley   25–6 Edw. III [1351–2]

A1/14/66 [GAR 95] Cam and Coaley   26–7 Edw. III [1352–3]

A1/14/67 [GAR 96]   28–9 Edw. III [1354–5]

A1/14/68 [GAR 98]   10–11 Ric. II [1386–7]

A1/14/69 [GAR 99]   12–13 Ric. II [1388–9]

Charter Roll

A1/14/70 [SR 13]   Hen. III to Hen. V

Abstracts of deeds concerning the manor of Cam, each entry numbered consecutively from no. 5 to no. 107, top damaged. Probably an original roll like A1/3/159 [SR 8–10], above.

OTHER TENANTS AND HOLDINGS

Maurice de Cam's holding

Maurice, who states in his charters that he was a son of Sir William de Berkeley (d. 1272), a younger brother of Maurice (II) Lord Berkeley (d. 1281), was almost certainly illegitimate since he failed to inherit from his father some entailed lands. Another indicator is that he was surnamed 'de Cam' rather than 'de Berkeley'.

A1/14/71 [GC 591]   Eve of St. Laurence, 21 Edw. I [2 Feb. 1293]

Thomas lord of Berkeleye and Maurice de Camme.

Thomas has granted to Maurice, for himself and his tenants in Cam, whatever they owe for Peter's Pence, viz. 3½*d.* a year.

Witnesses: Robert de Stone, Robert de Bradestone, Peter de Stintescumbe, Henry de Camme, Robert de Dreycot, Richard de Milkesham, Thomas de la Wodende.

At: Berkeley.

A1/14/72 [GC 602]   The Annunciation, 22 Edw. I [25 March 1294]

Miles de Stoke and Maurice de Camme, son of Sir William de Berkeleye.

Miles has granted to Maurice 3 a. of arable land in the field called Middulfeld, and Maurice has granted to Miles 1½ a. and 4 selions of arable land, above the road between Slimbrugge and the house of Walter Hathemare, and ½ a., in the field between Camme and Slimbrugge between the land which Sir Robert de Kingustone, knight, formerly held and the road between Camme and Cambrugge.

Witnesses: Peter de Stintescombe, William de Burgo, Reginald de Gosinton, Robert de Bradeston, Robert de Draycote, Robert de Coueleye, Richard de Salle.

At: Cam.

A1/14/73 [GC 1552]   n.d. [*c.* 1294]

Miles de Stoke and Maurice de Camme, son of Sir William de Berkeleye.

Miles has granted to Maurice 2 a. of land in the field called Middulfeld, and for this Maurice has granted to him 1 a. of land beside the road from Slimbrugge to the house which was of Walter Hathemare, and 4 selions lying between the two roads at Longetagge.

Witnesses: Peter de Stintuscombe, William de Burgo, Reginald de Gosintone, Robert de Bradeston, Robert de Draycote, Robert de Coueleye, Richard de Salle.

A1/14/74 [GC 633]   n.d. [1297]

Maurice de Camme and Alice of the mill (*de molend'*).

Maurice has leased to Alice 1 a. of arable land in Camme, from Michaelmas 25 Edw. I [29 Sept. 1297], for six autumn crops; she has given him 8*s.*

Witnesses: Robert de Dreycote, Henry de Camme, Walter Hathemere, Thomas de la Wodende, Robert Passelewe.

A1/14/75 [GC 1410]   n.d. [late 13th cent.]
Robert de Draycote of Cam and Maurice de Camme.

   Robert has quitclaimed to Maurice, for 50s., the land which Maurice bought from Robert
for a term of 6 years, lying in the croft called Thyckeleye in the vill of Camme.
Witnesses: Peter de Stynchescumbe, Adam de Laumport, Robert de Bradestone, Thomas de
Swonhongre, Thomas de Beoleye.

A1/14/76 [GC 1275]   n.d. [*temp.* Edw. I]
Ralph de Camme and Maurice son of Sir William de Berkel'.

   Ralph has granted to Maurice ½ a. of land in the field of Longeleg', and in exchange
Maurice has granted to Ralph two plots of land beside the street called Rudingestret and the
footpath to Stintescumb.
Witnesses: Peter de Stintescumbe, William de Burgo, Reginald de Gosinton, Robert de
Brothestan, Robert de Draycot, Robert de Couel, Walter de Corevegate.

A1/14/77 [GC 1214]   n.d. [*temp.* Edw. I]
Maurice son of Sir William de Berkel' and Walter de Corevegate.

   Maurice has granted to Walter 1 a. of land in the field called Witston, one fore-earth in
the furlong of Wowelond and one gore in . . . , in exchange for 1 a. of land in Purifurlong.
Witnesses: Peter de Stintescumbe, William de Burgo, Reginald de Gosinton, Robert de
Brothestan, Ralph de Camme, Robert de Draycot, Robert de Couel'.

The Woodend holding

A1/14/78 [GC 4107]   . . . 4 Hen. V [1416–17]
[William Kedon], cousin and heir of Richard WodeEnde of Cam; and [William] Longeforde
of Cam and John Cowley of Stinchcombe.

   William Kedon has quitclaimed to William Longeforde and John [Cowley] . . . land and
holdings [etc.] . . . which he inherited after the death of Richard his cousin, in Camme.
Witnesses: . . . Archer, Richard Hallyng, John Waryner, Thomas Tanner, John Mabbesone.
At: Cam.

A1/14/79 [GC 4114]   Thurs. before St. George, 6 Hen. V [21 April 1418]
John Cowley of Stinchcombe and William Longeford of Cam.

   John has quitclaimed to William the lands, holdings [etc.] in Camme which they had by
grant of William Kedon, cousin and heir of Richard WodeEnde of Camme.
Witnesses: John Archer, Thomas Tanner, Richard Hallyng, Henry Taillour, Roger Draycote.
At: Cam.

Grants by Reginald the cook

A1/14/80 [GC 728]   n.d. [late 13th cent.]
Reginald called the cook of Cam; and Gilbert de Longeworthe and Joan his wife.

   Reginald has leased to Gilbert and Joan, for their lives, 1 a. of land in the field called
Dunfeld next to the spring called Wolryhyceswelle; rent 1d. a year, and Gilbert has given
Reginald 12s.
Witnesses: Maurice de Camme, Henry de Camme, Robert de Draycot, Thomas de la
Wodende, Robert Passelewe.

A1/14/81 [GC 892]   n.d. [late 13th cent.]
Reginald called the cook; and Gilbert de Longeworthe and Joan his wife.

   Reginald has granted to Gilbert and Joan 1 a. of land in the field called Holemedforlong;
for their lives, rent 1d. a year, and they have given him 12s.
Witnesses: Maurice de Camme, Henry de Camme, Robert de Dreycote, Walter Hathemere,
Robert Passelewe.

A1/14/82 [GC 1291]   n.d. [*temp.* Edw. I]
Reginald the cook; and Gilbert de Langeford and Joan his wife.

Reginald has granted to Gilbert and Joan 2 a. of land in the field called le Hydefelde; for their lives, rent 6*d.* a year, and they have given him 16*s.*
Witnesses: Henry de Camme, Maurice de Camme, Robert Draycote, Robert Passelewe, Thomas de la Wodeynde.

A1/14/83 [GC 1290]   n.d. [*temp.* Edw. I]
Reginald the cook of Cam; and Adam le Neweme and Helen his wife.

Reginald has granted to Adam and Helen 1 a. of land in the vill of Camme at Inhechyng; for their lives, rent 1*d.* a year, and they have given him 12*s.*
Witnesses: Maurice de Camme, Robert de Draycot, Henry de Camme, Richard de Salle, Robert Passelewe.

A1/14/84 [GC 893]   n.d. [late 13th cent.]
Reginald the cook of Cam; and Adam and Helen his wife of the same.

Reginald has granted to Adam and Helen 1 a. of land called [Foelex]; for their lives, rent 1*d.* a year, and they have given him 14*s.*
Witnesses: Robert de Draycot, Henry de Camme, Maurice de Camme, Richard de Salle, Thomas ate Wodend.

Miscellaneous

A1/14/85 [SC 349]   n.d. [*temp.* Hen. III]
Roger de Camme, son of Eustace de Camme, and John le Blund.

Roger has granted to John the messuage, croft and 3 a. of land which William le Guldene sometime held of Sir Eustace his father, 1 a. lying at Tviseledewaga near the land of William de Berkeley, knight, 1 a. next to the land of Richard Pride, and 1 a. next to the land of Gilbert de Withia; rent 3*s.* a year, acknowledgement 2 marks to Roger and 10*s.* to Joan his wife.
Witnesses: Sir Richard de Clifford, Master Peter de Breus, Jordan de Budiford, William de Berkele, Richard Stut, Richard de la Wodende, James Cotel.

A1/14/86 [SC 382]   n.d. [*temp.* Hen. III]
Prioress Alice and the convent of Kington; and Henry de Hathemere of Cam.

The convent has granted to Henry the mill, with the pond and other appurtenances at Camme, which Walter de Hathemere, Henry's father, once held of them; rent 10*s.* a year, and Henry has given them 9 marks.
Witnesses: Roger de Camme, Robert de Dreycote, Reginald de Gosinton, William de Kyngeston, clerk, Richard the baker (*pistor*), Robert de Couele, Walter the butler (*pincerna*), James Cotele, William the baker of Hulemoncote, Walter de Sorveet, Walter the master of Gossington.

A1/14/87 [GC 511]   14 Kal. of April, 12 Edw. I [19 March 1284]
Walter de Corufgate of Cam and Master Thomas de Stoke, archdeacon of Gloucester.

Walter has received 15 marks from Master Thomas for which he has leased his mill to Thomas, with all the appurtenances, in surety to repay to the said Thomas at Michaelmas 12 Edw. I [29 Sept. 1284], and if he does not pay the mill remains with Thomas; and further he is bound in 15 marks to Sir Thomas de Berkeley; Walter's sureties being Miles de Langgetot, Robert de Olepenne, and Robert de Draycote.
At: Cam.

A1/14/88 [GC 2385]   Thurs. before the translation of St. Thomas the archbishop, 15 Edw. II [1 July 1322]

Richard de Salle of Cam and Robert Passelewe of the same.

Richard has granted to Robert, his heirs and assigns, for a certain sum of money, a rent of 1*d.* a year from 2 a. of land in the field of Farntone, which Gilbert de la Wodend and Alice his wife hold for life, with the reversion of the land; also a rent of 14*d.* a year from 1 a. of land in Longcrofte, which William le Couherd holds for life, with the reversion.

Witnesses: John de Coueleye, Stephen de Draykote, Henry de Camme, Walter Hathemare, Robert de Draykote, Alexander de Bernwode.

At: Cam.

A1/14/89 [GC 2703]   4 Kal. of June 4 Edw. III [29 May 1330]

Simon Martyn of Kyneltre; and Stephen de Kyneltre, Alice his wife and Margaret their daughter.

Simon has leased to Stephen, Alice and Margaret his holding at Kyneltre within the manor of Camme, in various parcels; for their lives, rent a rose a year.

Witnesses: Walter de Coumbe, Walter Toyt, Adam Moton, Adam de Mestesdone, William Godynow, William Gryp, William Cott.

At: Kineltre.

A1/14/90 [GC 3014]   Thurs. before the nativity of St. John the Baptist, 16 Edw. III [20 June 1342]

John de Lorwinge and Henry le Hayward.

John has granted to Henry a parcel of land in the field called Wlmworthy, beside the road from Mettesdone to Stintescombe.

Witnesses: Stephen de Keneltre, William in the Hurne, Robert Moton, Thomas le Wor, Richard Feror, Richard Aleyn, Nicholas Schot.

At: Cam.

A1/14/91 [GC 2568]   n.d. [mid 14th cent.]

William son and heir of Simon Martin and Stephen de Kyneltre.

William has granted to Stephen an annual rent of ½*d.* from William de Lorwynge for 2 selions of land in the furlong called Ecchedone extending above the meadow called Inwodesmede.

Witnesses: John Serjaunt, John de Egetone, John Purlewent, Thomas le Wor, Adam Purlewent, clerk.

A1/14/92 [SC 599]   30 April 29 Hen. VI [1451]

Alice Dorney of Nibley, widow, daughter and heir of the late William Ryel, and John Swanley the younger.

Alice has granted to John 4 selions of land in the field called Echedone, in the manor of Camme.

Witnesses: Thomas Smalcombe, John Dorney, Thomas Mundy, Maurice Robyn, William Longge, Walter Swanley, John Macy.

At: Nibley.

CAM: BREADSTONE

Breadstone was held of Alkington manor as a quarter of a knight's fee, but it was a hamlet of Cam in the 1327 subsidy.[1] It was held by the Breadstone (or Bradeston) family, the last active member of which, and certainly the most prominent, was Sir Thomas de Breadstone. His father Robert was an important servant of the Berkeley lords, and Thomas followed in his footsteps but moved on with Maurice de Berkeley of Stoke Giffard into the service of

[1] Smyth, iii. 113, 118–19.

Edward III. He rose to the rank of banneret and was summoned to parliament. He died in 1360 leaving as his successor a grandson Thomas de Breadstone, who died in 1374 shortly after coming of age, to be succeeded by a daughter Elizabeth.[1] See also below, A1/24/54 [GC 2571].

A1/15/1 [GC 3093]   24 May 18 Edw. III [1344]
Thomas lord of Berkele and Sir Thomas de Bradestone.

Thomas de Berkele has granted licence to Thomas de Bradestone to grant 3 messuages, 4 virgates of land, 12 a. of meadow, 6 a. of wood and 100*s.* rent in Hamme, Alkyntone, and Camme to the chapel of St. Michael of Bradestone, for the souls of Thomas [de Bradestone] and Isabel his late wife.
At: Berkeley.

CAM: CLINGRE
PLAUNCHE RENTS

A1/16/1 [GC 1434]   n.d. [late Hen. III]
John de Iwelegh and Sir Maurice de Berkel'.

John has granted to Maurice a rent of 1*d.*, which he had by grant of Thomas de la Plaunche, from Laurence de Wyke for his holding in Cleyhungre.
Witnesses: William de Mathem, Peter de Stintescumb, Roger de Dreycote, Ralph de Camme, Robert de Coueleyg'.

A1/16/2 [GC 801]   n.d. [late Hen. III]
Thomas de la Plaunch and Sir Maurice de Berkel'.

Thomas has granted to Maurice a rent of 1*d.* from Laurence de Cleyhungre for land in Cleyhungre, and a rent of 1*d.* from Henry de Dene for land at la Planche, and a rent of a clove from the land which Anselm Basset held of him in Eweleyg'.
Witnesses: Sir William de Derneford, William Maunsel, Robert de Kingeston, Nicholas le Lou, knights, William de Mathem, Ralph de Camme, Robert de Dreycote.

OTHER

A1/16/3 [GC 1747]   Sun. . . . John the Baptist, 3 Edw. II [21 June 1310?]
Thomas [de Berkeleye]; and [John] Godynow and Maud his wife.

Thomas has granted to John and Maud . . . perches of land above le . . . of Cleyhongre; to them and their issue, rent 2*s.* 6*d.* a year.
Witnesses: Richard de Avene, Thomas . . . , . . . Lorewynge, William de Kyneltre . . .
At: Berkeley.

A1/16/4 [GC 1866]   St. Matthew, 5 Edw. II [24 Feb. 1312]
Thomas de Berkelee, lord of Berkeley, and Thomas le Taylor of Clingre.

Thomas de Berkelee has granted to Thomas le Taylor the messuage with buildings, garden, curtilage and croft in Cleyhungre in the manor of Camme which John ate Cherche of Cleyhungre previously held of Thomas de Berkelee for life; to Thomas le Taylor, Margaret his wife and their issue, rent 5*s.* a year.
Witnesses: Robert de Berkelee, Maurice de Beleye, Thomas de Beleye, Henry de Camme, Roger de Gosynton, Walter de Gosynton, William le Botiler.
At: Clingre.

A1/16/5 [GC 4437]   20 May [3] Edw. IV [1463]
William Berkeley, son and heir of James Berkeley, lord of Berkeley; and Thomas Biscey, Sibyl his wife and John their son.

On the day that James died, William leased to Thomas, Sibyl and John a messuage with

---

[1] *GEC* ii. 273.

land and meadow which John Juipke now holds in [Cleangre] within the manor of Camme by grant of James.

CAM: PLANCHES

THE MONMOUTH HOLDING

Chorlemede

A1/17/1 [GC 1085]   n.d. [*c*. Feb. 1305]
Maud de Dene; and Robert de Berkle and Joan his wife.

Maud has granted to Robert and Joan all her meadow in Chorlemed; for their lives, rent 20*s.* a year for 11 years beginning at the Purification 33 Edw. I [2 Feb. 1305], and thereafter £20 a year.

Witnesses: Robert de Bradeston, Thomas de Boleye, Henry de Camme, Thomas Serjant, John de Crauleye, Walter de Gosinton, Sir Philip the chaplain.

A1/17/2 [GC 2039]   20 May 8 Edw. II [1315]
(1) Thomas son of Walter de Monemuth; (2) Roger le Archer and Edward Golde; (3) Robert de Berkeleye.

Thomas has appointed Roger and Edward his attorneys to receive the rent of 20*s.* from Robert de Berkeleye for a meadow in Chorlemede. [*In French.*]

At: Hereford.

A1/17/3 [GC 2053]   3 Sept. 9 Edw. II [1315]
Robert de Berkeleye and Sir Thomas de Berkeleye, lord of Berkeley.

Robert has quitclaimed to Thomas a meadow which Thomas previously had by grant of Thomas son of Walter de Monemuth in Chorlemede.

Witnesses: Thomas de Bradeston, Thomas de Boeleye, Henry de Camme, John le Serjant, Walter Sewaker.

At: Berkeley.

A1/17/4 [GC 2107]   Thurs. the feast of the nativity of St. John the Baptist, 9 Edw. II
                                                          [24 June 1316]
William Mody and Sir Thomas de Berkeleye, his lord.

William has granted to Thomas, his heirs and assigns 1 a. of meadow in Chorlemede called la Brodeacre, within the manor of Camme.

Witnesses: Henry de Camme, John de Coueleye, Stephen de Draycote, Walter Hathemare, Richard de Astmede, Robert de Draycote, William le Botyler.

At: Cam.

A1/17/5 [GC 2187]   1 Aug. 11 Edw. II [1317]
Thomas de Berkeleye, lord of Berkeley, and Walter Selymon.

Thomas has granted to Walter 2 a. of land above Barlichhulle extending to the street called Ruydingestret above the water called Baylokeswelle, and 1 a. of meadow in Chorlmede, in Camme; to him and his issue, rent 9*s.* a year.

Witnesses: Stephen de Draycote, Robert de Draycote, Walter de Gosyntone, Thomas atte Wodende, John Shydwalle.

At: Berkeley.

The entire holding

A1/17/6 [GC 2076]   Sat. the eve of St. Laurence, 9 Edw. II [9 Aug. 1315]
Thomas son of Walter de Monemuth and Sir Thomas de Berkeleye, lord of Berkeley.

Thomas de Monemuth has granted to Thomas de Berkeleye, his heirs and assigns all his lands and holdings at la Plaunche in the parish of Camme, with the reversion of the lands held for life by Katherine widow of John de Monemuth in dower and the reversion of the meadow called Chorlemede which Robert de Berkeleye holds at farm by demise of Maud de Monemuth.

Witnesses: John son of Nichol, lord of Hill, Thomas de Bradeston, Walter de Nasse, William Gamages, John de Saltmarsh (*de salso marisco*), John Peytevyn, John de Helyon, Ralph de Knulle, Robert le Warner.

At: La Plaunche.

A1/17/7 [GC 2371; *duplicate* GC 2372] Wed. in Epiphany, 15 Edw. II [6 Jan. 1322]
Maurice de Berkeleye, lord of Berkeley, and John de Berkeleye his son.

Maurice has granted to John all his land and holding at la Planche with all the appurtenances, in Camme, which Sir Thomas de Berkeleye, Maurice's father, had by enfeoffment of Thomas de Monemuthe, formerly lord of la Planche, except the meadow in Cherlemede which Sir Thomas took into the demesne of Camme; to him and his male issue, rent a rose a year.

Witnesses: Sir William de Wauton, Sir Simon le Chamberlein, knights, Walter de Nasse, Henry de Camme, Thomas de Bradeston, Thomas de Berkel' of Billow, Roger Archer.

At: Gloucester.

OTHER TENANTS AND HOLDINGS

A1/17/8 [GC 2031] 4 April 8 Edw. II [1315]
Thomas de Berkelee, lord of Berkeley; and William Modi and Mabel his wife.

Thomas has granted to William and Mabel four parcels of land at la Plaunche, one beside Lynhaledych, once called Flouredelond, one in Tokenhale, and one called Schortelond; for their lives, rent 5*s.* a year.

Witnesses: Stephen de Draycote, Walter Hathemare, Thomas atte Wodende, Henry de Camme, Robert de Draycote.

At: Berkeley.

A1/17/9 [GC 2185] Mon. the feast of St. James, 11 Edw. II [25 July 1317]
Thomas de Berkeleye, lord of Berkeley; and John de Generew and Edith his wife.

Thomas has leased to John and Edith 4 a. of land in the field called Hurlond at la Plaunche by Camme; to them and their issue, rent 2*s.* a year.

Witnesses: Henry de Camme, John de Coueleye, Stephen de Draycote, Walter de Gosyntone, Robert de Draycote.

At: Berkeley.

CAM: STINCHCOMBE

THE LORRIDGE HOLDING

A1/18/1 [SC 385] n.d. [*temp.* Hen. III]
John son of Walter de Lorwyng and Roger de Tumberleye.

John has granted to Roger 1 a. of land which Roger had by grant of Walter, John's father, lying in le Northfeld of Styntescumbe; rent 6*d.* a year to Peter de Styntescumbe, and Roger has given John 14*s.* 6*d.*

Witnesses: William de Burgo, Adam de Laumport, Maurice de Camme, Henry de Camme, Richard de Melksham.

A1/18/2 [GC 1924] 20 May 6 Edw. II [1313]
Peter de Styntescombe and Sir Thomas de Berkelee, his lord.

Peter has granted to Thomas 1 a. of land in le Northfeld of Styntescombe, which he had by grant of Roger de Tomberleie, in Camme.

Witnesses: Thomas de Stone, Thomas de Bradestone, John de Coueleye, Nicholas de Beoleie, Stephen de Draycote, Walter Hathemare, Richard de Astmed.

At: Berkeley.

INWOOD

Robert de Berkeley was the younger son of Sir Robert, younger brother of Thomas (II) Lord Berkeley.[1] He died in 1316 leaving a son and heir Thomas, who died 1340 × 1343 leaving a son and heir John. John died without issue in 1348 and his heir was his sister Margaret, who married Ralph Trye.

A1/18/3 [SC 461]   St. John the apostle and evangelist, 27 Edw. I [27 Dec. 1298]
Thomas lord of Berkeley and Robert de Berkeley, his nephew.
   Thomas has granted to Robert the wood of Inwode in Chamme; rent 40*s.* a year.[2]
Witnesses: Robert de Berkeley, Walter de Helyun, John de Wiliton, Robert le Veel, Peter Crok, knights, Richard de Byseleye, Robert de Bradestan, Robert de Stanes, Robert Wither, Richard de Avene, Thomas de Swanhongre.

A1/18/4 [GC 1106]   7 Jan. 34 Edw. I [1306]
Thomas de Berk', lord of Berkeley, and Robert de Berk', his nephew.
   Agreement concerning rights of way through Inwode, following from Thomas's enfeoffment to Robert. [*In French.*][3]
Witnesses: John de Button, John Basset, William de Wauton, knights, Robert de Bradeston, Thomas de Beoleye, Thomas de Stintescombe, John de Olepenne, Henry de Camme, Waryn le fiz Willam, Robert Wyther, Walter Hathemar.
At: Berkeley.

A1/18/5 [SC 634]   18 Aug. 16 Edw. IV [18 Aug. 1476]
William lord Berkeley; and William Try, esquire, and Isabel his wife, sister of William Berkeley.
   William Berkeley has granted to William Try the rent of 40*s.* which William Try ought to render to him for a certain land and wood at Stynchcombe (Glos.), the grant being in part payment of 30 marks to fulfil the will of James lord Berkeley, William's late father, to provide for Isabel's marriage.[4]
At: Gloucester.

OTHER

A1/18/6 [GC 2077]   Sun. the feast of St. Laurence, 9 Edw. II [10 Aug. 1315]
Thomas de Berkeleye, lord of Berkeley; and Robert le Wylde, Joan his wife, Isabel their daughter and Edith daughter of Walter Gylot.
   Thomas has leased to Robert, Joan, Isabel and Edith, for their lives, the cottage which the said Walter Gylot previously held of Thomas in villeinage at Styntescoumbe in the manor of Camme; rent 4*s.* a year.
Witnesses: Thomas de Bradeston, Thomas de Boeleye, Peter de Styntescombe, Stephen de Draycote, William le Botyler.
At: Berkeley.

COALEY

BERKELEY ACQUISITIONS
Grants by Elias de Coaley

A1/19/1 [GC 894]   n.d. [late Hen. III]
Elias de Coueleg' and Sir Maurice de Berkel'.
   Elias has granted to Maurice all his land between the land of William son of John and the land of John Eynolf in Couleg'; Maurice has given him 40*s.*
Witnesses: Sir Robert de Kyngeston, knight, William the serjeant (*serviens*), William Waryner, Ralph de Camme, Robert de Draycote.

---

[1] For Robert the younger see also above, pp. 64–7, Dangervilles Wick.
[2] *Transcript*: Smyth, iii. 350–1.   [3] *Transcript*: ibid. 351–2.   [4] *Transcript*: ibid. 353.

A1/19/2 [GC 740] n.d. [late Hen. III]

Elias de Couel' and Sir Maurice de Berkel'.

Elias has granted to Maurice 1 a. 5 perches of land in the vill of Couel' in the field called Westfeld; rent a rose a year, and Maurice has given him 20s.

Witnesses: Robert de Couel', William le Warener, William de Corfgate, John ate Forde, James Cotel, Elias le Botiller, Gilbert Huet, William le Serjaunt.

Grants by James Cotel

A1/19/3 [GC 774] n.d. [late Hen. III]

James Kotel of Coaley and Maurice de Berkel.

James has granted to Maurice 1½ a. of meadow.

Witnesses: Richard de Berkel', Robert de Kingeston, Elias le Botiller, Adam le Lung, Richard Alfrid, Michael de Wenden, clerk.

A1/19/4 [GC 1309] n.d. [late Hen. III]

James Cotel of Coaley and Sir Maurice de Berkel'.

James has granted to Maurice all his land in the furlong called Mudleye in the vill of Coueleye, between the land which Lady Joan de Berkel' held in dower and the water called Coueleysbrok; rent a rose a year, and Maurice has given him 20s. and half of 1 qr. of wheat.

Witnesses: Bartholomew de Olepenne, Roger de Lokintone, Robert de Draycote, Robert de Couel', Maurice de Camme, William de Burgo, William de Egeton.

A1/19/5 [GC 1311] n.d. [late Hen. III]

James Cotel of Coaley and Sir Maurice de Berkel'.

James has granted to Maurice 1 a. of meadow in the vill of Couel', and Maurice has given him 1 mark.

Witnesses: Richard de Berkel', Robert de Kingeston, Elias le Botiller, Adam le Lung, Richard Dis'do, Michael de Wenden, clerk.

A1/19/6 [GC 1312] n.d. [late Hen. III]

James Kotel of Coaley and Sir Maurice de Berkel'.

James has granted to Maurice . . . in the vill of Kouel', viz. that which lies in the furlong called . . . John de Berkel' and the land of Sir Richard his son; and Maurice has given him 14 . . .

Witnesses: . . . Peter de Stintescumbe, Elias de Kumbe, William de Marm. . . , . . . de Egeton, Bartholomew de Olepenne, Michael de Wenden . . .

Millham and associated holdings

A1/19/7 [GC 1018]   Sun. after the translation of St. Thomas [the archbishop], 29 Edw. I
[9 July 1301]

John de Iweleye and Sir Thomas de Berkeleye, lord of Berkeley.

John has granted to Thomas all his land lying in the furlong called Mulnham, which lies next to the stream of the mill of Coueleye, and all his meadow called Mormed in Coueleye; Thomas has given him 10 marks.

Witnesses: Sir John de Wylynton, Sir John de Akton, Sir John Basset, Sir John Lovel, Sir John de la Ryvere, knights, Thomas de Styntescombe, Henry de Camme, Robert de Coueleye, Thomas de Beoleye.

At: Berkeley.

A1/19/8 [GC 1017]   Sun. after the translation of St. Thomas [the archbishop], 29 Edw. I
[9 July 1301]

(1) John de Iweleye; (2) Walter Hathermare; (3) Sir Thomas de Berkel', lord of Berkeley.

John has appointed Walter to give seisin to Thomas of all the land and meadow which he had in the manor of Coueleye, as in his charter to Thomas.
At: Uley.

A1/19/9 [GC 1935]   1 Aug. [1313]
Thomas de Berkelee, lord of Berkeley; and John the miller (*molendinar*') and Joan his wife.

Thomas has granted to John and Joan two parcels of meadow beside the upper mill called Brechchesham and Whoelham, which Isabel de Berkelee his aunt formerly held, and a rent of 16*s.* a year from Walter Symond, chaplain, for two parcels of meadow beside the said meadow, which Walter holds of Thomas for life, with the reversion after Walter's death, in Hamme; to them and their issue, rent during Walter's life 32*s.* a year, and after his death 39*s.* a year.
Witnesses: Thomas de Stone, John Capel, Walter Sewaker, Robert Bastard, Nicholas Iweyn.
At: Berkeley.

A1/19/10 [GC 2342]   1 March 14 Edw. II [1321]
Walter Symond, chaplain, and Sir Thomas de Berkeleye, lord of Berkeley.

Walter has quitclaimed to Thomas 1 virgate of land which Henry Josep formerly held at Lyndweye in the manor of Hamme, also all the meadow called Brodehamme with appurtenances beside the mill of Hamme, which were of Isabel de Berkeleye, and further the furlong of arable land called Mulehamme in Couel', which was of John de Iweleye, all of which he previously had by grant of Thomas for his life.
Witnesses: John le Serjaunt, John de la Hay, John Capel, John Wyth, Roger Archer, Thomas Aleyn, John Abbot.
At: Berkeley.

Boseley and Elmcote rent

A1/19/11 [GC 590]   Michaelmas, 2[9] Edw. I [29 Sept. 1301]
Sir Thomas de Berkeleye, lord of Berkeley, and Henry de Camme.

Thomas has granted that Henry may enclose and . . . [hold in severalty?] . . . a furlong called Rudinge in Camme, also to improve his furlong of Bouresleye . . . Endorsed: *29 E.1.*
Witnesses: . . . Thomas de Stintescumbe, Thomas de Swonhungre, Thomas de Beoleye, John de . . . , . . . Budelescombe, Robert Wyther.
At: Berkeley.

A1/19/12 [GC 1024]   Sun. after Michaelmas, 29 Edw. I [1 Oct. 1301]
Henry de Camme and Sir Thomas de Berkel', lord of Berkeley.

Henry, with the assent of his wife Margaret, has granted to Thomas a rent of 24*s.* 6*d.* from John de Hulmaynecote and his heirs in Coueleye, in exchange for a furlong of land called Bouresleye which Thomas has granted to him.
Witnesses: Sir John de Botetourte, Sir John ap Adam, Sir Walter de Glouc', Sir William de Wauton, knights, Robert de Bradeston, Thomas de Stintescumbe, Thomas de Swonhungre, Thomas de Beoleye, John de Oulepenne, Robert de Butlescombe, Robert Wither.
At: Berkeley.

In Hinham meadow

A1/19/13 [GC 1656]   Whit-Sunday, 1 Edw. II [2 June 1308]
Richard le Waleys and Alice his wife; and Sir Thomas de Berkeley, lord of Berkeley.

Richard and Alice have granted to Thomas all their claim to 28 perches of meadow in Hyneham which Alice had in dower after the death of Hugh le Pestur her first husband, in Hulemancote and Couelee.
Witnesses: Robert de Bradestone, Robert de Berkeley, Thomas de Beoleye, Thomas de Styntescombe, Stephen de Draycote, Robert de Coueleye, Walter Hathemare.
At: Berkeley.

A1/19/14 [GC 1657]   Whit-Sunday, 1 Edw. II [2 June 1308]
William le Nyeucomene and Sir Thomas de Berkeley, lord of Berkeley.

William has granted to Thomas ½ a. 8 perches of meadow next to his meadow called Hyneham, in exchange for ½ a. 52 perches of meadow for the life of himself and Maud his wife, in Moremede in Coueleye.
Witnesses: Robert de Bradestone, Robert de Berkeley, Thomas de Beoleye, Thomas de Styntescombe, Stephen de Draycote, Robert de Coueleye, Walter Hathemare.
At: Berkeley.

A1/19/15 [GC 1664]   Wed. the eve of the Assumption, 2 Edw. II [14 Aug. 1308]
Robert son of Hugh le Pestur of Elmcote and Sir Thomas de Berkelee, lord of Berkeley.

Robert has granted to Thomas 2 selions of arable land next to the meadow of Hyneham, with 2 parcels of meadow in the same meadow, in Coueleye; Thomas has given him 20*s.* and 2 qr. of wheat.
Witnesses: Robert de Bradestone, Thomas de Belee, Robert de Berkelee, Thomas de Stintescumbe, John de Olepenne, Stephen de Draycote, Nicholas the clerk.
At: Berkeley.

The Starling holding

A1/19/16 [GC 1313]   n.d. [*temp.* Edw. I]
Robert de Coueleye; and Robert son of Miles de Stoke of Frampton and Helen his wife.

Robert has granted to Robert and Helen the holding which Thomas Starling held of Robert in villeinage in Coueleye, and also 6 a. of land in Coueleye, being 3 a. in Adgarescrofte, 1 a. in the field called Sogworthy and 2 a. in the field called Clyffeld; rent 1*d.* a year.
Witnesses: Thomas de Styntescombe, Henry de Camme, Stephen de Draycote, Walter Hathemare, John de Hulemonecote, William de Corefgate, Robert son of Elias de Stoke, Robert son of Elias Geffrey, William of the chamber (*de camera*).

A1/19/17 [GC 1682]   Sun. the feast of the Purification, 2 Edw. II [2 Feb. 1309]
Robert son of Miles de Stoke of Frampton and Sir Thomas de Berkeley, lord of Berkeley.

Robert has granted to Thomas the holding which Thomas Starlyng formerly held and 6 a. of land in Coueleye, being 3 a. in Adgarescroft, 1 a. in the field called Schoggeworthy and 2 a. in the field called Clyffeld, which land he had by grant of Robert de Coueleye his grandfather.
Witnesses: Robert de Berkeley, Robert de Bradestone, Thomas de Beoleye, Thomas de Styntescombe, Thomas de Stone, Walter Hathemare, Walter de Gosynton.
At: Berkeley.

A1/19/18 [GC 1685]   1 March 2 Edw. II [1309]
(1) Thomas de Berkelee, lord of Berkeley; (2) Sir Walter Symond, his chaplain; (3) Robert son of Miles de Stocke.

Thomas has appointed Walter his attorney to receive seisin in his name of the holding which Thomas Starling formerly held, with 6 a. of land, in Coueleye, from Robert.
At: Berkeley.

The Douce holding

A1/19/19 [GC 1863]   20 Feb. 5 Edw. II [1312]
John le Duk and Sir Thomas de Berkelee, his lord.

John has granted to Thomas all his land in the furlong called Bynethehay, which Richard le Duk his father had by grant of James Cotel, beside the land called Laumpacre above the stream of Coueleye.

Witnesses: Walter de Nasse, Thomas de Bradestone, Thomas de Stone, Peter de Styntescombe, John de Couelee, Robert Warner, Walter Hathemare.
At: Berkeley.

A1/19/20 [GC 1864]   20 Feb. 5 Edw. II [1312]
(1) John le Duk; (2) Walter Hathemare; (3) Sir Thomas de Berkeleye.
   John has appointed Walter his attorney to give seisin to Thomas of his land in the furlong called Binethehay, as in his charter.
Witnesses: Thomas de Bradestone, Thomas de Stone, Peter de Stintescombe, John de Coueleye, Robert Warner.
At: Berkeley.

A1/19/21 [GC 1873]   Wed. in Easter week, 5 Edw. II [22 March 1312]
Thomas de Berkelee, lord of Berkeley; and Roger son of Walter in the Hale and William son of William in the Hale, his villeins.
   Thomas has granted to Roger and William 17 selions of land in the field called Bynethehay, which he had by grant of John le Duk, in Couelee; for their lives, rent 6*s*. 8*d*. a year.
Witnesses: John de Couelee, Robert Warner, Stephen de Draycote, Walter Hathemare, Richard de Astmead.
At: Berkeley.

Llanthony Priory's manor

A1/19/22 [GC 3371]   27 July 25 Edw. III [1351]
King Edward III and Thomas son of Maurice de Berkelee, knight.
   The king has granted licence to Thomas to grant the advowson of Aure, held in chief, to Llanthony Priory, in exchange for the manor of Coueleye.
At: The Tower of London.

A1/19/23 [SC 527]   Tues. the eve of St. Matthew, 25 Edw. III [20 Sept. 1351]
Prior William [de Pendebury] and the convent of Llanthony by Gloucester; and Thomas lord of Berkeley.
   The convent have granted to Thomas their manor of Coueleye in exchange for the advowson of the church of Aure; to Thomas for life, with remainder to Maurice his eldest son and his male issue, remainder to the male issue of Thomas and Katherine his wife and to Thomas's right heirs.
Witnesses: Thomas de Bradeston, John Tracy, Simon Basset, knights, William de Chiltenham, John le Serjaunt.
At: Llanthony.

A1/19/24 [SC 528]   St. Matthew, 25 Edw. III [21 Sept. 1351]
The prior and convent of Llanthony by Gloucester; and Thomas lord of Berkeley.
   The convent have granted to Thomas their manor of Coueleye in exchange for the advowson of Aure, and they agree that if either should lose their acquisition, the exchange will be nullified.
At: Llanthony.

Other Berkeley acquisitions

A1/19/25 [GC 1367]   n.d. [late Hen. III]
John de la Forde of Coaley and Sir Maurice de Berkel'.
   John has granted to Maurice 1 a. of meadow in Couleyg' which he had by grant of James Cotele; and Maurice has given him 1 mark.
Witnesses: Sir Robert de Kingeston, William de Mathem, Gilbert son of Nigel, Elias le Botiler, William Wariner, Robert de Couleyg', Robert de Dreycot.

A1/19/26 [GC 2538]   n.d. [1281 × 1300]
John de Olepenne and Sir Thomas de Berkel'.

John has granted to Thomas a rent of 4s. from the lands which John de Farleye holds of
John at Berkel', and a rent of 6d. from the meadow which Richard Sypward holds of John,
in exchange for 4½ a. of land at Coueleye in the field called Cliffeld in the furlong called
Hothescumbe.
Witnesses: Sir Robert de Berkel', Robert de Stane, Robert de Bradestone, Peter de
Stintescumbe, Robert de Coueleye, Robert de Draycote, Maurice de Camme.

A1/19/27 [GC 1314]   n.d. [1281 × 1300]
Robert de Coueleye and Sir Thomas de Berkel'.

Robert has granted to Thomas a croft of land which he bought from James Cotele at
Coueleye and 2 selions in the furlong called Binethehay.
Witnesses: Sir Robert de Berkel, knight, Robert de Stan', Robert de Bradeston, Pcter de
Stintescombe, John de Olepenne, Robert de Draycote . . .

A1/19/28 [GC 1113]   13 April 34 Edw. I [1306]
William le Newcomene of Coaley and Sir Thomas de Berkelegh, lord of Berkeley.

William has quitclaimed to Thomas a messuage and 1 virgate of land, which Gilbert his
father and Alice his mother formerly held of Lord Maurice de Berkelee in Couelegh; and
Thomas has given him 40s.
Witnesses: Robert de Bradeston, Robert de Berkel', Robert de Couel', Thomas de
Styntescombe, Walter de Nasse, Robert le Warner, Stephen de Draycote, Robert atte
Churche, Walter Hathemare, Richard de Estmead, William de Corfgate.
At: Coaley.

A1/19/29 [SC 477]   Sun. the feast of St. Matthias, A.D. 1307 [24 Feb. 1308]
John de Oka, prior of St. Bartholomew's Hospital, Gloucester, and Lord Thomas de
Berkeley.

The prior has granted to Thomas an anniversary in full choir [etc.] for the souls of
Maurice, Thomas's father, and Isabel his mother and, after their deaths, for the souls of
himself, Joan his wife and Maurice their son; and in return Thomas has quitclaimed to them
suit of hundred and of his court of Berkeley due from part of a holding which belonged to
James Cotele in Coueleye.
At: Gloucester.

A1/19/30 [GC 1865]   Mon. before St. Peter in cathedra, 5 Edw. II [21 Feb. 1312]
(1) Thomas de Berklee, lord of Berkeley; (2) Nicholas de Stouwe, his constable, John
Notelyn and Robert Warner; (3) Adam of the mill (*de molend'*).

Thomas has appointed Nicholas, John and Robert his attorneys to receive seisin of a toft
and 16½ a. which he had by grant of Adam.
At: Berkeley.

LICENCES, LEASES AND OTHER GRANTS
Hulmanmoor

A1/19/31 [GC 1749]   Mon. the feast of St. Peter and St. Paul, 3 Edw. II [29 June 1310]
Thomas de Berkelee, lord of Berkeley, and Thomas de Wyggewolde.

Thomas de Berkelee has granted to Thomas de Wyggewolde licence to enclose 4 a. of
meadow in Hulmannemore beside the park of Frompton; rent 2s. a year.
Witnesses: Thomas de Styntescombe, Robert de Bradestone, Walter de Nasse, Robert le
Warner, Thomas de Stone, John de Bradeford, Walter Hathemare.
At: Berkeley.

A1/19/32 [GC 1750]   Mon. the feast of St. Peter and St. Paul, 3 Edw. II [29 June 1310]
Thomas de Berkelee, lord of Berkeley, and Sir Simon chaplain of Slimbridge.

Thomas has granted to Simon licence to enclose 4 a. of meadow in Hulmannemore beside the park of Frompton; rent 2s. a year.
Witnesses: Thomas de Styntescombe, Robert de Bradestone, Walter de Nasse, Robert le Warner, Thomas de Stone, John de Bradeford, Walter Hathemare.
At: Berkeley.

A1/19/33 [GC 1751]   Mon. the feast of St. Peter and St. Paul, 3 Edw. II [29 June 1310]
Thomas de Berkelee, lord of Berkeley, and Robert le Pestor.

Thomas has granted to Robert licence to enclose 4 a. of meadow in Hulmannemore beside the park of Frompton; rent 2s. a year.
Witnesses: Thomas de Styntescombe, Robert de Bradestone, Walter de Nasse, Robert le Warner, Thomas de Stone, John de Bradeford, Walter Hathemare.
At: Berkeley.

A1/19/34 [GC 1789]   Sat. before St. Laurence, 4 Edw. II [30 Jan. 1311]
Robert le Warner, William de Corfgate, William le Boteler, Richard Bat and John de Kyngestone; and the holders of the meadow.

At the request of Sir Thomas de Berkelee, lord of Berkeley, Robert, William, William, Richard and John have quitclaimed to the men who hold the meadow of Hulmannemore, beside the park of Fromptone, common in the meadow, and have granted to them that they may enclose it without challenge or disturbance.
Witnesses: Thomas de Styntescombe, Robert de Bradestone, Walter de Nasse, Thomas de Stone, John de Bradeforde.
At: Berkeley.

The Wiggold holding

A1/19/35 [GC 1822]   Tues. before St. George, 4 Edw. I [20 April 1311]
Thomas de Berkelee, lord of Berkeley; and Thomas de Wiggewolde and Maud his wife.

Thomas de Berkelee has granted to Thomas and Maud the virgate and 2 a. of foreland which Thomas de Wiggewolde previously held of him at his will, in Coueleye and Hulmanecote; to them and their issue, rent 40s. a year.
Witnesses: Robert de Bradestone, Robert de Berkelee, William de Corfgate, John de Iweleye, Robert le Warner.
At: Berkeley.

A1/19/36 [GC 2883]   Wed. after St. Peter in chains, 11 Edw. III [6 Aug. 1337]
Thomas de Berkelee, lord of Berkeley; and Thomas Top and Alice his wife.

Thomas has confirmed to Thomas and Alice, and Alice's issue, half of a messuage and 1 virgate of land which Thomas de Wyggewolde formerly acquired from Sir Thomas de Berkelee, his grandfather, in Coueleye and Hulmancote; rent half that paid by Thomas de Wyggewolde.
At: Berkeley.

Other

A1/19/37 [GC 1236]   n.d. [*temp.* Edw. I]
Thomas lord of Berkeleye and Maud daughter of Robert de Couele.

Thomas has granted to Maud the half-virgate which William ate Borgate formerly held in Couel', with all the appurtenances except the foreland; rent 21s. a year.
Witnesses: Peter de Styntescombe, Maurice de Camme, Henry de Camme, Robert de Draycote, William Birn', John de Hulmannecote, William de Corfgate.

A1/19/38 [GC 1686]   11 March 2 Edw. II [1309]
Thomas de Berkelee, lord of Berkeley, and his tenants of Coaley.

Thomas has granted to John de Hulemanecote, Thomas de Wiggewolde, Robert son of Elias de Stoke, John de Iweleye, and William de . . . and Maud his wife, free tenants, and to William le Rede and Henry atte Borgate, other tenants, for a term of . . . [50] years, . . . [meadow] at Hynham beside Coueleesbrok; to John, Thomas, Robert, John, William and Maud and their issue, and to William and Henry for life, rent 29s. a year.
Witnesses: Robert de Berkeley, Robert de Bradestone, Thomas de Beoelye, Thomas de Styntescombe, Walter Hathemare, Walter de Gosyntone, John le Duk.
At: Berkeley.

A1/19/39 [GC 1693]   Fri. the feast of St. Mark the evangelist, 2 Edw. II [25 April 1309]
Thomas de Berkelee, lord of Berkeley, and Walter son of Brounyng atte Wode.

Thomas has granted to Walter 1½ a. of land in Clyffelde, beside Throbburne, in Couelee; for life, rent 3s. a year.
Witnesses: Robert de Berkeley, Robert de Bradestone, Thomas de Beolee, Thomas de Styntescombe, John de Couelee, Robert Warner, Walter Hathemare.
At: Berkeley.

A1/19/40 [GC 3262]   n.d. [early 14th cent.]
Thomas de Berkeleye, lord of Berkeley, and William de Corfgathe.

Thomas has granted to William, his heirs and assigns 6½ a. 1 rood 20 perches of land and 1½ a. of meadow in the manor of Coueley; rent 15s. 6d. a year.
Witnesses: Robert de Coueleye, Thomas de Beoleye, Walter Hathermare, Elias le Botiler, John de Hulmanecote.

A1/19/41 [GC 1745]   Wed. the nativity of St. John the Baptist, 3 Edw. II [24 June 1310]
Sir Thomas de Berkeley, lord of Berkeley, and Robert atte Fischwere.

Thomas has granted to Robert 3½ a. 34 perches of land in the furlong called Lynch which Richard the miller (*molendinater*) previously held, in exchange for 1½ a. 32 perches of land in the field called Hulmanecotesfeld in Couelee; to him, Edith his wife and Isabel their daughter, for their lives, rent 2s. 3d. a year.
Witnesses: Robert de Bradestone, Robert de Berkelee, Robert le Warner, John de Couelee, William de Corgate.
At: Berkeley.

A1/19/42 [GC 1898; *a translation in 17th-cent. hand* GC 1989*; *duplicate* GC 1933]
                                                           24 Jan. 6 Edw. II [1313]
Thomas de Berkeley and his free tenants; and St. Peter's Abbey, Gloucester.

An agreement between Thomas and his free tenants [*named*] of Coueleye and Hulmancote, and the abbey, concerning common of pasture in the field called Southfeld, between the manors of Coueleye and Froucestre. [*In French*.]
At: Gloucester.

A1/19/43 [GC 1926]   1 June 6 Edw. II [1313]
Thomas de Berkelee, lord of Berkeley, and Robert le Wariner.

Thomas has granted to Robert all his land called Adegarescroft in the field called Schogworthy, which Walter Belamy, formerly vicar of Couelee, previously held of Thomas, in Couelee; to hold enclosed, to him and his issue, rent 2s. a year.
Witnesses: John de Coueleye, Henry de Camme, Stephen de Draycote, Walter Hathemare, John de Hulemanecote.
At: Berkeley.

A1/19/44 [GC 1938]   1 Aug. 7 Edw. II [1313]
Thomas de Berkelee, lord of Berkeley; and Thomas de Wyggewolde and Maud his wife.

   Thomas has granted to Thomas and Maud 6 selions of land in the field called Benhullesfeld; to them and their issue, rent 20*d.* a year.
Witnesses: John de Couelee, Robert Warner, Stephen de Draycote, Walter Hathemare, John de Hulmanecote.
At: Berkeley.

A1/19/45 [GC 2066]   7 Dec. 9 Edw. II [1315]
Thomas de Berkeleye, lord of Berkeley, and Walter of the mill (*de molend'*) of Coaley, clerk.

   Thomas has leased to Walter his meadow, garden, grove and croft called Grenemuydleye between Thomas's court of Coueleye and the mill of the said Walter; also the messuage with a curtilage and croft, 1 a. of land called Flodseteacre, 1 a. of land in the field called Northhamme and ½ a. of meadow in the meadow called Abboldesham, which Robert atte Forteye previously held of Thomas in villeinage, in Couelele; to Walter and his issue, rent 48*s.* a year, with licence to assart and enclose the garden and grove.
Witnesses: John de Coueleye, Robert le Warner, Stephen de Draycote, Walter Hathemare, John de Hulmanecote.
At: Berkeley.

A1/19/46 [GC 4106]   24 Feb. 24 Hen. VI [1446]
James Berkeley, lord of Berkeley, knight; and John Hurne, John Hals, Nicholas Gayner, John Kedyn, Robert Burgeys, Richard Herfordeshyre, Thomas Packer and John Brownyng.

   Indenture to testify that certain tenants of the manor of Cowley, viz. John, John, Nicholas, John, Robert, Richard, Thomas and John, having returned to the said lord James and paid the rent of Christmas last past, will hereafter be true tenants to James and his heirs. [*In English.*]

ADMINISTRATIVE DOCUMENTS

Coaley was often administered with Cam: see above, pp. 162–3.

A1/19/47 [GAR 97]   41–2 Edw. III [1367–8]
A1/19/48 [GRR 8]   n.d. [1368 × 1389]

THE HATHERMERE HOLDINGS
Stanfurlong and others

A1/19/49 [GC 1519]   n.d. [late Hen. III]
Amicia de Redmartun, widow, and Henry Hatemare of Cam.

   Amicia has granted to Henry 6 a. of land and 2 a. of meadow which her father gave to her in free marriage, of which 4 a. are called Stanforlong, 1 a. is called Brisacra and 3 selions in place of 1 a. in the same field, and 2 a. of meadow are called Medbreche; rent 2*d.* a year, and he has given her 9 marks.
Witnesses: Roger de Camme, Warin the butler (*pincerna*), W. de Kingeston, Robert de Dreicote, John de Egeton, John de Brotheston, W. the baker (*pistor*), W. de Gosinton, James Cotel.

A1/19/50 [GC 1315]   n.d. [late Hen. III]
Robert de Coueleye and Henry Hathemare.

   Robert has confirmed to Henry 6 a. of land and 2 a. of meadow in Couel', which Amicia de Redmartun, Robert's sister, in free widowhood granted to Henry, viz. 4 a. of land called Stanforlong, 1 a. called Briesacre and 5 selions (including one beside the pasture of Lady Joan de Berkeley), and 2 a. of meadow called Medbreche; rent to Amicia 2*d.* a year, and Henry has given him 1 mark.

Witnesses: Roger de Camme, Warin the butler (*pincerna*), William de Kingeston, clerk, Richard le Bruwer, William de Gosinton, William the baker (*pistor*), Walter de Corviet, Robert de Dreycote, James Cotel.

Other grants to Walter and Henry de Hathermere

A1/19/51 [SC 99]   n.d. [*temp.* John]
Richard de Couelege and Walter Hathemer.

Richard has granted to Walter 1 a. of land in Couelege, which lies opposite the cross of Apudupthrop in the field of Oldebiri; rent 6*d.* a year, and Richard has paid in acknowledgement 1 mark to Richard and 2*s.* to Richard's wife Maud.
Witnesses: Robert de Coulege, Varner the butler (*pincerna*), Walter de Benecumbe, James Cotele, John de Dreicote, Roger de Camme.

A1/19/52 [SC 145]   n.d. [*early 13th cent.*]
Henry son of Adam, chaplain of Coaley, and Walter Hathemer.

Henry has granted to Walter 1 a. of land in Couele at Oldeburi, viz. that lying between the land of Sir Thomas de Berkeley and David Ledbotare; rent 1*d.* a year, and Walter has paid 8*s.* in acknowledgement. Warranty by Henry and Henry his heir.
Witnesses: Sir Richard de Couele, Robert de Couele, Warin the butler (*pincerna*), John de Dreicote, James Cotele, Walter de Benecumbe, William Ulrich.

A1/19/53 [GC 414]   n.d. [*late Hen. III*]
David son of Walter le Plumber and Henry son of Walter Hathem' of Cam.

David has granted to Henry 3 a. in Couelee, viz. 1 a. between the land of Llanthony Priory and Henry, 1 a. between the lands of the lady of Wotton and Walter le Hackerman and 1 a. between the lands of Walter Hathem' and Walter le Hakerman; rent 1*d.* a year, and Henry has given David 2 marks.
Witnesses: Robert de Draycot, Robert de Couele, James Cotel, Warin le Botiler, Roger de Camme, William le Pestur, Walter de Coryethe, John de Hulmannecote, Alexander de Sumerford, clerk.

A1/19/54 [SC 360]   n.d. [*temp.* Hen. III]
Robert de Couelega and Walter Hathemer.

Robert has granted to Walter all his land in Hegelande of his demesne, at a rent of 2*d.* a year; in return for 30*s.* 8*d.* and a mare with her foal, value 10*s.*, and to Robert's wife Mary a pair of boots [*unas botas*], value 12*d.*
Witnesses: Richard de Couelege, Walter de Benethcombe, Peter de Ywele, Warin le Butiller, James Cotelle, William Marescal, Hugh the baker (*pistor*), John de Draicote, Roger de la Wdehend, Richard de Coruehete.

A1/19/55 [SC 359]   n.d. [*temp.* Hen. III]
James Cotell of Coaley, son of James Cotell, and Henry son of Walter Hathmere of Cam.

James has granted to Henry 16 selions of arable land in the field of Coueleye; rent 1*d.* a year, and Henry has given James 30*s.*
Witnesses: Robert de Coueleye, Robert de Draycote, Warin the butler (*pincerna*), Walter de Corfyet, Walter Hathemer, William the baker (*pistor*), Walter de Bennecumbe.

A1/19/56 [GC 1308]   n.d. [*temp.* Edw. I]
James Cotel of Coaley, son of James Cotel, and Henry Hathemare of Cam.

James has granted to Henry a portion of his land, viz. 16 selions in Couel' and 5 a. of land; rent ½*d.* a year, and Henry has given him 4 marks.
Witnesses: Robert de Couel, Robert de Draycote, Warin the butler (*pincerna*), Walter de Corvyet, Walter de Benecumbe, William the baker (*pistor*), Roger de Camme.

COALEY: ELMCOTE
THE BAKER HOLDING

A1/20/1 [SC 79]   n.d. [1190 × 1220]
Robert de Berkelay and St. Augustine's Abbey, Bristol.

Robert has granted to the abbey his servant Hugh the baker (*pistor*) and his heirs with the virgate of land at Hulemanecote for which Hugh pays a rent of 20*s.* a year, so that Hugh and his heirs can give to the canons two measures (*summae*) of corn for oblations and 10*s.* to buy wine every year at Michaelmas.

Witnesses: Roger son of Nicholas, Henry de Berkele, Adam son of Nigel, Simon de Olepenne, Richard de Couelege, John de Crauleigh, Elias de Bristoll, canon of Hereford, Henry and Adam, chaplains of Berkeley, John the chaplain, William the chaplain, Maurice son of Nigel, Richard de Cromhale, Elias de Slimbrugge, John de Egginton.

A1/20/2 [SC 339]   n.d. [1220 × 1243]
Thomas de Berkeley and St. Augustine's Abbey.

Thomas has granted to the abbey the rent of 20*s.* a year owed by Hugh the baker (*pistor*) for 1 virgate in Coaley with the appurtenances, which William de la Forcle held, and that of 5*s.* which Hugh son of Joel and Adam Chanterel owe for 3 burgages in Berkeley; further he has quitclaimed to the canons certain rents which the abbey owed to him, viz. a lamprey a year for land in Aldemunstre and 1 lb. of pepper a year for land in Berkeley which William Coby gave them; and he has confirmed rights of way in Berkeley.[1]

Witnesses: Sir William de Putot, Ralph de Wileton, Henry de Berkele, William de Berkele, Peter de Stintescumb, Master Hubert the bishop of Worcester's official, Roger de Andeure, rector of Cam, William dean of Arlingham, Arnulf de Berkele, clerk, John de Eginton, Walter de Sancto Jacobo, Adam Russel.

THE ELMCOTE HOLDING

A1/20/3 [GC 1083]   Sun. after Hilary, 33 Edw. I [17 Jan. 1305]
Thomas de Berkelee, lord of Berkeley, and John de Hulmanecot.

Thomas has rendered into the hands of John the croft of land which Walter Veysi, Thomas's villein, held at Hulmanecot, to render the same croft to Simon de Wendene, chaplain of the chapel of Slymbrugge, with 2 other crofts pertaining to the chapel, which John previously held, for 8¼ a. of land which Amicia de Hulmanecot, John's mother, gave in exchange to Sir Maurice de Berkelee, father of Thomas, for the said 3 crofts, and he has rendered to John the plot of land which Maurice retained at the time of the exchange with Amicia; and John has granted to Thomas the reversion of the croft which William le Rede and Edith his wife hold for their lives in Coueleye, which Amicia was granted by Maurice in exchange for the croft which Walter Veysi held at Hulmunecot; and John owes a rent of 3*s.* 9*d.* for the croft of Coueleye, for their lives; and Thomas has granted to John 6 a. of land below John's house at Hulmanecote in Coueleye; for his life, rent 3*s.* a year.

Witnesses: Robert de Bradestone, Thomas de Beoleye, Thomas de Styntescombe, Robert de Coueleye, William le Warner, Stephen de Draycot, Walter Hathemare, Richard de Estmede, Elias le Botyler, Walter de Gosynton, Walter de Porta, Roger Osbern, William le Muchele.
At: Berkeley.

A1/20/4 [GC 1092]   Sun. the feast of St. Ambrose, 33 Edw. I [4 April 1305]
Thomas de Berkelegh, lord of Berkeley, and John de Hulemanecote.

Thomas has granted to John, in fee, 1 a. of land in Oldelonde below Hulemanecote, which John previously held for life at a rent of 6*d.* a year, which rent Thomas has now remitted to him; for this John has rendered to Thomas a plot of land containing ¾ a. lying next to the king's highway to the park of Frompton. Further, Thomas has remitted to John a

---

[1] *Transcript*: *St Augustine's Cartulary*, no. 160.

rent of 9*d.* a year for a croft at Coueleye, which William le Rede and Edith his wife hold for their lives by grant of John, which reverts to Thomas on the death of William and Edith.
Witnesses: Robert de Bradeston, Thomas de Beolegh, Thomas de Styntescombe, Robert de Coulegh, William le Warner, Stephen de Draycote, Walter Hathemare, Richard de Estmede, Elias le Boteler, Walter de Gosinton, Walter de Porta, Roger Osbern, William le Muchele.
At: Berkeley.

CROMHALL

Cromhall was one of the detached portions of the hundred, lying a little south of the main body of the hundred. See also below, p. 291, Gossington.

CROMHALL RENTS

A1/21/1 [GC 718]   n.d. [late Hen. III]
Philip son of Bernard de Cromhal and Walter his son.
   Philip has granted to Walter all the land of Walter Hyrretmon, a rent of 4*s.* a year from the land which was of Richard the knight (*miles*) and a rent of 3*s.* a year from the land which Robert de Yuwelege held of Philip; rent a pair of white gloves or 1*d.* a year, and Walter has given him 40*s.*
Witnesses: John de Actun, William Mansel, Richard de Cromhale, Maurice de Saltmarsh (*de salso marisco*), John parson of Charfield, Alfred vicar of Tortworth, Alexander Colewith.

A1/21/2 [GC 1609]   n.d. [*temp.* Edw. I]
Walter de Cromhale, son of Philip de Cromhale, and Sir Thomas de Berkel'.
   Walter has granted to Thomas a rent of 6*s.* 1½*d.* in Cromhale, which he had by grant of Philip and of William de Cromhale, Walter's brother; Thomas has given him 6 marks.
Witnesses: Sir Robert le Veel, William de Wauton, Nicholas de Kingestone, Peter de Stintescumbe, William de Burgo, Robert de Bradeston, Thomas de Buleye.

OTHER

A1/21/3 [GC 2060]   12 Oct. 9 Edw. II [1315]
William Balon and Sir Thomas de Berkeleye, lord of Berkeley.
   William has granted to Thomas, his heirs and assigns all his lands, holdings, rents [etc.] in Cromhale.
Witnesses: Sir John Mautravers, Sir William de Wautone, knights, John son of Nichol, Thomas de Bradeston, Robert de Butlescoumbe, Walter de Nasse, William Gamage, John Capel, Walter Sewaker.
At: Cromhall.

A1/21/4 [GC 3267]   n.d. [mid 14th cent.]
Thomas lord of Berkelee; and Agnes wife of Robert Jurdan and Walter and William sons of Agnes and Robert.
   Thomas has granted to Agnes, Walter and William the holding which Robert previously held for his life in Cromhale; for their lives, at the customary rent.
Witnesses: John Sergeant the younger, John Capel, John Aleyn, Richard Corbet, Adam Pope.

DURSLEY

After the acquisition of Berkeley Herness by Robert FitzHarding, the original holders of the honour retained the manor of Dursley, which they held of the king in chief. A family distinct from the Berkeleys of Berkeley, the Berkeleys of Dursley were established at Dursley until they died out at the end of the 14th century.

MASON HOLDING

A1/22/1 [SC 26]   n.d. [*temp.* Hen. II]

Roger de Berkeley, son of Roger de Berkeley, and Reginald the mason (*mazo*) and Estrida his wife.

Roger has granted to Reginald and Estrida 3 a. of land and a burgage in Durseleg, of which 1 a. lies in Karswell, another in Wislade and the third above Wodemonecote, and the burgage lies near the mill of William son of Ota; rent 16*d.* a year at four annual terms.

Witnesses: Maurice de Berkeley, Robert his son, Elias Giffard, Philip, Eustace and Oliver, Roger's brothers, Ralph the butler (*pincerna*), Henry de Mumford, Robert de Sautem[ars], William de Planche, Adam son of Nigel, Richard de Couele.

A1/22/2 [GC 401]   n.d. [late Hen. III]

Nicholas son of Samson the mason (*mazo*) and Peter de Vike.

Nicholas has granted to Peter 3 a. of land in the manor of Durselege and a burgage in Dursleg'; of the 3 a., one lies at Karswelle, one in Wislade and one above Wodemanecote, and the burgage lies between the mill of Sir Odo son of William and the house of William the smith, to hold as in the charter of Roger de Berkele, son of Roger de Berkele, to Reginald the mason and Istrilda his wife; rent 1*d.*, and 16*d.* a year to chief lord of Dursleg'; acknowledgement 6 marks.

Witnesses: Thomas [?M]audut, steward, Sir Richard de Coulegh, Robert de la Plaunche, Peter de Yuelegh, James dean of Yueleg, Thomas the hunter (*venator*), Ralph de Brocuurthi, Henry de Wotton, John the fuller (*fullon'*), Gilbert Drake, William the whitesmith (*albus faber*), Walter the clerk, Herewic de Dodinton, Richard the clerk, Walter de Brocuurthi, Walter son of Hugh, Thomas the clerk, William the baker (*pistor*), William Ailrich.

A1/22/3 [SC 321]   n.d. [*temp.* Hen. III]

Alice widow of Samson Machun and Peter de Vike.

Alice has granted to Peter one third of the lands of her husband in Durseleg', which came to her in dower, for which Peter gave her [2] marks and 4*s.* in acknowledgement.

Witnesses: Thomas Mauduit, Sir Richard de Coueleg', Robert de la Planche, Peter de Yveleg', Roger de Camme, Thomas the hunter (*ven'r*), Ralph de Brocwurthe, John the fuller (*fullo*), Gilbert Drake, Richard the clerk.

ACQUISITION BY WILLIAM DE SYDE

A1/22/4 [GC 3333]   n.d. [mid 14th cent.]

Robert de Saintlo of Dursley and Sir William de Syde.

Robert has granted to William, his heirs and assigns the reversion of the holding which Agnes widow of Roger de Byberewe called le Tannare holds for life in Durseleye.

A1/22/5 [GC 1532]   n.d. [mid 14th cent.]

Robert de Saintlo of Dursley and Sir William de Syde.

Robert has quitclaimed to William the holding which Agnes widow of Roger de Byberewe holds for life in Durseleye.

OTHER

A1/22/6 [SC 374]   n.d. [*temp.* Hen. III]

Ralph Gule and Walter son of Henry [the minter (*monetarius*)].

Ralph has granted to Walter 6 a. from his free holding at . . . elega [Dursley]; rent 1 lb. of cumin a year.

Witnesses: . . . [Gilbert] the priest (*presbyter*) of Nibley (*Ni[b]lega*), Ralph de Durslega, Gervase de Bath, Swein de Bath, . . . , Geoffrey son of Sabilia.

A1/22/7 [GC 1440]   n.d. [1241 × 1245]
William Jussel and Alice his sister.

   William has granted to Alice the half-burgage in the vill of Duresl' which he bought from his brother Andrew, between the houses of John de Berkel' and of Cecilia, William's sister; rent ½d. to William and 6d. to the chief lord of the fee, and she has given him 12s.
Witnesses: Miles de Longetoht, Nicholas the reeve of Dursley, John de Berkel', Thomas Wenri, Richard the clerk, Walter de Brocworth.

A1/22/8 [GC 3798]   10 Nov. 9 Ric. II [1385]
Thomas de Berkeleye, lord of Berkeley, and John Copyner, son of Robert Copyner of Dursley.

   Thomas has granted to John, for his good and laudable service in the past and future, a half-burgage in Duresleygh and a burgage not built, 3½ a. of land in the field of Iweley and a rent of 12d. from the burgage in Duresleygh which Juliana Hathemere holds for life, with the reversion, which escheated to Thomas on the outlawry for felony of John Hathemere, son and heir of Robert Hathemere; for life, rent 12d. a year.
Witnesses: John Dybes, Robert Somynor, Walter Rawyn, Richard Tannere, John Wobbold.
At: Dursley.

ELBERTON

Elberton was a detached portion of Berkeley Herness. It was granted, with Beverston and King's Weston, by FitzHarding to his younger son Robert and passed to the Gurneys and then the ap Adams. It was bought from Thomas ap Adam in 1330 by Maurice de Berkeley of Stoke Giffard (d. 1347), younger son of Maurice (III) (d. 1326).[1] Maurice settled it in 1334 (below, A1/23/1) and it descended in the cadet line of Berkeley of Stoke Giffard.[2]

A1/23/1 [GC 2800]   17 Aug. 8 Edw. III [1334]
(1) Thomas lord of Berkeleye and William de Syde; (2) Robert Groundy; (3) Sir Maurice de Berkeleye.

   Thomas and William have appointed Robert to receive seisin in their names of the manors of Kyngeswestone and Ailbertone, as in the charter of Maurice.
At: Berkeley.

A1/23/2 [GC 4467*]   Eve of the Annunciation, 5 Hen. VII [24 March 1490]
William Berkeley of Gloucestershire, knight, and Thomas Marston, gentleman.

   William has granted to Thomas an annual rent of 40s. from the manor of Aylberton (Glos.); for his life.

HAM MANOR

BERKELEY ACQUISITIONS

Shockerwick ditch

A1/24/1 [GC 1546]   n.d. [late Hen. III]
William de Shokervith and Sir Maurice de Berkel'.

   William has quitclaimed to Maurice a ditch between Maurice's fishpond of Smethymor and William's meadow of Holemede.
Witnesses: Walter de Egeton, Geoffrey Neel, Robert de Egeton, Robert de Brothestan, Richard son of Alfred, John Sewaker, Thomas Cavel.

---

[1] *CPR* 1327–30, 507; PRO CP 25/1/77/57 no. 40.
[2] *CIPM* xviii, p. 409.

A1/24/2 [GC 427]   n.d. [early Edw. I]
William de Schokewich and Sir Thomas lord of Berkeley.

William has granted to Thomas his ditch outside Berkeley, between his meadow called Holemede and Thomas's fishpond; Thomas has given him 1 mark.
Witnesses: Robert de Br[othestan], Walter de Egeton, Thomas de Swonhongre, Thomas Aleyn, Henry de Weneswell, Geoffrey Neel.

Crawley rents and reversions

A1/24/3 [GC 1074]   Tues. in Michaelmas, 32 Edw. I [29 Sept. 1304]
John de Crawelegh and Sir Thomas de Berkelegh, lord of Berkeley.

John has granted to Thomas, for 10½ marks, an annual rent of 13s. from all his lands and holdings in the hundred of Berkelegh.
Witnesses: Robert de Bradestone, Robert de Berkelegh, Thomas de Beolegh, Thomas de Styntescombe, Robert Wyther, Walter de Nasse, John de Swonhungre.
At: Berkeley.

A1/24/4 [GC 1093]   Wed. in Easter week, 33 Edw. I [14 April 1305]
John de Craweleye and Sir Thomas de Berkelee.

John has granted to Thomas, for £9 4s., a rent of 9d. a year from John le Coppere for 19 a. of land and 1 a. of meadow, held for his life by John's grant in Hamme, a rent of 17d. a year from Walter Lacy for 9 a. of land and 2 a. of meadow, held in the same way, and a rent of 7d. from Philip Coby for 2 a. of land, held in fee, with the reversion of the lands held by John le Coppere and Walter Lacy.
Witnesses: Robert de Bradeston, Robert de Berkelee, Robert Wyther, Thomas de Styntescombe, John de Swonhungre, Richard de Avene, Robert Bastard, John Purlewent, Nicholas le Clerk of Pedington.
At: Berkeley.

A1/24/5 [GC 1320]   n.d. [c. April 1305]
John de Crawelee and Sir Thomas de Berkelee, lord of Berkeley.

John has quitclaimed to Thomas 10 a. of land called Manlond, in Bradestonesfelde, 9 a. of land and 1 a. of meadow which John le Cuppere holds for life with the rent of 9d. from the said land, 9 a. of land and 2 a. of meadow which Walter Lacy holds for life with the rent of 17d. from the said land and a rent of 7d. a year from 2 a. of land which Philip Coby holds in fee.
Witnesses: Robert de Bradeston, Robert de Berkelee, Thomas de Beolee, Robert Wyther, Thomas de Styntescombe, Henry le Gardener, Richard de Avene, Robert Bastard, John Porlewent.

A1/24/6 [GC 694]   n.d. [after 1305]
Thomas de Berkeleye, lord of Berkeley; and Gloucester Abbey and Stanley Priory.

Thomas has leased to the abbey and priory 10½ a. of land called Manlond, in the field called Bradestonesfeld in his manor of Hamme; rent 12s. a year.
Witnesses: Robert de Berkeleye, Robert de Bradeston, Thomas de Boeleye, Thomas de Styntescumbe, Henry de Camme, Stephen de Draycote, Robert de Coueleye, Robert le Warener, Walter Hathermare.

A1/24/7 [GC 1666]   Sat. the eve of Michaelmas, 2 Edw. II [28 Sept. 1308]
John de Craweleye; and Sir Thomas de Berkeley, his lord, and Lady Joan, Thomas's consort.

John has granted to Thomas and Joan all the rents and services of John le Vignour and Alice his wife for the lands which they hold of John in Hamme, with the reversion of 10 a. in the field called Newentoneshul after the death of John and Alice, and the reversion of the meadow called Worthyesmede, which lies between the field called Newentoneshul and the field called le Worthy, after the death of John.

Witnesses: Thomas de Styntescombe, Robert de Berkeleye, Thomas de Beoleye, Thomas de Stone, Thomas de Lorwynge, John de Swonhongre, Richard Olyver.

At: Berkeley.

A1/24/8 [GC 1678]   Sun. the feast of the Purification, 2 Edw. II [2 Feb. 1309]

Thomas de Berkelee, lord of Berkeley, and John le Cuppere and Maud his wife.

Thomas has granted to John and Maud 8½ a. 22 perches of land and 1½ a. 12 perches of meadow in 3 crofts (Luteleokworthy, Mucheleokworthy, and another), which he had by grant of John de Craweleye; further, the holding which Walter le Corder formerly held by the churchyard gate of Berkeley, with the appurtenances in Hamme and Berkeley; to them and their issue, rent during their lives 4*s.* 1*d.* a year and after their deaths 24*s.* a year.

Witnesses: Robert de Bradeston, Robert de Berkeley, Thomas de Beoleye, Thomas de Styntescoumbe, Thomas de Stone, Henry le Gardener, Roger le Cuppere.

At: Berkeley.

Gardener holdings

A1/24/9 [GC 1752]   Mon. the feast of St. Peter and St. Paul, 3 Edw. II [29 June 1310]

William called le Gardener of Berkeley and Sir Thomas de Berkelee, lord of Berkeley.

William has granted to Thomas his burgage and curtilage in the borough of Berkelee, all his land in Plaunkehulle, in Berclewode and in Wodewaldegrove, all his pasture in Pyneleshom in Hamme and all his land in Joelesaketres in Alkyntone.

Witnesses: Thomas de Stone, John Capel, Nicholas the clerk, Robert Bastard, John le Cuppere, Henry le Gardener, John Sewaker.

At: Berkeley.

A1/24/10 [GC 1753]   Mon. the feast of St. Peter and St. Paul, 3 Edw. II [29 June 1310]

William called le Gardener of Berkeley and Sir Thomas de Berkelee, lord of Berkeley.

William has quitclaimed to Thomas his pasture in Pynelesham next to the mill of the sacristan of St. Augustine's Abbey, Bristol, containing 63 perches, which he had by grant of William Pridy and Juliana his wife.

Witnesses: John le Cuppere, Henry le Gardener, John Sewaker, Roger le Cuppere, Adam Pynel.

At: Berkeley.

A1/24/11 [GC 1759]   Mon. the feast of St. Laurence, 4 Edw. II [10 Aug. 1310]

Thomas de Berkelee, lord of Berkeley; and Thomas son of Henry de Hamme and Maud his wife.

Thomas has granted to Thomas and Maud and their issue 1¼ a. 6 perches of pasture in Pyneleshom beside the mill of the sacristan of St. Augustine's Abbey, Bristol, which he had by grant of William le Gardener of Berkelee, in Hamme; rent 2*s.* a year.

Witnesses: John Capel, Robert Bastard, John le Cuppere, Henry le Gardener, Roger le Cuppere.

At: Berkeley.

A1/24/12 [GC 1836]   Thurs. before St. James, 4 Edw. II [22 July 1310]

William le Viegnor of Berkeley and Sir Thomas de Berkelee, lord of Berkeley.

William has granted to Thomas 1 a. of land in Plaunkehulle in Hamme; rent 3*d.* a year to St. Augustine's Abbey, Bristol.

Witnesses: John le Cuppere, Henry le Gardener, John Sewaker, Edward de Fromelode, Geoffrey Neel, Robert de Stanforde, Hugh de Costone.

At: Berkeley.

A1/24/13 [GC 1763]   Tues. the feast of St. Giles, 4 Edw. II [1 Sept. 1310]
Thomas de Berkelee, lord of Berkeley; and John le Schipward and Alice his wife.

   Thomas has granted to John and Alice 5¼ a. 4 perches of land which he had by grant of
William le Gardener and William le Viagnour of Berkelee, viz. one parcel in Berkelwode,
one in Wodewaldegrove, two in Plankehulle and one in Joelesaketre, in Hamme and
Alkyntone; to hold enclosed the parcel in Plankehulle, but not the others; to them and their
issue, rent 15s. a year.
Witnesses: Thomas de Stone, John Capel, Hugh de Costone, John le Cuppere, Henry le
Gardener, John Sewaker, Edward de Fromelode.
At: Berkeley.

Well croft and Pinels croft

A1/24/14 [GC 1722]   1 March 3 Edw. II [1310]
William Pridy and Juliana his wife; and Sir Thomas de Berkelee, lord of Berkeley.

   William and Juliana have granted to Thomas their croft called Wellecrofte, next to the
road of Pedyntone, and the croft of Joan widow of Bogo le Veel, 5 selions of land in the
furlong called Roulond, 3 selions in Tounmouneclyve, 3 selions in Hynegarstone, another
parcel of land above la Garstone, and ½ a. of meadow in Perhamesmore.
Witnesses: Robert de Berkelee, Robert de Bradestone, Thomas de Styntescombe, Thomas
de Beoleye, Robert Wyther, Robert Bastard, John Purlewent, John le Cuppere, Henry le
Gardyner.
At: Berkeley.

A1/24/15 [GC 1758]   Sat. the feast of St. James, 4 Edw. II [25 July 1310]
Thomas de Berkelee, lord of Berkeley; and Adam Pynel and Juliana his wife.

   Thomas has granted to Adam and Juliana, and their issue, the croft called Pynelescroft
which he had by grant of William Prydy and Juliana his wife, beside the land of Joan
widow of Bogo le Veel and the road from Hamme to Pedyntone, in Hamme; to hold
enclosed, rent 5s. 6d. a year.
Witnesses: John Capel, Nicholas the clerk, Nicholas Iweyn, John le Cuppere, Henry le
Gardener.
At: Berkeley.

Cupper holding

A1/24/16 [GC 1795]   St. Peter in cathedra, 4 Edw. II [22 Feb. 1311]
Maud widow of Robert le Coppare of Berkeley and Robert her son.

   Maud has granted to Robert all her holding in Hamme, beside the road to Berckel', of a
messuage, curtilage and 3 selions of land, also 1 a. of land in the field called Berclewode;
rendering the customary services to the chief lord, and to the hospital of Jerusalem for the
souls of Robert le Coppare and herself ½d. a year.
Witnesses: John le Coppare, Roger le Coppare, Richard Noblepas, Robert Bastard, Nicholas
Iweyn, John Purlewent, William Purlewent.
At: Ham.

A1/24/17 [GC 1956]   1 Dec. 7 Edw. II [1313]
Robert le Cuppere, son of the late Robert le Cuppere, and Sir Thomas de Berkelee, lord of
Berkeley.

   Robert has granted to Thomas his holding, viz. a messuage, curtilage and 3 selions of
land, which he had by grant of Maud his mother and by remise of John le Cuppere his
eldest brother, in Hamme.
Witnesses: Thomas de Stone, Thomas de Bradestone, John Capel, John With, William
Purlewent.
At: Berkeley.

Avery lands, rents and reversions

Framilode and Coston rents and reversions in Dolefield and Cobys lease

A1/24/18 [GC 1972]   Tues. the feast of St. George, 7 Edw. II [23 April 1314]
Robert Averay of Berkeley and Hugh de Costone.

   Robert has leased to Hugh 2 a. of land in Dolfeldeshulle in Hamme; to Hugh and Alice his wife, for their lives.
Witnesses: Robert de Stanforde, William Hert, John Sewaker, Edward de Fromilode, Thomas le Meleward.
At: Berkeley.

A1/24/19 [GC 2022]   10 March 8 Edw. II [1315]
Robert Averay; and Edward de Fromilode and Edith his wife.

   Robert has leased to Edward and Edith 6 selions of land in the field called Dolfelde in Hamme; for their lives, rent [. . .]d. [*figure cut out*].
Witnesses: Walter Sewaker, John le Serjant, Robert de Stanforde, William Gylemyn, John Sewaker.
At: Berkeley.

A1/24/20 [GC 1908]   Easter Day, 8 Edw. II [23 March 1315]
Robert Averay; and Edward de Fromilode and Edith his wife.

   Robert has leased to Edward and Edith 10 a. of land in Hamme in the field called Dolfeld; to hold enclosed, for their lives, rent 3d. a year.
Witnesses: Walter Sewaker, John le Serjant, Robert de Stanforde, William Gylemyn, John Sewaker.
At: Berkeley.

A1/24/21 [GC 2256]   1 Nov. 12 Edw. II [1318]
Robert Averay and Sir Thomas de Berkeleye, lord of Berkeley.

   Robert has granted to Thomas, his heirs and assigns 6½ a. of land in the field called Dolfelde in Hamme, a rent of 22d. a year from Edward de Fromelode and his heirs for a messuage and enclosure which Ralph, Edward's father, formerly had by grant of Alfred le Schipward, Robert's grandfather, a rent of 2s. a year from Edward and Edith his wife for a plot of land which they hold for life, with the reversion of the land, a rent of 3d. a year from Edward and Edith for 13½ a. of land in the field of Dolfelde which they hold for life, with the reversion of the land, and the reversion of 2 a. of land in the same field after the death of Hugh de Costone and Alice his wife.
Witnesses: John le Serjant, Walter Sewaker, John Capel, John Wyth, John le Cuppere, John Abbod, John Sewaker.
At: Berkeley.

A1/24/22 [GC 2345]   1 April 14 Edw. II [1321]
Thomas de Berkelee, lord of Berkeley; and John Abbod and Isabel his wife.

   Thomas has granted to John and Isabel 6½ a. of land in the field called Dolefeld, enclosed, which he had by grant of Robert Averay, in Hamme, and the pasture called Cobyeslese by Wyke containing 6¼ a., in Hamme; for their lives, rent 22s. a year.
Witnesses: John le Serjaunt, John Capel, John Wyth, Thomas de Craweleye, William Capel, Henry le Gardener, Edward de Fromelode.
At: Berkeley.

A1/24/23 [GC 2352]   16 May 14 Edw. II [1321]
Denise widow of Richard de Wyke and Sir Thomas de Berkelee, lord of Berkeley.

   Denise has quitclaimed to Thomas 6¼ a. pasture called Cobyeslese by Wyke, in Hamme.

Witnesses: John le Serjaunt, John Capel, John Wyth, Thomas de Craweleye, William Capel.
At: Berkeley.

A1/24/24 [GC 2884]   4 Aug. 11 Edw. III [1337]
Thomas lord of Berkele and William Capel.

Thomas has granted to William 7 a. of land and meadow, which John Abbot recently held for his life, in Hamme, called Cobyeslese; for his life, rent 13*s.* 4*d.* a year.
At: Berkeley.

Abbot and Cupper rents and reversions in Berkeley Wood and West Field

A1/24/25 [GC 1943]   Sat. in Michaelmas, 7 Edw. II [29 Sept. 1313]
Robert Averay and John called Abbod.

Robert has leased to John all his land in Berklewode in two plots, which John Averay his brother previously held of him, in Hamme; for life, rent 12*d.* a year.
Witnesses: John Capel, John de Swonhungre, John le Cuppere, Henry le Gardener, John Sewaker, Roger le Cuppere, Edward de Fromelode.
At: Berkeley.

A1/24/26 [GC 1944]   Sat. in Michaelmas, 7 Edw. II [29 Sept. 1313]
Robert Averay; and John called Abbod and Helen daughter of John de Porteshevede.

Robert has leased to John and Helen all his land in Berklewode in two plots, which John Averay his brother previously held of him, in Hamme; for their lives, rent a rose a year.
Witnesses: John Capel, John de Swonhungre, John le Coppere, Henry le Gardiner, John Sewaker, Roger le Cuppere, Edward de Fromelode.
At: Berkeley.

A1/24/27 [GC 2213; *duplicate* GC 2214]   Epiphany, 11 Edw. II [6 Jan. 1318]
Robert Averay of Berkeley; and John called Abbod and Maud his daughter.

Robert has leased to John and Maud his land in Bercklewode lying in two parcels, which John his brother previously held of Robert, in Hamme; for their lives, rent 6*d.* a year.
Witnesses: John le Serjaunt, John Capel, John le Coppere, John Sewaker, Roger le Coppere, Nicholas Neel, Edward Fromylode.
At: Berkeley.

A1/24/28 [GC 2889]   Tues. the feast of St. Katherine, 11 Edw. III [25 Nov. 1337]
Maud daughter of John Abbot and William Capel.

Maud has granted to William 2 a. of land in the field called Berklewode in Hamme; for her life, rent 12*d.* a year.
Witnesses: Robert Groundy, John de Lorewynge, John Sewaker, William Gillemyn, William de Swonhungre.
At: Berkeley.

A1/24/29 [GC 1953]   Thurs. the feast of St. Cecilia, 7 Edw. II [22 Nov. 1313]
Robert Averay of Berkeley; and John le Coppere of Berkeley, Isabel his daughter and John his son.

Robert has leased to John, Isabel and John 7 selions of land in the field called Westfelde; for their lives, rent a rose a year.
Witnesses: John Sewaker, Edward de Fremelode, Thomas the miller (*molendinar'*), Roger le Cuppere, Hugh le Proute.
At: Berkeley.

A1/24/30 [GC 2301]   Thurs. the feast of St. Valentine, 13 Edw. II [14 Feb. 1320]
Robert Averey of Berkeley and Sir Thomas de Berkeleye, lord of Berkeley.

Robert has granted to Thomas, his heirs and assigns a rent of a rose a year from John Abbod and Maud his daughter for the life of John, and 6*d.* a year from Maud after the death of John, for two parcels of land in Berkelewode, with the reversion of the land; also a rose a year from John le Cuppere and John his son for 7 selions of land in the field called Westfeld, which they hold for their lives, with the reversion of the land.

Witnesses: John le Serjaunt, John Capel, John Wyth, John Sewaker, John le Cuppere, Henry le Gardiner, Edward de Fromelode.

At: Berkeley.

A1/24/31 [GC 2467] Thurs. the feast of St. John before the Latin Gate . . . [6 May 1339?]
Maud daughter of John Abbod and William Capel.

Maud has quitclaimed to William . . . and also the land which Henry de Modybrok . . . while she lives.

Witnesses: Robert Groundy, John le Schipward, Henry de Modybrok . . .

At: Berkeley.

A1/24/32 [GC 2951] 1 June 13 Edw. III [1339]
Thomas lord of Berkeleye and William Capel.

Thomas has leased to William the land in Berklewode in two parcels, viz. that which John Abbod and Maud his daughter acquired from Robert Averay for their lives, in the manor of Hamme; for William's life, for the customary services.

Witnesses: John Serjaunt, John Capel, John de Melkesham, John de Eggetone, John Lorwyng.

At: Berkeley.

Hooper rent

A1/24/33 [GC 1525] All Saints, 33 Edw. I [1 Nov. 1305]
Robert son and heir of Richard Averay of Berkeley; and Thomas le Hopere, Alice his wife and John their son.

Robert has granted to Thomas, Alice and John a plot of land with trees; for their lives, rent 2*s.* a year, and they have given him a certain sum of money; and within 2 years after All Saints, 33 Edw. I, Thomas will build on the plot a house which Robert will roof.

Witnesses: Thomas le Serjant, Richard le Serjant, Thomas de Lorwenge, Philip Coby, Walter le Cuppere, Nicholas Coby, Walter the clerk.

A1/24/34 [GC 2421] 1 June 7 Edw. II [1314]
Robert Averay and Sir Thomas de Berkelee, his lord.

Robert has granted to Thomas a rent of 2*s.* a year from Thomas le Hopare, Alice his wife and John their son for the holding which they hold of Robert for their lives, with the reversion of the holding, in Homme.

Witnesses: John le Cuppere, Henry le Gardener, John Sewaker, Roger le Cuppere, John le Vignour, John le Schippard, Edward de Fromelode.

At: Berkeley.

Miller and Page rents in Berkeley Wood, and associated holdings

A1/24/35 [GC 1790] The Purification, 4 Edw. II [2 Feb. 1311]
Robert Averay of Berkeley and John the miller (*molen'*) of Berkeley.

Robert has leased to John all the land which Agnes le Schypward held in dower in the furlong called Yondereberclewode, viz. 3 selions, 3 butts of land and a parcel of pasture, near the fishpond of Smethemor; for their lives, and they have given him a certain sum of money.

Witnesses: John le Coppere, Henry le Gardiner, John Sewaker, John le Vyngnur, Richard Noblepas, Edward de Fromylode.

At: Berkeley.

A1/24/36 [GC 2021]   5 March 8 Edw. II [1315]
Robert Averay; and John le Meleward of Berkeley, Joan his first wife and John their eldest son.

Robert has granted to John, Joan and John 15 selions of land in the field called Yondereberclewode, by the fishpond of Smethemor, 13 selions in the field called Lutleberclewode, 3 selions in the same field, 5 selions in the field called Ochungre in the furlong called Oxenhamme and ½ a. of meadow in the meadow called Holemed, in Hamme; to them for their lives, rent 10*d.* a year for the life of John [the elder] and after his death 12*d.* a year from Joan and John [the younger].
Witnesses: John le Cuppere, John Sewaker, Henry le Gardyner, Robert Bastard, Robert Groundy.
At: Berkeley.

A1/24/37 [GC 2204]   Thurs. the morrow of St. Clement, 11 Edw. II [24 Nov. 1317]
Robert Averay; and William Page and Isabel his wife.

Robert has granted to William and Isabel, for their lives, 1 a. of land in the field of Berkelewode in Homme by Berkelee, between the road to the east and the fishpond called Smethemor to the west; rent ½*d.* a year.
Witnesses: John Serjaunt, John de Alkeleye, John Cuppare, Richard Serjaunt, John de Egetone.
At: Berkeley.

A1/24/38 [GC 2333]   Tues. the feast of St. Katherine, 14 Edw. II [25 Nov. 1320]
Robert Averay of Berkeley and Sir Thomas de Berkeleye, lord of Berkeley.

Robert has granted to Thomas, his heirs and assigns an annual rent of 10*d.* from John the miller (*molendinar'*) for his life and 12*d.* a year from his son John for his life, for the lands which they hold for the term of their lives by grant of Robert, with the reversion of the lands, viz. 15 selions of land with pasture in the field called Yondereberkelewode, 13 selions and 2 butts in the field called Lutleberkelewode, 5 selions and a fore-earth in the field called Ochungre in the furlong called Oxenham and ½ a. of meadow in the meadow called Holemede, in Hamme; also an annual rent of ½*d.* from William Page and Isabel his wife for 1 a. of land which they hold for their lives by lease of Robert, with the reversion of the land, in the field called Berkelewode, in Hamme.
Witnesses: John le Serjaunt, John Capel, John Wyth, John de Lorewynge, Thomas de Craweleye, William Capel, Edward de Fromelode.
At: Berkeley.

Avery hall and Purlewent rent

A1/24/39 [GC 2419]   Tues. after St. Gregory, 18 Edw. II [19 March 1325]
Robert Averay of Berkeley and Richard Averay his brother.

Robert has granted to Richard, his heirs and assigns a part of his hall with a plot of land, also 4 selions of his curtilage, and the reversion of the lands, holdings and rents which ought by right to come to Robert and his heirs.
Witnesses: John Capel, Nicholas Iweyn, John Sewaker, Robert Bastard, John Purlewent, Nicholas Neel, Edward de Fromylode.
At: Ham.

A1/24/40 [GC 575]   The nativity of St. John the Baptist, 18 Edw. II [24 June 1325]
Richard son of Richard Averay of Berkeley; and Nicholas le Vyngnur of Berkeley and Christine his wife.

Richard has leased to Nicholas and Christine the messuage with a plot and 4 selions of

land lying next to Berkeley which Richard had by gift of Robert Averay his brother, with the rent of 2*d.* from John Purlewent; for 10 years; rent 3*s.* 1*d.* a year.
Witnesses: John Capel, Nicholas Iweyn, Nicholas the clerk, John Sewaker, Adam Pynel.
At: Ham.

A1/24/41 [GC 3516]   n.d. [mid 14th cent.]
Richard Averay and Sir Thomas lord of Berkelee.

Richard has granted to Thomas, his heirs and assigns a messuage with a curtilage, which was the principal messuage of Robert his brother in Hamme, and an annual rent of 2*d.* from John Purlewent in the same vill.
Witnesses: William de Chiltenham, John de Clyve, John Wyth, John Sergeant, John Capel.

The Lockington holding

A1/24/42 [GC 2841]   Morrow of Palm Sunday, 10 Edw. III [25 March 1336]
Joan daughter of John de Lokyntone and Sir Thomas lord of Berkeley.

Whereas Thomas is bound to Joan in £20 by a bond to be paid at Christmas next, Joan grants that if Thomas makes one of her daughters a nun within a year of the present date the bond shall be void. [*In French.*]
At: London at Baynard's Castle in the parish of St. Andrew.

A1/24/43 [GC 2843]   27 March 10 Edw. III [1336]
Joan daughter of John de Lokynton and Sir Thomas lord of Berkeleye.

Joan has acknowledged all the holdings which Sir Thomas de Berkeley, lord of Wollaston, holds for life in Berkeleye and Hamme of her inheritance, to be the right of Sir Thomas lord of Berkeleye, and that after the death of Thomas of Wollaston the holding will revert to Thomas lord of Berkeleye. [*In French.*]
At: Berkeley.

Capel exchange

A1/24/44 [GC 3288]   n.d. [mid 14th cent.]
John Capel the elder and Sir Thomas lord of Berkeleye.

John has granted to Thomas 2 a. of land in Hamme in exchange for 2 a. of land in the same vill.
Witnesses: John le Serjaunt, Thomas de Swonhongre, Robert Groundi, John de Lorwynge, John Purlewent.

A1/24/45 [GC 3261]   n.d. [mid 14th cent.]
Thomas lord of Berkeleye and John Capel the elder.

Thomas has granted to John 2 a. of land in Hamme in exchange for 2 a. in the same vill; to hold enclosed, to John and his issue, with remainder to William Capel the elder and his issue, Walter Capel and his issue, and John Serjaunt the younger and his issue.
Witnesses: John le Serjaunt, Thomas de Swonhongre, Robert Groundy, John Lorwynge, John Purlewent.

Juddesmoor

A1/24/46 [GC 4067]   Mon. after Epiphany, 13 Hen. IV [11 Jan. 1412]
William Wallere and Richard Rycard.

William has granted to Richard, his heirs and assigns a parcel of meadow containing 4 a. called Joddesmore within the manor of Hamme.
Witnesses: Thomas Staunton, Richard Egeton, John Everard, William Gylmyn, Thomas ate Nelme.
At: Berkeley.

A1/24/47 [GC 4085]   Fri. the feast of the nativity of St. Mary, 1 Hen. V [8 Sept. 1413]
Richard Ricard and Thomas Berkeley, lord of Berkeley.

Richard has granted to Thomas, his heirs and assigns a parcel of meadow containing 4 a. called Joddesmore in the manor of Hamme.

Witnesses: Thomas FitzNichol, knight, Robert Poyns, John Grevel, John Rolves, Thomas Stauntone.

At: Berkeley.

Other acquisitions and grants

A1/24/48 [SC 160]   n.d. [1219 × 1220]
Robert de Berkeley, son of Maurice de Berkeley, and St. Augustine's Abbey, Bristol.

Robert has granted to the abbey the services of his mill at Berkeley, near to the bridge called Locfastebrige, also called the New Mill, with the custom and multure of Berkeley Castle, for the maintenance of a lamp; also 1 virgate of land in Ham near the said mill, viz. the half-virgates once held by Reginald the ploughman (*carucarius*) and by Alfred de Sindelford, for prayers and the maintenance of two lamps.[1]

Witnesses: Sir Nicholas Poinz, Sir Hugh his son, Sir Adam son of Nigel, Sir Thomas de Berkeley, Sir Simon de Olepenna, Henry the chaplain, Maurice son of Nigel, Richard and Philip de Hauberton.

A1/24/49 [SC 211]   n.d. [early Hen. III]
William son of Eustace the butler (*pincerna*) of Berkeley and Sir Thomas de Berkelay.

William has quitclaimed to Thomas a half-virgate of land in Ham, which Sewi once held and which Sir Robert de Berkelay gave to Eustace his father.

Witnesses: Henry de Berkelay, William de Berkelay, Richard de Coueleg', Richard de Lukinton, Robert son of Richard, Peter de Stintescumbe, Thomas de Tiringham, John de Eggentun, Arnulf the clerk, Jordan . . . ., Alexander de London.

A1/24/50 [SC 140]   n.d. [early 13th cent.]
Simon de Olepenna and Sir Thomas de Berkeley.

Simon has sold to Thomas two rents, one of 4*s.* a year from John de Eggeton for half a virgate of land in Abbewelle, the other of 16*d.* from Jordan de Waneswelle and William de Abbewelle for 2 a. of meadow in Bulewik; for which Thomas gave him 4 marks and pays 1*d.* a year.

Witnesses: Henry de Berkeley, William de Berkeley, Peter de Stintescumbe, Nicholas Rufus, Robert . . ., Elias the butler (*pincerna*), Arnulf the clerk.

A1/24/51 [GC 281]   Easter 35 Hen. III [16 April 1251]
Sir Maurice de Berkeley and Thomas Cavel.

Maurice has granted to Thomas 2 a. 10 perches land in the field of Alylond in exchange for all the land and appurtenances which Thomas had in the field called la Wurthy.

Witnesses: Peter de Wyk, John Sewaker, Adam Coby, Alfred Mariner, Robert Bastard, Robert le Herde.

A1/24/52 [GC 282]   Easter 35 Hen. III [16 April 1251]
Maurice de Berkeley and Robert Marescall.

Maurice has granted to Robert 1½ a. of land in Alylond in exchange for all his land with appurtenances in la Wurthy.

Witnesses: Peter de Wyke, Adam Cobi, John Sewaker, Alfred Mariner, Robert Bastard, Robert le Herde.

---

[1] *Transcript*: *St Augustine's Cartulary*, no. 145.

A1/24/53 [GC 1468]   n.d. [early Edw. I]
Alexander called de Loundres and Sir Thomas de Berkeley, his lord.

Alexander has granted to Thomas rents of 11*d.* a year from various tenants [*named*], in the manor of Hamme; Thomas has given him 6*s.* 8*d.*
Witnesses: Sir William Daubeny, Sir Roger de Lokinton, knights, Bartholomew de Olepenne, Robert de Stone, Robert de Bratheston, Thomas Serjant, Thomas Alayn.

A1/24/54 [GC 2571]   n.d. [late 13th cent.]
Robert de Bradestan and Sir Thomas de Berkel'.

Robert has granted to Thomas a rent of 2*s.* from John de Craweleye for lands and holdings formerly of William de Mettesdone in Hamme; and for this Thomas has remitted to Robert 2*s.* of the rent of 5*s.* which he pays for his lands and holdings at Bradeston in Chamme.
Witnesses: Robert de Stane, John de Egetone, Maurice de Chamme, Henry de Chamme, Thomas de Beoleye, Robert Wyther, Thomas de Swonhongre.

A1/24/55 [GC 1033]   Sun. the feast of St. Martin, 30 Edw. I [11 Nov. 1302]
Nicholas Iweyn of Pedington and Sir Thomas de Berk', his lord.

Nicholas has quitclaimed to Thomas whatever he has in Thomas's fields of Pedimersch and Banmersch in Hamme, and has granted that Thomas may enclose the said fields and hold them in severalty, and has quitclaimed common of pasture in his meadow of Honymed in Hamme from the Purification [2 Feb.] to Michaelmas [29 Sept.] each year.
Witnesses: . . . Robert de Berk', Thomas de Beolee, Thomas de Swonhungre, Nicholas the clerk, Robert Bastard.
At: Berkeley.

A1/24/56 [GC 1740]   26 May 3 Edw. II [1310]
Adam Pynel and Sir Thomas de Berkelee, lord of Berkeley.

Adam has granted to Thomas a rent of 1*d.* which came to him after the death of Robert Pynel, his father, from Richard de Wendene and Maud his wife for a holding in Hamme.
Witnesses: Robert de Bradestone, Robert Wyther, John Purlewent, Robert Bastard, John Capel, Nicholas the clerk, William Nortlone.
At: Berkeley.

A1/24/57 [GC 2146]   The Purification, 10 Edw. II [2 Feb. 1317]
Thomas de Berckel', lord of Berkeley; and Nicholas of the vine (*de vinea*), clerk, and Alice his wife.

Thomas has granted to Nicholas and Alice and their issue ½ a. of meadow in Matforde, beside the rhine called Matfordeshee, and a rent of 2 lb. of cumin which they ought to render for their holding in Hamme; and for this, Nicholas has granted to Thomas 1¾ a. of land in Oxenehome in Hamme.
Witnesses: Robert de Budescombe, Robert Wyther, Roger de la Garstone, Richard de Avene, John le Serjaunt, Walter Sewaker, John Capel.
At: Berkeley.

A1/24/58 [GC 2171]   12 May 10 Edw. II [1317]
John Capel and Sir Thomas de Berkeleye, lord of Berkeley.

John has granted to Thomas, his heirs and assigns 50 perches of land in the field called Pedymers', between Thomas's land and the road from Hamme to the mill of St. Augustine's Abbey, Bristol, in Hamme; and Thomas has released to John a rent of 6*d.* in exchange.
Witnesses: Roger de la Garstone, Walter Sewaker, Roger Archer, William le Golde, William de Kyneltre, William le Gryp, William Purlewent.
At: Berkeley.

A1/24/59 [GC 2565]   n.d. [early Edw. III]
William de Wauton, knight, and Sir Thomas lord of Berkeleye.

   William has granted to Thomas, his heirs and assigns all his lands, holdings, rents [etc.]
in Berkeleye, Hamme and Cloptone.
Witnesses: John Capel, John Milkesham, John de Egetone, William de Burgo, John
Purlewent.

A1/24/60 [GC 2863]   Wed. before St. Laurence, 11 Edw. III [29 Jan. 1337]
Thomas lord of Berkelee and Kingswood Abbey.

   Thomas has granted to the abbey 1 a. 1 rood 32 perches of land in Hamme in the field of
Rye, in exchange for 1 a. 1 rood 32 perches of land in the same vill.
At: Berkeley.

A1/24/61 [GC 4224]   28 Jan. 20 Hen. VI [1442]
James Berkeley, lord of Berkeley, knight, and John Phelypp ap Morgan.

   James has granted to John, for his good and laudable service, an annual rent of 60*s.* from
the manor of Appelrugge, one of 5 marks from a messuage lately of John Edward at
Clopton and one of 6*s.* 8*d.* from the manor of Hamme; for his life.
At: Berkeley Castle.

A1/24/62 [GC 4327]   11 Oct. 4 Edw. IV [1464]
William Lord Berkeley, knight, and Jane widow of James late Lord Berkeley, William's
father.

   Whereas William, by an indenture dated 4 March last past, granted to Jane an annual rent
of £40 for her life from the manor of Hamme (Glos.), of which £16 for the terms of the
Annunciation [25 March] and the nativity of St. John the Baptist [24 June] is unpaid,
beyond the £10 due to her now at Michaelmas [29 Sept.], Jane will take £15 at Christmas
next, and £15 at the Annunciation following, and £16 at the nativity of St. John the Baptist
following. [*In English.*]

A1/24/63 [GC 4431]   13 Dec. 22 Edw. IV [1482]
William Berkeley, Viscount Berkeley, and Joan his wife; and Thomas Berkeley, esquire, his
brother.

   William and Joan have granted to Thomas, for his good and laudable service, an annual
rent of £19 for Thomas's life, viz. £6 13*s.* 4*d.* from the manor of Wotton under Egge and
£12 6*s.* 8*d.* from the manor of Hamme.

BERKELEY LEASES
Peter de Wick

A1/24/64 [GC 868]   n.d. [late Hen. III]
Maurice lord of Berkel' and Peter de Wyke.

   Maurice has granted to Peter 3 a. of meadow in the moor [*mara*] above Longebrugge,
next to the stream of the the moor, in exchange for all his meadow in Perham; rent 12*d.* a
year.
Witnesses: Sir Maurice de Saltmarsh (*de salso marisco*), Sir Roger de Lokinton, Sir Walter
de Burgo, knights, John de Egeton, Robert Bastard, Robert le Herde, Adam Flamberd,
Adam Coby, Alfred Mariner, Nicholas de Coldewell.

A1/24/65 [SC 283; *duplicates* SC 284 *and* SC 285]   Ascension Day 28 Hen. III
                                                                   [12 May 1244]
Sir Maurice de Berkele and Peter de Wike.

   Maurice has leased to Peter for 6 years his land in the fields called Stapeling, Smalmor
and Oldefrihtgorst, with pastures lying between Walhamgarston and the lake called
Bradeflech, and between Stapeling field and the king's highway to Newenton, except the

portion of land which belongs to his mother, Joan de Berkele, by right of dower; rent, half the crop.

Witnesses: Sir Maurice de Saltmarsh (*de salso marisco*), William Mauduit, Roger de Lokinton, Richard de Cromhale, William de Aubemarle, Ralph Musard, Walter de Burgo, Robert de Hales, steward, Andrew de Bratheston, John de Egeton, Thomas Mathias.

A1/24/66 [GC 1205]   n.d. [late Hen. III]

Maurice de Berkel' and Peter de Wike.

Maurice has granted to Peter 24 a. of land in the field called Frythgorste lying between the land of Reginald le Shypward and the middle of the ditch of Walhamgarstone; to him and his heirs by Joan de Doghton his wife, rent 12*s.* a year, and Peter has given him 6 marks.

Witnesses: Sir Maurice de Saltmarsh (*de salso marisco*), Maurice de Stan', John de Brotheston, Adam Coby, John Sewaker, Alfred Mariner, Robert le Herde, William son of Eustace, Thomas Mathyas, Nicholas de Coldewell, Robert Bastard, Walter Sely, clerk.

Ashleworth holding in the Heath

A1/24/67 [GC 869]   n.d. [late Hen. III]

Maurice de Berkel' and Thomas de Asshelworth.

Maurice has granted to Thomas 7 a. of land in the manor of Hamme, next to the road between the new ditch and Bradeflet; rent 2*s.* 11*d.* a year, and Thomas has given him one bezant.

Witnesses: Sir Maurice de Saltmarsh (*de salso marisco*), Sir Warin de Raleyg, knights, Peter de Wika, Nicholas de Crauleg', John de Brotheston, Master Philip de Leycestre, Adam Coby, John Sewaker, Robert Bastard, Maurice de Stan', Adam Motun, Thomas de Wike, Walter Sely, clerk.

A1/24/68 [GC 871]   n.d. [late Hen. III]

Maurice lord of Berkel' and Thomas de Ahsseleworth.

Maurice has granted to Thomas 24 a. of land between Bradefleth and the heath (*bruera*) towards Egeton, saving the road to the spring; rent 10*s.* a year, and Thomas has given him 20*s.*

Witnesses: Sir Maurice de Saltmarsh (*de salso marisco*), Sir Roger de Lokinton, Sir Walter de Burgo, knights, Master William de Thaney, Maurice's steward, Master Philip de Leycestre, Peter de Wyke, Richard de Wyke, John de Egeton, William son of Eustace, Adam son of Nigel, Robert Bastard, Adam Flambard, Maurice de Stan', Walter Sely, clerk.

A1/24/69 [SC 387]   n.d. [*temp.* Hen. III]

Thomas Matthias and Sir Maurice de Berkeley.

Thomas has quitclaimed to Maurice, his lord, the land which Thomas de Asselworth holds in Maurice's close in the heath (*bruera*) next to Bradeflet.

Witnesses: John de Egeton, William son of Eustace, Maurice de Stanes, Peter de Wyk, Adam son of Nigel, Master Philip de Leycestre, Walter Sely, clerk.

Holding late of Adam Coby

A1/24/70 [SC 471]   Wed. the feast of St. Katherine, 33 Edw. I [25 Nov. 1304]

Thomas de Berkeley, lord of Berkeley; and Henry le Gardiner and Isabel his wife.

Thomas has granted to Henry and Isabel and Henry's issue 4¾ a. of meadow and 1 a. of arable land lying in four plots in Stokeshull field, of the holding which was of Adam Coby, in Ham; rent 6*s.* 6*d.* a year.

Witnesses: John de Crawelee, John de Swonhongre, Thomas de Lorewynge, Geoffrey Neel, Robert Averey, Robert Bastard, Nicholas Iweyn.

At: Berkeley.

A1/24/71 [GC 1076]   Wed. the feast of St. Katherine, 33 Edw. I [25 Nov. 1304]
Thomas de Berkelee, lord of Berkeley; and Edward de Fremelode and Edith his wife.

Thomas has granted to Edward and Edith 3 a. of land in 3 parcels in the field called Westfeld in the place called Lordeshull, of the holding which was of Adam Coby, in Hamme; to them and Edward's issue, rent 6s. 6d. a year.
Witnesses: John de Crawelee, John de Swonhungre, Thomas de Lorewyng, Geoffrey Neel, Robert Averay, Robert Bastard, Nicholas Iweyn.
At: Berkeley.

A1/24/72 [GC 1077]   Wed. the feast of St. Katherine, 33 Edw. I [25 Nov. 1304]
Thomas de Berkelee, lord of Berkeley; and William de Modibroc and Helen his wife.

Thomas has granted to William and Helen 3¼ a. 30 perches of land in 2 plots in the field called Okhungre next to Boggethorn, of the holding which was of Adam Coby, in Hamme; to them and William's issue, rent 5s. a year.
Witnesses: John de Crawelee, John de Swonhungre, Thomas de Lorewyng, Geoffrey Neel, Robert Averay, Robert Bastard, Nicholas Iweyn.
At: Berkeley.

A1/24/73 [GC 1097]   6 May 33 Edw. I [1305]
Thomas de Berkel', lord of Berkeley, and William aten Abbeye.

Thomas has granted to William half of the meadow called Holemed, which was of Adam Coby, in Hamme; to him and his issue, rent 5s. 6d. a year.
Witnesses: Robert de Berk', Robert de Bradestone, John de Swonhungre, Thomas de Lorewynge, John le Cuppere, Philip Coby, Henry le Gardiner, Walter le Cuppere, Roger le Cuppere.
At: Berkeley.

Sewacres
A1/24/74 [GC 3887]   Sat. after the Assumption, 18 Ric. II [16 Aug. 1394]
Thomas de Berkeley, lord of Berkeley; and Thomas Frye and Anne his wife.

Thomas has leased to Thomas and Anne, for Thomas Frye's good service, his lands and holdings called Sewacres within Berkeley and Hamme, and also all his land in Horsmersche and elsewhere; for their lives, rent the old rent for Sewacres and 1d. a year for the other.
Witnesses: Ralph Waleys, John Rolves, William Smalcombe, Richard Egton, John Egtone, smith.
At: Berkeley.

A1/24/75 [GC 4030]   St. Thomas the apostle, 10 Hen. IV [21 Dec. 1408]
Thomas Berkeley, lord of Berkeley; and Thomas Staunton and Amicia his wife.

Thomas has leased to Thomas and Amicia, for Thomas Staunton's good service, all his lands and holdings called Sewacres within Berkeley and Hamme, and also all his land in Horsmersch, and 1 a. of land in Stodefeld; for their lives, at the customary rent for Sewacres and 1d. a year for the other.
Witnesses: John Rolves, Thomas Kendale, Richard Ectone, John Archer, Henry Gosyngton, John FitzRobert.
At: Berkeley.

A1/24/76 [GC 4237]   20 Nov. 22 Hen. VI [1443]
James Berkeley, lord of Berkeley, knight, and John son of John Wythe.

James has demised at farm to John, and his first wife and eldest son, a messuage in Berkeley called Sewacresplace with all the appurtenant lands [etc.] and 3 a. of meadow in the meadow called Parham; for their lives, rent 40s. a year.
At: Berkeley Castle.

Villein land

A1/24/77 [GC 1742]   Thurs. in Ascension, 3 Edw. II [28 May 1310]

Thomas de Berkelee, lord of Berkeley; and Margaret atten Elme and William her son.

Thomas has granted to Margaret and William the half-virgate with a foreland which Walter atten Elme and Margaret previously held in villeinage in Hamme; for their lives, rent 20s. a year.

Witnesses: Robert de Bradestone, Robert de Berkelee, Thomas de Boelee, Thomas de Styntescombe, Thomas de Stone, John de Swonhongre, Robert de Stanford.

At: Berkeley.

A1/24/78 [GC 2133]   1 Dec. 10 Edw. II [1316]

Thomas de Berkeleye, lord of Berkeley, and John Abbod.

Thomas has granted to John 1 a. of meadow in the meadow of Longebrugge, which Richard Imeke previously held of Thomas in villeinage, in Hamme; to him and his issue, rent 4s. a year.

Witnesses: John Capel, John le Serjaunt, John de Swonhungre, John Wyth, John le Cuppere, Henry le Gardener, William de Kyneltre.

At: Berkeley.

A1/24/79 [GC 2357]   1 June 14 Edw. II [1321]

Thomas de Berkelee, lord of Berkeley; and Margaret atten Elme, William her son and Agnes his wife and William their son.

Thomas has leased to Margaret, William, Agnes and William the half-virgate with a foreland and appurtenances which Walter atten Elme and Margaret formerly held of Thomas in villeinage in Hamme; to Margaret for life, with remainder to William, Agnes and William for their lives, rent 20s. a year.

Witnesses: Thomas de Bradeston, Thomas de Craweleye, Richard le Serjaunt, John le Serjaunt, John Wyth, William Gylemyn, Hugh de Costone.

At: Berkeley.

Other

A1/24/80 [SC 166]   n.d. [c. 1220]

Thomas de Berkele and William son of Osbert the parker (*parcarius*).

Thomas has given and confirmed to William the land which Osbert his father held of Robert, Thomas's brother, and of himself, and 1 a. of meadow in Perhamesmor; rent 5s. 7d. a year, and William has given 2 oxen to Thomas and a talent to Thomas's wife Joan in acknowledgement.

Witnesses: Peter de Stintescumbe, Thomas de Tyringeham now steward, Robert son of Maurice, Ralph de Stanes, Arnulf the clerk, John de Eggeton, Robert son of Walter de Hineton.

A1/24/81 [SC 288]   Easter, 32 Hen. III [19 April 1248]

Maurice de Berkeley and St. Augustine's Abbey.

Maurice has granted to the abbey common of pasture in Walmegerston for 24 oxen, 7 sows, 1 boar and their offspring of one year old; further, . . .

Witnesses: Sir Richard de Cromhall, Sir Roger de Lukinton, Sir Maurice de Saltmarsh (*de salso marisco*), Alan de Hales, Thomas the serjeant (*serviens*) de Berkeley, Thomas Matthias, John de Eggeton, William the marshal (*marescallus*).

A1/24/82 [SC 312]   n.d. [c. 1250]

Sir Maurice de Berkeley and St. Augustine's Abbey.

In exchange for 8½ a. 6 perches of arable land and 2½ a of meadow, Maurice has granted to the abbey 5¼ a. 20 perches of arable land and 2 a. of meadow [*individually described*].[1]

---

[1] *Transcript*: *St. Augustine's Cartulary*, no. 171.

Witnesses: Sir Maurice de Saltmarsh (*de salso marisco*), Sir Roger de Lokinton, Sir Walter de Burgo, knights, Peter de Wik, Richard de Wik, Maurice de Stanes, Thomas Mathias, Adam Coby, Ralph Dangervile, Robert Bastard.

A1/24/83 [SC 351]   n.d. [*temp.* Hen. III]
Maurice de Berkeley and Sir Nicholas vicar of Berkeley.

Maurice has granted to Nicholas 19 a. of land in the field called la Frythegorst, of which 12 a. lie between the land which Peter de Wike holds of him and the road from Berkeley to Brathestone and 7 a. lie between the land of Thomas Cavel and the cross of Bradeflete; rent 9*s.* 6*d.* a year, and Nicholas has given him 4 marks.
Witnesses: Sir Maurice de Saltmarsh (*de salso marisco*), Sir Henry de Baylol, Sir Henry de Berkele, knights, Peter de Wik, William son of Robert, Thomas the serjeant (*serviens*), William de Mathem, John de Egeton, Thomas Mathias, Thomas Cavel, Henry de Egeton, John Sewake, Robert le Herde, Walter Sely.

A1/24/84 [SC 352]   n.d. [*temp.* Hen. III]
Maurice lord of Berkeley and Alfred le Skypward.

Maurice has granted to Alfred all the land in Ochungre which Walter Dole sometime held, next to the road to Shonhongre, in exchange for other land there. Endorsed: *Hyneton*.
Witnesses: Adam Coby, John Sewak', Adam son of Nigel, Robert le Herde, William Gust', Thomas the serjeant (*serviens*).

A1/24/85 [GC 870]   n.d. [late Hen. III]
Maurice lord of Berkeleg' and Thomas the serjeant (*serviens*).

Maurice has granted to Thomas 3¼ a. of land in the field called Worthlond towards Suonhungre between the land of Richard Everard and the land called Alilond and next to the gateway which leads from Berkel' to Suonhungre; rent 10*d.* a year, entry fine 3½ marks.
Witnesses: Sir Maurice de Saltmarsh (*de salso marisco*), John de Bradeston, Peter de Wyke, William Mauduch of Billow (*Beley*), Nicholas de Crauleg', Adam Cobi, John Sewaker.

A1/24/86 [GC 692]   n.d. [*temp.* Edw. I]
 Sir Thomas de Berkeleye and Roger le Cuppare of Berkeley.

Thomas has leased to Roger 1 a. of arable land in the field called Ochungre between the land of Peter son of Warin and Juliana de la Slo and between the land of Alexander Dole and Gilbert de Haleyate, in exchange for 1 a. in the enclosure of Juliana de la Slo called Truelgarstone which Roger leased to Thomas; and Roger will pay to Thomas a rent of 12*d.* a year.
Witnesses: Thomas le Serjant, Richard de Avene, Richard de Wyke, Richard de Wenden, John Sewaker.

A1/24/87 [GC 995]   Fri. after St. Barnabas, 28 Edw. I [17 June 1300]
Thomas de Berkeleye, lord of Berkeley, and John le Cuppere.

Thomas has leased to John a ditch called Mordych running from Pedymers' to Perhamesthron with a parcel of pasture; to hold as Adam Purlewent held it, for life, rent 6*s.* a year, and Thomas has reserved the right to dig in the ditch and carry away earth to improve his land.
Witnesses: Robert de Bradeston, Thomas de Swonhungre, Robert Wyther, Richard de Wenden, Robert Bastard, William son of Robert, Nicholas Iweyn.
At: Berkeley.

A1/24/88 [GC 454]   Fri. in Michaelmas, 1 Edw. I [29 Sept. 1307]
Thomas de Berkelegh, lord of Berkeley, and Roger le Cuppere.

Thomas has granted to Roger 3 a. of land which Isabel de Berkeley, his aunt, previously held in the field called Ochungere, with appurtenances, in Hamme; to Roger and Isabel his wife and their issue, rent 6*s.* a year.

Witnesses: Robert de Berkeleye, Thomas de Beoleye, Robert de Stanford, Geoffrey Neel, Richard le Serjaunt, Thomas de Lorewynge, William de Keneltre.

At: Berkeley.

A1/24/89 [GC 453]   Fri. in Michaelmas, 1 Edw. I [29 Sept. 1307]
Thomas de Berkeleye, lord of Berkeley, and William le Smale.

Thomas has granted to William the holding which he previously held for life of Isabel de Berkeleye, Thomas's aunt, in Hamme; to William, Isabel his wife and their issue, rent 7*s.* a year.

Witnesses: Robert de Berkeleye, Robert de Bradeston, Robert Wyther, Robert Bastard, Robert de Stanford.

At: Berkeley.

A1/24/90 [GC 1676]   Sun. the feast of the Purification, 2 Edw. II [2 Feb. 1309]
Thomas de Berkeley, lord of Berkeley; and Richard Olyver and Joan his wife.

Thomas has granted to Richard and Joan 6 a. of land in the field called Lokkedoune, which Richard de Wendene formerly held, in Hamme; rent 7*s.* a year.

Witnesses: Robert de Bradestone, Robert de Berkeley, Thomas de Beoleye, Thomas de Lorwynge, Robert Stanford, Geoffrey Neel, Nicholas Neel.

At: Berkeley.

A1/24/91 [GC 1711]   Fri. before the nativity of St. Mary, 3 Edw. II [5 Sept. 1309]
Thomas de Berkelee, lord of Berkeley, and Alan Skot.

Thomas has granted to Alan the croft which Nicholas atte Slo previously held, and a building plot, in Hamme; to him and his issue, rent 2*s.* a year for his life, and after his death 3*s.* 4*d.* a year.

Witnesses: Roger de la Garstone, Walter Sewaker, Nicholas Iweyn, Robert Bastard, John Purlewent.

At: Berkeley.

A1/24/92 [GC 1738]   22 May 3 Edw. II [1310]
Thomas de Berkelee, lord of Berkeley, and Adam Pynel.

Thomas has granted to Adam a small building plot beside his house, measuring 1 by ½ perch; to Adam and Juliana his wife and their isse, rent 1*d.* a year.

Witnesses: John le Cuppere, Roger le Cuppere, Henry le Gardin', John le Schipward, William Iweyn, John the miller (*molend'*), John Page.

At: Berkeley.

A1/24/93 [GC 1754]   Mon. the feast of St. Peter and St. Paul, 3 Edw. II [29 June 1310]
Thomas de Berkelee, lord of Berkeley; and Roger le Cuppere and Isabel his wife.

Thomas has granted to Roger and Isabel all the meadow called Amyeshom lying between the field called la Worthy and the stream called la [Ee] in Hamme; for their lives, rent 18*s.* a year.

Witnesses: Robert Bastard, Nicholas Iweyn, John le Cuppere, Henry le Gardener, John the miller (*molend'*).

At: Berkeley.

A1/24/94 [GC 1764]   Mon. in the Exaltation of Holy Cross, 4 Edw. II [14 Sept. 1310]
Thomas de Berklee, lord of Berkeley; and Robert Bastard and Joan his wife.

Thomas has granted to Robert and Joan and their issue 1 selion of land in Lakemerchs, which he had by grant of Philip Coby of Berkelee, in Hamme; rent 2*s.* 6*d.* a year.

Witnesses: Thomas de Stone, John Capel, William Purlewent, Henry le Gardener, John Sewaker.
At: Berkeley.

A1/24/95 [GC 1810]   1 April 4 Edw. II [1311]
Thomas de Berkelee, lord of Berkeley; and William Heort and Mabel his wife.

Thomas has granted to William and Mabel ½ a. 4 perches of land between his holding and the road, in Homme; to hold enclosed, to them and their issue, rent 9*d.* a year.
Witnesses: Thomas de Stone, John Capel, John Waifer, Robert de Stanford, Matthew Hatholf, John le Frig.
At: Berkeley.

A1/24/96 [GC 1910]   20 April 6 Edw. II [1313]
Thomas de Berkelee, lord of Berkeley; and Robert le Gardener and Alice his wife.

Thomas has granted to Robert and Alice the land in Plankehulle which they previously held, in Hamme; to them and their issue, with remainder to Henry, Robert's brother, and his issue, rent 10*d.* a year.
Witnesses: John le Cuppere, Henry le Gardener, John Sewaker, Roger le Cuppere, John le Schippard.
At: Berkeley.

A1/24/97 [GC 1957]   1 Jan. 7 Edw. II [1314]
Thomas de Berkelee, lord of Berkeley, and William son of William le Frigg of Ham.

Thomas has granted to William 3 selions of land containing 42 perches in Hamme; to him and his issue, rent 20*d.* a year.
Witnesses: John Capel, Robert Bastard, Nicholas the clerk, Nicholas Iweyn, William Purlewent.
At: Berkeley.

A1/24/98 [GC 2189]   Thurs. in Michaelmas, 11 Edw. II [29 Sept. 1317]
Thomas de Berkeleye, lord of Berkeley, and Alan Skot.

Thomas has granted to Alan custody of the mill which John le Muleward and Joan his wife, recently deceased, held of Thomas in the vill of Hamme, with the lower garden, Mulecroft and Alrenesgrove, and with the suit of all the villeins of Hamme and Hynetone, and the millpond, until the full age of William, son and heir of John and Joan, rendering the same services as John and Joan.
Witnesses: John Capel, Walter Sewaker, William Capel, John Wyth, John Abbod.
At: Berkeley.

A1/24/99 [GC 2825]   Trinity Sunday, 9 Edw. III [11 June 1335]
Thomas de Berkeleye, lord of Berkeley; and John le Cuppere and Alice his wife.

Thomas has granted to John and Alice 3 a. of land which Walter le Cuppere previously held in the field called Hokhongre, in Hamme; to them and their issue, rent 6*s.* a year.
Witnesses: John de Clyve, John Wyth, William Curteys, John Capel, John de Egeton.
At: Berkeley.

A1/24/100 [GC 3121]   Thurs. before St. Barnabas, 19 Edw. III [9 June 1345]
Thomas de Berkeleye, lord of Berkeley; and Robert Lyndeweye, clerk, and Walter his brother.

Thomas has leased to Robert and Walter a croft of land called Alysaundresrudynge which was of William de Wauton, knight, in Hamme; for their lives, rent 2*s.* a year.
Witnesses: John Serjaunt the younger, John Capel, John Purlewent, William son of Robert, Richard Adames.
At: Ham.

A1/24/101 [GC 3264]   n.d. [mid 14th cent.]
Thomas de Berkelee; and John de Fromylode and Alice his wife.

Thomas has leased to John and Alice and their issue 1 a. of land in Homcroft in Hamme; rent a rose a year, with remainder to John's son Edward and his issue and to John's assigns for a term of 100 years.
Witnesses: John Serjaunt, John Purlewent, Henry de Egetone, John ate Boure, John Bastard.

A1/24/102 [GC 3921]   The Annunciation, 20 Ric. II [25 March 1397]
Thomas de Berkley, lord of Berkeley, and William Caulegh, his esquire.

Thomas has granted to William, for his good services, a plot with adjacent land and with a watermill appurtenant in the vills of Wodeforde, Alkyngtone and Hamme, which Ralph Cook previously held by grant of Thomas for his life, and also a holding in Berkley in the street called Chirchelone which Ralph previously held; for life, rent a crossbow bolt [*catapulta*] a year.
At: Berkeley.

A1/24/103 [GC 4188]   St. George, 13 Hen. VI [23 April 1435]
James Berkeley, lord of Berkeley; and John Somere of Pedington and Thomas Somere, his son.

James has leased to John and Thomas the reversion of a pasture in Hamme called la Worthy, which John Eddewardes holds; for their lives, rent 28s. 4d. a year.
At: Berkeley Castle.

A1/24/104 [GC 4235]   15 Oct. 22 Hen. VI [1443]
James Berkeley, lord of Berkeley, knight; and John Legge of Ham and Elizabeth his wife.

James has leased to John and Elizabeth the reversion of a messuage and enclosure which Thomas Herbarde and his wife Isabel hold in Hamme, after their deaths; for the lives of John and Elizabeth, rent the same as Thomas and Isabel.
At: Berkeley Castle.

A1/24/105 [GC 4260]   26 Oct. 22 Hen. VI [1443]
James Berkeley, lord of Berkeley, knight; and William Brystowe of Ham and Edith his wife.

James has leased to William and Edith the fishery in the Severn at le Throwre, which John Greyell of Hamme lately held; for their lives, rent 12d. a year.
At: Berkeley Castle.

A1/24/106 [GC 4246]   22 April 23 Hen. VI [1445]
James Berkeley, lord of Berkeley, knight, and David Jenkyns *alias* David Legge.

James has leased to David the reversion of a messuage and half-virgate of land and the other parcels of land which Thomas Rycardes holds and which John Legge held in Hamme, after the death or surrender of Thomas; for David's life, rent the same as Thomas.

A1/24/107 [SC 612]   20 June 5 Edw. IV [20 June 1465]
William Lord Berkeley; and Maurice Kynge and Juliana his wife.

William has leased to Maurice and Juliana, for their lives, the messuage and fardel of land which Agnes Boure held, with a foreland and pastures called Nethirmede and Pedemersch, and parcels of land called Cattemersh, Oldmere and Longerugge; rent 7s. yearly.

ADMINISTRATIVE DOCUMENTS
Manorial account rolls

A1/24/108 [GAR 100]   14 April to 1 Aug. 9 Edw. I [1281]
A1/24/109 [GAR 101]   14–15 Edw. I [1286–7]
A1/24/110 [GAR 102]   Michaelmas 17 to 19 June 18 Edw. I [1289–90]

A1/24/111 [GAR 103]	21–2 Edw. I [1293–4]
A1/24/112 [GAR 104]	24–5 Edw. I [1296–7]
A1/24/113 [GAR 105]	25–6 Edw. I [1297–8]
A1/24/114 [GAR 106]	26–7 Edw. I [1298–9]
A1/24/115 [GAR 107]	27–8 Edw. I [1299–1300]
A1/24/116 [GAR 108]	30–1 Edw. I [1302–3]
A1/24/117 [GAR 109]	2–3 Edw. II [1308–9]
A1/24/118 [GAR 110]	3–4 Edw. II [1309–10]
A1/24/119 [GAR 111]	10–11 Edw. II [1316–17]
A1/24/120 [GAR 112]	15–16 Edw. II [1321–2]
A1/24/121 [GAR 113]	16–17 Edw. II [1322–3]
A1/24/122 [GAR 114]	17–18 Edw. II [1323–4]
A1/24/123 [GAR 115]	18–19 Edw. II [1324–5]
A1/24/124 [GAR 116]	18–19 Edw. II [1324–5]
A1/24/125 [GAR 117]	19–20 Edw. II [1325–6]
A1/24/126 [GAR 118]	20 Edw. II to 1 Edw. III [1326–7]
A1/24/127 [SR 42]	Michaelmas 20 Edw. II to Michaelmas 1 Edw. III [1326–7]
A1/24/128 [GAR 119]	2–3 Edw. III [1328–9]

Two rolls; Michaelmas to St. Maurus [15 Jan.] and St. Maurus to Michaelmas.

A1/24/129 [GAR 120]	6–7 Edw. III [1332–3]
A1/24/130 [GAR 121] Scribal error in heading.	7–8 Edw. III [1333–4]
A1/24/131 [GAR 122]	9–10 Edw. III [1335–6]
A1/24/132 [GAR 123]	11–12 Edw. III [1337–8]
A1/24/133 [GAR 124]	13–14 Edw. III [1339–40]
A1/24/134 [GAR 125]	17–18 Edw. III [1343–4]
A1/24/135 [GAR 126]	20–1 Edw. III [1346–7]
A1/24/136 [GAR 127]	21–2 Edw. III [1347–8]
A1/24/137 [GAR 128]	22–3 Edw. III [1348–9]
A1/24/138 [GAR 129]	23–4 Edw. III [1349–50]
A1/24/139 [GAR 130]	24–5 Edw. III [1350–1]
A1/24/140 [GAR 131]	26–7 Edw. III [1352–3]
A1/24/141 [GAR 132]	27–8 Edw. III [1353–4]
A1/24/142 [GAR 133]	28–9 Edw. III [1354–5]
A1/24/143 [GAR 134]	29–30 Edw. III [1355–6]
A1/24/144 [GAR 135] Two rolls attached at the head.	35–6, 39–40 Edw. III [1361, 1365]
A1/24/145 [GAR 136]	36–7 Edw. III [1362–3]
A1/24/146 [GAR 137]	37–8 Edw. III [1363–4]
A1/24/147 [GAR 138]	47–8 Edw. III [1373–4]
A1/24/148 [GAR 139]	48–9 Edw. III [1374–5]
A1/24/149 [GAR 140]	49–50 Edw. III [1375–6]
A1/24/150 [GAR 141]	50 Edw. III to 1 Ric. II [1376–7]
A1/24/151 [GAR 142]	1–2 Ric. II [1377–8]
A1/24/152 [GAR 143]	2–3 Ric. II [1378–9]

A1/24/153 [GAR 144]	3–4 Ric. II [1379–80]
A1/24/154 [GAR 145]	4–5 Ric. II [1380–1]
A1/24/155 [GAR 146]	5–6 Ric. II [1381–2]
A1/24/156 [GAR 147]	7–8 Ric. II [1383–4]
A1/24/157 [GAR 148]	8–9 Ric. II [1384–5]
A1/24/158 [SR 48]	9–10 Ric. II [1385–6]
A1/24/159 [GAR 149]	10–11 Ric. II [1386–7]
A1/24/160 [GAR 150]	11–12 Ric. II [1387–8]
A1/24/161 [GAR 151]	12–13 Ric. II [1388–9]
A1/24/162 [GAR 152]	12–12 Edw. IV [*sic*] [1472]

Rentals

A1/24/163 [GRR 13]	4 Edw. II [1310–11]
A1/24/164 [GRR 12]	n.d. [*temp.* Edw. II]
A1/24/165 [GRR 11]	1 Ric. II [1378]

Rental with, attached, (i) copy of three charters of hospital of St. Katherine of Robert de Berkeley and his brother Thomas de Berkeley; (ii) memorandum of the leased demesne.

A1/24/166 [GRR 9]	May 10 Hen. IV [1409]
A1/24/167 [GRR 10]	n.d. [*temp.* Hen. VI]

Extents

A1/24/168 [GMR 27]	13 Edw. I [1285]
A1/24/169 [GMR 26]	n.d. [*temp.* Edw. II]

Court roll

A1/24/170 [GCR 8]	21 Sept. 6 Hen. V [1418]

Court of Richard Beauchamp, earl of Warwick, and Elizabeth his wife.

Charter rolls

A1/24/171 [SR 16]	Hen. III to Hen. V

Abstracts of charters relating to the manor of Ham, begining with no. 7 and continuing to no. 256; top and bottom missing.

A1/24/172 [SR 15]	Hen. III to Hen. V

Brief abstracts of charters relating to the manor of Ham, with current holders and rents.

THE STONE HOLDING

The large holding of Robert de Stone at the end of the 13th century passed briefly to his grandson Thomas de Stone. Thomas died in 1316 leaving two daughters, who married John Serjeant and John de Saniger respectively. The Serjeant purparty passed through a series of heiresses while the Saniger portion remained in that family until it passed to the Thorpes, by marriage to an heiress, *c.* 1400. Other lands were held by the Stone, Serjeant and Saniger families elsewhere in the hundred.

Partition of Stone lands

A1/24/173 [GC 2678]	1 May 3 Edw. III [1329]

John son of John de Swonhungre and Alice his wife; and John son of John Serjant and Joan his wife.

Covenant between John and Alice on the one part, and John and Joan on the other, daughters and heirs of Thomas de Stone, for the partition of lands in Stone, Nether Stone, Wodeford. [*In English, 15th-cent. translation.*]

At: Berkeley.

A1/24/174 [SR 132] [late 15th cent.]
Pedigree reciting descent from Robert de Stone, lord of Wanswell and Stone, through his son Thomas and Thomas's two daughters Joan and Alice to the mid-15th century.

The Serjeant purparty

A1/24/175 [GC 2169] 6 May 10 Edw. II [1317]
Thomas de Bradeston and John son of Richard le Serjaunt.

Thomas has granted to John the custody of the lands of the late Thomas de Stone, Thomas's brother, at Wanneswelle in the field called Burifeld, until the legal age of the heir or heirs of Thomas [de Stone].
Witnesses: John Capel, John de Swonhongre, John Wyth, William Capel, John Abbod, Thomas de Craweleye, Henry le Gardener.
At: Breadstone.

A1/24/176 [GC 3542] Sun. after the nativity of St. John the Baptist, 37 Edw. III
[25 June 1363]
John Sergeaunt of Stone and Walter Oldelonde.

John has granted to Walter his capital messuage at Waneswelle, with the croft [etc.] which he inherited after the death of his father; to Walter and his male issue, rent 20*s*. a year.
Witnesses: William Capel, John Aleyn, William Modbroke, Henry Egetone, John Draycote.
At: Berkeley.

A1/24/177 [GC 3865] Two weeks after Easter, 15 Ric. II [28 April 1392]
Thomas Norton, chaplain, and William Shawe, chaplain; and Edmund Forde and Joan his wife.

Copy of final concord (made one week after the Purification, 15 Ric. II [9 Feb. 1392]) concerning 9 messuages, a toft, 2 carucates and 100 a. of meadow, 15 a. of pasture, 10 of wood, 40*s*. rent and half of a toft in Stone, Hamme, Alkynton, Waneswell, Falefeld and Nubbeley and the advowson of the chantry of St. Mary in Stone; Edmund and Joan have acknowledged the right of Thomas and William, and they have given £100 to Edmund and Joan.
At: Westminster.

A1/24/178 [GRR 31] Thurs. after St. Katherine, 23 Hen. VI [26 Nov. 1444]
Rental of tenants of Joan Greyndour made for the information of the bailiff for taking the acknowledgements of the tenants at the fourth term.

The Saniger purparty

In Ham
A1/24/179 [GC 4163] 11 Sept. 8 Hen. VI [1429]
John Thorpp of Wanswell by Berkeley; and John Wyth of Berkeley parish, Isabel his wife and John their son.

John Thorpp has leased to John Wyth, Isabel and John 11 parcels of land containing 62 selions in the field called Walmegarstone; for their lives, rent 9*s*. 8*d*. a year.
Witnesses: John Oldelond, Walter Toyt, Richard Ricard.
At: Berkeley.

A1/24/180 [GC 4255] 25 Nov. 9 Hen. VI [1430]
John Thorpp; and Maurice Browne, Margery his wife and John their son.

John has leased to Maurice, Margery and John the reversion of a holding at Wyke with a dovecot, after the death of William Browne and Agnes his wife, and a croft called Redecroft, a croft called Stapelone, an enclosure called Frethegastone beside the road called Frethegastonyslane [etc.]; for their lives, rent 22*s*. a year.

Witnesses: Richard Ecton of Berkeley, John Taylour, John Dyar the elder, John Bowyar, John Trebelle.

At: Berkeley.

A1/24/181 [GC 4338**]   31 Jan. 6 Edw. IV [1467]

John Thorppe and Agnes Kyng, widow of the late Richard Kyng of Berkeley.

John has leased to Agnes a messuage with a curtilage and a parcel of meadow beside the curtilage and other parcels of meadow called Holmede, and 1 selion of land in the field called Nokeshull and 1 selion in the field called Berkelewode; for her life, rent 4*s*. 4*d*. a year.

Witnesses: Richard Clavyle, Robert Ricardis, William Barbur.

At: Berkeley.

A1/24/182 [GC 4357*]   4 Oct. 9 Edw. IV [1469]

Richard Thorppe of Wanswell; and John Rycardus and Richard and Robert his sons.

Richard has leased to John, Richard and Robert a pasture called Buschylese between the road from the Severn to Newport, and the lane called Wynemulfeld lane; for their lives, rent 10*s*. a year. [*In English*.]

Witnesses: John Hervy, Robert Rycardus, Henry Strongge, Robert Herne, Maurice Russell.

At: Wanswell.

In Saniger

A1/24/183 [GC 3386]   20 April 26 Edw. III [1352]

William de Swonhongre and William le Panyter, son of William Oldelynch.

William de Swonhongre has leased to William le Panyter and his first wife a messuage with a curtilage and garden and two crofts called Homcroftes, which Matthew de Oulepenne sometime held, and other lands in Swonhongre, and two staithes in the Severn for burrocks [i.e. fish-traps], from which William de Swonhungre is to have all the fish caught on Fridays; for their lives, rent 6*s*. 8*d*. a year and 40*s*. a year during the life of the wife if she survives William le Panyter.

Witnesses: Henry de Egetone, John Serjaunt, John atte Boure, John Fraunceys, John in the Hurne.

At: Saniger.

A1/24/184 [GC 3446; *a late 15th-cent. copy* GC 4438]   Sun. after Easter, 30 Edw. III
                                                               [1 May 1356]

William Swonhungre, brother and heir of Thomas Swonhungre of Wanswell; and John Neel and Agnes his wife.

William has inspected a charter of John Swonhungre, his father, son and heir of John Swonhungre, to John son of Isolda Neel, Isabel his wife and John their son leasing to them his holding which Isolda Neel formerly held in Swonhungre; for their lives, rent 10*s*. a year; and he has confirmed it to John son of John son of Isolda and Agnes his wife and their issue.[1]

Witnesses: John Serjaunt, John Capel, John Draicote, Henry de Egetone, Thomas Payn, John Bil.

At: Berkeley.

A1/24/185 [GC 3709]   11 April 51 Edw. III [1377]

Elias de Swonhongre and William Panyter.

Whereas William holds for his life, by lease of William Swonhongre, late father of Elias, a messuage with a curtilage, and garden, and two crofts called Homecroftes, two parcels of land, meadow and pasture, and an *elond* [i.e. land?] called Homemersch, Homemeode and Homeolond, two parcels of land called Luyteleradelynch and Mecheleradelynch, and two

---

[1] *Transcript*: Smyth, iii. 380–1.

staithes in the Severn for the construction of fish-traps, at a rent of 26*s*. 8*d*. a year, Elias has granted that the rent shall be 13*s*. 4*d*. a year, and that after William's death Amicia his wife shall have the holding for her life.

Witnesses: John Sergeant of Stone, John ate Bowre, William Modybroke, Nicholas Schippard, John Fraunceys.

At: Berkeley.

A1/24/186 [SC 552]					3 June 51 Edw. III [3 June 1377]
Elias de Swonhongre and Richard de Egton of Saniger.

Elias has granted to Richard, for life, half of a staithe with a fishery called 'le longstath' in the river Severn at Swonhongre, and the other half after the death of John Serjaunt of Stone [who holds it of Elias for his life], rent 1*d*. a year, and after Richard's death it will pass to John de Egton, Richard's brother, for his life.

Witnesses: William Modibroc, Richard Gylemyn, John Bastard, William Purlewent, William Panyter.

At: Berkeley.

In Wanswell

A1/24/187 [GC 1581]					n.d. [early Edw. I]
Henry de Weneswell, son and heir of Master Philip de Weneswell, and Sir Thomas de Berkeley.

Henry has granted to Thomas a plot of land in his field called Windmulfeld with the windmill built on it, and Thomas has given him 5 marks.

Witnesses: Sir Robert le Veel, Sir Roger de Lokinton, Sir Maurice de Saltmarsh (*de salso marisco*), knights, Bartholomew de Olepenne, Robert de Stanes, Elias de Cumbe, Robert de Brathestone.

A1/24/188 [GC 2482]					n.d. [early 14th cent.]
Thomas lord of Berkeleye and Thomas son of John de Swonhungre.

Thomas de Berkeleye has granted to Thomas de Swonhungre the plot of land at Wyndmullefelde where his windmill is situated in Hamme; to him and his issue, rent a rose a year.

A1/24/189 [GC 1234]					n.d. [early 14th cent.]
Thomas de Berkelegh, lord of Berkeley, and Thomas de Stone, son and heir of Robert son of Robert de Stone.

Thomas de Berkelegh has granted to Thomas de Stone 1 virgate of land which Hugh de la Stompe holds in villeinage in Waneswelle, with Hugh and his issue and chattels; also a half-virgate of land which Hugh Bouchard formerly held at Waneswelle, the half-virgate which Isabel Snyte formerly held, a field called Wyntmellefeld with an enclosed pasture called Oldefischwere, 2 a. of land which William le Rom formerly held at Stone within the manor of Hamme and 4 a. of land which were of the holding of Ralph Symond at Wodeford in Alkynton; to him and his issue, rent £4 10*s*. a year.

Witnesses: Sir John Basset, Sir William de Wauton, knights, John de Saltmarsh (*de salso [marisco]*), John de Lokyunton, Robert de Bradeston, Robert de Berkelegh, Thomas de Beolegh, Robert de Butlescombe, Thomas de Stintescombe, Walter de Nasse, Robert Wyther, John de Olepenne, John de Swonhongre.

A1/24/190 [GC 2558]					n.d. [*c*. 1304]
Thomas de Stone, son and heir of Robert son of Robert de Stone, and Sir Thomas de Berkelegh.

Whereas Sir Thomas sometime enfeoffed Robert, grandfather of Thomas de Stone, of certain lands and holdings [*details*], to him and his issue, rent £11 a year, Thomas now has difficulty in paying the rent, for which reason, on the advice of Master William de Kyngescote, Robert de Bradeston, Juliana his mother, Robert Wyther and his other friends, he has given up the said holdings to Sir Thomas and quitclaimed them to him; and for this Thomas has granted to him the virgate [formerly of Hugh de Stompe in Waneswell], the half-virgates of Isabel Snyte [and Hugh Bouchard in Hamme], [the field] called Wyntmellefeld and the pasture called Oldefyschwere, and [the half-virgate] formerly of William le Rom [in Stone], at a rent of £4 10s. . . . as in Thomas's charter of enfeoffment.

Witnesses: Sir John Basset, [Sir William de Wauton, knights, John de Saltmarsh (*de salso*] *marisco*), John de Lokynton, Robert de Bradeston, Robert de Berkelee, Thomas de Beoleye, Robert de Butlescombe, . . . Robert Wyth', John de Olepenne, John de Swonhongre.

A1/24/191 [GC 2120]   1 Sept. 10 Edw. II [1316]
Thomas de Berkeleye, lord of Berkeley, and John de Swonhungre.

Thomas has leased to John 48 a. 45 perches of land in various fields at Wanneswelle in enclosures, 3½ a. 10 perches of meadow in enclosures and 2 a. 22 perches of pasture in enclosures, which Thomas de Stone, recently deceased, held of Thomas by knight service in Hamme; to hold until the full age of the heir or heirs of Thomas, rent 6s. 8d. a year to Thomas, 26s. 8d. a year to Thomas's daughter Isabel and 60s. a year to Thomas's daughter Margaret.

Witnesses: John son of Nichol, Thomas de Bradeston, Peter de Stintescombe, John Capel, John le Serjaunt.
At: Berkeley.

A1/24/192 [GC 3660]   Sun. after St. Mary Magdalen, 47 Edw. III [24 July 1373]
Thomas lord of Berkele; and Walter Oldelonde and John Oldelonde, his brother, of Berkeley.

Thomas has granted to Walter and John custody of all the lands [etc.] which William Swonhongere held of Thomas in chief in Wanneswell within the hundred of Berkele, until the full age of Elias, William's son and heir, rendering the customary services to Thomas.
At: Berkeley.

A1/24/193 [GC 4019*]   Mon. before the Annunciation, 8 Hen. IV [21 March 1407]
John Thorpe, burgess of Bristol, and Isabel his wife; and Richard Richard of Hinton by Berkeley and Joan his wife.

John and Isabel have leased to Richard and Joan the field called Courtefelde, in Waneswelle by the road called Puttebroke, a croft called Prestefeld, a pasture called Oldefisshewere, beside Courtefelde, and 3 a. of meadow in le More; for their lives, rent 40s. a year.

Witnesses: Thomas Stauntone, William Gilmyn, Robert Smyth of Pedington, John atte Hurne.
At: Berkeley.

OTHER TENANTS AND HOLDINGS
Avery leases and grants

To John and Maud Abbot
A1/24/194 [GC 1951]   Tues. after St. Martin, 7 Edw. II [13 Nov. 1313]
Robert Averay and John called Abbod.

Robert has leased to John 1 a. of land in the furlong called Berklewode in Hamme; for life, rent a rose a year.

Witnesses: Thomas de Stone, John Capel, John le Cuppere, Henry le Gardener, John Sewaker, Roger le Cuppere, Edward de Fromelode.
At: Berkeley.

A1/24/195 [GC 2736]   Fri. after St. Martin, 5 Edw. III [15 Nov. 1331]
Geoffrey Martyn of Bristol and his wife Beatrice; and William atte Wode of Berkeley.

   Geoffrey and Beatrice have granted to William 1 a. of land which they have for the term
of the life of John Abbud in Berkelwode, which was of William le Someter; for the life of
John Abbud, rent a rose a year. [*In French.*]
At: Bristol.

A1/24/196 [GC 2892; *duplicate* GC 2893]   Mon. after the translation of St. Wulfstan,
                                                          11 Edw. III [9 June 1337]
Maud daughter of John Abbod and Henry de Modibrok.

   Maud has leased to Henry 1 a. of land in the field called Berkelode in Hamme; for her
life, rent 1½*d*. a year.
Witnesses: Robert Groundy, John Sewaker, Edward de Fromelode, John Schipward, John de
Fromelode.
At: Berkeley.

A1/24/197 [GC 2880]   Mon. after St. Peter, 11 Edw. III [4 Aug. 1337]
Maud daughter of John Abbod, unmarried woman, and Henry de Modibrok.

   Maud has leased to Henry 1 a. of land in the field called Berclode; for her life, rent 1*d*. a
year.
Witnesses: John Serjaunt, John de Lorwynge, William Selewyn, Edward de Fromelode,
John Sewaker.
At: Berkeley.

A1/24/198 [GC 2872]   St. Aldhelm, 12 Edw. III [25 May 1338]
John Payn of Berkeley and William Capel.

   John has leased to William 1 a. of land in the furlong called Berklewode; for the term of
the life of Maud daughter of John Abboth, for the previous services to the chief lord.
Witnesses: John le Serjaunt, John de Lorwynge, William Gylemyn, Thomas de Costone,
Adam Purlewent, clerk.
At: Berkeley.

A1/24/199 [GC 2906]   St. Aldhelm, 12 Edw. III [25 May 1338]
Henry de Modybroc and William Capel.

   Henry has leased to William 1 a. of land in the furlong called Berklewode in Hamme; for
the life of Maud daughter of John Abbod, rendering the customary services to the chief lord.
Witnesses: John le Serjaunt, John de Lorwynge, William Gylemyn, Thomas Costone, Adam
Purlewent, clerk.
At: Berkeley.

   To Thomas le Serjaunt
A1/24/200 [GC 2138]   Tues. after St. Nicholas, 10 Edw. II [7 Dec. 1316]
Robert Averay of Berkeley and Thomas le Serjaunt.

   Robert has leased to Thomas all his meadow in Wynemed in Hamme; for life, rent 1*d*. a
year.
Witnesses: John Coppere, Henry Gardener, Edward de Fromelode, John Sewaker, Robert
Groundy.
At: Berkeley.

A1/24/201 [GC 2259]   Fri. after St. Nicholas, 12 Edw. II [8 Dec. 1318]
Robert Averay of Berkeley; and John son of Richard le Serjaunt and John his son.

   Robert has granted to John and John a rent of 1*d*. a year from Thomas son of Richard le
Serjaunt, for 3 a. of meadow lying in the meadow called Wynemed, which he holds for life
by lease of Robert, in Hamme, with the reversion of the meadow after the death of Thomas;

to the said John le Serjaunt and John his son and the heirs of John le Serjaunt.
Witnesses: Thomas de Bradeston, John Capel, John Wyth, Thomas de Craweleye, William Capel, John le Cuppere, John Judde.
At: Berkeley.

To Alan le Scot and family

A1/24/202 [GC 2411]   St. Matthew, 17 Edw. II [21 Sept. 1323]
Robert Averay of Berkeley; and Alan le Scott of Ham, Juliana his wife and Henry and John their sons.

Robert has leased to Alan, Juliana, Henry and John his grange, wagon-shed, lower gate and a plot of land, beside the stream running to the Severn and la Sleche, with free access and sufficient way [*via*] with wagons and carts to the doors of the buildings, and they are each to have a key to open and close the gate; for their lives, rent 6*d.* a year.
Witnesses: John le Serjaunt, John Capel, Nicholas of the vine (*de vynea*), Nicholas Iweyn, John Sewaker, Nicholas Neel, Adam Pynel.
At: Berkeley.

A1/24/203 [GC 2414]   St. Nicholas, 17 Edw. II [6 Dec. 1323]
Robert Averay of Berkeley; and Alan le Scott of Ham, Juliana his wife Juliana and Henry and John their sons.

Robert has leased to Alan, Juliana, Henry and John his messuage called the byre, extending above Robert's hall, with a plot of land adjacent which extends from the freestones lying in the wall beside the doorway of the said byre to the willows growing in Robert's ditch and to the lower gate, also another plot of land between the road and Robert's curtilage; to hold the said messuage, lower gate and two plots of land, with the trees growing there; for their lives, saving to Robert free access with wagons and carts through the said gate to repair his croft, and to Richard Payn and Isabel his wife to cultivate their 5 selions; rent 1*d.* a year.
Witnesses: John le Serjaunt, John Capel, John Sewaker, Nicholas Neel, Nicholas Iweyn.
At: Berkeley.

A1/24/204 [GC 2422]   St. Barnabas, 17 Edw. II [11 June 1324]
Alan le Scott of Ham and Juliana his wife; and Robert Averay.

Whereas Robert has enfeoffed Alan and Juliana of three hedges with the adjacent ditches for 24*s.* which they gave him, if Robert or his attorney pay to them the 24*s.* in the church of Berckel' on Michaelmas Day next coming they will give up the charter and seisin, and if Robert fails then the charter and seisin will remain with Alan and Juliana.
Witnesses: John Capel, Nicholas of the vine (*de vynea*), Nicholas Iweyn, Robert Bastard, Adam Pynel.
At: Ham.

Other

A1/24/205 [GC 2473]   n.d. [early 14th cent.]
Robert Averay; and Edward de Fromelode and Edith his wife.

Robert has leased to Edward and Edith 3 a. of land and three quarters of 1 a. of meadow in Hamme, the land lying in the field called Dolveld and the meadow in the meadow called Bolewykesterste; for their lives.
Witnesses: John Sewaker, John Coppere, Henry Gardiner, William Bodde, John de Fromelode.

A1/24/206 [GC 1729]   St. Ambrose, 3 Edw. II [4 April 1310]
Robert son and heir of Richard Averey of Berkeley; and Edward de Fromilode and Edith his wife.

Robert has granted to Edward and Edith his meadow in Yondreholemede, for their lives, rent 1*d.* a year.
Witnesses: John Sewaker, John le Coppere, Roger le Coppere, William Bodd, John le Vynor, John de Fromilode, clerk.
At: Berkeley.

A1/24/207 [GC 1723]   St. Gregory, 3 Edw. II [12 March 1310]
Robert Averay of Berkeley; and Henry le Gardiner of Berkeley and Isabel his wife.

Robert has leased to Henry and Isabel all his meadow in Holemed near Berckelegh, beside Holemedespolle; for their lives, rent a rose a year, and they have given him a certain sum of money.
Witnesses: John le Coppere, John Sewaker, Edward de Fromyde, William de Vyngnur, William Bodde.
At: Berkeley.

A1/24/208 [GC 2378]   The Invention of Holy Cross, 15 Edw. II [3 May 1322]
Robert Averay of Berkeley; and Richard atte Slo, Margery his wife and John their son.

Robert has leased to Richard, Margery and John his pasture in Hamme beside the rhine running through the Castle meadow and the common way called Walstret above the stream running towards the Severn; for their lives, rent a rose a year, and they have given him a certain sum of money.
Witnesses: John Capel, Nicholas of the vine (*de vynea*), Nicholas Iweyn, John Purlewent, Robert Bastard.
At: Ham.

A1/24/209 [GC 2406]   St. Augustine, 16 Edw. II [26 May 1323]
Robert Averay of Berkeley; and Richard Reynaldes of Aust and Isabel his wife.

Robert has leased to Richard and Isabel 5 selions of land in Robert's croft with two fore-earths, and with free access with wagons and carts, and sufficient way [*via*] at la Sleche beyond Robert's pasture to improve the land; for their lives, doing the customary services to the chief lord.
Witnesses: John le Serjaunt, John Capel, John Sewaker, Adam Pynel, Thomas Page, William Iweyn, John Swele.
At: Berkeley.

Ashleworth and Kingswood Abbey

A1/24/210 [SC 308]   n.d. [*c.* 1250]
Kingswood Abbey and Thomas de Esselwrth.

The abbey has granted to Thomas all the land in Hamma which Walter de Horsford held; rent 20*s.* a year, and 20*s.* for relief at a change of heirs, and whatever royal service pertains to a half-virgate in that vill.
Witnesses: Sir Geoffrey de Chausi, Sir Richard de Cromhale, Sir Roger de Lokinton, Sir Maurice de Sautemareis, Sir Walter de Burgo, Nicholas de Chausi, John de Egintun, Andrew de Bradestun, Thomas Mathias.

A1/24/211 [GC 1040]   The conversion of St. Paul, 1303 [25 Jan. 1303]
Thomas de Assleworthe, son and heir of Thomas de Assleworthe, and Kingswood Abbey.

Thomas has granted to the abbey a half-virgate of land in the vill of Hamme, with all the land and a certain pasture in the field called Stonhamfeld next to Marebrok, with 2½ a. of meadow in Swynemor.
Witnesses: Sir Thomas de Berkeleye, lord of Berkeley, Sir Maurice, Sir Thomas and Sir John his sons, knights, Robert de Bradeston, Thomas de Beoleye, John de Olepenne.

A1/24/212 [GC 1061; *duplicate* GC 1065]   May 1304
Thomas de Berkeleye, lord of Berkeley, and Kingswood Abbey.

Thomas has inspected and confirmed the charter of Thomas de Assleworth [above, A/1/24/211 (GC 1040)].

Witnesses: Sir Maurice, Sir Thomas and Sir John, Thomas's sons, and Sir William de Wauton, knights, Robert de Bradestone, Thomas de Beoleye, John de Olepenne.

A1/24/213 [GC 1458]   n.d. [early 14th cent.]
Kingswood Abbey and Thomas de Assleworthe, son and heir of the late Thomas de Assleworthe.

The abbey has quitclaimed to Thomas 5 a. and 1 selion of land in Banmers within the manor of Hamme, which Thomas granted to Sir Thomas de Berkeleye.

Witnesses: Sir Thomas de Berkeleya, Sir Maurice, Sir Thomas and Sir John, his sons, knights, Robert de Bradeston, Robert de Berkel', Robert de Kouel', Henry de Camme, Thomas de Beoleya.

A1/24/214 [GC 1457]   n.d. [early 14th cent.]
Kingswood Abbey and Thomas de Assleworthe, son and heir of the late Thomas de Assleworthe.

The abbey has quitclaimed to Thomas 5 a. and 1 selion of land in Banmers within the manor of Hamme, which Thomas granted to Sir Thomas de Berkeleye; also a rent of 20*s.* which he owed for a half-virgate held of the abbey in the vill of Hamme.

Witnesses: Sir Thomas de Berkeleya, Sir Maurice, Sir Thomas and Sir John, his sons, knights, Robert de Bradeston, Thomas de Beoleya, John de Olepenne.

The Waleys holding

A1/24/215 [GC 828]   n.d. [before 1291]
Nigel de Staniteford and Martin Waleys (*Walensis*) of Saniger.

Nigel has granted to Martin 1 a. of land called Nelescroft in the vill of Suonhungre; rent 4*d.* a year, and Martin has given him 3 marks.

Witnesses: Peter de Wyk, Thomas the serjeant (*serviens*), John de Egethon, Philip de Leycestr', Walter Sely, Ralph Bulcard, Roger the clerk.

A1/24/216 [GC 721]   n.d. [before 1291]
Adam le Cuppere and Martin son of Walter Waleys (*Walensis*).

Adam has granted to Martin 1 a. of land in 'west feld' next to Wodewaldegrave; rent 2*d.* a year, and Martin has given him 20*s.*.

Witnesses: Sir Maurice de Saltmarsh (*de salso marisco*), John de Wodeford, Maurice de Stan, Adam Coby, Alfred Mariner, John Sewaker, William son of Eustace, Andrew de Brothestan, Robert le Herde, Walter Sely, clerk.

A1/24/217 [GC 586]   Sun. before Michaelmas, 19 Edw. I [23 Sept. 1291]
Robert le Waleys, son and heir of Martin le Waleys, and Philip his brother.

Robert has granted to Philip all the lands and holdings which came to him after the death of Martin, their father.

Witnesses: Robert de Egetone, Adam Hathulf, Robert le Waleys, William Eustace, Walter the parker (*parcarius*).
At: Berkeley.

The Tece holding

A1/24/218 [GC 1558]   n.d. [late Hen. III]
Thomas Tece, son of Jordan Tece, and Elias Blacbaruoht.

Thomas has granted to Elias a part of his demesne beside his [Thomas's] principal house in Hamme; rent 4*d.* a year, and Elias has given him 15*s.*

Witnesses: Sir Maurice de Saltmarsh (*de salso marisco*), Sir Walter de Burgo, knights, Peter de Wyke, Richard de Wyke, John de Egeton, Nicholas de Coldewell, Adam Coby, Alfred le Shipward, Richard Pinel, William son of Eustace, Robert Bastard, William son of Robert, Maurice de Stane, Walter Sely, clerk.

A1/24/219 [GC 699]   n.d. [late Hen. III]
Elias Blacbaruoht and Hugh son of Roger de Pedinton.

Elias has granted to Hugh all the land which he had by grant of Thomas Thece, son of Jordan Thece, in the vill of Hamme, and Hugh has given him 4 marks.
Witnesses: Sir Nicholas Wolf (*Lupus*), steward of Berkeley, Sir Maurice de Saltmarsh (*de salso marisco*), knights, Maurice de Stan, Peter de Wike, Nicholas de Crauleygh, John Sewaker, Adam Coby, Robert Bastard, Nicholas de Coldewell, Walter Sely, clerk.

The Framilode holding in West Field

A1/24/220 [GC 1343]   n.d. [*temp.* Edw. I]
John de Egetone; and Ralph de Fromylode and Alice his wife.

John has granted to Ralph and Alice 6 selions of land and half of Hopynghullesych; to hold of the lord of Berkeleye, rent to the lord 2*d.* a year, and they have given him a certain sum of money.
Witnesses: Robert de Stone, Thomas le Serjant, John Sewaker, Richard Auveray, William de Clerk [*sic*].

A1/24/221 [GC 1583]   n.d. [*temp.* Edw. I]
Reginald and Walter, sons of Roger le White; and Edward de Fremilode and Edith his wife.

Reginald and Walter have granted to Edward and Edith 1 a. of land in the furlong called Loverdeshulle, to hold of the hospital of Holy Trinity of Longebrugge; rent ¼*d.* a year, and Edward and Edith have given them 40*s.*
Witnesses: Robert de Bradestone, Robert de Berkeleye, John le Coppare, Robert Averey, Thomas the miller (*molendin'*), John Sheyare, William le Vinea, Thomas Aleyn.

A1/24/222 [GC 2527]   n.d. [*temp.* Edw. I]
John Marescall of Berkeley; and Edward de Fromilode and Edith his wife.

John has granted to Edward and Edith 1 a. of land in Berkeleye in the field called Westfeld; for their lives, rent 1*d.* a year.
Witnesses: John Sewaker, John le Coppere, Robert Averey, Henry le Gardiner, William le Vynor, Thomas Molender'.

A1/24/223 [GC 3605]   Sun. the eve of Christmas, 42 Edw. III [24 Dec. 1368]
Edward de Fromylode, son and heir of John de Fromylode of Berkeley, and John Coby the elder.

Edward has granted to John, his heirs and assigns two thirds of a parcel of land in the furlong called Lordeshulle in le Westfelde, with the reversion of one third after the death of Alice widow of John de Fromylode, and the parcel contains 12 selions.
Witnesses: John Aleyn, Walter Oldelonde, William Modebroke, Richard Groundy, John Byl.
At: Berkeley.

A1/24/224 [GC 3597]   Tues. after St. John at the Latin Gate, 42 Edw. III [9 May 1368]
Edward Fromelode of Berkeley and John Coby the elder of the same.

Edward has quitclaimed to John 6 selions, two fore-earths and a certain parcel of land with half of Hopynghullessych in le Westfeld of Berkel' which John previously held for life by grant of John Fromelode, Edward's father.
Witnesses: John Serjaunt, John Aleyn of Hill, Walter Oldelond, William Modebrok, William Purlewent.
At: Berkeley.

Marybrook holding in West Field

A1/24/225 [GC 1394]   n.d. [*temp.* Edw. I]
Henry Grout of Berkeley; and William de Modebrock and Helen his wife.

Henry has granted to William and Helen all the land in the field of Westfeld called Rudingaker, next to the road called Muleweye; rent 4*d.* a year and they have given him 34*s.*
Witnesses: Thomas Alein, Thomas le Serjant, Walter Shipward, John Sewaker, John Bonserjant, Richard Marescall, Richard Shipward.

A1/24/226 [GC 1477]   n.d. [*temp.* Edw. I]
Richard called Marescall of Berkeley; and William de Modibroc and Helen his wife.

Richard has granted to William and Helen, for a certain sum of money, all his land in Westfeld; rent a rose a year.
Witnesses: Thomas Alein, Richard Averey, John Sewaker, John le Cuppere, Henry le Cuppere.

A1/24/227 [GC 2429]   Sun. the feast of St. Simon and St. Jude, 18 Edw. II [28 Oct. 1324]
William son and heir of William Modibroc of Berkeley; and Henry de Modibroc, his brother, and Edania his wife.

William has granted to Henry and Edania, and their heirs and assigns, 3 selions of land in the field called le Westfelde.
Witnesses: John le Serjaunt, John de Swonhungre, John de Egetone, John Judde, John Sewaker, Nicholas Neel, Edward de Fromylode.
At: Berkeley.

A1/24/228 [GC 3147]   Sun. after Michaelmas, 20 Edw. III [1 Oct. 1346]
William Modebrok and Henry Modebrok, his father.

William has leased to Henry a house with a curtilage and two parcels of land in le Westfelde, which he had by grant of Henry in fee; for life, rent a rose a year.
Witnesses: Robert Groundy, Walter Payn, Henry Jodde, John Gomylef, Henry Swele.
At: Berkeley.

The Pynel holding

A1/24/229 [GC 1060]   Sun. after Easter, 32 Edw. I [5 April 1304]
Adam Pinel of Berkeley and Juliana Maundwere.

Adam has granted to Juliana the messuage which he had by grant from Denise Pinel in the vill of Hamme, with the adjacent curtilage; for Juliana's life, rent 7*d.* a year, and she has given him a certain sum of money.
Witnesses: Robert Bastard, Henry de Hamme, William le Hopere, William le Frigg, Maurice de Wenden, William Purlewent, clerk.
At: Berkeley.

A1/24/230 [GC 1876]   8 April 5 Edw. II [1312]
Adam Pynel of Berkeley and Robert Gaugy.

Adam has granted to Robert his holding at Homme and a rent of 7*d.* from Juliana Maundeware, with the reversion on her death of the house and curtilage which she holds for life, which holding he had by grant of Denise Pynel his sister, between the field called Pedymerche and the holding of Elias le Hopere.
Witnesses: John Capel, Robert Bastard, Nicholas Iweyn, Thomas son of Henry atte Watere, William Purlewent.
At: Ham.

The Marybrook holding in Oakhunger

A1/24/231 [GC 2174]   St. Aldhelm, 10 Edw. II [25 May 1317]
William de Modibrok and Helen his wife; and William de Modibrok, their son.
  William and Helen have granted to William 2 selions of land in the field called
Ochungre; William has given them a certain sum of money.
Witnesses: John le Coppare, Henry le Gardiner, John Sewaker, John Jodde, John le
Vyngnur, Roger le Coppare, William Bodde.
At: Berkeley.

A1/24/232 [GC 2795]   Mon. before St. Augustine, 8 Edw. III [23 May 1334]
Henry Modybrok of Berkeley; and Nicholas le Vyngnur of Berkeley and Margaret his wife.
  Henry has granted to Nicholas and Margaret 2 selions of land in the field called
Ochungre beside the land of Sir Peter le Veel; they have given him a certain sum of money.
Witnesses: John le Gardiner, Robert Groundi, William Judde, Edward de Fromylode, John
le Coppere, Robert Peke, Robert le Schypward.
At: Berkeley.

The Sewaker holding in West Field

A1/24/233 [GC 2412]   St. Luke, 17 Edw. II [18 Oct. 1323]
John Sewaker of Berkeley; and Richard le Serjaunt of Berkeley and Alice his wife.
  John has leased to Richard and Alice 13 selions of land with two fore-earths in the field
called le Westfeld in the furlong called Bradeforlong; for their lives, rent a rose a year, and
they have given him a certain sum of money.
Witnesses: John le Serjaunt, John de Egetone, William Gylemyn, Richard de Stanford,
Nicholas Neel.
At: Berkeley.

A1/24/234 [GC 2751]   5 July 5 Edw. III [1331]
Margery widow of John Sewaker of Berkeley and Alice widow of Richard le Sergeaunt.
  Margery has quitclaimed to Alice her dower rights in 13 selions and two fore-earths of
land in the field called le Westfeld in the furlong called Bradeforlong, which Richard and
Alice previously had by lease of John Sewaker.
Witnesses: John le Cuppere, Edward de Fromelode, Robert Groundi, Henry de Modybrok,
William Gylemyn.
At: Berkeley.

The Marybrook (later Judd) holding in Alylond

A1/24/235 [GC 2438]   Mon. after Palm Sunday, 18 Edw. II [1 April 1325]
William Modibroc of Berkeley and Helen his wife; and John Judde of Berkeley and Alice
his wife.
  William and Helen have granted to John and Alice, and their heirs and assigns, 8 selions
of land in the furlong called Alylond, extending to the road called le Muleweye.
Witnesses: John de Swonhungre, Henry le Gardiner, Robert Groundy, Nicholas Neel, John
Sewaker, Edward de Fromylode, Alan Skott.
At: Berkeley.

A1/24/236 [GC 2625]   Tues. after Easter, 1 Edw. III [14 April 1327]
William son and heir of Helen Modibrok of Berkeley; and John Judde of Berkeley and
Alice his wife.
  William has quitclaimed to John and Alice a parcel of land in the furlong called Alylond.
Witnesses: John Capel, Robert Groundy, Edward de Fromylode, John Sewaker, Thomas
Page, William Bodde, Adam Pynel, Nicholas Neel, Thomas Aleyn.
At: Berkeley.

The Hooper holding

A1/24/237 [GC 3065]   Thurs. before St. Luke, 17 Edw. III [16 Oct. 1343]
Richard le Smyth of Ham and John le Hopare of Berkeley.

Richard has quitclaimed to John the lands and holdings [etc.] which . . . by grant of Isabel la Hopare within the manor of Hamme.

Witnesses: Robert Groundy, Robert Pryk, Edward de Fromelode, Robert Bastard, John Purlewent.

At: Ham.

A1/24/238 [GC 3071]   Sun. after All Souls, 17 Edw. III [9 Nov. 1343]
Richard le Smyth of Ham; and John le Hopare of Berkeley and Edith his wife.

Richard has quitclaimed to John and Edith the lands and holdings [etc.] which he had by grant of Isabel la Hopare within the manor of Hamme.

Witnesses: Robert Groundy, Robert Prikke, Edward de Fromelode, Robert Bastard, John Purlewent.

At: Ham.

The Shoyar holding in Berkeley and West Field[1]

A1/24/239 [GC 3622]   Mon. after St. James, 44 Edw. III [29 July 1370]
John Coby the younger of Berkeley and Amicia widow of John Coby the elder, his brother.

John has leased to Amicia a holding with a curtilage in Berkelee called Schoyarestenement and 3 a. of land in the field called Westfeld in various parcels; for her life, paying the customary services to the chief lord, with remainder to John son of John Coby the elder and of Amicia, for his life, and to John Coby the grantor.

Witnesses: John Sergeaunt, William Modibrok, Robert Balstake, John Byl, John Gamel.

At: Berkeley.

A1/24/240 [GC 3807]   Wed. the feast of St. Peter in chains, 10 Ric. II [1 Aug. 1386]
John Cobi the elder of Berkeley and John de Egeton, son of Robert de Egeton.

John Cobi has leased to John de Egeton a holding with a curtilage in Berkeley called Schoyarestenement and 3 a. of land in the field called Westfeld; for a term of 70 years, rent 1d. a year to John, and the customary services to the chief lord.

Witnesses: Robert Balstake, Thomas Lucas, Thomas Opynton, John Clerk, William Packere.

At: Berkeley.

A1/24/241 [GC 4009]   Sun. after Epiphany, 6 Hen. IV [11 Jan. 1405]
John son and heir of John Coby, brother of the late John Coby the elder of Berkeley, and John Egetone, son of the late Robert Egetone.

John Coby has leased to John Egetone the holding in Berkeley called Schoyarestenement and also 3 a. of land in Westfeld and 1 selion in Okongre; for a term of 50 years, rent 4s. a year.

Witnesses: William Oteclyf, chaplain, Richard Egetone, Thomas Staunton, Thomas Lucas, John Stanley.

At: Berkeley.

The Warminster holding in Parham and Berkeley

Halling holding in Parham

A1/24/242 [GC 3625]   Sun. after the Exaltation of Holy Cross, 44 Edw. III [15 Sept. 1370]
(1) John Aleyn of Hill; (2) John Smyth of Saniger; (3) Nicholas atte More.

John Aleyn has appointed John Smyth to give seisin to Nicholas of 1 a. of meadow in Perham which William Hallyng sometime held of John and recently surrendered to him.

At: Berkeley.

---

[1] Cf. below, p. 217, the Coby holding.

A1/24/243 [GC 3627]   Sun. after All Saints, 44 Edw. III [3 Nov. 1370]
John Aleyn of Hill and Nicholas atte More; and John Smyth of Saniger and Joan his wife.

    John and Nicholas have leased to John and Joan 1 a. of meadow in Perham which
William Hallyng previously held of John Aleyn; for their lives, rent 3*s.* a year.
Witnesses: Walter Oldelond, Richard Gylmyn, William Modebrok, William Purlewent, John
Bastard.
At: Berkeley.

Budd holding in Berkeley

A1/24/244 [GC 3633]   Tues. before St. Peter in chains, 45 Edw. III [29 July 1371]
John Halys and John Aleyn; and Alice widow of Thomas Bodde of Berkeley.

    John and John have leased to Alice a messuage with a curtilage in the vill of Berkel' beside
the road from Lokfastebrugge to the marketplace, and also all the lands and holdings which
William Bodde sometime held by lease of Thomas Aleyn, father of John; for her life, rent to
John Halys while he lives 18*s.* a year and to John Aleyn 2*s.* a year, and after the death of
John Halys 20*s.* a year to John Aleyn.
Witnesses: William Modibroke, Robert Balstake, John Coby, John Byl, Nicholas Sopere.
At: Berkeley.

The combined holding

A1/24/245 [GC 3759]   6 March 6 Ric. II [1383]
Nicholas atte More of Gloucestershire and William Wermynstre, burgess of Bristol.

    Nicholas has granted to William all his estate in a rent of 28*s.* 2*d.* from Alice Bodde of
Berkeley, John Smyth of Sonongger and Agnes Ricardys, his tenants in the parish of
Berkeley.

A1/24/246 [GC 3758]   8 March 6 Ric. II [1383]
Nicholas atte More of Gloucestershire and William Wermynstre, burgess of Bristol.

    Whereas Nicholas granted to William all his estate in a rent of 28*s.* 2*d.* from Alice Bodde
of Berkeley, John Smyth of Sonongger and Agnes Ricardys, his tenants in the parish of
Berkeley, for Nicholas's life, and whereas Nicholas is bound to William in 20 marks,
William has granted that if he holds the rent for a term of 10 years, the bond will be void.
[*In French*.]
At: Bristol.

A1/24/247 [GC 3852]   24 June 15 Ric. II [1391]
Robert Poyns of Iron Acton (Glos.) and William Wermystre, burgess of Bristol.

    Robert has quitclaimed to William an annual rent of 28*s.* 2*d.* from lands and holdings in
Berkley in the said county, which William had by grant of Nicholas atte More, for
Nicholas's life.
Witnesses: Thomas FitzNicoll, knight, John atte Yate, Edmund Basset, William Smalcombe,
Laurence Berley.
At: Berkeley.

A1/24/248 [GC 3869]   21 June 15 Ric. II [1392]
Robert Poyns of Iron Acton and William Wermynstre, draper of Bristol and burgess.

    Robert has granted to William, his heirs and assigns the rents and services of John Carter
and Christine his wife, of Ralph Coke and of Alice Cloude for the lands which they hold of
Robert for their lives in Berkeley, with the reversion of the holdings after their deaths,
which he had by grant of George atte More and Thomas Deneys chaplain.
Witnesses: Thomas FitzNicholl, knight, John Rolves, John Skeye, John Trye, Luke Tanner.
At: Berkeley.

The Stamp holding

A1/24/249 [GC 3769; *duplicate* GC 3770]   Mon. after the Purification, 7 Ric. II
[8 Feb. 1384]

Nicholas Stompe of Dursley and Ralph Cok.

Nicholas has leased to Ralph a house with a curtilage and garden in the street called Modbrokestret at Berkeley, a parcel of land in le Westfeld and a parcel of land in Aketre, which he inherited after the death of his brother, Adam atte Herne, in the manors of Hamme and Alkyntone; for a term of 70 years, rent to Nicholas 18*d.* a year and to the chief lord 2*s.* 6*d.* a year.

Witnesses: John Waltone, Richard Gylmyn, Thomas Lucas, Thomas Uppyntone, John Byl.
At: Berkeley.

A1/24/250 [GC 3823]   Thurs. the feast of St. Gregory, 11 Ric. II [12 March 1388]
Nicholas Stompe of Dursley and Ralph Coke.

Whereas Nicholas leased to Ralph a house [etc., as above A1/24/249 (GC 3769)], for a term of 70 years, rent 12*d.* a year, Nicholas has quitclaimed the same and the rent to Ralph, his heirs and assigns.

Witnesses: John Sergeaunt of Stone, Ralph Waleys, William Smalcombe, Thomas Lucas, Richard Gylmyn, Thomas Oppyntone, John Schypward.
At: Berkeley.

The Coby holding in Berkeley and West Field[1]

A1/24/251 [GC 4051]   Wed. after St. Kalixtus, 12 Hen. IV [15 Oct. 1410]
John Coby, son and heir of John Coby, and Walter Toyt of Breadstone.

John has quitclaimed to Walter a holding in Berkeley and an annual rent of 12*d.* from the holding of William Barbour.

Witnesses: Thomas Stanton, John Flour, Richard Gilbert, John Stanley, William Daker.
At: Berkeley.

A1/24/252 [GC 4052]   Thurs. before St. Luke, 12 Hen. IV [16 Oct. 1410]
John Coby, son and heir of John Coby, and Walter Toyt of Breadstone.

John has quitclaimed to Walter 3 a. of land in Westfeld and 1 selion in Okongre, which John Egeton son of Robert Egeton has for life.

Witnesses: Thomas Stanton, John Flour, John Dier, William Barbour, Thomas Carter.
At: Berkeley.

A1/24/253 [GC 4053]   Mon. before St. Simon and St. Jude, 12 Hen. IV [27 Oct. 1410]
Walter Toyt of Breadstone; and John BonJohn and John Wynter.

Walter has granted to John and John, and their heirs and assigns, a holding, a rent of 12*d.* a year from the holding of William Barbour of Berkeley, and 3 a. and 1 selion of land within the hundred of Berkeley, which he had by grant of John Coby.

Witnesses: Thomas Kendale, Thomas Stantone, John Flour, John Dier, Richard Gilbert.
At: Berkeley.

The Dolley holding in West Field

A1/24/254 [GC 4232]   4 Aug. 21 Hen. VI [1443]
William Doly, burgess of Berkeley, and Walter Hevyner of Saniger.

William has leased to Walter 7 selions of land in Westfeld; for his life, rent 12*d.* a year.

Witnesses: John Staunton, Richard Rycardes, Robert de Egton.
At: Berkeley.

---

[1] Cf. above, p. 215, the Shoyar holding.

A1/24/255 [GC 4233]   4 Aug. 21 Hen. VI [1443]
William Doly, burgess of Berkeley; and Walter Hevyner of Saniger and Maud his wife.
    William has leased to Walter and Maud 7 selions of land in Westfeld; for their lives, rent
12*d.* a year.
Witnesses: John Staunton, Richard Rycardes, Robert de Egton.
At: Berkeley.

Other acquisitions and grants

West Field

A1/24/256 [GC 1465]   n.d. [late Hen. III]
John de Loreinge and Richard his son.
    John has granted to Richard ½ a. of land in the furlong called Hoverdeshulle, which he
had from Emma le Cuppare; to Richard and his issue, rent ½*d.* a year.
Witnesses: Sir Maurice de Saltmarsh (*de salsomarisco*), John de Egetun, John de
Brod[estone], Nicholas de Craul', Peter de Stintescumbe, Peter de Wike, Thomas the
serjeant (*serviens*), Adam Mutun, Robert le Herde.

A1/24/257 [GC 816]   n.d. [late 13th cent.]
Alfred le Schypward of Berkeley and Walter le Scypward his brother.
    Alfred has granted to Walter 1 a. of arable land in the field called Westfeld; rent to the
chief lord of the fee 4*d.* a year, and Walter has given him 20*s.*
Witnesses: Richard le Schipward, John Sewoker, Henry le Gruth, Walter the miller
(*molendinarius*), John Bonsergant.

A1/24/258 [GC 1633]   n.d. [*temp.* Edw. I]
William Grout and Henry le Cuppere.
    William has granted to Henry 2 a. of land in the field of Westfeld, lying in 10 selions;
rent to the chief lord 8*d.* a year, and Henry has given him 3½ marks.
Witnesses: Thomas Alein, John Sewaker, Walter Shipward, Walter le Cuppere, Henry Grout.

A1/24/259 [GC 1960]   23 Jan. 7 Edw. II [1314]
Robert son and heir of John le Schoyare of Berkeley and Sir Thomas de Berkelee, lord of
Berkeley.
    Robert has granted to Thomas a rent of 1*d.* from Edward de Fromelode and Edith his
wife for 1 a. of land in the field called Westfeld, with the reversion of the land after their
deaths, in Hamme.
Witnesses: Thomas de Stone, John Capel, Henry le Gardener, Robert Averay, Nicholas
Neel.
At: Berkeley.

A1/24/260 [GC 2299]   Sun. after conversion St. Paul, 13 Edw. II [27 Jan. 1320]
John Abbod; and John Judde of Berkeley and Alice his wife.
    John Abbod has granted to John and Alice, and their heirs or assigns, 2 selions of land in
the field called Westfeld, in Hamme; for the lives of John and Maud his daughter.
Witnesses: John Wyth, Thomas de Craweleye, Edward de Fromelode, John Sewaker,
William de Modybroc.
At: Berkeley.

A1/24/261 [GC 2376]   St. Mark the evangelist, 15 Edw. II [25 April 1322]
Denise Bolcard, widow, and Philip son of Richard Couthulf of Saniger.
    Denise has leased to Philip 1 selion of land in the field called Westfeld in the furlong
called Kyngakre, beside the path from Berkel' to Swonhungre; for life, rent ½*d.* a year.

Witnesses: Richard le Serjaunt, Walter Tylemyn, Richard de Stanford, Nicholas Neel, William de Swonhungre.

At: Saniger.

A1/24/262 [GC 2444]   Translation of St. Thomas the martyr, beginning of 18 Edw. II
[7 July 1324][1]

Hervey Kyllecote of Berkeley and John Judde of Berkeley.

Hervey has granted to John, his heirs and assigns an annual rent of 5*d.* from William de Aure and Alice his wife for a croft of land which they hold of Hervey for their lives, lying in the field called le Westfeld beside the king's highway and the footpath from Berckel' to Swonhungre, with the reversion of the land.

Witnesses: Richard le Serjaunt, William Gylemyn, Henry le Gardiner, Robert Groundy, John Sewaker, Edward de Fromylode.

At: Berkeley.

A1/24/263 [GC 2805]   Wed. the feast of St. Clement, 8 Edw. III [23 Nov. 1334]

Walter son of Hugh le Fraunckeleyn of Berkeley and John son of Thomas le Hopare of Berkeley.

Walter has granted to John, his heirs and assigns 1 selion of land in the field called le Westfeld in the furlong called Wodewellegrof, beside the road from Berckel' to Swonhungre called le Cherichweye.

Witnesses: John le Serjaunt, John de Egetone, William de Swonhungre, William Gylemyn, Nicholas Neel, William Andrews.

At: Ham.

A1/24/264 [GC 3908]   St. Mark the evangelist, 19 Ric. II [25 April 1396]

Richard le Frere of Nass and Philip ate Berwe.

Richard has leased to Philip 3 parcels and a half-selion of land in Westfeld and a pasture; for a term of 60 years, rent a rose a year.

Witnesses: Thomas Swonhungre, John FitzRobert, Richard Gylmyn, Walter Toyt, Thomas Upynton, John Clerk, John Byl.

At: Berkeley.

Alylond, in West Field

A1/24/265 [GC 820]   n.d. [late 13th cent.]

William de Shokerwich; and Roger de Metesdone and Helen his wife.

William has granted to Roger and Helen 1¼ a. of land in Alilond, next to the road called Muleweie; rent 1*d.* a year, and they have given him 6*s.*

Witnesses: Thomas Alein, Thomas Serjant, Geoffrey Neel, Henry Cuppere, John Bonserjant, Roger Tannar'.

A1/24/266 [GC 1555]   n.d. [*temp.* Edw. I]

Thomas de Swonhungre, son of Thomas de Esshelesworth, and Henry le Grout of Berkeley.

Thomas has granted to Henry 4½ a. of land in the field called Alilonde; rent 1*d.* a year and 1 lb. of cumin, and Henry has given him 7 marks.

Witnesses: Master Philip de Leycestre, Walter de Egetone, Geoffrey Neel, John de Crauley, Richard le Shipward, John Sewaker, Robert the clerk.

A1/24/267 [GC 2636]   Michaelmas Day, 1 Edw. III [29 Sept. 1327]

William son and heir of William Modibrok of Berkeley; and Henry de Modibrok, his brother, and Edania his wife.

William has granted to Henry and Edania, and Henry's heirs and assigns, 4 selions of land in the furlong called Alylonde.

[1] Edward II's regnal year began on 8 July, so 7 July 18 Edw. II was in fact in 1325.

Witnesses: Robert Groundy, Edward de Fromylode, Thomas Page, Adam Pynel, William Judde, Hugh le Proute, William de Aure.
At: Berkeley.

Lugdown

A1/24/268 [GC 2328; *duplicate* GC 2329]   10 Nov. 14 Edw. II [1320]
John son of Philip Broun of Wanswell and Helen Adames of Pedington.

John has granted to Helen ½ a. of land at Lokkedonne in Hamme; for her life, rent 6*d.* a year.
Witnesses: Robert Wyther, John Capel, Robert Bastard, Nicholas of the vine (*de vinea*), William Purlewent.
At: Berkeley.

A1/24/269 [GC 4376]   12 Nov. 13 Edw. IV [1473]
John Doly, burgess of Berkeley; and Richard Webbe of Saniger, Margaret his wife and Joan their daughter.

John has leased to Richard, Margaret and John 5 selions of land, two in the field called Luckedon, one in the furlong called Alelond and two in the field called Westfeld; for their lives, rent 8*s.* 10*d.* a year.
Witnesses: Richard Thorppe, John Rycardes, Robert Attwood.
At: Berkeley.

Berkeley Wood

A1/24/270 [GC 1487]   n.d. [*temp.* Edw. I]
Mary daughter of Ivo de Morevil' and Richard le Schipward.

Mary has granted to Richard 1 a. of land in Berkeleyswod, between the land of Sibyl and of Margery, her sisters, which Alfred le Schipward granted to Ivo, her father, with Mabel, her mother, in free marriage; Richard has given Mary 17*s.*
Witnesses: Robert de Bradestan, Walter de Egeton, John de Crauleye, Thomas de Rolee, Thomas le Sergant.

A1/24/271 [GC 1395]   n.d. [*temp.* Edw. I]
Henry son of Henry Grout of Berkeley and Richard le Herl.

Henry has granted to Richard 1 a. of land in the furlong called Berclewode, beside the road from Berkel' to Weneswell; rent ¼*d.* a year, and Richard has given him 20*s.*
Witnesses: Walter Shipward, reeve of Berkeley borough, John Bonserjant, John Sewaker, Richard de la Schambre, Thomas le Serjant, Thomas Alayn.

A1/24/272 [GC 763]   n.d. [late 13th cent.]
Henry son of Henry Grout of Berkeley and Richard le Herl.

Henry has granted to Richard a plot of arable land with a fore-earth, in the furlong called Berclewode, next to the road from Berkel' to Weneswelle; rent ¼*d.* a year, and Richard has given him 24*s.*
Witnesses: Walter Shipward, John Bonsergeant, John Sewaker, Richard de la Chambre, Thomas de Swonhungre, Thomas Alayn.

Miscellaneous

A1/24/273 [SC 434]   Morrow of Quasimodo Sunday [5 April] 1266]
St. Augustine's Abbey and Adam de Loreweng.

The abbey has granted to Adam 10½ a. of land near the field called Newenthonehulle; for the lives of Adam and his wife, rent 4*s.* a year and the services which John his father owed; and for this grant, Adam has granted to the abbey a croft which his father once held, next to the wood of Loreweng, and an entry fine of 10*s.*

A1/24/274 [GC 316]   The Purification, 53 Hen. III [2 Feb. 1269]
Richard le Shipward and Alexander de Purlewent.

Richard has leased to Alexander, for 18*s.*, 2 a. of meadow in the meadow called Parham; for 6 years.
Witnesses: John Sewaker, Robert le Bastard, Richard the cook, Hugh de Pedintone, William Frig.

A1/24/275 [GC 1545]   n.d. [late Hen. III]
Mabel daughter of Alfred le Shipward and Richard her brother, heir of the said Alfred.

Mabel has granted to Richard all the meadow in Perham which she had by grant of the said Alfred in free marriage, for 40*s.*
Witnesses: Peter de Wyke, John Sewaker, William son of Robert, Robert Bastard, Thomas de Ahsselworthe, John de Egeton, Henry de Egeton, Walter Sely.

A1/24/276 [GC 367]   n.d. [late Hen. III]
Robert Caudel and Sir Maurice de Saltmarsh (*de salso marisco*).

Robert, with the assent of Maud his wife, has granted to Maurice 1 a. of land lying above Shadewell, between the land of Mabel de Stane and the land of Eve, Maurice's wife, in exchange for a road between Robert's house and the croft of Hugh of the bridge (*de ponte*). Endorsed: *Alkynton.*
Witnesses: Sir Roger de Lokinton, Sir Walter de Burgo, Sir Henry Droys, Maurice de Stane, William de Stane, Henry Langbord, Andrew de Bratheston.

A1/24/277 [GC 1435]   n.d. [late Hen. III]
Henry Joel, son of Hugh Joel, and Roger de Cantilupo.

Henry has granted to Roger 2¼ a. 11 perches of land in the furlong called Breriforlong; rent ½*d.*, a year and Roger has given him 26*s.*
Witnesses: Sir Maurice de Saltmarsh (*de salso marisco*), Sir Roger de Lokinton, Sir Walter de Burgo, knights, Thomas the serjeant (*serviens*), Andrew de Brothestan, John de Egeton, Robert le Herde, Adam Coby, Alfred Skypward, John Sewaker, Walter Sely, clerk.

A1/24/278 [GC 443]   n.d. [Hen. III × Edw. I]
William de Sokerwyk and St. Augustine's Abbey, Bristol.

William has quitclaimed to the abbey a rent of 12*d.* from land at Plankehulle in the manor of Berkele.
Witnesses: Walter de Egynton, John de Craweleye, John de Wyke, Richard son of Alfred, Robert de Bradeston.

A1/24/279 [GC 1490]   n.d. [*temp.* Edw. I]
Geoffrey Neel and Alan Anger.

Geoffrey has granted to Alan, in free marriage with Agnes his daughter, all his land called [Wittelinen] next to the field of Lockedone, 1 a. of meadow in Bolewyke and the reversion of the land held in dower by Symond his mother and of the land held at farm by Nicholas of the vine (*de vinea*); to them and their issue.
Witnesses: Thomas de Swonhungre, John de Egeton, Thomas Alain, Richard de Stanford, Adam Hathulf.

A1/24/280 [GC 1418]   n.d. [*temp.* Edw. I]
Richard le Hopere of Ham and Clarice his daughter.

Richard, with the assent of Alice his wife, has granted to Clarice a messuage with a garden in Maggeford, which Bridget, Alice's mother, formerly held; to her and her issue, rent 1*d.* a year.
Witnesses: William Capele, Robert Bastard, Richard de Wendene, Henry de Homme, Robert Pynel.

A1/24/281 [GC 767]   n.d. [late 13th cent.]
William son of Richard le Hopere and Thomas his brother.

William has quitclaimed to Thomas the croft in Hamme at Maggeford next to Pedimersh which he had from Alice his mother.

Witnesses: Thomas Alein, Thomas le Serjant, Richard de Wendene, Robert Bastard, Hervid de Hamme, Henry Grout.

A1/24/282 [GC 732]   n.d. [late 13th cent.]
Eve Clotleye and Helen daughter of John de Killecote.

Eve has granted to Helen 4 selions of land in the field called Plankehulle between the land of St. Augustine and the land of Walter le Gardiner; rent 1½d. a year to the chief lord of the fee.

Witnesses: Geoffrey Neel, Henry Cuppere, Walter Cuppere, Henry Gardiner, Henry Grout.

A1/24/283 [GC 726]   n.d. [late 13th cent.]
John de Crauleye; and John le Vinor and Agnes his wife.

John has granted to John and Agnes, for their lives, 10 a. of land in the field called Mimtoneshull; rent 6d. a year, and John has given him 6 marks and all the land which John had from John le Coppare for his life in exchange.

Witnesses: John le Coppare, Walter Seuwoker, Thomas de Lorewinge, Roger le Coppare, John de Swonhungre.

A1/24/284 [GC 759]   Easter, 25 Edw. I [14 April 1297]
Helen daughter of William Frig of Ham; Robert Wyther and Sibyl his wife.

Helen has leased to Robert and Sibyl 2 perches of meadow in Perhame, one in Dupemore and the other in the meadow called Hunimed; from Easter 25 Edw. I until five crops have been taken.

Witnesses: Richard de Wenden, Robert Bastard, John Purlewent, William son of Robert.

A1/24/285 [GC 760]   n.d. [*c.* 1297]
Helen daughter of William le Frig of Ham, widow; and Robert Wyther and Sibyl his wife.

Helen has granted to Robert and Sibyl all her meadow in Perhame which lies next to la Mordich to the west, for a certain sum of money; rent ½d. to the chief lord of the fee.

Witnesses: Robert de Stan, Robert de Bradeston, Thomas le Serjant, John de Crauley, Robert Bastard, John Purlewent, William son of Robert.

A1/24/286 [GC 1602]   n.d. [*temp.* Edw. I]
Adam ate Barre of Berkeley and John Sewaker.

Adam has granted to John 1 a. of land in Adam's croft, beside the land of St. Augustine's Abbey, Bristol, called Leye; rent 7½d. a year, and John has given him 11s.

Witnesses: Walter Schipward, reeve of Berkeley, Thomas Aleyn, John Bonserjant, William Cuppere, Henry Cuppere.

A1/24/287 [GC 984]   n.d. [early 14th cent.]
Henry de Weneswell and John le Frig.

Henry has granted to John, for a certain sum of money, 8 selions with a fore-earth at each head in Leyfeld, opposite la Lane, all the land at Marshull, 1 selion in Schurchfeld, 1 selion in the same beyond Marbroc and all the land in Nortfeld below Lutlehom; to hold of the lord of Berkel', rent a rose a year.

Witnesses: Nicholas de Wodeford, Walter de Bathon', Richard Brun, Nicholas Frankelan, William Nouthon.

A1/24/288 [GC 425] n.d. [*c.* 1310]
John Sewaker the elder and Richard le Gardiner.

John has granted to Richard, in free marriage with Isabel his daughter, 14 selions of land in the furlong called Plankehulle, lying among the land of Robert Gamel, which John gave to Robert in marriage with Gunnilda his daughter; rent 6*d.* a year and the royal service which pertains to 2 *a.* Endorsed: *Cowley.*
Witnesses: John de Eggeton, John Sewaker the younger, reeve, Adam Gobi, Alfred le Scipward, Hugh Joel, William the palmer (*palmerius*), Richard the deacon (*diaconus*).

A1/24/289 [GC 1780] Wed. the feast of St. Katherine, 4 Edw. II [25 Nov. 1310]
Henry Pridy son of Margery de Morvyle; and William Page and Juliana his wife.

Henry has granted to William and Juliana a messuage with a curtilage, garden, croft [etc.], which he holds of St. Augustine's Abbey in Hamme near Berckeleye, and 1 a. of land in the field called Berckeleyewode, beside the fishpond called Smethemore, also the croft at Marebrok in Hamme which formerly was of Walter de Haggeleye, 2 selions in the field called Westfeld and 4 selions in the croft called Barricroft; for their lives, rendering the customary services to the lord of the fee, and they have given him a certain sum of money.
Witnesses: John de Alkeleye, John le Cuppere, John Sewaker, John le Serjaunt, John Schipward, Edward de Fremelode, Thomas le Muleward.
At: Berkeley.

A1/24/290 [GC 1837] Fri. after the Assumption, 5 Edw. II [20 Aug. 1311]
Robert Nottestok of Stone and William son of Walter Doucesone of Hinton.

Robert has granted to William 1 a. of land in the croft called Frithecroft in the manor of Hamme, which came to him on the death of his mother Alice; to hold of the chief lord by the customary services, and William has given him a certain sum of money.
Witnesses: Roger de la Garstone, Thomas de Stone, John Capel, Nicholas Iweyn, Walter Snyte, John de Lyndeseye, William Northlane.
At: Stone by Berkeley.

A1/24/291 [GC 2494] n.d. [early 14th cent.]
Joan widow of John Bonserjaunt of Berkeley; and Roger le Coppare of Berkeley and Isabel his wife.

Joan has granted to Roger and Isabel 4 selions of land in the field called Nokeshulle; rent to the lamp of the Blessed Virgin Mary in Berckel' church 3*d.* a year.
Witnesses: John le Coppare, Henry le Gardiner, Richard Noblepas, John le Vyngnur, Adam Pynel, William Bodde, Walter le Coppare, Robert Swele, Robert Groundy.

A1/24/292 [GC 2387] Sun. the feast of St. James, 16 Edw. II [25 July 1322]
John Abbod and John de Lorewynge.

John Abbod has quitclaimed to John de Lorewynge the lands which he previously had in Walmegarstone and Frithegorst and 1 a. of meadow in Stapelynge, in Hamme.
Witnesses: John le Serjaunt, John de Egeton, John de Swonhongre, Edward de Fromelode, Hugh de Costone.
At: Berkeley.

A1/24/293 [GC 2680] St. Augustine, 3 Edw. III [26 May 1329]
William son of Alice Bolcard and John Broun.

William has quitclaimed to John the holding which John has of the holding formerly of Alice, his mother.
Witnesses: John le Serjaunt, John Capel, John de Swonhungre, John de Egeton, John Wyke, Richard de Stanford, Nicholas Neel.
At: Wanswell.

A1/24/294 [GC 2881]   Fri. after St. Peter and St. Paul, 11 Edw. III [4 July 1337]
Isabel la Hopare of Ham, unmarried woman; and John le Hopare and Elizabeth his wife.

Isabel has granted to John and Edith a curtilage and 1 selion in Hamme; to them and John's issue, rent a rose a year.
Witnesses: Robert Groundy, John Schipward, John le Webbe, John Payn, William Fryg, Richard the smith (*fab'*), John de Fromelode.
At: Ham.

A1/24/295 [GC 2935]   Fri. the feast of St. Wulfstan [*sic*], 13 Edw. III [19 Jan. 1340]
John le Clerkes of Berkeley and Maud his wife; and John Payn and Alice his wife.

John and Maud have leased to John and Alice a parcel of land in Yonderaketre; for Maud's life, rent 3*s.* a year.
Witnesses: Robert Groundy, John le Schipward, John Gomylef, John le Sopare, John le Bil.
At: Berkeley.

A1/24/296 [GC 2986]   Fri. after St. Peter in cathedra, 15 Edw. III [23 Feb. 1341]
Juliana daughter of William le Hopare and John le Hopare of Berkeley.

Juliana has granted to John, his heirs and assigns all her lands and holdings [etc.] in Hamme which she inherited after the death of William her father.
Witnesses: John Capel, Robert Groundy, John Purlewent, William son of Robert, Robert Bastard, William Smyth, Adam Purlewent.
At: Ham.

A1/24/297 [GC 3134; *duplicates* GC 3135 *and* GC 3136; *an early 15th-cent. copy* GC 3137]
                                                      14 March 20 Edw. III [1346]
(1) John Capel; (2) Thomas de Swonhongre; (3) John de Lorewyng.

Partition of the inheritance of John de Wyke in Hamme between John, Thomas and John as the sons and heirs of Joan Capel, Alice de Swonhongre and Agnes de Lorewynge. [*In French.*]
At: Berkeley.

A1/24/298 [GC 2606]   n.d. [mid 14th cent.]
Sibyl daughter of the late Thomas Page; and Richard le Paniter and Alice his wife.

Sibyl has granted to Richard and Alice her status in a croft called Sterte and in 3 parcels of land in Walmegarstone, and in 2 a. of meadow in the marsh [*mora*] of Wyke held of Thomas de Swonhungre in Hamme, as appears in an indenture made with John de Swonhungre; also in 5 a. of land in various parcels in Walmegarstone in Hamme held of John Capel, as in the indenture made with him, which indentures have been delivered to Richard and Alice.
Witnesses: John de Egetone, William de Swonhungre, John de Lorewyng, Robert Groundy, Robert Bastard.

A1/24/299 [GC 3530]   Sat. the feast of St. Denis, 35 Edw. III [9 Oct. 1361]
William Modebroke, son and heir of Henry Modebroke of Berkeley; and John Scherare of Berkeley and John Jinke of Stinchcombe.

William has granted to John and John, and their heirs and assigns, 8 a. of land within the manor of Hamme.
Witnesses: John Sergeaunt, John Aleyn, Thomas Goldhop, Thomas Payn, John Byl.
At: Berkeley.

A1/24/300 [GC 3595]   Fri. the eve of Christmas, 41 Edw. III [24 Dec. 1367]
Edward Fromelode of Berkeley; and Sir Walter Goldemere and Sir William Wynbaud, chaplains.

Edward has granted to Walter and William, and their heirs and assigns, all his meadow and pasture in Oxenham and Wynmed, within the lordship of Berkele.
Witnesses: John Sergeant, John Aleyn of Hill, Henry Egetone, William Modebroke, John Coby.
At: Berkeley.

A1/24/301 [GC 3339]   n.d. [late 14th cent.]
Nicholas le Shipward of Berkeley; and William le Smith of Ham and Margery his wife.

Nicholas has leased to William and Margery 1½ a. of land in the field called Shiplyng in Hamme; for their lives, rent 2*s.* a year.
Witnesses: William Modebroke, John Bastard, William Balstake, John Purlewent, John Gare.

A1/24/302 [GC 3874]   Sun. the feast of St. Aldhelm, 16 Ric. II [25 May 1393]
Thomas Bathe of Berkeley and Joan his wife; and Thomas James and Joan his wife.

Thomas Bathe and Joan have leased to Thomas James and Joan the holding with a foreland that John Syngare formerly held in Hamme; for a term of 69 years, rent 20*s.* a year.
Witnesses: John FitzRobert, John Purlewent, John Edward, William Clerk, Andrew Carter.
At: Berkeley.

A1/24/303 [GC 3922]   The Annunciation, 20 Ric. II [25 March 1397]
Robert Schippard, son and heir of the late Nicholas Schippard of Berkeley; and John Coke, Joan his wife and Margaret their daughter.

Robert has leased to John, Joan and Margaret a meadow called le Quabbe beside the road from Berkel' to Hamme; for their lives, with licence to fell trees, rent 3*s.* a year.
Witnesses: Richard Toukere, Richard Panyter, William ate Berwe, Richard Scot, John Byl.
At: Berkeley.

HAM MANOR: LAND IN BERKELEY

The deeds below relate to arable land in Berkeley vill, administered with Ham manor, not with the borough, although clearly the two overlap.

BERKELEY FAMILY

A1/25/1 [SC 57]   n.d. [*c.* 1200]
Alice de Berkele and Thomas her son.

Alice has granted to Thomas all her land of Berkeley; rent 12*d.* a year.
Witnesses: John abbot of St. Augustine's, William abbot of Keynsham, Master Maurice de Slimbridge, William de Morevill, Maurice and Henry de Berkeley, Alice's sons, Gilbert and William, chaplains of Slimbridge, Wiot de Vilers and Walter his brother, William de Hulle, Elias de Slimbridge.

A1/25/2 [SC 327]   n.d. [*temp.* Hen. III]
Thomas de Berkeley and Peter de Wike.

Thomas has granted to Peter the land which Richard Wager held of him in Berkeley; rent 12*d.* a year.
Witnesses: Peter de Stintescumbe, Henry de Berkele, William de Berkele, Elias the butler (*pincerna*), John de Eggeton, Adam Cobi, John Sewaker, William the clerk.

A1/25/3 [SC 303]   Sun. after Easter [11 April] 1260
Richard son of Robert, merchant, and Maurice de Berkele, his lord.

Richard has granted to Maurice, for [50]*s.*, land lying in front of the castle gate.
Witnesses: Thomas Cavel, reeve of Berkeley, Peter de Wike, John Sewak', Adam Coby, Thomas son of Alan, John Bonserjaunt, William Cole, William Cuppere, Walter Sely.

A1/25/4 [GC 530]   Sun. after the Assumption, 15 Edw. I [17 Aug. 1287]
Robert le Grip, son and heir of Walter le Grip, of Newport, and Sir Thomas de Berkel, his lord.

Robert has quitclaimed to Thomas a croft with appurtenances in the west part of Berkel towards Swonhungre called Alagrene street, which descended to him by inheritance after the death of his father Walter.
At: Berkeley.

A1/25/5 [GC 2270]   12 March 12 Edw. II [1319]
Alice widow of Thomas le Hopere and John le Hopere her son; and Sir Thomas de Berkeleye, lord of Berkeley.

Alice and John have granted to Thomas a rent of 3s. from a messuage with a curtilage at Berkeleye in Hamme; for their lives.
Witnesses: John le Serjaunt, John Capel, John Wyth, John le Cuppere, John Sewaker.
At: Berkeley.

A1/25/6 [GC 3281]   n.d. [mid 14th cent.]
Thomas de Berkelee, lord of Berkeley; and Robert Balstake, his cook [keu], and Margaret his wife.

Thomas has granted to Robert and Margaret and their issue his part of a parcel of land in Berkelee; for the customary rent. [*In French.*]
Witnesses: John de Clyve, constable of Berkeley Castle, William Modebrok, John Coby, John Bil, Thomas Goldhoppe.

OTHER TENANTS AND HOLDINGS
Grants to Peter de Wick

A1/25/7 [SC 326]   n.d. [*temp.* Hen. III]
Adam Cube and Peter de Wike, son of Hugh de Wike.

Adam has granted to Peter a messuage with appurtenances lying between the land of Stanley Priory which Peter the forester (*forestarius*) held of the priory and the land which Richard Wager held of Sir Thomas de Berkeley; rent 1d. a year to Adam and 2d. a year to the chief lord, and Peter gave Adam 7s.
Witnesses: Adam Cobi, John Sewaker, Alan de Clotleg', Gilbert Corveiser, William Bonsergant, Jordan Tece.

A1/25/8 [GC 1278]   n.d. [late Hen. III]
William de Canvill and Peter de Wike.

William has granted to Peter all the land, with meadow, pasture [etc.], in the town of Berkeley which he had by grant of Maurice son of Maurice son of Negell, except the messuage which Thomas Cavel holds of William and 1 a. of land which John Sewaker holds of William, with the services of Thomas and John; rent 12s. a year.
Witnesses: Sir Maurice de Saltmarsh (*de salso marisco*), Sir Robert le Veel, Sir Robert de Kingeston, knights, John de Brothestan, John Sewaker, Thomas the serjeant (*serviens*), John de Craweleye, Geoffrey Neel, Walter Sely.

A1/25/9 [GC 1276]   n.d. [late Hen. III]
William de Canville and Peter de Wyke.

William is bound to Peter to warrant him for all the land which Peter had by William's grant in the territory of Berkel, as in his charter [above, A1/25/8, GC 1278].
Witnesses: Sir Nicholas vicar of Berkeley, Roger de Lokinton, John de Brothestan, Richard de Stanford, Thomas the serjeant (*serviens*), Geoffrey Carbonel, John Sewaker.

Coby Mortgage
A1/25/10 [GC 2902]   Tues. after the Invention of Holy Cross, 12 Edw. III [5 May 1338]
Walter son and heir of Roger le Cuppare of Berkeley and John Cobi of Berkeley, the elder.

Walter has leased to John his croft in Berkeley; to hold, with the spring, hedges and ditches, for John's life, but if he dies within 12 years then his heirs or assigns shall hold the holding until the end of the term.

Witnesses: Robert Groundy, John le Cuppare, John le Schipward, Henry de Modybrok, John le Webbe, Alexander de Bathe.

At: Berkeley.

A1/25/11 [GC 2903]   Tues. after the Invention of Holy Cross, 12 Edw. III [5 May 1338]
John Cobi of Berkeley, the elder, and Walter le Cuppare of Berkeley.

Whereas Walter has granted to John a croft in Berkel' for his life, John has granted that if he receives 24*s*. from Walter at Michaelmas next after the completion of 12 years after this date, the enfeoffment will be void.

Witnesses: John Gomylef, John de Fromelode, Robert le Schipward, Robert Prykke, John Bil.

At: Berkeley.

Dolley leases

A1/25/12 [GC 4207]   4 May 15 Hen. VI [1437]
William Doly of Berkeley; and Robert Gybbus of Marsh (Mersch), Joan his wife and Richard their son.

William has leased to Robert, Joan and Richard a croft of land called Gardynerysfeld; for their lives, rent 10*s*. a year.

Witnesses: David Chepmon, Robert Ecton, Robert Wytt'.

At: Berkeley.

A1/25/13 [GC 4228]   The Annunciation [25 March], 20 Hen. VI, A.D. 1442
William Doly, burgess of Berkeley, and Richard Clavyle of the same.

William has leased to Richard 12 selions of land in the field called Okeshull; for a term of 11 years, rent a red rose a year.

Witnesses: Robert Batyn, chaplain, Thomas Clyfford, Richard Lee, John Payn, Robert Wytte.

At: Berkeley.

A1/25/14 [GC 4257]   10 May 25 Hen. VI [1447]
John Doly, burgess of Berkeley; and Walter Hevyn the younger, Maud his wife, John their son and Joan their daughter.

John has leased to Walter, Maud, John and Joan a parcel of land in the field called Nokeshull; for their lives, rent 12*d*. a year.

Witnesses: Richard Lee, Robert Rycardes, John Payn.

At: Berkeley.

Payn grants

A1/25/15 [GC 4264]   28 April 26 Hen. VI [1448]
John Payn of Berkeley; and John Thorpe of Berkeley and Margaret his wife.

John Payn has granted to John and Margaret, and John's heirs, an annual rent of 2*s*. from the land and holdings in Berkeley which he had by grant of John Dyrlyng, burgess of Bristoll, and Isabel his wife.

Witnesses: John Dyer, Richard Lee, Richard Ecton.

A1/25/16 [GC 4265]   30 April 26 Hen. VI [1448]
(1) John Payn of Berkeley; (2) Joan widow of Richard Skott; (3) Richard Kyng; (4) John Dyrlyng and Isabel his wife.

John has granted to Joan a messuage and 8 a. of land, 1 a. of meadow and 1 a. of pasture called le Avereys in Berkeley parish, and has granted to Richard a messuage in Berkeley, to each for their lives, rent from Richard 13*s*. 4*d*. a year; and he has granted to John and Isabel and their issue a messuage in Berkeley [etc.]

Witnesses: John Dyer, Richard Lee, Richard Ecton.

Other

A1/25/17 [SC 92]   n.d. [1190 × 1216]
Guy prior of Southwick and J[ohn] abbot of St. Augustine's.

The prior has granted to St. Augustine's Abbey all the land in Berkelaio which Sir Robert de Berkelaio and Juliana his wife gave to the priory.[1]
Witnesses: Sir Robert de Berkeley, Juliana his wife, R. prior of St. Augustine's, brother J. the chamberlain, brother W. the sacristan, on the one part, and on the other Owen (*Audoenus*) sub-prior, and canons Luke, Robert and Walkelin.

A1/25/18 [SC 492]   n.d. [late Edw. I]
John de Newenton, warden and prior of Holy Trinity Hospital near Longbridge, outside Berkeley, and Robert Wyther.

The prior has quitclaimed to Robert a rent of 2*s.* from lands in Berkeley which were of Gilbert the baker (*pistor*) and Robert will pay to them a rent of 2*s.* a year.
Witnesses: Robert de Stane, Thomas Alein, Richard Averey, John Sewaker, Walter Cuppere, Richard le Savon.

A1/25/19 [GC 597]   4 Aug. 21 Edw. I [1293]
Peter de Hacham, prior of the hospital of St. John of Jerusalem in England, and Henry le Gardiner.

The prior notifies that Henry is the hospital's free tenant in Berkeley.
At: Berkeley.

A1/25/20 [GC 3091]   Thurs. after St. Gregory, 18 Edw. III [18 March 1344]
Sibyl and Joan daughters and heirs of Thomas Page; and John Sley of Berkeley.

Sibyl and Joan have granted to John, his heirs and assigns a parcel of land in Berkeleye.
Witnesses: Robert Groundy, Robert Prikke, John le Webbe, Richard ate Panetre, Henry Swele.
At: Berkeley.

A1/25/21 [GC 3784]   Tues. after St. Gregory, 8 Ric. II [14 March 1385]
Thomas de Berkeley of Coberley, sheriff of Gloucestershire, and John Deneys.

Memorandum that on the Tuesday after St. Gregory, 8 Ric. II, Thomas received from John a writ of warranty by which John is petitioning against Peter de Veel of Tortworth, knight, for a toft, 35 a. of land, 2 a. of meadow, 33 a. of pasture, 10 a. of wood and 6*d.* rent in Berkele.

HAM: BEVINGTON
BERKELEY FAMILY
Pavicroft

A1/26/1 [GC 748]   n.d. [*temp.* Hen. III]
Elias le Iskermisur and Maud his younger daughter.

Elias has granted to Maud half of the croft in Bevintun called Pavicroft, viz. the eastern part, and ½ a. of land in the furlong called Longenacre; rent ½*d.* a year.
Witnesses: Adam Flamberd, Maurice de Stanes, William de Mandewer, Nicholas the Scot (*Scoticus*), Luke Russel, . . . , Elias de Wikkestowe.

A1/26/2 [GC 2492]   n.d. [1300 × 1306]
John Bochard; and Sir Thomas de Berkelegh, lord of Berkeley, and Lady Joan his wife.

John, with the assent of Maud his wife, daughter of the late Elias le Skyrmysour, has granted to Thomas and Joan his cottage with a croft called Pavycroft, which Maud previously had by grant of the said Elias in Bevynton.
Witnesses: Robert de Berkelee, Robert de Bradestone, Thomas de Beolee, Robert Wyther, John Porlewent, Robert Bastard, Nicholas the clerk (*cler'*).

---

[1] *Transcript*: *St Augustine's Cartulary*, no. 136.

A1/26/3 [GC 1129]   Sat. after St. Laurence, 34 Edw. I [13 Aug. 1306]
William Cole, son and heir of Maud daughter of Elias le Skyrmisour; and Sir Thomas de
Berk', lord of Berkeley, and Lady Joan his wife.

William has quitclaimed to Thomas and Joan a cottage and adjacent croft called Pavicroft
at Bevynton in Hamme, which Thomas previously had by grant of Maud, William's mother.
Witnesses: Robert de Berkelee, Robert de Bradeston, Thomas de Beolee, Robert Wyther,
John Porlewent, Robert Bastard, Nicholas Clerk.
At: Berkeley.

A1/26/4 [GC 1640]   10 Dec. 35 Edw. I [1306]
Thomas de Berkeleye, lord of Berkeley; and John Nabbescal and Eleanor his wife.

Thomas has granted to John and Eleanor the holding which he had by grant of John
Bochard and Maud his wife at Bevynton in Hamme; to them and their issue, rent 4*s*. 6*d*. a
year.
Witnesses: Robert Wyther, John Porlewent, Robert Bastard, Nicholas the clerk, Nicholas
Iweyn.
At: Berkeley.

Wyther rent

A1/26/5 [GC 1883]   1 June 5 Edw. II [1312]
Isabel widow of John de Ayschscheleworthy and Sir Thomas de Berkelee, lord of Berkeley.

Isabel has granted to Thomas a rent of 6*d*. a year from Robert Wither for the holding
which Thomas le Carpenter holds in Bevynton, in Hamme.
Witnesses: Thomas de Stone, John Capel, Thomas Aleyn, Robert Bastard, John de
Purlewent.
At: Berkeley.

A1/26/6 [GC 1894]   All Saints, 6 Edw. II [1 Nov. 1312]
Robert de Ayschscheleworthy and Sir Thomas de Berkelee, lord of Berkeley.

Robert has inspected the charter of his mother, Isabel de Ay[schscheleworthy], whereby
she granted to Thomas a rent of 6*d*. from Robert Wither in Bevynton, and has quitclaimed it
to Thomas.
Witnesses: Thomas de Stone, Thomas de Bradestone, John Capel, Robert Bastard, Nicholas
Iweyn.
At: Berkeley.

Other

A1/26/7 [GC 711]   n.d. [late 13th cent.]
Edith daughter of Robert de Bybury, widow, and Sir Thomas de Berkeleye, her lord.

Edith has granted to Thomas, for 4*s*., her part of a house, curtilage and croft in Bevinton
which she inherited from Maud her mother, lying between the high street and the field
called Dedefeld.
Witnesses: Peter de Stintescumbe, William de Burgo, Robert de Bradeston, Thomas de
Swonhungre, Thomas de Beolye, Robert Bastard, Nicholas Iwein.

A1/26/8 [GC 1766]   Tues. in Michaelmas, 4 Edw. II [29 Sept. 1310]
Thomas de Berkelee, lord of Berkeley; and Thomas de Carswelle and Margaret his wife.

Thomas has granted to Thomas and Margaret the holding which Elias le Cran formerly
held in Bevynton, beside the road from Bevyntone to Hulle, containing 1 a., in Hamme; to
hold enclosed, to them and their heirs, rent 4*s*. a year.
Witnesses: Thomas de Stone, Robert Wither, John Capel, John Purlewent, Nicholas the
clerk, Robert Bastard, Nicholas Iweyn.
At: Berkeley.

OTHER TENANTS AND HOLDINGS
Ross holding

A1/26/9 [SC 367]   n.d. [*temp.* Edw. I]
Robert de Egeton and Reginald son of William Buddig of Bevington.

Robert has granted to Reginald the holding in Bevinton which Roger le Ros sometime held; rent 6*d.* a year, for which Reginald has given Robert 10*s.*
Witnesses: Walter de Egeton, Thomas de Swonhongre, Richard the cook (*coquus*), Alexander Purlewent, Hugh Wayneterre, Nicholas Scoth.

A1/26/10 [GC 2572]   n.d. [late 13th cent.]
Reginald Budding; and Robert Wyther and Sibyl his wife.

Reginald has granted to Robert and Sibyl all his holding at Bevinton for a certain sum of money.
Witnesses: Richard de Biseleye, steward, Robert de Stone, William Capel, Thomas Alein.

Kingswood Abbey

A1/26/11 [SC 233]   St. Ciricus and St. Julitta [16 June] 1234
Roger Aillard of Bristol and Kingswood Abbey.

Roger has granted to the abbey 1 virgate of land, which Maud Bulcard held from him in Bevinton, and the land called Colehide nearby; the abbey to pay him 18*d.* a year, but Roger will pay the 6*d.* a year for the virgate and the 6*d.* for Colehide due to the lords of the fee, and 6*d.* relief on change of heirs.
Witnesses: Geoffrey de Chausi, Walter Cauvel, Richard Aillard, Richard le Warre, William Beumund, Richard de Bochoure, Hugh de Howelle, Geoffrey de Rodmerton, Thomas de la Planche.

A1/26/12 [SC 237]   St. Ambrose [4 April] 1236
Thomas de Berkelay and Kingswood Abbey.

Thomas has confirmed to the monks the grant by Roger Ailard of 1 virgate at Bevintun and the holding called Colehide, both previously held by Maud Bulcard, and further has remitted and quitclaimed to the monks the services which Roger owed him for the two holdings.
Witnesses: Ralph de Wilintun, Nicholas son of Roger, Geoffrey de Chausi, Oliver de Berkeley, Simon de Olepenne, Henry and William de Berkeley, sons of the grantor, Bartholomew Labanch, Roger de Ducton, Thomas de la Planche, Walter his brother, John de Egintun, Robert Veel (*Vitulus*), William de Bradeleg', Matthew le Scay, Robert de Soreston, Adam Russel, Arnulf the clerk.

Other

A1/26/13 [GC 362]   n.d. [1230 × 1261]
Maurice de Bevintone and Adam Flaumbard.

Maurice has granted to Adam, in free marriage with his daughter Hawise, the messuage which Roger Rot once held in the vill of Bevintone, 2 a. of land in Henacre, 1 a. in Lutlecrofte, 4 selions with 2 fore-earths (*forherdis*) at Worthi, 1 a. in Goldemere, 1 a. above Graveberwe, 2 selions and all that land in Heldegerstone and all the land called la Berwe and the charter of Sir Thomas de Berkeley of the said Berwe [etc.]; rent 8½*d.*
Witnesses: Sir Nicholas son of Roger, Sir Richard de Cromhale, Sir Henry de Berkelai, Maurice de Stanes, Andrew de Bradestone, John de Egeton, Adam son of Nigel, Adam Cobi, Nicholas the Scot (*Scoticus*), William Mandewerre, Luke Russel.

A1/26/14 [SC 281]   One weeks after St. John the evangelist [27 Dec.], A.D. 1243
(1) Abbot William [Long] and the abbey of St. Augustine's; (2) Maurice de Bevintun; (3) Maurice de Berkeley.

The abbot has declared that he will allow no loss from the land in Bevington which Maurice de Bevintun leased to the abbey to fall on either Maurice de Bevinton or Maurice de Berkeley, in consideration of the confirmation by Maurice, son and heir of Thomas de Berkeley, of the grants made to the abbey by Maurice de Bevintun of a court, two crofts called la Burlonde, 36 a. of arable land, 7¾ a. of meadow, 3 a. of pasture, rent of 1 bu. of wheat from Elias le Eskermissur and rent of 1*d*. from Elias son of Maurice de Bevintun.

Witnesses: Sir William de Putot, Roger de Lukinton, Maurice de Saltmarsh (*de salso marisco*), Thomas Long (*longus*), William de Beaumont (*de Bello Monte*), Robert de Legh, Robert de Hales, John Tike, Adam Russel, Adam de Portesheved.

A1/26/15 [GC 1403]   n.d. [*temp*. Edw. I]

Henry de Hamme and Robert Wyther.

Henry has granted to Robert, for a certain sum of money, 3 a. and 2 fore-earths of land in Bevintun, which is called Wythicroft and lies beside the great road from Bevintun to Clopton; rent to the lord of Berkel' 1*d*. a year.

Witnesses: Robert de Stone, William Capel, Thomas Alein, Richard de Wendene, Robert Bastard, Richard le Savoner, clerk.

HAM: CLAPTON

THE BASTARD HOLDING

A1/27/1 [SC 93]   n.d. [1190 × 1216]

Robert de Berkeleia and Robert Bastard.

Robert de Berkeleia has granted to Robert Bastard 1 virgate of land in Cloptune in Ham, which Aldwin Coppe held, the land next to it which was held by Sewin son of Richard, and 4 a. of meadow in Robert de Berkeleia's meadow of Perham; rent 1 lb. of pepper a year, and Robert Bastard has become Robert de Berkeleia's man.

Witnesses: John abbot of St. Augustine's, William abbot of Kingswood, Adam son of Nigel, Maurice his brother, Robert de Aubemare, Ralph his brother, Walter dean of . . . , Walter chaplain of Berkeley, Reginald de Gosintone, Bernard de Stanes, Bernard de Brotheston, Hugh de Camme, Roger de Planca, Richard Cotell.

A1/27/2 [GC 676]   n.d. [late Hen. III]

Robert Bastard and Richard his son.

Robert has granted to Richard 3 a. of arable land in Cloptune, viz. 1 a. in the furlong called Cloplinge, and 2 selions in the furlong of Cottenhale, and 1 selion in the same and 2 selions in the furlong called Cotfourforlong; also 2 a. of meadow in the meadow of Perham'; rent a rose a year.

Witnesses: Sir William de Berkel, Sir Richard his brother, knights, Philip de Leycestre, Walter de Egetune, Robert de Egetun, John de Craweleg', Geoffrey Neel, Walter Sely.

A1/27/3 [GC 1186]   n.d. [late Hen. III]

Robert Bastard and Sir Maurice de Berkel'.

Robert has granted to Maurice 5 a. of arable land in the marsh called Beningehemmersh next to the Severn, viz. 1 a. in the furlong called la Worthy, 3 a. in Oxenehay, and 1 a. in the upper furlong of Oxenehay containing 3 selions, extending to Longepullesdich; Maurice has given him 6 marks.

Witnesses: Sir Warin de Raleg', Sir Nicholas Wolf (*Lupus*), Sir Robert de Kingestun, knights, William Gulafre, William Capel, Robert de Ston', Robert de Bratheston, Walter de Egetun, John de Craweleye.

THE ALVARDE HOLDING

A1/27/4 [GC 3970]   28 Feb. 1 Hen. IV [1400]

Thomas Berkeleye, lord of Berkeley; and Thomas Browne and Isabel his wife.

Thomas Berkeleye has leased to Thomas Browne and Isabel, for Thomas's good and laudable service, the holding and virgate of land which Robert Alvarde held of Thomas in

Cloptone within the manor of Hamme, with 8 a. of foreland; for their lives, rent for the virgate 1*d.* a year and for the foreland 8*s.* a year.
At: Berkeley.

A1/27/5 [GC 4071]   1 June 13 Hen. IV [1412]
Thomas Berkeley, lord of Berkeley; and Thomas Browne and Maud his wife.

Thomas Berkeley has leased to Thomas Browne and Maud, for Thomas's good and laudable service, the holding and virgate of land which Robert Alvarde held of Thomas Berkeley in Clopton within the manor of Hamme, with 8 a. of foreland; for their lives, rent for the virgate 1*d.* a year and for the foreland 8*s.* a year.
At: Berkeley.

THE ADAMS HOLDING

A1/27/6 [GC 4204]   Mon. before St. Luke, 15 Hen. VI [15 Oct. 1436]
James Berkeley, lord of Berkeley, knight; and William Smyth, son of John Smyth, of Hinton and Eleanor his wife.

James has leased to William two messuages and two half-virgates of land in Cloptone and a pasture in Peddemershe which Edmund Adames held; to William and Eleanor for their lives, rent 52*s.* 8*d.*
At: Berkeley Castle.

A1/27/7 [GC 4242]   . . . Easter, 22 Hen. VI [*c.* April 1444]
James Berkeley . . . , and John Adams, son of Thomas Adams late of . . .

James has leased to John two half-virgates of land in le Yondir Cloptone and a pasture in Peddemersch . . . ; for his life, rent 52*s.* 8*d.* a year.
At: Berkeley Castle.

THE EDWARDS HOLDING

A1/27/8 [GC 4220]   19 Sept. 20 Hen. VI [1441]
James Berkeley, lord of Berkeley, knight; and John Broune the younger, Cecilia his wife and John their son.

James has granted to John, Cecilia and John a messuage and 1 virgate and a half-virgate of land in Cloptone and also two messuages in Hamme called Magfordes, all the lands, holdings [etc.] which John Edward and Juliana his wife held in her right; for their lives, rent 66*s.* 7*d.* a year.
Witnesses: Master John Tumbrell, vicar of Berkeley, Nicholas Stanschawe, John Thorpp.

A1/27/9 [SC 611]   31 Oct. 3 Edw. IV [1463]
James Lord Berkeley and Thomas Berkeley, esquire, his son.

James has granted to Thomas the messuage in Clopton, with all the lands, etc. which pertain to it within Berkeley hundred which John Edward lately held, and further all the lands in the county of Gloucester which James holds in fee simple.
Witnesses: Walter Ferys, Lord Ferys, John Barre, knight, Maurice Berkeley of Beverston, esquire, Maurice Deneys, esquire, John Thorpp.
At: Berkeley.

OTHER

A1/27/10 [GC 284]   St. Vincent 37 Hen. III [22 Jan. 1253]
Denise widow of Robert Forestar and Sir Maurice de Berkeley.

Denise has granted to Maurice the land which she held in the field of Berunerhersshe in dower, Maurice to render 2*s.* 8*d.* a year to Denise while she lives; and further Denise has leased to Maurice the land which lies between her garden and Maurice's land, for her life, with conditions regarding sowing, harvesting, pasture [etc.]
Witnesses: Maurice de Stane, Robert Bastard, Nicholas de Coldewelle, William Cust', William son of Robert, Robert le Herde.

A1/27/11 [GC 729]   n.d. [late Hen. III]
Richard the cook (*cocus*) of Clapton and Sir Maurice de Berk', his lord.

Richard has granted to Maurice the grove with appurtenances next to Maurice's wood of Whiteclive, being part of the land which Richard had from Sir Thomas de Berk' his father in the vill of Clopton, for a reasonable exchange from Maurice.
Witnesses: Sir Roger de Lokinton, Sir Maurice de Saltmarsh (*de salso marisco*), Sir Walter de Burgo, knights, Maurice de Stanes, Peter de Wyke, Robert Bastard, Adam Flambert, Adam Coby, Alfred Marenar'.

A1/27/12 [GC 689]   n.d. [late Hen. III]
Maurice lord of Berkele and Sir Roger de Lokinton.

Maurice has granted to Roger 30 a. of land in his manor of Hamme, viz. 17 a. in the field called Wowethurn south of the way from Clopton to the Severn, 8½ a. in the field similarly called Wowethurn north of the same way, and 4½ a. in the field called Redecroft, in exchange for 31 a. in the same manor.
Witnesses: Sir Maurice de Saltmarsh (*de salso marisco*), Sir Richard de Cromhal, knights, Master William, Maurice's steward, John de Egeton, Robert le Bastard, Maurice de Stanes, Adam Flamberd, Robert le Herde, Walter Sely, clerk.

A1/27/13 [GC 2891]   5 Dec. 11 Edw. III [1337]
Thomas lord of Berkele; and Nicholas le Sopare and Joan Tysoun.

Thomas has leased to Nicholas and Joan the holding which Maud Tysoun sometime held in Cloptone; for their lives, rent 2s. a year.
Witnesses: John fiz Nichol, John Capel, Nicholas Iweyn, Robert Groundy, Alexander de Bathon'.
At: Berkeley.

A1/27/14 [GC 3389; *duplicate* GC 3390]   12 May 26 Edw. III [1352]
Eleanor widow of William Tril, and one of the heirs of the late Nicholas Iweyn, and Sir Thomas lord of Berkelee, knight.

Eleanor has quitclaimed to Thomas all the lands and holdings which Nicholas held in Cloptone and Pedynton in Hamme, and elsewhere within the hundred of Berkele.
Witnesses: William de Chiltenham, John de Clyve, John Serjant the elder, John Capel, John de Milkesham.
At: Berkeley.

HAM: HAMFALLOW

Hamfallow, a sub-manor within the Berkeleys' manor of Ham, was held by the FitzWarrens and then by the Veels (below, pp. 553–5) until it passed, through a daughter, to the Moigne family in the mid 14th century. It appears in the Ham accounts of 1347–56 during the time when Katherine, widow of Peter le Veel (d. 1343) was married to Thomas (III) Lord Berkeley (d. 1361). Other charters for Ham may well relate to this sub-manor.

A1/28/1 [GC 2738]   Thurs. before St. Andrew, 5 Edw. III [28 Nov. 1331]
Peter le Veel, lord of Tortworth, and Adam son of William Purlewent of Ham.

Peter has leased to Adam, for a certain sum of money, a rent of 5s. a year from William Purlewent for two plots [*hammis*] of land which William holds of Peter for his life within the manor of Hamme, with the reversion of the land, for Adam's life; rent 5s. a year.
Witnesses: John le Serjaunt, John Capel, John de Swonhungre, John Purlewent, Robert Bastard, William son of Robert.
At: Ham.

HAM: PEDINGTON

A1/29/1 [GC 756]   n.d. [1230 × 1243]

Robert the forester (*forestarius*) and Thomas de Berkel'.

Robert has quitclaimed to Thomas all the land which he had in Pedinton.

Witnesses: Sir Nicholas son of Roger, Sir Elias Giffard, Roger de Lokinton, Henry de Berkel, Walter de Burgo, Philip de Cromhale, William the marshal (*marscallus*), Maurice de Bevintun, Robert Bastard, Adam Flambard, John de Eketun, Andrew de Bradestan.

A1/29/2 [GC 363]   n.d. [1220 × 1243]

Thomas de Berkeley; and Robert de Bokovere, Isabel his wife and Adam their son.

Thomas has granted to Robert, Isabel and Adam, for their lives, all the land in Pedintun which Richard le Honte once held; rent 3*s.* a year.

Witnesses: Sir G. de la Wertun, Thomas's steward, Sir Henry de Berkeley, Maurice de Bevintun, Maurice de Stanes, Adam Flambard, Elias de Bevinton.

A1/29/3 [GC 683]   n.d. [late Hen. III]

Maurice de Berkel; and Robert de Bochoure and Isabel his wife and Isabel their daughter.

Maurice has granted to Robert and Isabel and Isabel, for their lives, 2 a. of land in Buttewelle in the vill of Pedinton which Walter le Bonde once held; rent 2*s.* a year, and Robert has given him 2*s.*

Witnesses: Peter de Wika, Maurice de Estan, Henry Marscall, Robert Bastard, Nicholas de Coldewell, William son of Robert.

A1/29/4 [GC 321]   Fourth Sun. in Lent, 54 Hen. III [23 March 1270]

Laurence de Cleyhungre and Hawise his wife; and Sir Maurice de Berkeley.

Laurence and Hawise have quitclaimed to Maurice the land which Nicholas de Coldewell once held in Pedinton.

Witnesses: Sir Thomas de Pina, Peter de Wik, William son of Robert, Richard son of Alfred, Robert Bastard, Walter Sely.

A1/29/5 [GC 1805]   20 March 4 Edw. II [1311]

Walter Willies of Pedington, son and heir of Hugh de Pedyntone, and Sir Thomas de Berkelee, lord of Berkeley.

Walter has granted to Thomas his holding in Homme which he inherited through the death of his father Hugh, with the reversion of the dower in the same after the death of Maud his mother.

Witnesses: Thomas de Stone, Robert Wither, John Capel, John le Cuppere, Henry le Gardener, Robert Bastard, Nicholas Iweyn.

At: Berkeley.

A1/29/6 [GC 2485]   n.d. [mid 14th cent.]

Thomas de Berkeleye, lord of Berkeley; and John le Gar, Joan his wife and John's son John.

Thomas has granted to John, Joan and John the holding in Pedynton which Richard Adames held of Thomas for his life; for their lives, rent 10*s.* a year.

Witnesses: John Serjaunt, John Capel, John de Egetone, John Purlewent, John Bastard.

HAM: SANIGER

BERKELEY FAMILY

A1/30/1 [GC 1345]   n.d. [late Hen. III]

John de Egetone, son and heir of John de Egeton, and Sir Maurice de Berkel'.

John has quitclaimed to Maurice common of pasture in the park of Shobenasse, and for this Maurice has granted to John a quarter-virgate of land in the vill of Shonhongre, which William Couthulf formerly held.

Witnesses: Sir Maurice de Saltmarsh (*de salso marisco*), Sir Nicholas Wolf (*Lupus*), Sir Warin de Ral[egh], knights, Peter de Wyke, Thomas the serjeant (*serviens*), John de Brotheston, John Sewaker, Geoffrey Carbonel, Adam Coby.

OTHER
The Aunger holding

A1/30/2 [GC 2535]					n.d. [*temp.* Edw. I]

Geoffrey Nel of Saniger in the parish of Berkeley and Walter Waleys (*Walenc'*) of Purton.

Geoffrey has granted to Walter, his heirs and assigns a plot of land in the field called Stodfelde, beside the land of Sir Thomas de Berkeleye, and 3 selions of land in the same field; rent a rose a year, and Walter has given him 7½ marks.

Witnesses: Thomas le Serjaunt, John de Eggetone, Nicholas Nel, Adam Hathulf, John Warin, John de Auste, Richard the clerk.

A1/30/3 [SC 415]					n.d. [*temp.* Edw. I]

Walter de Piriton called Waleys (*Walensis*); and Alan Ang' and Agnes his wife.

Walter has granted to Alan and Agnes, for a certain sum of money, all his land in the furlong at Swanhungre called Stodfeld, in the parish of Berkeley; rent a rose a year.

Witnesses: Robert de Stanes, Robert de Bradeston, Thomas de Swonhungre, Geoffrey de Neel, Nicholas Neel, Adam Hathulf.

A1/30/4 [GC 2184]		Sun. after the translation of St. Thomas [the archbishop], 11 Edw. II
[10 July 1317]

Alan Aunger and Agnes his wife; and Nicholas Neel and Margaret his wife.

Alan and Agnes have demised to Nicholas and Margaret all their land in Hamme formerly of Walter le Walshe of Piritone, with the reversion of a third part held in dower by Joan Neel, mother of Nicholas, lying near Swonhungre, in the field called Stodfold; for their lives, rent 6*d.* a year.

Witnesses: Richard Serjaunt, William Gilemin, William Bochard, Hugh de Costone.

At: Berkeley.

Other

A1/30/5 [SC 427]				Easter, 39 Hen. III [March 1255]

Peter de Wike and Arnulf de Berkeley.

Peter has granted to Arnulf for 7 years all his land in Swanhunger with the fishery and appurtenances, which Reginald Luffing sometime held at farm, reserving to himself two days' fishing in the week, namely [Wednesdays and Fridays].

Witnesses: Nicholas vicar of Berkeley, John de Egetun, Adam Cobi, John Sewaker, Thomas the serjeant (*serviens*), Adam son of Nigel, William de Boifeld, Robert le Herde.

A1/30/6 [SC 320]					n.d. [1262 × 1264]

Abbot William [Long] and St. Augustine's Abbey; and Robert le Hunde.

The abbey has granted to Robert the land at Suanhangre which Reginald Luffing held called C. . . croft; rent 30*s.* a year, for which Robert gave them 40*s.*

Witnesses: Sir Henry de Berkele, knight, Thomas . . . . . . , Andrew de Bradestan, John de Eginton, Nicholas Rufus, Adam Cobi.

A1/30/7 [GC 3400]			Wed. after St. Tiburtius and St. Valerianus, 27 Edw. III
[17 April 1353]

Isabel Broun of Bristol, widow; and Richard Heved and Margery his wife, Isabel's daughter.

Isabel has granted to Richard and Margery all her land, wood, pasture and meadow which is of her inheritance in Swonhangre (Glos.) within the lordship of Berkele; to them and their issue, with remainder to the right heirs of Margery.

Witnesses: Walter de Fromptone, Walter Derby, John Blanket, Thomas Brywere, John Scryveyn.

At: Bristol.

HAM: STONE
BERKELEY INTERESTS
The Falfield holding

A1/31/1 [GC 1357]   n.d. [before 1281]
Alice daughter of Matthew de Falefeld, unmarried woman, and Sir Maurice de Berkel'.

Alice has granted to Maurice the land with appurtenances called la Langecroft in Nethere Stan'.

Witnesses: Sir Nicholas le Lou, Robert Caudel, Henry de Baton', Robert Brun, William Capel, Richard son of Alfred, Robert Bastard.

A1/31/2 [GC 1359]   n.d. [before 1281]
Alice daughter of Matthew de Falefeld and Sir Maurice de Berkel'.

Alice has granted to Maurice the land in the vill of Nethereston beside his land called Perhamesfeld; and he has given her 2 marks.

Witnesses: Sir Nicholas Wolf (*Lupus*), Robert de Stane, Henry de Baton', Robert Caudel, Nicholas de Wodeford, William Capel, Walter de Egeton, Geoffrey Neel.

A1/31/3 [GC 1358]   n.d. [before 1281]
Alice daughter of Matthew de Falefeld and Sir Maurice de Berkel'.

Alice has quitclaimed to Maurice two crofts in Netherestone beside Maurice's land called Perhamesfeld; and he has given her 10*s*.

Witnesses: Sir Nicholas Wolf (*Lupus*), knight, William Capel, Robert de Stane, Henry de Baton', Robert Caudel, Nicholas de Wodeford.

A1/31/4 [GC 496]   n.d. [before 1281]
Alice daughter to Matthew de Falefeld and Sir Maurice de Berkel.

Alice has granted to Maurice ½ a. of meadow in Opingeapeldure; and he has given her 8*s*.

Witnesses: Sir Nicholas Wolf (*Lupus*), Nicholas de Wodeforde, Robert Caudel, Henry de Batton', Robert de Stan', Robert Bastard, William [his son?].

The Stone holding

A1/31/5 [GC 1400]   n.d. [late Hen. III]
Cecilia daughter of Walter de Hagel' and William son of Ralph de Stane.

Cecilia has quitclaimed to William half of his land in the vill of Stan', in exchange for 3½ a. of land.

Witnesses: Peter de Wike, John de Brothestan, Nicholas de Wodeford, Henry de Batonia, Walter de Hagel', William de Aungervill, Robert de Ston, Robert Caudel.

A1/31/6 [GC 1362]   n.d. [late Hen. III]
Matthew de Falefeld and William son of Ralph de Stane.

Matthew has quitclaimed to William the lands which William has inherited in the vill of Stane.

Witnesses: Nicholas de Wodeford, Henry de Batonia, Walter de Hagel, Robert de Stane, Robert Caudel.

A1/31/7 [GC 1361]   n.d. [late Hen. III]
Cecilia daughter of Matthew de Falefeld and William son of Ralph de Stane.

Cecilia has quitclaimed to William half of the land which he has in the vill of Stane, viz. 1 a. at Hoxhaham, 1 a. at Newelond, 1 a. at Heppelton and ½ a. in the field called

Chureschesfeld; and for this he has given her 3½ a. of land, as in his charter.
Witnesses: Peter de Wike, John de Brothestan, Nicholas de Wodeford, Henry de Baton', Robert de Stan', Robert Caudel, Simon de Wodeford.

A1/31/8 [GC 826]   n.d. [late Hen. III]
Walter de Stan', son of Ralph de Stan', and Sir Maurice de Berkel'.

Walter has granted to Maurice all his land in the vill of Stan' and elsewhere within Maurice's fee, with rents [etc.], which he inherited after the death of William his brother; and Maurice has given him 10 marks.
Witnesses: Sir Nicholas Wolf (*Lupus*), Sir Robert de Kingestun, Sir Richard de Berkel, knights, Robert de Stan', William Capel, Henry de Baton, Nicholas de Wodeforde, Robert Caudel, Walter Sely.

The Bath holding

A1/31/9 [GC 1187]   n.d. [*temp.* Edw. I]
Henry de Bathon' and Margery his daughter.

Henry, with the assent of his wife Alice, has granted to Margery a house with a curtilage and 2 crofts in Nethereston, ½ a. of land in Schurichfeld, 1 a. above Appeltone and all his land in Richyerd; to her in fee, rent 1½d. a year, and a further 7d. a year to celebrate masses in the chapel of Stan' for the souls of Cecilia de Stan', Amicia de Stan' and Maud de Stan' and for the souls of Henry and Alice in the future.
Witnesses: Robert de Stan', William Capel, Henry de Weneswelle, Nicholas de Wodeford, Thomas Aleyn, Richard le Turch, Richard le Savoner.

1/31/10 [GC 1188]   n.d. [*temp.* Edw. I]
Alice widow of Henry de Bathon' and Margery her daughter.

Alice has granted to Margery, for laudable service, her croft called Berecroft with the adjacent enclosure, all her meadow in Matford between the meadow of Stanley Priory and that which William Herieth formerly held with a head above the water called Matforde, 2 a. of land in Beworthe with the adjacent enclosure, all her land in Cherchefelde, 2 a. in Schardewhul and 7 selions of land above Appelton, in Stone within the manor of Hamme; to hold of the chief lord of the fee.
Witnesses: Robert de Bradeston, Thomas de Swonhungre, Thomas de Beolee, Thomas de Styntescombe, Roger de la Garstone, Robert Bastard, Nicholas the clerk (*cler'*), John Porlewent, Nicholas Iweyn.

A1/31/11 [GC 2474]   n.d. [*temp.* Edw. I]
Alice de Ba, widow of Henry de Ba, and Walter de Stone her son.

Alice has granted to Walter, his heirs and assigns, for 14 marks, all her land in Opeliapeldore and in Oxenham.
Witnesses: Robert de Bradeston, Nicholas de Wodeford, Richard Broun, Robert Bastard, William Northlone, Walter Snyte, Nicholas Frankeleyn, William de Stone, mason.

A1/31/12 [GC 1604]   n.d. [*temp.* Edw. I]
Walter de Bathon' and Walter Donintoun, vicar of Berkeley.

Walter de Bathon has granted to Walter Donintoun all his land in the furlong called Yert and all the land which he had by the enfeoffment of Alice his mother in Opeliapeldore and Oxenham; to hold of the chief lord by the customary services, and Walter Donintoun has given him a certain sum of money.
Witnesses: Robert de Bradeston, Thomas de Beoleye, Thomas le Serjant, Walter Snyte, William Northlone, Richard Broun, Nicholas de Pedinton, clerk.

A1/31/13 [GC 2510]   n.d. [*c.* Feb. 1302]
Walter Donyntoun, vicar of Berkeley, and Agnes widow of Walter de Bhaton' of Stone.

Walter has granted to Agnes, her heirs and assigns all the land which he has in Stone in the furlongs called Yert and Opeliopeldore and in Oxenham, by grant of Walter de Bhaton'.
Witnesses: Robert de Bradestone, Thomas de Boelee, Thomas le Serjaunt, Robert Wither, Nicholas de Wodeford, Richard Broun, Walter Snyte.

A1/31/14 [GC 1031]   Wed. after St. Agatha, 30 Edw. I [7 Feb. 1302]
(1) Walter Douninton, vicar of Berkeley; (2) Nicholas de Pedintone, clerk; (3) Agnes widow of Walter de Ba.

Walter has appointed Nicholas as his attorney to give seisin to Agnes of all his land in Opeliapeldore, Oxheneham, and Yartcrucisham.
At: Berkeley.

A1/31/15 [GC 1765; *duplicate* GC 1839]   Fri. after the Exaltation of Holy Cross, 4 Edw. II
                                                                  [18 Sept. 1310]
John de Lyndesee and Agnes his wife; and Sir Thomas de Berkelee, lord of Berkeley.

John and Agnes have granted to Thomas 17½ a. of land at Stone, which they had by grant of Sir Walter Dounyntoun, vicar of Berkelee, of which 11 a. lie in the field called Apeliapeldore, 4 a. in the field called Oxenehom and 2 a. and 2 selions in the field called Yherd.
Witnesses: Robert de Bradestone, Thomas de Styntescombe, Roger de la Garstone, Thomas de Stone, Richard de Avene, Robert Wyther, John Capel.
At: Berkeley.

A1/31/16 [GC 1771]   Fri. after Michaelmas, 4 Edw. II [2 Oct. 1310]
Thomas de Berkelee, lord of Berkeley; and John de Lyndesee and Agnes his wife.

Thomas has granted to John and Agnes 17½ a. of land at Stone, which he had by their grant, in Hamme; for their lives, rent 12*d.* a year.
Witnesses: Thomas de Stone, Robert Wyther, John Capel, Nicholas the clerk, Nicholas Iweyn.
At: Berkeley.

A1/31/17 [GC 1886]   One week after the nativity of St. John the Baptist, 5 Edw. II
                                                                   [1 July 1312]
Thomas de Berkeleye the elder, by Robert de Prestebury, and John de Lyndeseye and his wife Agnes.

Final concord concerning 17½ a. of land in Stone near Berkeleye; John and Agnes have acknowledged the right of Thomas, and Thomas has given them £20.
At: Westminster.

The Walbrook holding
A1/31/18 [GC 1918]   1 May 6 Edw. II [1313]
Roger Walebrok of Stone and Sir Thomas de Berkelee, his lord.

Roger has granted to Thomas a messuage with a curtilage at Stone in Hamme.
Witnesses: Thomas de Stone, Richard de Avene, John Capel, Maurice de Beoleie, Walter Sewaker.
At: Berkeley.

A1/31/19 [GC 1958]   1 Jan. 7 Edw. II [1314]
Thomas de Berkelee, lord of Berkeley; and Ralph de Northlone, Maud his wife and Hugh their son.

Thomas has granted to Ralph, Maud and Hugh a messuage with a curtilage, which he had by grant of Roger Walebrok of Stone; to them and Hugh's issue, or the issue of Ralph and Maud if Hugh dies without issue, rent 2*s.* 8*d.* a year.

Witnesses: Thomas de Stone, John Capel, Walter Sewaker, Nicholas Iweyn, Walter Snyte.

At: Berkeley.

The Cranford holding

A1/31/20 [GC 2118]   Sun. the feast of St. Bartholomew, 9 Edw. II [24 Aug. 1315]
(1) Robert de Berkeleye; (2) Hugh de Cranforde and Margery his wife; (3) [Thomas] lord of Berkeleye.

Whereas Hugh and Margery had agreed to sell to Robert lands and holdings in Nethereston, Robert, at the request of Hugh and Margery, has released the agreement, saving to Robert the money, and granted that they may sell the land to his lord of Berk'. [*In French.*]

Witnesses: Sir John Mautravers the son, Sir William de Wautone, knights, Thomas de Bradeston, . . . , Walter Sewaker, John le Sergant, Henry le Gardener, John le Cuppere.

At: Berkeley.

A1/31/21 [GC 2151]   St. Valentine's Day, 10 Edw. II [14 Feb. 1317]
Thomas de Berckel', lord of Berkeley; and Hugh de Cranford and Margery his wife.

Thomas has granted to Hugh and Margery the holding which he had in Hamme by their acknowledgement in the king's court, viz. a messuage, land, meadow, pasture [etc.], which they hold for their lives, rendering the services which they owe, as in the acknowledgement.

Witnesses: John le Serjaunt, Walter Sewaker, John Capel, Nicholas of the vine (*de vinea*), Nicholas Iweyn, Walter Snyte, Richard Broun.

At: Berkeley.

A1/31/22 [GC 2163]   Three weeks after Easter, 10 Edw. II [24 April 1317]
Thomas de Berkeleye the elder by Richard de Salle; and Hugh de Croweford and Margery his wife.

Final concord concerning a messuage, 16 a. of land and 2 a. of meadow in Hamme and Alkintone; Hugh and Margery have acknowledged the right of Thomas, and Thomas has given them 20 marks.

At: Westminster.

The Marybrook holding

A1/31/23 [GC 2137]   6 Dec. 10 Edw. II [1316]
Thomas de Berkeleye, lord of Berkeley; and Richard atte Marlputte and Leticia his wife.

Thomas has leased to Richard and Leticia 6½ a. 24 perches of land which Dulcia de Marebrok previously held of Thomas in villeinage in Stone, in 22 parcels, in Hamme; to them and their issue, rent 6*s.* 8*d.* a year.

Witnesses: John Capel, Roger de la Garstone, Walter Sewaker, Roger Archer, John de Lyndeseye.

At: Berkeley.

A1/31/24 [GC 2075]   1 Feb. 10 Edw. II [1317]
Thomas de Berkeleye, lord of Berkeley; and Richard Broun of Stone and Margery his wife.

Thomas has leased to Richard and Margery 4½ a. of land and pasture in the field of Stone called Lobbethornesfeld, in 10 parcels, which Dulcia de Marebrok formerly held of Thomas in villeinage in Hamme; to them and Richard's issue, rent 5*s.* 3*d.* a year.

Witnesses: Roger de la Garstone, Walter Sewaker, John Capel, Nicholas of the vine (*de vinea*), Roger Archer, Hugh le Busschare.

At: Berkeley.

A1/31/25 [GC 2167]   6 May 10 Edw. II [1317]
Thomas de Berkeleye, lord of Berkeley; and John de Lyndeseye and Agnes his wife.

Thomas has granted to John and Agnes ½ a. 5 perches of land beside John's land in the field called Yert, beside the road from Berkeleye to Rockhamptone, which Dulcia de Marebrok formerly held in villeinage, in Hamme; to them and their issue, rent 8*d.* a year.
Witnesses: John Capel, Walter Sewaker, Robert Bastard, Nicholas Iweyn, Nicholas of the vine (*de vinea*).
At: Berkeley.

Other

A1/31/26 [GC 361]   n.d. [1220 × 1243]
Thomas de Berkeley and . . .

Thomas has granted to . . . assart next to Appelrugge . . . [Reg]inald Tassel at Stanes and pasture of Bernard de Stanes, and between . . . of the house of the said Reginald Tassel at Walthaves . . .
Witnesses: . . . Adam son of Nigel, Oliver de Berkeley, Simon de Olepenne, . . . , Peter de Stintescombe, Richard de Cromhale, Reginald de Gosinton, . . . , Adam the clerk.

A1/31/27 [GC 719]   n.d. [1243 × 1261]
Henry Cauval and Sir Maurice lord of Berkel', his lord.

Henry has granted to Maurice all the land, with meadow, pasture, rents [etc.], in the vill of Stan which he inherited on the death of Cecilia de Stan, sister and heir of Sir William de Stan; and Maurice has given him 100*s.*
Witnesses: Sir Nicholas son of Roger, Sir Maurice de Saltmarsh (*de salso marisco*), Sir Henry de Berk', Sir Henry de Baylol, knights, Walter de Wimbvill, steward of Berkeley, Peter de Wyk, Maurice de Stan, Ralph de Angervilla, Walter Sely, clerk.

A1/31/28 [GC 568]   n.d. [late Hen. III]
Margaret daughter of Cecilia de Stanes and Maurice de Berkel'.

Margaret has quitclaimed to Maurice pasture for four oxen or four cows, as in the charter of Cecilia her mother. Endorsed: *Hamme*.
Witnesses: Elias de Cumbe, William de Mathone, William de Burgo.

A1/31/29 [SC 457]   n.d. [*temp.* Edw. I]
Thomas de Berkeley, lord of Berkeley, and William le Veysee.

Thomas has granted to William 4 perches of land at Stone lying against his house; rent 1*d.* a year.
Witnesses: Richard de Avene, Walter Moton, William le Golde, Robert le Boschare, Alexander the clerk.

A1/31/30 [GC 1229]   n.d. [*temp.* Edw. I]
Thomas de Berkelee, lord of Berkeley, and Thomas the mason (*cementarius*) son of Henry de la Lupeghat.

Thomas de Berkeley has granted to Thomas the mason the holding which came to him after the death of William called Wolf (*lupus*), and which William de Stone held for life, and ½ a. of meadow which Rose of the cross (*de cruce*) formerly held in the meadow called Luttleham at Stone in Hamme; to Thomas and Joan his wife and Thomas's issue, rent 3*s.* a year for their lives, and 5*s.* a year after the deaths of Thomas and Joan; further, he has granted to Thomas for his life one wagonload a year from Mukulwode, viz. underwood, thorns or branches, by the view and livery of the forester of the same.
Witnesses: Robert de Bradeston, Robert de Berkelee, John de Saltmarsh (*de salso marisco*), Thomas de Beolee, Thomas de Swonhungre, Robert Wyther, Roger de la Garston, Richard de Avene, Nicholas of the vine (*de vinea*), clerk.

A1/31/31 [GC 1235]   n.d. [*temp.* Edw. I]
Thomas de Berkelee, lord of Berkeley, and Richard Broun.

    Thomas has granted to Richard 5 perches of land against his house at Stone in Hamme; to him and his issue, rent 1*d.* a year.

Witnesses: Roger de la Garston, Walter Sewoker, Robert le Boschare, Alexander the clerk (*cler'*), Philip the smith (*fabr'*).

A1/31/32 [GC 1078]   Sun. the eve of St. Andrew, 33 Edw. I [29 Nov. 1304]
Thomas de Berkelee, lord of Berkeley; and Walter Snyte and Isabel his wife.

    Thomas has granted to Walter and Isabel a messuage and a half-virgate which they previously had by grant of Robert de Stone, also 3¼ a. of pasture in the enclosure called Carswellescroft at Stone in Hamme; to them and Walter's issue, rent 20*s.* a year.

Witnesses: Thomas de Stone, Robert de Bradestone, Roger de Garston, John de Lokynton, Robert Wyther, Robert Bastard, Nicholas Iweyn, Nicholas le Clerk, Thomas the mason (*cementarius*).

At: Berkeley.

A1/31/33 [GC 1123]   5 June 34 Edw. I [1306]
Kingswood Abbey and Sir Thomas de Berkelee.

    The abbey has granted to Thomas the rent of 12*d.* a year from Alice de Baa in Stone, which the abbey was granted by Cecilia de Stanes, daughter of Sir Bernard de Stanes. [*In French.*]

Witnesses: John de Sautemareis, William Malerbe, Roger de la Garston, Thomas de Stanes, Robert de Buttlescombe, Robert Wyther, Walter Sewaker, Nicholas le Clerk, Robert Bastard.

At: Berkeley.

A1/31/34 [GC 1677]   Sun. the feast of the Purification, 2 Edw. II [2 Feb. 1309]
Thomas de Berkel', lord of Berkeley, and Ralph Northlone.

    Thomas has granted to Ralph 7 perches of land in two parcels next to his holding at Stone; to him and his issue, rent 2*d.* a year.

Witnesses: Roger de la Garstone, Walter Sewaker, Richard Broun, Philip the smith (*fabr'*), William Cut.

At: Berkeley.

A1/31/35 [GC 1715]   Mon. after St. Andrew, 3 Edw. II [1 Dec. 1309]
Thomas de Berkelee, lord of Berkeley, and Nicholas Iweyn.

    Thomas has granted to Nicholas ½ a., 1 fardel and 38½ perches of land at Marebrok and a plot of land at Overestone; to hold enclosed, to him and his issue, rent 3*s.* a year.

Witnesses: Robert de Berk', Robert de Bradestone, Roger de la Garstone, Nicholas the clerk, Robert Bastard.

At: Berkeley.

A1/31/36 [GC 1720]   1 Feb. 3 Edw. II [1310]
Thomas de Berkelee, lord of Berkeley, and William de Nortlone.

    Thomas has granted to William a messuage and 6 a. of land, which Rose of the cross (*de cruce*) held of Thomas at Stone in Hamme; to him and his issue, rent 8*s.* a year.

Witnesses: Thomas de Stone, Robert de Bradestone, Roger de Garstone, Robert Bastard, Nicholas Iweyn, Nicholas the clerk, Thomas the mason (*cement'*).

At: Berkeley.

A1/31/37 [GC 1782]   1 Jan. 4 Edw. II [1311]
Thomas de Berkelee, lord of Berkeley; and Ralph de Thachham and Cecilia his wife.

    Thomas has granted to Ralph and Cecilia 1 a. of land in Thachhammestrete beside the

road from Stone to Thornbur, in Hamme; to hold enclosed, to them and their issue, rent 16*d.* a year.
Witnesses: Thomas de Stone, John Capel, Walter Sewaker, Nicholas the clerk, Nicholas Iweyn.
At: Berkeley.

A1/31/38 [GC 1857]   Thurs. in Epiphany, 5 Edw. II [6 Jan. 1312]
Thomas de Berkelee, lord of Berkeley; and John de Lyndesee and Agnes his wife.
   Thomas has granted to John and Agnes 4 a. of land at Netherestone and towards Rokhamtone, taken from the half-virgate which Dulcia de Marebrok, his villein, holds, in exchange for 4 a. of land in the field called Oxeneham which Dulcia holds through taking those 4 a. in the said field; for their lives, rent a rose a year.
Witnesses: Thomas de Stone, John Capel, William de Northlone, Nicholas the clerk, Nicholas Iweyn.
At: Berkeley.

A1/31/39 [GC 1906]   1 March 6 Edw. II [1313]
Thomas de Berkelee, lord of Berkeley; and Hugh de Northlone and Maud his wife.
   Thomas has granted to Hugh and Maud 46 perches of land in the high street at Netherestone, which John de Cleihongre previously held of Thomas, in Hamme; to hold enclosed, to them and their issue, rent 4*d.* a year.
Witnesses: Walter Sewaker, John Capel, Nicholas Iweyn, Walter Snyte, Hugh le Boschare.
At: Berkeley.

A1/31/40 [GC 2264]   The Purification, 12 Edw. II [2 Feb. 1319]
Thomas de Berkeleye, lord of Berkeley; and John son of Robert the clerk, Edith his wife and Walter and Isabel their children.
   Thomas has leased to John, Edith, Walter and Isabel, a messuage and 2 a. of land, which Richard Dreth formerly held at Stone in Hamme; for their lives, rent 5*s.* a year.
Witnesses: John Capel, John de Lyndeseye, Walter Snyte, Hugh de Crauforde, William Northlone.
At: Berkeley.

OTHER TENANTS AND HOLDINGS
The Harald holding

A1/31/41 [SC 408]   n.d. [*temp.* Hen. III]
William de Stanes, son of Walter the clerk of Stone, and Robert Harald.
   William has granted to Robert the land in Stonhemefeld which lies between the land of Maurice de Stanes and the rivulet of Shadewell; rent 1*d.* a year and the royal service which pertains to 1a. in the same fee, and Robert has paid a fine of 10*s.*
Witnesses: Sir Maurice de Saltmarsh (*de salso marisco*), Sir Roger de Lokinton, Andrew de Bratheston, John de Egeton, Maurice de Stanes, Robert le Herde, John de Wodeford, Walter Sely, clerk.

A1/31/42 [GC 1404]   n.d. [late Hen. III]
Walter Harald, son and heir of Robert Harald, and Sir Maurice de Saltmarsh (*de salso marisco*).
   Walter has granted to Maurice all the land which Robert his father had by grant of William de Stane, son of Walter the clerk of Stane, beside the rhine of Shadewell.
Witnesses: Peter de Wyke, John de Brothestan, Adam Moton, Robert son of Maurice de Stane, Robert Caudel, Thomas de Asshelworth, Walter Sely, clerk.

Other

A1/31/43 [GC 730]   n.d. [*temp.* Hen. III]

Reginald Coby and Hugh son of the priest of Breadstone.

Reginald has granted to Hugh all the land of Stanes which Robert *perincarius* [the stone-cutter?] held of him when he died; to Hugh and his wife Isabel, for their lives, rent 8*s.*, acknowledgement 12*s.* 4*d.*

Witnesses: Thomas de Tyringeham, John de Wudeford, Maurice de Stanes, William son of the clerk, Robert the merchant (*mercator*), Robert the forester (*forestar*'), Geoffrey the forester, Adam the white (*albus*) of Wick, John de Wyca.

A1/31/44 [GC 386]   n.d. [late Hen. III]

Richard de Haselcote and Elias de Cumbe.

Richard has quitclaimed to Elias the land of Stanes which Cecilia de Stanes once held and which fell to Richard by hereditary descent from Cecilia; Elias has given him 40*s.*

Witnesses: Sir Henry de Berkelay, knight, Maurice de Stanes, Peter de Wyke, John de Egetone, John de Brotheston, Adam Flambard, William son of Robert, Nicholas de Craulegh, Henry Marescall.

A1/31/45 [GC 825]   n.d. [late Hen. III]

Mabel daughter of Thomas de Stan' and Sir Maurice de Saltmarsh (*de salso marisco*).

Mabel has granted to Maurice 1 a. of land in Stan'; rent ½*d.* a year.

Witnesses: Maurice de Stan', Peter de Wyke, Henry de Haweye, John Sewaker, Adam Coby, Robert Bastard, Adam Flambard, Walter Sely, clerk.

A1/31/46 [GC 824]   n.d. [late Hen. III]

Mabel daughter of Thomas de Stanes and Stephen her son.

Mabel has granted to Stephen 5 a. of arable land, one above Marstral', one above Leyfeld, one above Stonhamveld of 6 selions, one in the furlong called Jonesworthi and one in the furlong called Gerth; rent 1*d.* a year to the hospital of Queninthon for her soul.

Witnesses: Sir Nicholas vicar of Berkeley, Maurice de Stanes, Robert Caudel, Henry de Bathe, Roger the smith, Nicholas the Scot (*Scoticus*), Maurice Fraunkeleyn, Robert Brun, Richard Carpentar', Robert son of William de Stanes, Roger . . . of Berkeley.

A1/31/47 [GC 1594]   n.d. [late Hen. III]

Richard de Wyka, son of Hugh de Wyka, and Peter de Wyka, his brother.

Richard has granted to Peter all the land in the field called Oxeneham which he had by grant of William son of Walter the clerk of Stane, also 1¼ a. of land which he had by grant of Nicholas de Coldewell in the same field; rent 2*d.* a year, and Peter has given him 12 marks.

Witnesses: Sir Roger de Lokinton, Sir Maurice de Saltmarsh (*de salso marisco*), Sir Henry de Berk', knights, Maurice de Stane, Adam Flambard, Robert Bastard, John de Egeton, William son of Eustace, Adam Coby, John Sewaker, Alfred Mariner, Robert le Herde, Walter Sely, clerk.

A1/31/48 [GC 1360]   n.d. [late Hen. III]

Alice daughter of Matthew de Falefeld and Stephen le Herre of Stone.

Alice has granted to Stephen a plot of land in the furlong called Newelond; rent a rose a year, and he has given her 12*d.*

Witnesses: Nicholas de Wodeford, Henry de Batonia, Robert Caudel, Robert son of William, clerk, Robert Brun, Richard de Stan', carpenter, Maurice le Frankeleyn, William Russel of Woodford.

A1/31/49 [GC 1288]   n.d. [*temp.* Edw. I]

John Cavel; and Cecilia Purlyng and Edith her daughter.

John has quitclaimed to Cecilia and Edith the messuage which Richard Leuwine held of

John in the vill of Stane; rent to John 5 grains of pepper, and 12*d.* a year to the mother church of Tornebur' for the lamp of the Blessed Virgin and 1*d.* to All Saints' church, Stanes, for a lamp, and Cecilia and Edith have given John 2*s.*
Witnesses: Maurice de Stone, Thomas the serjeant (*serviens*), Matthew de Falefeld, Robert de Stone, Robert Caudel, Richard Carpentar', Roger clerk.

A1/31/50 [GC 2004]   30 Dec. 8 Edw. II [1314]
William son of Walter Doucesone of Hinton and Roger son of Adam de Pedyntone.
    William has granted to Roger, his heirs and assigns 1 a. of land in the croft called Frithecroft at Stone, which he had by grant of Robert Notestoke of Stone, and 8 selions of land in the field called Cherichfield at Stone beside Comewellebrok, which he had by grant of Richard son of John the miller (*molend*') of Wodeford, in Hamme.
Witnesses: John Capel, Walter Sewaker, Nicholas the clerk of Pedington, Nicholas Iweyn, John Porlewent, Robert Bastard, Walter Snyte, Richard Broun, John de Lyndeseye.
At: Stone.

A1/31/51 [GC 2355]   St. Augustine, 14 Edw. II [26 May 1321]
Roger son of Adam de Pedyntone; and Philip son of John le Frigg of Stone and Alice his wife.
    Roger has granted to Philip and Alice, and Philip's heirs and assigns, 1 a. of land in Stone in the furlong called Frithecroft; rendering the customary services to the chief lord, viz. ¼*d.* a year, and they have given Roger a certain sum of money.
Witnesses: John Capel, Nicholas of the vine (*de vinea*), Nicholas Iweyn, John de Lyndeseye, Walter Snyte, Richard Broun, Hugh de Cranford.
At: Stone.

A1/31/52 [GC 2691]   St. Silvester, 3 Edw. III [31 Dec. 1329]
Hugh de Cranford and John Swele of Berkeley.
    Hugh has granted to John, his heirs and assigns 6 selions of land, of which four lie in the field of Stone called le Churchfeld and two in the furlong called Vylothe, which he had by grant of Maud wife of the late Robert Daungervyle.
Witnesses: John Capel, Nicholas Iweyn, Nicholas of the vine (*de vynea*), Robert Bastard, John de Lyndeseye, William Nortlone.
At: Stone.

A1/31/53 [GC 3019]   Mon. before St. Margaret the virgin, 16 Edw. III [15 July 1342]
Edith widow of John le Wyn of Falfield and Thomas Swele of Berkeley.
    Edith has quitclaimed to Thomas the lands and holdings at Netherestone which John Swele his father [had by grant of] John le Wyn.
Witnesses: John Capel, John Scewaker, Hugh de Crauford, Thomas Scnyte.
At: Stone.

A1/31/54 [GC 3545]   Thurs. after St. Luke, 37 Edw. III [19 Oct. 1363]
Roger atte Garstone, son and heir of John atte Garstone, and John Sergeaunt of Stone.
    Roger has quitclaimed to John all lands and holdings which John had by his grant at Stone in Hamme and Alkyntone.
Witnesses: John FitzNichol, lord of Hill, William de Chiltenham, Robert Palet, Robert Bruyse, John de Coueleye.
At: Stone.

A1/31/55 [GC 4123]   20 Feb. 7 Hen. V [1420]
William Gothay of Falfield; and John Thommes of the same and Adam Gothay, William's brother.
    William has granted to John and Adam, and their heirs and assigns, his parcel of land at

Stone within the hundred of Berkeleye.

Witnesses: John Lewyn, John Morice, John Smyth, Richard Galyan, John Seysell.
At: Stone.

HAM: WANSWELL
BERKELEY FAMILY
Eustace holding

A1/32/1 [GC 303]   Quadragesima, 46 Hen. III [26 Feb. 1262]
William son of Eustace and Sir Maurice de Berkeley.

William has granted to Maurice, his lord, 1 a. and ½ a. and $^1/_5$ a. and 2 perches with the buildings on it, in the vill of Weneswell, for 5 marks.
Witnesses: Sir Richard de Wygorn, steward of Berkeley, Sir Maurice de Saltmarsh (*de salso marisco*), knights, Peter de Wyke, John de Brodeston, Nicholas de Craulegh, John de Egeton, William Maudut, Henry de Egeton, William son of Robert.

A1/32/2 [GC 1329]   n.d. [late Hen. III]
Edith la Cuppere, widow of William Eustace, and Sir Maurice de Berkel'.

Edith has quitclaimed to Maurice her dower rights in the lands and holdings which were of William her husband; further, she has granted to Maurice all the land which she had by grant of William de Shokerwych.
Witnesses: Peter de Wyke, John de Bratheston, John de Crauleyg, Thomas the serjeant (*serviens*), Geoffrey Neel.

A1/32/3 [GC 1210]   n.d. [late Hen. III]
Maurice de Berkeley and William le Cuppere.

Maurice has granted to William 2 a. of land of the holdings which were of William son of Eustace in the vill of Weneswell; to him and his issue, rent 10*d.* a year, and William has given him 2 marks and a lamprey.
Witnesses: Peter de Wyk, Philip de Leycestre, Thomas the serjeant (*serviens*), Geoffrey Carbonel, John Sewaker, Richard Shipward.

A1/32/4 [GC 1212]   n.d. [late Hen. III]
Maurice de Berkely and William son of William Eustace.

Maurice has granted to William all the land which Maurice had from William, William's father, with the rents and appurtenances except 2 a. of land which Maurice has sold to William le Cuppare; rent 3*s.* a year, and William has given him 100*s.*
Witnesses: Sir Richard de Berkely, Peter de Wike, Walter de Egeton, Thomas Servient, Richard de Stanford, John de Crauleye, Richard le Scipward, Adam Hathulf.

A1/32/5 [GC 449]   Tues. after St. [James], 21 Edw. I [28 July 1293]
[Richard] son of William le Cuppere of Berkeley and William Eustace.

Richard has quitclaimed to William, for a certain sum of money, . . . and Oldegarston in Weneswell, which he had by grant of [William] le Cuppere, his father.
Witnesses: [Richard] de Wendene, Richard Averey, Richard Erl, . . . John le Cuppere.
At: Berkeley.

A1/32/6 [GC 598]   Mon. the feast of St. Nicholas, 22 Edw. I [7 Dec. 1293]
Denise widow of William le Cuppere of Berkeley and William Eustasse of Wanswell.

Denise has quitclaimed to William her dower rights in the lands in Weneswell which William had from William her husband.
Witnesses: Thomas Alein, John Sewaker, John le Cuppere, Henry le Cuppere, Walter le Cuppere.
At: Berkeley.

The Philips rent and reversion

A1/32/7 [GC 2910]   Trinity Sunday, 12 Edw. III [7 June 1338]
Richard Phelippes of Wanswell; and Thomas son of Andrew le Serjant and Joan his wife.

   Richard has granted to Thomas and Joan a messuage and 7 a. of land; for their lives, rent 10s. 10d. a year.
Witnesses: John le Serjaunt, John de Egetone, Walter Matheus, William Gylemyn, Thomas Costone.
At: Wanswell.

A1/32/8 [GC 2923]   Mon. after All Saints, 12 Edw. III [2 Nov. 1338]
Richard Phelippes and Margery Phelippes.

   Richard has granted to Margery, her heirs and assigns a rent of 10s. 10½d. from Thomas Andrewes and Joan his wife for a messuage and 7 a. of land lying enclosed in Hamme, with the reversion of the holding after their deaths; customary rent to the chief lord.
Witnesses: John Serjaunt, John de Egetone, John de Lorwynge, William de Swonhungre, William Gelemyn.
At: Wanswell.

A1/32/9 [GC 2927]   Sun. the feast of St. Lucy, 12 Edw. III [13 Dec. 1338]
Margery Phelippes of Wanswell and Sir Thomas lord of Berkele.

   Margery has granted to Thomas, his heirs and assigns a rent of 10s. 10½d. from Thomas Andreu and his wife Joan for a messuage and 7 a. of land lying enclosed in Weneswell within the manor of Hamme, with the reversion of the holding.
Witnesses: John le Serjaunt, John de Egetone, John de Lorewynge, William de Swonhungre, William Gillemyn.
At: Berkeley.

Other

A1/32/10 [SC 21]   n.d. [1170 × 1190]
Roger de Berkeley and Maurice son of Nigel.

   At the request of Mahel de Skenefrid, Roger has confirmed to Maurice the land which Walter son of Alwin held of Mahel at Wanswell and the land of Wudewellegrof, which are of Roger's fee.[1]
Witnesses: Sir Maurice de Berkeley, Nicholas his brother, Robert de Berkeley, Richard his brother, Master Maurice, Reginald and Thomas, chaplains, Adam the seneschal, Adam son of Nigel, Richard de Euhalla, Elias de Saltmarsh (*de salsomarisco*), Roger de Stintescombe, Bernard de Stanes, Walter son of Albert, Walter de Iwele, Bartholomew de Olep[enne], Hugh de Plancha, Eustace de Camma, William Wenri, William de Paris, Ralph de Stintescombe, Richard de Stintescombe, Robert Gansel, Robert son of the seneschal, Nicholas Punc', Henry de Stanes, Peter de Haia, Roger the hunter, Richard son of William, Alfred the doorkeeper.

A1/32/11 [SC 162]   n.d. [early Hen. III]
Robert de Berkeley and Richard the sailor (*nauta*).

   Robert has granted and confirmed to Richard the half-virgate which he held of Robert's father and of Robert at a rent of 8s. a year, and 12 a. of land in Dolfelde; to him and his eldest son, to hold for life and a rent of 10s. a year; and if the eldest son dies without children then Richard's second son will hold it for life in the same way; and after the deaths of Richard and his son the land will return to Robert and his heirs; acknowledgement four good oxen.
Witnesses: Adam son of Nigel, Maurice his brother, Bernard de Stanes, Bernard de Brothestone, Harding de Hunteneford, Elias de Bevintun, Maurice his son, Robert Bastard, John de Crauleye, Gilbert son of Osmund, William Cobi.

---

[1] *Transcript*: Smyth, iii. 373.

A1/32/12 [GC 437]   n.d. [1220 × 1243]
Thomas de Berkel and Alfred Sipward.

Thomas has granted to Alfred 8 a. in Dolvelde which Lethewith[1] de Waneswell held of
him in the manor of Hamme; rent 2s. a year, and Alfred has given Thomas 1 mark.
Witnesses: Ralph de Redleg', Henry de Berkel, William de Berkel, John de Eginton,
Maurice de Bevinton, Maurice de Stanes.

A1/32/13 [SC 289]   n.d. [1243 × 1245?]
Philip de Leycestria and Sir Maurice de Berkele.

Philip has quitclaimed to Maurice the common in Maurice's lands which Philip has for
the land of Weneswell which he bought from Walter de Stanton, in exchange for 65 a. of
land which Maurice granted to Philip.
Witnesses: Sir Maurice de Saltmarsh (*de salso marisco*), Sir Roger de Lokinton, Robert de
Hales, steward, Andrew de Brodestan, John de Eginton, Thomas Mathias, Robert le Herde.

A1/32/14 [SC 287]   n.d. [1243 × 1245]
Maurice lord of Berkeley and Peter de Wika.

Maurice has granted to Peter the land which John le Vale sometime held in Weneswelle
in the manor of Ham; rent a pair of gilt spurs price 6d. a year; and in exchange Peter has
released and quitclaimed to Maurice the land which he held in Aketre, in Alcrintone manor,
by grant of Thomas de Berkeley, Maurice's father, and has given Maurice 20 marks.
Witnesses: Sir Maurice de Saltmarsh (*de salso marisco*), Sir Roger de Lokinton, Robert de
Hales, steward of Berkeley, Andrew de Bradestan, John de Egeton, Adam son of Nel,
William Eustace, Nicholas de Crauele Henry de Egetun, Maurice de Stanes, William de
Stanes, John de Wodeford, Hugh the clerk, Robert le Herde, Adam Flaumbard.

A1/32/15 [GC 447]   n.d. [early Edw. I]
Henry de Weneswell and Sir Thomas lord of Berkeley.

Henry has quitclaimed to Thomas a fishpond at Waneswell which his father Philip de
Weneswell had by the grant of Maurice de Berkeley, Thomas's father; and Thomas has
given him 20s. Endorsed: *Hyneton*.
Witnesses: Sir Roger de Lokynton, Sir Maurice de Saltmarsh (*de salso marisco*), Walter de
Egeton, Robert de Brotheston, Richard de Stanford, Thomas de Swonhungre, William Wariner.

A1/32/16 [GC 1813]   1 April 4 Edw. II [1311]
Thomas de Berkelee, lord of Berkeley; and Richard le Serjant and John his son.

Thomas has granted to Richard and John 3 a. of land at Weneswelle between Luytelhul
and the road from Egetone to Swonhongre in Homme; to hold enclosed, to them and
Richard's issue, rent 3s. a year.
Witnesses: Robert de Bradestone, Thomas de Stone, John Capel, Robert de Stanford,
Matthew Hatholf.
At: Berkeley.

A1/32/17 [SC 534]   Mon. before St. George, 23 Edw. III [22 April 1349]
Maurice de Berkeley, son of Sir Thomas de Berkeley, and the hospital of Holy Trinity of
Longbridge near Berkeley.

Maurice has granted to the hospital an annual rent of 2s. 6d. due from John Nel and his
heirs male for land in Wanneswelle in the manor of Hamme, and confirms the land which
they had by grant of William Burel, sometime held by Robert Russel; and the hospital will
distribute 1d. to the chaplain, 2d. among the clerks and 6d. among the poor on the
anniversaries of Margaret, Maurice's mother, and of Maurice, and 1d. to the chaplain, 2d.
among the clerks and 13d. among the poor on the anniversaries of his wife Elizabeth, of
Katherine lady of Berkeley, and of Sir Nicholas de Poyns.

---

[1] The final *th* is written as a thorn.

Witnesses: Thomas de Bradeston, knight, John le Serjaunt the elder, John le Serjaunt the younger, John de Egeton, John Capel.
At: Berkeley.

OTHER TENANTS AND HOLDINGS
The Butler holding

A1/32/18 [GC 4299]					28 Dec. 38 Hen. VI [1459]
Thomas Fromelode of Kingston and Richard Cleyvele of Berkeley; and John Botiller of Wanswell.

Thomas and Richard have granted to John, his heirs and assigns their lands and holdings [etc.], in Baggepath and Waneswell and elsewhere in Gloucestershire, which they had by grant of the said John.
Witnesses: John Oldelond, Thomas Berkeley, John Ricardes, Richard Nelme, Robert at Wode.

A1/32/19 [GC 4300]					31 Dec. 38 Hen. VI [1459]
John Botyller of Wanswell in Berkeley parish (Glos.); and Walter Herne of Tetbury and John ap Adam of Dursley in the said county.

John has granted to Walter and John, and Walter's heirs and assigns, his lands and holdings [etc.], in Baggepath and Waneswell and elsewhere in Gloucestershire.
Witnesses: Edward Berkeley, esquire, John Estecourte, Robert Heynes, clerk, Thomas Garesdon, John Jones.

A1/32/20 [GC 4301]					12 Jan. 38 Hen. VI [1460]
John ap Adam of Dursley and Walter Herne of Tetbury.

John has quitclaimed to Walter the lands and holdings [etc.] in Baggepath and Waneswell and elsewhere in Gloucestershire which they had by grant of John Botyller of Waneswell.
Witnesses: Edward Berkeley, esquire, John Estecourte, Robert Heynes, clerk, Thomas Garesdon, John Jones.

A1/32/21 [GC 4452]					22 Dec. 2 Hen. VII [1486]
Thomas Herne of Tetbury, cousin and heir of Walter Herne, late of Tetbury, and Richard Butteler of Wanswell, son of John Butteler late of Wanswell.

Thomas has granted to Richard, his heirs and assigns all his lands, holdings [etc.], in Waneswell and Baggpathe (Glos.), which Thomas lately had by grant of Edward Barkeley, esquire, Thomas Whyttyngton, Thomas Holford, John Erton, John Spicer, John Hale, John Lane, Laurence Hamond, Thomas Hattecombe, William Bedell, Robert Payn and John Coke; and has appointed Thomas Tyler and John at Wode to deliver seisin.
Witnesses: William Trye, esquire, Richard Thorppe, Thomas Oldland.

Other

A1/32/22 [GC 851]					n.d. [late 13th cent.]
William Abbewelle of Wanswell; and Walter Hirebeu of Wanswell and Maud daughter of Juliana Peris of Bevington, his wife.

William has granted to Walter and Maud all his holding in Weneswell between the holdings of Walter Snyte and Hugh de Stompe, which he bought from the said Walter; to them and Walter's heirs.
Witnesses: Thomas de Swonhungre, Thomas de Lorwyng, Richard le Serjaunt, Robert de Stanford, Geoffrey Nel, Alan Aunger, William Purlewent, clerk.

A1/32/23 [SC 455]				Nativity of St. Mary, 6 Edw. I [8 Sept. 1278]
Henry de Weneswell; and Robert Mathias of Egeton and Joan his wife.

Henry has granted to Robert and Joan, for their lives, a certain meadow above his

fishpond in Weneswell, near the king's highway which leads from Wanswell to Egeton, reserving the right of driving his wagons and carts over the meadow; rent 6*d.* a year.
Witnesses: Walter de Egeton, Thomas de Swonhongre, William de Schokerwich, Robert de Egeton, Geoffrey Neel, Adam Hathulf, Thomas Aleyn, Richard le Savoner, clerk.

A1/32/24 [GC 2639]   Sun. after Christmas, 1 Edw. III [27 Dec. 1327]
John son of Richard Serjaunt and Richard son of Robert Phelippes.

John has quitclaimed to Richard a croft at Weneswelle called Hopkynescroft, which he had by lease of Robert Phelippes his father, and Richard grants that he and his heirs are bound to pay to the lord of Berkeleye 10*s.* a year for the windmill at Weneswelle for the life of Richard le Serjaunt, which mill he had by grant of Sir Thomas late lord of Berkeleye.
Witnesses: John de Swonhungre, William de Swonhungre, William Gilmyn, Thomas Frigge, John ate Boure.
At: Berkeley.

A1/32/25 [GC 4132]   St. Chad, 8 Hen. V [2 March 1421]
William Doly of Berkeley; and Thomas Kyng of Wanswell and [*blank*] his wife

William has leased to Thomas and his wife a parcel of his house in Waneswelle, the southerly portion, 27 by 24 feet, and the land lying between the house and the road; for their lives, rent 4*d.* a year.
Witnesses: Richard Scot, John Trebell, Richard Ricard, John Everard, Walter Camme.
At: Berkeley.

A1/32/26 [GC 4391]   10 Dec. 14 Edw. IV [1474]
John Dolly of Berkeley; and John Cockys of Wanswell, Joan his wife and William their son.

John has leased to John, Joan and William a holding in Wansewell at the cross called Whytecros, a croft beside Gayworthyslane and a parcel of meadow in Holmede; for their lives, rent 9*s.* 4*d.* a year.
Witnesses: John Rycardes, Walter at Well, John Don.
At: Wanswell.

Rental

A1/32/27 [GRR 14]   6 Edw. IV [1466–7]

HAM: WHITCLIFF PARK

A1/33/1 [SC 448]   n.d. [late Hen. III]
Richard the cook (*chocus*) of Clopton and Sir Maurice de Berkeley.

Richard has granted to Maurice, for 15*s.*, land in Wyteclyve Park.
Witnesses: William de Mathem, steward of Berkeley, William Capel, William son of Robert, Robert de Stanes, William Golafre, Robert Caudel, John de Bratheston, John de Crauleygh, Geoffrey Neel.

A1/33/2 [GC 863]   n.d. [late Hen. III]
Isabel widow of Thomas de Aysshelworth and Sir Maurice de Berkel.

Isabel has granted to Maurice, for her life, 2 a. of land within the park of Wyteclyv which she holds in dower after the death of Thomas.
Witnesses: Sir Nicholas Wolf (*Lupus*), knight, Robert de Stan', William Capel, Robert Caudel, Nicholas de Wodeford.

A1/33/3 [GC 1620]   n.d. [late Hen. III]
Adam de Pedintune, cook (*cocus*), and Sir Maurice de Berkel', his chief lord.

Adam has quitclaimed to Maurice the land which he had next to Wyteclive, which is now included in the park of Wyteclive.

Witnesses: Sir Nicholas Wolf (*Lupus*), William de Matheme, William Capel, Robert de Stane, Robert Caudel, Nicholas de Wodeford.

A1/33/4 [GC 798]   n.d. [late Hen. III]
Robert Pinel and Sir Maurice de Berkel'.

Robert has granted to Maurice the ditch opposite his land in the northern part of Witeclyve.

Witnesses: Sir Warin de Raleyg', Sir Nicholas Wolf (*Lupus*), knights, William Capel, William son of Robert, Robert Bastard, Richard the cook (*cocus*).

A1/33/5 [GC 1614]   n.d. [late Hen. III]
Richard le Hopere of Ham and Sir Maurice de Berkel', his lord.

Richard has granted to Maurice all his ditch opposite his land to the north of Maurice's park of Whiteclyve.

Witnesses: Sir Warin de Raleyg', Sir Nicholas Wolf (*Lupus*), knights, William Capel, William son of Robert, Robert Bastard, Richard the cook (*cocus*).

A1/33/6 [GC 3331]   n.d. [mid 14th cent.]
John Purlewent and Sir Thomas lord of Berkeleye.

John has granted to Thomas ½ a., 1 rood, 35 perches of land enclosed within Wyteclyve park in Hamme, in exchange for ½ a. 12 perches of land which he had by Thomas's grant.

A1/33/7 [GC 3414]   1 June 28 Edw. III [1354]
John le Clerk of Pedington and Sir Thomas lord of Berkelee.

John has quitclaimed to Thomas 2 parcels of land and wood which Thomas has enclosed in his park of Whiteclyve in Hamme, and which Thomas had by John's grant in exchange for a parcel of land in Colverfeld in the said vill of Hamme.
At: Berkeley.

HILL

With Nympsfield, Hill was granted by Robert FitzHarding to his younger son Nicholas (I) (d. 1189) and descended through Nicholas's son Roger (d. 1230), Roger's son Nicholas (II) (d. 1261), that Nicholas's son Ralph (d. 1290–1) and Ralph's son Nicholas (III) (d. 1312), who all used patronymic surnames. The last Nicholas was succeeded by his son John FitzNichol (d. 1375), whose long life seems to have established FitzNichol as the surname for his successor, his son Reginald's son Thomas, was also known as FitzNichol. Sir Thomas FitzNichol died in 1418 leaving two daughters.

TENURE AND SUIT OF COURT

A1/34/1 [SC 25]   n.d. [*temp.* Hen. II]
Robert FitzHarding and Nicholas his son.

Robert has granted to Nicholas Hulla and Nimdesfeld, which the king granted to him, to hold by the service of half of one knight's fee.

Witnesses: Richard [de Warwick] abbot of St. Augustine's, William the prior, Henry archdeacon of Exeter, Lady Eve, Robert her son, Adam de Saltemareis, John de Cogan, Robert de Worle, Moyses Bertelot, John de Paris, Gregory, Roger de Weston, Ailwin the despenser (*dispensator*), Richard the notary.

A1/34/2 [GC 688]   n.d. [1243 × 1261]
 Sir Maurice de Berkel and William Golafre.

Maurice has claimed that William owes suit to his foreign (*forinsec*) court of Berkeley as the other free men of Hull for a holding which William has in Hull, and William has acknowledged that he owes suit twice a year for the lawdays, and warrants this to Maurice against Sir Nicholas son of Roger; Maurice has released William from the suit, for his life, for 1 mark and one ox.

Witnesses: Sir Nicholas son of Roger, Sir Maurice de Saltmarsh (*de salso marisco*), Sir William Maunsel, knights, Peter de Wik, Thomas the serjeant (*serviens*), William Maundewer, Roger the smith.

A1/34/3 [SC 439]   n.d. [1243 × 1261]

Sir Maurice de Berkelay and Nicholas son of Roger.

Nicholas has acknowledged the right of Maurice to have the suit of the free men and villeins to his hundred court from Nicholas's manors of Hulle and Nimdesfeld twice a year and the associated judicial rights, and in return Maurice has released Nicholas and his heirs from their personal suit to the court.

Witnesses: Sir James de Frivile, Sir Maurice de Saltmarsh (*de salso marisco*), Sir Roger de Lokinton, Sir Adam de Eston, Sir William de Eston, Robert de Hales, steward of Berkeley, Humphrey de la Barre, Maurice de Stanes, John de Wodeford, Andrew de Bradestan, Walter le Butiller, Ralph de Bagepuz.

A1/34/4 [GC 2337]   n.d. [*c.* 1303]

Nicholas son of Ralph, lord of Hill, and Sir Thomas de Berk'.

Nicholas has granted to Thomas and his heirs the suit of his villeins of his manors of Hulle and Nymedesfelde to two lawdays every year of the hundred of Berk', so that the villeins of each manor go by three men and the reeve.

Witnesses: Sir John Lovel, Sir Peter Crok, Sir John Basset, Sir William de Wauton, knights, Robert de Bradeston, Robert de Bedelescombe, Thomas de Styntescombe, Miles de Rodeborwe, Richard de Bysel', John Champeneys, Thomas de Swonhungre, Thomas de Beol', John de Olepenne.

KINGSWOOD ABBEY'S HOLDINGS
Grants by Robert and Sibyl Wyther

The Russell holding

A1/34/5 [GC 422]   n.d. [late Hen. III]

Luke Russel of Hill and John de Boleya.

Luke has granted to John, for 2½ marks, 2½ a. of land in the field next to la Wildepurie in the manor of Hulle; rent 1*d.* a year.

Witnesses: Adam Flambard, Henry de Hauwey, Nicholas the Scot (*Scotticus*), William de Berhamthon, John de Falice, William Mandewar', Robert de Beyby, Maurice de Stanes.

A1/34/6 [GC 528]   Sat. before St. John the Baptist, 15 Edw. I [21 June 1287]

Robert Russel, son and heir of Luke Russel of Hill, and William de Roppeley.

Robert has confirmed to William all the land which Luke his father gave to John de Beleya in the field next to Wildepyre in the manor of Hulle.

Witnesses: Thomas de Swonhongre, Thomas Aleyn, Gilbert Tynedon, John Corebet, Henry Finypeni, Walter of the wood (*de bosco*).

At: Gloucester.

A1/34/7 [GC 807]   n.d. [late 13th cent.]

William de Roppesleye; and Robert Wyther and Sibyl his wife.

William has granted to Robert and Sibyl 2½ a. of land with a fore-earth in the field next to Wyldepurie within the manor of Hulle, which Luke Rossel once held; to hold of the chief lord of the fee at 1*d.* a year, and they have given him a certain sum of money.

Witnesses: Robert de Ston', Thomas le Serjant, William Mareys, John Goule, William de Webbeleye, clerk.

A1/34/8 [GC 1529]   n.d. [1312 × 1320]
Edith widow of William de Roppesleye and Kingswood Abbey.

Edith has quitclaimed to the abbey the portion of the lands of her late husband which came to her after his death within the manor of Hulle as dower, with regard to the lands which Robert Wyther had by William's grant; the abbey has given her a certain sum of money.

Witnesses: John son of Nicholas, lord of Hill, William Martel, Thomas Alayn, Peter de Stintescombe, William le Knigt of Hill.

Other

A1/34/9 [GC 1744]   One week after Trinity, 3 Edw. II [21 June 1310]
Kingswood Abbey; and Robert Wyther and Sibyl his wife.

Final concord concerning a messuage, 1 virgate and 26 a. of land in Hulle; Robert and Sibyl have acknowledged the right of the abbey by their gift, and the abbey has given them £40.

At: Westminster.

A1/34/10 [GC 1717]   Sun. after St. Benedict [7 Dec. 1309]
Robert Wyther of Hill and Kingswood Abbey.

Robert has quitclaimed to the abbey all the lands which he has previously given to them of the fee of the lord of Hulle.

Witnesses: Sir John de Wylinton, Sir Hugh [*sic*; *recte* Nicholas] son of Ralph, lord of Hill, Sir John de Berkeleye, Sir William de Wautone, Sir Nicholas de Kyngeston, knights, Robert de Bradeston, Thomas de Styntescumbe, John de Olepenne, Thomas de Beoleye, Adam Waleys, Robert de la Churche, Warin son of William.

A1/34/11 [SC 311]   St. Katherine [25 Nov. *c*. 1310]
Nicholas son of Ralph, lord of Hill, and Kingswood Abbey.

Nicholas has confirmed to the abbey the grants made to them by Robert Wyther and Sibyl his wife in Hull.

Witnesses: Robert de Bradeston, Robert de Berkeleye, Thomas de Stintescombe, Thomas de Beoleye, Nicholas de Stowe, constable of Berkeley, Thomas de Lude, William de Colewych, Thomas de Swanhungre, Nicholas of the vine (*de vinea*), clerk.

At: Hill.

A1/34/12 [GC 2939]   Thurs. in the Annunciation, beginning 1339 [25 March 1339]
Kingswood Abbey and Sir Matthew vicar of Berkeley.

To resolve the dispute between the abbey and the vicar over the lesser tithes from a holding of the abbey which was once of Robert Wyther in the vill of Hulle by Berkel', the abbey has agreed to pay to the vicar 2*s.* a year.

At: Kingswood.

Grants by Nicholas FitzRoger and Nicholas FitzRalph

A1/34/13 [SC 328]   n.d. [1230 × 1261]
Nicholas son of Roger and Kingswood Abbey.

Nicholas has granted to the abbey a road through the middle of the mere called Stukemere, 2 perches wide including the ditch, to begin from the way which goes to Willepulle as far as the way which comes from Berkeley and goes to Thornbury.

Witnesses: Humphrey de la Barre, Maurice de Bevintone, Nicholas Ruffus, Adam Flaumbard, William Mandewerre, Luke Russel, Osbert Bulcard, Robert Selewine, Robert de Besebury.

A1/34/14 [SC 336]   n.d. [1230 × 1261]
Nicholas son of Roger and Kingswood Abbey.

Nicholas has granted to the abbey, for the souls of himself and Sibyl his wife, right of
way from Hulle to Wilepille, and through his pasture near the Severn to their pasture, and
right of carrying hay and corn through his land and meadow and pasture.
Witnesses: Geoffrey de Chausi, Oliver de Berkelay, Simon de Olepenne, John de
Egintun, William de Bradele, William de Hulle, John de Berkele, Matthew le Scay, John
Herman.

A1/34/15 [GC 2537]   n.d. [1290 × 1312]
Nicholas son of Ralph son of Nicholas, formerly lord of Hill, and Kingswood Abbey.

Nicholas has granted to the abbey a path in the fields of Hulle, 2 perches wide, from their
land called Colehyde to the king's highway running from Berkeley to Thornbury, viz. from
the land of Nicholas and his men called la Stocke to the place called Stukemere along the
ditch.
Witnesses: Sir Roger de Lokynton, Sir Peter son of Warin, knights, Robert de Stone, Gilbert
Tynedon, Alexander Purlewent, Robert Bastard, William de Bruhampton, Nicholas le
Scock, Robert Russel, Walter of the wood (*de bosco*), Roger le Oyselur.

Other

A1/34/16 [GC 552]   n.d. [early Edw. I]
William Golafre and Kingswood Abbey.

William has granted to the abbey a certain portion of land in Hulle lying at the eastern
head of his land called la Stocke, 9 by 2 perches, with the adjacent ditch which extends
towards the abbey's land called Colehide.
Witnesses: Sir William Maunsel, knight, Roger de Lokynton, Robert de Stone, Henry de
Bathonia, Robert le Vouler of Hill.

A1/34/17 [GC 2050]   Thurs. after St. James, 9 Edw. II [31 July 1315]
Adam le Waleys, knight, and Sir John le Bryd, abbot of Kingswood.

Adam has received from John a charter which was of Adam le Waleys, his uncle, for a
messuage and 1 virgate of land in the vill of Hulle by Berkelegh, which he (Adam the
uncle) had by grant of Nicholas son of Ralph.
At: Kingswood.

OTHER INTERESTS
Wyther acquisitions
These were possibly granted to Kingswood Abbey but there is no direct evidence.

Barrow holdings
A1/34/18 [GC 1423]   n.d. [1290 × 1294]
Nicholas son of Ralph, lord of Hill, and Ivo de la Berwe.

Nicholas has granted to Ivo 1 virgate of land with appurtenances which William Gulafre
formerly held in the vill of Hulle; for the life of Ivo and one assign, rent 1*d.* a year.
Witnesses: Gilbert Tyndan, William de Brughampton, John Goule, Walter of the wood (*de
bosco*), Nicholas le Scot, Hugh Wayunetre.

A1/34/19 [GC 1424]   n.d. [1290 × 1294]
Nicholas son of Ralph, lord of Hill, and John de la Berwe.

Nicholas has granted to John all the land and meadow which Matthew de Bagepathe held
of Nicholas his grandfather in the vill of Hulle; for the life of John and one assign, rent 1*d.*
a year.
Witnesses: Gilbert Tyndan, William de Brughampton, John Goule, Nicholas le Scot, Hugh
Wayunetre.

A1/34/20 [GC 678]   n.d. [1290 × 1294]
Ivo de la Berewe and Robert Wyther.

Whereas Nicholas son of Ralph, lord of Hulle, granted to Ivo 1 virgate of land in the vill
of Hulle, for his life, Ivo has now granted the virgate to Robert Wyther.
Witnesses: Sir Robert le Veel, Sir Robert de Berkel, Robert de Bradeston, Thomas de
Swonhungre, . . .

A1/34/21 [GC 604]   Sun. 18 Kal. of July 22 Edw. I [14 June 1294]
Nicholas son of Ralph, lord of Hill, and Robert Wyther.

Nicholas has quitclaimed to Robert the lands and holdings in Hulle which he once gave
to Ivo de la Berwe and John de la Berwe.
At: Hill.

Other acquisitions
A1/34/22 [GC 1576]   n.d. [*temp.* Edw. I]
Hugh Waynetere of Hill; and Robert Wither and Sibyl his wife.

Hugh has granted to Robert and Sibyl, for a certain sum of money, his meadow in Hulle
called Waynetereslese.
Witnesses: Robert de Stane, William Capel, Thomas Alein, Robert Bastard, Robert Russel,
Nicholas le Scot, Richard le Savoner, clerk.

A1/34/23 [GC 961]   n.d. [early 14th cent.]
Denise daughter of Robert le Scot of Hill, unmarried woman; and Robert Wyther and Sibyl
his wife.

Denise has granted to Robert and Sibyl 3 a. of land in Hulle, one at la Noyte, one in
Purtegarston and the third in 2 selions, one in Longebengrote next to le Somerweye and the
other in Litlecroft; rent 1*d.* a year to Nicholas le Scot of Hulle, and they have given her 40*s.*
Witnesses: Robert de Stan', William Capel, Thomas Alein, Robert Bastard, William son of
Robert, Robert Russel.

A1/34/24 [GC 853]   n.d. [early 14th cent.]
Alice widow of Thomas Alayn of Berkeley; and Robert Wyther and Sibyl his wife.

Alice has granted to Robert and Sibyl her meadow called Dockemed as enclosed, in the
manor of Hulle, with an annual rent of 2*d.* from Robert le Sygare; the meadow extends
towards Rochamebricgg above Bretonestret in the south part and the other head lies above
the croft of Adam le Waleys called le Oke in the east part; for a certain sum of money.
Witnesses: Robert de Bradeston', Robert de Berkel', Thomas le Serjaunt, John Coule,
William Martel, William le Knytht, John Purlewent, Robert Bastard, William Purlewent,
clerk.

Other

Reginald son of Walter, merchant, is presumably the same man as Reginald the merchant,
and also as Reginald called 'le chepmon', the chapman.

A1/34/25 [GC 1497]   n.d. [early Hen. III]
Bernard de Oldebyr' and Thomas his son.

Bernard has granted to Thomas, for 10*s.*, the holding in Hulle which he holds of William
Mandewerre, also the holding at Landpulle in the parish of Thornebyr' which he holds of
William le Archer, and 1 a. of meadow in la Northamme; rent to Bernard 12*d.* a year.
Witnesses: Sir John de Saltmarsh (*de salso marisco*), Richard de Bochovere, Thomas de
Barry, Robert de Suthmed, Gilbert de Notheswell, Luke Russel, Peter Sumer, Richard the
black (*niger*), Richard the franklin (*frankelanus*), Sebastian de Oldebyr', Hippolyte de
Oldebyr', Thomas le Weyte, Thomas the clerk.

A1/34/26 [GC 938]   n.d. [1290 × 1312]
Nicholas son of Ralph and Reginald son of Walter, merchant.

Nicholas has granted to Reginald the messuage with appurtenances which Walter his
father once held of Nicholas in his manor of Hulle, also the land of Natelonde which Adam
Flambard released at Nicholas's request, and ½ a. of meadow in Suthepulle; rent 4s. a year,
and Reginald has given him 2 marks.
Witnesses: Sir Adam rector of St. Fagans, Adam Flambard, Matthew de Bagapathe, Maurice
de Stanes, William Mandewe', Luke Russel, Nicholas le Fort.

A1/34/27 [GC 932]   n.d. [late 13th cent.]
Reginald the merchant (*mercator*) of Hill and William his eldest son and heir.

Reginald has granted to William 8 selions of land in the croft called Holecroft within the
manor of Hulle and the pasture called Morsplot; rent 1½d. a year.
Witnesses: Sir William Golafre, William de Burghamton, Gilbert Tynedon, Nicholas le Scot,
Robert le Scot, Robert Russell, Hugh Waynetere.

A1/34/28 [GC 1889]   Sun. after St. Luke, 6 Edw. II [22 Oct. 1312]
Reginald called 'le chepmon' of Hill and Thomas son of Reginald de la Fortheye of
Rockhampton.

Reginald has granted to Thomas all his holding in the vill of Hulle, rendering the
customary services to the chief lord.
Witnesses: William Martel, Gilbert Dyndan, John de Brughamptone, Thomas Alayn, Peter
Waynter, Roger Scot, William le Knyth.
At: Hill.

A1/34/29 [GC 3774]   16 May 7 Ric. II [1384]
Nicholas atte More of Tickenham and William Wermynstre, burgess and merchant of
Bristol.

Nicholas has granted to William the annual rent of 16s. which John Janys of the parish of
Rokymton renders to Nicholas for lands and holdings within the lordship of Hulle; for the
life of Nicholas.

HILL: WICKSTOWE

Wickstowe, now lost, was in Hill or Ham but cannot certainly be located. Like Hamfallow,
it passed from the FitzWarrens to the Veels and then to the Moignes.

A1/35/1 [GC 497]   9 Edw. I [1281]
Peter de la More and Peter son of Warin.

Peter de la More has granted to Peter son of Warin all his lands and holdings at
Wykestowe and a messuage and 1½ virgates of land in Bulee (Glos.), and a messuage and
1½ virgates of land in Bridham and Westschenore (Sussex); Peter son of Warin has given
Peter de la More 120 marks and £40 for the corn growing on the land and the chattels [etc.]
Witnesses: Sir William Dune, Sir John Cormeylles, knights, Herbert de Stok, Thomas de
Mere, Ivo de Capehulle, John de Stok, John de Heliwere, Robert Michel, John le Longe,
John Lece, Arnald de Howode, John le Mareschal, Adam le clerk of Charlton, Henry Brun,
William, John Walter, Adam Walrent, Henry Pynd, Robert le Taillour, John the clerk.
At: Ablington.

A1/35/2 [GC 2920]   Sun. before the nativity of St. Mary, 12 Edw. III [6 Sept. 1338]
Peter le Veel, lord of Charfield; and William FitzWaryn of Rudloe (*Riggelawe*) and Clarice
his wife and William their son.

Peter has quitclaimed to William, Clarice and William, and the heirs and assigns of

William [the younger?], the lands and holdings which William has in Wykestowe (Glos.), by demise of Alice FitzWaryn, Peter's aunt.
Witnesses: Sir Robert Seleman, Sir John Pavely, Sir Simon Bassatt, John FitzNichole, Richard Dausie, Nicholas FitzWaryn, Walter Sewale.
At: Ablington.

A1/35/3 [GC 2921]   Morrow of Michaelmas, 12 Edw. III [30 Sept. 1338]
William FitzWaren the elder of Rudloe (*Ruggelawe*) and Clarice his wife; and Bogo FytzWaren, William's brother, and Sir John de Lamertone, chaplain.
   William and Clarice have granted to Bogo and John all their lands and holdings, rents and services at Wykestowe by Wodende of Hulle which they had by grant of Alice FytzWaren, daughter and one of the heirs of Sir Peter FytzWaren, knight; to them, their heirs and assigns.
Witnesses: John FytzNicol, William Martel, Thomas Alein, John Capel, John Milkesham.
At: Wixstowe.

A1/35/4 [GC 2926]   Eve of St. Andrew, 12 Edw. III [29 Nov. 1338]
Bogo FitzWaryn and John de Lamyntone, chaplain; and William FytzWaryn the elder of Rudloe (*Rugglawe*), Clarice his wife and William their son.
   Bogo and John have granted to William, Clarice and William all the lands and holdings, rents and services, which they had in Wykestowe by Wodhende of Hulle; to them and the issue of William the younger, with remainder to the issue of William the elder and to the heirs and assigns of William the younger.
Witnesses: Sir Robert Seleman, Sir Simon Basset, knights, John FytzNicole, William Martel, John Melkesham, Thomas Alayn, William de Budustone.
At: Wixstowe.

A1/35/5 [GC 2982]   14 Edw. III [*sic*] [1340–1]
Adam de Shareshull and Alice his wife; and William FizWaryn of Rudloe (*Rugelawe*).
   Adam and Alice have quitclaimed to William the lands and holdings, rent and services of tenants [*named*] for the holdings which they previously held of Adam and Alice in Wykkestowe by Hulle, with 2 a. of meadow in Hamme by Berkeley.
Witnesses: Sir William de Wautone, knight, John fiz Nycole, William Martel, John de Mylkesham, Thomas Aleyn.
At: Wixstowe.

A1/35/6 [GC 874]   n.d. [*c.* 1350]
Thomas de Berke', lord of Berkeley; and William son of Warin, Clarice his wife, and William their son.
   Thomas, wishing to enclose certain lands and holdings in his manor of Appelrug' to make a park, and to make a hedge on the land of William, Clarice and William at Wyxtouwe, has granted to them and their heirs that he will maintain the ditch between the park and their land, and if the wild beasts escape from the park, he will make good any damage.

A1/35/7 [GC 3425]   Sun. after the Annunciation, 29 Edw. III [29 March 1355]
William FitzWaryn, Clarice his wife and William their son; and John Aleyn of Hill.
   William, Clarice and William have leased to John all their lands, holdings, rents [etc.] at Wyckestouwe with 2 a. of meadow in Perhamesmed and all the appurtenances except a grove called Cattegrove; for his life, rent for the first 12 years 40*s.* a year to them and 2*s.* a year to the lord of Hulle, and thereafter 100*s.* a year to them, and he will maintain the hall, chamber, chapel, dovecot and kitchen at Wyckestouwe.
Witnesses: John Serjaunt, John Capel, John le Clerck, John Purlewent, John Sparwe.
At: Berkeley.

A1/35/8 [GC 3490]   Mon. the feast of St. Mary Magdalen, 33 Edw. III [22 July 1359]
William FitzWaryn the elder and Clarice his wife; and John Aleyn of Hill and Emma his wife.

   William and Clarice have granted to John and Emma all the lands, holdings [etc.] at Wyxtowe by la Wodende of Hulle, with all appurtenances including two groves called Cattegrove and Hongyngegrove, and 2 a. of meadow in Perham, as fully as they and their son William had them by grant of Alice FitzWaryn, daughter and coheir of Sir Peter FitzWaryn, knight; to them and John's male issue, remainder to Margaret, John's daughter, and her male issue, Joan his daughter and her male issue, and Maud his daughter and her male issue; rent 60*s.* a year.

Witnesses: John Serjaunt, John Capel, John Draicote, John Purlewent, John Bastard.
At: Berkeley.

A1/35/9 [GC 3489]   Mon. the feast of St. Mary Magdalen, 33 Edw. III [22 July 1359]
(1) William FitzWaryn the elder, and Clarice his wife; (2) John Gar; (3) John Aleyn of Hill and Emma his wife.

   William and Clarice have appointed John Gar to give seisin to John and Emma of all the lands, holdings [etc.] of 2 a. of meadow in Perham and all their meadow at Wyxtowe by la Wodende of Hulle.
At: Berkeley.

A1/35/10 [GC 3495]   Mon. after Michaelmas, 33 Edw. III [30 Sept. 1359]
William FitzWaryn the elder of Rudloe (*Regelawe*) and Clarice his wife; and John Aleyn of Hill.

   William and Clarice have quitclaimed to John all the lands and holdings at la Wodende of Hulle called Wixstowe, and an annual rent of 60*s.* in which John was bound for the said lands.

Witnesses: John Sergeaunt the elder, John Sergeaunt the younger, John Capel, John Purlewent, John Bastard, John Russel.
At: Berkeley.

A1/35/11 [GC 609]   St. Giles, 23 Edw. I [1 Sept. 1295]
Roger de Keynsham and Sir Thomas de Berkeleya.

   Roger has granted to Thomas a rent of 8*s.* from Thomas Aleyn and Alice his wife for a holding in the vill of Hulle at Beyebury; Thomas de Berkeleya has given Roger 5 marks.
Endorsed: *Hamme*.

Witnesses: Sir Nicholas son of Ralph, Sir Robert de Berkeleya, Sir Peter son of Warin, knights, Robert de Stanes, Robert de Bradeston, Robert Wither, Richard de Wenden, John Coule, John Kenet.
At: Berkeley.

A1/35/12 [GC 3497]   Mon. after St. Andrew, 33 Edw. III [2 Dec. 1359]
John Aleyn of Hill and Sir Thomas de Berkele, lord of Berkeley.

   John has granted to Thomas a grove called Hongyngegrove and 8½ a. of land of the land of Wixstowe beside Thomas's park, in exchange for Thomas's releasing to him the rent of 8*s.* a year which he pays to Thomas for the land of his inheritance in Hulle.

Witnesses: John FitzNichol, John Sergeant, John Bastard, John Purlewent, William FitzRobert.
At: Berkeley.

A1/35/13 [GC 3498]   Mon. after St. Andrew, 33 Edw. III [2 Dec. 1359]
Thomas de Berkele, lord of Berkeley, and John Aleyn of Hill.

   Thomas has quitclaimed to John an annual rent of 8*s.* from the lands of John's

inheritance in Hulle, in exchange for the grove called Hongyngegrove and 8½ a. of land of the land of Wixstowe.
At: Berkeley.

A1/35/14 [GC 3795]   St. Matthew, 9 Ric. II [21 Sept. 1385]
William FitzWaryn; and Henry Moigne, Sir William Moigne his brother, rector of Shipton Moyne, William Smalcombe the younger and John Gerneyes of Biddestone.
    William has granted to Henry, William, William and John, and their heirs and assigns, all his lands and holdings in Wyxtowe by Wodehende of Hulle.
Witnesses: Sir Thomas FitzNichol of Hill, knight, John Sergeaunt, William Smalcombe the elder, Thomas Skay.
At: Wixstowe.

A1/35/15 [GC 3841]   Sun. before St. Nicholas, 14 Ric. II [4 Dec. 1390]
(1) Thomas de Berkeley, lord of Berkeley; (2) Ralph Waleys; (3) William FitzWaryn.
    Thomas has appointed Ralph to receive seisin from William of all the lands and holdings that William had in the vill of Hamme and elsewhere within the hundred of Berkeley, and which were of William FitzWaryn, his father. [*In French.*]
At: Wotton.

A1/35/16 [GC 3843]   Monday before St. Nicholas, 14 Ric. II [5 Dec. 1390]
William FitzWaryn and Thomas de Berkeley, lord of Berkeley.
    William has granted to Thomas, his heirs and assigns all his lands, holdings, rents and services in Hamme and elsewhere within the hundred of Berkeley which were of William FitzWaryn his father.
Witnesses: John Berkeley, knight, Ralph Waleys, John atte Yate, William Smalcombe, John Rolves.
At: Ham.

A1/35/17 [GC 3844]   n.d. [*c.* 5 Dec. 1390]
(1) Henry Moygne, William Moigne, rector of Shipton Moyne, William Smalcombe the younger and John Gerneys of Biddestone; (2) William FitzWaryn; (3) Thomas de Berkeley, lord of Berkeley.
    Whereas William FitzWaryn granted to Thomas all his lands and holdings in Wixstowe by Wodende of Hulle in the hundred of Berkeley, Henry, William, William and John have quitclaimed to Thomas.
Witnesses: Gilbert Deneys, Thomas FitzNicol, knights, Ralph Waleys, John Coueley, John Trye.
At: Berkeley.

A1/35/18 [GC 4059]   14 May 12 Hen. IV [1411]
Richard Denys, son and heir of John Denys, heir of John Alayn, and Sir Thomas lord of Berkeley.
    Richard has quitclaimed to Thomas all the lands [etc.], that were of William FitzWaryn.
At: Portbury.

HINTON

BERKELEY ACQUISITIONS
Stanford holding

A1/36/1 [GC 3300]   n.d. [mid 14th cent.]
Walter Goldemere and Walter Payn; and John Fraunceys and Alice de Stanford.
    Walter and Walter have granted to John and Alice all their lands, holdings, rents and services which they had by Alice's grant in Hynetone.

Witnesses: John le Serjaunt, John de Lorewynge, John de Egetone, John Porlewente, Walter Matheu.

A1/36/2 [GC 3299]   n.d. [mid 14th cent.]

John Fraunceys and Alice his wife; and John le Vey, clerk.

John and Alice have granted to John, his heirs and assigns all their lands, holdings and reversions in Hyneton and elsewhere within the hundred of Berkelee.

Witnesses: John le Sergeant the elder, John de Clyve, John le Sergeant the younger, John de Eketone, [John de] Lorewynge.

A1/36/3 [GC 3349]   n.d. [mid 14th cent.]

John le Vey clerk; and John Fraunceys and Alice his wife.

John has granted to John and Alice, and their heirs and assigns, all the lands and holdings which he had by their grant in Hyneton and elsewhere within the hundred of Berkeley.

Witnesses: John le Serjaunt the elder, John de Clyve, John le Serjaunt the younger, John de Egetone, John de Lorewynge.

A1/36/4 [GC 3866]   Wed. 14 Feb. 15 Ric. II [1392]

Robert Fraunces, son and heir of John Fraunces and of Alice Stanford his wife; and John Camme, chaplain, William FitzWaryn and Ralph Coke.

Robert has granted to John, William and Ralph, and their heirs and assigns, all his lands, holdings, rents [etc.], which he inherited after the death of his mother in Hyntone and elsewhere within the hundred of Berkeley.

Witnesses: Ralph Waleys, John Trye, Richard Egton, Richard Gylmyn, John Egton, smith.

At: Hinton.

A1/36/5 [GC 3867]   16 Feb. 15 Ric. II [1392]

Robert Fraunceys of Hinton and Thomas de Berkeley, lord of Berkeley.

Robert is bound to Thomas in £20 to be paid at Easter next.

A1/36/6 [GC 3878]   Mon. before Christmas, 17 Ric. II [22 Dec. 1393]

John Camme, chaplain, William FitzWareyn and Ralph Coke; and Sir Thomas de Berkeley, lord of Berkeley.

John, William and Ralph have quitclaimed to Thomas the lands, holdings, rents [etc.], that they had by grant of Robert Fraunceys, son and heir of John Fraunceys.

Witnesses: Ralph Waleys, William Smalcombe, John Trye, Richard Gylmyn, Richard Egtone.

At: Berkeley.

Other grants and acquisitions

A1/36/7 [GC 2567]   n.d. [*c*. Sept. 1296]

John Wither of Hinton and Sir Thomas de Berkeleya.

John has rendered and quitclaimed to Thomas all the lands and holdings which he inherited in the manor of Hynentone.

Witnesses: Sir Robert de Berkeleya, Sir Robert le Veel, knights, Robert de Bradeston, John de Egetone, John de Craweleye, Robert Wither, Thomas de Swonhongre.

A1/36/8 [GC 618]   Morrow of Michaelmas, 24 Edw. I [30 Sept. 1296]

John Wyther of Hinton and Sir Thomas de Berkel.

John has quitclaimed to Thomas all the lands which he had in the manor of Hyneton; and Thomas has granted to him an annual rent of 10*s*. from Reginald de Holeweya for his lands in Camme and a forest bailiwick (*bailey forestarie*) of Camme or Wottone, for John's life.

Witnesses: Sir Robert de Berkel, Sir Robert de Veel, knights, Robert de Bradeston, John de Egeton, John de Craweleye, Robert Wyther, Thomas de Swonhungre.

A1/36/9 [GC 1019] Sat. the feast of St. Mary Magdalen, 29 Edw. I [22 July 1301]
Thomas de Berkeleye, lord of Berkeley, and Robert the tailor (*cissor*).

Thomas has granted to Robert his villein John son of Richard ate Stompe of Hyneton, with all his issue and chattels.

Witnesses: Robert de Bradeston, Robert de Berkeleye, Thomas de Beoleye, Thomas de Swonhungre, John de Egeton.

At: Berkeley.

A1/36/10 [GC 1696] Whit-Sunday, 2 Edw. II [18 May 1309]
Adam Elyot, son and heir of John Elyot of Hinton, and Sir Maurice de Berkel'.

Adam has quitclaimed to Maurice the lands which he had by grant of William, brother and heir of Adam Hatholf, in Hynetone.

Witnesses: Robert de Bradestone, Thomas de Beoleye, Robert de Berkel', Thomas le Sergant, Robert de Stanforde.

At: Berkeley.

A1/36/11 [GC 2097] 6 May 9 Edw. II [1316]
Adam Elyot of Hinton and Sir Thomas de Berkeleye, his lord.

Adam has granted to Thomas a rent of 3*s.* from Adam and his heirs for all his lands and holdings which he has by his charter in Hamme and Hynetone.

Witnesses: Thomas de Bradeston, Thomas de Boeleye, Peter de Stintescombe, John le Serjant, John Wyth.

At: Berkeley.

A1/36/12 [GC 3255] n.d. [mid 14th cent.]
John Aunger and Sir Thomas lord of Berkeleye.

John has granted to Thomas, his heirs and assigns all the lands and holdings [which he] held for life or for terms of years in Hynitone or elsewhere within the lordship of Berkel'.

Witnesses: John le Serjant, John de Milkesham, Peter de Styntescombe, William de Swonhungre, John de Egetone.

A1/36/13 [GC 4088] Mon. before St. Nicholas, 1 Hen. V [4 Dec. 1413]
Thomas de Berkeley, lord of Berkeley; and Philip Waterton and Cecilia his wife.

Thomas has granted to Philip and Cecilia, for their good service, various rents and services in Hyntone and Halmare, holdings in Heystrete and Longbrugstret in Berkeley, and others; to them and their issue.

Witnesses: Thomas Kendale, Thomas Stauntone, Geoffrey Skey, Richard Scotte, John Floure.

At: Berkeley.

A1/36/14 [GC 4290] 16 June 34 Hen. VI [1456]
James Berkeley, lord of Berkeley, knight, and his beloved Walter Devreux, knight.

James has granted to Walter, for his good service, an annual rent of 20 marks from the manor of Hynton (Glos.); for his life.

BERKELEY LEASES
Hekeriches marsh

A1/36/15 [GC 1004] St. Clement, 28 Edw. I [23 Nov. 1299]
Sir Thomas de Berkel' and Thomas de Swonhungre.

Thomas de Berkel' has granted to Thomas de Swonhungre all his land of Hekerichesmers in Hyneton, for his homage and service and for 6 a. of land which Richard de Wendene holds for life in Benmers; rent 21*s.* a year while Richard lives and after his death 15*s.* a year; and Thomas de Swonhungre has quitclaimed to Thomas de Berkel' his land of Benmers in Hamme which Richard holds for life.

Witnesses: Sir John Boteturte, Sir William de Wauton, Sir Nicholas de Kyngeston, knights, Robert de Bradeston, John de Egeton, Robert de Berkel', Thomas de Beoleye, Henry de Camme, Robert de Draycote, Robert Wyther, William le Wariner.

A1/36/16 [GC 1005]   Mon. the feast of St. Clement, 28 Edw. I [23 Nov. 1299]
Sir Thomas de Berkel' and Thomas de Swonhungre.

Thomas de Berkel' has quitclaimed common of pasture in Hekerichesmers within the manor of Hyneton, for himself and all his tenants in villeinage, to Thomas de Swonhungre.
Witnesses: Robert de Bradeston, Thomas de Beleye, John de Egeton, Geoffrey Neel, William de [Web]bel', clerk.

A1/36/17 [GC 1817]   Easter Day, 4 Edw. II [11 April 1311]
(1) Sir Thomas de Berkelee, lord of Berkeley; (2) Thomas de Swonhongre; (3) Maurice son and heir of Sir Thomas.

Thomas has appointed Thomas his attorney to give the rents and services of the field called Hekerisschesmersch to Maurice. [*In French.*]
At: Berkeley Castle.

Hinham moor and le Hey pastures

A1/36/18 [GC 3740]   Mon. after All Saints, 4 Ric. II [5 Nov. 1380]
Thomas de Berkleye, lord of Berkeley, and John Fraunceys of Hinton.

Thomas has leased to John two pastures called Hynhammor and le Hey by Thomas's park of Shobbenassh; for life, rent 20*s.* a year.
Witnesses: Thomas Skay, Richard Gilemyn, Thomas Purlewent, John . . .
At: Berkeley.

A1/36/19 [GC 4139]   20 Feb. 2 Hen. VI [1424]
James de Berkeley, lord of Berkeley, and John Amkys.

James has leased to John a messuage and half-virgate of land in Hyntone which John Drew previously held, and a parcel of pasture called Hymmamore, and a parcel of land called le Hey beside the enclosure of the park of Shoppenmarshe, and all the houses and buildings in the court [*curia*] of Hyntone, viz. the hall [etc.]; for life, with remainder to Eleanor his wife for her life and to John their son for his life, rent 50*s.* a year, and they have paid a fine of 5 marks.
Witnesses: Thomas Staunton, William Brownin', Richard Ricards.
At: Berkeley.

Other

A1/36/20 [GC 2486]   n.d. [early 14th cent.]
Thomas de Berkel' and Robert le Gardiner, tailor.

Thomas has granted to Robert the messuage and land which Agnes atte Halle formerly held of the holding formerly of Robert le Brut in Hynetone, also a messuage with a curtilage and two small crofts which were formerly of John Wyther, 1 a. of land which Walter Balstake formerly held, 1½ a. of land which Adam de Appelhulle formerly held, ⅓ a. of meadow which Isilia Kyng formerly held and 2 a. of land of Thomas's demesne of which one is called Cleyacre and the other Langetag, in Hynetone; to him and his issue, rent 6*s.* 8*d.* a year while Robert lives, with 2*d.* a year customary aid, and 10*s.* a year after Robert's death and 2*d.* aid.
Witnesses: Robert de Stane. Robert de Bradeston, John de Eketone, John de Crawleye, Thomas de Swonhunger', Robert Wyther, John Sewaker.

A1/36/21 [GC 1000]   Michaelmas, 28 Edw. I [29 Sept. 1300]
Sir Thomas lord of Berkeleye and John Elyoth of Hinton.

Thomas has granted to John the stage [*stagium*] for putts and other fishing engines in the Severn called Pullamouthe between the stage which was of Sir Robert de Kyngeston and the stage of Denise la Whyth in Hyneton; rent 4*d.* a year, and saving to Thomas all the fish caught at all the putts or other fisheries in the said stage on two days each week, Wednesdays and Fridays.
Witnesses: Robert de Bradestone, Thomas de Beoleye, Thomas de Swonhungre, Robert de Stanford, Adam Hatholf.

A1/36/22 [GC 1012]   Thurs. before St. Barnabas, 29 Edw. I [8 June 1301]
Thomas lord of Berkeley; and John Everard, Alice his wife and John and Walter their sons.

Thomas has granted to John, Alice, John and Walter, for their lives, a messuage and a half-virgate of land with 1 a. of foreland in Hynetone, which John previously held of Thomas in villeinage; rent 20*s. 8*d. a year, and they have given him 10 marks.
Witnesses: Nicholas de Stowa, constable of Berkeley, Robert de Bradeston, Thomas de Beoleye, Thomas le Serjant, Robert de Stanford, Adam Hatholf, William de Webbel, clerk.
At: Berkeley.

A1/36/23 [GC 1986]   1 Aug. 8 Edw. II [1314]
Maurice de Berkelee; and John de Oldelynch and Maud his wife.

Maurice has leased to John and Maud the rent of 14*s.* a year from Robert le Taillour for his holding, viz. a messuage, garden, curtilage, lands and meadow, which he holds of Maurice for life, with the reversion of the same holding, in Hyneton; for their lives, rent 14*s.* a year while Robert lives, and 40*s.* a year thereafter, and their issue will remain in servile condition.
Witnesses: Robert de Stanford, William Gylemyn, Richard le Serjant, Matthew Hatholf, William in the Hurne.
At: Berkeley.

A1/36/24 [GC 3275]   n.d. [mid 14th cent.]
Thomas lord of Berkelee; and Thomas son of William de Swonhongre, Maud his wife and John the younger their son.

Thomas has leased to Thomas, Maud and John a messuage and half-virgate of land which Robert Wyntur previously held in villeinage in Hynetone; for their lives, rent 20*s.* a year, and the customary maintenance of the woodward.
Witnesses: John Serjaunt the elder, John Serjaunt the younger, John Purlewent, John Capel, John ate Boure.

A1/36/25 [GC 3671]   Thurs. before St. Simon and St. Jude, 48 [Edw. III, 26 Oct. 1374]
Thomas lord of Berkelee; and John Ricardes, Alice his wife and William their son.

Thomas has leased to John, Alice and William a messuage and half-virgate of land which John Oldelynch sometime held . . . ; for their lives, rent . . . a year.
At: Berkeley.

A1/36/26 [GC 4238]   16 April 22 Hen. VI [1444]
James Berkeley, lord of Berkeley, knight; and Thomas Adames and Joan his wife.

James has leased to Thomas and Joan a messuage in the manor of Hynton and a half-virgate of land, with a foreland and a fishery nearby at Chiselhongre which John Sonehungre lately held; for their lives, rent 41*s.* a year.
At: Berkeley Castle.

ADMINISTRATIVE DOCUMENTS
Account rolls

A1/36/27 [GAR 153]	14–15 Edw. I [1286–7]
A1/36/28 [GAR 154]	17–18 Edw. I [1289–90]
A1/36/29 [GAR 155]	20–1 Edw. I [1292–3]
A1/36/30 [GAR 156]	21–2 Edw. I [1293–4]
A1/36/31 [GAR 157]	n.d. [1297–8]
A1/36/32 [GAR 158]	26–7 Edw. I [1298–9]

Two rolls, Michaelmas to 1 Aug. and 1 Aug. to Michaelmas.

A1/36/33 [GAR 159]	n.d. [*c.* 1300]
A1/36/34 [GAR 160]	3–4 Edw. II [1309–10]
A1/36/35 [GAR 161]	5–6 Edw. II [1311–12]
A1/36/36 [GAR 162]	6–7 Edw. II [1312–13]
A1/36/37 [GAR 163]	8–9 Edw. II [1314–15]
A1/36/38 [GAR 164]	16–17 Edw. II [1322–3]
A1/36/39 [GAR 165]	18–19 Edw. II [1324–5]
A1/36/40 [GAR 166]	18–19 Edw. II [1324–5]
A1/36/41 [GAR 167] Early draft.	n.d. [1324–5]
A1/36/42 [SR 43]	18–19 Edw. II [1324–5]
A1/36/43 [GAR 168]	20 Edw. II to 1 Edw. III [1326–7]
A1/36/44 [GAR 169]	1–2 Edw. III [1327–8]
A1/36/45 [GAR 171]	7–8 Edw. III [1333–4]
A1/36/46 [GAR 172]	8–9 Edw. III [1334–5]
A1/36/47 [GAR 173]	n.d. [1335–6]
A1/36/48 [GAR 174]	10–11 Edw. III [1336–7]
A1/36/49 [GAR 175]	12–13 Edw. III [1338–9]
A1/36/50 [GAR 176]	13–14 Edw. III [1339–40]
A1/36/51 [GAR 170]	n.d. [1341–2]
A1/36/52 [GAR 177]	19–20 Edw. III [1345–6]
A1/36/53 [GAR 178]	30–1 Edw. III [1356–7]
A1/36/54 [GAR 179]	31–2 Edw. III [1357–8]
A1/36/55 [GAR 180]	32–3 Edw. III [1358–9]
A1/36/56 [GAR 181]	33–4 Edw. III [1359–60]
A1/36/57 [SR 47]	Mich. 41 to 8 June 42 Edw. III [1367–8]
A1/36/58 [GAR 182]	4 [Jan.] to Mich. 48 Edw. III [1374]
A1/36/59 [GAR 183]	48–9 Edw. III [1374–5]
A1/36/60 [GAR 184]	49–50 Edw. III [1375–6]
A1/36/61 [GAR 185]	50 Edw. III to 1 Ric. II [1376–7]
A1/36/62 [GAR 186]	2–3 Ric. II [1378–9]
A1/36/63 [GAR 187]	4–5 Ric. II [1380–1]
A1/36/64 [GAR 188] Three rolls.	10–13 Ric. II [1386–9]
A1/36/65 [GAR 189]	3–4 Hen. V [1415–16]
A1/36/66 [GAR 322]	1–2 Hen. VI [1422–3]
A1/36/67 [GAR 190]	38–9 Hen. VI [1459–60]

Rentals

A1/36/68 [GRR 15]   Jan. 5 Hen. VI [1427]

A1/36/69 [GRR 16]   n.d. [*temp.* Hen. VI]

OTHER INTERESTS

A1/36/70 [GC 753]   n.d. [late Hen. III]
Richard [Fediht?] and William Hildermon.

Richard has granted to William 1 a. of arable land in the furlong called Nelescrofte containing 8 selions and 2 fore-earths, next to the road from the house of William son of Eustace to Oldeminstre; rent 3*d.* a year, and William has given him 27*s.*
Witnesses: Adam Coby, John Sewaker, Alfred Mariner, Adam son of Nigel, Henry de Abbewell, Andrew de Bratheston, John de Egeton, Thomas de Ahsselworth, Walter Sely, clerk.

A1/36/71 [GC 1257]   n.d. [late Hen. III]
Robert le Breht and Philip de Leycestria.

Robert has granted to Philip 23⅜ and $\frac{1}{20}$ a. and 1¾ perches of land, 1 a. of meadow, half the meadow called Welleacre and all his right in the meadow called Cockesmede in the field called Cotteworth [etc.]; rent 6*d.* a year, and Philip has given him 24 marks.
Witnesses: Sir Maurice de Saltmarsh (*de salso marisco*), Sir Roger de Lokinton, Sir Walter de Burgo, knights, Andrew de Brothestone, Thomas . . . , John de Egeton, Peter de Wike, Robert de la Plaunche, Robert Bastard, Peter de Eweleya, Robert le Herde.

HINTON: POCKINGTON

THE CRAWLEY HOLDING

A1/37/1 [GC 1322]   n.d. [1281 × 1300]
John de Crauleye and Sir Thomas de Berkeleye.
. John has granted to Thomas all the lands and holdings which he had by grant of Isabel de Waneswelle in Pochampton and Hyneton in the parish of Berkeleye; rent 1*d.* a year, and Thomas has given him £20.
Witnesses: Sir Robert de Berkeleye, Sir Robert le Veel, knights, Robert de Stone, Robert de Bradestone, Peter de Styntescumbe, Thomas de Swonhungre, John de Egetone.

A1/37/2 [GC 3295]   n.d. [late 14th cent.]
Joan de Craweley of Gloucestershire and Sir Thomas lord of Berkeley.

Joan has quitclaimed to Thomas all the lands, holdings [etc.] which John C[raweleye] had by grant of Isabel de Waneswelle in Pocampton within the hundred of Berkeleye.
Witnesses: John Sergeant of Stone, Ralph Waleys, William Porlewent, William Modbroke, Richard Gillymyn.

OTHER INTERESTS

A1/37/3 [SC 68]   n.d. [*c.* 1200]
Robert de Berkelaia and Kingswood Abbey.

Robert has confirmed grants to the abbey by William the white (*albus*) of 1 virgate of land (granted on 11 June 1200) and eight pennyworth (*nummatai*) of land in the same vill, and other land; and he has further granted pasture for 7 sows and a year's litter, 1 boar and 50 sheep, and certain fishing rights in the Severn near Chiselhanger Wood.
Witnesses: Ralph [Su]mery, William de Punthdelarch, Richard de Clifford, Oliver de Berkeley, Bernard de Stanes, Walter the chaplain, Hugh the chaplain, Robert the chaplain, Maurice son of Nigel, Robert le Bastard, Gilbert son of Osmund, Hugh de Cimma, John de Crauleia.

A1/37/4 [GC 1560]   n.d. [*temp.* Edw. I]
Nicholas Thedulf of Alkington and Robert Wyther, constable of Berkeley.

Nicholas has granted to Robert, for a certain sum of money, the services of Walter Cloterhet for his holding in Pocamton.
Witnesses: Robert de Stone, Robert de Bradestone, John de Crauleye, Thomas de Swonhungre, Thomas Alein.

HORFIELD

A1/38/1 [GC 2461]   Sun. after the Assumption of St. Mary, 20 Edw. II [17 Aug. 1326]
Ralph atte Welle of Syde and Maud his daughter.

Ralph has granted to Maud, her heirs and assigns all his land and meadow in the furlong of Horfeld above the hill called Asselyneshulle in the lordship of Elias de Filtone, which he had by grant of Adam le Norreys, formerly burgess of Bristoll'.
Witnesses: Elias de Filtone, John de Oldebur', Robert Jordan, Richard de Stoke, Ralph le Hopere.
At: Stoke Gifford.

HURST

The manor was very closely associated with neighbouring Slimbridge, with which it was, indeed, often administered, and it is sometimes difficult to disentangle the two, particularly with regard to the vill of Gossington.

BERKELEY ACQUISITIONS
Land in Aspley

A1/39/1 [GC 1511]   n.d. [*c.* March 1293]
Henry Pinel and William de Bernwod.

Henry has leased to William 2 a. of land in the furlong called Aspeleye, between the stream called Holdelondesborc [*sic*] and the footpath from Gosinton to Camme, from Easter 21 Edw. I [29 March 1293] for a term of 20 years; William has given him 14*s*.
Witnesses: Reginald de Gosintone, Robert de Draycote, Henry de Camme, Walter de Gosintone, Richard le Duc.

A1/39/2 [GC 1039]   28 Edw. I [1299–1300]
Henry Pynel and Robert de Berkeleye.

Henry has quitclaimed to Robert the arable land in the furlong called Aspeleye which William de Bernwode bought from him [Henry]; for a term of 20 years.
Witnesses: Robert de Bradeston, Thomas de Belegh, Thomas de Swonhungre, Philip the chaplain, Elias le Botyler, Walter de Gosyngton.
At: Breadstone.

A1/39/3 [GC 2585]   n.d. [*c.* 1330]
Thomas de Berkeleye of Billow (*Beoleye*) and Sir Thomas lord of Berkeleye.

Thomas of Billow has granted to Thomas of Berkeley 2 a. of land in the furlong called Aspeleye in Hurste.
Witnesses: John le Serjaunt, John de Milkesham, John de Avene, John de Egetone, John de Kyngestone.

Other grants and acquisitions

A1/39/4 [GC 4143]   Fri. after Epiphany, 3 Hen. VI [12 Jan. 1425]
James Berkeley, lord of Berkeley, and Richard Venables, his esquire.

James has granted to Richard, for his good service, an annual rent of 10 marks from the manor of Hurste, to him and his assigns for 60 years if he lives that long, and has demised at farm to Richard the site of the manor of Hurst with the houses and buildings and all the

demesne lands [etc.], and 16 a. of meadow; for a term of 60 years if he lives that long, rent 16 marks a year.
At: Berkeley Castle.

A1/39/5 [GC 4296]   4 Aug. 36 Hen. VI [1458]
James lord of Berkeley, knight; and John Lord Beauchamp, Richard Beauchamp and John Cotford and John Kyrton, mercers of London.

James has made an enfeoffment of the manor of Hurste in the parish of Sclymbrugge (Glos.), to John, Richard, John and John until such time as £147 13s. 4d. is levied from the manor at £20 a year, to the use of John Cotford and his said feoffees. [*In English.*]

BERKELEY LEASES
Pool half-virgate
A1/39/6 [SC 480; *duplicate* GC 2035]   1 May 8 Edw. II [1315]
Thomas de Berkeley, lord of Berkeley; and William de la Pulle and Mabel his wife.

Thomas has granted to William and Mabel, for their lives, the half-virgate which John de la Pulle once held, and 1½ a. of meadow in Lottesmore and a certain plot of land, in Hurst; rent 26s. 9½d. a year.
Witnesses: Thomas de Bradeston, Roger de Gosyntone, William le Botyler, Walter de Gosynton, John le Duk, Richard Bat, John de Kyngestun.
At: Berkeley.

A1/39/7 [GC 2759]   27 Nov. 6 Edw. III [1332]
Thomas lord of Berkelee; and Robert le Cook of Leonard Stanley and Maud his wife.

Thomas has leased to Robert and Maud a messuage and a half-virgate of land with a plot 5 perches by 1 perch, which William atte Pulle previously held in Hurste; for their lives, rent 20s. 1½d.
Witnesses: John Serjaunt, John de Melkesham, John Colynes, Robert de Coueleye, Robert le Waryner.
At: Berkeley.

Villein land
A1/39/8 [GC 1658]   5 June 1 Edw. II [1308]
Thomas de Berkelee, lord of Berkeley; and Isabel la Rede and John her son.

Thomas has granted to Isabel and John the half-virgate which she previously held in villeinage in Hurste; for their lives, rent 20s. a year, and their issue will remain in servile condition.
Witnesses: Robert de Bradeston, Robert de Berkelee, Thomas de Beolee, Thomas de Styntescombe, Elias le Boteler, John le Duk, Walter de Gosynton.
At: Berkeley.

A1/39/9 [GC 1659]   5 June 1 Edw. II [1308]
Thomas de Berkelee, lord of Berkeley; and Richard le Man and Edith his wife.

Thomas has granted to Richard and Edith the half-virgate which Adam Sake previously held in villeinage in Hurste; for their lives, rent 20s. a year.
Witnesses: Robert de Bradeston, Robert de Berkelee, Thomas de Beolee, Thomas de Styntescombe, Elias le Boteler, John le Duk, Walter de Gosynton.
At: Berkeley.

A1/39/10 [GC 2310]   10 April 13 Edw. II [1320]
Thomas de Berkeleye, lord of Berkeley; and John atte Pulle and Maud his wife.

Thomas has leased to John and Maud the virgate of land, with a house and foreland, which William Sake formerly held in villeinage, in Hurste; for their lives, rent 42s. a year.

Witnesses: Stephen de Draycote, Walter Hathemare, Walter de Gosyntone, William le Botyler, John de Kyngestone.
At: Berkeley.

Other leases

A1/39/11 [GC 1867]   1 March 5 Edw. II [1312]
Thomas de Berkelee, lord of Berkeley; and Thomas the tailor (*Sissor*) of Clingre and Margaret his wife.

Thomas has granted to Thomas and Margaret his croft called Hardynggesherne which he had by grant of Thomas de Styntescoumbe, in Hurste; to hold enclosed, to them and their issue, rent 12*s.* a year.
Witnesses: Thomas de Bradestone, Nicholas de Beolee, Roger de Gosyntone, Walter de Gosyntone, Stephen de Draycote.
At: Berkeley.

A1/39/12 [GC 1868]   1 March 5 Edw. II [1312]
Thomas de Berkelee, lord of Berkeley; and John Pynel and Joan his wife.

Thomas has granted to John and Joan a plot of land beside John's house in Hurste; to hold enclosed, to them and their issue, rent 12*d.* a year.
Witnesses: Roger de Gosyntone, Robert Warner, Walter de Gosyntone, William le Boteler, Richard Bat.
At: Berkeley.

A1/39/13 [GC 1870]   1 March 5 Edw. II [1312]
Thomas de Berkelee, lord of Berkeley; and Thomas le Thechchare and Mabel his wife.

Thomas has granted to Thomas and Mabel 2 a. and a fardel of land at Palmaresherne in Hurste; to hold enclosed, to them and their issue, rent 9*s.* a year while Thomas lives and 10*s.* thereafter.
Witnesses: Roger de Gosyntone, Nicholas de Beolee, Robert Warner, Walter de Gosyntone, William le Boteler, Richard Bat, John de Kyngestone.
At: Berkeley.

A1/39/14 [GC 1915]   1 May 6 Edw. II [1313]
Thomas de Berkelee, lord of Berkeley; and Isabel le Rede and John her son.

Thomas has leased to Isabel and John 1½ a. 5 perches of meadow in Ademede, in Hurste; for their lives, rent 7*s.* 8*d.* a year.
Witnesses: Thomas de Bradestone, Roger de Gosintone, Nicholas de Beoleie, Walter de Gosintone, William le Botiler.
At: Berkeley.

A1/39/15 [GC 1921]   20 May 6 Edw. II [1313]
Thomas de Berkelee, lord of Berkeley; and John le Kyng and Maud his wife.

Thomas has leased to John and Maud 4 a. 20 perches of meadow in Ademede, next to the meadow of Isabel la Rede, in Hurste; for their lives, rent 18*s.* 4*d.* a year.
Witnesses: Thomas de Bradestone, Roger de Gosintone, Nicholas de Beoleie, Walter de Gosynton, William le Boteler.
At: Berkeley.

A1/39/16 [GC 2001]   12 Nov. 8 Edw. II [1314]
Thomas de Berkeleye, lord of Berkeley, and Thomas son of Thomas de Boeleyestret.

Thomas de Berkeleye has granted to Thomas son of Thomas a rent of 4*s.* from Walter Gylebert and Edith his wife for a holding and a plot of land adjacent containing 2 a. which

they hold for life in Hurste, with the reversion of the land and holding after their deaths; to Thomas son of Thomas and his issue, rent 5*s.* a year.
Witnesses: Thomas de Bradeston, Thomas de Boeleye, John Capel, Stephen de Draycote, Robert de Stanford.
At: Berkeley.

A1/39/17 [GC 2038]   4 May 8 Edw. II [1315]
Thomas de Berkeleye, lord of Berkeley; and William atte Pulle and Mabel his wife.

Thomas has remitted to William and Mabel, for their lives, suit to the mills of Camme and Cambrugge and to the two lawdays [*lawhalymotas*] of Camme each year, for 12*d.* a year paid to the manor of Hurste.
Witnesses: Thomas de Bradeston, Roger de Gosyntone, William le Botyler, John le Duk, Richard Bat.
At: Berkeley.

A1/39/18 [GC 3256]   n.d. [*c.* 1338 × 1361]
 Sir Maurice de Berkelee, lord of Hurst, and Richard son of Sir Richard de Ryvers, knight.

Maurice has granted to Richard 2 roods of land in the field called Lynch in exchange for 2 roods of land in the field called Elmes.
Witnesses: John Draycotes, John Hulles, John Mon, Thomas Hallyng, Thomas Colynes.

A1/39/19 [GC 3391]   Mon. after Ascension, 26 Edw. III [21 May 1352]
Maurice de Berkelee, lord of Hurst; and Simon Mody, Joan his wife and Thomas their son.

Maurice has leased to Simon, Joan and Thomas a messuage and 1 fardel of land which William Davy sometime held in Hurste; for their lives, rent 12*s.* a year.
Witnesses: John de Draycote, John Howes, John le Mon.
At: Berkeley.

A1/39/20 [GC 4444]   6 Nov. 1 Hen. VII [1485]
John Andrews and the lord [William Berkeley]

Extract from court roll: John came and gave the lord a fine of £4 to have the reversion of 'le courte of Hirst' which John Man held; to John Andrews and Agnes his wife for their lives.

ADMINISTRATIVE DOCUMENTS
Account rolls
Since the manor was often administered with Slimbridge there are some joint accounts: see below, p. 285.

A1/39/21 [GAR 191]	20–1 Edw. I [1292–3]
A1/39/22 [GAR 192]	26–7 Edw. I [1298–9]
A1/39/23 [GAR 193]	27–8 Edw. III [1353–4]
A1/39/24 [GAR 194]	Michaelmas 28 Edw. III for 12 weeks [1354]
A1/39/25 [GAR 195]	29–30 Edw. III [1355–6]
A1/39/26 [GAR 196]	31–2 Edw. III [1357–8]
A1/39/27 [GAR 197]	32–3 Edw. III [1358–9]
A1/39/28 [GAR 198]	33–4 Edw. III [1359–60]
A1/39/29 [GAR 199]	34–5 Edw. III [1360–1]
A1/39/30 [GAR 200]	36–7 Edw. III [1362–3]
A1/39/31 [GAR 201]	37–8 Edw. III [1363–4]
A1/39/32 [GAR 202]	38–9 Edw. III [1364–5]
A1/39/33 [GAR 203]	39–40 Edw. III [1365–6]
A1/39/34 [GAR 204]	40–1 Edw. III [1366–7]

Bailiff's allowances

A1/39/35 [GAR 419]   28 Edw. III [1354]

OTHER INTERESTS
Monk rent

A1/39/36 [GC 2651]   Morrow of St. Augustine, 2 Edw. III [27 Aug. 1328]
William ate Pulle of Gossington and John his son.

William has granted to John a rent of 12*s.* a year from a messuage, garden, curtilage and croft held by Reginald le Monek and Alice his wife for their lives, in Hurste, and all the land and meadow which William acquired with the said holding in the fee of William son of Henry de Camme, with the reversion of the holding.
Witnesses: Roger Archer, Thomas Hallyng, John Bradeford, John de Kyngestone, William Botiler.
At: Hurst.

A1/39/37 [GC 2963]   Wed. before St. Luke, 13 Edw. III [13 Oct. 1339]
Henry de Furneaux, rector of Slimbridge; and John son of the late William ate Pulle of Gossington and Maud his wife.

Henry has granted to John and Maud an annual rent of 12*s.* from the holding which Reginald le Moneke and Alice his wife hold for their lives in Hurste, with the reversion of the holding, and also all the lands [etc.] which he acquired from John in the parish of Slymbrugge; to them and their issue, with remainder to John's right heirs.
Witnesses: William le Botiler, John de Kyngestone, Richard de Kyngestone, John Knyght, Thomas Halling.
At: Slimbridge.

Other

A1/39/38 [GC 3966]   n.d. [late 13th cent.]
Robert de Berkeleya, knight, lord of Arlingham; and Thomas de Beleystrete and Isabel his wife.

Robert has granted to Thomas the holding towards Beleystrete which he had by grant of John le Granval and Isabel his wife, and 1 a. of land in Hurste which he had by grant of Thomas de Berkeleya; to Thomas and Isabel, and their heirs and assigns, rent 5*s.* a year. Memorandum that this copy is true, sealed by John Passelew. [*Early 15th-cent. copy.*]
Witnesses: Robert de Bradestone, John de Craweley, Thomas de Beley, John de Beyvile, Walter de Wyke, Richard de Wyke, Richard of the wood (*de bosco*).

KINGSCOTE
THE KINGSCOTE HOLDING

A1/40/1 [GC 1446]   n.d. [early Edw. I]
Nigel de Kingescot and Alice his daughter.

Nigel has granted to Alice a rent of 5*s.* a year from the half-virgate which he sold to Richard de Heselcote, and which John le Neweman formerly held; to her and her issue.
Witnesses: Sir Nicholas Burdon, Henry de Dene, Peter de Stintescumbe, Robert de Olepenne, Maurice son of Sir William de Berkel', Peter Jake.

A1/40/2 [GC 1447; *duplicate* GC 1449]   n.d. [early Edw. I]
Nigel de Kyngescote and Alice his daughter.

Nigel has granted to Alice the half-virgate which Hugh the baker (*pistor*) formerly held of Nigel, in the territory of Haselkote; rent a rose a year.
Witnesses: Henry de Dene, Philip de la Hulle, Maurice son of Sir William de Berkel', Peter Jake, Nicholas de Newinton, Richard de Aselcote, Walter de Styntescumbe, clerk.

A1/40/3 [GC 1448]   n.d. [early Edw. I]
Nigel de Kingescote and Alice his daughter.

Nigel has granted to Alice two crofts in la Rode of Kingescote which John de la Rode formerly held; rent a rose a year.

Witnesses: Sir Nicholas Burdon, Henry de Dene, Peter de Stintescumbe, Robert de Olepenne, Maurice son of Sir William de Berkel', Peter Jake.

A1/40/4 [GC 3704]   Mon. after the Purification, 51 Edw. III [9 Feb. 1377]
Elias Swonhongre; and Thomas Clavylle of Uley, Maud his wife and their first son, called Maurice.

Elias has leased to Thomas, Maud and Maurice a croft called Rodecroft by Kyngescote; for their lives, rent 1*d.* a year.

Witnesses: Maurice Basset, Edmund Basset, John Clavylle, John Oulepenne, William Clavyle.
At: Berkeley.

OTHER

A1/40/5 [GC 3700]   St. Andrew, 50 Edw. III [30 Nov. 1376]
Elias de Wannswelle; and John Andrew of Hazlecote, Eleanor his wife and James their son.

Elias has leased to John, Eleanor and James a half-virgate of land in Kyngguscote which Giles Maynel sometime held; for their lives, rent 7*s.* 6*d.* a year.

Witnesses: John de Olpen, Thomas Clavyle, William Edward, Roger Aynleye.
At: Kingscote.

KINGSCOTE: HAZLECOTE

BERKELEY INTERESTS

A1/41/1 [GC 2006]   20 Jan. 8 Edw. II [1315]
Peter de Styntescombe and Sir Thomas de Berkeleye, lord of Berkeley.

Peter has granted to Thomas, his heirs and assigns a rent of 4*s.* from a messuage with a croft and 15½ a. of land in Haselcote, which Thomas atte Clive and Eve his wife hold for their lives by his grant, with the reversion of the said holding after their deaths, in Haselcote and Kyngescote.

Witnesses: John de Olepenne, Stephen de Draycote, Robert de Bennecoumbe, Robert of the gate (*de porta*), John de Bradeforde, John Giffard of Nympsfield, Thomas le Eyr.
At: Berkeley.

A1/41/2 [GC 2009]   The Purification, 8 Edw. II [2 Feb. 1315]
Thomas de Berkelee, lord of Berkeley, and Thomas atte Clive of Hazlecote and Eve his wife.

Thomas has leased to Thomas and Eve, for their lives, their messuage and croft and 15½ a. of land in Haselcote, of which the messuage and croft lie in the vill of Haselcote, 7 a. in the west field and 8½ a. in the east field; rent 4*s.* a year.

Witnesses: William de Kyngescote, Thomas le Eyr, John Richardes, William de Beuleye, Walter Jordan.
At: Berkeley.

A1/41/3 [GC 2837]   Wed. the feast of St. John the evangelist, 9 Edw. III [27 Dec. 1335]
Thomas de Berkele, lord of Berkeley; and Thomas atte Clyve of Hazelcote, and Agnes his wife.

Thomas has leased to Thomas and Agnes a messuage and 15½ a. of land which Eve atte Clyve held of Thomas for her life in Haselcote by Kyngescote; for their lives, for the customary services.

Witnesses: William de Kyngescote, Robert le Heyward of Beverston, Philip Smart, John Robert of Kingscote.
At: Berkeley.

OTHER INTERESTS

A1/41/4 [GC 1952]   St. Brice, 7 Edw. II [13 Nov. 1313]

Thomas de Stone and Nigel son of John Richard of Kingscote.

Thomas has leased to Nigel the half-virgate which Hugh le Prestour formerly held in Haselcote; to Nigel for life, with remainder to William son of the said John, for life, if he survives Nigel, rent 12s. a year.

Witnesses: Nigel de Kyngescote, John de Houlpenne, Henry de Camme, Stephen de Draycote, Walter Petit.

At: Berkeley.

OWLPEN

Owlpen was a sub-manor held of the Berkeleys of Berkeley by the de Owlpen family until the mid 15th century when it passed through an heiress to John Daunt. It was held as half a knight's fee and for a rent of 5s. paid to Wotton manor. The greater part of its lands lay in Newington Bagpath.[1]

A1/42/1 [GC 4218]   Fri. before St. George, 19 Hen. VI [21 April 1441]

Robert Oulepen; and Christopher Hylton, William Notyngham, William Wangford, John Kendale, William Pomeray, Richard Pygot, Richard Brugge, John Busce, Lambert Lee, Robert Basset, Philip parson of Nympsfield, Henry Payne, Robert Raubyn, John Loughton, John Huggys and John Oulepen.

Robert has granted his manor of Oulepen and all his lands, holdings [etc.] within the hundred of Berkeley to Christoper and the others, and their heirs and assigns.

Witnesses: Robert Clavyle, John Oldelond, John Thorp the younger.

SLIMBRIDGE

The manor was granted to FitzHarding's son Maurice (I) (d. 1190) by Roger de Berkeley of Dursley in marriage with Roger's daughter. Thereafter it passed with the rest of Berkeley Herness. It comprised the vills of Cambridge, Gossington and Kingston.

BERKELEY ACQUISITIONS AND GRANTS
Exchange with Longbridge Hospital

A1/43/1 [SC 436]   A.D. 1270 [1270–1]

Prior Henry of Holy Trinity, Longbridge, and Sir Maurice de Berkeley.

The priory has granted to Maurice the pasture called la Sterte which lies between la Newelond and la Warth in exchange for 5½ a. of land in Gosintune called Suthwrthi.

Witnesses: Sir Robert de Kingestun, Sir Richard de Berkeley, knights, Reginald de Gosintun, Thomas de Belegh, Robert de Bratheston, Walter de Egetun, Geoffrey Neel, Walter Sely.

A1/43/2 [GC 325]   A.D. 1270 [1270–1]

Prior Henry and the convent of Holy Trinity, Longbridge; and Sir Maurice de Berkeley.

Prior Henry and the brothers have granted to Maurice the pasture called la Sterte lying between the furlong called la Newelonde and la Warth, rendering to the chief lord of Frompton 4s. a year in the name of the brothers, and in return Maurice has granted to them 5½ a. of land in the field of Gosintone called Suthworthy, viz. 3 a. lying next to the land of Elias le Butiler, from the land of Sir Robert de Kingestone to Lithingbroc, and 2½ a. next to the land of John Halling, between the land of Reginald de Gosinton and Walter Pynel, for the brothers to hold in free alms. Endorsed: *Hurste*.

Witnesses: Sir Robert de Kingestun, Sir Richard de Berkeley, knights, Roger de Gosinton, Thomas de Belegh, Robert de Bratheston, Walter de Egeton, Geoffrey Neel, Walter Sely.

[1] Smyth, iii. 311–12.

Exchanges with Adam Long

A1/43/3 [GC 928]   n.d. [late Hen. III]
Adam le Lung of Slimbridge and Sir Maurice de Berkel', his lord.

Adam has quitclaimed to Maurice ½ a. of land which Maurice holds in the vill of Slimbrugge in the furlong called Eforlong.

Witnesses: Sir Robert de Kingestun, knight, Henry de Clifford, Elias le Botiler, Walter de Salle, Robert Wyther, Walter de Wyke, William the serjeant (*serviens*) of Kingston.

A1/43/4 [GC 1213]   n.d. [late Hen. III]
Maurice de Berkel' and Adam Long.

Maurice has granted to Adam ½ a. of land in the furlong called Long Garstone, in exchange for ½ a. in the field of Aldeford.

Witnesses: Sir Robert de Kyngeston, William de Mathem, William the serjeant (*serviens*), Elias le Botiler, Gilbert son of Hugh, Walter Sely.

A1/43/5 [GC 684]   n.d. [late Hen. III]
Maurice de Berkel and Adam Longe.

Maurice has granted to Adam 1½ selions of land in the furlong called Longelonda, one next to the land of Walter Selewine and half next to the land of Elias le Botiler, extending to the road called Guldenemile, and further 1½ selions in the furlong called Cattesham, and for this Adam has granted to Maurice 1 selion and a gore of land in the said furlong of Longelonde and 1 selion in Marhscroft; Adam will render to Maurice 1*d.* a year.

Witnesses: Sir Robert de Kingeston, William de Gosinton, Elias le Botiler, Gilbert son of Hugh, William son of Robert, Walter Sely.

Lease from and exchange with William le Duce

A1/43/6 [GC 462]   Thurs. before the translation of St. Thomas the martyr [5 July] 1274
William le Duc and Sir Maurice de Berkel', his lord.

William has leased to Maurice a gore of the land which William Young (*Juvenis*) granted to him for a term of 30 years, in the furlong called Parva Longelond, to hold for all his term as in the charter of William Young.

Witnesses: Sir Robert de Kingeston, William the serjeant (*serviens*), Elias le Botiler, Gilbert son of Hugh, William Baht.

A1/43/7 [GC 1340]   n.d. [late Hen. III]
William le Duc of Slimbridge and Alice his wife; and Sir Maurice de Berkel'.

William and Alice have granted to Maurice 2 selions of land in the furlong called le Muchele Longelond, beside le Guldenmile, in exchange for 3 selions in the furlong called Fifrug'.

Witnesses: Sir Robert de Kyngeston, John de Kyngeston, Elias le Butiler, Robert de Draycote, Ralph de Camme, Robert de Couel', William Warner.

Meadow in Brewers ham

A1/43/8 [GC 886]   n.d. [late 13th cent.]
Ismannia la Bruere and Thomas Flambard.

Ismannia has granted to Thomas her meadow in the furlong called le Bruereshomm', which ham lies between the meadow called Wyteneye and the rhine called Cambrok; rent 1 lb. of cumin a year, and Thomas has given her 20*s*.

Witnesses: Walter de Egeton, Robert de Bradeston, Thomas the serjeant (*serviens*), Richard le Duc, Robert Mathias, Elias le Boteler, Walter de Gosinton.

A1/43/9 [GC 755]   n.d. [1281 × 1300]
Thomas Flambard and Sir Thomas de Berkel', his lord.

Thomas Flambard has granted to Thomas de Berkel' all the land which he had by grant of

Joan le Bruware called la Brewereshamme . . .

Witnesses: Sir Robert de Berkel', Sir William de Aubigny, Bartholomew de Olepenne, Robert de Bradestone, Robert de Stan.

Other Brewer holdings

A1/43/10 [GC 1630]   n.d. [late Hen. III]

Richard le Bruare of Slimbridge and Sir Maurice de Berkel', his chief lord.

Richard has granted and quitclaimed to Maurice 3 a. of land in the manor of Slimbrugge, being 2 a. in the field called Vifrugge and 1 a. in the field called Aldevord; and Maurice has given him 20*s*.

Witnesses: Sir Robert de Kingestun, knight, Reginald de Gosintun, Robert de Coueleg', Robert de Dreicote, Gilbert son of Hugh, William the serjeant (*serviens*), Ralph de Camme.

A1/43/11 [GC 2496]   n.d. [late 13th cent.]

Ismannia daughter of Richard le Brewere of Slimbridge and Sir Maurice de Berkel'.

Ismannia has granted to Maurice 2 selions and two headlands (*birri*) in the furlong called le Michele Longelond, in exchange for 2 selions in the furlong called Fifmor.

Witnesses: Sir Robert de Kyngestone, John de Kyngestone, Elias le Butiler, Robert de Draicote, Ralph de Kamme, Robert de Couel', William Warner.

A1/43/12 [GC 1607]   n.d. [late Hen. III]

Sir Maurice de Berkel' and Ismannia at the gate (*ad portam*).

Maurice has granted to Ismannia ½ a. of land in the furlong called Longarston, in exchange for ½ a. of land in the field of Aldeford.

Witnesses: Sir Robert de Kingestone, William de Mathem, William the serjeant (*serviens*), Elias le Botiler, Gilbert son of Hugh, Walter Sely.

A1/43/13 [GC 331]   St. Katherine [25 Nov.] A.D. 1271

Ismannia widow of Roger at the gate (*ad portam*) and Sir Maurice de Berkeley.

Ismannia has quitclaimed to Maurice ½ a. of land in the field called Eforlong, beside the king's highway. Endorsed: *carta dom. de Berkel ex dono Ismanie ad portam de Slimbrigge*.

Witnesses: Sir Robert de Kingestun, knight, William the serjeant (*serviens*), Elias le Butiler, Richard le Briare, William Bath, Gilbert son of Hugh.

The Yate holding in Mill croft and in Coaley

A1/43/14 [GC 1600]   n.d. [*temp.* Edw. I]

John de la Yate of Slimbridge and Sir Thomas de Berkeleye, his lord.

John has quitclaimed to Thomas 2 a. of land in the furlong called Mulcroft in Slymbrugg', beside the road to la Guldinemyle; and for this Thomas has granted to him 3½ a. 13 perches of land in the furlong called la Hyde in Slymbrugge.

Witnesses: Robert de Bradeston, Thomas de Beoleye, Henry de Camme, Maurice de Camme, Walter Hathemare, Elias le Botiller of Slimbridge, John le Duk.

A1/43/15 [GC 1628]   n.d. [late Edw. I]

Thomas de Berkelee, lord of Berkeley, and Sir Simon de Whytynton, chaplain of Thomas's chapel of Slimbridge.

Thomas has granted to Simon 2 a. of land in Slymbrugge, viz. those which he had by grant of John de la Yate of Slymbrugge, and ½ a. 6 perches of land in the field called Ocheye in Coueleye; to him and his successors as chaplain, rent 8*s*. a year.

Witnesses: Robert de Bradeston, Robert de Berkelee, Thomas de Beoleye, Henry de Camme, Maurice de Camme, Thomas de Styntescombe, Walter Hathemar', Elias le Botyller of Slimbridge, John le Duc.

The Hathemare Holding

A1/43/16 [GC 1128]   10 Aug. 34 Edw. I [1306]
Roger Hathemare, son and heir of Roger Hathemare, and Walter Hathemare.

   Roger has quitclaimed to Walter 1 a. of meadow in Whyteneye.
Witnesses: Robert de Bradestone, Robert de Berkelee, Thomas de Beolee, Thomas de Styntescombe, Robert of the church (*de ecclesia*), Robert Wyther, Richard de Wyk.
At: Berkeley.

A1/43/17 [GC 1130]   20 Aug. 34 Edw. I [1306]
Walter Hathemare and Sir Thomas de Berkelee, lord of Berkeley.

   Walter has quitclaimed to Thomas 1 a. of meadow in Whyteneye which his nephew, Roger Hathemare, son and heir of Roger Hathemare, quitclaimed to him. [*In French.*]
Witnesses: Robert de Bradeston, Robert de Berkelee, Thomas de Beolee, Thomas de Styntescombe, Robert atte Cherche, Robert Wyther, Richard de Wyke.
At: Berkeley.

Weston rents and reversions

A1/43/18 [GC 2248]   Thurs. the feast of St. Margaret, 12 Edw. II [20 July 1318]
William son of Simon de Westone of Slimbridge; and John son of Nicholas de Kingestone and Mabel his wife.

   William has granted to John and Mabel, and John's heirs, a rent of 1*d.* a year from Maud, William's sister, in Slimbrugge, for a messuage, garden and curtilage, with all the lands that Maud holds of William for her life, with the reversion of the holding after Maud's death.
Witnesses: Walter de Gosinton, Thomas de Kingestone, John Duyke, Walter Oldelonde, Thomas Halling, William ate Broke.
At: Slimbridge.

A1/43/19 [GC 2249]   20 July 12 Edw. II [1318]
William son of Simon de Westone of Slimbridge and Sir Thomas de Berkeleye, lord of Berkeley.

   William has granted to Thomas all the rents and services of John son of Nicholas de Kyngestone, for half of a messuage and of a virgate of land held of William in Slymbrugge, with the reversion of the holding after the death of John, which he inherited after the death of Isabel, daughter and heir of the late Gilbert Huyet, who was the said John's wife.
Witnesses: Odo de Actone, Thomas de Bradeston, John le Serjant, Walter de Gosyntone, Thomas le Spenser, Roger Archer, Edward Golde.
At: Berkeley.

A1/43/20 [GC 2251]   Mon. before St. James, 12 Edw. II [24 July 1318]
William son of the late Simon de Westone and Maud his sister.

   William has leased to Maud all his holding with 1 a. of land which he inherited after the death of Margery, his mother, in Slymbrugge; for her life, rent 1*d.* a year to William, and 12*d.* a year to the chief lord.
Witnesses: Walter de Gosyntone, William le Botiler, John Duyke, John de Kyngestone, John de la Yate.
At: Slimbridge.

A1/43/21 [GC 2287]   Wed. in the decollation of St. John the Baptist, 13 Edw. II
                                                                        [29 Aug. 1319]
John son of Nicholas de Kyngestone and Sir Thomas de Berkeleye, lord of Berkeley.

   John has quitclaimed to Thomas and his heirs a rent of 1*d.* a year with the reversion of the holding of Maud daughter of Simon de Westone, at Slymbrugge, for her life, by lease of William son of Simon de Westone, her brother, which rent and reversion he had by grant of William, and a rent of 12*d.* a year from Maud for the same holding.

Witnesses: Thomas de Bradeston, Walter de Nasse, John le Serjaunt, Walter Sewaker, Stephen de Draycote, Robert le Warner, Walter de Gosyntone.
At: Berkeley.

Butler holdings

A1/43/22 [GC 3636]   Mon. after the Purification, 46 Edw. III [9 Feb. 1372]
John Boteler of Slimbridge and John Cutul.

John Boteler has leased to John Cutul 2 selions of land in Longelond and 8 selions in Bovenhay, from Michaelmas 46 Edw. III [29 Sept. 1372] for a term of 12 years.
Witnesses: John Fromilode, Robert Willies, Walter Knyghth, William Catare, John Basset.
At: Slimbridge.

A1/43/23 [GC 3719]   Mon. the feast of St. Matthew, 1 Ric. II [21 Sept. 1377]
John Botiler of Slimbridge and Ralph Waleis.

John has granted to Ralph, his heirs and assigns 2 selions of land in Slymbrugge in Muchullangelonde.
Witnesses: John de Coueleie, Henry de Gosyntone, John Fromlode, John Archer, John Man, John de Trie.
At: Slimbridge.

A1/43/24 [GC 3947]   St. Clement, 22 Ric. II [23 Nov. 1398]
John Boteler of Slimbridge and Sir Thomas de Berkeleye, lord of Berkeley.

John has quitclaimed to Thomas a parcel of land which Ralph Waleys acquired from John for his life in Slymbrugge. Attached is a memorandum of the land and meadow which Ralph held for life of John Boteler, of which the first parcel was called Cattesbrayn.
Witnesses: John ate Yate, John Trye, John Archer, Henry de Gosyntone, John Fromylode.
At: Slimbridge.

The Clevedon holding

A1/43/25 [GC 3903]   Mon. after the Purification, 19 Ric. II [7 Feb. 1396]
John Botiler of Slimbridge and Alexander Clyvedon.

John has leased to Alexander all his land at Cattesbrayn in Slymbrugge, and 3 parcels of land in Litellongelond and 2 a. in Bitwenestrete [etc.]; for his life, rent a rose a year.
Witnesses: Henry Gosyntone, John Archer, John Fromlode, Walter Knyght, John Trye.
At: Slimbridge.

A1/43/26 [GC 3943]   Mon. the nativity of St. John the Baptist, 22 Ric. II [24 June 1398]
Alexander de Clyvedone and Joan his wife; and Thomas Berkeley, lord of Berkeley.

Alexander and Joan have granted to Thomas all the lands [etc.] that they had in the parish of Slymbrigge (Glos.), except a croft which John Archer formerly held; for Joan's life, rent 5 marks a year.

A1/43/27 [GC 3930]   Wed. after the nativity of St. John the Baptist, 21 [?*recte* 22] Ric. II
                            [27 June 1397, ?*recte* 28 June 1398]
(1) Alexander Clyvedone and Joan his wife; (2) John Archer of Slimbridge; (3) Thomas Berkeley, lord of Berkeley.

Alexander and Joan have appointed John to deliver to Thomas seisin of all the lands [etc.] which they had in the parish of Slymbrugge; to hold for Joan's life.

A1/43/28 [GC 3958]   20 May 22 Ric. II [1399]
Alexander de Clyvedone and Joan his wife; and Thomas Berkeley, lord of Berkeley.

Alexander and Joan have quitclaimed to Thomas lands [etc.] in the parish of Slymbrigge.
Witnesses: John Yate, William Smalcombe, John Archer, John Framlode.
At: Slimbridge.

The Kingston (later Acton) holding

The holding, which included lands in Kingston, Gossington and Hurst, was created by a cadet branch of the Berkeley family which was not recognised by Smyth, one descended from Richard, younger brother of Robert (II) Lord Berkeley (d. 1220) and Thomas (I) Lord Berkeley (d. 1243). Richard's son Sir Robert was known as Robert FitzRichard and as Robert de Kingston, and that Robert's son, Sir Robert (II) de Kingston, died without issue in 1275 leaving a widow Maud. His heirs were his sister Alice and his nephew Robert de Downton, son of his sister Letuaria.

Kingston acquisitions in Slimbridge, Gossington and Kingston

A1/43/29 [SC 23]   n.d. [1185 × 1189]
Maurice de Berkeley and William his son.

With the consent of Robert his son and heir, Maurice has granted to William, in fee, the half of his land of Gosinton; to hold by the service of a quarter of a knight's fee.[1]
Witnesses: William [de Saltmarsh] bishop of Llandaff, John abbot of St. Augustine's, Geoffrey [de Henlow] prior of Llanthony, William earl of Salisbury, Master Maurice, Master Peter de Par[is], Reginald the chaplain, Adam de Saltemareis, Henry and Elias his brothers, John de Cogan, Bernard de Stane, Richard de Cohill, William de Moreville, Maurice son of Nigel.

A1/43/30 [GC 878]   n.d. [1220 × 1221]
Thomas de Berkele and Robert son of Richard, his nephew.

Thomas has granted to Robert all the land in Gosynton which William de Berkele his brother held and pannage for 20 pigs in his wood of Mudewode; to hold as a quarter of a fee. [*Late 14th-cent. copy.*]
Witnesses: Sir Maurice de Gant, Sir Roger son of Nicholas, Sir Henry de Berkele, Simon de Olepenn, Richard de Couelegh, Peter de Styntescomb, John de Craulegh, Maurice son of Nigel, Roger de Gosynton, Adam the clerk.

A1/43/31 [SC 276]   n.d. [1220 × 1221]
Robert son of Richard and Thomas de Berkeley.

Declaration by Robert of the terms under which he received his land of Gosintun from Thomas de Berkeley, his lord, viz. that the land should revert to Thomas if Robert has no legitimate children.
Witnesses: Sir Maurice de Gaunt, Roger son of Nicholas, Henry de Berkeley, Richard de Coueleg', Peter de Stintescumb, John de Crauleg', Maurice son of Nigel.

A1/43/32 [GC 788]   n.d. [before 1275]
Christine widow of Sir Ralph Musard; and Sir Robert de Kingeston, knight, and Lady Maud his wife.

Christine has granted to Robert and Maud 19 a. of arable land and ½ a. of meadow in the territory of Kingeston, viz. 4 a. in the field called Linch, 5 a. in the furlong called Woresle, 5 a. in the furlong called Rowelond, 2 a. in the furlong called Heylinemed, 1 a. in Heystanberewe, 2 a. at Hawethorne, 1 a. at Beuleg', and 1½ a. in Camme[2] [etc.]; rent 1*d.* a year, and they have given her 24 marks.
Witnesses: Sir Maurice lord of Berkel', Sir William de Berkel', Sir Richard de Berkel', Sir Robert le Veel, knights, Peter de Wik, Peter de Stintescumb, Elias de Cumbe, Reginald de Gosinton, William de Kingeston, Richard le Duc, Walter de Stintescumb, clerk.

---

[1] *Transcript*: Smyth, iii. 200–1.
[2] The total number of acres specified is 21½, not 19½ as stated earlier.

A1/43/33 [GC 2569]   n.d. [late Hen. III]
Elias le Wylde of Worthwode and Sir Robert de Kyngestone.

Elias has quitclaimed to Robert, his heirs and assigns an annual rent of 2*d.* which Robert renders for the land which Roger Stuttetott formerly held of Elias.
Witnesses: Master Robert rector of Slymbruch', Reginald de Cosyntone, William called Berthat', Walter de Cosyntone, William de Cosyntone, Richard le Duc.

A1/43/34 [GC 1441]   n.d. [*temp.* Hen. III]
Walter Young (*Juvenis*) of Kingston; and Robert de Kyngestone and Maud his wife.

Walter has granted to Robert and Maud a croft lying between Walter's grange and Robert's court, extending to the croft formerly of Arnold de Berkeley, and 8 selions of land, 2 in the furlong below Stanberwe next to Lihtingbroke, and 6 in the furlong called la Brech; rent 1*d.* a year, and they have given him 5 marks.
Witnesses: Reginald de Gosint', Robert de Bradeston', John de Kyngestone, William le Serjant, Elias le Butiler, Walter de Gosintone.

A1/43/35 [GC 1450]   n.d. [1275 × 1281]
Maud widow of Sir Robert de Kingeston and Sir Maurice de Berkel'.

Maud has granted to Maurice all the lands and holdings which came to her on the death of Robert; rent to the chief lord 2*d.* a year, and Maurice has given Maud 20 marks.
Witnesses: Sir William de Maunsel, knight, Peter de Stintescumbe, Bartholomew de Olepenn', Reginald de Gosintone, Ralph de Camme, Thomas de Beoleye, William le Serjant of Kingston, Michael de Wendene, clerk.

Alice's purparty
A1/43/36 [GC 2469]   Mon. before St. Bartholomew, 3 Edw. I [19 Aug. 1275]
Alice daughter of Sir Robert son of Richard and Robert de Duntone, her nephew.

Alice acknowledges the right of Robert to half of the lands of which Sir Robert de Kyggestone died seized, as his purparty after the death of Letuaria his mother, and, within a week after St. Bartholomew following [31 Aug.], each will appoint two men to make the partition, and each is bound to the other in £100 if either prevents the partition.
Witnesses: Sir William de Derneford, Sir John de Actone, Robert de Hyldesleygh, William Basset, William le Serjant.

A1/43/37 [SC 286]   n.d. [1275 × 1281]
Alice de Kingeston and Sir Maurice de Berkeley.

Alice has granted to Maurice a fishery in the Severn and a holding in Kingeston and Gosinton which came to her on the death of Sir Robert de Kingeston, her brother; for which Maurice gave her 100*s.*
Witnesses: Sir Roger de Lokinton, Sir Maurice de Saltmarsh (*de salso marisco*), Henry of the bridge (*de ponte*), Bartholomew de Olepenne, Thomas de Buleye, Elias the butler (*pincerna*), William le Serjant.

A1/43/38 [GC 1454; *duplicate* GC 1455]   n.d. [1275 × 1281]
Alice de Kyngeston and Sir Maurice de Berkeley.

Alice has granted to Maurice the services of Robert de Dounton, her nephew, for the lands which he inherited after the death of Robert de Kyngeston, her brother; Maurice has given her 100*s.*
Witnesses: Peter de Stintescumbe, Robert de Coueleye, Robert de Draycote, Ralph de Camme, Bartholomew de Olepenne, William de Egeton, Michael de Wendene, clerk.

Downton purparty and its passage to the Actons

A1/43/39 [GC 1334]   n.d. [*temp.* Edw. I]
Robert de Duntone, son and heir of Letuaria daughter of Sir Robert son of Richard de
Kyngestone, and Sir John de Acton.

Robert has granted to John all the land which he inherited after the death of Sir Robert de
Kyngeston, his uncle, in the vills of Slymbrugge, Kyngestone and Gosyntone; rent 1*d.* a
year, and John has granted to him 60*s.* worth of land in Somerset.
Witnesses: Sir Jordan la Warre, Sir Richard de Berkeley, Ralph de Haddleye, Peter Croc,
Thomas de Barry, Roger de Hyldesleye, Richard de Balun.

A1/43/40 [GC 1335]   n.d. [*temp.* Edw. I]
Robert de Dounton, son and heir of Letuaria de Kyngeston, and Sir Thomas de Berkel'.

Robert has granted to Thomas the homage and service of Sir John de Acton for the land
which John held of Robert in Kingeston; Thomas has given Robert 100*s.*
Witnesses: Sir Ralph de Wylinton, Sir Robert le Veel, Sir Roger de Lokinton, Nicholas de
Apperleye, William de Burg', Robert de Stan', Robert de Bradeston, Maurice de Camme,
Thomas Alayn.

A1/43/41 [GC 527]   Tues. after St. Barnabas, 15 Edw. I [17 June 1287]
Robert de Dounton, son and heir of Letuaria de Kingeston, and Sir Thomas de Berkel.

Robert has granted and quitclaimed to Thomas the homage and service of Sir John de
Acton and his heirs for the land which John previously held of Robert in the vill of
Kingeston.
At: Gloucester.

A1/43/42 [GC 1336]   n.d. [*c.* 1279–80]
Robert de Dounton, son and heir of Robert de Dounton, and Sir John de Acton, knight.

Robert has quitclaimed to John 30*s.* worth of land in Walkyngthrop (Som.) which he had
by grant of Sir John de Acton, father of John, in exchange for his right to land in Kyngeston
(Glos.), which 30*s.* worth William de Insula and Baldric de Noneton recovered at Somerton
before the king's justices itinerant in Somerset, 8 Edw. I [1279–80]; John has given him £10.
Witnesses: Sir John Tregoz, lord of Storidon, John de Clyvedon, Henry de Tistelden, Robert
de Bradeston, Henry of the marsh (*de marischo*), Roger de Hildesleye, Andrew de Burgo.

A1/43/43 [GC 1829]   Thurs. before Trinity, 4 Edw. II [3 June 1311]
Robert de Dountone, son and heir of Letuaria de Kyngestone, sister of the late Robert de
Kyngestone, knight, and Odo de Actone.

Robert has quitclaimed to Odo all the lands and holdings in Kyngestone by Slymbrugge
(Glos.) which were of his uncle Robert de Kyngestone, with the lands which Lady Maud,
widow of Robert, held in dower.
Witnesses: John le Botiller, Peter de Draycote, John Haydene, John Flori, Robert Colebarre.
At: Horsington [Som.]

A1/43/44 [GC 1828]   Thurs. before Trinity, 4 Edw. II [3 June 1311]
Robert de Dountone, son and heir of Letuaria de Kyngestone, sister of the late Robert de
Kyngestone, knight, and Odo de Actone.

Robert has quitclaimed to Odo all the lands and holdings in Kyngestone by Slymbrugge,
Gosyntone and Hurste (Glos.) which were of his uncle Robert de Kyngestone, with the
lands which Lady Maud, widow of Robert, held in dower.
Witnesses: John le Botiller, Peter de Draycote, John Haydene, John Flori, Robert Colebarre
of Somerset; William de Wauton, knight, Warin son of William, Thomas le Spenser,
Richard Bat, William le Botiller, John son of Thomas de Swonhungre, Richard Sone,

William de Clyfford, Peter le Kyng, Walter Wyth, John le Duk, John le Frankeleyn of Arlingham, of Gloucestershire.

At: Horsington [Som.]

Acquisition by the Actons of Richard son of Alfred's holding

A1/43/45 [GC 582]   One week after Trinity, 19 Edw. I [24 June 1291]
John de Actone and Richard son of Alfred.

Copy of final concord concerning a messuage and 1 virgate of land in Kyngeston by Slymbrygge. Richard has acknowledged the right of John, and John has granted the holding to Richard for life, rent 5*s.* a year, to revert to John after his death.

At: Westminster.

A1/43/46 [GC 1003]   n.d. [*c.* Oct. 1300]
Richard le Clerk, son of Alfred de Kyngeston, and Odo de Acton.

Richard has granted to Odo all his lands and holdings in Kyngeston by Slymbrugg, for a certain sum of money.

Witnesses: Walter de Gosynton, Thomas de Kyngeston, William Clifford of Frampton, Richard Balon, Walter Wyth.

A1/43/47 [GC 999]   Mon. after Michaelmas, 28 Edw. I [3 Oct. 1300]
Odo de Acton and Richard le Clerk, son of Alfred de Kyngeston.

Odo has leased to Richard, for his life, all the lands and holdings which Odo had by grant of the said Richard, in Kyngeston, rent 12*s.* 6*d.* a year.

Witnesses: Walter de Gosynton, Thomas de Kyngeston, William Clifford of Frampton, Richard Balon, Walter Wyth.

At: Kingston.

A1/43/48 [GC 2282]   Wed. after St. John the Baptist, 12 Edw. II [27 June 1319]
John de Gosintone and Odo de Actone.

John has quitclaimed to Odo and his heirs his inheritance in the lands which Richard his uncle held in Kyngestone by Slymbrugge.

At: Stonehouse.

Passage of both purparties and lands in Hurst from Acton to Berkeley

A1/43/49 [GC 1965]   St. Valentine, 7 Edw. II [14 Feb. 1314]
Odo de Actone and Master Roger Cantok.

Odo has granted to Roger all his lands in Kingestone by Slimbrugge (Glos.).

Witnesses: Sir Thomas de Berkeleye, lord of Berkeley, Sir John de Berkeleye, his son, knights, John de Berkeleye, lord of Arlingham, William Clifford, John le Serjaunt, Elias de Filtone, John le Duk.

At: Kingston.

A1/43/50 [GC 1982]   One week after Holy Trinity, 7 Edw. II [9 June 1314]
Odo de Actone and Elizabeth his wife; and Roger Cantok.

Final concord concerning 2 messuages, 1 carucate of land, 30 a. of meadow, 20 a. of pasture and 100*s.* rent in Kyngeston and Gosyntone; Odo has acknowledged the right of Roger, by his gift, and Roger has granted the same to Odo and Elizabeth and Odo's heirs.

At: Westminster.

A1/43/51 [GC 2830]   Sun. before Michaelmas, 9 Edw. III [24 Sept. 1335]
Odo de Actone and Robert de la Felde.

Odo has granted to Robert, his heirs and assigns all his lands and holdings in Kyngestone by Slymbrugge, Gosyntone and Hurste, with all the appurtenances.

Witnesses: Robert Dabetot, John Capel, Nicholas de la Niewelonde of Frampton, John le Knygt of Slimbridge, John de Monemewe.
At: Kingston by Slimbridge.

A1/43/52 [GC 2831; *duplicate* GC 2382]   Sun. after All Saints, 9 Edw. III [5 Nov. 1335]
Robert de la Felde; and Odo de Actone and Amicia his wife.

Robert has granted to Odo and Amicia all the lands and holdings in Kyngestone by Slymbrugge, Gosyntone and Hurste which he had by Odo's grant; for their lives, with remainder to Isabel their daughter for her life and to Odo's right heirs.
Witnesses: John Serjaunt, John de Milkesham, Henry de Clifford, John de Ekynton, John de Lorwynch, John Nichol, Nicholas de la Niewelond.
At: Kingston by Slimbridge.

A1/43/53 [GC 2964]   Sun. after St. Matthew, 13 Edw. III [28 Feb. 1339]
Odo de Actone and Robert de la Felde.

Odo has granted to Robert, his heirs and assigns all his lands and holdings in Kyngestone by Slymbrugge, Gosintone and Hurste.
Witnesses: Robert Dabetot, John de Kyngustone, John le Knyt, Thomas le Muchele, Thomas Halling.
At: Kingston.

A1/43/54 [GC 3717]   [Two weeks after Easter, 13 Edw. III, 11 April 1339][1]
Odo de Acton and Anne his wife; and [Robert de la Felde].

Final concord concerning a messuage, 1 carucate of land, 30 a. of meadow, 30 a. of pasture and 100[*s*. rent in Gosynton], Hurste and Kyngestone by Slymbrugge. Odo and Anne have acknowledged the right of Robert as by [Odo's] gift, and Robert has granted the holding to them, for their lives, with remainder to Isabel, [Odo's daughter, for her life] and to the right heirs of Odo.
At: Westminster.

A1/43/55 [GC 3565]   Sat. before Christmas, 38 Edw. III [21 Dec. 1364]
John son of Odo de Actone and Sir Maurice lord of Berkele.

John has quitclaimed to Maurice the lands and holdings which Maurice holds in Slymbrugge, Kyngestone, Gosyntone and Hurste, and elsewhere within the lordship of Berkele, which Odo his father formerly held.
Witnesses: Sir Richard de Actone, knight, William de Chiltenham, John Serjant.
At: Berkeley.

A1/43/56 [SC 539; *duplicate* SC 540]   Sat. before Christmas, 38 Edw. III [21 Dec. 1364]
John son of Odo de Acton and Maurice lord of Berkeley.

John has quitclaimed to Maurice all the lands in Slymbrugge, Kyngestone, Gosynton and Hurste, or elsewhere within the lordship of Berkelee, which his father, Odo de Acton, formerly held.
Witnesses: Richard de Acton, knight, William de Cheltenham, John Sergeaunt.
At: Berkeley.

A1/43/57 [GC 3581]   Thurs. after Holy Trinity, 40 Edw. III [4 June 1366]
John son of Odo de Actone and Sir Maurice lord of Berkele.

Whereas John and his heirs are bound to warrant to Maurice and his heirs all the lands and holdings which Maurice holds in Slymbrugge, Kyngestone, Gosyntone and Hurste, Maurice has granted that if he or his heirs should be impleaded by John or his heirs the warranty shall be invalid and Maurice shall recover the value of the lands from John. [*In French*.]
At: Berkeley.

---

[1] Details illegible in the document are supplied from PRO CP 25/1/77/62 no. 174 [bis].

A1/43/58 [GC 2596]   n.d. [late 14th cent.]
Richard atte Felde of Dindesleye and Thomas lord of Berkelee.

Richard has quitclaimed to Thomas all the lands which were late of Odo de Actone in Slymbrugge, Gosyntone and Kyngeston. [*In French*.]
Witnesses: Robert Palet, William atte Merssch, John Clyfford, William Westhale.

Grants of annuities

A1/43/59 [GC 4222]   21 Jan. 20 Hen. VI [1442]
James Berkeley, lord of Berkeley, knight, and John Wyche.

James has granted to John, for his good and laudable service, an annual rent of 40*s.* from the manor of Slymebrugge, viz. from a pasture called le Warth and le Newlese; for his life.

A1/43/60 [GC 4223]   21 Jan. 20 Hen. VI [1442]
James Berkeley, lord of Berkeley, knight, and John Dunstable *alias* Gloucestre.

James has granted to John, for his good and laudable service, an annual rent of 40*s.* from the manor of Slymebrugge, viz. from a pasture called le Warth and le Newlese; for his life.

A1/43/61 [GC 4231]   24 Sept. 21 Hen. VI [1442]
James Berkeley, lord of Berkeley, knight, and John Byforde.

James has granted to John, for his good and laudable service, an annual rent of 40*s.* from the manor of Slymbrugge, viz. from the pasture called le Warth, Newlese and Hogenesplotte; for his life.
At: Berkeley Castle.

Other grants and acquisitions

A1/43/62 [SC 4]   n.d. [1153 or later]
Robert FitzHarding and Roger de Berckele.

Agreement made in Robert's house at Bristol, in the presence of Henry duke of Normandy, for Robert's son Maurice to marry Roger's daughter, with Slimbridge, being £10 worth, for her portion, and for Roger's son Roger to marry Robert's daughter, with the manor of Siston near Bristol for her dowry. Pledged by eight men on behalf of each party: on Roger's, William son of Henry, Roger de Sckai, Ralph de Huelega, Walkelin, Engebald de Gosintunia, Guy de Rupe, Gwaiferus de Planca, Hugh de Planca his brother; on Robert's, Hugh de Hasela, Nigel son of Arthur, Robert de Saltemareis, Elias brother of Robert FitzHarding, Jordan his brother, Jordan le Warre, Nicholas son of Robert, David Duncepucke.[1]

A1/43/63 [GC 1573]   n.d. [late Hen. III]
William Wariner of Coaley and Sir Maurice de Berkel'.

William has quitclaimed to Maurice 3¼ a. of land in the field called la Westveld at la dene, beside the land which Lady Joan de Berkel' holds in dower.
Witnesses: Sir Richard de Berkeleya, Sir Robert de Kyngestona, Peter de Stintescumbe, Elias le Butiler, Gilbert son of Hugh, William le Serjant.

A1/43/64 [GC 682]   n.d. [*c.* 1270]
Sir Maurice de Berkel and Simon de Weston.

Maurice has granted to Simon 2 selions of land in the field of Bovenhay next to the land of Walter Selewine, in exchange for 1 selion in the furlong called Eforlong.
Witnesses: Sir Robert de Kingeston, William de Mathem, Gilbert son of Hugh, William the serjeant (*serviens*), Elias le Botiler, Walter Sely.

A1/43/65 [GC 772]   n.d. [late Hen. III]
William Young (*Juvenis*) of Kingston and Edania his wife; and Sir Maurice de Berkeleye.

William and Edania have granted to Maurice 2 selions and 2 headlands (*birri*) in the

---

[1] *Transcript*: Smyth, iii. 325–6; Jeayes, pp. 4–6. For the date, above, Introduction, p. xxii.

furlong called Michelelongelond, one head towards 'la guldene mile', in exchange for 3 selions of land in the furlong called Fifrug.

Witnesses: Sir Robert de Kyngeston, John de Kyngeston, Elias le Butiler, Robert de Draycote, Ralph de Kamme, Robert de Couel', William Warner.

A1/43/66 [GC 2539]   n.d. [*c*. 1300]

John de Olepenne and Sir Thomas de Berkel', his lord.

John has granted to Thomas, his heirs and assigns all his meadow which he had in the meadow called Whyteneye by Slimbrugge, and also all his land lying in two parcels in the field called Symondeshalesdone; Thomas has given him 100*s*.

Witnesses: Richard de Biseleye, Peter de Stintescombe, Richard de Kingescote, Robert de Stane, Robert de Bradeston, Maurice de Camme, Henry de Camme.

A1/43/67 [GC 1927]   5 June 6 Edw. II [1313]

John ate Yate of Slimbridge and Sir Thomas de Berkelee, lord of Berkeley.

John has granted to Thomas a rent seck of 8*d*. from Joan wife of Walter le Chepmon for a messuage and curtilage and croft in Slymbrugge, the curtilage above the water running towards the mill of Cambr[ugge], and the croft called Bokcroft above Lutlelongelond.

Witnesses: Odo de Actone, Richard de Ryvers, William le Boteler, Richard Bat, John de Kyngestone.

At: Berkeley.

A1/43/68 [GC 905]   n.d. [early 14th cent.]

Margery de Falefeld and Maurice de Berkel'.

Margary has granted to Maurice 2 a. of land in the field called Newelond next to the meadow called Rolvesmed; Maurice has given her 6*s*. 8*d*.

Witnesses: William Capel, Henry de Bath', Robert de Stanes, Nicholas de Wodeford, Robert Caudel, Richard Iwein.

A1/43/69 [GC 2718]   Morrow of the Circumcision, 4 Edw. III [2 Jan. 1331]

Thomas de Berkley, lord of Berkeley; and Sir Richard Rivers and Sarah his wife.

Thomas has granted to Richard and Sarah common of pasture in the pasture called le Warth in the vills of Kingston and Slimbridge. [*Early 17th-cent. copy.*]

Witnesses: Robert de . . . , William de Chiltingham, John le Serjant, Richard Gillins, John Collins.

At: Berkeley.

A1/43/70 [GC 2979]   Sun. after All Saints, 14 Edw. III [5 Nov. 1340]

William le Botiller and Sir Thomas lord of Berkeleye.

William has granted to Thomas the reversion of the lands and holdings which John Colynes holds of William for his life in Slymbrugge.

At: Berkeley.

A1/43/71 [GC 3285]   n.d. [mid 14th cent.]

William le Botiller and Sir Thomas lord of Berkelee.

William has granted to Thomas an annual rent of 6*d*. from Walter le Botiller, his brother, for a holding which he holds of William for his life, in Slymbrugge, with the reversion of the holding after Walter's death.

Witnesses: John le Sergeant, John de Egeton, John de Lorewynge, John de Kyngestone, John le Knyght.

A1/43/72 [GC 4173*]   27 Oct. 11 Hen. VI [1432]
[James] lord of Berkeley and John Archer.

Extract from court roll: the homage came and said that half of Newhurst pertains to the lord of Berkeley and half to John. Sealed by William Payn, under-steward.
At: Sages.

BERKELEY GRANTS

A1/43/73 [SC 54]   n.d. [late 12th cent.]
Alice de Berkel' and Guy son of Roger de Vilers.

Alice has granted to Guy 1 virgate of land which she holds in free marriage in Slimbridge, which William son of Selewin held; annual rent a pair of gilt spurs.
Witnesses: Roger de Berkele, Philip de Berkele, John Wolf (*Lupus*), Henry de Berkele, William his brother, Thomas de Berkele, Bernard de Stanes, Hugh de Wike, Roger de Linz, Elias, Master Peter.

A1/43/74 [SC 55]   n.d. [late 12th cent.]
Alice de Berkele and Elias son of Toke.

Alice, at the request and with the consent of Robert de Berkele, her son, has granted to Elias, son of her nurse and servant Toke, a half-virgate of land in Slimbridge, which William Blundus held, together with Slimbridge mill and the tolls for grinding corn [etc.]; rent 10s. a year.
Witnesses: Roger de Berkele, Philip his brother, John Wolf (*Lupus*), Peter de Paris, Thomas de Tiringham, Henry de Berkele and Thomas her brothers, Henry de Couelei, Maurice son of Nigel, William de Kingestune.

A1/43/75 [SC 279]   n.d. [1220 × 1243]
Thomas de Berkeley and Hugh son of Alfred, son of Aymer de Slimbridge.

Thomas de Berkeley, at the request of Thomas de Tyringeham, has granted to Hugh his freedom, and quitclaims to him all services from him and his offspring, for the service of Thomas de Tyringeham, and grants to Hugh 1 virgate of land at Slimbridge which Alfred his father held; to hold freely [etc.], for a rent of 20s. a year. For this Thomas de Tyringeham has given to Thomas de Berkeley 3 marks and a measure of wine, and to Joan his wife 4s.
Witnesses: Robert son of Richard, Peter de Stintescumbe, Richard de Couele, Robert son of Maurice, Elias the butler (*pincerna*), Arnulf the clerk.

A1/43/76 [GC 329]   Sun. after St. Denis [11 Oct.] 1271
Maurice de Berkeley and Elias le Butiler.

Maurice has confirmed to Elias, son and heir of William le Butiler of Slimbrugge, all the land which Thomas de Berkeley, Maurice's father, gave to Elias le Butiler, grandfather of the said Elias son of William; Elias has given Maurice 1 mark.
Witnesses: Sir Richard de Berkeley, Maurice's brother, Sir Robert de Kingestone, knights, Reginald de Gosinton, William Wariner, William the serjeant (*serviens*), William son of Robert, Robert de Dreyecote, Robert de Coueleye, Ralph de Camme.

A1/43/77 [GC 1215]   n.d. [late Hen. III]
Maurice de Berkel' and Alfred le Shypward.

Maurice has confirmed to Alfred all the lands, holdings [etc.] which Alfred had by grant of Sir Thomas de Berkel', Maurice's lord and father, to hold of Maurice, and Maurice has quitclaimed to Alfred his rights to cart and drive stock in Alfred's land between his house and the water called la Hyderhe as far as Somerford; Alfred has given him 36s.
Witnesses: Sir Maurice de Saltmarsh (*de salso marisco*), Sir Warin de Ral[egh], knights, Peter de Wyke, Philip de Douhgton, Maurice's constable, John de Egeton, John de Brotheston, William Maudut, Adam Coby, John Sewaker, Walter Sely, Maurice's clerk.

A1/43/78 [GC 1243]   n.d. [*temp.* Edw. I]
Thomas lord of Berkeleye; and William Bode, Margery his wife and Thomas, Margery's son.

    Thomas has leased to William, Margery and Thomas 1 a. of land in the vill of Slymbrugge in the furlong called Everlong; to hold enclosed, for their lives, rent 4*s.* a year.
Witnesses: Elias le Botiler, Walter de Gosintone, John le Duc, John of the gate (*de porta*), Richard Bat.

A1/43/79 [GC 2135]   4 Dec. 10 Edw. II [1316]
Thomas de Berkelee, lord of Berkeley; and Agnes le Garlaundere of Slimbridge and Alice her daughter.

    Thomas has granted to Agnes and Alice the holding which Richard Pokel sometime held in Slymbrugge, with the appurtenances, as in the charter of Sir Maurice de Berkelee, his father, for the life of Agnes; to them for their lives and to the issue of Alice de Bathon, once wife of Richard de Blakeneye, rent as in the charter of Maurice; and also a certain acre of land called Pochesacre.
Witnesses: Roger de Gosyntone, Walter de Gosyntone, Thomas de Kyngestone, William le Botyler, John de Kyngestone.
At: Berkeley.

A1/43/80 [GC 2136]   6 Dec. 10 Edw. II [1316]
Thomas de Berkeleye, lord of Berkeley, and Nicholas Selewyne of Slimbridge.

    Thomas has granted to Nicholas 2¼ a. 22 perches of meadow in the meadow called Whyteneye, which Walter vicar of Berkeley previously held of Thomas in Slymbrugge; to him and his issue, rent 10*s.* a year.
Witnesses: Thomas de Bradeston, Thomas de Craweleye, Walter de Gosyntone, Thomas de Kyngestone, William le Botyler.
At: Berkeley.

A1/43/81 [GC 4236]   17 Nov. 22 Hen. VI [1443]
James Berkeley, lord of Berkeley, knight, and Edmund Carter.

    James has demised at farm to Edmund, his first wife and eldest son a messuage in Slymbrugge with 1 virgate of land, a pasture there called Lordesmersch and a parcel of meadow pertaining to the said virgate; for their lives, rent 49*s.* a year.
At: Berkeley Castle.

A1/43/82 [GC 4362]   29 Sept. 11 Edw. IV [1471]
William Berkeley, knight, lord of Berkeley; and Laurence Teste and Joan his wife.

    William has granted to Laurence and Joan all the lands, holdings [etc.] called Newlese and le Warth in the manor and lordship of Slymebrygge; for their lives, and if they die within 6 years 4 months with remainder to their heirs and executors for the remainder of that term, rent for the first 6 years 4 months a red rose a year, and afterwards 10 marks a year.
Witnesses: William Trye, James Clyfford, William Raymond, Richard Cowley, John Davy.

ADMINISTRATIVE DOCUMENTS
Account rolls

A1/43/83 [GAR 207]   n.d. [*temp.* Edw. I]
A1/43/84 [GAR 208]   10–11 Edw. I [1282–3]
A1/43/85 [GAR 209]   14–15 Edw. I [1286–7]
A1/43/86 [GAR 210]   17–18 Edw. I [1289–90]
A1/43/87 [GAR 211]   20–1 Edw. I [1292–3]
Two rolls; Michaelmas to the morrow of St. Petronilla [1 June], and the morrow of St. Petronilla to Michaelmas.
A1/43/88 [GAR 212]   25 Edw. I [1297–8]

A1/43/89 [GAR 213]	26–7 Edw. I [1298–9]
A1/43/90 [GAR 214]	27–8 Edw. I [1299–1300]
A1/43/91 [GAR 215]	Michaelmas 30 Edw. I to Christmas 31 Edw. I [1302]
A1/43/92 [GAR 216]	n.d. [*c.* 1315–20]
A1/43/93 [GAR 217] Slimbridge and Hurst	n.d. [*c.* 1322–4]
A1/43/94 [GAR 218] Slimbridge and Hurst	*temp.* John Frelond, keeper during the forfeiture [1324–5]
A1/43/95 [GAR 219] Slimbridge and Hurst	19–20 Edw. II [1325–6]
A1/43/96 [SR 44] Slimbridge and Hurst	19–20 Edw. II [1325–6]
A1/43/97 [SR 45; SR 46 *a translation*] Slimbridge and Hurst	20 Edw. II to 1 Edw. III [1326–7]
A1/43/98 [GAR 220]	3–4 Edw. III [1329–30]
A1/43/99 [GAR 221]	6–7 Edw. III [1332–3]
A1/43/100 [GAR 222] Fragment; head missing.	n.d. [1333–4]
A1/43/101 [GAR 223]	9–10 Edw. III [1335–6]
A1/43/102 [GAR 224]	11–12 Edw. III [1337–8]
A1/43/103 [GAR 225] Michaelmas to St. Thomas the apostle [21 Dec.] 13 Edw. III [1339]	
A1/43/104 [GAR 226] St. Thomas the apostle 13 Edw. III to Michaelmas 14 Edw. III [1339–40]	
A1/43/105 [GAR 227]	16–17 Edw. III [1342–3]
A1/43/106 [GAR 229]	20–1 Edw. III [1346–7]
A1/43/107 [GAR 230]	31–2 Edw. III [1357–8]
A1/43/108 [GAR 231]	33–4 Edw. III [1359–60]
A1/43/109 [GAR 232]	36–7 Edw. III [1362–3]
A1/43/110 [GAR 233]	37–8 Edw. III [1363–4]
A1/43/111 [GAR 234]	38–9 Edw. III [1364–5]
A1/43/112 [GAR 235]	39–40 Edw. III [1365–6]
A1/43/113 [GAR 236]	40–1 Edw. III [1366–7]
A1/43/114 [GAR 237]	41–2 Edw. III [1367–8]
A1/43/115 [GAR 238]	50 Edw. III to 1 Ric. II [1376–7]
A1/43/116 [GAR 239]	1–2 Ric. II [1377–8]
A1/43/117 [GAR 240]	2–3 Ric. II [1378–9]
A1/43/118 [GAR 241]	3–4 Ric. II [1379–80]
A1/43/119 [GAR 242]	5–6 Ric. II [1381–2]
A1/43/120 [GAR 243]	6–7 Ric. II [1382–3]
A1/43/121 [GAR 244]	7–8 Ric. II [1383–4]
A1/43/122 [GAR 245]	8–9 Ric. II [1384–5]
A1/43/123 [GAR 246]	Michaelmas to 1 May 10 Ric. II [1386–7]
A1/43/124 [GAR 228]	. . . [. . .]
A1/43/125 [GAR 247]	3–4 Hen. V [1415–16]
A1/43/126 [GAR 248]	6–7 Hen. VI [1427–8]
A1/43/127 [GAR 249] Slimbridge and Sages	22–3 Hen. VI [1443–4]
A1/43/128 [GAR 250] Slimbridge and Sages	27–8 Hen. VI [1448–9]
A1/43/129 [GAR 251] Slimbridge and Sages	28–9 Hen. VI [1449–50]

Charter rolls

A1/43/130 [SR 5]   Hen. III to Hen. V

Abstracts of charters concerning the manor of Slimbridge; fair copy, entries numbered 16, 17, 24, 25, 84, 27, unnumbered entry concerning a pasture in Awre, 32, 34, 36, 37, 39, 44, 45, 53, 55, 66, 69, 12/8/15 (composite entry concerning Maurice (IV)'s purchase of Sageslond from John son of Odo de Acton), three unnumbered entries, 8/12/13 (composite entry concerning another purchase by Maurice (IV) from John son of Odo de Acton), 14, 42; last two entries unnumbered (memoranda about Maurice (I)'s grant of half of Gossington to his son William and about the holding called Hugeteslond held by John Colyns who died without heirs). The current tenant of each holding has been added, as also in the right-hand margin, which is missing, the current rent.

A1/43/131 [SR 18]   Ric. I to Hen. V

Abstracts of charters concerning the manor of Slimbridge, top missing; entries numbered 18–88, the numbers corresponding to those in A1/43/130 [SR 5].

OTHER INTERESTS
The Mitchell holding in Slimbridge and Coaley

The holding was possibly acquired from the Waleys' feoffees by Thomas (IV) Lord Berkeley.

A1/43/132 [GC 3626]   Mon. after St. Dunstan, 44 Edw. III [20 May 1370]

Thomas Muchele of Slimbridge; and Sir John le Coke, chaplain of St. Mary of the same, and Walter Bath.

   Thomas has granted to John and Walter, and their heirs and assigns, all the lands and holdings which he had in Slymbrugge and Coueleye.

Witnesses: Henry Gosintone, John Boteler, Philip Archer, John Fremelode, Philip Howes, Philip le Man, Robert Willies.

At: Slimbridge.

A1/43/133 [GC 3689]   Fri. 4 Jan. 49 Edw. III [1376]

John Cook, chaplain, and Walter Bat; and Ralph Waleys, William Smalcombe and Ralph Coke.

   John and Walter have granted to Ralph, William and Ralph all the lands [etc.] which they had by grant of Thomas le Muchele in Slymbrugge and Coueley; to them and the heirs and assigns of Ralph Waleys.

Witnesses: John Clyfforde, John Whyte, John Fromylode, John Archer the younger, John Botiller.

At: Slimbridge.

A1/43/134 [GC 3673]   Mon. before the conversion of St. Paul, 49 Edw. III [24 Jan. 1376]

Peter le Reve of Wheatenhurst; and Ralph Waleys, William Smalcombe and Ralph Coke.

   Peter has quitclaimed to Ralph, William and Ralph, and the heirs and assigns of Ralph Waleys, the lands and holdings which were of Thomas le Muchele in Slymbrugge and Coueley and which they had by grant of John Cook, chaplain, and Walter Bat.

Witnesses: John Clifforde, John Whyte, John Fromylode, John Botiller, John Archer the younger.

At: Slimbridge.

A1/43/135 [GC 3868]   Wed. after Palm Sunday, 15 Ric. II [10 April 1392]

Ralph Waleys; and Sir Richard Wynchecombe, parson of Slimbridge, John Raso, chaplain, and William Kemote of Almondsbury.

   Ralph has granted to Richard, John and William, and their heirs and assigns, all his lands, holdings, rents [etc.] within the parish of Slymbrugge.

Witnesses: John de Coueleie, William Smalcombe, John Trie, John Archer, John Boteler.
At: Slimbridge.

The Joliffe holding

A1/43/136 [GC 3856]   Nativity of St. Mary, 15 Ric. II [8 Sept. 1391]
Walter Jolyff of Cam and Leticia his wife; and John Herfordschyre of Gossington.

Walter and Leticia have granted to John, his heirs and assigns 1 a. of land in the field called Dodforlong.
Witnesses: John Archer, John Fromylode, Henry de Gosyntone, John Boteler, Thomas Hallyng.
At: Slimbridge.

A1/43/137 [GC 4006]   Sun. the feast of St. Matthew, 5 Hen. IV [21 Sept. 1404]
John Herfordschyre of Gossington and Thomas Herdfordschyre, his son.

John has granted to Thomas, his heirs and assigns 1 a. of land in the field called Dodforlong.
Witnesses: John Archer, Henry de Gosyntone, Richard Hallyng, John Fromlode, Richard Boteler.
At: Slimbridge.

A1/43/138 [GC 4007]   Mon. after St. Matthew, 5 Hen. IV [22 Sept. 1404]
(1) John Herfordschyre of Gossington; (2) John Monk of the same; (3) Thomas son of John Herfordschyre.

John Herfordschyre has appointed John Monk to deliver seisin of 1 a. of land to Thomas.
At: Gossington.

A1/43/139 [GC 4093]   Assumption of St. Mary, 2 Hen. V [15 Aug. 1414]
Robert Rodes and Thomas Herfordshire of Gossington.

Robert has quitclaimed to Thomas 1 a. of land in the field called Dodfurlong.
Witnesses: John Archer, John Fromelode, Thomas Fromelode, Richard Knyght, Henry Clerk.
At: Slimbridge.

The Byford holding in Slimbridge, Kingston, Cambridge and Stinchcombe

Acquisition of the Rhodes holding in Kingston
A1/43/140 [GC 4115]   Eleven Thousand Virgins, 6 Hen. V [21 Oct. 1418]
Robert Rodes; and John Byford and Joan his wife.

Robert has granted to John and Joan, and their heirs and assigns, a messuage with a garden in the vill of Kyngestone, 1 a. of meadow in Lytilbrodmed, ½ a. of meadow in Parva Lotesmore and 1 a. of arable land in Dodfurlong.
Witnesses: John Archer, Richard Hallyng, Walter Clerke, Thomas Gosyngtone, Richard Knyght, John Boteler.
At: Slimbridge.

A1/43/141 [GC 4116]   Eleven Thousand Virgins, 6 Hen. V [21 Oct. 1418]
(1) Robert Rodes; (2) Thomas Fromelode and Richard Hallyng; (3) John Byford.

Robert has appointed Thomas and Richard to deliver seisin to John of a messuage and other lands in Kynggestone, as by his grant.

Acquisition of the Butler holding
A1/43/142 [GC 3504]   Sun. before the translation of St. Thomas the martyr, 34 Edw. III
                                                                    [5 July 1360]
John le Boteler of Slimbridge; and Richard le Boteler, his son, and Walter, Richard's brother.

John has leased to Richard and Walter the messuage and croft in Slymbrugge called

Aleysescroft, and 3 a. of land and ½ a. of meadow; for their lives, rent a rose a year.
Witnesses: Richard Ryvers, John Archer, John Hulles, Thomas Colynes, John le Mon.
At: Slimbridge.

A1/43/143 [GC 3882]   24 Feb. 17 Ric. II [1394]
John Boteler of Slimbridge, son and heir of John Boteler; and Richard Boteler, his brother,
and Alice his wife.

John has quitclaimed to Richard and Alice and their issue a messuage and croft called
Aleysecroft in Slymbrugge, with 3 a. of land and ½ a. of meadow, which Richard acquired
from John their father, for his life.
Witnesses: John Archer, . . . Gosyntone, John Fromelode, Walter K. . . , Richard Hallang.
At: Slimbridge.

A1/43/144 [GC 4144]   Thurs. before Palm Sunday, 3 Hen. VI [29 March 1425]
John Boteler of Slimbridge; and John Byforde of Slimbridge and Joan his wife.

John Boteler has quitclaimed to John and Joan the lands and holdings which Richard
Boteler lately held of him in Slymbrugge, two parcels of meadow in Whiteney and le
Hydforerdde, etc.
Witnesses: John Archere the elder, John Fremelode, Richard Knyght, Richard Hallynge,
John Archere the younger, Thomas Fremelode, John Taylour of the court (*de curia*) of
Slimbridge.
At: Slimbridge.

Acquisition of the Fleming holding in Slimbridge and Stinchcombe
A1/43/145 [GC 4160]   Sun. before the Invention of Holy Cross, 7 Hen. VI [1 May 1429]
Joan Colewyche, widow, and John Byforde.

Joan has granted to John, his heirs and assigns all her lands and holdings [etc.], in the
vills of Slymbrugge and Stynchecombe (Glos.) after the death of Margaret Flemynge.
Witnesses: John Clerke of Wotton, Nicholas Dawnte, Robert Purches.
At: Wotton.

A1/43/146 [GC 4229; *duplicate* GC 4230]   Thurs. after the nativity of St. John the Baptist,
                                                      20 Hen. VI [28 June 1442]
Margaret Flemmynge of Slimbridge, widow, and John Byforde.

Margaret has quitclaimed to John her messuage at Morehende and the croft called
Middulhomme and all her other lands and holdings in the vills of Slymbrygge and
Stynchecombe (Glos.).
Witnesses: Thomas Fremelode, John Archer, Thomas Gylmyn, Walter Selewyn, Walter
Clerk.
At: Slimbridge.

Other acquisitions
A1/43/147 [GC 4151]   The Purification, 4 Hen. VI [2 Feb. 1426]
Walter Wodeward of Cam; and John Byforde of Slimbridge and Joan his wife.

Walter has granted to John and Joan various parcels of land.
Witnesses: Walter Purlewent, John Archer, Richard Knyght, Henry Taylour, Nicholas
Selewy.
At: Slimbridge.

A1/43/148 [GC 4157]   St. Peter in cathedra, 6 Hen. VI [22 Feb. 1428]
John Byford of Slimbridge and Richard Knyght of the same.

John has granted to Richard, his heirs and assigns a messuage in Kyngeston and 1 selion
in Lynche at Wytherewe, for a croft of the said Richard at Cambrugge called
Cambruggyshurne and 1 a. of land.

Witnesses: John Archer, Thomas Fromelode, Richard Hallyng, Henry Archer, Nicholas Selewyne.
At: Slimbridge.

A1/43/149 [GC 4178]   Michaelmas, 13 Hen. VI [29 Sept. 1434]
John Byforde of Slimbridge and Nicholas Selewyn.
    John has granted to Nicholas 1 a. of land in the field called Lyefelde and 2 butts in the same field, for 1 a. of land in Camrysfelde.
Witnesses: Thomas Framelode, John Archer, Walter Wodewarde, Walter Clerc, Henry Archer.
At: Slimbridge.

   Roger Wall's holding
A1/43/150 [GC 4348]   Thurs. after the Purification, 7 Edw. IV [4 Feb. 1468]
John Byforde and Roger Walle.
    John has granted to Roger, his heirs and assigns a sheepfold and 1 a. of land adjacent in Slymebrugge, in a furlong called Monescrofte.
Witnesses: Richard Fromelode, John Robardes, John Mede, Thomas Hallyng, William Rogeres.
At: Slimbridge.

A1/43/151 [GC 4365]   St. Katherine, 11 Edw. IV [25 Nov. 1471]
Roger Wall of Arlingham; and Thomas Payne, gentleman, of Gloucester, John Trye, gentleman, William Wall of Arlingham and Thomas Myll of Slimbridge.
    Roger has granted to Thomas, John, William and Thomas, and their heirs and assigns, a sheepcot (*domus ovium*) *alias* 'shepehowse' and 1 a. of land in the furlong called Mancroft in Slymbrygge, which Roger had from John Byfort.
Witnesses: William Rogers, John Roberts, John Longney, William Cordy, John Cordy.
At: Arlingham.

Other

A1/43/152 [GC 1310]   n.d. [late Hen. III]
James Cotel of Coaley; and Peter le Buch' and Alice his wife.
    James has granted to Peter and Alice, for 44s., 1 a. of meadow in the meadow called Wyteneye; rent 1d. a year.
Witnesses: Miles de Langetoth, Peter de Stintescumb, Robert de Couel', Robert de Draycote, William Warner, Walter de Corevegate, Walter de Stintescomb, clerk.

A1/43/153 [GC 2546]   n.d. [late 13th cent.]
Ismannia widow of Roger called of the gate (*de porta*) and Alice her daughter.
    Ismannia has granted to Alice a messuage with a curtilage in the vill of Slimbrugge, which Roger le Brasur formerly held, and 1 selion of land called Longelond; to her and her issue, rent 1d. a year, and if Alice dies without issue then the holding will revert to Ismannia.
Witnesses: Sir Robert de Kyngestone, knight, John de Kyngestone, Elias le Botyller, William the serjeant (*serviens*), Richard le Duc, Gilbert son of Hugh of Slimbridge, Walter de Stintescumbe, clerk.

A1/43/154 [GC 2317]   Fri. after Holy Trinity, 13 Edw. II [30 May 1320]
John de le Yate of Slimbridge; and Thomas de Muchele and Eleanor his wife.
    John has granted to Thomas and Eleanor and Thomas's heirs a sheepfold with fore-earth beside it, beside the Wowevorerde in the marsh of Slimbrugge, for a certain sum of money.
Witnesses: Walter de Gosintone, John de Kingestone, William Botiler, John Duyk, Walter Oldelonde.
At: Slimbridge.

SLIMBRIDGE: CAMBRIDGE
THE FLERDING HOLDING

A1/44/1 [GC 1239]   n.d. [*temp.* Edw. I]
Thomas lord of Berkeleye and William Flerding.

Thomas has leased to William the house which Edith de Cambrugge formerly held next
to the mill of Cambrugge; for the lives of William, his first wife and his issue, rent 5*s.* a year.
Witnesses: Robert de Bradeston, Thomas de Beoleye, Elias le Botiler, Richard le Duc, John
Halling.

A1/44/2 [GC 1757]   Wed. the feast of St. Mary Magdalen, 4 Edw. II [22 July 1310]
Thomas de Berkelee, lord of Berkeley; and William Flerdyng and Margaret his wife.

Thomas has granted to William and Margaret the messuage, garden, curtilage and croft
which Edith de Cambrugge formerly held, beside the mill of Cambrugge, with common of
pasture for 40 sheep and 1 cow; to William, Margaret and Peter their son, for their lives,
rent 5*s.* a year, and reserving to Thomas sufficient land of the holding to improve the
millpond.
Witnesses: Thomas de Styntescombe, Robert de Bradestone, Thomas de Beoleye, William
le Boteler, John le Duk.
At: Berkeley.

OTHER

A1/44/3 [GC 1048]   Mon. the feast of the nativity of St. John the Baptist, 31 Edw. I
[24 June 1303]
Thomas de Berkelee, lord of Berkeley; and John le Bakere and Agnes his wife.

Thomas has granted to John and Agnes the messuage and enclosure at Cambrugge which
John the smith once held, with 2 a. 12 perches of Thomas's land lying in the furlongs called
Alres (1 a.) and Okheye (1 a.12 perches); to John and Agnes and John's issue, rent 10*s.* a
year.
Witnesses: Robert de Bradestone, Robert de Berkelee, Thomas de Beolee, Thomas de
Swonhungre, John de Egeton, Elias le Boteler, Walter de Gosyntone, Roger Osbern, John
atte Yate.
At: Berkeley.

SLIMBRIDGE: GOSSINGTON

BERKELEY INTERESTS
The Gossington holding

Hawling half-virgate
A1/45/1 [GC 2020]   Wed. before St. Matthew, 8 Edw. II [19 Feb. 1315]
Walter Lespec', burgess of Gloucester, and Sir Thomas de Berkeleye.

Walter has granted to Thomas, his heirs and assigns, for a certain sum of money, the
messuage with a garden, curtilage and half-virgate of land which Walter Halling formerly
held in Gosyntone, which Walter and Walter his son had by grant of Roger de Gosintone for
the lives of the same Walter Lespec' and Walter his son; to hold of Roger during the lives of
Walter Lespec' and his son Walter; rent to Roger 1 lb. of cumin a year.
Witnesses: William de Wautone, Thomas de Berkeleye, John de Berkeleye, Walter
Gascelyne, Stephen de la More, knights, John son of Nicholas, Thomas de Bradeston, John
de Coueleye, Robert of the church (*de ecclesia*).
At: Berkeley.

A1/45/2 [GC 2504]   Mon. the feast of St. Matthew, [8] Edw. II [24 Feb. 1315]
Roger de Gosintone and Reginald son of Juliana ate Cherche, daughter of Robert ate
Cherche.

Roger has granted to Reginald, for a certain sum of money, the messuage with a garden, curtilage and half-virgate of land which Walter Hallyng formerly held in Gosyntone; for Reginald's life, with remainder to John son of Sir Maurice de Berkeleye for his life, rent 1 lb. of cumin.

Witnesses: Thomas de Bradeston, Thomas de Beleye, John de Coueleye, Stephen de Draycote, Maurice de . . . , Walter de Gosyntone, Robert de . . .

At: Gossington.

A1/45/3 [GC 2024]   20 March 8 Edw. II [1315]

Roger de Gosyntone; and Reginald son of Juliana daughter of Robert de la Churche and John son of Sir Maurice de Berkeleye.

Roger has granted to Reginald, for his life, and after his death to John, for his life, a messuage and half-virgate of land which Walter Halling formerly held of Roger in villeinage in Gosyntone, and for a term of 30 years after the death of the survivor; rent 1 lb. of cumin a year, and 100s. after the end of the term of 30 years.

Witnesses: John son of Nicholas son of Ralph, Odo de Actone, Thomas de Bradeston, John de Oulepenne, John de Coueleye, Robert le Warner, Stephen de Draycote.

At: Gossington.

Cromhall rent

A1/45/4 [GC 1761; *duplicate* GC 1762]   Sat. the feast of the Assumption of St. Mary,
                                                            4 Edw. II [15 Aug. 1310]

Roger de Gosyntone and Odo de Actone.

Roger has granted to Odo a rent of 19s. 6d. a year from Jordan de Bibberston and Hugh de Tounewelle for their holdings in Cromhale; to hold of the chief lord for the customary services and, after a term of 10 years, at a rent of 10 marks a year to Roger and his heirs, and Odo has given him 10 marks.

Witnesses: Robert de Berkleye, Stephen de Draycote, Robert de Bradeston, John de Oulepenne, William son of Warin.

At: Cromhall.

A1/45/5 [GC 2023]   20 March 8 Edw. II [1315]

Roger de Gosyntone; and Reginald son of Juliana, daughter of Robert de la Churche, and John son of Sir Maurice de Berkeleye.

Roger has granted to Reginald, for his life, and after his death to John, for his life, a rent of 19s. 6d. from Jordan de Bibberston and Hugh de Tounewelle for lands in Cromhale, and for a term of 36 years after the death of the survivor; rent 100s. after the end of the term of 36 years; for this, Sir Thomas de Berkeleye, lord of Berkeley, at the request of Reginald and John, has released to Roger all actions for dower of Sibyl de Gosyntone, Roger's mother, by the lease of Walter Lespecer, and has given to him all the writings concerned with the said dower.

Witnesses: John son of Nicholas son of Ralph, Odo de Actone, Thomas de Bradeston, John de Oulepenne, John de Coueleye, Robert le Warner, Stephen de Draycote.

At: Gossington.

A1/45/6 [GC 2036]   Tues. before St. Philip and St. James, 8 Edw. II [29 April 1315]

Odo de Actone and Sir Thomas de Berkeleye, lord of Berkeley.

Odo has quitclaimed to Thomas land and rent in Cromhale which he had from Roger de Gosyntone. [*In French.*]

Witnesses: William le Botyler, Walter de Gosyntone, Robert de Budlescombe, William le Brid, Henry de Mareis.

At: Berkeley.

Meadow in Little Lots moor

A1/45/7 [GC 1919]   Sun. after the Exaltation of Holy Cross, 6 Edw. II [6 May 1313]
Roger de Gosinton and Odo de Actone.

Roger has granted to Odo his meadow in Parva Lottesmore at la Geze; rent, after 4 years,
40s. a year, and Odo has given him a certain sum of money.
Witnesses: Walter de Gosinton, William le Butiler, Richard Bat, William le Muchele, John
le Duk.
At: Kingston.

A1/45/8 [GC 2062]   Sun. the feast of St. Clement, 9 Edw. II [23 Nov. 1315]
Roger de Gosyntone; and Reginald son of Juliana de Nibley and John son of Sir Maurice de
Berkeleye.

Roger has granted to Reginald, for his life, and after his death to John, for his life, 1½ a.
53 perches of meadow in the meadow called Lottesmor, in Gosyntone, and for a term of 36
years after the death of the survivor; rent a rose a year.
Witnesses: John son of Nicholas son of Ralph, Odo de Actone, Thomas de Bradeston, John
de Oulepenne, John de Coueleye, Robert le Warner, Stephen de Draycote.
At: Gossington.

The combined holding

A1/45/9 [GC 2794]   24 May 8 Edw. III [1334]
Roger le Archer and Sir Thomas de Berkelee, lord of Berkeley.

Roger has granted to Thomas 34s. 8d. from Edward Golde and William de Draycote, viz.
26s. 8d. from Edward for a half-virgate of land which he holds in Gosyntone within the
manor of Camme, and 8s. from William for 2 a. of meadow in Lottesmor within the said
manor; to hold the said rent during the minority of John son and heir of Roger de
Gosyntone, which Sir Thomas late lord of Berkeley, grandfather of the present lord, granted
to Roger le Archer.
At: Berkeley.

A1/45/10 [GC 2840]   Sat. in Epiphany, 9 Edw. III [6 Jan. 1336]
Robert de Aulton and Edward Golde, executors of John de Berkeleye; knight, and Thomas
de Berkel', lord of Berkeley.

Whereas Roger de Gosyntone lately leased to John for his life 1 virgate of land, which
Edward holds for life, at Gosyntone within the manor of Camme, and also 1½ a. 53 perches
of land and meadow in the place called Luttesmour in the same manor, and also 19s. 6d.
rent from holdings in Cromhale, viz. from Jordan de Bibberstone and Hugh de Toneswelle,
to John for his life and after his death to his assigns for 36 years; and whereas John
appointed Robert and Edward his assigns to hold the holdings for the said term, and
whereas the lord of the fee seized the holdings by reason of the minority of John son and
heir of the said Roger de Gosyntone, Robert and Edward have granted all the said holdings
to Thomas for the said term.
At: Berkeley.

A1/45/11 [GC 2918]   Sun. before the nativity of St. Mary, 12 Edw. III [6 Sept. 1338]
John son of Roger de Gosyntone and Sir Thomas de Berkeleye, lord of Berkeley.

John has quitclaimed to Thomas a half-virgate of land held by Richard le Man and John
his son, in Gosyntone within the manor of Camme, by grant of the said Thomas, and 2 a. of
meadow and a rent of 20s. from holdings in Cromhale.
At: Berkeley.

Other

A1/45/12 [GC 1152]   23 June 35 Edw. I [1307]

Thomas de Berkelee, lord of Berkeley, and Roger de Gosynton, his kinsman.

Thomas has granted to Roger licence to enclose the field called Oldelond lying next to his court of Gosynton.

Witnesses: Robert de Bradeston, Robert de Berkelee, Thomas de Beolee, Thomas de Styntescombe, Walter de Gosynton.

At: Berkeley.

A1/45/13 [GC 2079]   6 Feb. 9 Edw. II [1316]

Roger de Gosyntone and Sir Thomas de Berkeleye, lord of Berkeley.

Roger has granted to Thomas, his heirs and assigns a rent of 20s. a year from all the lands and holdings which John Pynel holds of Roger at la Fortheye in Gosyntone, and a rent of 4s. a year from a croft at le Fortheye and 1 a. of land in the field called Schipeyate, which Christine widow of Henry Pynel holds for life, with the reversion of the croft and acre after her death, in Gosyntone.

Witnesses: Thomas de Bradeston, Peter de Stintescombe, Henry de Camme, John de Coueleye, Stephen de Draycote, Walter de Gosyntone, John le Duk.

At: Gossington.

A1/45/14 [GC 2152]   St. Valentine's Day, 10 Edw. II [14 Feb. 1317]

Roger de Gosyntone and Sir Thomas de Berkel', lord of Berkeley.

Roger has granted to Thomas a rent of 10s. a year from William ate Broke for the holding which he holds of Roger in Slymbrugge, Gosintone and Hurste.

Witnesses: Thomas de Bradeston, Peter de Styntescombe, John le Serjant, Thomas de Craweleye, Walter de Gosyntone, William le Botyler, John de Kyngestone.

At: Gossington.

A1/45/15 [GC 2353]   20 May 14 Edw. II [1321]

Thomas de Berkelee, lord of Berkeley, and Roger Archer of Woodford.

Thomas has granted to Roger custody of two thirds of the lands and holdings which Roger de Gosyntone, lately deceased, held of Thomas in chief by knight service in Hurste and Slymbrugge, with the reversion of the one third which Desiderata, Roger's wife, holds in dower, until the full age of John, Roger's son and heir, for the rent as Roger paid it, with the marriage of John.

Witnesses: John le Serjaunt, John Capel, John de la Hay, John Wyth, John Abbod.

At: Berkeley.

Other Berkeley interests

A1/45/16 [SC 192]   n.d. [1197× 1209]

Roger de Berkele and Maurice de Berkele, his nephew.

Roger has granted to Maurice the meadow at Gosintun called Lutlemede, next to the furlong called Smethem's, at a rent of a pair of gilt spurs and 6d. a year, for which Maurice gave to Roger an unmewed falcon worth 16s. and to Hawise Painel, Roger's wife, a besant.

Witnesses: Robert de Berkele, Eustace and Oliver, Roger's brothers, Roger de Haggele, Reginald de Gosintun, Harding de Hunteneford, Adam and Maurice sons of Nigel, Hugh and Richard de Bradele, John de Craule, William Cotele, John the baker (*pistor*), Robert Bastart, William de Berkele, Roger de Planca, Bernard de Brodestan.

A1/45/17 [GC 2087]   8 March 9 Edw. II [1316]

John son and heir of Henry Pynel of Gossington and Sir Thomas de Berkeleye, lord of Berkeley.

John has granted to Thomas, his heirs and assigns a rent of 5s. a year from William le

Lung' and Margaret his wife for a messuage and 1 fardel of land held of John in Gosyntone, of Margaret's inheritance.

Witnesses: Thomas de Bradeston, Thomas de Boeleye, Odo de Actone, Robert de Berkeleye, Peter de Styntescombe, Roger de Gosyntone, Walter de Gosyntone.
At: Berkeley.

OTHER INTERESTS
The Kingswood Abbey holding

A1/45/18 [GC 1452; *duplicate* GC 1453]   n.d. [late Hen. III]
Robert de Kyngestune and Kingswood Abbey.

   Robert, for the souls of himself and Maud his wife, has granted to the abbey a rent of 10*s.* from a half-virgate in the vill of Gosynton, which John Halling sometime held.
Witnesses: Sir Maurice de Berkeleya, Sir William le Mansel, Sir Robert le Veel, knights, Robert de Bradestone, Elias le Botiller, Robert de Dreycote, Robert de Coueleye, Richard le Duc.

A1/45/19 [GC 1605]   n.d. [late Hen. III]
Maurice de Berkeley and Kingswood Abbey.

   Maurice has confirmed to the abbey all the grants of Sir Robert de Kyngeston of a rent of 10*s.* from a half-virgate in the vill of Gosynton, which John Halling formerly held, and a half-virgate of land at Beoleye, which escheated to Robert on the death of William Mauduyt.
Witnesses: Sir William le Maunsel, Sir Robert le Veel, knights, Robert de Bradestone, Elias le Butyller, Robert de Dreycote, Robert de Coueleye.

A1/45/20 [GC 593]   The Invention of Holy Cross, 21 Edw. I [3 May 1293]
Kingswood Abbey and Constance widow of John Halling of Gossington.

   The abbey has granted to Constance the wardship of lands in the vill of Gosinton after the death of John, son and heir of the said John her late husband and Maud formerly his wife, until the full age of the heir of the said John Halling, her late husband; Constance rendering the customary services plus an increment of 5*s.* a year, and she has given the abbey 20*s.*
Witnesses: Reginald de Gosinton, Robert de Dreicot, Robert de Bradeston, Thomas le Serjaunt, Thomas de Beule, Henry de Camme, Richard le Duyk.

Other

A1/45/21 [GC 2894]   Sat. the eve of the conversion of St. Paul, 11 Edw. III [24 Jan. 1338]
John de Lorwynge of Matson and Edith daughter of William Redhod of Gossington.

   John has leased to Edith all the land and holdings which he had by grant of Richard de Lorwynge except a croft called Homcroft; for her life, rent 7*s.* 6*d.* a year.
Witnesses: Stephen de Kyneltre, William ate Herne, Henry le Eyr, William Gryp, Adam Purlewent, clerk.
At: Matson.

A1/45/22 [GC 3212]   Thurs. after St. Mildred, 23 Edw. III [26 Feb. 1349]
Robert Hallyng of Gossington, and Nicholas his son.

   Robert has granted to Nicholas 2½ a. of land in Hale; to him and his issue.
Witnesses: Richard le Riveris, John Sage, John le Man, John Taylur, Thomas Hallyng.
At: Gossington.

A1/45/23 [GC 3756]   Sun. after St. James, 6 Ric. II [27 July 1382]
John le Engleys of Longford; and Thomas Kynge of Gossington and Isabel his wife.

   John has leased to Thomas and Isabel a holding in villeinage in Gosyngton; for their lives, rent 6*s.* a year.
Witnesses: John Fromlode, John Archer, Walter Sygryth, Thomas Hallynge, John Yaneworth.
At: Gloucester.

SLIMBRIDGE: KINGSTON

BERKELEY INTERESTS

A1/46/1 [GC 357]   n.d. [late Hen. III]

Sir Maurice de Berkeley and William Young (*Juvenis*) of Kingston.

Maurice has granted to William ¼ a. of land in the furlong called Bovenhay between the land of Walter Selwyn and Walter Burel, in exchange for ½ a. of land in the field of Heforlonge. Endorsed: *Kyngston*.

Witnesses: Sir Robert de Kyngeston, William de Mathem', William the serjeant (*serviens*), Elias le Botiler, Gilbert son of Hugh.

A1/46/2 [GC 1242]   n.d. [*c*. 1300]

Thomas de Berkel' and Richard le Touhte.

Thomas has quitclaimed to Richard his issue and chattels and all services for his life; and he has leased to Richard all the land with meadow which Walter le Touhte held of Thomas in Kingeston, to Richard and his first wife for their lives, rent 7*s*. a year, and Richard has given Thomas 10 marks; after Richard's death his issue will take the servile condition of Richard as it was before the making of this charter.

Witnesses: Robert de Stone, Robert de Bradestone, Thomas Aleyn, Thomas de Beleye, Richard le Duc.

A1/46/3 [GC 1781]   Mon. the feast of St. Thomas the apostle, 4 Edw. II [21 Dec. 1310]

Thomas de Berkelee, lord of Berkeley; and Roger atte Watere and Joan his wife.

Thomas has granted to Roger and Joan 3 a. 4 perches of land at Kyngestone beside Lyhttyngbrok, in Slymbrugge; to them and their issue, rent 10*s*. a year.

Witnesses: Robert le Warner, Walter de Gosinton, William le Boteler, Richard Baat, John de Kyngestone.

At: Berkeley.

A1/46/4 [GC 2253]   10 Sept. 12 Edw. II [1318]

Thomas de Berkeleye, lord of Berkeley, and Walter le Botyler.

Thomas has granted to Walter 1¼ a. of land in the field called Bovenhay beside the road called Burellestret in Slymbrugge; to him and his issue, rent 5*s*. a year.

Witnesses: Thomas de Bradeston, William le Botyler, Thomas le Spenser, Walter de Gosyntone, John Colynes of Kingston.

At: Berkeley.

OTHER INTERESTS
The Kingston holding

A1/46/5 [GC 1451]   n.d. [late Hen. III]

Robert de Kyngeston and Edith daughter of John Duc.

Robert has granted to Edith two messuages with curtilages in the vill of Kyngeston, which Walter Maignard and Reginald the lame (*claudus*) formerly held; rent 6*d*. a year, and she has given him 4 marks.

Witnesses: Master Robert Baion, rector of Slimbridge, Reginald de Gosintone, William de Kyngestone, William de Bradefeld, Roger son of Hugh, William de Gosintone, Richard Duc.

A1/46/6 [GC 898]   n.d. [late 13th cent.]

Edith daughter of John le Duc; and Nicholas de Kingeston and Eleanor his wife.

Edith has granted to Nicholas and Eleanor, for a certain sum of money, all the holding and meadow in the vill of Kingeston which she had from Sir Robert de Kingeston; rent 6*d*. a year to the chief lord of the fee.

Witnesses: John de Kingeston, Richard Duc, William le Sergant, Elias le Butiler, Thomas de Kingeston, Walter de Gosinton.

Richard Falwell

A1/46/7 [SC 541]　　　　Thurs. after the translation of St. Thomas the martyr, 39 Edw. III
[10 July 1365]
Maurice de Berkelee and Richard de Acton, knight.
　Maurice has granted to Richard his villein Richard Fallewelle of Kyngustone.
At: Berkeley.

A1/46/8 [GC 3571]　　　　Wed. after St. Bartholomew, 39 Edw. III [27 Aug. 1365]
John de Actone and Cecilia wife of William le Voltere of Gloucester.
　John has granted to Cecilia his villein Richard Falwelle of Kyngestone.
At: Gloucester.

Other

A1/46/9 [GC 1875]　　　　　　　　　　　　　　6 April 5 Edw. II [1312]
Agnes de Madresdon; and Richard de Rivers (*de Ripariis*) and Sarah de la Haghe, Agnes's niece.
　Agnes has granted to Richard and Sarah a messuage and 1 carucate of land in Kyngestone and Gosintone in the parish of Slymbrugg, which were of Sir Robert de Kyngeston.
Witnesses: Sir Thomas le Blound, Sir John le Rous, knights, Robert de Haddele, John de Alkele, Thomas de Bule, Robert de Berkele, Walter de Gosington.
At: Kingston.

A1/46/10 [GC 2524]　　　　　　　　　　　　　n.d. [*temp.* Edw. I]
William le Jevene and John Wyth' of Arlingham.
　William has granted to John his claim to a plot of land in the vill of Kingestone which Margery, widow of Walter le Jevene his father, holds in dower and which she granted to John, and also another plot of land; John has given him 10*s*.
Witnesses: Walter de Gosintone, Richard le Duck, Thomas de Kingestone, John de Kingestone, Elias le Botiler, Gilbert son of Hugh of Slimbridge.

A1/46/11 [GC 4048]　　　　　　　　　　　　14 May 11 Hen. IV [1410]
John Wyntour and Henry Taylour of Cam; and Robert Rode and Alice Pullare.
　John and Henry have granted to Robert and Alice, and Robert's heirs and assigns, all the lands, holdings [etc.] that they had by grant of Alice Boteler in Kyngestone and within the parish of Slymbrugge.
Witnesses: Henry Gosyntone, John Archer, John Fromlode, Richard Knyght, John Boteler.
At: Kingston.

SLIMBRIDGE: SAGES

Sages, a large holding within Slimbridge bought either from John Sage by Thomas (III) Lord Berkeley *c*. 1344[1] or from John son Odo de Acton by Thomas's son Maurice (IV),[2] gained a separate identity during the Great Dispute of the 15th century because the heirs general claimed that it had not been included in the entail of 1349. When in Berkeley hands it was usually administered with Slimbridge.

CHARTERS

A1/47/1 [GC 3283]　　　　　　　　　　　　　n.d. [mid 14th cent.]
Thomas lord of Berkele; and Robert Willyes, Alice his wife and John their younger son.
　Thomas has leased to Robert, Alice and John a messuage with a dovecot, which was the capital messuage of John Sage, with 21a. of land and meadow parcel of the said messuage, in Kyngestone; for their lives, rent 26*s*. 8*d*. a year.
Witnesses: Richard Ryvers, John Arch', John Howes, John le Man, John le Botiller.

---

[1] Smyth, i. 328.　　　　　　　　　[2] Above, A1/43/130 [SR 5].

ADMINISTRATIVE DOCUMENTS[1]

A1/47/2 [GRR 18] Rental n.d. [*c.* 1400]

A1/47/3 [GRR 19] Rental 5 Hen. VI [1426–7]

A1/47/4 [GCR 9] Court roll 19 Sept. 6 Hen. V [1418]

Court of Richard Beauchamp, earl of Warwick, and Elizabeth his wife.

SYMOND'S HALL

Symond's Hall was a small manor closely associated with the large manor of Wotton, with which it was occasionally administered. It formed one of the vills of Wotton. Many charters concerning the vill are therefore included among those for Wotton (below, pp. 339–47.)

KINGSWOOD ABBEY

A1/48/1 [GC 1221] n.d. [mid Hen. III]

Thomas de Berkel' and Thomas his son.

Thomas the elder has granted to Thomas the younger all the land in Simundeshal at Egge which Osbert Wixi and Roger de Bradepenn formerly held, except 4 a. which Thomas the elder has given to Kingswood Abbey, also all the land at Egge which Adam de Holeya holds, with the grove and Adam and all his issue, also 2 a. of land next to Thomas the younger's land extending above Fulemor, and 4 a. of land between Thomas the younger's land and the path and the half-virgate which Andrew holds, with Andrew and all his issue; rent two silver pennies a year.

Witnesses: Sir William Large (*Grassus*), Sir Peter de Stintescumbe, Henry de Berkel', Simon de Ollepenn, Richard de Brimelham, Nicholas Ruffus, Elias de Cumbe, William de Bradeleya, Nigel de Kingescote.

A1/48/2 [SC 335] n.d. [*temp.* Hen. III]

Thomas de Berkeley, son of Sir Thomas de Berkeley, and Kingswood Abbey.

Thomas has granted to the abbey, for the souls of Thomas his father and Joan his mother, the land in Symundeshale at Egge which Osbert Wyxi and Roger de Bradpenne sometime held, except 4 a. which the monks had before, also the land at Egge which Adam de Holeweya held with the grove which he also held, with Adam and his issue, also 2 a. on Fulemore and 4 a. lying near the road and the half-virgate which Andrew held, with Andrew and his issue, saving to Thomas his father and his heirs a rent of 2*d.* a year and the royal service as in Thomas the elder's charter to Thomas the younger.

Witnesses: Sir Peter de Eggeworth, Sir Geoffrey de Chausi, Sir Oliver de Berkeley, Geoffrey the clerk of Derhurste, Nicholas Ruffus, Herevic de Fleg', Nicholas de Chausi, Humphrey de la Barre, Robert Joye, Stephen de Wyka, Thomas the Scot (*Scottus*), Peter de Yweleg', Matthew le Scay, Walter Tysun.

A1/48/3 [SC 248] n.d. [*c.* 1238]

Thomas de Berkelay, son of Sir Thomas de Berkeley, and Kingswood Abbey.

Thomas has granted to the abbey all his wood in the manor of Symundeshale, lying between the valley called la Throte and the road called Cullingewey, and a croft called la Penne; doing the services to Sir Thomas de Berkeley, his father, as in his charter to Thomas the younger, viz. 8*d.* at Christmas each year for the souls of Thomas his father and Joan his mother.

Witnesses: Sir Peter de Eggewrthe, Sir Geoffrey de Chausi, Oliver de Berkelay, Geoffrey the clerk of Derherste, Nicholas Ruffus, Humphrey de la Barre, Matthew le Scay, Peter de Yweleye, Walter Tysun.

---

[1] See also above, A1/43/130 [SR 5].

A1/48/4 [GC 550]   n.d. [*temp.* Hen. III]
Thomas de Berkeley, son of lord Thomas de Berkeley, and Kingswood Abbey.

Thomas has granted to the abbey all the liberty which he had from Elias de Cumb in the manor of Symundeshale and in the field there called Fulmore, to hold as in Elias's charter to him.
Witnesses: Peter de Eggewrthe, Geoffrey de Chausi, Nicholas Ruffus, Matthew le Scay, Roger Petipas.

A1/48/5 [SC 301]   n.d. [1241 × 1248]
Thomas de Berkelay, son of Sir Thomas de Berkeley, and Kingswood Abbey.

For the souls of himself and Sir Thomas his father and Lady Joan his mother, Thomas has granted to the abbey a rent of 10*s.* a year from his land of Symundeshale to provide a pittance for the monks every year on St. Andrew's day [30 Nov.].
Witnesses: Sir Robert the prior, brothers Odo, John, Vitalis, William the cellarer, and Andrew, monks of Kingswood.

A1/48/6 [GC 390]   n.d. [1243 × 1246]
Kingswood Abbey and Sir Maurice lord of Berkeley, son of Thomas de Berkeley.

The monks have granted to Maurice and all his tenants of Symundeshal free ingress and egress in their land of Egge, which they had by grant of Thomas de Berkeley, Maurice's brother, to lead and drive all animals to the water called Lodewell and to water them there.
Witnesses: Sir Peter de Stanford, sheriff of Gloucester, Master Peter de Brewys, Humphrey de la Barr, Robert de Hales, steward of Berkeley, William de Sanford, John de Dreycote, Andrew de Bratheston, William de Berkeley, Richard de Wik, Thomas Alein.

A1/48/7 [SC 468]   10 Feb. 31 Edw. I [1303]
Robert de Tetbury, abbot of Kingswood; and Thomas de Berkeley and Maurice his son.

Arbitration by Walter Bordun, archdeacon of Gloucester, William de Kingescote, canon of Hereford, Sir Nicholas de Kyngeston, Sir Peter Crok, Sir Simon le Chaumberlayn, knights, and others to end the controversies between the parties concerning a fold of 200 sheep at Simondshall: that the abbey should provide the fold each year from the Invention of Holy Cross [3 May] to All Saints [1 Nov.], except three days for shearing, and in return Thomas and Maurice agree that the fold need not be found if the abbey have no sheep on their granges of Egge, Ozleworth or Caldecot because of murrain [etc.]
At: Cromhall.

ADMINISTRATIVE DOCUMENTS
Account rolls
There are several joint accounts for Wotton and Symond's Hall: see below, p. 346.

A1/48/8 [GAR 258]	Michaelmas to June, 8 Edw. II [1314–15]
A1/48/9 [GAR 260]	9–10 Edw. II [1315–16]
A1/48/10 [GAR 264]	14–15 Edw. II [1320–1]
A1/48/11 [GAR 269]	n.d. [1345]

Extent
A1/48/12 [GMR 28]   n.d. [*temp.* Edw. I]

KING'S WESTON
The manor formed a detached portion of Berkeley Herness. For the principal manor, which was granted to FitzHarding's younger son Robert and was bought from his descendant Thomas ap Adam in 1330 by Maurice de Berkeley of Stoke Giffard, see above, p. 183, Elberton. The additional holdings here purchased by Maurice (III) Lord Berkeley (d. 1326) were merged with the neighbouring holdings at Lawrence Weston (below, p. 498) and

passed to his younger son John. On John's death without issue in 1336 they reverted to Thomas (III) Lord Berkeley (d. 1361) and passed to the Beverston cadet line. See also below, p. 477, Over.

BERKELEY INTERESTS
The Legat holding

A1/49/1 [GC 2194]   Sun. before Michaelmas, 11 Edw. II [25 Sept. 1317]
Alice widow of Hugh Legat and Sir Maurice de Berkeleye, lord of Portbury.

Alice has granted to Maurice 13 a. of land, ½ a. 1 rood of meadow, 7 parcels of pasture and 1 a. of wood in Kyngeswestone, with rents of 2*s*. and ½*d*. and the reversion of 16 a. of land and 2 a. of meadow and of 7 a. of land and 4 a. of meadow [etc.]
Witnesses: Sir Stephen de la More, Sir William de Wautone, knights, John de Alkeley, William Waleys, Elias de Filtone, John atte Combe, William de Thriddelonde.
At: Portbury.

A1/49/2 [GC 2191]   Sun. before Michaelmas, 11 Edw. II [25 Sept. 1317]
(1) Alice widow of Hugh Legat of King's Weston; (2) Richard de la Marche and John Wale; (3) Sir Maurice de Berk', son and heir of Sir Thomas de Berk'.

Alice has appointed Richard or John her attorneys to give seisin to Maurice in all the lands and holdings [etc.], as in her charter.
At: Portbury.

A1/49/3 [GC 2201]   Wed. after St. Leonard, 11 Edw. II [9 Nov. 1317]
(1) Maurice de Berk'; (2) Richard de la Marche; (3) Alice widow of Hugh Legat.

Maurice has appointed Richard his attorney to receive seisin of the lands, holdings [etc.] that he had by Alice's grant.
At: Portbury.

A1/49/4 [GC 2252]   Tues. the feast of St. Peter in chains, 12 Edw. II [1 Aug. 1318]
Maurice de Berkeleye, son and heir of Sir Thomas de Berkel', and Alice Legat of King's Weston.

Maurice has leased to Alice 13½ a. of land, ½ a. 1 rood of meadow and 1 a. of wood in Kyngesweston, and 6*d*. a year from 3 parcels of pasture at le Merdyche, le Lynche and le Warth, 2*d*. a year from a parcel of pasture at le Waschtone, 4*d*. every other year from 3 parcels of pasture at the gate [*portam*] of Hemecrofte, the gate of Hemelond and the gate of Berlond, a rent of 2½*d*. a year from the holding of Agnes le Smale, and a rent of 2*s*. a year from the holding of John Leoveys; for her life, rent a rose a year.
Witnesses: Sir Stephen de la More, Sir William de Wauton, knights, John de Alkeleye, William Waleys, Elias de Fylton, John atte Combe, William de Triddelonde.
At: Portbury.

The Munne holding, in King's Weston and Henbury[1]

A1/49/5 [GC 1942]   Sat. the feast of the nativity of St. Mary, 7 Edw. II [8 Sept. 1313]
John Munne, son and heir of John Munne of Glaston[bury], and John de Bartone.

John Munne has granted to John de Bartone his messuage in the vill of Kyngesweston by Bristol (Glos.), with the lands, holdings [etc.], in the same vill and that of Salso Marisco.
Witnesses: John de Northelode, Thomas de Juethorne, John de Mere, Adam le Ferour, William le Baker, Robert le Cooc, John de Suthfolk, Roger le Somer', Richard le Messag', Philip Payn, John Broun.
At: Glastonbury.

---

[1] See also below, A1/49/9.

A1/49/6 [GC 2144]   Wed. after the conversion St. Paul, 10 Edw. II [26 Jan. 1317]
(1) John de Barthon of Somerset; (2) Thomas Jacob of Stowey; (3) Sir Maurice de
Berkeley, son of Sir Thomas de Berkeley.

John has appointed Thomas his attorney to give seisin to Maurice of all the lands and
holdings which he had in Kyngesweston and in Salso Marisco by Hembury, as in his
charter.
At: Portbury.

A1/49/7 [GC 2148]   Sun. after the Purification, 10 Edw. II [6 Feb. 1317]
John de Barthone of Somerset and Sir Maurice son of Sir Thomas de Berkelee.

John has quitclaimed to Maurice, his heirs and assigns the holding which John Monne of
Glastonia formerly held in Kynggeswestone and in Salso Marisco by Hembury (Glos.).
Witnesses: Sir Thomas le Botiler, Sir William de Wautone, knights, Elias de Fyltone, John
de Alkelegh, William de la Hay, Florentinus de Stoke, John de Combe.
At: Portbury.

Various acquisitions and grants

A1/49/8 [GC 2192]   Sun. before Michaelmas, 11 Edw. II [25 Sept. 1317]
Walter Golde, son of John Golde 'by Hembury', and Sir Maurice de Berkeley, lord of
Portbury.

Walter has granted to Maurice and his heirs a plot of land and meadow within an
enclosure called la Nywelond, within the manor of Kyngusueston.
Witnesses: Sir Stephen de la More, Sir William de Waweton, knights, John de Alkeley,
William le Waleys, Elias de Fylton, John ate Combe, William de Thrydelond.
At: Portbury.

A1/49/9 [GC 2294]   Mon. the feast of St. Silvester, 13 Edw. II [31 Dec. 1319]
Maurice de Berkeleye, son of Sir Thomas de Berkeleye, knight, and John de Berkeleye, his
son.

Maurice has granted to John all his holding in Kyngguswestone (Glos.), with the
appurtenances, and with the reversion of the holding and homage which Joan widow of
John Monne of Glastyngbury holds in dower; to John and the heirs male of his body, rent
1*d.* a year.
Witnesses: Sir William de Suhtleye, Sir William de Wautone, Sir Stephen de la More,
knights, John de Button, Richard de la Marche.
At: Wotton.

A1/49/10 [GC 2296]   Mon. the feast of St. Silvester, 13 Edw. II [31 Dec. 1319]
(1) Maurice de Berkeleye, son of Sir Thomas de Berkeleye; (2) Nicholas de Westone;
(3) John de Berkeleye, Maurice's son.

Maurice has appointed Nicholas his attorney to give seisin to John of all the lands and
holdings which John had by Maurice's grant in Kyngguswestone and Westone Sancti
Laurencii (Glos.), as in his charters.
At: Wotton.

A1/49/11 [GC 2297]   Mon. the feast of St. Silvester, 13 Edw. II [31 Dec. 1319]
(1) John de Berkeleye, son of Sir Maurice de Berkeleye, knight; (2) Richard de la Marche;
(3) Sir Maurice de Berkeleye.

John has appointed Richard his attorney to receive seisin of all the lands and holdings
which he had by Maurice's grant in Kynguswestone and Westone Sancti Laurencii.
At: Wotton.

A1/49/12 [GC 3104]   29 Oct. 18 Edw. III [1344]
Walter Goldemere and Sir William de Syde.

Walter has granted to William all the lands, holdings and reversions that he had in Kyngeswestone and Westone Sancti Laurencii; for his life, with remainder to Sir Thomas lord of Berkel' for his life, to Sir Thomas's son Thomas son and his issue, and to Sir Thomas's right heirs.

Witnesses: William de Chiltenham, John de Clyve, William Curteys, Henry Peche, Robert Groundy.

At: Berkeley.

A1/49/13 [GC 3714]   n.d. [1330 × 1361]
Thomas lord of Berkelee; and John [Barri] and Agnes his wife.

Thomas has granted to John and Agnes a messuage and 4 a. of land in Kyngcswestone . . .

A1/49/14 [GC 3190; *duplicates* GC 3191 *and* GC 3192]   Tues. the feast of St. Martin,
                                                         22 Edw. III [11 Nov. 1348]
Thomas de Besforde, parson of Beverston, Roger de Estham and John le Vey clerk; and Thomas son of Maurice de Berk', Katherine his wife and Thomas their son.

Thomas, Roger and John have confirmed to Thomas, Katherine and Thomas the reversion of the manor of Kyngeswestone, which William de Syde holds of them for his life; to them and the male issue of Thomas the younger, with remainder to the male issue of Thomas and Katherine, Alphonse de Berkelee and his male issue, and Thomas's right heirs.

Witnesses: William de Syde, William de Chiltenham, John de Clyve, John le Serjaunt the younger, William Curteys.

At: Beverston.

OTHER INTERESTS

A1/49/15 [GC 1592]   n.d. [1230 × 1270]
Nicholas de Wyke and Thomas son of Richard de Boreford.

Nicholas has granted to Thomas all his land in la Nuelonde in the vill of Kyngesweston, beside the land of Sir Robert Gurnay and between Smethemerise and le Merediche; rent 6*d.* a year, and Thomas has given him 2 marks and 10*s.*

Witnesses: William de Veyin, John Saltmarsh ([*de*] *salso marisco*), Peter Croc, Adam de Thridelonde,[1] Henry de Werkebur', William Savage, Roger le Botiller, Robert Jurdan.

WOTTON-UNDER-EDGE BOROUGH

The borough was created in 1253 by Joan Lady Berkeley, who held the manor in dower as widow of Thomas (I) Lord Berkeley (d. 1243). Thenceforth a distinction was made between Wotton *Intrinseca*, the borough, and Wotton *Forinseca*, the manor.

BERKELEY ACQUISITIONS
The Sone burgage

A1/50/1 [GC 849]   n.d. [late 13th cent.]
Edith widow of William le Sone and Richard Wocok.

Edith has granted to Richard her burgage in the town of Wotton, and he has given her 60*s.*

Witnesses: Henry the baker (*pistor*), Alexander le Hore, Richard the skinner (*pellipar'*), Adam the dyer (*tinctor*), Simon the weaver (*textor*), Hugh Forestar, William Wither.

A1/50/2 [GC 844]   n.d. [late 13th cent.]
Richard Wokoc and Sir Thomas de Berkel', his lord.

Richard has quitclaimed to Thomas, for a certain sum of money, his burgage which he had by grant of Edith widow of William le Sone, in the vill of Wotton.

---

[1] The initial character of 'Thridelonde' is written as the runic letter wen.

Witnesses: Walter de Chaldefeld, Thomas de Lude, Henry the baker (*pistor*), Alexander le Hore, Richard the skinner (*pellipar'*), Geoffrey the baker, Simon the weaver (*textor'*).

Noblepas rents in Wotton and Acton

A1/50/3 [GC 942]   n.d. [*c.* April 1311]
Richard Noblepas of Berkeley and Sir Maurice de Berkel'.

Richard has granted to Maurice, for a certain sum of money, a rent of 2*s.* . . . for a messuage and croft at Egeton in the manor of . . . [Hinton]; also a rent of 1*d.* in Wotton from Richard son of Henry the baker (*pistor*) . . .
Witnesses: . . . de Berkel, Thomas de Beoleye, Thomas de Lude, Robert de la Churche, Maurice de . . . , Warin son of . . .

A1/50/4 [GC 1815]   2 April 4 Edw. II [1311]
Richard Noblepas and Richard son of Henry the baker (*pistor*) of Wotton.

Richard Noblepas notifies Richard son of Henry of his grant to Sir Maurice de Berkel' of the rent of 1*d.* from the messuage in which John de la Fermerie lives.
At: Wotton.

Rolves rents in Wotton and Billow (in Cam)

A1/50/5 [GC 2130]   Tues. the feast of St. Clement, 10 Edw. II [23 Nov. 1316]
Philip Rolves of Wotton and Sir Thomas de Berkeleye, lord of Berkeley.

Philip has granted to Thomas an annual rent of 18*d.* from William Wyther for the holding between the holding of the lord of Wottone and the holding of Lucy Rolves, in the borough of Wottone.
Witnesses: William de Colewych, Walter Sewaker, Roger Archer, Maurice de Chapstowe, Thomas Brounyng.
At: Wotton.

A1/50/6 [GC 2236]   Mon. the morrow of St. George, 11 Edw. II [24 April 1318]
Thomas de Berkeley, lord of Berkeley, and Maurice de Berkeley, son of Maurice, his [Thomas's] son.

Thomas has granted to Maurice a rent of 9*s.* a year in Beoleye within the manor of Camme, which he acquired from Thomas de Beoleye from all his lands and holdings in the same place, and a rent of 12*d.* a year acquired from Philip Rolves in the borough of Wotthone; to him and his male issue.
Witnesses: Thomas de Bradeston, Peter de Stintescombe, John de Coueleye, Robert le Wariner, Stephen de Draycote.
At: Berkeley.

Acquisitions by William de Syde and passage to Thomas (III) Lord Berkeley

Hawcroft rent and reversion in Wotton manor
A1/50/7 [GC 3308]   n.d. [mid 14th cent.]
Richard Henegge and Sir William de Syde.

Richard has granted to William an annual rent of 8*s.* from Richard le Smyth of Wottone sub Egge for a croft called Hawecroft between the land of the lord of Wottone and Hawe park, which Richard holds for his life in Wottone sub Egge, and the reversion of the croft after Richard's death.
Witnesses: John le Skey, Elias de Berleye, John de Clyve, William Curteys, Geoffrey Neel.

A1/50/8 [GC 3292]   n.d. [mid 14th cent.]
Elias son of William de Combe the elder and Sir William de Syde.

Elias has quitclaimed to William a rent of 8*s.* from the croft called Hawecroft which Richard le Smyth holds for life in Wottone sub Egge, and also for the reversion of the croft.

Witnesses: John de Clyve, Elias de Berleye, William Curteys, Geoffrey Neel, Robert Groundi.

A1/50/9 [GC 2589]   n.d. [mid 14th cent.]
John son of William de Combe the younger and Sir William de Syde.

John has quitclaimed to William a rent of 8*s.* a year from a croft called Hawecroft which Richard le Smyth holds for life in Wotton sub Egge, and the reversion of the holding.
Witnesses: John de Clyve, Elias de Berleye, William Curteys, Geoffrey Neel, Robert Groundi.

Two parts of the Chepstow burgage in Wotton borough
A1/50/10 [GC 2588]   n.d. [mid 14th cent.]
Leticia widow of Maurice de Chapstowe of Wotton and Sir William de Syde.

Leticia has granted to William, his heirs and assigns, for a certain sum of money, two thirds of a burgage in Wottone beside the high street.
Witnesses: Elias de Berleye, William Curteys, Geoffrey Neel, Adam de Colewych, William le Weose.

A1/50/11 [GC 3079]   Thurs. the feast of St. Edmund the king, 17 Edw. III [20 Nov. 1343]
(1) William de Syde; (2) Roger de Estham and Roger le Duynyssch; (3) Leticia widow of Maurice de Chepstowe.

William has appointed Roger and Roger his attorneys to receive seisin of two thirds of a burgage which Leticia granted to him in Wottone.
At: Berkeley.

A1/50/12 [GC 3185]   Wed. after Michaelmas, 22 Edw. III [1 Oct. 1348]
Robert Waleys and Sir William de Syde.

Robert has quitclaimed to William all the lands and holdings formerly of Maurice de Shepstowe and Leticia his wife in Wottone.
Witnesses: William Curteys, Geoffrey Neel, Adam Colewych, Robert le Fysshare, William Smalcombe.
At: Wotton.

Scholar rent and reversion in Nibley
A1/50/13 [GC 2988]   Thurs. in Easter week, 15 Edw. III [12 April 1341]
Roger le Duynisshe of Nibley and Sir William de Syde.

Roger has granted to William, his heirs and assigns a rent of 2*s.* a year from Richard Scholar of Nubbelegh, for 2½ a. of land which Richard holds for life in Nubbel', with the reversion of the land.
Witnesses: John de Milkesham, John Skay, William Curteys, William de Romesbur', Geoffrey Neel.
At: Nibley.

Grant to Thomas (III) Lord Berkeley
A1/50/14 [GC 3196]   Sun. the feast of St. Andrew, 22 Edw. III [30 Nov. 1348]
William de Syde and Sir Thomas lord of Berkelee, his lord.

William has granted to Thomas, his heirs and assigns all the land which Richard le Smyth held of William for his life in Wottone, the holding which William had by grant of Leticia de Chepstowe in the same vill, a rent of 2*s.* a year from 2½ a. of land which Juliana Scolar holds for her life at Horende in Nubbeleye and the reversion of the land, and a rent of 3*s.* a year from Robert Luteman for the land which he holds of William in fee in Nubbeleye.

Witnesses: Sir Simon Basset, knight, William de Chyltenham, John de Clyve, William Curteis, Robert Groundy.
At: Wotton.

A1/50/15 [GC 3197]   Sun. the feast of St. Andrew, 22 Edw. III [30 Nov. 1348]
(1) William de Syde; (2) John de Eggesworthe chaplain; (3) Sir Thomas lord of Berkelee, William's lord.

William has appointed John to deliver seisin to Thomas of all the lands and holdings which Thomas had by grant of William in Wottone and Nubbeleye.
At: Wotton.

The Sheppard holding

A1/50/16 [GC 2829]   Fri. in Michaelmas, 9 Edw. III [29 Sept. 1335]
Alice widow of Walter le Scepehurde of Wotton and Adam Colewyth.

Alice has granted to Adam, his heirs and assigns the holding which was left to her by Walter in the town of Wotton market (*mercatoria*).
Witnesses: Thomas Brounyng, John le Hore, William de Renesburi, William the marshal (*marescallus*), William Picard.
At: Wotton.

A1/50/17 [GC 3539]   2 April 37 Edw. III [1363]
Katherine de Berkeleye, lady of Wotton, William Smalcombe, William de Aldryntone, John Welles and Robert Thomas of Wotton; and Adam Colewych and Juliana his wife.

Katherine and the others have leased to Adam and Juliana their holding in Wottone formerly of Alice widow of Walter Schepherde, which they had by Adam's grant; for the lives of Adam and Juliana, rent a red rose a year.
Witnesses: Elias de Berleye, Adam Legat, John Daunt, William Phyppes, Walter Glovere.
At: Wotton.

The Welles holding in Sone Lane

A1/50/18 [GC 3728]   6 April 2 Ric. II [1379]
John Welles of Wotton; and William Smalcombe and Ralph Coke.

John has granted to William and Ralph, and their heirs and assigns, the holding with a curtilage and other appurtenances, between the holding in which Nicholas Locare lives and the lane called Sonelane, and a rent of 13s. 4d. from the holding held by the said Nicholas and his wife for their lives, opposite the Lower Cross, and the reversion of the holding.
Witnesses: Adam Legat, William Fisschere, John Whitsire, Roger Pyngul, Alexander Heore.
At: Wotton.

A1/50/19 [GC 3745; *duplicate* GC 3746]   11 Sept. 5 Ric. II [1381]
William Smalcombe and Ralph Coke; and Joan wife of John de Bristewe and Thomas her son.

William and Ralph have leased to Joan and Thomas the holding with a curtilage in Wottone subtus Egge between the holding in which Nicholas Lokare lives and the lane called Sonelane, and a rent of 13s. 4d. from the holding which the said Nicholas and Joan his wife hold for their lives opposite the Lower Cross, with the reversion of the holding; for the lives of Joan and Thomas, rent a rose a year, with remainder after their deaths to Sir Thomas lord of Berkeley and his heirs and assigns.
Witnesses: William Fisshere, Roger Pingul, John Whitesire, Nicholas Wynegod, John Staverton.
At: Wotton.

A1/50/20 [GC 3937]   Mon. after Christmas, 21 Ric. II [31 Dec. 1397]
John Lyncolne and Alice his wife; and Thomas Berkeleye, lord of Berkeley.

John and Alice have quitclaimed to Thomas a holding which Thomas recently acquired from John Welles, Alice's father, in Wotton undur Hegge.

Leggat holdings in Bradley Street

The Webb half-burgage

A1/50/21 [GC 1652]   4 Kal. of April 1 Edw. II [29 March 1308]
William le Webbe, son of Nicholas le Webbe of Oldbury, and Henry le Weose.

William has granted to Henry a half-burgage in the new town of Wottone, on the street to Bradeleye, to hold of the lord of the fee; Henry has given him 2½ marks.
Witnesses: Maurice Chepstowe, Walter le Chepmon, Walter Schail, Hugh le Wodeward, William Picard.
At: Wotton.

A1/50/22 [GC 570]   n.d. [1308 × 1322]
Henry le Weose and Matthew Latyn.

Henry, for a certain sum of money, has granted to Matthew a half-burgage between two holdings of the lord in Bradeleyestret in Wotton.
Witnesses: Maurice de Chepustowe, John le Hore, William Pycard, Thomas Brounyng, Walter le Chepmon.

A1/50/23 [GC 2383]   Sun. in Holy Trinity, 15 Edw. II [6 June 1322]
Matthew Latyn and Philip le Hunte.

Matthew has granted to Philip, his heirs and assigns a holding between two holdings of the lord in Bradeleyesstret in Wotone.
Witnesses: Maurice de Chappestowe, John le Hore, William Pycard, Thomas Bround, Walter le Chepmon.
At: Wotton.

A1/50/24 [GC 2391]   Sun. before St. Edmund the king, 16 Edw. II [14 Nov. 1322]
Philip le Hunte; and Matthew Latyn and Eleanor his wife.

Philip has granted to Matthew and Eleanor his holding between the holdings formerly of Sir Maurice de Berkeleye in Bradeleyesstret in Wottone; to them and their issue.
Witnesses: Maurice de Chepustowe, John le Hore, William Pykard, Walter le Chepmon, Thomas Brounyng.
At: Wotton.

A1/50/25 [GC 3119]   Sun. before Ascension, 19 Edw. III [1 May 1345]
Eleanor widow of Matthew Latyn and John her son.

Eleanor has granted to John, his heirs and assigns her holding in Bradeleyestrete in the town of Wottone.
Witnesses: William de Henlond, William Tannare, Adam Colewich, William Marchal.
At: Wotton.

A1/50/26 [GC 3150]   St. Luke, 20 Edw. III [18 Oct. 1346]
John son of the late Macy [*sic*] Latyn and Alice Macy [*sic*] his sister.

John has granted to Alice half of the half-burgage which he had by grant of Eleanor his mother in Bradeleyestrete in the borough of Wottone.
Witnesses: William de Henlond, Robert Fisschare, Geoffrey Neel, William Tannare, Thomas Badecoke.
At: Wotton.

A1/50/27 [GC 3151]   St. Luke, 20 Edw. III [18 Oct. 1346]
John son of the late Macy [*sic*] Latyn and Juliana his sister.

John has granted to Juliana half of the half-burgage which he had by grant of Eleanor his
mother in Bradeleyestrete in the borough of Wottone.
Witnesses: William de Henlond, Robert Fisschare, Geoffrey Neel, William Tannare,
Thomas Badecoke.
At: Wotton.

A1/50/28 [GC 3397]   Wed. in the decollation of St. John the Baptist, 26 Edw. III
                                                                      [29 Aug. 1352]
Juliana Macy and Alice Macy her sister, daughters of the late Matthew Latyn; and Adam
Legat and Margery his wife.

Juliana and Alice have granted to Adam and Margery, and Adam's heirs and assigns, their
half-burgage in Bradeleyestrete.
Witnesses: Geoffrey Neel, Robert le Fysshere, William Heynes, William Phippes, Thomas
Matheu.
At: Wotton.

The Hall (*later Fox*) *holding*

A1/50/29 [GC 2382]   Sun. before St. Aldhelm, 15 Edw. II [23 May 1322]
Henry Legat and Walter ate Halle of Cromhall.

Henry has granted to Walter, his heirs and assigns, for a certain sum of money, his
holding in the town of Wottone in the street to Bradeleye, between the holdings of Sir
William de Wautone and the lord of Wottone.
Witnesses: Maurice de Chapstowe, John le Hore, William Pykard, Thomas Brounyng,
Thomas Badecok.
At: Wotton.

A1/50/30 [GC 2428]   Sun. after St. Bartholomew, 18 Edw. II [26 Aug. 1324]
Walter ate Halle of Cromhall; and John le Vox and Joan his wife.

Walter has leased to John and Joan his holding in Wottone containing four burgages in
Bradeleyestret in the south part; to hold, with the houses, curtilages, enclosures, lands,
hedges and ditches, for their lives, rent 6*s.* a year.
Witnesses: Maurice de Chapstowe, Thomas Brounyng, John le Hore, James the miller
(*molendinar'*), William Mareschal, Thomas Badecok, Walter de Hareford.
At: Wotton.

A1/50/31 [GC 2898]   Thurs. . . . Mary, 12 Edw. III [26 March 1338]
Alice atte Halle, widow of Walter atte Halle of . . . , and Adam Legat son of Henry Legat of
Wotton.

Alice has granted to Adam an annual rent of 18*d.* from Alice's holding in Bradeleyestret,
with the reversion of the holding after the deaths of John le Fox and Joan his wife.
Witnesses: William de Romesbury, . . . lpride, . . . , Adam Colewych, Thomas Badecok,
Richard le Webbe.
At: Wotton.

A1/50/32 [GC 2899]   Fri. after the Annunciation, 12 Edw. III [27 March 1338]
Alice atte Halle, widow of Walter atte Halle of Cromhall, and Adam Legat son of Henry
Legat of Wotton.

Alice has quitclaimed to Adam the holding in Wottone in Bradeleyestret.

Witnesses: William de Romesbury, Geoffrey Neel, Thomas le Deyare, Thomas Matheu, Adam Colewych, Thomas Badecok, Richard le Webbe.
At: Wotton.

A1/50/33 [GC 2901]   Mon. after St. Mark, 12 Edw. III [27 April 1338]
John le Fox and Joan his wife; and Adam Legat son of Henry Legat of Wotton.

John and Joan have quitclaimed to Adam the holding with a curtilage and croft in Bradeleyestret.
Witnesses: William Curteys, William de Romesbury, Thomas le Deyare, William de Henlond, Thomas Matheu, William Pycard, Thomas Badecoke.
At: Wotton.

A1/50/34 [GC 3020]   Sun. the morrow of St. Laurence, 16 Edw. III [11 Aug. 1342]
John le Fox of Wotton and Adam Legat of Wotton.

John has granted to Adam, his heirs and assigns his messuage in Wottone in Bradeleyestret, beside the holding formerly of Sir William de Wauton, knight, with the curtilage and croft.
Witnesses: William de Romesbury, Adam Colewyth, Robert le Fysshere, William Henlond, Thomas Matheu.
At: Wotton.

A1/50/35 [GC 3138]   Sun. after the Annunciation, 20 Edw. III [26 March 1346]
Alice atte Halle, widow of Walter atte Halle of Cromhall, and Adam Legat of Wotton.

Alice has quitclaimed to Adam her dower rights in the holding in the town of Wottone, which was of Walter in Bradeleyestret.
Witnesses: Adam Colewych, William Smalcombe, Robert le Fysshere, Thomas le Deyare, Thomas Matheu.
At: Wotton.

   The Brown holding
A1/50/36 [GC 3022]   Thurs. before Michaelmas, 16 Edw. III [26 Sept. 1342]
John Broun of Wotton and Adam Legat son of Henry Legat of Wotton.

John has granted to Adam his holding with a croft in Wottone in Bradeleyestret.
Witnesses: William de Romesbury, William Henlond, Thomas le Deyar, Thomas Matheu, Roger Pent'.
At: Wotton.

A1/50/37 [GC 3021]   Tues. after Michaelmas, 16 Edw. III [1 Oct. 1342]
John Broun of Wotton and Adam Legat son of Henry Legat of Wotton.

John has quitclaimed to Adam his holding with a croft in Bradeleyestret.
Witnesses: William de Romesburgh, William Henlond, Thomas le Deyar, Thomas Matheu, Roger Pent'.
At: Wotton.

A1/50/38 [GC 3140]   Fri. the morrow of St. Peter and St. Paul, 20 Edw. III [30 June 1346]
Maud widow of John Broun and Adam Legat of Wotton.

Maud has quitclaimed to Adam the holding late of John in Bradeleyestret.
Witnesses: Geoffrey Neel, William Smalcombe, Adam Colewych, William le Weose, Thomas Matheu.
At: Wotton.

The Wyther holding
A1/50/39 [GC 3583]   18 July 40 Edw. III [1366]
Alice widow of Henry Wyther of Wotton and William Gayner of the same, executors of
Henry; and Adam Legat and Margery his wife.
    Alice and William have granted to Adam and Margery, and Adam's heirs and assigns, a
holding with a curtilage and croft in Bradeleystret of Wottone.
Witnesses: Elias de Berleye, William Smalcombe, William Phippes, Robert Thomas,
William le Fysshare.
At: Wotton.

A1/50/40 [GC 3584]   31 July 40 Edw. III [1366]
John Wyther, son and heir of Henry Wyther of Wotton; and Adam Legat and Margery his wife.
    John has quitclaimed to Adam and Margery a holding with a curtilage and croft in
Bradeleystret of Wottone.
Witnesses: Elias de Berleye, William Smalcombe, William Phippes, Robert Thomas,
William le Fysshare.
At: Wotton.

Other
A1/50/41 [GC 3024]   Fri. before Michaelmas, 16 Edw. III [27 Sept. 1342]
Thomas Badecoke and Adam Legat of Wotton.
    Thomas has granted to Adam, his heirs and assigns a messuage with a curtilage in
Bradeleyestret; rent to the chief lord 4*d.* a year.
Witnesses: William de Romesbury, Adam Colewych, Thomas Matheu, William Henlond,
Thomas le Deyare.
At: Wotton.

A1/50/42 [GC 3023]   Fri. after Michaelmas, 16 Edw. III [4 Oct. 1342]
William de Romesbury and Joan his wife; and Adam Legat of Wotton.
    William and Joan have quitclaimed to Adam a cottage with a curtilage and croft, which
Joan held in dower after the death of Walter le Chapman, late her husband.
Witnesses: Adam Colewych, Thomas Deyar, Thomas Matheu, William Henlond.
At: Wotton.

A1/50/43 [GC 3131]   Sun. after St. Valentine, 20 Edw. III [19 Feb. 1346]
William Smalcombe of Wotton and Adam Legat of the same.
    William has granted to Adam, his heirs and assigns his messuage in Bradeleyestret.
Witnesses: Adam Colewych, Robert le Fysshere, Thomas Matheu, Thomas le Deyare,
William le Weose.
At: Wotton.

A1/50/44 [GC 3146]   Tues. in the Exaltation of Holy Cross, 23 Edw. III[1] [15 Sept. 1349]
Agnes Curteys, widow and executor of William Curteys; and Adam Legat of Wotton and
Margery his wife.
    Agnes has granted to Adam and Margery, and Adam's heirs and assigns, her holding in
Bradeleyestret with a curtilage and croft.
Witnesses: Geoffrey Neel, Robert le Fysshere, William Phippes, Thomas Matheu, Roger Pent'.
At: Wotton.

A1/50/45 [GC 3383]   Sun. before the Annunciation, 26 Edw. III [18 March 1352]
Agnes Curteys, executor of William Curteys her husband; and Adam Legat of Wotton and
Margery his wife.

---

[1] The feast of the Exaltation of Holy Cross, 14 Sept., fell on Monday in 1349.

Agnes has granted to Adam and Margery her messuage in Wottone in Bradeleyestret, with free access to the water-pit to draw water.

Witnesses: Robert le Fysshere, Adam Colewych, William Heynes, William Phippes, Thomas Matheu.

At: Wotton.

A1/50/46 [GC 3455]   Thurs. the feast of the conception of St. Mary, 30 Edw. III
[8 Dec. 1356]

Thomas Daunt of Wotton; and Adam Legat of the same and Margery his wife.

Thomas has granted to Adam and Margery, and Adam's heirs and assigns, his holding in Wottone in Bradeleystret.

Witnesses: Adam Colwych, William Heynes, Walter Glovare, William Aldrynton, Thomas Mathu.

At: Wotton.

A1/50/47 [GC 3634]   Sun. in the Exaltation of Holy Cross, 45 Edw. III [14 Sept. 1371]

William le Tannere; and Adam Legat and Margery his wife.

William has granted to Adam and Margery, and Adam's heirs and assigns, his half-burgage in the vill of Wottone in Bradeleystret, with the croft and all other liberties.

Witnesses: William Smalcombe, William Henyes, William Fysshere, Thomas Daunt, John Whitsire.

At: Wotton.

Leases by the Leggats

A1/50/48 [GC 3364]   Fri. the feast of St. John before the Latin Gate, 25 Edw. III
[6 May 1351]

Adam Legat of Wotton; and John Cole, Alice his wife and Walter their son.

Adam has leased to John, Alice and Walter his messuage in Bradeleyestrete; for their lives, rent 3*s*. a year, and they will maintain the walls and roof in their present state.

Witnesses: Geoffrey Neel, Walter le Glovere, Robert le Fysshere, William Heynes, Thomas Matheu.

At: Wotton.

A1/50/49 [GC 3469]   Palm Sunday, 32 Edw. III [25 March 1358]

Adam Legat of Wotton and Richard le Rous.

Adam has leased to Richard a messuage in Bradeleyestret; for his life, rent 2*s*. a year.

Witnesses: Geoffrey Neel, William Phippes, Walter le Glovere, Roger Pent, John Cole.

At: Wotton.

A1/50/50 [GC 2581]   n.d. [mid 14th cent.]

Thomas lord of Berkeleye; and Adam Legat and Margery his wife.

Thomas has granted to Adam and Margery two half-burgages in Bradeleyestret in Wottone, formerly held by Thomas le Rous and Denise Davy; for their lives, rent a rose a year.

Witnesses: Robert le Fyssher, Walter le Glovare, William Heynes, William Phippes.

Passage to Berkeley

A1/50/51 [GC 3767]   Thurs. before the conversion of St. Paul, 8 Ric. II [19 Jan. 1385]

Hugh de Byseleye, cousin and heir of Margery Legat, and William atte Nasshe; and Ralph Coke and John Wyntur.

Hugh and William, executors of Margery, have granted to Ralph and John, and their heirs and assigns, all the lands and holdings which were of Adam Legat and Margery his wife in Wottone, in Bradeleiestret.

Witnesses: William Smalcombe, Nicholas Lokere, Roger Pyngul, Richard Panter, John Heynes.
At: Wotton.

A1/50/52 [GC 3783]   Sat. before the conversion of St. Paul, 8 Ric. II [21 Jan. 1385]
Hugh de Byseleye, cousin and heir of Margery Legat, and William atte Nasshe; and Ralph Coke and John Wyntur.

Hugh and William, executors of Margery, have granted to Ralph and John all their right and claim to all the lands and holdings which were of Adam Legat and Margery his wife in Wotton, in the street called Bradeleyestret.
Witnesses: William Smalcombe, Nicholas Lokere, Roger Pyngul, Richard Panter, John Heynes.
At: Wotton.

A1/50/53 [GC 3814]   Mon. after Epiphany, 10 Ric. II [7 Jan. 1387]
Thomas lord of Berkeleye and Richard Panyter.

Thomas has leased to Richard, for his good and laudable service in the past and future, the holding with an enclosure and cottages in Wottone Underegge, in Bradeleyesstrete, which he lately acquired from Hugh de [Byselegh] and William atte Nassche, executors of Margery Legat; for life, rent a rose a year.
At: Wotton.

The Phipps holding in the high street
A1/50/54 [GC 3855]   Wed. after the decollation of St. John the Baptist, 15 Ric. II
[30 Aug. 1391]
John Whitsyre and William atte Nasche; and John vicar of Cam, John Cley, William Sowhy chaplain and Ralph Coke.

John and William have granted to John, John, William and Ralph, and their heirs and assigns, a holding which was of Edith Phippus opposite le Chepynglane in the borough of Wottone Underegge.
Witnesses: William Smalcombe, Thomas Skay, Laurence Jewet, Richard Panyter, John Heignus.
At: Wotton.

A1/50/55 [GC 3857]   Thurs. after St. Denis, 15 Ric. II [12 Oct. 1391]
Thomas de Berkeley, lord of Berkeley; and Simon Daunt, Juliana his wife and John their son.

Thomas has leased to Simon, Juliana and John a holding with a garden in the borough of Wotton Underegge, which was sometime of Edith Fippus opposite le Chepynglane; for their lives, rent 12*s.* 10*d.* a year.
Witnesses: John Whitsyre, Alexander Hore, Richard Panyter, Roger Pyngul, William atte Nasche.
At: Wotton.

A1/50/56 [GC 3972]   24 Feb. 1 Hen. IV [1400]
Thomas Berkeley, lord of Berkeley; and Robert Horblyng, barber, Thomas's servant, and Alice his wife.

Thomas has leased to Robert and Alice, for Robert's good and laudable service, the new building in the town of Wottone under Egge with four cottages and curtilages in the land called Chepynglane and rents of 12*s.* 10*d.* a year from the holding which Simon Daunt and Juliana his wife hold for their lives in the high street of Wottone, opposite Chepynglane, and 12*s.* 4*d.* from Robert Bailly and Joan his wife, with the reversion of the holdings, and other things; for their lives, for the customary services.
At: Wotton.

The shop called Copt Hall and a burgage in the high street

A1/50/57 [GC 3527]   Mon. after St. Matthew, 35 Edw. III [27 Sept. 1361]
Maud Amy, widow of Roger Amy of Wotton; and Reginald de Castre, tailor, and Alice his wife.

Maud has granted to Reginald and Alice, and Reginald's heirs and assigns, a shop called Coppedehalle in the vill of Wottone, with free access to the water-pit to draw water.
Witnesses: Adam Legat, William Smalcombe, Walter le Glovere, William Phyppes, William Heynes.
At: Wotton.

A1/50/58 [GC 3616]   15 April 44 Edw. III [1370]
Alice Brounyng of Wotton, widow of Reginald le Frensshe, and John Welles of the same.

Alice has leased to John a shop called Coppudhalle in the vill of Wottone; for her life, rent a rose a year.
Witnesses: Adam Legat, William Smalcombe, Walter le Glovere, William Phippes, William Heynes.
At: Wotton.

A1/50/59 [GC 3623]   Thurs. before St. Peter in chains, 44 Edw. III [25 July 1370]
Thomas son and heir of the late Reginald le Frensshe and John Welles of Wotton.

Thomas has quitclaimed to John the shop called Coppudhalle in the town of Wottone subtus Egge.
Witnesses: Adam Legat, William Smalcombe, Walter le Glovere, William Phippes, William Heynes.
At: Wotton.

A1/50/60 [GC 3638]   Mon. after St. Ambrose, 46 Edw. III [5 April 1372]
John Welles and Robert Thomas of Wotton.

John has quitclaimed to Robert the shop called Coppedhalle in the town of Wottone subtus Egge.
Witnesses: Adam Legat, William Smalcombe, William Fischere, Walter Glovere, William Phippes, William Heynes.
At: Wotton.

A1/50/61 [GC 3950]   20 Feb. 22 Ric. II [1399]
Thomas Berkeley, lord of Berkeley; and John atte Worthe and Isabel his wife.

Thomas has granted to John and Isabel, and their heirs and assigns, a burgage in the town of Wottone in the high street, by le Nethercrosse, in exchange for a shop called le Coppithall by Chepynglane.
Witnesses: William Smalcombe, Laurence Berley, Richard Panter, Richard Sprynget, Thomas . . . , Simon Daunt.
At: Wotton.

A1/50/62 [GC 4014]   15 . . . , 7 Hen. IV [1405–6]
Thomas Bakere and Alice his wife of Wotton; and Thomas Berkeley, lord of Berkeley.

Thomas and Alice have granted to Thomas, his heirs and assigns a burgage in the vill of Wottone, which they had by grant of Isabel atte Worthe, widow of John atte Worthe, in the high street of the vill, by Nethercrosse.
Witnesses: Simon Daunt, John . . . , . . . atte Nasche, John Sprynget, Thomas Chamberleyn.
At: Wotton.

The Marshall holding by the Upper Cross

A1/50/63 [GC 3005]   Sun. one week after St. Martin, 15 Edw. III [18 Nov. 1341]
William le Marescal of Wotton and John his son.

William has granted to John, his heirs and assigns his holding in the vill of Wottone by the Upper Cross.

Witnesses: William de Remesburi, Walter le Glovare, William Smalecumbe, Thomas Matheu, John Pinnoc.

At: Wotton.

A1/50/64 [GC 3620]   Fri. the eve of St. Margaret the virgin, 44 Edw. III [12 July 1370]
John le Mareschal, son and heir of John le Mareschal of Wotton, and Reginald Davy of the same.

John has granted to Reginald his corner holding in the town of Wottone opposite the Upper Cross beside the lane leading to le Oldeton, and an annual rent of *6d.* from the curtilage which William Phippes and his wife Edith hold for the life of Edith, with the reversion of the holding.

Witnesses: Adam Legat, William Smalcombe, William Fysshere, Robert Thomas, William Heynes.

At: Wotton.

A1/50/65 [GC 3621]   Tues. after St. Mary Magdalen, 44 Edw. III [23 July 1370]
Richard Porter, parson of Castle Eaton (*Eton*), and William Wattes of Cricklade; and Reginald Davy of Wotton.

Richard and William have quitclaimed to Reginald all the holding with rents and reversions which were of John son and heir of John le Mareschal in the borough town of Wottone.

Witnesses: Adam Legat, William Smalcombe, William Fysshere, Robert Thomas, John Whitsire.

At: Wotton.

A1/50/66 [GC 3629]   18 Jan. 44 Edw. III [1371]
John Mareschal, son and heir of the late John Mareschal of Wotton, and Reginald Davy.

John has quitclaimed to Reginald the holding in the borough town of Wottone opposite the Upper Cross beside the road to Heorteworth.

Witnesses: Adam Legat, William Smalcombe, William Fysshere, Robert Thomas, John Whitsire.

At: Wotton.

A1/50/67 [GC 3781]   3 Sept. 7 Ric. II [1383]
John Davy, son and heir of Reginald Davy of Wotton, and Roger Pyngul of the same.

John has granted to Roger, his heirs and assigns his corner holding in the town of Wottone opposite the Upper Cross between the lane to Oldetone and the holding which Henry Torteworthe and Alice his wife hold as Alice's dower, and also an annual rent of *6d.* from the curtilage which Edith Phippes holds for life and an annual rent of *4d.* from the curtilage which Alice wife of Henry Torteworthe holds for life, with the reversion of the holdings.

Witnesses: William Smalcombe, John Whitesire, William Heynes, Richard Spryngot, John Staverton.

At: Wotton.

A1/50/68 [GC 3763]   20 Sept. 7 Ric. II [1383]
John Davy, son and heir of Reginald Davy, and Roger Pyngul of Wotton.

John has granted and quitclaimed to Roger, his heirs and assigns his claim to a corner holding in the town of Wotton opposite the Upper Cross, a curtilage, an annual rent of *6d.* from the curtilage which Edith Phippes holds for her life and an annual rent of *4d.* from a curtilage which Alice wife of Henry Torteworthe holds for her life.

Witnesses: William Smalcombe, William Heygnes, John Whitesire, Richard Spryngot, John Staverton.
At: Wotton.

A1/50/69 [GC 3848]   10 April 14 Ric. II [1391]
Roger Pyngul of Wotton; and Thomas Laurence and John Taillour of Iron Acton.

Roger has granted to Thomas and John his corner holding in Wottone opposite the Upper Cross, with a long house situated beside the curtilage of Margaret Davy, and a curtilage adjacent and a latrine (*latrina*) at the end of the curtilage, and also an annual rent of 6*d.* from a cottage which Margaret Davy holds in fee.
Witnesses: John Whitesire, Richard Panter, Richard Spryngot, Thomas Bradeford, John Heignes.
At: Wotton.

A1/50/70 [GC 3850]   28 May 14 Ric. II [1391]
Thomas Laurence of Iron Acton and John Taillour of the same; and Roger Pyngul of Wotton and Eleanor his wife.

Thomas and John have granted to Roger and Eleanor their corner holding [etc., as in A1/50/69, GC3848], to them and their issue, and if they die without issue then the holdings are to be sold for their souls and distributed to pious uses.
Witnesses: John Whitesire, Richard Panter, Richard Spryngot, Thomas Bradeforde, John Heignes.
At: Wotton.

A1/50/71 [GC 3933]   Thurs. in the Exaltation of Holy Cross, 21 Ric. II[1] [13 Sept. 1397]
Roger Pyngul of Wotton; and Simon Daunt of the same and Juliana Daunt his wife.

Roger has leased to Simon and Juliana a parcel of a certain curtilage which Edith Phippes sometime held of Roger; for their lives, rent 6*d.* a year.
Witnesses: Richard Panyter, John Thresshere, John Stavertone, Thomas Bradeforde, Thomas Hulle.
At: Wotton.

A1/50/72 [GC 4020]   22 May 8 Hen. IV [1407]
Edith Pyngul, widow of Roger Pyngul of Wotton, and John Pyngul, Roger's son; and Thomas Bruge, John Wythyndon and Thomas Heyward, clerks.

Edith and John, executors of Roger Pyngul, have granted to Thomas, John and Thomas, and their heirs and assigns, the corner holding in the borough town of Wottone opposite the Upper Cross, beside the lane to Herteswerthe, and also a barn and two holdings beside the said house and a rent of 6*d.* a year, and other things.
Witnesses: Laurence Juwet, Thomas Bradeford, Thomas Chaumburleyn, John Springot, John Whytemor, Simon Daunt, Richard Purchas.
At: Wotton.

A1/50/73 [GC 4023]   Wed. before the Annunciation, 9 Hen. IV [21 March 1408]
Thomas Berkeley, lord of Berkeley; and Robert Purchas and Joan his wife.

Thomas has granted to Robert and Joan a burgage in Wottone, except two cottages in which Richard Brut and John Hunte live, and a rent of 6*d.* from a garden which Simon Daunt and Juliana his wife hold for life, which he had by grant of Edith Pyngul and John Pyngul, executors of Roger Pyngul; for their lives, rent 13*s.* 4*d.* a year.
Witnesses: Laurence Juet, John Spryngot, Simon Daunt, William Sowey, John Pent.
At: Wotton.

---

[1] The feast of the Exaltation of Holy Cross, 14 Sept., fell on Friday in 1397.

House in Church Lane

A1/50/74 [GC 3420]   Fri. the feast of St. Stephen, 28 Edw. III [26 Dec. 1354]
William Sendy of Wotton and John Daunt of the same.

William has granted to John a house in the new town of the borough of Wottone, opposite the Lower Cross beside the road to the church.
Witnesses: Adam Legat, Geoffrey Nel, Robert Fysshare, William Phippus, Thomas Mathu.
At: Wotton.

A1/50/75 [GC 3421]   Mon. after Christmas, 28 Edw. III [29 Dec. 1354]
John Daunt of Wotton; and John le Reve of the same and Lucy his wife.

John Daunt has granted to John and Lucy a house in the new vill of the borough of Wottone, opposite the Lower Cross, beside the road to the church.
Witnesses: Adam Legat, Robert Fysshare, William Phippus, Thomas Mathu, William Heynes.
At: Wotton.

A1/50/76 [GC 3667]   Sun. after Michaelmas, 48 Edw. III [1 Oct. 1374]
Isabel le Reve, daughter and heir of John le Reve of Wotton; and John Dressour of the same and Edith his wife.

Isabel has granted to John and Edith a house in the new borough town of Wottone opposite the Lower Cross . . .
Witnesses: Adam Legat, William Smalcombe, William Fysschare, Robert Thomas, John Whitsyre.
At: Wotton.

A1/50/77 [GC 4024]   Maundy Thursday (*Cena domini*), 9 Hen. IV [12 April 1408]
Simon Daunt of Wotton and Juliana his wife and William Haukesbury and Margaret his wife; and Sir Thomas lord of Berkeley.

Simon, Juliana, William and Margaret have granted to Thomas a house in the new borough town of Wottone, opposite the Lower Cross beside Churchelane.
Witnesses: John Spryngot, Robert le Hore, John Pyngul, John le Hore, John Heynus.
At: Wotton.

Pent holdings in the high street and Bradley Street

A1/50/78 [GC 4026]   Mon. after the Assumption of St. Mary, 9 Hen. IV [20 Aug. 1408]
John Pent of Wotton and Thomas Berkeley, lord of Berkeley.

John has granted to Thomas, his heirs and assigns three holdings in Wottone of which two are in the high street and one in Bradeleyestret.
Witnesses: Laurence Juet, Simon Daunt, Richard Phelpus, Richard Colwyth, Robert Hore.
At: Wotton.

A1/50/79 [GC 4027]   Mon. before the nativity of St. Mary, 9 Hen. IV [3 Sept. 1408]
Thomas Berkeley, lord of Berkeley; and John Pent of Wotton and Joan his wife.

Thomas has granted to John and Joan three holdings in Wottone, two in the high street and one in Bradeleystret; for their lives, for the customary services.
Witnesses: Laurence Juet, Simon Daunt, Richard Phelpus, Richard Colwych, Robert Hore.
At: Wotton.

The Webb holding

A1/50/80 [GC 4035]   24 May 10 Hen. IV [1409]
Thomas Berkeley, lord of Berkeley, and John Webbe.

Thomas has granted to John, his heirs and assigns a holding in the borough of Wottone in which William Haukesbury lived, in exchange for a parcel of meadow beside the mill of Wottone.

Witnesses: Edmund Basset, Laurence Berle, Simon Daunt, Robert Hore, John Whitemore.
At: Wotton.

A1/50/81 [GC 4036]   24 May 10 Hen. IV [1409]
(1) Thomas Berkeley, lord of Berkeley; (2) John Whitemore; (3) John Webbe.

Thomas has appointed John Whitemore to deliver seisin to John Webbe of a holding in the borough of Wotton in which William Haukesbury lived.
At: Wotton.

A1/50/82 [GC 4037]   24 May 10 Hen. IV [1409]
John Webbe, and the nobleman Thomas Berkeley, lord of Berkeley.

John has granted to Thomas, his heirs and assigns a parcel of meadow beside the lord's mill at Wottone under Egge.
Witnesses: Edmund Basset, Laurence Berle, Simon Daunt, John Whitemore, Robert Hore.
At: Wotton.

A1/50/83 [GC 4136]   24 May 10 Hen. IV [1409]
Thomas Berkeley, lord of Berkeley, and John Whitemour.

Thomas has appointed John to receive seisin of a holding in . . . in the town of Wottone Underegge.
At: Wotton.

The Wyther holding

A1/50/84 [GC 3880]   Fri. after the Purification, 17 Ric. II [6 Feb. 1394]
Thomas Wyther, chaplain, son and heir of Henry Wyther of Wotton, and William Westerle.

Whereas Alice Wyther, widow of Henry, holds certain lands and holdings in the vill of Wottone Underegge for her life, of which the reversion belongs to Thomas, Thomas has granted to William, his heirs and assigns the reversion of the holding called Wytherholding.
Witnesses: John Pente, portreeve, John [Chapman], catchpoll, Richard Panter, Roger Pyngel, Simon Daunte, John Hayns, John Whiteschire.
At: Wotton.

A1/50/85 [GC 3881]   Fri. after the Purification, 17 Ric. II [6 Feb. 1394]
Thomas Wyther, chaplain, son and heir of Henry Wyther of Wotton, and John Crompe.

Whereas Alice Wyther, widow of Henry, holds certain lands and holdings in the vill of Wottone Underegge for her life, of which the reversion belongs to Thomas, Thomas has granted to John, his heirs and assigns the reversion of the holding called Wytherholding in the said town, after Alice's death.
Witnesses: John Pente, portreeve, John Chapman, catchpoll, Richard Panter, Roger Pyngel, Simon Daunt, John Hayns, John Whiteschire.
At: Wotton.

A1/50/86 [GC 3931]   Fri. after St. Peter, 21 Ric. II [3 Aug. 1397]
Elias Taylour of Tetbury and John Crompe of Wotton.

Elias has quitclaimed to John a holding in the new town of Wottone, which Alice Withur holds for life by grant of Henry Withur.
Witnesses: Laurence Juwet, Simon Daunt, John Stavertone, John Flourer of Woodford.
At: Wotton.

A1/50/87 [GC 4055]   Sun. after Christmas, 12 Hen. IV [28 Dec. 1410]
William Westerley, burgess of Bristol, and John Crompe of Wotton, his brother; and Thomas Berkeley, lord of Berkeley.

William and John have quitclaimed to Thomas all the lands and holdings in Wottone sub Egge which were of Thomas Wyther of Wotton.

Witnesses: Laurence Juwet, Simon Daunt, John Pent, John Hore, William Sowey.
At: Wotton.

Other

A1/50/88 [SC 460]   Gules of August, 26 Edw. I [1 Aug. 1298]
Richard de Wike and Denise his wife; and Lady Joan de Berkeley, wife of Thomas de
Berkeley.

Richard and Denise have granted to Joan, for 7 years, a burgage in Wottone; rent 12*d.* a
year. [*In French.*]
Witnesses: Robert de Stane, Robert de Bradestone, Richard de Byseleye, Robert Wyther,
John Champeneys, Henry de Ledebury, Alexander le Hore, Philip Draysyd, Richard le
Peleter.

A1/50/89 [GC 822]   n.d. [late 13th cent.]
William Springeld of Wotton and Sir Thomas de Berkel, lord of Berkeley.

William has granted to Thomas the messuage with the buildings on it which he bought
from Ralph Marescall in the borough of Wotton.
Witnesses: Peter de Styntescumbe, Richard de Byseleye, Robert de Ston', Walter de
Chaldefeld, Thomas de Lude, Henry the baker (*pistor*), Alexander le . . .

A1/50/90 [GC 1977]   20 May 8 Edw. II [1315]
Richard de Wyke and Sir Thomas de Berkeleye, lord of Berkeley.

Richard has granted to Thomas, his heirs and assigns his burgage in the borough of
Wottone which he previously had by grant of Margaret de Rachefort.
Witnesses: Maurice de Boeleye, Robert of the church (*de ecclesia*) of Nibley, John le Skey,
Maurice de Chepstowe, John le Hore, William Pycard, Walter le Chepmon.
At: Berkeley.

A1/50/91 [GC 3229]   Tues. after Holy Trinity, 23 Edw. III [9 June 1349]
Agnes Curteys, widow and executrix of William Curteys, and Sir Thomas lord of
Berkeley.

Agnes has quitclaimed to Thomas five holdings in Wottone which were William's.
Witnesses: Geoffrey Neel, Adam Legat, Robert le Fysshere, Adam Colewych, Thomas
Matheu.
At: Wotton.

A1/50/92 [GC 3537*]   Mon. before St. Simon and St. Jude, 36 Edw. III [24 Oct. 1362]
Henry Wythur of Wotton; and Sir Maurice de Berkele, lord of Berkeley, and Katherine de
Berkele, lady of Wotton.

Henry has quitclaimed to Maurice and Katherine, and Maurice's heirs, a half-burgage in
Wottone.
Witnesses: Elias de Berleye, John Draycote, Thomas Skay, Adam Legat, William Heynes.
At: Wotton.

LEASES AND ADMINISTRATIVE DOCUMENTS
Leases

A1/50/93 [GC 2580]   n.d. [mid 14th cent.]
Thomas lord of Berkelee; and John le Corrayour, Denise his wife and John their son.

Thomas has leased to John, Denise and John a messuage with a curtilage formerly of
Denise de Bathe; for their lives, rent 3*s.* a year.
Witnesses: Adam Legat, William Heynes, William Phipp, Thomas Mathun, John Daunt.

A1/50/94 [GC 3915]   Mon. before the Exaltation of Holy Cross, 20 Ric. II [11 Sept. 1396]
Thomas lord of Berkeley; and Richard Panter and Isabel his wife.

Thomas has leased to Richard and Isabel the holding in the borough of Wottone undur Egge opposite the Upper Cross; for their lives at the previous rent, but Thomas wills that they should be quit of the rent during Richard's life.

Witnesses: Roger Pyngull, Thomas Bradeford, Simon Daunt, John Pente, Thomas Chamburleyn.

At: Wotton.

A1/50/95 [GC 3919]   Mon. the feast of St. Gregory, 20 Ric. II [12 March 1397]
Thomas de Berkeleye, lord of Berkeley; and Simon Daunt, Juliana his wife and John their son.

Thomas has leased to Simon, Juliana and John a burgage with a curtilage in the town of Wottone under Egge; for their lives, rent 5*s.* a year.

Witnesses: William Smalcombe, Richard Panyter, Roger Pyngull, William atte Nasshe, Richard Spryngot.

At: Wotton.

A1/50/96 [GC 3924]   . . . Palm Sunday, 20 Ric. II [*c*. April 1397]
Thomas de Berkeleye, lord . . . ; and John Stephenes and Joan his wife.

Thomas . . . John and Joan the holding . . . ; for their lives, rent . . .

Witnesses: . . . [Roger] Pyngul, Richard Panyter, Simon Daunt, Walter . . . , John . . .

A1/50/97 [GC 3938]   Mon. after Relic Sunday, 21 Ric. II [9 July 1397]
Thomas Berkeleye, lord of Berkeley; and John Lyncolne and Alice his wife.

Thomas has leased to John and Alice a messuage with a curtilage in the town of . . . between the holdings of Nicholas Batyn and John Teynton; for their lives, rent 1*d.* a year.

Witnesses: William Smalkombe the elder, John Rowles, Laurence Jwet, Richard Panter, Roger Pyngul.

At: Wotton.

A1/50/98 [GC 3969]   Fri. after the conversion of St. Paul, 1 Hen. IV [30 Jan. 1400]
T[homas] de Berkeley; and Robert Loker and Joan his wife.

Thomas has leased to Robert and John . . . Wottone; . . . rent 13*s.* 4*d.* a year.

Witnesses: . . . William Nasshe, Thomas Chamberleyn, Thomas . . .

A1/50/99 [GC 3971]   28 Jan. 1 Hen. IV [1400]
Sir Thomas Berkeleye, lord of Berkeley; and John Whytemore, Alice his wife and John, Alice's son.

Thomas has leased to John, Alice and John, for the good service of John the elder, the new building at the marketplace gate, except one house for 'tolfelde', and a parcel of land in the croft of the said marketplace and a cottage with a curtilage which he acquired from Thomas Chaumburleyne in the street called Chepynglane, next to the said new building; for their lives, rent 12*d.* a year.

At: Berkeley.

A1/50/100 [GC 3991]   Morrow of St. Wulfstan, 3 Hen. IV [20 Jan. 1402]
Thomas Berkeley, lord of Berkeley; and Simon Daunt of Wotton and Juliana his wife.

Thomas has leased to Simon and Juliana a holding in Wottone which escheated to Thomas, between the holding called Proutyng and the highway by Skymeresput; for their lives, rent 4*s.* a year.

At: Wotton.

A1/50/101 [GC 3996]   Sun. after St. Gregory, 3 Hen. IV [19 March 1402]
Thomas Berkeley, lord of Berkeley; and John Chynham of Wotton and Joan his wife.

Thomas has leased to John and Joan, for good and laudable service, a messuage with a curtilage in Wotton in the street called Chepynglane; for their lives, at the customary rent.

Witnesses: William Smalcombe, Thomas Chamburleyn, John Pent, William Sowey, William atte Nasshe.
At: Wotton.

A1/50/102 [GC 4010]   Sun. after the Annunciation, 6 Hen. IV [29 March 1405]
Thomas Berkeley, lord of Berkeley; and John Spryngat, Margaret his wife and their first child.

   Thomas has leased to John and Margaret and their first child a burgage in Wottone which John Whytsyre previously held, and also 5 a. of land in Combysfeld and Bradeleyesfelde, which Walter Bakere and the said John Spryngat previously held; for their lives, rent 1*d.* a year.
Witnesses: Laurence Berley, Simon Daunt, Thomas Chamburleyn, William atte Nasshe, William Sowey.
At: Wotton.

A1/50/103 [GC 4025]   Thurs. before Easter, 9 Hen. IV [12 April 1408]
Thomas lord of Berkeley; and Simon Daunt and Juliana his wife.

   Thomas has granted to Simon and Juliana, and their heirs and assigns, the cottage with a curtilage between the holdings of John Hopere and the said lord; rent 1*d.* a year.
Witnesses: Laurence Juwet, John Skey, Robert Hore.
At: Wotton.

A1/50/104 [GC 4040]   Thurs. before the nativity of St. Mary, 10 Hen. IV [5 Sept. 1409]
Thomas Berkeley, lord of Berkeley; and John Wyntur and Alice his wife.

   Thomas has granted to John and Alice, for John's good and laudable service, a holding in Wotton borough and a croft called Stoncroft and a dovecot in Wotton manor (*Forinseca*); for their lives, rent 12*d.* a year.
Witnesses: Laurence Juwet, Simon Daunt, John Spryngat, Robert Hore, Richard Purchas.
At: Wotton.

A1/50/105 [GC 4045]   Fri. before Epiphany, 11 Hen. IV [3 Jan. 1410]
Thomas Berkeley, lord of Berkeley; and Richard Hey[sogge], Alice his wife and John their son.

   Thomas has granted to Richard, Alice and John a holding in Wotton borough . . . ; for their lives, rent 10*s.* a year.
Witnesses: Laurence Juet, Simon Daunt, Robert Hore, John Whytemore, William Sowey.
At: Wotton.

A1/50/106 [GC 4046]   The Purification, 11 Hen. IV [2 Feb. 1410]
Thomas Berkeley, lord of Berkeley; and Bartholomew Fypeyn, Joan his wife and Edith their daughter.

   Thomas has granted to Bartholomew, Joan and Edith a holding in Wotton borough which Walter Kernere previously held and a parcel of the croft called Chepyngcroft; for their lives, rent 3*s.* 4*d.* a year.
Witnesses: Laurence Juet, Simon Daunt, Robert Hore, John Whytemore, William Sowey.
At: Wotton.

A1/50/107 [GC 4091]   Sat. before St. George, 2 Hen. V [21 April 1414]
Thomas Berkeleye, lord of Berkeley, knight; and Thomas Hopere, Alice his wife and Thomas their son.

   Thomas has leased to Thomas, Alice and Thomas a burgage with a curtilage in Wottone Underegge; for their lives, at the previous rent.

Witnesses: Simon Daunt, Robert Hore, John Chapman, Robert Purchas, Richard Purchas.
At: Wotton.

A1/50/108 [GC 4102]   Sunday in Epiphany, 2 Hen. V [6 Jan. 1415]
Thomas lord of Berkeley and Philip Chamberleyn, his servant.

Thomas has leased to Philip, for his good service, a holding in the borough of Wottone Underegge and a croft of land called Wesecroft, containing 2 a., and other things; for his life, rent a rose a year.
Witnesses: Thomas Rugge, John Grevell, Robert Poyns, Robert Hore, Simon Daunt.
At: Wotton.

A1/50/109 [GC 4110]   16 June 5 Hen. V [1417]
Thomas Berkeley; and Richard Daunt and Alice his wife.

Thomas has granted to Richard and Alice a holding with a curtilage in the borough of Wottone; for their lives, rent 6*s.* 8*d.* a year.
Witnesses: Lionel Sebroke, John Wyntere, John Austille, Richard Tornour, Simon Daunt.
At: Berkeley Castle.

A1/50/110 [GC 4359]   10 May 10 Edw. IV [1470]
John Taskar and the lord [William Berkeley].

Extract from court roll: John came and gave the lord a fine of 30*s.* to have entry into a burgage with a curtilage; to him and Ellen his wife for their lives, rent 13*s.* 4*d.* a year.

Account rolls

The borough was apparently usually administered with the manor, so there are very few separate accounts.

A1/50/111 [GAR 279]   21–2 Edw. I [1293–4]
A1/50/112 [GAR 280]   Michaelmas 8 to June 9 Edw. II [1314–15]
A1/50/113 [GAR 281]   5–6 Hen. VI [1426–7]

OTHER INTERESTS
Acquisitions by Adam de Ashleworth

A1/50/114 [GC 708]   n.d. [*temp.* Hen. III]
Walter Brutur. . . , clerk, and Sir Adam de Escelworth, chaplain.

Walter has granted to Adam the burgage . . . which he held by grant of Philip Drayside; to hold of the chief lord at a rent of 12*d.* a year for his life, with remainder to . . . Chepestowe and Alice his wife.
Witnesses: Roger de Berleye, William de . . . , . . . Skynare, William Drayside, . . . de Drayside.

A1/50/115 [SC 366]   n.d. [*temp.* Hen. III]
Philip Dreyside and Sir Adam de Esscelwurthe, chaplain.

Philip has granted to Adam a burgage in Wottone; rent to the chief lord 12*d.* a year, for which Adam has given him 3 marks.
Witnesses: Elias de Cumbe, Thomas le Archer, John le Sone, William Dreyside, Hugh de Dimmoch, Walter Dreyside, Thomas de Esscelworth.

The Sone half-burgage in Sone Lane

A1/50/116 [GC 823]   n.d. [late 13th cent.]
Richard le Sone, son of John le Sone, burgess of Wotton, and Ralph the smith son of Adam the smith of the same.

Richard has granted to Ralph, for a certain sum of money, his half-burgage which he had by grant of John his father in the borough of Wotton, next to the road and between the street

called Sonelone to the east and the holding of John de la Wast to the east, with free entry to the water-pit in the holding of John de la Wast whenever necessary.
Witnesses: Alexander le Hore, Adam the dyer (*tingtor*), Hugh le Wodeward, Walter Chepman, Walter Schayl.

A1/50/117 [GC 2804]   Sun. after St. Martin, 8 Edw. III [13 Nov. 1334]
Richard son of Ralph the smith of Wotton and Agnes and Margaret, Ralph's daughters; and Walter Baldwyne of Wotton.

Richard, Agnes and Margaret have granted to Walter their holding and curtilage in the town of Wottone beside the holding called le Wast.
Witnesses: John Lydyard, William Curteys, John Averey, John le Hore, Thomas Brounyng.
At: Wotton.

A1/50/118 [GC 2874]   Sat. the eve of Whit-Sunday, 11 Edw. III [7 June 1337]
Walter le Glovare of Wotton; and Walter Baldwyne and Christine his wife.

Walter has granted to Walter and Christine his holding in the borough of Wottone beside the holding called le Wast; to them and their issue.
Witnesses: William Curteys, John Lydiard, William de Romesbury, Elias Geffrey, Geoffrey Neel.
At: Wotton.

Wyther acquisitions

A1/50/119 [GC 1528]   n.d. [*temp.* Edw. I]
Lucy Rolves and William Wyther the younger.

Lucy has granted to William her holding in the borough of Wottone; rent 4*d.* a year, and he has given her a certain sum of money.
Witnesses: Maurice de Chepustowe, John le Hore, Henry Bron, Walter le Chepmon, William Pyngul.

A1/50/120 [GC 2708]   Tues. before St. Peter in chains, 4 Edw. III [31 July 1330]
William le Botyler of Wotton and William Wyther of Wotton.

William le Botyler has granted to William Wyther his holding in the borough of Wottone.
Witnesses: Thomas Brounyng, John le Hore, William le Marchal, Roger Huchynes, Elias Geffrey, Richard Pyngul, James the miller (*molendinar'*).
At: Wotton.

The Batyn burgage in Bradley Street

A1/50/121 [GC 391]   n.d. [early 14th cent.]
Henry de Kynemersforde, chaplain, and Walter de Hareforde, son of Walter Batyn.

Henry has granted to Walter his burgage in the borough of Wotton, between the holding of Alexander de Hertesworthy and the holding of Walter le Ladzetare in the street which leads to Bradel; to hold of the chief lord of the fee.
Witnesses: Maurice de Chepstowe, John le Hore, William Pycard, Thomas Brounyng, Henry Broun.

A1/50/122 [GC 2384]   Sun. before St. John the Baptist, 15 Edw. II [20 June 1322]
Walter son of Walter Batyn of Hareforde; and Walter atte Halle of Cromhall, and Alice his wife.

Walter has granted to Walter and Alice, and Walter's heirs and assigns, for a certain sum of money, his holding in the town of Wottone, in the street to Bradeleye.
Witnesses: Maurice de Chepestowe, William Marchal, John le Hore, William Pycard, Thomas Brounyng, Thomas Badecok, Adam le Glovare.
At: Wotton.

The Chapman holding in Bradley Street

A1/50/123 [GC 1095]   St. Philip and St. James, 33 Edw. I [1 May 1305]
Reginald le Parmunter of Wotton and Walter le Chepman of the same.

Reginald has granted to Walter, for 2 marks, two thirds of his burgage, and the outer (*forinsec*) land appurtenant, and his claim to the reversion of the other third of the burgage after the death of Margery, widow of Peter de Bayles, in the new town of Wotton, next to the king's highway to Bradeleye; rent 2*s.* a year to the chief lord of the fee, viz. 8*d.* for two thirds of the burgage, 8*d.* for the land and 8*d.* for the other third.

Witnesses: Maurice de Cheppustowe, reeve of the borough, John the miller (*molend'*), John the smith, Walter Schayl, Adam le Glovar, William le Dressour.

At: Wotton.

A1/50/124 [GC 2468; *duplicate* GC 1626]   n.d. [*temp.* Edw. I]
Edith Adames, daughter of Margery widow of Peter Stiwardesman, and Walter Chepman of Acton.

Edith has granted to Walter a burgage in the town of Wottone in the street to Bradeleye; rent 2*s.* a year to the chief lord.

Witnesses: Henry the baker (*pistor*), Alexander le Hore, Richard the skinner (*pelliparius*), Adam the dyer (*tinctor*), Maurice Chepstowe, Philip Draydisid, Reginald the skinner.

A1/50/125 [GC 2448]   9 Oct. 19 Edw. II [1325]
Juliana daughter of Walter le Chepmon late burgess of Wotton, unmarried woman, and Maud her sister.

Juliana has granted to Maud a length 3 royal feet to the east of Juliana's house, beside Maud's house, in the vill of Wottone, with one part of the adjacent curtilage, in the street called Bradeleghstret in the north part, 28 royal feet long by 4 wide, also a plot of land between Maud's house and her land in Bradesleghstret, 28 royal feet long by 28 wide, also a width of 4 royal feet through half of her croft in Wottone.

Witnesses: John de Romesia, mayor of Bristol, John Franceys and Walter Prentiz, bailiffs, Roger Turtle, John de Axebrugge, John ate Walle, Richard le White, William de Kilhendre.

At: Bristol.

A1/50/126 [GC 2451]   Tues. the morrow of St. Simon and St. Jude, 19 Edw. II
[29 Oct. 1325]

Juliana daughter of Walter Chepmon of Wotton and her sister Maud.

For a certain sum of money, Juliana has granted to Maud, her heirs and assigns her holding containing two burgages with the appurtenances in the town of Wottone in the south part of Bradeleyestret, beside Maud's holding; rent 2*s.* a year to the chief lord.

Witnesses: Thomas . . . , Maurice de Chepstowe, John Hore, William Pykard, William Marescall.

At: Wotton.

A1/50/127 [GC 2631]   Mon. after St. Barnabas, 1 Edw. III [15 June 1327]
Maud daughter of the late Walter Chapman of Wotton and John Brun.

Maud has granted to John, his heirs and assigns her holding in the town of Wottone containing four burgages, in the south part of Bradeleyestret.

Witnesses: Thomas Brunyng, Maurice Chepstowe, William Pykard, James the miller (*molendinar'*), Peter the tailor (*cissor*).

At: Wotton.

The Hartsworth burgage in Bradley Street

A1/50/128 [GC 1109]   St. Matthew, 34 Edw. I [24 Feb. 1306]
Nicola de Hertusworth, burgess of Wotton, and Juliana her daughter.

Nicola has granted to Juliana half a burgage next to the part which Alexander, Nicola's son, had as a legacy from Thomas de Hertusworth, his father.

Witnesses: John the smith, Alexander le Hore, Maurice de Chepstowe, Robert Tannar', Walter le Lyminor.

At: Wotton.

A1/50/129 [GC 3124; *duplicate* GC 3125]   Tues. in All Saints, 19 Edw. III [1 Nov. 1345]
Alexander de Hertesworth; and John le Mey of Wotton and Isabel his wife.

   Alexander has granted to John and Isabel, and their heirs and assigns, his burgage in the town of Wottone, extending above Bradeleyestret.

Witnesses: William Smalecombe, Adam Legat, Walter le Glovare, Richard le Webbe and William le Tannare.

At: Wotton.

The Dresser burgage holding in Bradley Street

A1/50/130 [GC 2511]   n.d. [early 14th cent.]
Adam le Dressor of Wotton; and Richard le Dunysch of Nibley and Joan his wife.

   Adam has granted to Richard and Joan, and their heirs and assigns, his holding in the street leading to Bradel' in the borough of Wottone.

Witnesses: Maurice de Chepstowe, John le Hore, William Pycard, Walter Chepmon, Adam le Glovare.

A1/50/131 [GC 2594]   n.d. [*temp.* Edw. II]
Richard le Duynisse of Nibley; and Henry le Legat and Maud his wife.

   Richard has granted to Henry and Maud the holding which he had by grant of Adam le Dressur in the town of Wottone containing one third of a burgage in the street to Bradeley.

Witnesses: Maurice de Chepstowe, John le Hore, William Pycard, William de Oldebury, Adam le Glovare.

The Dresser (later Leggat) holding in Bradley Street

A1/50/132 [GC 1748]   Eve of St. Peter and St. Paul, 3 Edw. II [28 June 1310]
Adam le Dressur, burgess of Wotton, and Richard Caumvile.

   Adam has granted to Richard, for a certain sum of money, all his holding in the borough of Wottune in Bradeleystrete, beside the holding formerly of Walter le Lumenor.

Witnesses: Maurice de Chepstowe, John le Hore, Gregory le Hore, Walter le Chepmon, William Pycard.

At: Wotton.

A1/50/133 [GC 1279]   Fri. after St. Luke, 6 Edw. II [20 Oct. 1312]
Richard Canvyle, burgess of Wotton; and Henry le Legat and Maud his wife.

   Richard has granted to Henry and Maud, for a certain sum of money, all the holding which he had from Adam le Dressur in the borough of Wotton, situated in Bradeleystrete, and all the land in the manor of Wotton of the said holding, above the field called Overemyddel.

Witnesses: Maurice de Chepstowe, John le Hore, William Pycard, Thomas . . . , Adam le Glovar.

At: Wotton.

The Sone burgage in Haw Street

A1/50/134 [GC 1945]   n.d. [*c.* Sept. 1313]
Edith called le Sone and John Averay.

   Edith has granted to John her burgage, which William le Sone previously gave to her and William and John her sons, in Hawestrete in Wottone.

Witnesses: Maurice de Chepstowe, John le Hore, William Pycard, Walter le Chepmon, Adam le Glovar.

A1/50/135 [GC 1948]   Sun. the morrow of Michaelmas, 7 Edw. II [30 Sept. 1313]
William son of William le Sone and John Averay.

William has inspected the charter of Edith his mother concerning a burgage in
Hawestrete in Wottone, and has confirmed it.
Witnesses: Maurice de Chepstowe, John le Somenur, John le Hore, William de Oldebury,
William Pycard.
At: Wotton.

A1/50/136 [GC 1946]   Wed. after Michaelmas, 7 Edw. II [3 Oct. 1313]
John son of William le Sone and John Averay.

John has inspected the charter of his mother and the confirmation of William his brother
to John Averay of a burgage in Hawestrete in Wottone, and has quitclaimed to John.
Witnesses: Maurice de Chepstowe, Hugh de Brughampton, John le Hore, Adam le Glovare,
William Pyngul.
At: Wotton.

The Picard burgage

A1/50/137 [GC 2320] Fri. the feast of the translation of St. Martin, 13 Edw. II [4 July 1320]
Richard le Muleward, son of the late Henry le Muleward of Wotton; and William Picard of
Wotton and Agnes his wife.

Richard has granted to William and Agnes, and William's heirs and assigns, for a certain
sum of money, his burgage with a curtilage between the garden of William le Scrivein and
the holding of Peter le Taillur.
Witnesses: Maurice de Chepstowe, [John] le Hore, Walter le Chepmon, John Averay,
William Pyngul, Henry Broun, Thomas Brounyng.
At: Wotton.

A1/50/138 [GC 2839]   Sat. after the Circumcision, [4?] Edw. III [5 Jan. 1331]
William Picard of Wotton and William his son.

William the elder has granted to William the younger his burgage in the town of Wottone
within the liberty of Berkeleye; rent to the chief lord 12*d.* a year.
Witnesses: John Lydyard, Thomas Brounyng, John le Hore, Walter le Glovare, Thomas le
Deyar'.
At: Wotton.

The Chepstow holding

A1/50/139 [GC 2648]   Mon. after St. Ambrose, 2 Edw. II [11 April 1328]
Maurice de Cheppestowe and Ralph le Webbe of Wotton.

Maurice has granted to Ralph, his heirs and assigns his holding in the town of Wottone
between the holding formerly of Reginald le Skynnare and the holding of John Lydyard.
Witnesses: John Lydyard, John le Hore, Thomas Brounyng, William Curteys, Adam le
Glovare, Philip Baldewyne, William le Vycoryz.
At: Wotton.

A1/50/140 [GC 2658]   7 Aug. 2 Edw. III [1328]
Ralph le Webbe of Wotton; and Maurice de Chepestowe and Leticia his wife.

Ralph has granted to Maurice and Leticia his holding in the town of Wottone between the
holding formerly of Reginald le Skynnare and the holding of John Lydyard; to them and
Leticia's heirs and assigns.
Witnesses: John Lydyard, William Curteys, John le Hore, Richard Pyngel, Hugh Pydons.
At: Wotton.

A1/50/141 [GC 3028]   St. Martin, 16 Edw. III [11 Nov. 1342]
Leticia widow of Maurice de Chepestowe and Roger Hayl of Wortley.

Leticia has granted to Roger, his heirs and assigns her holding in the town of Wottone, which she and Maurice had by grant of Ralph le Webbe of Wottone.
Witnesses: William Curteys, John Lydyard, William de Remmesbury, Adam Collewych, Geoffrey Neel, John Pynnoc.
At: Wotton.

A1/50/142 [GC 3059]   St. James, [17] Edw. III [25 July 1343]
Roger Hayl of Wortley and Leticia widow of Maurice de Chepestowe.

Roger has granted to Leticia his holding in the vill of Wottone, which he had by Leticia's grant.
Witnesses: William Curteys, John Lydyard, Adam Collewych, Geoffrey Neel, John Pynnoc, William de Remmesbury.
At: Wotton.

The Wyther (later May) holding in Bradley Street

A1/50/143 [GC 2720]   Sat. before St. Gregory, 5 Edw. III [9 March 1331]
William Wythur of Wotton; and John le Mey and Isabel his wife.

William has granted to John and Isabel his burgage in Wottone; to them and their issue, with remainder to William and his heirs.
Witnesses: Thomas Brounyng, John le Hore, William called le Marchal, Reginald Jurdan, Henry Leget.
At: Wotton.

A1/50/144 [GC 2992]   Fri. after St. Augustine, 15 Edw. III [1 June 1341]
Juliana widow of William Wether; and John le Mei and Isabel his wife.

Juliana has quitclaimed to John and Isabel, and Isabel's issue, a holding in Bradeleystret, which William Wether granted to John and Isabel in free marriage.
Witnesses: Geoffrey Neel, William de Rommesbur', William le Marshal, William Were, William Smalcombe.
At: Wotton.

The Dyer holding

A1/50/145 [GC 3004]   Thurs. the feast of St. Luke, 15 Edw. III [18 Oct. 1341]
Alice widow of John le Deuare of Wotton and John Dhetforde.

Alice has granted to John, his heirs and assigns her holding in the town of Wottone market (*mercatoria*).
Witnesses: William de Remesburi, John Pinoc, Walter le Glovere, Robert the fisher (*piscator*), William Henlond.

A1/50/146 [GC 3110]   Sat. after Epiphany, 18 Edw. III [8 Jan. 1345]
John Deppforde and Robert le Wysschar of Wotton.

John has granted to Robert, his heirs and assigns his holding in the market town of Wottone which he had by grant of Alice widow of John Deiare of Wotton.
Witnesses: William Corteis, Geoffrey Neel, William Smalecombe, John the fisher (*piscator*).

Brown (later Matthew) holding

A1/50/147 [GC 3168]   23 Nov. 21 Edw. III [1347]
Maud widow of William Broun of Wotton and Thomas Matheu of Wotton.

Maud has granted to Thomas her holding, which she had as a legacy from William.
Witnesses: Adam Legat, William Smalcoumbe, Robert Fisschere, William Phippes, John Daunt.
At: Wotton.

A1/50/148 [GC 3204]   Thurs. after St. Hilary, 22 Edw. III [15 Jan. 1349]
Maud widow of William Broun of Wotton and Thomas Matheu of Wotton.

Maud has granted to Thomas her holding with a curtilage in the town of Wottone, which she had by grant of her late husband.
Witnesses: Geoffrey Neel, Adam Legat, William Smalcombe, Robert le Fysshere, Thomas le Deyare.
At: Wotton.

Acquisitions by William de Syde and Walter Goldmere[1]

The Schayl half-burgage
A1/50/149 [GC 2564]   n.d. [mid 14th cent.]
John Waterschyp; and William de Syde and Walter Goldemere.

John has granted to William and Walter, and their heirs and assigns, his half-burgage, which he had by grant of Edith Schayl in the town of Wottone under Egge.
Witnesses: William de Chiltenham, John de Clyve, William Curteys, Elias de Berleye, Geoffrey Neel, William Smalecombe, Adam Colewych.

A1/50/150 [GC 3173]   24 Feb. 22 Edw. III [1348]
William de Syde and Walter Goldemere; and William Curteys.

William and Walter have appointed William to receive seisin of a half-burgage in . . . in the town of Wottone undiregge.
At: Wotton.

The Lydiard (later Fisher) messuages
A1/50/151 [GC 3176]   Mon. before St. Gregory, 22 Edw. III [10 March 1348]
John Lydiard of Wotton and Robert le Fysschare of the same.

John has granted to Robert, his heirs and assigns two messuages with curtilages in Wottone.
Witnesses: William Curteys, Geoffrey Neel, Adam Legat, William Smalcombe, Thomas le Deyare.
At: Wotton.

A1/50/152 [GC 3178]   Mon. before the Annunciation, 22 Edw. III [24 March 1348]
Robert le Fysschere of Wotton; and Sir William de Syde and Sir Walter Goldemere.

Robert has granted to William and Walter two messuages with curtilages in Wottone.
Witnesses: William de Cheltenham, John de Clyve, William Curteys, Elias de Berleye, Geoffrey Neel.
At: Wotton.

A1/50/153 [GC 3316]   n.d. [mid 14th cent.]
John Lydiard of Wotton; and Sir William de Syde and Sir Walter Goldemere.

John has granted to William and Walter, and their heirs and assigns, two messuages with curtilages in Wottone.
Witnesses: William de Cheltenham, John de Clyve, William Curteys, Elias de Berleye, Geoffrey Neel.

The Waleys messuage
A1/50/154 [GC 3184]   Wed. after Michaelmas, 22 Edw. III [1 Oct. 1348]
Robert Waleys; and Sir William de Syde and Sir Walter Goldemere.

Robert has granted to William and Walter, and their heirs and assigns, a messuage with a curtilage in the new town of Wottone, extending from William's holding to the road.

---

[1] Syde and Goldmere often acted together as agents for Thomas (III) Lord Berkeley and may have been doing so here.

Witnesses: William Curteys, Geoffrey Neel, William Smalcombe, William de Romesbur', Robert le Fisshare.

At: Wotton.

A1/50/155 [GC 3186]   . . . after Michaelmas, 22 Edw. III [Oct. 1348]
(1) Robert Waleys; (2) William Curteys and Roger the clerk; (3) Sir William de Syde and Sir Walter Goldemere.

William de Syde and Walter have appointed William Curteys or Roger to receive seisin of the lands which they had by grant of Robert in Wottone.

At: Wotton.

   Other

A1/50/156 [GC 3289]   n.d. [mid 14th cent.]
John de Clyftone, executor of Peter le Frensshe; and William de Syde and Walter Goldemere.

John has granted to William and Walter, and their heirs and assigns, the holding which he had by demise of Peter in Wottone.

Witnesses: Elias de Berleye, John Skaay, Geoffrey Neel, William Smalcombe, Roger Dunyssh.

The Tortworth holding

A1/50/157 [GC 3189]   Thurs. after All Saints, 22 Edw. III [6 Nov. 1348]
John le Hopare of Wotton and Richard Torteworthe of the same.

John has granted to Richard, his heirs and assigns his house in the town of Wottone.

Witnesses: Adam Legat, William Smalcombe, Robert le Fysshare, Thomas Mathu, John Pynnoc.

At: Wotton.

A1/50/158 [GC 3228]   Sat. the eve of Whit-Sunday, 23 Edw. III [30 May 1349]
John le Mareschal, son and heir of the late William le Mareschal of Wotton, and Richard de Torteworthe.

John has quitclaimed to Richard a messuage with a curtilage which John le Hopare sometime acquired from the said William in the high street of Wottone.

Witnesses: Geoffrey Neel, Adam Legat, Robert le Fysshare, Adam Colewych, Thomas Matheu.

At: Wotton.

A1/50/159 [GC 3523]   Sun. in the decollation of St. John the Baptist, 35 Edw. III
                                                                       [29 Aug. 1361]
Richard Torteworthe and Tybota his daughter.

Richard has granted to Tybota, her heirs and assigns his house in the town of Wottone, with a curtilage.

Witnesses: Adam Legat, William Phippus, William Aldryntone, Thomas Mathu, William Hayl.

At: Wotton.

The Fisher holding

A1/50/160 [GC 3361]   Mon. after St. Philip and St. James, 25 Edw. III [2 May 1351]
Robert le Fysschere of Wotton and William Cendy of the same.

Robert has granted to William, his heirs and assigns his holding in the borough of Wottone in the street extending from the Upper Cross to the old town, beside the road to Hertesworth.

Witnesses: Walter le Glovare, William Heynes, Thomas Mathu, William Aldryngton, John Mareschal.

At: Wotton.

A1/50/161 [GC 3478]   12 Nov. 32 Edw. III [1358]
Isolda widow of William de Westbury and Reginald de Castre.

Isolda has leased to Reginald the cottage with a curtilage which William had by grant of William Sendy in the borough of Wottone, in the street extending from the Upper Cross to the old town of Wottone; for a term of 14 years from Christmas next.
Witnesses: Adam Legat, William Smalcombe, William Scndy, William Phippes, Thomas Matheus.
At: Wotton.

The Lydiard burgage

A1/50/162 [GC 3405]   Thurs. after St. Kenelm, 2[7] Edw. III [18 July 1353]
John Lydyard and Robert atte Halle of Cromhall, clerk.

John has granted to Robert, his heirs and assigns his . . . [land] with houses, buildings, liberties [etc.], in Wottone Underegge, and 1 a. of land to the south of the holding.
Witnesses: William Croke of Gloucester, Adam Legat, William Heynus, William Henlond, William Phippus, Roger Pont.
At: Wotton.

A1/50/163 [GC 3411]   7 April 28 Edw. III [1354]
Robert ate Halle and William de Westone.

Robert has granted to William, his heirs and assigns the burgage in the town of Wottone Underegge which he had by grant of John Lidyard.
Witnesses: Robert le Visshare, Adam Legat, William Heynes, Walter le Glovare.
At: Wotton.

Acquisitions by Thomas Daunt

The Walton burgage in Bradley Street
A1/50/164 [GC 1743]   Sun. after St. Barnabas, 3 Edw. II [14 June 1310]
Walter le Lumenur, burgess of Wotton, and Richard Caumvylle.

Walter has granted to Richard, for a certain sum of money, all his burgage in the borough of Wottone in the street called Bradeleystrete and ⅓ a. of land in the manor of Wottone lying between the said burgage and the field called Overemyddel.
Witnesses: Robert atte Churche, Maurice de Chepustowe, John le Hore, William Picard, Adam le Glovar.
At: Wotton.

A1/50/165 [GC 716]   n.d. [1310 × 1317]
Richard Caumvyle, burgess of Wotton, and William Soudmor.

Richard has granted to William his burgage in the borough of Wotton in the street called Bradeleystret, and ⅓ a. which pertains to it, lying between the said burgage and the field called Overemyddel.
Witnesses: Maurice de Chepstowe, John le Hore, William Pycard, William de Oldeburi, Adam le Glovare.

A1/50/166 [GC 2153]   Tues. after St. Valentine, 10 Edw. II [15 Feb. 1317]
William de Suthmore, son of Robert de Suthmore, and Sir William de Wautone, knight.

William de Suthmore has granted to William de Wautone and his heirs the burgage which he had by grant of Richard de Caumvyle in the borough of Wottone in the street called Bradeleghestrete, and ⅓ a. lying between the burgage to the north and the field called Overemyddel to the south.
Witnesses: Maurice de Chepstowe, John le Hore, William Pichard, William de Oldebury, Adam le Glovare.
At: Wotton.

A1/50/167 [GC 2154]   Wed. after St. Valentine, 10 Edw. II [16 Feb. 1317]
(1) Sir William de Wautone, knight; (2) Robert de Wyke; (3) William de Suthmor.

William de Wautone has appointed Robert his attorney to receive seisin of a burgage and ⅓ a. of land in the borough of Wottone, which William de Suthmore granted to him.
At: Cromhall.

A1/50/168 [GC 3166]   Sat. the eve of St. Simon and St. Jude, 21 Edw. III [27 Oct. 1347]
Alice de Wautone and Richard le Theyn her son.

Alice has granted to Richard the rent of 3*s.* a year from a burgage held by Robert Perot of Wottone Undiregge for his life, with the reversion of the burgage.
At: Ashton.

A1/50/169 [GC 3165]   Sat. the eve of St. Simon and St. Jude, 21 Edw. III [27 Oct. 1347]
Alice de Wautone and Robert Perot of Wotton.

Whereas Alice has granted to Richard le Theyn her son the rents and services which Robert owes for the burgage that he holds of Alice in the town of Wotton Undiregge, with the reversion of the burgage, she commands Robert to attorn for the rents and services to Richard.
At: Ashton.

A1/50/170 [GC 3445]   Sun. before St. Martin, 30 Edw. III [6 Nov. 1356]
Richard Theyn, son and heir of Alice de Wautone, wife of the late William de Wautone, knight, and Thomas Daunt of Wotton.

Richard has granted to Thomas, his heirs and assigns his burgage in Wottone in Bradeleystret.
Witnesses: Adam Colwych, William Phipp, Thomas Mathu, William Aldryntone, Robert Thomas.
At: Wotton.

Other

A1/50/171 [GC 3613]   18 Feb. 44 Edw. III [1370]
Maud widow of Peter Pycard and Thomas Daunt of Wotton.

Maud has quitclaimed to Thomas her dower rights in a holding in the town of Wottone.
Witnesses: Adam Legat, William Smalcombe, William Fysshere, Walter Glovere, William Phyppes.
At: Wotton.

A1/50/172 [GC 3628]   Sat. the feast of St. Clement, 44 Edw. III [23 Nov. 1370]
Maud Mathu, widow of Thomas Mathu of Wotton, and Thomas Daunt of the same.

Maud has granted to Thomas, his heirs and assigns her holding in Wottone between the holdings of Walter Glovare and William Smalcombe.
Witnesses: Adam Legat, William Smalcombe, William Fisshare, William Phippus, John Daunt.
At: Wotton.

A1/50/173 [GC 3694]   Thurs. before St. Mark the evangelist, 50 Edw. III [24 April 1376]
John Daunt of Wotton and Thomas Daunt of the same.

John has granted to Thomas, his heirs and assigns two cottages in Wottone.
Witnesses: Adam Legat, William Fisshere, John Whitesyre, John Dressur, Alexander le Hore.
At: Wotton.

The Currier holding

A half-burgage in Haw Street

A1/50/174 [GC 3520]   Eve of St. Bartholomew, 35 Edw. III [23 Aug. 1361]
John Welsche of Wotton and Agnes his wife; and Thomas Daunt of Wotton.

John and Agnes have granted to Thomas, his heirs and assigns a half-burgage and half-curtilage with a water-pit in the new town of the borough of Wottone.
Witnesses: Adam Legat, William Fischare, William Phippes, John Daunt, John Weytosyr.
At: Wotton.

A1/50/175 [GC 3521]   Eve of St. Bartholomew, 35 Edw. III [23 Aug. 1361]
Agnes Kademon, late wife of John Welsche of Wotton, and Thomas Daunt of Wotton.

Agnes has quitclaimed to Thomas a half-burgage in Hawestret in Wottone.
Witnesses: Adam Legat, William Fischare, William Pheppus, John Daunt, John Weytesyr.
At: Wotton.

A1/50/176 [GC 3739]   5 Oct. 4 Ric. II [1380]
Thomas Daunt of Wotton and Agnes widow of John Correour of the same.

Thomas has granted to Agnes, her heirs and assigns his burgage curtilage with a water-pit in the borough town of Wottone.
At: Wotton.

A cottage in Haw Street

A1/50/177 [GC 3632]   Thurs. before St. Mark the evangelist, 45 Edw. III [24 April 1371]
Richard Adams of Wotton and Richard Rous of the same.

Richard Adams has granted to Richard Rous, his heirs and assigns his cottage in Hawestret.
Witnesses: William Fysshere, Walter Glovere, William Phippes, William Heynes.
At: Wotton.

A1/50/178 [GC 3736]   Sun. before the Purification, 3 Ric. II [29 Jan. 1380]
Richard le Rous; and Agnes widow of John Corrayour and William their son.

Richard has granted to Agnes and William, and William's heirs and assigns, his cottage in Hawestret in the borough town of Wottone.
Witnesses: Adam Legat, William Fisschere, Thomas Deyare, John Stavertone, Thomas Daunt.
At: Wotton.

Passage from Currier to Ryhall

A1/50/179 [GC 4008]   3 Oct. 6 Hen. IV [1404]
William Coryour of Wotton and Richard Ruyhale.

William has granted to Richard, his heirs and assigns the burgage in the town of Wottone Underegge in the street called Bradeleyestrete, beside the way called Cartereslone, and also his burgage in the street called Hawestrete with a cottage.
Witnesses: Simon Daunt, John Whytemore, John Spryngot, Richard Purchas, Robert Hore.
At: Wotton.

The Brut messuage in Chipping Lane

A1/50/180 [GC 3591]   Wed. after St. Ambrose, 41 Edw. III [7 April 1367]
Walter Brutt of Wotton; and Agnes his daughter and Edith daughter of Agnes.

Walter has granted to Agnes and Edith, and Edith's heirs and assigns, his messuage in the borough of Wottone with a curtilage, in the street called le Chepynglane.
Witnesses: William Fisschere, John Daunt, Alexander le Hore, William Phippes, Walter Glovere.
At: Wotton.

A1/50/181 [GC 3836]   6 Feb. 13 Ric. II [1390]
Walter Plasch and Agnes Brutt his wife; and Laurence Juwet.

Walter and Agnes have granted to Laurence, his heirs and assigns their messuage in the borough town of Wottone subtus Egge with a curtilage, in the street called Chepynglane.

Witnesses: John Heygnus, bailiff of the said borough, John Wythsyre, Alexander le Hore, Nicholas Bayly, John Stavertone.
At: Wotton.

A1/50/182 [GC 3849]   Whit-Sunday, 14 Ric. II [14 May 1391]
Laurence Juwet and Maud his wife; and Walter Plasch of Wotton and Agnes his wife.

Laurence and Maud have leased to Walter and Agnes, and their heirs and assigns, their messuage in the borough town of Wottune with a curtilage, which Laurence previously had from Walter and Agnes, in the street called Chepinglane.

Witnesses: John Whitschire, bailiff of the same, Simon Daunt, catchpoll, John Heynus, Nicholas Bayly, Richard Panter.
At: Wotton.

A1/50/183 [GC 3862]   Epiphany, 15 Ric. II [6 Jan. 1392]
Walter Plasch of Wotton and Agnes Bruth his wife; and John Chynnham of Wotton and Joan his wife.

Walter and Agnes have granted to John and Joan, and their heirs and assigns, their messuage in the borough town of Wottone, with a curtilage, in the street called Chepynglane.

Witnesses: John Heygnus, Nicholas Bayly, Walter Godun, Richard Panter, Simon Daunt.
At: Wotton.

The Williams messuage

A1/50/184 [GC 3646]   Mon. before Easter, 47 Edw. III [11 April 1373]
Richard Wilym, son and heir of William Wilym called Tannere; and Adam Legat and Robert Thomas.

Richard has granted to Adam and Robert, and their heirs and assigns, his messuage in the town of Wottone beside his corner holding, with an adjacent curtilage.

Witnesses: William Smalcombe, William Fysshere, Thomas Daunt, John Daunt, Roger Pyngul.
At: Wotton.

A1/50/185 [GC 3741]   Wed. the morrow of the Circumcision, 4 Ric. II [2 Jan. 1381]
Adam Legat; and William Penkoke, chaplain, Henry Torteworth, John Heynes and Richard Spryngot.

Adam has granted to William, Henry, John and Richard, and their heirs and assigns, his messuage with a curtilage in the borough town of Wottone, beside the corner holding of Richard Willymes, which he had by grant of Richard Willomes.

Witnesses: William Smalcombe, William Fysschere, Thomas Daunt, John Whitsire, Roger Pyngul.
At: Wotton.

A1/50/186 [GC 3755]   Thurs. after the nativity of St. John the Baptist, 6 Ric. II
                                                                    [26 June 1382]
William Pendoke, chaplain, Henry Torteworth, John Heynes and Richard Springgot; and Thomas atte Broke and Denise his wife.

William, Henry, John and Richard have leased to Thomas and Denise the holding with a curtilage in the borough town of Wottone beside the corner holding of Richard Wylmes; for their lives, rent 3*s.* a year.

Witnesses: John Wyghtsyre, Nicholas Baylye, Simon Daunt, Richard Purchas, John Wylmes.
At: Wotton.

Acquisitions by Simon and Juliana Daunt

A1/50/187 [GC 3731]   31 July 3 Ric. II [1379]
William Smalcombe, William Fysschere, Thomas Daunt, John Whitsire, Richard Springgot, John Thresschere, John Staverton; and Simon Daunt and Juliana his wife.

William, William, Thomas, John, Richard, John and John, and other parishioners of the church of Wottone, have confirmed to Simon and Juliana their corner holding in the borough town of Wottone, beside the street to Kynggeswode.
Witnesses: Adam Legat, Roger Beuley, William Haynes.
At: Wotton.

A1/50/188 [GC 3907]   Mon. the feast of St. Cuthbert, 19 Ric. II [20 March 1396]
Thomas Daunt chaplain; and Simon Daunt of Wotton and Juliana his wife.

Thomas has granted to Simon and Juliana, and Simon's heirs and assigns, his holding in the borough town of Wottone in the street extending from the Upper Cross to the old town.
Witnesses: Laurence Juet, John Pente, Richard Paniter, Roger Pynghull, John Thresschere.
At: Wotton.

A1/50/189 [GC 3999]   5 Oct. 4 Hen. IV [1402]
Richard Wottone of the parish of Brockworth and Juliana wife of Simon Daunt of Wotton.

Richard has quitclaimed to Juliana the corner holding opposite the holding of the lord of Berkele, inhabited by William atte Nasch, by the Lower Cross in Wotton.
Witnesses: Sir William parson of Newington, Laurence Berlygh, John Wytmore, John Spryngget, Robert Churchhey.
At: Wotton.

The Bradford (formerly Daunt) holding

A1/50/190 [GC 3796]   20 Oct. 9 Ric. II [1385]
Thomas Daunt of Wotton and Thomas Bradeford of the same.

Thomas Daunt has granted to Thomas Bradeforde, his heirs and assigns his holding in Wottone between the holdings of William Smalcombe and John Stavertone.
Witnesses: William Smalcombe, John Whitesire, Roger Pyngul, Richard Spryngot, John Staverton.
At: Wotton.

A1/50/191 [GC 3797]   . . . Oct. 9 Ric. II [1385]
(1) Thomas Daunt of Wotton; (2) [Richard] Spryngot, Henry Ste. . . the younger and John Threschere; (3) Thomas Bradeford.

Thomas Daunt has appointed Richard, Henry and John [to deliver seisin] to Thomas Bradeford of the holding . . . William Smalcombe and John Stavertone.

A1/50/192 [GC 3811]   Tues. after St. Simon and St. Jude, 10 Ric. II [30 Oct. 1386]
Margery Daunt of Wotton and Thomas Bradeforde of the same.

Margery has granted to Thomas all her dower rights and claim to the holding which he recently acquired from Thomas Daunt, late her husband.
Witnesses: John Heignes, Richard Panyter, Roger Pyngul, John Whitesire, John Staverton.
At: Wotton.

The Pyngel burgage

A1/50/193 [GC 3808]   Sun. after Michaelmas, 10 Ric. II [30 Sept. 1386]
Joan Pyngel of Wotton, widow; and Thomas Scharp of Wotton and Agnes his wife.

Joan has granted to Thomas and Agnes, and Thomas's heirs and assigns, a burgage in Wottone between the holdings of Isabel Squabbe and the house of St. Mary.

Witnesses: Richard Panyter, Roger Pyngel, Richard Spryngot, John Wylteschire, Simon Daunt.
At: Wotton.

A1/50/194 [GC 3851]   Sun. after St. Barnabas, 14 Ric. II [18 June 1391]
Thomas Sharp of Wotton and Agnes his wife; and Thomas Hopere of la Ende of Kingswood and Alice his wife.

Thomas and Agnes have granted to Thomas and Alice, and their heirs and assigns, a burgage in Wotton between the holding of Isabel Squabbe and the house of St. Mary, which they had by grant of Joan Pyngul.
Witnesses: Richard Panyter, Roger Pyngel, Richard Spryngot, John Wylteschire, Simon Daunt.
At: Wotton.

The Thomas holding at the Cloud
A1/50/195 [GC 3990]   St. Wulfstan, 3 Hen. IV [19 Jan. 1402]
Isabel Tomas of Wotton, widow; and John [Rolfus], Nicholas Hulle and John Camme.

Isabel has granted to John, Nicholas and John, and their heirs and assigns, a holding in Wottone . . .
Witnesses: William Smalcombe the elder, Laurence Juet, William Sowey, John Spryngat, Thomas Chamburleyn.
At: Wotton.

A1/50/196 [GC 3993]   The Purification, 3 Hen. IV [2 Feb. 1402]
John Rolfus, Nicholas Hulle and John Camme; and Isabel Tomas of Wotton.

John, Nicholas and John have leased to Isabel a holding with appurtenances in Wottone beside the road called le Cloude; for life, rent a red rose a year.
At: Wotton.

Other Thomas holdings
The Chamber holding in Chipping Lane
A1/50/197 [GC 2142]   4 Jan. 10 Edw. II [1317]
Richard called of the chamber (*de camera*) of Wotton and Walter Wollewerye, miller, of the same.

Richard has granted to Walter, in free marriage with Edith his daughter, his holding in Wottone in the lane called Chepyngelane, beside the wall of the marketplace; to them and their heirs and assigns.
Witnesses: Elias Berle, Geoffrey Neel, Henry Legate, Reginald Jurdan, Randolph Webbe, John Macschal, William Wylymys.
At: Wotton.

A1/50/198 [GC 2897]   Tues. the eve of the Annunciation, 12 Edw. III [24 March 1338]
Walter Wollewerye, miller, and Edith la Brutt his wife; and Walter le Brutt the elder, son of the said Edith.

Walter Wollewerye and Edith have granted to Walter le Brutt, his heirs and assigns their messuage in the borough of Wottone with a curtilage, in the street called le Chepinglane, extending to the gate of the marketplace.
Witnesses: William de Romesbury, Adam Colewych, William Henlond, Thomas le Deyare, Thomas Matheu.
At: Wotton.

A1/50/199 [GC 3461]   1 April 31 Edw. III [1357]
Walter le Brut the elder of Wotton and Robert Thomas of Wotton.

Walter has granted to Robert, his heirs and assigns his messuage with a curtilage in the lane called Chepynglone by the gate of the market town of Wottone.
Witnesses: Adam Legat, William Smalcombe, William Phyppus, John Daunt, Thomas Daunt.
At: Wotton.

Other

A1/50/200 [GC 3558]   Mon. after the translation of St. Thomas of Canterbury, 38 Edw. III
[8 July 1364]
Maud Amy, widow of Roger Amy of Wotton, and Robert Thomas of Wotton.

Maud has granted to Robert, his heirs and assigns her holding in the new town of the borough of Wottone.
Witnesses: William Smalcoumbe, William Fisschere, William Phippes, Walter Glovere, John Daunt, John Whitesir.
At: Wotton.

A1/50/201 [GC 3610]   Sun. after All Saints, 43 Edw. III [4 Nov. 1369]
Thomas de Myghte and Agnes his wife; and Robert Thomas of Wotton.

Thomas and Agnes have granted to Robert, his heirs and assigns a selion of curtilage land in Chepynglane of Wottone.
Witnesses: Adam Legat, William Smalcombe, William Fysshere, William Phyppes, William Heynes.
At: Wotton.

Settlement

A1/50/202 [GC 3992]   Sat. after St. Wulfstan, 3 Hen. IV [21 Jan. 1402]
Agnes Thomas of Wotton, executrix of Robert Thomas of Wotton; and [John] de Camme, William Otleve, clerk, William Cauley and Nicholas Hulle.

Agnes has granted to John, William, William and Nicholas four shops in Wo. . . . . .
Witnesses: William Smalcombe the elder, Laurence Juet, . . . Roger Pyngul, . . .
At: Wotton.

A1/50/203 [GC 3994]   Mon. after the Purification, 3 Hen. IV [6 Feb. 1402]
John Camme, William Otcleve, clerk, William Cauley and Nicholas Hulle; and Thomas Chamburleyn of Wotton and Agnes Thomas his wife.

John, William, William and Nicholas have leased to Thomas and Agnes . . . four shops in Wotton in Chepynglane, with a curtilage adjacent and a half-burgage, which were of Robert Thomas of Wotton; for their lives, rent a red rose a year.
At: Wotton.

A1/50/204 [GC 3986]   Mon. after the Purification,[1] 3 Hen. IV [6 Feb. 1402]
John Camme, William Otcleve clerk, William [Cauley] and Nicholas Hulle; and Thomas Chamburleyn of Wotton and Agnes Thomas [his wife].

John, William, William and Nicholas have leased to Thomas and Agnes . . . four shops in Wotton in Chepynglane, with a curtilage adjacent and a half-burgage, which were of Robert Thomas of Wotton; for their lives, rent a red rose a year.
At: Wotton.

---

[1] The deed is dated, evidently in error, Mon. after the *conception* of St. Mary, 3 Hen. IV [12 Dec. 1401], eight weeks before the conveyance to the feoffees.

Other

Sone Lane

A1/50/205 [GC 3888]   Tues. the feast of the nativity of St. Mary, 18 Ric. II [8 Sept. 1394]
John ate Forde and Isabel his wife; and Thomas Chamburlayn and Agnes his wife.

John and Isabel have granted to Thomas and Agnes, and their heirs and assigns, their holding in the borough of Wottone Unduregge beside the road called Sonelane.
Witnesses: Laurence Juwet, John Chepman, Thomas Baker, John Haynes.
At: Wotton.

Haw Street

A1/50/206 [GC 1947]   n.d. [*c.* Sept. 1313]
Elias the baker (*pistor*) of Wotton and John Averay.

Elias has granted to John a burgage in Hawestrete in Wottone.
Witnesses: Maurice de Chepstowe, John le Hore, William Pycard, Philip Baldwyne, Adam le Glovare.

A1/50/207 [GC 2332]   Thurs. the feast of St. Edmund the king, 14 Edw. II [20 Nov. 1320]
Thomas Boggepolle, cook, and Juliana his wife; and Henry Legat and Maud his wife.

Thomas and Juliana have, for a certain sum of money, demised and leased to Henry and Maud, and their heirs and assigns, their holding in the vill of Wottone in Hawestret, for a term of 200 years, rent a rose a year.
Witnesses: Maurice de Chapstowe, John le Hore, Thomas Brounyng, Richard de Blakeneye, William Pykard.
At: Wotton.

A1/50/208 [GC 3374]   Mon. after Michaelmas, 25 Edw. III [3 Oct. 1351]
Juliana Cademan of Wotton and Adam Colewych of the same.

Juliana has granted to Adam, his heirs and assigns a messuage with a curtilage in Hawestret.
Witnesses: Geoffrey Neel, Walter Glovere, Robert le Fisschare, William Heynes and William Smalcombe.
At: Wotton.

A1/50/209 [GC 3392]   Mon. before the nativity of St. John the Baptist, 26 Edw. III
[18 June 1352]
Geoffrey Neel of Wotton and William Sendy of the same.

Geoffrey has granted to William, his heirs and assigns his cottage in Hawestrete.
Witnesses: Walter Glovere, William Heynes, Edward Brevel, William Phippes, William Aldryntone.
At: Wotton.

Bradley Street

A1/50/210 [GC 1415]   n.d. [*temp.* Edw. I]
Denise Holacre of Wotton; and Edith Suryng and Isabel her sister.

Denise has granted to Edith and Isabel her holding in the street to Bradeley, in the town of Wottone; rent ½*d.* to the lamp of the Virgin Mary of Wotton.
Witnesses: Maurice de Chepstowe, John le Hor', Walter le Chepmon, Henry Broun, Adam le Glovare.

A1/50/211 [GC 2453]   Mon. before the conversion of St. Paul, 19 Edw. II [20 Jan. 1326]
Alice daughter of Walter le Ledurtare of Wotton and John le Vox.

Alice has granted to John two thirds of a burgage in the town of Wottone between Bradeleghstret to the north and the land of Walter atte Halle to the south.

Witnesses: Thomas Brounyng, John le Hore, James le Moleward, Adam le Glovare, Walter atte Halle.

A1/50/212 [GC 2689]   Fri. before St. Edmund the king, 3 Edw. III [17 Nov. 1329]
John le Vox and William Corteys, clerk.

John has granted to William two parts of a burgage in the town of Wottone in the street called Bradeleyestret, beside the holding of Lady Isabel de Berkeleye, lady of Wottone.
Witnesses: Thomas Brouning, John le Hore, James le Meleward, Walter atte Halle, John Lydyard.
At: Wotton.

Unspecified

A1/50/213 [SC 112]   n.d. [*temp.* Hen. III]
William Veisin and Philip Draesid.

William has granted to Philip half a burgage in Vectun at a rent of 6*d.* a year, for which Philip has given him 5*s.*
Witnesses: Elias de Cumba, John le Sune, William Drawesid, Robert Herding, Hugh de Dimmoc, Walter Drawesid.

A1/50/214 [SC 378]   n.d. [*temp.* Hen. III]
Thomas le Huthlae and John de la Porte of Frocester.

Thomas has granted to John one house, being one third of a burgage, in the town of Wotton, between the house of Thomas and the house of Nicholas son of Nicholas le Moliner; rent 5*d.* a year to the chief lord of the fee; John has given Thomas 2 marks and 2*s.*
Witnesses: Philip Drayside, William de Cumbe, Henry the baker (*pistor*), William le Seone, Walter le Luminur, Nicholas the miller (*molendinarius*), Alexander le Hore, Richard le Scynnar, Richard le Glovare, Ralph the marshal (*marescallus*), Geoffrey the baker.

A1/50/215 [GC 705]   n.d. [late 13th cent.]
Peter de Breles and Margaret ate Castle of Sandhurst (*Sondhurste*).

Peter has granted to Margaret, for a certain sum of money, the messuage and curtilage between the burgage formerly of Hugh le Belmon and the messuage which Sir Geoffrey the chaplain once held in the new town of Wotton; rent to the chief lord 8*d.* a year and to Peter a rose a year.
Witnesses: Henry the baker (*pistor*), Philip Draysid, Alexander le Hore, Richard the skinner (*pellipar*'), Richard le Glovar.

A1/50/216 [GC 2495]   n.d. [late 13th cent.]
William de Bradeleg' and Peter de Breyles.

William has granted to Peter part of his burgage with the house built on it in the new borough of Wottone, lying beside the messuage which Peter bought from Henry Wayfer, and has also granted to Peter the rent of 4*d.* from the said messuage which was of Henry Wayfer; rent a clove a year, and Peter has given him 12*s.*
Witnesses: Elias de Cumbe and Richard de Stanford, bailiffs of Wotton, Henry the baker (*pistor*), reeve of Wotton, William Draysid, Philip Draysid, Philip the long (*longus*).

A1/50/217 [GC 1166]   n.d. [*temp.* Edw. I]
Thomas ate Boure of Malmesbury and William the miller (*molendinar*)' of Wotton.

Thomas has granted to William his burgage in the new town of Wottone, to hold of the chief lord of the fee; William has given him 100*s.*
Witnesses: Alexander le Hore, reeve of the town, Henry the baker (*pistor*), Philip Draysid, Richard the skinner (*pellipar*'), Ralph the marshal (*mariscallus*).

A1/50/218 [GC 887]   n.d. [late 13th cent.]
Edith widow of Thomas de la Bure of Malmesbury and William Pingel of Wotton.
　　Edith has quitclaimed a burgage to William.
Witnesses: Philip Dreisid, Henry the baker (*pistor*), Adam the dyer (*tinctor*), Alexander le Hore, Richard the skinner (*pellipar'*).

A1/50/219 [GC 1574]   n.d. [*temp.* Edw. I]
John le Warre of Sodbury, son and heir of Adam le Warre, and Nicholas the clerk of Wotton.
　　John has granted to Nicholas, for a certain sum of money, a cottage and curtilage in which Edith the laundress (*lotrix*) lives, situated in the corner opposite the garden of the parson of Wottone, beside the king's highway from the new town of Wottone to the lord's court.
Witnesses: William de Coumbe, Nicholas Lovekoc, Maurice de Chepstowe, Gregory le Hore, John le Hore, William de Oldeburi, Thomas Brounyng.

A1/50/220 [GC 1548]   n.d. [*temp.* Edw. I]
Maud le Soutar' of Wotton, widow, and Edith her daughter.
　　Maud has granted to Edith half of her house in the new town of Wottone, beside the road to the marketplace, and a plot of land beside the house; rent 2*s.* 9*d.* a year while she lives; for this Edith will sustain a chaplain celebrating in the church of Wottone for half a year.
Witnesses: John the smith (*fabr'*), Maurice Chepstowe, Alexander le Hore, Walter Chepman, Walter Schayl, Geoffrey the baker (*pistor*), Adam the dyer (*tingtor'*).

A1/50/221 [GC 2526]   n.d. [*temp.* Edw. I]
Edith widow of Ralph le Marchal of Wotton; and William son of Richard the clerk of Oldbury and Edith, Edith's daughter.
　　Edith has granted to William and Edith, and their heirs and assigns, for their love and service, the burgage which she had in the new town of Wottone in the east corner, doing the customary services to the chief lord and paying 6*d.* a year to the lamp of the Blessed Mary in the church of Wottone.
Witnesses: Maurice de Chepstowe, Walter le Chepman, Gregory le Hore, John le Hore, Geoffrey the baker (*pistor*), William Pycard, Adam le Glovare.

A1/50/222 [GC 2561]   n.d. [early 14th cent.]
John formerly huntsman of Sir Thomas de Berkel' and William called le Webbe of Wotton.
　　John has granted to William, his heirs and assigns, for 27*s.*, his house and curtilage; rent 6*d.* a year to the chief lord.
Witnesses: Maurice de Cheppustowe, John the smith (*fab'*), Walter Chepman, John the miller (*molend'*), Walter Sayl, William le Dresour, Walter Lydyard.

A1/50/223 [GC 1939]   Eve of the Assumption, 7 Edw. II [14 Aug. 1313]
Maud Balrych; and Sir Richard de Iwel', chaplain, and Maurice de Chepstowe.
　　Maud has granted to Richard and Maurice her holding in the borough of Wottone.
Witnesses: Walter le Chepmon, William Pycard, Adam le Glovare, Geoffrey the baker (*pistor*), Gregory le Hore.
At: Wotton.

A1/50/224 [GC 2098]   Sat. before Ascension, 9 Edw. II [15 May 1316]
Edith widow of William le Dressur of Wotton and Adam le Dressur her son.
　　Edith has quitclaimed to Adam, for her life, her holding in Wottone which she had in dower after the death of her husband.
Witnesses: Maurice de Chepstowe, Gregory le Hore, William Pycard.
At: Wotton.

A1/50/225 [GC 2798]   18 [July] 8 Edw. III [1334]
Robert de Cliftone and William le Bowiare; and William Curteys of Wotton, clerk, and
Agnes Trenchesoyl his wife.

Robert and William have granted to William and Agnes, and their issue, the holding in
the borough of Wotton Underegge opposite the Lower Cross of the vill and rents and other
things; with remainder to William's heirs.
Witnesses: Roger de Berleye, John le Skay of Nibley, Walter de Coumbe, John Lydyard,
Geoffrey de Wottone, Thomas Brounyng, John le Sometour.
At: Wotton.

A1/50/226 [GC 2915]   Sat. before St. Margaret the virgin, 12 Edw. III [11 July 1338]
William le Tannare, son of Agnes le Tannare of Wotton; and John le Moy and Isabel his
wife.

William has granted to John and Isabel free access to a water-pit by a path at the head of
his curtilage; rent 1*d.* a year.
Witnesses: William de Romesbur', Adam Legat, John le Fox, James the miller (*molend'*),
John Teynton.
At: Wotton.

A1/50/227 [GC 3230]   Mon. after the nativity of St. John the Baptist, 23 Edw. III
                                                                    [29 June 1349]
Geoffrey Neel of Wotton and Henry atte Ree, executors of Alice le Taillur; and Richard de
Wottone, rector of the same.

Geoffrey and Henry have granted to Richard their holding in Wottone, which they had by
Alice's grant.
Witnesses: Adam Legat, Robert le Fysschare, William Wylym, Thomas Matheu, Walter le
Glovere.
At: Wotton.

A1/50/228 [GC 634]   Sat. after St. Martin, 26 Edw. [III, 17 Nov. 1352]
Robert le Fysschar of Wotton and William Cendy of the same.

Robert has granted to William a cottage with a curtilage in the borough of Wotton.
Witnesses: Walter Glover, William Heynus, Thomas Mathu, William Aldrynton, John
Marich.
At: Wotton.

A1/50/229 [GC 3450]   Tues. the morrow of St. James, 30 Edw. III [26 July 1356]
Thomas Mathu of Wotton and Walter Brut of the same.

Thomas has granted to Walter, his heirs and assigns his holding in Wottone extending to
Walter's curtilage.
Witnesses: Adam Legat, Adam Colwych, William Phippus, William Aldryntone, John
Daunt.
At: Wotton.

A1/50/230 [GC 3459]   Mon. after St. Hilary, 30 Edw. III [16 Jan. 1357]
Roger Huychons of Wotton; and Elias de Berleye, Adam Legat, William Smalcombe and
Walter Glovere.

Roger has granted to Elias, Adam, William and Walter, and their heirs and assigns, his
holding in Wottone beside the road to the river at the end of the town.
Witnesses: John Draycote, Thomas Skay, John Oulepenne, William Phippus, Robert
Fysschare.
At: Wotton.

A1/50/231 [GC 3463]   Mon. in Easter week, 31 Edw. III [3 April 1357]
John le Cartere and John le Daunt of Wotton.

John le Cartere has granted to John le Daunt, his heirs and assigns his messuage in Wottone and the rent of a rose from a curtilage which Robert Thomas holds of John le Cartere for his life, with the reversion of the curtilage which is parcel of the said messuage.
Witnesses: Adam Legat, Adam Colwych, William Heynes, William Phippes, Thomas Mathu.
At: Wotton.

A1/50/232 [GC 3543]   [August 1363]
Copy of two deeds:
(i) Thurs. the feast of St. Laurence, 37 Edw. III [10 Aug. 1363]. Grant by John son of Simon le Carpont' of Cirencester to Robert Thomas of Wotton and Alice his wife, and their heirs and assigns, of all the lands and holdings in Wottone which he inherited from Simon his father, witnessed by Adam Legat, William Smalecumbe, William Fischare, Adam Colliwiche, Walter Glovere and William Heynes;
(ii) Sun. before the Assumption of St. Mary 3[7] Edw. III [13 Aug. 1363]. Quitclaim of the same by Margaret daughter of Simon Carpont' of Cirencester to Robert and Alice.
At: Wotton.

A1/50/233 [GC 3611]   6 Nov. 43 Edw. III [1369]
William Fisschare of Wotton and Robert Thomas of the same; and John Welles of Wotton.

William and Robert have granted to John, his heirs and assigns the corner holding between Robert's shop called Coppedehalle and the street to the marketplace.
Witnesses: Adam Legat, William Smalcoumbe, John Whytsyre, William Phippes, William Sandy, John Daunt.
At: Wotton.

A1/50/234 [GC 3663]   31 May 48 Edw. III [1374]
John Welles of Wotton; and Richard Curte of the same, Edith his wife and Juliana [their daughter].

John has leased to Richard, Edith and Juliana the holding in the borough vill of Wottone . . . ; for their lives, rent 8*s.* a year.
Witnesses: [Adam] Legat, William Smalcoumbe, John Whytsyre, William Fisshere, John Daunt.
At: Wotton.

A1/50/235 [GC 3676]   10 Feb. 49 Edw. III [1375]
John Oldelond, parson of King's Stanley; and Robert Thomas of Wotton, Agnes his wife and Isabel and Margery, Robert's daughters.

John has leased to Robert, Agnes, Isabel and Margery his holding in Wottone beside the holding which Robert inhabits; for their lives, rent 6*s.* a year.
Witnesses: Adam Legat, William Fisshare, Thomas Daunt, William Phippes, Robert Pyngyl.
At: Wotton.

A1/50/236 [GC 3765]   19 Nov. [7] Ric. II [1383]
Roger Pyngul of Wotton and Joan widow of William Wynegot of the same.

Roger has quitclaimed to Joan a holding with a curtilage in the town of Wottone.
Witnesses: Richard Panyter, John Whitesire, William [Sowy], John Staverton, Richard Spryngot.
At: Wotton.

A1/50/237 [GC 3817]   Wed. before St. Valentine, 10 Ric. II [13 Feb. 1387]
William Smalcombe and John Welles; and Sir Walter Burnel, rector of Brean, and Ralph Coke.

William and John have granted to Walter and Ralph, and their heirs and assigns, their holding with appurtenances in Wottone, which they had by grant of Adam Colewyche of Wottone.
Witnesses: Laurence Juwet, Richard Panyter, Roger Pyngul, John Heygnes, Richard Spryngot.
At: Wotton.

A1/50/238 [GC 3828]   3 Nov. 12 Ric. II [1388]
Hugh de Byseley; and Ralph Waleys and John Couele.

Hugh has granted to Ralph and John, and their heirs and assigns, all his holdings in the new town of Wottone, which sometime were of Geoffrey Neel.
Witnesses: William Smalcombe, Thomas Skay, William FitzWaryn, John Whitesire.
At: Wotton.

A1/50/239 [GC 3838]   Mon. after the nativity of St. John the Baptist, 14 Ric. II
                                                                        [27 June 1390]
Laurence Juwet of Combe; and Walter Plasch and Agnes his wife.

Laurence has leased to Walter and Agnes an annual rent of 5s. from a messuage and curtilage which William Proute and Edith his wife hold for the term of 6 years in Wottone in the street called Chepynglane, with the reversion of the holding; for their lives, rent 2 lb. of cumin a year.
Witnesses: John Heigns, John Wytsire, Alexander le Hore, Nicholas Bailly, Richard Spryngot.

A1/50/240 [GC 3898]   20 May 18 Ric. II [1395]
Joan Might, daughter and heir of Agnes Might, and John Chynham called Chapman.

Joan has granted and quitclaimed to John her claim to two messuages in the town of Wottone Unduregge (Glos.).
Witnesses: John Tresour of Monmouth, Thomas Bakere of Lydney, Richard Spryngot of Wotton, Nicholas Bayluf, Simon Daunt, Walter Godeman.
At: Wotton.

WOTTON-UNDER-EDGE MANOR
BERKELEY GRANTS AND ACQUISITIONS
The advowson

A1/51/1 [SC 39]   n.d. [1193 × 1195]
H[enry de Soilly], bishop of Worcester, and St. Augustine's Abbey.

On presentation by the abbot, the bishop has admitted William the clerk of Hesl' to the church of Wotton with the chapels of Symundeshale and Nibbeleg, on an annual pension of 3 marks.
Witnesses: Peter archdeacon of Worcester, Richard archdeacon of Gloucester, Master Jordan, Master Herbert, William of the oak (*de quercu*), Ulger de Bruge, Master Robert de Beintona, Master Arnold de Bathonia, Walter dean of Cam (*Camma*), Savaric dean of Bristol, Lewis de Teinton, David the scrivener (*scriptor*) of Worcester (*Wirec*).

A1/51/2 [GC 1149]   1 June 35 Edw. I [1307]
St. Augustine's Abbey; and Sir Thomas de Berkel', lord of Berkeley, and Sir Maurice his son.

The abbey has agreed with Thomas and Maurice to exchange the advowson of the church of Wotton for the fisheries in Erlyngham, saving to the abbey the fisheries which it has on its own land.

Witnesses: Sir John de Wylyngtone, Sir John Mautravers, Sir Nicholas son of Ralph, Sir William de Wauton, Sir Nicholas de Kyngestone, knights, Robert de Bradeston, Walter de Nasse, Richard de Byseleye, John de Alkeleye.
At: Bristol.

A1/51/3 [SC 475]   1 June 35 Edw. I [1307]
Thomas de Berkeley and Maurice his son; and St. Augustine's Abbey.

Thomas and Maurice have confirmed to the abbey all the grants of their predecessors, and have further granted, for them and their tenants, freedom from suit to their courts; and the abbey has quitclaimed to Thomas and Maurice the advowson of the church of Wotton.
Witnesses: John de Wylyngtone, John Mautravers, Walter de Gloucestre, escheator, Nicholas FitzRalph, William de Wautone, Nicholas de Kyngestone, Thomas le Botyler, knights, Robert de Bradeston, Walter de Nasse, Richard de Byseleye, Robert Wyther.
At: Berkeley.

A1/51/4 [GC 1150]   1 June 35 Edw. I [1307]
St. Augustine's Abbey, Bristol; and Sir Thomas de Berkeleye, lord of Berkeley, and Sir Maurice, his son, lord of Wotton.

The abbey has quitclaimed to Thomas and Maurice the advowson of the church of Wottone, and has bound itself to celebrate the anniversaries of Thomas and Maurice and of the Lady Joan, Thomas's wife; for which Thomas and Maurice have confirmed all the abbey's liberties within their lands in the counties of Gloucester and Somerset, and have given the abbey £100.
Witnesses: Sir John de Wylyngtone, Sir John Mautravers, Sir Thomas le Botyler, Sir William de Wauton, Sir Nicholas de Kyngeston, Sir Nicholas son of Ralph, Sir Walter de Gloucestre', the king's escheator, knights, Robert de Bradestone, Richard de Byseleye, Robert Wyther, Walter de Nasse.
At: Bristol.

The Lude holding in Wotton and Bradley

A1/51/5 [GC 1470]   n.d. [*c.* 1290]
Thomas de Lude and Eleanor his wife; and Sir Thomas lord of Berkeley.

Thomas and Eleanor have granted to Thomas a messuage, 1 carucate of land and rents of 50*s.*, of Eleanor's inheritance, in Wottone and Bradeleye; Thomas has given them £100.
Witnesses: Robert de Berkeley, Robert le Veel, John de Chausy, knights, Peter de Stintescombe, William de Burgo, Robert de Bradeston, Thomas de Swonhungre, Thomas de Beoleye, Walter de Chaldefeld, William de Cumbe, Thomas Alayn.

A1/51/6 [GC 1471]   n.d. [*c.* 1290]
Thomas de Lude and Eleanor his wife; and Sir Thomas lord of Berkeleye.

Thomas and Eleanor have granted to Thomas a messuage, 1 carucate of land and rents of 50*s.*, of Eleanor's inheritance, in Wottone and Bradeleye; Thomas has given them 100 marks.
Witnesses: Robert de Berkeley, Robert le Veel, John de Acton, knights, Peter de Stintescombe, William de Burgo, Walter de Chaldefelde, Robert de Bradeston, William de Cumbe, Thomas de Swonhungre.

A1/51/7 [GC 2570]   n.d. [*c.* 1290?]
Thomas lord of Berkel'; and Thomas de Lude and Eleanor his wife.

Thomas de Berkel' has granted to Thomas and Eleanor the holding, land, meadow, pasture, grove and rents with appurtenances which he had by grant of Thomas and Eleanor within the manor of Wottone at Bradeleye and Wottone; to them and Eleanor's issue, rent 18[*d.*] at Michaelmas, a rose at the nativity of St. John the Baptist, and 4½*d.* at St. Peter in chains [1 Aug.]. *Witnesses*: . . . [*Later copy*; *unfinished*] Endorsed: *Transcriptum carte Alyanore de Bradeleye*.

A1/51/8 [GC 587]   St. Philip and St. James, 20 Edw. I [1 May 1292]
Thomas de Luda and Eleanor his wife; and Thomas de Berkeleye.

Thomas and Eleanor have granted to Thomas all their holding of Bradeleye and of Wotton of Eleanor's inheritance, which Thomas recovered in the royal court and then granted to Thomas and Eleanor.

Witnesses: Sir Rauf chamberlain of St. Augustine's, Bristol, Robert de Stone, Robert de Bradeston, Thomas le Serjaunt, Thomas Aleyn.

At: Berkeley.

A1/51/9 [GC 1002]   Two weeks after Michaelmas, 20 Edw. I [13 Oct. 1292]
Thomas de Berkel'; and Thomas de Lude and Eleanor his wife.

Final concord concerning a messuage, 1 carucate of land and [50*s.* rent] in Wottone and Bradeleye; Thomas and Eleanor have acknowledged the right of Thomas by their gift, and warrant for themselves and Eleanor's heirs; Thomas has given them 100 marks.

At: Shrewsbury.

The Bellamy holding in Wotton, Nibley and Alkington

A1/51/10 [GC 358]   n.d. [1193 × 1220]
Robert de Berkeleya and Adam de Grava.

Robert has granted to Adam 1 virgate of land which Roger Eschermissur held of Robert in the vill of Nubbeleya towards Swunhaia; rent 1 lb. of cumin a year; acknowledgement 10 marks. Endorsed: *Nybbeleye in Wotton de ten[emento] quond[am] Walteri Belamy.*

Witnesses: Osbert chaplain of Nibley, William de Heseleya, parson of Wotton, Adam son of Nigel, Henry de Coueleya, Bernard de Stanes, Thomas de Tiringham, Maurice son of Nigel, Harding de Hunteneford, John de Crauleya, William de Haggeleya, Richard de Cromhale, Bernard de Cromhale, Bernard de Brotheston, Walter de Angervillis.

A1/51/11 [GC 2460]   Sun. before the nativity of St. John the Baptist, 19 Edw. II
                                                                [22 June 1326]
Richard atte Grove, son and heir of Nicholas atte Grove, and Walter Belamy.

Richard has quitclaimed to Walter, his heirs and assigns all the lands and holdings, to the right to which he succeeded after Nicholas's death, in the manors of Wottone and Alkyntone.

Witnesses: Roger le Duynyssh, Richard le Caunvyle, Richard le Duynyssh, Nicholas Draysid, John le Chausy.

A1/51/12 [GC 2779]   Mon. after Michaelmas, 7 Edw. III [4 Oct. 1333]
Richard de Foxcote, sheriff of Gloucester, and Walter Belamy of Nibley.

Richard has received from Walter 10*s.* of his fine to have a licence of agreement with Richard le Grovere for holdings in Nubbeleye by Wottone.

At: Gloucester.

A1/51/13 [GC 2947]   Thurs. in Ascension, 13 Edw. III [6 May 1339]
Walter Belamy and Sir Thomas lord of Berkel'.

Walter has sold to Thomas all his goods and chattels in all his lands and holdings in Nubbeleye, Wottone and Alkyntone, which were of Richard le Grovare.

At: Nibley.

A1/51/14 [GC 2948]   n.d. [7 May 1339]
Walter Belamy of Nibley and Sir Thomas lord of Berkeleye.

Walter has granted to Thomas, his heirs and assigns all his lands and holdings in Nubbeleye, Wottone and Alkyntone, viz. the holding which was formerly of Richard le Grovare.

Witnesses: William de Borough, John le Serjaunt, John de Milkesham, John de Egetone, John Skey of Nibley.

A1/51/15 [GC 2949]   Fri. the morrow of Ascension, 13 Edw. III [7 May 1339]
Walter Belamy and Sir Thomas de Berkel'.

Memorandum that on Friday the morrow of Ascension, 13 Edw. III, Walter came to Berkel' and, in the presence of the lord, William de Borough, John de Egetone, John de Nubbel' and others of the lord's household (*familia*), sold to the lord all his land and holdings which he held of the lord in fee of the holding formerly of Richard le Grovare within the manors of Wottone and Alkyntone, except those which he had previously sold to William de Borough and John de Nubbel'; and memorandum of the tenants [*named*] who hold for life of this holding.
At: Berkeley.

A1/51/16 [GC 2946]   Sun. after Ascension, 13 Edw. III [9 May 1339]
(1) Thomas lord of Berkel'; (2) John de Clyve and John de Nubbeleye; (3) Walter Belamy.

Thomas has appointed John and John his attorneys to receive seisin of all the lands and holdings which Walter granted to Thomas in Nubbeleye, Wottone and Alkyntone.
At: Berkeley.

A1/51/17 [GC 3259]   n.d. [mid 14th cent.]
Thomas de Berkeleye, lord of Berkeley; and Walter Belamy of Nibley, Gunnilda his wife and John their son.

Thomas has leased to Walter, Gunnilda and John all the lands and holdings which Walter granted to Thomas in Nubbeleye, Wottone and Alkyntone; for their lives, rent during the lives of Walter and Gunnilda 2*s.* a year, and of John alone 20*s.* a year.
Witnesses: John de Milkesham, William le Borugh, Roger Duynissch.

The Smalcombe holding

A1/51/18 [GC 3912; *duplicate* GC 3913]   Tues. before the nativity of St. Mary, 20 Ric. II
                                                                    [5 Sept. 1396]
William Smalcombe the elder; and Walter Godeman, Margery his wife and John their son.

William has leased to Walter, Margery and John his holding with meadow in Wottone Underegge; for their lives, rent 18*s.* a year.
Witnesses: Richard Panyter, Roger Pyngull, John Pente, Richard Spryngot, John Heygnes.
At: Wotton.

A1/51/19 [GC 3987]   Sat. after Christmas, 3 Hen. IV [31 Dec. 1401]
William Smalcombe the elder and Thomas Berkeley, lord of Berkeley.

William has granted to Thomas, his heirs and assigns a holding in Wottone Underegge.
Witnesses: Thomas FitzNicoll, knight, John atte Yate, John Skey, Laurence Juet.
At: Wotton.

A1/51/20 [GC 3988]   Sat. after Christmas, 3 Hen. IV [31 Dec. 1401]
(1) William Smalcombe the elder; (2) William Smalcombe the younger, his son; (3) Thomas Berkeley, lord of Berkeley.

William the elder has appointed William the younger to deliver seisin to Thomas of a holding in Wottone Underegge.
At: Wotton.

A1/51/21 [GC 3989]   Sat. after Christmas, 3 Hen. IV [31 Dec. 1401]
(1) Thomas Berkeley, lord of Berkeley; (2) William Godefelagh; (3) William Smalcombe the elder.

Thomas has appointed William Godefelagh to receive seisin from William Smalcombe of a holding in Wottone Underegge.
At: Wotton.

Other Berkeley Interests

A1/51/22 [GC 1302]   n.d. [*temp.* Edw. I]
Ivo de Combe and Sir Maurice de Berkelee.

Ivo, with the assent of Maud his wife, has rendered and quitclaimed to Maurice all the lands and holdings which he held of him in Wottone and Combe.
Witnesses: Walter de Chaldefeld, Robert of the church (*de ecclesia*), Warin son of William, Richard de Wik, Nigel de Kingescote, John de Olepenne, William de Combe, John With, Richard Wocock.

A1/51/23 [GC 1190]   n.d. [1285 × 1300]
Thomas de Boleg' and James de Berkeley, son of Sir Thomas de Berkel'.

Thomas has granted to James 2 a. of meadow in the meadow called Brademed, extending towards Eghamersch; rent a rose a year, and John has given him 3½ marks.
Witnesses: Sir Robert de Berkel', Sir William de Ailbeygni, Sir Roger de Lokyngton, Robert de Stanes, Robert de Bradeston, Elias de Cumbe, Bartholomew de Olepenne.

A1/51/24 [GC 1224]   n.d. [early Edw. I]
Thomas de Berkeley, son and heir of Sir Maurice de Berkeley, and Kingswood Abbey.

For the souls of himself and Joan his wife, Thomas has granted to the abbey a plot of land below Blakeleyesegge which was held by Henry de la Welle of Combe, viz. to the east of Thomas's quarry, between the foot of the said hill of Blakeleyesegge and the king's highway from the quarry to la Stapele below the hill, and the stone they dig from it, and free access with carts and wagons along the said road to the said place . . .
Witnesses: Sir Robert de Berkeley, Thomas's brother, Sir John de [Chausy], knights, Robert de Stone, Robert de Bradeston, William de Burgo, Peter de Stintescumbe, Walter de Chaldefeld.

A1/51/25 [GC 1641]   Mon. before St. Peter in chains [31 July] A.D. 1307
Edith widow of Ralph le Mareschal of Wotton and Sir Maurice de Berkeleye.

Edith has quitclaimed to Maurice all actions which she has or might have against him for dower in the holdings which were Ralph's in Wottone.[1]
Witnesses: Robert atte Churche of Nibley, Warin son of William, Maurice de Chepstowe, Hugh le Wodeward, Alexander le Hore, Walter Chepmon, William Pykard.
At: Wotton.

A1/51/26 [GC 2573]   n.d. [early 14th cent.]
Richard Noblepas of Berkeley and Sir Maurice de Berkel'.

Richard has granted to Maurice a rent of a clove a year in Wottone from Elias de Coumbe for a croft between Hawecroftes and the king's highway beside the park of Hawe.
Witnesses: William Colewych, Roger de Berleye, Robert ate Cherche, John de Olepenne, Warin son of William, Richard de Wyke, John le Sckey of Nibley.

A1/51/27 [SC 549]   26 Jan. 49 Edw. III [1375]
Thomas de Berkeleye, lord of Berkeley, and Lady Katherine de Berkeley, lady of Wotton.

Thomas has granted that Katherine may cut and sell wood in Southwood for a term of 10 years, the profits to be divided between them. [*In French.*]
At: Wotton.

---

[1] The quitclaim may relate to the Marshall holding in Wotton borough: above, p. 311.

BERKELEY GRANTS
The Coterel holding and two assarts

A1/51/28 [GC 360]   n.d. [1220 × 1243?]
Thomas de Berkeley and Robert Crispin.

Thomas has granted to Robert the land which Peter Coterel held in Thomas's manor of Wotton and 2 assarts in the same manor, viz. those which Walter the old reeve held, called the ridding of Abbeleye and the ridding of Hore, and ½ a. of meadow in Monmed; rent 6*d.* a year, acknowledgement 5 marks.
Witnesses: Richard de Cromhale, Oliver de Berkeley, William de Bradele, William son of Elias, John de Berkeley, Robert the forester.

A1/51/29 [SC 277]   n.d. [1220 × 1243]
Robert Crispin and Henry de Berklai, knight, son of Thomas de Berkelay, his lord.

Robert has sold to Henry, for 4 marks, the land which the said Thomas gave to him in his manor of Wotton, viz. the land which Peter Coterel held and 2 assarts called the ridding of Abbeleia and the ridding of Hage; Henry to pay the rent of 6*d.* a year to Thomas.
Witnesses: Oliver de Berkelay, Simon de Olepenne, Peter de Stintescumbe, Richard de Coueleia, William de Berkeleya, knight, Arnulf the clerk, William de Bradele.

A1/51/30 [SC 344]   n.d. [*temp.* Hen. III]
Henry de Berkelay, son of Sir Thomas de Berkelay, and Thomas de Estsexia.

Henry has granted to Thomas the land in the manor of Wttune which Robert Crispin sold to him and which Peter Coterel held and two assarts which Walter the reeve held called the riddings of Abbeleia and Hage; rent to Henry and his heirs 1*d.* a year and to Sir Thomas de Berkeley 6*d.* a year; and Thomas has paid 100*s.* entry fine.
Witnesses: Oliver de Berkeley, Peter de Stintescumbe, Richard de Couleia, Nicholas Rufus, Richard de Brimelham, Colin de Chausi, Adam Russel, Nicholas Minot, Walter de Sancto Jacobo.

Other grants

A1/51/31 [GC 695]   n.d. [1220 × 1243]
Thomas de Berkel and William de Berkel his younger son.

Thomas has granted to William 1 virgate in his manor of Wutton which Henry Chocki held of Sir Robert de Berkel, Thomas's brother, in fee; rent 4*d.* a year. Endorsed: *Borrowed from Wm. Basset Esquire 1606.*
Witnesses: Sir Henry de Berkel, Sir William de Berkel, Peter de Stintescumbe, Simon de Olepenne, Thomas de Tyringeham, John de Eggeton, John de Berkel, Nicholas Rufus, Elias the butler (*pincerna*), Arnulf the clerk.

A1/51/32 [GC 1669]   Michaelmas Day, 2 Edw. II [29 Sept. 1308]
Maurice de Berkeleye, son and heir of Sir Thomas de Berkel', and Robert de Bassett of Wotton.

Maurice has granted to Robert 3 a. of land in the manor of Wottone, next to le Soutlone in the croft called Chepyngcroft; to hold enclosed, to him and his issue, rent 9*s.* a year.
Witnesses: Robert de la Churche, Richard de Wyke, John le Skey, William de Combe, Maurice de Chepestowe, Walter le Chepmon, William Pycard.
At: Wotton.

A1/51/33 [GC 1712]   Michaelmas, 3 Edw. II [29 Sept. 1309]
Maurice de Berkel', son and heir of Sir Thomas de Berkel'; and Adam Waterschup and Maud his wife.

Maurice has granted to Adam and Maud 2½ a. 16 perches of land in Maurice's manor of Wottone, lying above le Oldebur', between the path from Wurtel' to Kyngeswod and the

path from Wottone to Alreleye; to hold enclosed, to them and their issue, rent 7*s*. 6*d*. a year.
Witnesses: Robert de la Churche, Richard de Wyke, William de Coumbe, William Warlemund, Maurice de Chepistowe.
At: Wotton.

A1/51/34 [GC 4090]   10 April 2 Hen. V [1414]
Thomas Berkeley, lord of Berkeley; and Robert Shypward, burgess of Bristol, and Joan his wife.

Thomas has leased to Robert and Joan his holding in Wottone Foreyn called Curteysplace, which John Whytemore lately held at Thomas's will, and an annual rent of 13*s*. 4*d*. from John Purchas for a holding which he held of Thomas for his life, with the reversion of the holding; for their lives.
Witnesses: John Clers, Maurice Couthel, Robert Purchas.
At: Wotton.

A1/51/35 [GC 4310]   30 March A.D. 1461
(1) Robert Batyn, clerk, and Richard Warde; (2) James Berkeley, lord of Berkeley, knight; (3) Maurice Berkeley of Beverston, esquire, Edward Hopton, Thomas Holt, Thomas Campdene, John Turnour, clerk, and David Berkeley.

Whereas the late James, by his charter dated the Monday before St. Simon and St. Jude, 29 Hen. VI [26 Oct. 1450], granted to Richard and Robert, and their heirs and assigns, his manors of Wottone Underegge, Cauley, Wortley, Swymondsale, Nybley, Combe and Synawell, and all his lands and holdings there, Robert has now leased the said manors and lands to Maurice, Edward, Thomas, Thomas, John and David, and their heirs and assigns.
Witnesses: John Thorpe, Richard Clayvele, Thomas Berkeley, John Oldlond, Henry Taylour.

A1/51/36 [GC 4395]   10 April 15 Edw. IV [1475]
William Viscount and lord of Berkeley and Robert Loege, clerk, rector of Wotton-under-Edge (Glos.).

William has demised at farm to Robert a certain parcel of land called le Courte Orchyard and a parcel of meadow, in the manor of Wotton; from Christmas for a term of 60 years, rent 28*s*. a year.

A1/51/37 [GC 4404*]   7 April 17 Edw. IV [1477]
William Dorney and the lord [William Berkeley].

Extract from court roll: William Dorney came and took from the lord a messuage and 1 virgate of land lately in the tenure of Robert Dangerfeld; to hold to him and Agnes his wife and John their son, for their lives, rent 32*s*. a year.

ADMINISTRATIVE DOCUMENTS
Acknowledgements of receipt of annuity
William Lord Berkeley and Joan his wife granted an annuity of £100 from the manor (or the manor and borough) of Wotton-under-Edge to Henry Bodrugan, esquire, and Margaret Viscountess Lisle, his wife, lately wife of Thomas Talbot, Viscount Lisle. The following record the receipt of quarterly instalments of £25.

A1/51/38 [SC 629]	2 Aug. 13 Edw. IV [1473]
A1/51/39 [GC 4381]	3 May 14 Edw. IV [1474]
A1/51/40 [GC 4385]	Nativity of St. John the Baptist, 14 Edw. IV [24 June 1474]
A1/51/41 [GC 4394]	2 Feb. 14 Edw. IV [1475]
A1/51/42 [GC 4407]	7 Nov. 16 Edw. IV [1476]
A1/51/43 [GC 4411]	2 Feb. 16 Edw. IV [1477]
A1/51/44 [GC 4416]	7 Nov. 17 Edw. IV [1477]
A1/51/45 [GC 4424]	7 Nov. 20 Edw. IV [1480]

Account rolls

A1/51/46 [GAR 252] Wotton and Symond's Hall		n.d. [1290s]
A1/51/47 [GAR 271]	Michaelmas to St. Thomas the apostle 22–3 Edw. I[1]	[1294]
A1/51/48 [GAR 253]		26–7 Edw. I [1298–9]
A1/51/49 [GAR 254]		n.d. [c. 1300]
A1/51/50 [GAR 255] Wotton and Symond's Hall		1–2 Edw. II [1307–8]
A1/51/51 [GAR 256]		5–6 Edw. II [1311–12]
A1/51/52 [GAR 257]		7–8 Edw. II [1313–14]
A1/51/53 [GAR 259]		Michaelmas to June , 8 Edw. II [1314–15]
A1/51/54 [GAR 261]		11–12 Edw. II [1317–18]
A1/51/55 [GAR 262]		12–13 Edw. II [1318–19]
A1/51/56 [GAR 263]		13–14 Edw. II [1319–20]
A1/51/57 [GAR 265] Wotton and Symond's Hall		15–16 Edw. II [1321–2]
A1/51/58 [GAR 266] Wotton and Symond's Hall		16–17 Edw. II [1322–3]
A1/51/59 [GAR 267] Wotton and Symond's Hall		18–19 Edw. II [1324–5]
A1/51/60 [GAR 268]		Michaelmas 20 Edw. II, for 32 weeks [1326–7]
A1/51/61 [GAR 270]		20–1 Edw. III [1346–7]
A1/51/62 [GAR 272]		[1351–2]
A1/51/63 [GAR 273]		29–30 Edw. III [1355–6]
A1/51/64 [GAR 276]		n.d. [late 14th cent.]
A1/51/65 [GAR 274]		n.d. [1361 × 1385]
A1/51/66 [GAR 275]		n.d. [temp. Ric. II]
A1/51/67 [GAR 277]	Michaelmas 5 Hen. V to the Purification 8 Hen. V [1417–19]	

Rentals

A1/51/68 [GRR 20] Tenants of Eleanor de Bradeleye	45 Hen. III [1260–1]
A1/51/69 [GRR 22]	28 Edw. I [1300]

List of payers of aid 28 Edw. I; dorse has list of payers of Peter's Pence, 35 Edw. I [1307].

A1/51/70 [GRR 21]	Michaelmas, 8 Edw. IV [29 Sept. 1468]

Court rolls

A1/51/71 [GCR 10] Halimot	19 Oct. 8 Hen. V [1420]
A1/51/72 [GCR 11]	18 April 28 Hen. VI [1450]

Halimot, of John [Talbot] earl of Shrewsbury and Margaret his wife, Edmund [Beaufort] duke of Somerset and Eleanor his wife, and George Lord Latimer and Elizabeth his wife.

Charter rolls

A1/51/73 [SR 3]	early Hen. III to Hen. V

Abstracts of charters concerning the manor and borough of Wotton, numbered in margin but not consecutively; current tenant and current rent added, or blank spaces for such information.

A1/51/74 [SR 20, incorporating SR 21]	Ric. I to Hen. V

Abstracts of charters concerning the manor and borough of Wotton; top missing, entries numbered 78–373, the numbers corresponding with those in A1/51/73 [SR 3].

A1/51/75 [SR 22]	43–4 Edw. III [1369–70]

Copies of five deeds concerning lands in Wotton.

Other

A1/51/76 [GMR 15]	
Custumal	n.d. [temp. Edw. I]

---

[1] The account is for 12 weeks; the feasts specified indicate Edw. I, not Edw. III.

OTHER INTERESTS
The Bradley half-virgate

A1/51/77 [SC 75]   n.d. [*temp.* John]

Hugh de Bradeleia and Juliana de Ponte Arche, wife of Robert de Berkeleia.

Hugh has granted to Juliana a half-virgate of land in Wotton which Odo Russell held next to the parson's court; Juliana has given as acknowledgement a horse valued at ½ mark; rent 1 lb. of cumin at Michaelmas.[1]

Witnesses: Adam son of Nigel, Maurice de Berkeleia, William de Berkeleia, Henry de Coueleia, Bernard de Stanes, Roger de Boivillis, Henry the chaplain, Walter the chaplain, Hugh the chaplain, Harding de Hunteneford, Maurice son of Nigel, Richard de Cromhale, Bernard de Cromhale, Elias de Bevintuna, Maurice his son, Elias de Cumba, Gilbert son of Osbert, Walter de Angervillis.

A1/51/78 [GC 364]   n.d. [1220 × 1230]

William de Bradelegh and St. Augustine's, Bristol.

William has confirmed to the canons of St. Augustine's the grant by Reginald de Camme to them of a half-virgate of land in Wotton, which Lady Juliana de Berkeley, once wife of Robert de Berkeley, granted to Reginald, and which Juliana bought from Hugh de Bradelegh, William's brother; for 7 marks and a horse, rent 1 lb. of cumin a year to William and his heirs; and the canons gave him 10s.[2]

Witnesses: Sir Robert de Laxinton, Maurice de Gant, Ralph Musard, Jordan Warr', William the chamberlain (*camerarius*), Thomas de Tiringham, John de Egeton.

Other

A1/51/79 [SC 340]   n.d. [*temp.* Hen. III]

Alice, widow, daughter of William sometime rector of Wotton, and William de Watersip.

Alice has granted to William the messuage which Ralph the smith sometime held in Wttone with the land lying next to the house which Walter the sexton (*sixtor*) once held; rent 1*d.* a year or a pair of gloves, and William has given her ½ mark.

Witnesses: Henry Lyvet, Thomas de Rodeberge, Elias de Cumbe, Nicholas de Chausi, Nicholas Hwinebaud, Thomas le Archer.

WOTTON: BRADLEY
BERKELEY INTERESTS
La Hamme

A1/52/1 [GC 715]   n.d. [late 13th cent.]

Maurice de Camme, son of Sir William de Berkeleie, and Sir Odo Archdiakene.

Maurice has granted and quitclaimed to Odo whatever he has in the land of Bradeleie, which he had by grant of Sir William de Berkeleie, and Odo has given him £10.

Witnesses: Sir Thomas de Berkeleie, Sir Ralph de Wilinton, Sir Robert le Vel, John de Acton, Sir William Mauncel, Robert de Bradeston, William de Bourwe.

A1/52/2 [GC 571; *duplicate* GC 572]   Thurs. after the conversion of St. Paul, 18 Edw. I
                                                          [26 Jan. 1290]

Amicia la Ercedekene, widow of Sir Odo le Ercedekene, and Thomas de Luda.

Amicia has quitclaimed to Thomas and his wife the holding at la Hamme in the manor of Wotton, next to Kingswood Abbey; Thomas has given her £40.

Witnesses: Reginald de Boterewes, knight, Walter le Venur, clerk, Adam de Lamport, Robert de Bradeston, Walter de Chaldefeld, John de Iweley, John le Botiler.

At: London.

---

[1] *Transcript*: *St Augustine's Cartulary*, no. 266.

[2] *Transcript*: ibid. no. 270.

A1/52/3 [GC 573]   3 April 18 Edw. I [1290]
Amicia widow of Odo le Ercedekene and Sir Thomas de Berkeley.

Whereas Lady Joan de Berkeley enfeoffed William de Berkeley, her son, and his issue of
a certain land called la Hamme at Bradeley, so that if he died without issue the said land
would revert to Joan and her heirs, and Sir William gave the land to Master John de
Sechevile and his heirs, and John enfeoffed Amicia and her heirs; and Sir William died
without issue, and Thomas succeeded as next heir of Joan and pursued Amicia and Odo in
the royal courts for the land, during which Odo, her second husband, died; Amicia has
quitclaimed to Thomas.
Witnesses: Sir John de Acton, Sir John Botetourte, Sir Richard de Rivers (*de Ripar'*), Sir
Robert le Veel, Sir Robert de Berkeley, knights, Robert de Bradeston, Walter de Chaldefeld,
Thomas le Noreys, William de Burgo.
At: Ruan Lanihorne [Cornw.].

A1/52/4 [GC 2479]   n.d. [*c.* 1298]
Maurice de Berkeley, son of Sir Thomas de Berkeley, and John de Berkeley, his brother.

Maurice has inspected the charter of the lands and holding of la Homme at Bradeleye
which his father has granted to John and his issue, and has confirmed it.
Witnesses: Sir Robert de Berkeley, Sir Robert le Veel, Sir William de Wautone, Sir Thomas
de Gorneye, Sir Roger Perceval, knights, Richard de Bisleye, Robert de Stone, Robert de
Bitlescumbe, Robert de Bradestone.

The Parker holding

A1/52/5 [GC 4173; *duplicate* GC 4041]   One month after Michaelmas, 11 Hen. IV
                                                                    [27 Oct. 1409]
Robert Stanshawe and Isabel his wife; and William Parker and Alice his wife.

Final concord concerning a messuage, 9 a. of land and 5 a. of meadow in Bradeley,
Wottone and Worteley; William and Alice have acknowledged the right of Robert and
Isabel by their gift, and Robert and Isabel have given them 20 marks.
At: Westminster.

A1/52/6 [GC 4039]   St. Margaret the virgin, 10 Hen. IV [20 July 1409]
William Parkere, citizen of London, and Alice his wife, daughter and heir of Robert
Churcheheye; and Robert Poyntz, John Grevell, Robert Stanshawe and Isabel his wife.

William and Alice have granted to Robert, John, Robert and Isabel a messuage called . . .
in . . . by Wottone subtus Egge with 11 a. of land and 5 a. of meadow . . .
Witnesses: Thomas [FitzNicol] knight, John Rolves, John Vele.

A1/52/7 [GC 4050]   Thurs. the eve of St. James, 11 Hen. IV [24 July 1410]
Robert Stanshawe and Sir Thomas Berkeley, lord of Berkeley.

Robert has quitclaimed to Thomas a messuage, 11 a. of land and 5 a. of meadow in
Bradeley.
At: Wotton.

Other

A1/52/8 [GC 1196]   n.d. [1264 × 1276]
Joan de Berkel', widow of Sir Thomas de Berkel', and Sir Richard [de Malmesbury], abbot
of St. Augustine's Abbey, Bristol.

Joan has quitclaimed to Sir Richard, in pure alms, all services due from the holding
which was of John de Bradeleya, son and heir of Reginald Buchard at Bradeleya in the
manor of Wotton', whether rents, suits to her courts of Wottone and Camme, wardships [etc.]
Witnesses: Elias de Cumbe, Walter de Chaldefeld, Ivo de Cumba, Richard de Bradeleya,
John le Skey, Nicholas de Bradeleya, mason, Roger le Skey.

A1/52/9 [GC 348]   n.d. [*temp.* Hen. III]
Lady Joan de Berkeley, widow of Sir Thomas de Berkeley, and William de Berkeley, her son.

Joan has granted to William all her land which she bought from Ralph de Wiplex in Bradeleye in the manor of Witune, viz. a messuage and 1 virgate of land which Adam de Bradeleye once held and 7 a. of land which Thomas le Pacchare held in the same manor of Wottune; to him and his issue, performing the due services to the chief lord of the fee, viz.18*d.* a year, and if William dies without issue, then the lands are to revert to Richard de Berkeleye, his brother.
Witnesses: Sir Henry de Berkeleye, Robert le Vel, Elias de Comba, Thomas le Archer, Reginald de Ysetebury, Robert Hardine.

A1/52/10 [GC 883]   5 Feb. . . . [1361 × 1385]
Alice Brounyng of Wotton and Lady Katherine de Berkeleye, lady of Wotton.

Alice has made over to Katherine all that she has in the lands [etc.] which she had by grant of St. Augustine's Abbey in Bradeleye next to Wotton and within the lordship of Wotton for her life; to Katherine for Alice's life, rendering to the abbey 46*s.* 8*d.* a year.
Witnesses: Nicholas de Kyngescote, Walter Bourgh, William Fysshare, William Heynes, Thomas Daunt.
At: Wotton.

OTHER INTERESTS

A1/52/11 [GC 457]   May 1273
St. Augustine's Abbey, Bristol, and John son of Reginald de Jastesbury.

John has granted to the abbey all his land of Bradeleya which he held of Lady Joan de Berkeley and all his land of Wotton which his father held of the abbey in the vill of Wotton; and for this the abbey has granted to John for life 5 marks a year and also to Peter and Reginald his brothers 6 qr. of pure wheat and 6 qr. of good barley each year for their lives.

A1/52/12 [GC 2777]   Morrow of St. Matthew, 7 Edw. III [22 Sept. 1333]
Agnes widow of John le Schay of Bradley; and John Fader and Joan his wife.

Agnes has leased to John and Joan her house with a curtilage and garden, her part of the adjacent croft and all that she has within enclosures in Bradeleye in dower; from Michaelmas, for a term of 8 years, and the garden for a further 3 years, for the customary services to the chief lord.
Witnesses: William Corteys, John le Hore, Robert Slydewyne.
At: Bradley.

A1/52/13 [GC 3572]   Mon. in Michaelmas, 39 Edw. III [29 Sept. 1365]
Walter Henreys, son and heir of Henry Slydewyne of Bradley; and Adam Legat of Wotton and Margery his wife.

Walter has leased to Adam and Margery 1 a. of land in Ebbrokesfeld; for their lives, rent a red rose a year.
Witnesses: William Smalcombe, John Daunt, William Fysshare, Robert Thomas, William Phippes.
At: Wotton.

WOTTON: COMBE

FALWELL RENT AND REVERSION, AND ASSOCIATED HOLDINGS, IN COMBE AND BRADLEY

A1/53/1 [GC 2430]   Sun. the feast of St. Martin, 18 Edw. II [11 Nov. 1324]
Robert son of Ivo de Cumbe; and Thomas Fallewolle and Isabel his wife.

Robert has granted to Thomas and Isabel, for a certain sum of money, the plot of land where his buildings and curtilage were situated next to Thomas's holding in Cumbe, and

also 4½ a. of land in Wottone, of which one lies at Revenescumbe, one at Henleye, one at Secheleye, one in Cumbes at Oldecherche and ½ a. in the same field; to Thomas and Isabel and their issue, rent 2d. a year for their lives and 40s. a year after their deaths.
Witnesses: Roger Berieye, John Skey of Nibley, Warin son of William, John ate Cherche of Nibley, John ate Halle of Combe.
At: Combe.

A1/53/2 [GC 2433; *duplicate* GC 2434]   Sun. the morrow of St. Wulfstan, 18 Edw. II
                                                                                [20 Jan. 1325]
Robert son of Ivo de Cumbe; and Thomas Fallewolle and Isabel his wife.
   Robert has granted to Thomas and Isabel, for a certain sum of money, 4 a. in the fields of Cumbe, of which 3½ a. lie above Lawepen and ½ a. at Codespenne; to them and their issue, rent a rose a year during their lives, and after their deaths 6d. a year.
Witnesses: Roger Berleye, John Skey of Nibley, Warin son of William, John ate Cherche of Nibley, John ate Halle of Combe.
At: Combe.

A1/53/3 [GC 2985]   Fri. the feast of St. Laurence, 15 Edw. III [10 Aug. 1341]
Hugh son and heir of Robert Ives of Combe; and William Curteys of Wotton, Agnes his wife and William their son.
   Hugh has granted to William, Agnes and William all his lands and holdings in Combe which he inherited after the death of Robert Ives his father, also a rent of 13½d. a year from 2 a. of land and 1 a. of meadow which Robert le Heyward and Juliana his wife hold of Hugh for their lives, with the reversion of the land, and a rent of 2d. and a rose a year from a house and curtilage and 9 a. of land which Isabel Fallewolle holds for life, with the reversion; to them and the heirs and assigns of William Curteys.
Witnesses: Elias de [Berley], John Averay, Geoffrey Neel, Nicholas Lovekoc, Elias de Combe, John de Combe.
At: Wotton.

A1/53/4 [GC 2984]   Fri. the feast of St. Laurence, 15 Edw. III [10 Aug. 1341]
Hugh son of Robert Yves of Combe; and William Curteys of Wotton, Agnes his wife and William their son.
   Hugh has quitclaimed to William, Agnes and William all his lands and holdings in Combe, with reversions, as in his charter.
At: Wotton.

A1/53/5 [GC 3001]   Fri. the feast of St. Laurence, 15 Edw. III [10 Aug. 1341]
Hugh son of Robert Ives of Combe; and William Curteys of Wotton, Agnes his wife and William their son.
   Hugh has granted to William, Agnes and William, and the heirs and assigns of William [the elder], an annual rent of 15½d. from 2 a. of land and 1 a. of meadow which Robert le Hayward of Combe and Juliana his wife hold of Hugh for their lives, with the reversion of the holding, and from 9 a. of land which Isabel Fallewolle holds of Hugh for life, with the reversion of the holding, and also 1 a. of land above Lilleweye.
Witnesses: Elias de Berleye, John Averay, Geoffrey Neel, Nicholas Lovecoke, Elias de Combe, John de Combe.
At: Wotton.

A1/53/6 [GC 3363]   Sat. before the Invention of Holy Cross, 25 Edw. III [30 April 1351]
Agnes widow of William Curteys of Wotton; and Adam Legat of Wotton and Margery his wife.
   Agnes has leased to Adam and Margery all her lands and holdings in Combe which

William acquired from Hugh Ives of Combe, and an annual rent of 16*d.* from 2 a. of land and 1 a. of meadow which Richard le Heyward holds for life, with the reversion of the holding; for her life, for the customary rent.
Witnesses: Elias de Berleye, Geoffrey Neel, Walter le Glovare, Robert le Fysshare, Adam Colewych.
At: Wotton.

A1/53/7 [GC 3372]   Mon. before St. Peter in chains, 25 Edw. III [24 July 1351]
Nicholas Curteys, son and heir of the late William Curteys; and Adam Legat of Wotton and Margery his wife.
 Nicholas has quitclaimed to Adam and Margery his lands and holdings in Combe which he inherited after William's death, and an annual rent of 16*d.* from Richard le Heyward for his life, with the reversion of the land.
Witnesses: Elias de Berleye, Geoffrey Neel, Walter le Glovere, Robert le Fysshere.
At: Wotton.

A1/53/8 [GC 3472]   Sat. in Whitsun week, 32 Edw. III [19 May 1358]
Adam Legat of Wotton and Sir Thomas lord of Berkeleye.
 Adam has granted to Thomas, his heirs and assigns all the lands, holdings, rents and reversions in Combe which he had by grant of Nicholas son and heir of William Curteys, and which were of Robert Ives of Combe, in exchange for a messuage with an enclosure and land, which Richard Phelpes sometime held in Bradeleye.
Witnesses: Elias de Berleye, Thomas le Skay, Geoffrey Neel, Warin FitzWaryn, Roger Chausi.
At: Berkeley.

A1/53/9 [GC 3473]   Sat. in Whitsun week, 32 Edw. III [19 May 1358]
Thomas de Berkeleye, lord of Berkeley; and Adam Legat, Margery his wife, Edith daughter of John Legat, and William Legat.
 Thomas has leased to Adam, Margery, Edith and William the messuage with an enclosure and land which Richard Phelpes sometime held of him in Bradeleye in exchange for lands and holdings which he had by Adam's grant in Combe; for their lives, rent a rose a year.
Witnesses: Elias de Berleye, Thomas Skay, Geoffrey Neel, Warin FitzWaryn, Roger Chausy.
At: Berkeley.

THE PORTER HOLDING IN COMBE AND BRADLEY

A1/53/10 [GC 508]   One month after Easter, 11 Edw. I [16 May 1283]
Henry de Thisteldon; and Thomas le Porter and Joan his wife.
 Final concord concerning 30 a. of land, 7 a. of wood, 2 a. of pasture and 17*s.* 3*d.* rent in Wooton; Thomas and Joan have acknowledged the right of Henry, and Henry has given them 40 marks.
At: Shrewsbury.

A1/53/11 [GC 2545]   n.d. [May × Sept. 1283]
Henry de Thistelden and Sir Thomas de Berkeley.
 Henry has quitclaimed to Thomas the holding with land, rents, and appurtenances which Henry bought from Thomas le Porter and Joan his wife in Bradeley and Cumbe in the manor of Wottone by a fine levied in the king's court, which fine he has now handed over to Thomas; Thomas has given him 25 marks.
Witnesses: Sir Thomas de Wylond, king's justice, Sir William le Gras, Sir Robert de Berkeley, Sir Roger de Lokinton, Elias de Cumbe, Bartholomew de Olepenne.

A1/53/12 [GC 510]   Michaelmas, 11 Edw. I [29 Sept. 1283]
Sir Thomas de Berkley; and Henry the baker (*pistor*) of Wotton and his wife.

Thomas has leased to Henry and his wife all the land and pasture which he bought from
Henry de Thystelden in the vill of Cumbe, except the land which William Gile held and the
wood; for their lives at 10*s.* a year.
Witnesses: Elias de Cumbe, William de Cumbe, Ivo de Cumb, Alexander le Hore, Richard
the skinner (*pellipar'*).

OTHER INTERESTS

A1/53/13 [SC 11]   n.d. [*c.* 1150 × 1160]
Robert FitzHarding and Elias his brother.

Robert has granted to Elias in fee 1 hide of land in Combe, which Robert bought from
Mahihele son of Ansger de Combe; for the service of one fifth of a knight's fee.
Witnesses: Lady Eve, Maurice, Nicholas, Robert, Robert's sons, Alan de Furnellis, Odo son
of William, Adam de Saltemareis, Nigel son of Arthur, Roger de Stintescombe, Harding de
Stintescombe, William son of Bernard, Richard son of Harding de Couele, Ralph de
Draicote, Simon son of Richard de Couele, Roger de Scai, Henry de Saltemareis, Robert de
Hanum.

WOTTON: HAW PARK

A1/54/1 [GC 507]   Eve of St. Laurence [9 Aug.] 1283
Thomas de Berkeley and Kingswood Abbey.

The abbey has agreed that Thomas may enclose into his park of Hawe the land between
the garden of the monks called Wyneerd and the park.

WOTTON: HUNTINGFORD

BERKELEY INTERESTS

A1/55/1 [GC 2220]   8 March 11 Edw. II [1318]
John [C]hausy of Alderley and Sir Maurice de Berkel', son and heir of Sir Thomas de
Berkel'.

John has granted to Maurice, for a certain sum of money, all his meadow called
[El]ynemed at Hunteneford in Wottone; to Maurice and his issue, rent for 20 years a rose a
year, and afterwards 40*s.* a year.
Witnesses: . . . Richard de Wyke of Nibley, Richard ate Churche, John le Skey of Nibley,
Walter Bellamy.
At: Wotton.

A1/55/2 [GC 2265]   The Purification, 12 Edw. II [2 Feb. 1319]
John de Chausy of Nibley and Sir Maurice de Berkeleye, son and heir of Sir Thomas de
Berkeleye.

John has granted to Maurice, for a certain sum of money, all his meadow in the meadow
called Elynemed at Huntenford in Wottone, with the reversion of the dower in the same
meadow; to Maurice and his issue, rent a rose a year for 20 years, and 60*s.* a year thereafter.
Witnesses: William Colewich, Roger de Berleye, Warin son of William, Thomas de Wyke,
John le Skey of Nibley.
At: Wotton.

THE VEEL MANOR

The Veels held Huntingford as a sub-manor of Wotton manor as a quarter of a knight's fee.[1]

---

[1] Smyth, iii. 234.

A1/55/3 [GC 342] n.d. [late Hen. III]
Eleanor de Alrely and Sir Robert le Veel.

Eleanor has granted to Robert the corner of her meadow of Huntingeford, which extends to Robert's garden; Robert has given her 28s. 8d.
Witnesses: Elias de Cumbe, Peter de Stintescumbe, Bartholomew de Olepenne, Ivo de Cumbe, Thomas le Archer, Richard de Colewiche, Nicholas de Culkerton.

A1/55/4 [GC 1566] n.d. [*temp.* Edw. I]
Robert le Veel and Robert de Stone.

Robert le Veel has granted to Robert de Stone a part of his demesne land of Huntenford called Sybelyehale; rent a rose a year.
Witnesses: Walter de Chaldefeeld, Robert de Bradestone, William de Burgo, William de Cumbe, Richard de Colewyth, Adam de la Cnolle.

WOTTON: NIBLEY

BERKELEY INTERESTS
The Woodford holding in Nibley and Pedington (in Ham)

A1/56/1 [SC 73] n.d. [*c.* 1200]
John de Wodeford and Juliana de Ponte Arche, wife of Robert de Berkeleia.

John has granted to Juliana a half-virgate of land with 15 a. of assart in Nubbeleia, which John recovered from Margaret the wife of Odo son of William; Juliana has given John 70s. of silver and a gold ring for acknowledgement, and will hold the land at a rent of 1 lb. of cumin at Michaelmas.
Witnesses: Adam son of Nigel, Oliver de Berkelaia, Bernard de Stanes, Bernard de Cromhale, Richard de Cromhale, Reginald de Gosintuna, Roger de Boivill, Maurice de Berkel', William de Berkel', Walter the chaplain, Henry the chaplain, Harding de Hunteneford, Maurice son of Nigel, Bernard de Brotheston.

A1/56/2 [SC 74] n.d. [*c.* 1200]
Juliana wife of Robert de Berkeley and Richard de Pinkeni.

Juliana has granted to Richard the half-virgate of land with appurtenances which she holds of John de Wodeforde; to hold of John for the same services, i.e. 1 lb. of cumin at Michaelmas.
Witnesses: The abbot [William] of Kingswood, Adam son of Nigel, John de Erlei, Robert son of Richard, Ralph the chaplain, Master John de Godestan, Master William de Bristol, Robert Musard, Peter Fish (*Piscis*), Henry the clerk of Berkeley, Reginald de Chamme.

A1/56/3 [GC 565] n.d. [late Hen. III]
Richard de Pynkeneya and Sir Maurice lord of Berkeley.

Richard has granted to Maurice all the land in the vill of Nibeleya which he had by grant of Lady Juliana wife of Sir Robert de Berkel'; to hold of John de Wodeford at a rent to John of 1 lb. of cumin a year; further he has granted to Maurice all the land in Pedinton and 5 a. of land in the marsh which he had by grant of Sir Thomas de Berkel', Maurice's father.
Witnesses: Maurice de Saltmarsh (*de salso marisco*), Henry de Berkel', Richard de Cromhale, Roger de Lokinton, knights, Andrew de Brothestan, John de Egeton, Henry Habbehors, William Eustace, Robert Bastard.

A1/56/4 [GC 1584] n.d. [late Hen. III]
John de Wodeford and Maud de Berkel', daughter of Sir Maurice lord of Berkel'.

John has confirmed to Maud the land with appurtenances in Nibeleye which Maurice her father . . . to hold as John granted to Lady Juliana wife of Sir Robert de Berkel' . . .

Witnesses: Sir Maurice de Sautemareys, Sir Roger de Lokinton, Sir Henry de Berk', Andrew de Bratheston, John de Egeton, Thomas Mathias, William Eustace, Adam Coby, John Sewaker.

A1/56/5 [GC 841]   n.d. [late Hen. III]
John de Wodeford and Sir Maurice lord of Berkel'.

John has quitclaimed to Maurice the land in the vill of Nibel' which Arnold in la Felde once held with the rents etc. and all the services which Maud de Berkel', daughter of the said Maurice de Berkel', and her heirs owed and rendered to him and his heirs.
Witnesses: Sir Richard de Cromhal, Sir Roger de Lokinton, Sir Walter de Burg', knights, Maurice de Ston, Peter de Wyke, Richard de Wyk, Robert Bastard, John de Egeton.

The Basset Holding

A1/56/6 [SC 406]   n.d. [*temp.* Hen. III]
Matthew le Schay and Lady Joan de Berkeley.

Matthew has quitclaimed to Joan [4] a. of land in Moldeclive and Beckedescombe.
Witnesses: Sir Henry de Berkeley, Thomas de Rodeberge, Michael le Venur, . . . , Robert Brun, Richard de Pedyntun.

A1/56/7 [GC 713]   n.d. [*temp.* Hen. III]
Adam son of Thomas de Byverichesleye and Sir Maurice lord of Berkel'.

Adam has quitclaimed to Maurice the land in Byverichesl' which Royers de Beverichesl' had by grant of Sir Robert de Berkel'.
Witnesses: Sir Richard de Cromhal, Sir John Mautravers, Sir Maurice de Saltmarsh (*de salso marisco*), Sir Roger de Lokinton, Andrew de Brotheston, John de Egeton, Maurice de Stan, Nicholas Ruffus, William de Berkel'.

A1/56/8 [GC 1218]   n.d. [late Hen. III]
Richard de Berkel, knight, and Master John de Sechevile.

Richard has granted to John 10 a. of land with appurtenances in the vill of Nubbeleye, which he had by grant of Lady Joan de Berkel', his mother, of which 6 a. lie towards Byverchesl' in the field of Teppecumbe below Haselhurste and 4 a. lie in the fields of Nubeley (3 a. in Modesclive and 1 a. in Beckedescumbe); rent 1*d.* a year, and John has given Richard 12 marks.
Witnesses: Sir Robert le Veel, Sir William Maunsel, Sir Bartholomew de la More, knights, Elias de Cumbe, Richard de la Grave, Richard de la Chireche, William de Wyke.

A1/56/9 [GC 1217]   n.d. [1265 × 1280]
Richard de Berkeley; and Sir Anselm Basset and Margaret his wife.

Richard has granted to Anselm and Margaret, and Anselm's heirs, 30½ a. of land in the vills of Camme and Chosleye, viz. at Chosleye 3 a. held of James Cotele, 7 a. held of Adam Fynch, 3 a. held of Richard Duc and 1 a. held of Robert de Chosleye, and at Camme 16½ a. held of Adam the cook (*cocus*), and a rent of 1*d.* from Sir Robert le Veel for 18 a. of land in Huntoneford and a rent of 2*d.* from Master John de Siccavilla for 10 a. of land, of which 6 a. was of Rose de Byverlychesleg' and 4 a. was of Matthew le Schey.
Witnesses: Sir Maurice de Berkelay, Sir Walter de Bromthon', Sir William de Mancel, knights, Miles de Langetot, Peter de Stintecumbe, Elias de Cumba, Robert de Olepenne, Robert de Benecumbe, Ralph de Camme, Walter de Chaldefeud, Richard de Sanford.

Bradley exchanges

A1/56/10 [GC 702]   n.d. [1281 × 1300]
Thomas de Berkeley and Richard de Bradeley.

Thomas has granted to Richard a certain plot of land in the field of Bekedescumb in the furlong called Lungefurlung next to the road, in exchange for a certain plot which Richard has granted to him in the field called Middel next to the road from Wotton to Hawe Park, which Richard held of him in the manor of Wotton.[1]

Witnesses: Sir Robert de Berkel', Bartholomew de Olepenn, Elias de Cumbe, Robert de Stone, Peter de Stintescumb, William de Cumbe, Ivo de Cumbe.

A1/56/11 [GC 1238]   n.d. [1281 × 1300]

Thomas de Berkel' and Richard de Bradeleye.

Thomas has granted to Richard a plot of his land in the field of Beckedecumbe, in the furlong called Scorteforlunge, next to the road from Wuttone to Nubbeleye, in exchange for two plots of land, one in the field called Myddel, next to the road from Wuttone to Hawe Park, to the west, and the other in the field called Thistelslade to the east of the said road.

Witnesses: Sir Robert de Berkel, Bartholomew de Olepenne, Elias de Cumbe, Robert de Stan', Peter de Stintescumb, William de Cumbe, Ivo de Cumbc.

The Puttock grant

A1/56/12 [GC 3466]   Mon. after Michaelmas, 31 Edw. III [2 Oct. 1357]

John Pottok and Alice his wife; and Sir Thomas lord of Berkele.

John and Alice have granted to Thomas, his heirs and assigns all their lands and holdings in Nubbeleye in the hundred of Berkele.

Witnesses: John Draycote, Robert Coueleye, John de Olepenne, Elias de Berleye, Thomas Skay.

At: Nibley.

A1/56/13 [GC 3484]   Three weeks after Easter, 33 Edw. III [12 May 1359]

Thomas de Berkele; and John Pettok and Alice his wife

Final concord concerning a messuage and 3 a. of land in Wottone Underegge; John and Alice have acknowledged the right of Thomas and have quitclaimed for themselves and Alice's heirs, and Thomas has given them 10 marks.

At: [Westminster].

A1/56/14 [GC 3499]   n.d. [*c*. April 1359]

(1) Robert de Hildesle, sheriff of Gloucester; (2) Sir Thomas de Berkele of Berkeley; (3) John Puttok and Alice his wife.

Robert has received from Thomas 6*s*. 8*d*. for licence to agree with John and Alice for the holding in Wottone Underegge for the terms of Trinity and Michaelmas 32 Edw. III and Hilary and Easter 33 Edw. III.

Other

A1/56/15 [GC 1232]   n.d. [1281 × 1300]

Thomas de Berkel' and William de Burgo of Nibley.

Thomas has granted to William a half-virgate which Richard le But formerly held in villeinage in the vill of Nubbeleye; rent 20*s*. a year.[1]

Witnesses: Sir Robert de Berkel', Peter de Stintescumbe, Elias de Cumbe, William de Cumbe, Warin son of William.

A1/56/16 [GC 1117]   1 May 34 Edw. I [1306]

John de Berkelee and Sir Thomas de Berkelee, his father.

John has remitted and quitclaimed to Thomas his claim in 2 marks rent and other services from Richard de Wyke at Sharnclive in Nebbelee.

Witnesses: Robert de Bradeston, Robert de Berkelee, Thomas de Beolee, Thomas de Styntescombe, Robert atte Churche.

At: Berkeley.

[1] *Transcript*: Smyth, iii. 275.

A1/56/17 [GC 2820]   Mon. after St. John before the Latin Gate, 9 Edw. III [8 May 1335]
Isabel widow of Sir Maurice de Berkeleye and John de Nybbeleye.

Isabel has granted to John the reversion of the holding which Richard le Smyth of
Nybbel' holds of her for life, in Nibbeleye; to John for the term of Isabel's life.
Witnesses: John le Skay, John le Hunte, Walter Belamy, Roger le Duynysssche, Richard
Draysyd.
At: Wotton.

A1/56/18 [GC 4358]   23 March 10 Edw. IV [1470]
William Berkeley, lord of Berkeley and Wotton, knight, and his beloved brother, Maurice
Berkeley, esquire.

William has granted to Maurice an annual rent of 10 marks, for his life, from the vill of
Nybbeley (Glos.).

OTHER INTERESTS
Preth holdings conveyed to John de Sackville

A1/56/19 [GC 336]   Easter [24 April] 1272
Amicia daughter of Adam Preth, late of Nibley, and Master John de Secchevile.

Amicia has granted to John a croft in Swinhay called Dedecroft, 1 rod and a hedge; rent
1*d.* a year.
Witnesses: Elias de Cumbe, Richard de Bradeley, Roger le Skay, William de Wike, Richard
de la Grave.
At: Wotton.

A1/56/20 [GC 340]   1272
Cecilia widow of Adam Preth and Master John de Secchevile.

Cecilia has quitclaimed to John whatever right she has in dower in the croft in Swinheye
called Dedecroft, 1 rod and a hedge.
Witnesses: Elias de Cumbe, Richard de Bradeleye, Roger le Skay, William de Wyke,
Richard de la Grave.
At: Wotton.

A1/56/21 [GC 338]   n.d. [*c.* 1272]
Amicia Preth, daughter and heir of Adam Preth, and Master John de Sicca Villa.

Amicia has granted to John 1 a. of land in the fields of Nubbelegh lying in the furlong
called Forlond; rent ½*d.* a year, and John has given her 8*s.*
Witnesses: Sir Robert le Veel, knight, Elias de Cumbe, John le Schay, Thomas of the church
(*de ecclesia*), Roger le Schay.

A1/56/22 [GC 337]   n.d. [*c.* 1272]
Amicia Preth and Master John de Sechevill.

Amicia has granted to John ½ a. of land in the field of Nubbel called Forlond; rent 1*d.* a
year, and John has given her 2*s.* 8*d.*
Witnesses: Richard de Bradel', John le Schay, Robert de Wik, William de Wik, William le
Frend, Walter le Frend.

A1/56/23 [GC 339]   n.d. [*c.* 1272]
Amicia Preth, daughter of Adam Preth late of Nibley, and Master John de Secchevile.

Amicia has granted to John all that land called Upstotenelond in the field called
Frothlond; rent 1*d.* a year.
Witnesses: Elias de Cumbe, Richard de Bradeleye, John le Schay, Roger le Schay, William
de Wyke.

A1/56/24 [GC 1518]   n.d. [*temp.* Edw. I]
Amicia Preth, daughter and heir of Adam Preth, and Master John de Sicca Villa.

Amicia has granted to John two thirds of 1 a. of land in the field of Nubbel', in the furlong called Holewehechene, in the northern part; rent ½*d.* a year, and he has given her 5*s.*
Witnesses: Elias de Cumbe, Ivo de Cumbe, John le Schay, Thomas of the church (*de ecclesia*), Robert de Wike, William de Wike.

Scay grant to Kingswood Abbey

A1/56/25 [GC 1537]   n.d. [*temp.* Edw. I]
John le Scay of Nibley and Kingswood Abbey.

John has granted to the abbey a mill at Bisford, with the meadow to the south of the millpond, and two crofts, one called Homcrofte and the other Pikedecroft.
Witnesses: Robert le Veel, William Maunsel, knights, Richard de Bradeleye, Thomas de la Chireche of Nibley, William de Knabwelle, Walter de Chaldefeld, Ivo de Cumbe.

A1/56/26 [GC 1702]   St. Barnabas, 2 Edw. II [11 June 1309]
John le Scay, son and heir of John le Scay of Nibley, and Kingswood Abbey.

John le Scay has inspected the charter of his father granting to the abbey the mill at Bisford with appurtenances and confirms it.
Witnesses: Robert de Bradeston, Robert de Berkeleye, Thomas de Lude, Thomas de Beoleye, Thomas de Swonhungre, Robert Wyther, Richard de Wyke, William Colewich, Robert de la Churche, Warin son of William, John Hermon.

Other

A1/56/27 [SC 404]   n.d. [late Hen. III]
Peter son of Matthew le Schey, and Kingswood Abbey.

Peter has granted to the abbey, for the support of a lamp to burn daily at the mass of the Blessed Virgin, a messuage which he was given by John le Schey, his uncle, at Bisford near the road, close to the bridge called Bisfordesbruge.
Witnesses: Sir Robert le Veel, knight, Sir John de Wautone, knight, Elias de Cumbe, Thomas le Archer, Richard Colewiche.

A1/56/28 [GC 2674]   Sun. before St. Gregory, 3 Edw. III [5 March 1329]
Adam de Lorewyng and Roger de Beverston.

Adam has quitclaimed to Roger 3½ a. of land which Roger had by enfeoffment of Adam in Nubbel' within the manor of Wottone.
Witnesses: John de Milkesham, John le Skay, Richard le Duynyssh, Walter Belamy, Richard le Caumvyle, John le Frend.
At: Nibley.

A1/56/29 [GC 3418]   Mon. after Michaelmas, 28 Edw. III [6 Oct. 1354]
William Swonhongre, cousin and one of the heirs of Thomas de Stone; and Walter Hurste and Joan his wife, cousin and coheir of the said Thomas.

Indenture between William, and Walter and Joan, to divide a messuage and 1 virgate of land in Nibbeleye, viz. of the messuage, William shall have the hall and the high chamber with half of the garden except three apple trees, and Walter and Joan shall have the grange and the house called Waynhous and half of the garden with the three apple trees, and of the land, William shall have the eastern half and Walter and Joan the western, as they have measured it. [*In French.*]
At: Berkeley.

WOTTON: ULEY

BERKELEY INTERESTS
Peter de Uley to William de Berkeley

A1/57/1 [SC 432]   Fri. before St. Dunstan [12 May] 1262
Peter de [Uley] and Sir William de Berkeley, knight.

Peter has granted to William all his land in Ywelege, . . . , and all his land in Schubbeleg', . . ., and all his land in Brunesleg', . . . ; and in return William has granted to Peter a certain holding in Bradel' for life and 50 marks in acknowledgement.
Witnesses: Sir Maurice de Berkeley, Sir John de Wauton, Sir Maurice de Saltmarsh (*de salso marisco*), Sir Richard de Berkeley, Robert de Kingestun, Elias de Cumb, Thomas le Archer.

A1/57/2 [GC 305]   Fri. before St. Dunstan [12 May] 1262
Peter de Ywel and Sir William de Berkeley, knight.

Peter has granted to William all his land in the vill of Ywel [*detailed*] with his tenants, escheats, wardships etc., and for this William has granted to him a holding in Bradley for life and has given him 40 marks in acknowledgement.
Witnesses: Sir Maurice de Berkeley, Sir John de Wauton, Sir Maurice de Saltmarsh (*de salso marisco*), Sir Richard de Berkeley, Robert de Kingeston, Elias de Cumbe, Thomas le Archer.

A1/57/3 [SC 216]   n.d. [*c.* 1262]
Peter de Yweleye and Sir William de Berkeleye, knight.

Peter has granted to William all his lands with all appurtenances in Yweley, for which gift William has given him 50 marks in acknowledgement.
Witnesses: Sir Maurice de Berkele, Sir Maurice de Saltmarsh (*de salso marisco*), Nigel de Kyngescote, Bartholomew de Olepenne, Robert de Kyngestone, Robert de Ywele, Peter de Stintescumbe, John de Brothestane.

A1/57/4 [GC 299]   Michaelmas [29 Sept.] 1262
Amicia daughter of Peter de Ywel and Sir William de Berkeley, knight.

Amicia has quitclaimed to William the lands, woods and rents in Ywel which he had of the gift of her father Peter de Ywel, and in return William will maintain her until Michaelmas and will provide her with 1 virgate of land for her marriage or becoming a nun.
Witnesses: Elias de Cumb, Robert le Veel, Robert de Kingeston, Peter de Stintescumb, John de Brothestan, Roger de Camme, William de Wike, Laurence de Wike.

Thomas (I) Lord Berkeley to his daughter Margaret

A1/57/5 [GC 1222]   n.d. [mid Hen. III]
Thomas de Berkel' and Margaret his daughter.

Thomas has granted to Margaret half of the manor of Eweleg' and half of the mill, also 1 virgate of land which Idonia de Estgate formerly held of Thomas; to her and her issue, for the service of a quarter of a knight's fee and two suits each year to the hundred court.[1]
Witnesses: Sir William Large (*Grassus*) the elder, Sir Odo son of William, Henry de Berkel', Peter de Stintescumba, Simon de Ollopenn, Walter de Burgo, John de Duresleg', Thomas Mauduit, Nicholas Ruffus, Roger de Camme, John de Draicot.

A1/57/6 [GC 436]   n.d. [*c.* 1240]
Thomas de Berkel and Margaret his daughter.

Thomas has granted to Margaret half of his manor of Eweleg, including the services of the land which Walter de Sancto Jacobo, Adam Stut, John de Egkenton and Walter of the churchyard (*de cimiterio*) held of him in fee, the land and persons of nine villeins, and half

---

[1] *Transcript*: Smyth, iii. 182

of the mill; to her and her issue, for the service of a quarter of a knight's fee and two suits to the hundred court each year.[1] Endorsed: *Borrowed of Wm. Basset anno 1606.*

Witnesses: Sir William Large (*Grassus*) the elder, Odo son of William, Richard de Cromhale, Peter de Stintescumba, Henry de Berkel', Simon de Ollepenn', Richard de Brumelham, Philip de Cromhale, Nicholas Ruffus, John de Draicot, Henry le Drois, Roger de Camma.

OTHER INTERESTS
Lude holding in Uley and Owlpen

A1/57/7 [GC 1381]   n.d. [*temp.* Edw. I]
Walter de Gloucestre, knight, and Thomas de Luda.

Walter has granted to Thomas 30 a. of land in the vills of Iweleye and Olepenne which he had by grant of Bartholomew de Olepenne and Peter Jakes. Endorsed: *Borrowed of William Basset Esq. 19 Oct. 1606.*

Witnesses: Sir Robert rector of Iweleye, Robert de Bradestone, Maurice de Camme, John de Olepenne, John de Iweleye, Henry de Camme, Robert atte Churche of Nibley.

A1/57/8 [GC 2525]   n.d. [*temp.* Edw. II]
Thomas de Lude; and Richard de Lude and John de Lude, his brothers.

Thomas has granted to Richard and John an annual rent of a rose from Adam Shaterel, chaplain, for lands and holdings which Adam holds for life by Thomas's grant in the vills of Yweley and Olepenne, with the reversion of the lands after Adam's death, and also the holding which Christine de la Grenestrete held by Thomas's grant in the vill of Yweley and afterwards released to him; they have given him £40. Endorsed: *Borr. of Wm. Basset Esq. 19 Oct. 1606.*

Witnesses: John de Olepenne, Robert atte Churche of Nibley, Robert de Benecombe, Richard de Estmede, Walter Araz, John Simond, Adam de Tettepenne.

Other

A1/57/9 [GC 3917]   Thurs. in the conversion of St. Paul, 20 Ric. II [25 Jan. 1397]
Hugh Pepir and Margaret his wife, widow of Robert Clavylle late burgess of Bristol; and William Clavylle of Gloucestershire.

Whereas William has a holding in the parish of Uley within the hundred of Berkeleye called Clavylesplace, of which one third pertains to Margaret in dower, the reversion of that third belonging to William after her death, Hugh and Margaret have granted to William their status in the holding, and for this William has granted to them that he will render to them 3 qr. of wheat a year during Margaret's life.
At: Uley.

WOTTON: WORTLEY
BERKELEY INTERESTS
Exchange with William de Coombe

A1/58/1 [SC 164]   n.d. [1281 × 1298]
Thomas de Berkeley and William de Cumbe.

William has granted to Thomas the half-virgate of land in Wotton which William de Wyke formerly held of him, and Thomas has granted to William, for life, the virgate of land at Wurtheleye in Wotton manor which Peter de Hawe formerly held in villeinage.

Witnesses: Sir Robert de Berkeley, Sir William Daubigny, Sir Roger de Lokinton, Elias de Cumbe, Bartholomew de Olepenne, Robert de Stane, Yvo de Cumbe.

A1/58/2 [GC 693]   n.d. [*temp.* Edw. I]
Thomas lord of Berkel and William de Cumbe.

Thomas has granted to William a half-virgate in the vill of Wutton, viz. that which he had by grant from the same William in exchange for 1 virgate at Wurteleye which William

---

[1] *Transcript*: Smyth, iii. 182–4.

held of Thomas for life; to William and his heirs, rent 30s. a year, and William has given him 40s.

Witnesses: Sir John de Chausy, knight, Peter de Stintescumb, Elias de Cumbe, Walter de Chaldefeld, Ivo de Cumbe, Henry the baker (*pistor*), Alexander le Hore.

Agreement with Kingswood Abbey regarding Haw Park

A1/58/3 [GC 1026]   Christmas Day, 30 Edw. I [25 Dec. 1301]
Kingswood Abbey and Sir Maurice de Berkel, son and heir of Sir Thomas de Berkel'.

The abbey has granted to Maurice 1 a. of land lying in the field of Wrtelegh, between the footpath from Wotton to Kyngeswod, and extending above the rhine from Hawebrugg to Kyngeswode next to his park of Hawe, with the monks' right to common of pasture in all the land between the footpath and the rhine and between the rhine and the park, and Maurice has granted to the abbey free passage to the park.

Witnesses: Sir Thomas de Berkel', lord of Berkeley, Sir Thomas his son, Sir William de Wauton, knights, Robert de Bradeston, Walter de Chaldefelde, Thomas de Swanhungre, Robert de la Chureche, of . . . , bailiff of Wotton, John de Bradeford, clerk.

A1/58/4 [GC 1456]   n.d. [1301 × 1312]
Kingswood Abbey and Sir Maurice de Berkeleye, son and heir of Sir Thomas de Berkeleye.

The abbey has quitclaimed to Maurice 1 a. of land in Wrtelegh, between the footpath from Wottone to Kyngeswod and the rhine from Hawebrugge to Kyngeswod, next to his park of Hawe, and common of pasture in all the land between the footpath and the park, to be enclosed in the said park.

Witnesses: Sir Nicholas son of Ralph, Sir John de Sancto Laudo, Sir Thomas de Berkeleye, son of Sir Thomas de Berkeleye, Sir William de Wauton, knights, Robert de Bradeston, Henry de Chamme, Thomas de Swonhungre.

Other

A1/58/5 [GC 2699; *duplicate* GC 2700]   1 April 4 Edw. III [1330]
Thomas lord of Berkelee and Walter de Coumbe.

Thomas has granted to Walter and his issue a plot of land called le Churchehey containing $^1/_8$ a. at Wirteleye within the manor of Wottone, to build a chapel in honour of St. John the Baptist; rent 1d. a year. If Walter dies without issue it will remain to Elias de Coumbe, his brother, and his issue, with remainder to Thomas and his heirs. For this Walter has promised that all the chaplains celebrating in the chapel will have Thomas in memory when celebrating masses there.

Witnesses: John de Melkesham, John le Skay, Robert de Couelee, William Corteys, William de Coumbe.

At: Berkeley.

COOMBE HOLDINGS
The Bacon holding

A1/58/6 [GC 837]   n.d. [late Hen. III]
John de Waterchip and William son of William de Cumbe.

John has quitclaimed to William the holding in Wrtheleg' in the parish of Wotton which Reginald Bacon his uncle held of Wotton church, and William has given him 20s.

Witnesses: Sir Henry de Berk', Sir Thomas de Radeleg', Elias de Cumbe, Peter de Stintescumb, Reginald de Igetesbur', Thomas le Archer, Robert Harding.

A1/58/7 [GC 317]   Wed. after St. Mark the evangelist, 53 Hen. III [1 May 1269]
Agatha de Writtel, daughter of Robert the cook (*cocus*) of Bristol, and William de Combe.

Agatha has quitclaimed to William land in the vill of Writtel which Reginald Bacon once held, concerning which a plea was heard between them before the king's justices itinerant in Gloucestershire.

Witnesses: Sir William le Mansel, Walter de Wall, Peter de Stintescombe, Nigel de Kingiscote, Roger de la Berge, Robert de Dreicote, Robert Wyc.

At: Gloucester.

Acquisition of the Archer virgate

A1/58/8 [GC 346]   n.d. [late Hen. III]
Thomas son of Thomas le Archer of Wortley and William de Cumbe.

Thomas has granted to William, for 60 marks, 1 virgate of land in the vill of Wyrtele which William held of him for life and a half-virgate which Maud his mother holds in dower; rent a clove a year.

Witnesses: Sir John de Chausi, knight, Walter de Chalvesfeld, Robert le Franseys, Peter de Stintescombe, Maurice de Berkele, Robert the clerk.

A1/58/9 [GC 1160]   n.d. [late Hen. III]
Thomas le Archer, son of Thomas le Archer, and William de Cumbe.

Thomas has quitclaimed to William a messuage and 1 virgate of land in the vill of Writtelee and 1 a. of meadow lying in the meadow called Matteford.

Witnesses: Sir John de Chaucy, knight, Elias de Cumbe, Geoffrey de Chaucy, John Denlee, Geoffrey Reynebaud.

Caylly marriage settlement, 1318

A1/58/10 [GC 2590]   n.d. [*c.* 1318]
William de Combe of Wortley (Glos.) and John de Caylly.

William has granted to John, his heirs and assigns all his holdings in Wyrteleye and in Wottone and in all other places in Gloucestershire, with all the appurtenances.

Witnesses: John de Annesleye, deputy constable of Bristol Castle, Elias de Fylton.

A1/58/11 [GC 2591]   n.d. [*c.* 1318]
William de Combe of Wortley (Glos.) and Maud de Caylly, daughter of John de Caylly.

William has granted to Maud a messuage in the vill of Wottone by Kyngeswode with 20 a. of land in the west field of the same vill, viz. 8 a. lying between the vill and le Stonystyle, 2 a. between Combe and Sinewell, and 10 a. between the cross of Worteleye and le Stonystyle; for life, rent 1*d.* a year.

Witnesses: [*unfinished but sealed*].

A1/58/12 [GC 2239]   Thurs. before St. John the Baptist, 11 Edw. II [22 June 1318]
John de Combe and Maud his wife; and William de Combe, John's father.

John and Maud have leased to William all the lands which they had by grant of John de Caylly in Wyrtel' and Wottone, with all the appurtenances except a messuage and 20 a. of land which William previously gave to Maud; for his life, rent 38*s.* 8*d.* a year.

Witnesses: Sir John de Chausy, Roger de Berleye, John le Skay.

At: Wortley.

A1/58/13 [GC 1301]   n.d. [*c.* 1318]
John de Combe, son and heir of William de Combe of Wortley, and Maud daughter of John de Caylli; and William de Combe of Wortley, John's father.

John and Maud have granted to William, for his great benevolence, each and every holding in the vill of Worteleye and in Wotton (Glos.), with all the appurtenances, except a messuage and 20 a. of land which William previously granted to Maud, which holdings William granted to them; for William's life.

Witnesses: [*unfinished*].

Grants by John de Coombe

A1/58/14 [GC 2743]   Sat. after St. Gregory, 6 Edw. III [14 March 1332]
John son and heir of William de Coumbe and William Corteys, clerk.

John has leased to William, for his life, 1 a. of land in le Estfeld of Worteleye, beside the land of Kingswood Abbey appurtenant to le Walkemulle, extending beyond Romescoumbe; rent a rose a year.
Witnesses: John Lydyard, Geoffrey de Wottone, Walter Sephdem, Roger Hayl, Richard Wynterbourne.
At: Wortley.

A1/58/15 [GC 2791]   28 April 8 Edw. III [1334]
John de Cumbe, son and heir of the late William de Cumbe of Wortley, and Walter le Schepherde of Wortley.

John has granted to Walter, his heirs and assigns 1 a. of land in the east field of Wurtel' below Sondayseshulle; rent a rose a year.
Witnesses: Walter de Cumbe, Nicholas Lovekoc, Roger Hayl.
At: Wortley.

A1/58/16 [GC 2818]   Sat. the eve of Easter, 9 Edw. III [15 April 1335]
John son and heir of William de Combe of Wortley; and William Curteys of Wotton, Agnes Trenchesoil his wife and Nicholas their son.

John has leased to William, Agnes and Nicholas 2 a. of land in the west field of Wrteleye; for their lives, rent a rose a year.
Witnesses: John Lydiard, Walter de Combe, Geoffrey de Wottone, Walter le Schephurde, Nicholas Lovekoc.
At: Wotton.

A1/58/17 [GC 3006; *duplicate* GC 3007]   Sun. before St. Edmund the king, 15 Edw. III
                                                                    [18 Nov. 1341]
John de Combe, son of the late William de Combe of Wortley, and Thomas his brother.

John has leased to Thomas a plot within the enclosure by John's garden and le Weleserd; for life, rent 2*d.* a year.
Witnesses: Elias de Combe, William de Combe, Roger Hayl.
At: Wortley.

Sale by Maud de Coombe

A1/58/18 [GC 3296]   n.d. [*c.* 1384]
Maud widow of John de Combe of Wortley; and Sir Adam Dangerville, chaplain, and John Howes.

Maud has granted to Adam and John, and their heirs and assigns, all the lands, holdings, rents and reversions which she has in Wottone and Worteleigh and elsewhere in Gloucestershire.
Witnesses: Elias Daubeneys, Elias de Berleigh, Thomas Skay, John Draicote, Richard Schausy.

A1/58/19 [GC 4308]   n.d. [*c.* 1384]
Henry de Neuport; and Sir Adam Daungerville, chaplain, and John . . .

Henry has quitclaimed to Adam and John the lands and holdings which they had by grant of Maud de Coumbe in Worteleye and elsewhere in Berkele hundred.

A1/58/20 [GC 3782]   18 Jan. 8 Ric. II [1385]
Adam Daungervylle, chaplain; and William FitzWaryn and Ralph Coke.

Adam has granted to William and Ralph, and their heirs and assigns, all the lands,

holdings, rents [etc.] that he had in Wottone and Wortelegh and elsewhere within Gloucestershire.
Witnesses: Ralph Waleis, Henry Waryner, John Joye, Thomas Skay, Laurence Juwet.
At: Wotton.

Other

A1/58/21 [GC 850]   n.d. [1243 × 1276]
John del Overayne, son of Master Robert le Masun of Salebyr', and William de Cumbe.

John has granted to William, for 40 marks, a messuage and a half-virgate in the vill of Wottone which he held of Lady Joan de Berkele, who holds the vill in dower, and a quarter-virgate and messuage in the vill of Wurtele, held of Joan.
Witnesses: Sir Robert de Tridehull, Elias de Cumbe, Walter de Chaldefelde, Peter de Stintescumbe, Maurice de Berkelee, Robert de Bradestone, Robert de Dreikote.

A1/58/22 [GC 2257]   St. Martin, 12 Edw. II [11 Nov. 1318]
Clarice widow of William de Combe and Walter de Combe, her son.

Clarice has granted to Walter, for her life, all her lands and holdings with appurtenances in Wurtelegh which she holds in dower, as appears by the indenture by which she was dowered by Sir Thomas lord of Berkelegh; rent 40*s.* a year.
Witnesses: John de Chausy, lord of Alderley, Laurence de Tresham, William Colewich, Roger de Berlegh, John le Scay, William Warlemound, Nicholas Lovecok.
At: Wortley.

A1/58/23 [GC 2466]   Sat. in All Saints, 20 Edw. II [1 Nov. 1326]
William de Combe of Wortley; and William the cook (*cocus*) del Ende and Maud his first wife.

William de Combe, with the assent of John his son and heir, has granted to William and Maud 1½ a. of land in the west field of Worteleye, of which 1 a. lies in Holobrok and ½ a. in Alreham beside the stream which runs through the abbey of Kyngeswode against Wyneshulle; for their lives and for one year after their deaths, rent 12*d.* a year.
Witnesses: Nicholas Lovecok, Roger Hayl of Wortley, John de Slymbrugge, William le Dressour, Edward the cook (*cocus*) del Ende.
At: Wortley.

A1/58/24 [GC 2849]   Sun. the eve of St. Mary Magdalen, 10 Edw. III [21 July 1336]
Joan widow of William de Combe; and Geoffrey Neel, son of Geoffrey Neel, baker of Wotton, and Joan his wife.

Joan has leased to Geoffrey and Joan 6 plots of land and 2 of meadow and pasture; for her life, rent 6*s.* a year.
Witnesses: William Curteys, Nicholas Lovecoke, Walter le Schepherde, John Wylotes, Roger Hayl.
At: Wotton.

THE MATSON HOLDING

The holding extended into Cam and Alkington and eventually passed to Thomas (II) Lord Berkeley *c.* 1301.

GRANTS TO WILLIAM DE MATSON BY NICHOLAS AND JOHN DE CRAWLEY IN ALKINGTON
A1/59/1 [GC 1323]   n.d. [early Edw. I]
Nicholas de Crauleye and William de Mettesdun.

Nicholas has granted to William all his meadow in Matforde between the meadow of Maurice de Stan' and the meadow formerly held by Cecilia de Stan'; rent 12*d.* a year, and William has given him 2 marks.

Witnesses: Maurice de Stan', Ralph de Angervill, John de Berk', Henry Marescall, Adam Mutun, Robert le Herde, Sir Richard chaplain of Bradestone.

A1/59/2 [SC 362]   n.d. [*temp.* Hen. III]
Nicholas de Crauleg' and William de Mettesdune.
   Nicholas has granted to William the croft which William the smith of Berkeley once held of him; rent 1*d.* a year, and William has given Nicholas 2½ marks.
Witnesses: Thomas Mathias, Philip de Leycestria, John de Egetun, John de Brodeston, Adam Nel, William son of Eustace, Robert le Herde.

A1/59/3 [GC 1324]   n.d. [early Edw. I]
Nicholas de Crauleygh and William de Mettresdun.
   Nicholas has granted to William all his meadow in Matford between the meadow of Maurice de Stan' and the meadow formerly held by Cecilia de Stan'; rent 2*d.* a year, and William has given him 36*s.*
Witnesses: Peter de Wik, John de Egeton, Thomas de Wik, Adam son of Nigel, Thomas Math', John Sewaker, Adam Coby.

A1/59/4 [GC 737]   n.d. [*temp.* Edw. I]
Nicholas de Crauleg' and William de Mettesdune.
   Nicholas has granted to William 4 a. of land in the furlong called Netherebreche, rent 12*d.* a year, and William has given him 2 marks.
Witnesses: Philip de Leycestre, Peter de Wik, Thomas Mathias, John de Egetun, John de Brodestone, Adam Neel, Robert le Herde, Henry Marescall.

A1/59/5 [SC 361]   n.d. [*temp.* Hen. III]
Nicholas de Crauleyg and William de Mettesdune.
   Nicholas has granted to William the land called Netherebreche; rent 22½*d.* a year, for which William has given to Nicholas 5 marks and to Hawise, Nicholas's wife, 10*s.*
Witnesses: Sir Nicholas vicar of Berkeley, Thomas Mathias, John de Egetun, Philip de Leycestria, Peter de Wike, Adam Mutun, Robert le Herde, Adam Nel, Henry Marescall.

A1/59/6 [GC 1319]   n.d. [*temp.* Edw. I]
John son and heir of Nicholas de Crauleg'; and William de Mettesdon and Isabel his wife.
   John has quitclaimed to William and Isabel 2*s.* 7½*d.* of their rent of 3*s.* 7½*d.* which they owe for the holding that they had from Nicholas de Crauleg' his father, viz. the rent for the holding shall now be 12*d.* a year; they have given him 2 marks.
Witnesses: Peter de Wik, Peter de Stintescumb, Walter de Egeton, William de Egeton, John Sewaker, William Herith, Nicholas de Wodeford, Robert the marshal (*marescallus*), Walter Grip, Walter de Stintescomb, clerk.

A1/59/7 [GC 1321]   n.d. [*temp.* Edw. I]
John de Crauleg', son and heir of Nicholas de Craul'; and William de Mettesdon and Isabel his wife.
   John has granted to William and Isabel a croft called Puricroft at Kekesfled, which he had by grant of Gilbert son of Edwin de Longebrugg of Berkeley; rent 2*s.* a year, and they have given him 10 marks.
Witnesses: Sir Thomas de Evercy, knight, Peter de Stintescumbe, Robert de Brotheston, Walter de Egeton, Nicholas de Wodeforde, Robert the marshal (*marescallus*), William Herith, William de Wik, Adam Motun, Walter de Stintescomb, clerk.

A1/59/8 [GC 1208]   n.d. [late Hen. III]
Maurice de Berk' and William de Mettesdone.

Maurice has granted to William free ingress to the croft which he had by grant of John de Crauley, which was of Gilbert Edwyne.

Witnesses: John de Craul', William Herith, Richard Averey.

A1/59/9 [GC 895]   n.d. [late 13th cent.]
John de Crauleye and William de Mettesdon.

John has quitclaimed to William the land called Overebreche, that called Netherebrech, that called Smithescroft, that called Puricroft and 1 a. of meadow in Matford; to hold of John, rent 3*s*. a year.

Witnesses: Robert de Stan', Robert de Bradeston, Thomas de Swonhungre, Robert Bastard, Richard le Savoner, clerk.

A1/59/10 [GC 611]   St. Laurence, 24 Edw. I [10 Aug. 1296]
John de Crauleye and Thomas de Berkel'.

John has sold to Thomas a rent of 3*s*. from William de Mettesdon for Purycroft, Overebreche, Netherebreche and Smytecroft.

At: Berkeley.

A1/59/11 [GC 612]   n.d. [*c*. 1296]
John de Craweleye and Sir Thomas de Berkeley.

John has sold to Thomas the rent of 3*s*. from William de Mettesdon for Puryecroft, Overebreche, Netherebreche and Smytecroft, saving free ingress and egress for himself and his heirs to his house towards the church and vill of Berkeleye, for a certain sum of money.

Witnesses: Sir Robert de Berkel', Sir Robert le Veel, Sir Richard de Rivers (*de Ripar'*), knights, Richard de Byseleye, Robert de Stane, Robert de Bytlescumbe, Maurice de Camme, Henry de Camme, Robert Wither.

GRANTS TO WILLIAM DE MATSON BY JOHN DE ALBEMARLE IN CAM AND STINCHCOMBE
A1/59/12 [GC 661]   n.d. [late Hen. III]
John de Albemarl; and William de Mettesdon and Isabel his wife.

John has granted to William and Isabel 11 selions of land in the field of Bollecroft, lying between the land of William Hathewi and the land of Nicholas de Stanleg'; rent a rose a year at Mettesdon, and William has given him 20*s*.

Witnesses: Peter de Wik, John de Brothestan, Peter de Stintescumb, Ralph de Camme, John de Egeton, Thomas the serjeant (*servians*), John de Crauleg', Nicholas de Wodeford, Walter de Stintescumb, clerk.

A1/59/13 [GC 662]   n.d. [late Hen. III]
John de Albemarl; and William de Mettesdon and Isabel his wife.

John has granted to William all his land in the furlong [Schortest]ockes next to Stintescumb; to William and Isabel . . . 3*s*.

Witnesses: . . . Peter de Stintescumb, John de Brotheston, William de Camvill, William . . . , John de Craul', Walter de Stintescumbe, clerk.

A1/59/14 [GC 1157]   n.d. [late Hen. III]
John de Albemarl; and William de Mettesdon and Isabel his wife.

John has granted to William and Isabel all his land in the furlong called Tenrugge in Stintescumbe, and all his meadow called Lese next to the furlong called Broderuding, and all his meadow in the meadow of Hynwodesmed, and 11 selions of land in the field of Bollecroft, and all his land in the furlong called Schortestockes; and they have given him 7 marks.

Witnesses: Peter de Stintescumbe, Peter de Wike, John de Brothestan, William de Canvill,

Walter de Egeton, William de Wike, John de Craul', Adam Motun, William de Angervill, Walter de Stintescombe, clerk.

A1/59/15 [GC 852]   Sun. before the nativity of St. Mary, 18 Edw. I [3 Sept. 1290]
Edith widow of John de Abbemarle and William de Mettesdone.

Edith has quitclaimed to William her dower rights in the meadow called Inwodesmed, and he has given her 9*s.*
Witnesses: Peter de Stintescumbe, Thomas de Buleye, Robert de Bradeston, John de Crauleye, Thomas Alein, Richard le Savoner, clerk.
At: Berkeley.

GRANTS BY OTHERS TO WILLIAM DE MATSON IN ALKINGTON

A1/59/16 [GC 1156]   n.d. [before 1255]
William de Alba Mara, knight, and William de Mettresdon.

William de Alba Mara has granted to William de Mettresdon the land called Clohtlond lying between the heath (*bruera*) and the land which Walter de Kyneltre formerly held; rent 3*s.* a year, and William de Mettresdon has given him 8 marks.
Witnesses: Peter de Stintescumbe, Philip de Leycestre, John de Egeton, Nicholas de Crauleygh, John de Lorwing, Robert de Kineltre, Henry Marescall, Adam Moton, Walter Sely, clerk, Robert le Herde.

A1/59/17 [GC 1568]   n.d. [late Hen. III]
Martin Waleys (*Walensis*) of Purton and William de Mettesdune.

Martin has granted to William 1 a. of land in the furlong called Aketre; rent 2*d.* a year, and William has given him 16*s.*
Witnesses: John de Egetun, John de Brodestone, Nicholas de Crauleg', Adam Mutun, Robert le Herde, Henry the marshal (*marescallus*), William Eustace.

A1/59/18 [GC 379]   n.d. [late Hen. III]
Thomas de Evercy, knight, and William de Mettesdon.

Thomas has quitclaimed to William the house and buildings which Walter de Mettesdon, William's father, once held; and William has given him 20*s.* Endorsed: *Alkynton.*
Witnesses: Peter de Stintescumbe, John de Brothestan, John de Egeton, John de Craul', Thomas the serjeant (*serviens*), Osbert de Kyneltre, Thomas de Wike.

A1/59/19 [GC 2559]   n.d. [*c.* 1300]
Ralph Symon of Woodford and William de Mettesdon.

Ralph has granted to William, his heirs and assigns all his land in Baynham; rent a rose a year, and William has given him 40*s.*
Witnesses: Walter Moton, William de Kineltre, Adam de Lorewinge, William Gold, Richard the long (*longus*), William Pothering, Richard le Savoner.

A1/59/20 [GC 1241]   n.d. [*c.* 1300]
Thomas lord of Berkel'; and William de Mettesdon and Alice his wife.

Thomas has leased to William and Alice 2 a. of land of the holding which Geoffrey the forester (*forestar'*) and Simon his son held by grant of Sir Robert de Berkel' for their lives, in Baynham; for their lives, rent a rose a year.
Witnesses: Richard de Biseleye, steward, Robert de Stan', Robert de Bradeston, John de Crauleye, William Moton, Adam Godmon.

THE COMBINED HOLDING, AND ITS PASSAGE TO THOMAS (II) LORD BERKELEY

A1/59/21 [GC 1481]   n.d. [*temp.* Edw. I]
William de Mettesdon and Alice, daughter of Adam le Hayward of Hinton, his wife.

William has granted to Alice, in dower, for all the land which he has in the vills of

Berkeley, Stintescumbe and Camme, all his holding in Mettesdon; further, 9 a. of land and 1 a. of meadow, of which 6 a. lie in the furlong called Breche which he had by grant of Nicholas de Craweleye, 1 a. in the field called Stinthemefeld by grant of John de Aumarle, 2 a. in the field called Bainham by grant of Ralph Symundes of Woodford, and 1 a. of meadow in the meadow called Matford by grant of Nicholas de Craweleye; for her life.
Witnesses: Robert de Brothestone, Robert de Stone, William Capel, Thomas de Swonhungre, Richard de Stanford, Thomas Alayn, Adam Hathulf.

A1/59/22 [GC 1013]   Sun. the feast of St. Barnabas, 29 Edw. I [11 June 1301]
John Everard of Hinton and Sir Thomas lord of Berkeley.

John has quitclaimed to Thomas all the lands, holdings [etc.] which he may have inherited on the death of William de Mettesdone within the hundred of Berkeleye.
Witnesses: Robert de Bradeston, John de Egeton, Thomas le Serjant, John de Crauleye, Walter Moton, William le Gold, William de Webbeleye, clerk.
At: Berkeley.

A1/59/23 [GC 1042]   St. Gregory, 31 Edw. I [12 March 1303]
Thomas de Berckel', lord of Berkeley, and Alice widow of William de Mettesdone.

Thomas has granted to Alice the holding with two crofts which William had by grant of William de Aumarle, and four crofts called Overebreche, Netherbrech, Puricrofft and Smythescrofft with 1 a. of meadow in Matford which William had by grant of Nicholas de Crauweleye, John de Crauweleye and Robert de Bradestone, also 2 a. of land in Baynham with 1 a. in Aketre, all of which Thomas had by gift of John Everard, Thomas's villein and William's heir; for her life, rent 17*s.* a year.
Witnesses: Thomas de Beoleye, Robert de Bradestone, Thomas le Serjaunt, Walter Moton, Adam Hathulf, William Purlewent, clerk.
At: Berkeley.

A1/59/24 [GC 1119]   Thurs. in Ascension, 34 Edw. I [12 May 1306]
Thomas de Berkelee, lord of Berkeley; and Adam son of Walter Doucesone of Hinton and Joan his wife.

Thomas has granted to Adam and Joan the holding with two crofts which William de Mettesdone had by grant of William de Aumarle, also four crofts called Overebreche, Netherebreche, Puricroft and Smythescroft with 1 a. of meadow in Matford, which William had by grant of Nicholas de Crauweleye, John de Crauweleye and Robert de Bradestone, also 2 a. of arable land in Baynham and 1 a. in Aketre, which Thomas had by demise of John Everard, heir of William de Mettesdone; to them and their issue, rent 30*s.* a year to the manor of Camme.
Witnesses: Robert de Bradestone, Robert de Berkelee, Thomas de Beoleye, Walter Hathemare, Robert Wyther, Robert le Warner, William de Kyneltre.
At: Berkeley.

THE SYDE HOLDING

William de Syde, a priest, was one of Thomas (III) Lord Berkeley's most valued servants and he acted as Thomas's agent in creating chantry chapels at Syde, Cambridge (in Slimbridge), Newport (in Alkington) and Wortley (in Wotton) in 1343. It is unlikely, therefore, to be a coincidence that most of the charters connected with him are concerned with Alkington and Wortley, and it is likely that the acquisitions there were made with a view to providing for the chantry chaplains. William had other lands, however, and after his death *c.* 1352 his heir granted them to Thomas. It is a feature of William's charters that remarkably few are dated.

ACQUISITIONS IN ALKINGTON
The Morkyns holding in Alkington and Newport

Through Richard Aleyn

A1/60/1 [GC 3015]   Sat. the eve of St. Peter and St. Paul,[1] 16 Edw. III [28 June 1342]
John son and heir of William Morkyns of Newport and Richard Aleyn of Newport.

John has granted to Richard, his heirs and assigns all the lands and holdings in Alkyntone which he inherited after the death of his said father William and the reversion of the lands held in dower by Leticia Morkyns, his mother, of his inheritance in Alkyntone.
Witnesses: Stephen de Kyneltre, Richard le Feror, Henry le Eyr, Thomas le Woor, William Gryp.
At: Alkington.

A1/60/2 [GC 2575]   n.d. [*c.* 1344]
Richard Aleyn of Newport and Sir William de Syde.

Richard has granted to William, his heirs and assigns all the lands and holdings which he had by grant of John son and heir of William Morkyns of Newport, viz. that which he inherited on the death of his father in Alkyntone and Neweport, also all the reversions of lands held for lives in Alkyntone and Neweport.
Witnesses: John de Clyve, William Curteys, Robert Groundi, William Saundres, Thomas le Woor.

A1/60/3 [GC 3039]   n.d. [after 1342]
John son and heir of William Morkyns of Newport and Sir William de Syde.

John has quitclaimed to William all the lands, holdings and reversions which he inherited after the death of William Morkyns, his father, and which William [de Syde] had by grant of Richard Aleyn in Alkyntone.
Witnesses: John de Clyve, William Curteys, Robert Groundi.

Through John Cook

A1/60/4 [GC 3031]   Sun. after St. Edmund the archbishop, 16 Edw. III [17 Nov. 1342]
John Morsus, son and heir of William Morsus of Newport, and John Coc of Woodford.

John Morsus has granted to John Coc, his heirs and assigns a half-selion of land in the field called le Redeleye, and the reversion of one third of the said selion after the death of Leiticia, John's mother.
Witnesses: Stephen Kyneltre, Robert Dangervile, Thomas le Wyn, John le Tornor, Robert le Masun.
At: Newport.

A1/60/5 [GC 2593]   n.d. [*c.* 1344]
John Coc of Woodford and Sir William de Syde.

John has granted to William two thirds of a selion of land in the field called Redeleye in Alkyntone, with the reversion of the one third held in dower by Leticia widow of William Morkyns of Neweport, which he had by grant of John son and heir of William.
Witnesses: John de Clyve, William Curteys, Robert Groundi, Richard Aleyn, Henry le Heyr.

Through Stephen de Kyneltre

A1/60/6 [GC 2603]   n.d. [mid 14th cent.]
John son and heir of William Morkynes of Newport and Stephen de Kyneltre.

John has quitclaimed to Stephen the meadow in Matforde which he had by grant of William his father.

---

[1] The feast of St. Peter and St. Paul, 29 June, fell on Saturday in 1342; cf. below, A1/60/15 [GC 3016].

Witnesses: John de Egeton, John Sewaker, Thomas le Wor, Richard Aleyn, Adam Purlewent, clerk.

A1/60/7 [GC 3315]   n.d. [mid 14th cent.]
Stephen de Kyneltre and Sir William de Syde.

Stephen has quitclaimed to William all the lands, holdings and reversions which he had by grant of William Morkyns of Neweport and of John, William's son and heir, in Alkyntone.
Witnesses: John de Clyve, Robert Groundi, Richard le Feror, Henry le Heyr, Richard Aleyn.

The dower portion
A1/60/8 [GC 2604]   n.d. [mid 14th cent.]
Leticia widow of William Morkyns of Newport and Sir William de Syde.

Leticia has granted to William her part of two parcels of meadow in Matford which she had in dower, and which Stephen Kyneltre and Nicholas Cuc hold for their lives, in the manor of Alkyntone.
Witnesses: John de Clyve, William Curteys, Robert Groundi, William Saundres, Thomas le Woor.

A1/60/9 [GC 2605]   n.d. [mid 14th cent.]
Leticia widow of William Morkyns and Sir William de Syde.

Leticia has attorned and done fealty to William for all the lands which she holds in dower after the death of William her husband in Alkyntone and Neweport.
Witnesses: John de Clyve, Robert Groundy, Richard Aleyn.

A1/60/10 [GC 3338]   n.d. [mid 14th cent.]
John le Sergeant the younger and Sir William de Syde.

John has quitclaimed to William the lands and holdings which Leticia widow of William Morkyns holds in dower in Neweport.
Witnesses: William de Chiltenham, John de Clyve, Robert Groundy.

Other
A1/60/11 [GC 2586]   n.d. [*c.* 1344]
Richard son of Maurice Bernard of Newport and Sir William de Syde.

Richard has granted to William 5 selions of land in the field called Churchehull which he had by grant of Maurice his father for his [Richard's] life in Alkyntone, the reversion of which belongs to William by reason of the holding which he acquired from John Morkyn.
Witnesses: John de Clyve, William Curteys, Robert Groundi.

A1/60/12 [GC 2587]   n.d. [*c.* 1344]
John de Charefeld of Newport and Sir William de Syde.

John has granted to William a plot of land and a parcel of meadow in Alkyntone which he had by grant of John son and heir of William Morkyns of Neweport.
Witnesses: John de Clyve, Robert Groundi, Stephen de Kyneltre, Henry le Heir, Richard Aleyn.

Hayward grants in Alkington

Former Vithelar holdings
A1/60/13 [GC 2993; *duplicate* GC 2994]   Whit-Sunday, 15 Edw. III [27 May 1341]
Edith le Vythelare; and Henry le Hayward, Alice his wife and Thomas Imeke.

Edith has leased to Henry, Alice and Thomas a parcel of land in the field called Brerylond in Alkintone; for their lives, rent a rose a year.
Witnesses: John de Avene, Stephen de Keneltre, John ate Grene, Nicholas Schot, Richard Alayn.
At: Alkington.

A1/60/14 [GC 3012]   Whit-Sunday, 16 Edw. III [19 May 1342]
Edith la Vythelar and Henry le Hayward.

Edith has quitclaimed to Henry the land which Henry holds in the field called Brerylond in Alkintone.
Witnesses: Richard Aleyn, John de Lorwinge, John ate Grene, William ate Hurne, Nicholas Schot.
At: Alkington.

Former Morkyns holdings
A1/60/15 [GC 3016]   Fri. the eve of St. Peter and St. Paul, 16 Edw. III [28 June 1342]
John son and heir of William Morkyns of Newport and Henry le Haiward of Newport.

John has quitclaimed to Henry the meadow in Matforde which Alice, Henry's wife, holds for her life by grant of William, John's father, and Leticia his mother, in Alkyntone.
Witnesses: John Sewaker, Stephen de Kyneltre, Thomas Snyte, Thomas le Wor, Richard Aleyn.
At: Alkington.

A1/60/16 [GC 3307]   n.d. [mid 14th cent.]
Henry le Hayward of Newport and Sir William de Syde.

Henry has granted to William, his heirs and assigns a parcel of meadow in Mathforde, which he had by grant of John son and heir of William Morkines of Neuport, and a parcel of land in the field called Brerylond and a curtilage, which he had by grant of Edith Vithelar, in Alkyntone.
Witnesses: John de Clyve, William Curteys, Robert Groundi, Richard Aleyn, William Gryp.

A1/60/17 [GC 3043]   Sat. before St. Laurence, 17 Edw. III [9 Aug. 1343]
William de Syde; and Henry le Heyward of Alkington and Alice his wife.

William has leased to Henry and Alice a parcel of meadow in the meadow of Mathforde in Alkyntone; for Alice's life, rent 2*d.* a year.
Witnesses: John de Clyve, William Curteys, Robert Groundi, Richard Alayn, William Gryp.
At: Alkington.

Lorridge grants in Alkington and Ham
A1/60/18 [GC 3066; *duplicate* GC 3067]   Sat. after St. Luke, 17 Edw. III [25 Oct. 1343]
Maurice de Lorewynge and Sir William de Syde.

Maurice has granted to William 2 a. of land, of which one lies in the field called Aketre in Alkyntone and the other in le Westfelde in Hamme; for the term of Maurice's life.
Witnesses: William de Chiltenham, John de Clyve, Robert Groundy, Stephen de Kyneltre, John Payn.
At: Berkeley.

A1/60/19 [GC 3088]   n.d. [*c.* 1343]
Maurice de Lorewynge and Sir William de Syde.

Maurice has granted and quitclaimed to William all the lands and holdings which William holds in Hamme, Berkelee and Alkyntone and elsewhere within the hundred of Berkelee.
Witnesses: John de Clyve, Robert Groundy, Richard Aleyn.

Former Veysy holding in Alkington
A1/60/20 [GC 2768]   Tues. before St. Gregory, 7 Edw. III [9 March 1333]
Thomas called le Coke of Dursley; and John called le Copyner of Tortworth and Alice his wife.

Thomas has leased to John and Alice the messuage with a curtilage and 16 a. of land lying enclosed in the field called Knottefeld, with two water-mills, one a corn mill and the other a fulling mill, with their ponds and races, which messuage, land and mills Richard le Enveysy formerly held at Wyke in Alkyntone; to John and Alice for their lives, rent 3s. a year.

Witnesses: Walter de Coumbe, John de Milkesham, Nicholas Kuc, Stephen Kyneltre, Richard le Ferur.

At: Wick.

A1/60/21 [GC 2592]   n.d. [*c.* 1344]
John le Copener of Tortworth and Sir William de Syde.

John has leased to William the messuage with a garden, curtilage and 16 a. of enclosed land in the field called Knottefelde and two water-mills, viz. a corn mill and a fulling mill, with their millponds and races, which Richard le Enveysy formerly held and which he had by lease of Thomas le Cooke of Dursleye for the term of Thomas's life, at Wyke in Alkyntone; to William for Thomas's life, rent 3s. a year to Thomas and the customary services to the chief lord of the fee.

Witnesses: John de Clyve, William Curteys, Robert Groundy, Richard Aleyn, Henry le Eyr.

A1/60/22 [GC 3095]   1 June 18 Edw. III [1344]
Thomas son and heir of John called le Cooke of Dursley and Sir William de Syde.

Thomas has quitclaimed to William an annual rent of 3s. from the lands which William holds by grant of John le Copener of Torteworthe, for the term of Thomas's life, in Alkyntone, a messuage, garden, curtilage and 16 a. of land in the field called Cnottefeld and two water-mills.

Witnesses: John de Clyve, Robert Groundy, Richard Aleyn, William Dosy, Henry le Heyr.

At: Berkeley.

A1/60/23 [GC 3097]   Sun. before St. Laurence, 18 Edw. III [8 Aug. 1344]
Alice widow of John le Mareschal and Sir William de Syde.

Alice has quitclaimed to William the lands which William had by grant of John le Copyner of Torteworthe, in Wyke within the manor of Alkyntone, which were sometime of Richard le Veysi her father.

Witnesses: John de Clyve, William Corteys, Robert Groundy, Richard Aleyn, William le Gryp.

At: Alkington.

The Bernard holding of meadow in Matford

A1/60/24 [GC 2697]   Mon. before St. Gregory, 4 Edw. III [5 March 1330]
William son of Maurice Bernard of Newport and Stephen de Kyneltre.

William has leased to Stephen 1 a. of meadow in the meadow called Matford; for life, rent a rose a year.

Witnesses: Walter de Coumbe, Adam Moton, Adam de Metesdone, William Cocc, William Gryp, William Godynou.

At: Newport.

A1/60/25 [GC 2696]   Mon. before St. Gregory, 4 Edw. III [5 March 1330]
(1) William son of Maurice Bernard of Newport; (2) Adam Moton; (3) Stephen de Kyneltre.

William has appointed Adam his attorney to give seisin to Stephen of 1 a. of meadow in Matford.

At: Newport.

A1/60/26 [GC 3314]   n.d. [mid 14th cent.]
Stephen de Kyneltre and Sir William de Syde.

Stephen has granted to William, his heirs and assigns 1 a. of meadow in Matforde in Alkyntone which he had by grant of William son of Maurice Bernard of Neweport.

Witnesses: John de Clyve, Robert Groundi, Richard le Feror, Henry le Heyr, Richard Aleyn.

The Potter land and meadow in Alkington

A1/60/27 [GC 802]   n.d. [mid 14th cent.]
William Potuur; and John de Lorwynge and Edith his wife.

   William has granted to John and Edith all his land in the field called Kyngesfethele and
one piece of meadow in Alkintone; to hold of the chief lord of the fee.
Witnesses: John de Avene, Stephen de Keneltre, John ate Grene, Richard Aleyn, Nicholas
Schot.

A1/60/28 [GC 3317]   n.d. [mid 14th cent.]
Edith widow of John de Lorewynge of Matson and Sir William de Syde.

   Edith has granted to William, his heirs and assigns all the land and meadow in
Kyngesvithele which she and John acquired from William Potuur in Alkyntone.
Witnesses: John de Clyve, Robert Groundi, Richard Aleyn.

A1/60/29 [GC 3342]   n.d. [mid 14th cent.]
John de Swanleye and Sir William de Syde.

   John has quitclaimed to William the land and meadow which William had by demise of
Edith widow of John de Lorewynge of Mettesdone, and which John and Edith had by
demise of William Potuur in Kyngesvythele in Alkyntone.
Witnesses: John de Clyve, Robert Groundy, Richard Aleyn.

The Henley holding in Alkington

A1/60/30 [GC 2600]   n.d. [*c*. 1344]
Richard de Henleye of Newport, carpenter, and Sir William de Syde.

   Richard has granted to William, his heirs and assigns a messuage, 14 a. of land, 2 a. of
meadow and 1 a. of wood in Alkynton.
Witnesses: William de Chiltenham, John de Clyve, William Curteys, Robert Groundy,
Richard Aleyn.

A1/60/31 [GC 3305]   n.d. [mid 14th cent.]
Robert son of William le Gryp of Newport and Sir William de Syde.

   Robert has quitclaimed to William a messuage, 14 a. of land, 2 a. of meadow and 1 a. of
wood in Alkynton which William had by grant of Richard de Henleye of Neweport,
carpenter.
Witnesses: William de Chiltenham, John de Clyve, Robert Groundy, Walter Payn, Richard
Aleyn.

A1/60/32 [GC 3343]   n.d. [mid 14th cent.]
William de Syde; and Richard de Henlegh of Newport, carpenter, and Isabel his wife.

   William has leased to Richard and Isabel a messuage and 10 a. of land, 2 a. of meadow
and 1 a. of wood in Alkyntone; for Isabel's life, with reversion to William and his heirs
without impediment from Isabel's heirs.
Witnesses: William de Chiltenham, John de Clyve, William Curteys, Robert Groundy,
Richard Alein.

The Robert holding in Newport

A1/60/33 [GC 2960]   Wed. the feast of St. Matthew, 13 Edw. III [24 Feb. 1339]
Alice widow of Thomas Robat; and Margery, Emma and Walter her children.

   Alice has granted to Margery, Emma and Walter a house in Neweport; to them and their
heirs.
Witnesses: Stephen de Keneltre, Henry le Heyr, William le Gryp, Richard Aleyn, Nicholas
le Schot.
At: Newport.

A1/60/34 [GC 3058]   Sun. after the translation of St. Thomas the martyr, 17 Edw. III
[13 July 1343]
Walter, Margery and Emma, children of Alice widow of Thomas Robat; and William
Maltman of Newport.

Walter, Margery and Emma have granted to William, his heirs and assigns the plot in
Neuport which they had by grant of the said Alice.
Witnesses: Stephen de Kyneltre, Henry le Heir, Nicholas Skot, Thomas le Wor, William le
Grip.
At: Newport.

A1/60/35 [GC 2601]   n.d. [mid 14th cent.]
William le Maltman of Newport and Sir William de Syde.

William le Maltman has granted to William de Syde, his heirs and assigns the plot of land
which he had by grant of Walter, Margery and Emma, children of Alice Robat, in Alkyntone.
Witnesses: John de Clyve, William Curteys, Robert Groundy, Richard Aleyn, Henry le
Heyr.

The Sely holding acquired by Syde and passed to Newport chapel

A1/60/36 [GC 2161]   Sat. after the Annunciation, 10 Edw. II [26 March 1317]
Nicholas son and heir of Adam Sely of Newport; and Robert Groundy, Sibyl his wife and
Robert their son.

Nicholas has leased to Robert, Sibyl and Robert his messuage in Neuport, with a garden
and curtilage, and all his land in Riham, with reversion of the one third held in dower by
Alice Sely his mother, also a rent of 16*d.* from Edith and Isabel, his sisters, and their heirs
for two cottages in Neuport; for their lives, rent 3*s.* 6*d.* a year.
Witnesses: John le Serjant, Walter Sewaker, John le Cuppere, Roger le Cuppere, Henry de
Killecote, Maurice Bernard, Adam le Herde.
At: Newport.

A1/60/37 [GC 3054]   28 May 17 Edw. III [1343]
Nicholas Sely son and heir of Adam Sely of Newport and Sibyl widow of Robert Groundy
of Berkeley.

Nicholas has quitclaimed to Sibyl all the lands, holdings and reversions that Sibyl and
Robert her son hold in Neuport in the manor of Alkyntone, for their lives, by his grant.
Witnesses: John de Clyve, Robert Groundy, William Curteis, Richard Aleyn, Henry le Heir.
At: Berkeley.

A1/60/38 [GC 3053]   28 May 17 Edw. III [1343]
John son and heir of Nicholas Sely of Newport and Sibyl widow of Robert Groundy of
Berkeley.

John has quitclaimed to Sibyl all the lands, holdings and reversions that Sibyl and Robert
her son hold in Neuport in the manor of Alkyntone, for their lives, by grant of Nicholas his
father.
Witnesses: John de Clyve, Robert Groundy, William Curteis, Richard Aleyn, Henry le Heir.
At: Berkeley.

A1/60/39 [GC 3304]   n.d. [mid 14th cent.]
Sibyl widow of Robert Groundy of Berkeley and Sir William de Syde.

Sibyl has granted to William, his heirs and assigns all the lands, holdings and reversions
which she had in Neuport within the manor of Alkyntone by grant of Nicholas son and heir
of Adam Sely.
Witnesses: John de Clyve, William Curteys, Stephen de Kyneltre, Richard Aleyn, Henry le
Eyr.

A1/60/40 [GC 3303]   n.d. [mid 14th cent.]
Robert son of Robert Groundy of Berkeley and Sir William de Syde.

Robert has quitclaimed to William all the lands, holdings and reversions in Neuport within the manor of Alkyntone [which he had by grant of] Sibyl Groundy his mother.
Witnesses: John de Clyve, Stephen. . . , Henry le Heir.

A1/60/41 [GC 3323]   n.d. [mid 14th cent.]
Alice Mortymer of Newport and Sir John Snede, keeper of Newport chapel.

Alice has quitclaimed to John and his successors one third of 1 a. of land in Ryham in Selyescrofte in Alkyntone.
Witnesses: Richard Aleyn, Stephen Kenultre, William Grip.

Other grants to Syde in Alkington

A1/60/42 [GC 3070]   1 Nov. 17 Edw. III [1343]
William de Syde and William Dosy of Alkington.

William de Syde has granted to William Dosy ½ a. of land in the field of Ryham in Alkyntone in exchange for ½ a. of land in the same field.
Witnesses: John de Clyve, William Curteys, Robert Groundy, Richard Aleyn, Henry le Eyr.
At: Berkeley.

A1/60/43 [SC 513]   11 April 18 Edw. III [11 April 1344]
Maurice de Berkeley, son of Maurice de Berkeley, and Sir William de Syde.

Maurice has granted to William the rent of 2*s.* a year due from a messuage and curtilage in Neweport in the manor of Alkyngton, which Reginald de Milkesham holds of Maurice for life, and the reversion of the holding after Reginald's death.
Witnesses: Sir Thomas lord of Berkeley, Maurice his son, John de Milkesham, John le Serjaunt, John Capel.
At: Berkeley.

A1/60/44 [GC 3198]   Tues. the morrow of the Conception, 22 Edw. III [9 Dec. 1348]
Elias de Combe and Sir William de Syde.

Elias has surrendered to William 1 a. of land in the field called Wynleye within the manor of Alkyntone, which he held of William for his life.
Witnesses: John de Clyve, William Curteys, Roger de Estham.
At: Beverston.

A1/60/45 [GC 3337]   n.d. [mid 14th cent.]
John le Sergeant the younger and Sir William de Syde.

John has granted to William an annual rent of 4*d.* from William Gryp and Leticia his wife for 3 a. of land which they hold of John for their lives in Alkyntone, with the reversion of the holding after their deaths, the reversion of 1 a. of land beside the said 3 a. after the death of Maud wife of Walter de Whytefelde, which she holds in dower, an annual rent of ½*d.* from Henry Jones and his wife Agnes for 1 a. of land which they hold of John for their lives in Baynham, and the reversion after their deaths.
Witnesses: William de Chiltenham, John de Clyve, Robert Groundy.

A1/60/46 [GC 2612]   n.d. [mid 14th cent.]
Edith la Vithelere, daughter and heir of Alice la Vithelere of Newport, and Sir William de Syde.

Edith has granted to William, his heirs and assigns a garden between Goldelone and the holding of Henry le Hayward in Alkyntone, also 2½ a. of land of which 3 parcels lie in the field of Hawe and 1 a. in the field of Hamstal in Alkyntone.
Witnesses: John de Clyve, Robert Groundi, Henry le Heyr, Richard le Feror, Richard Aleyn.

A1/60/47 [GC 3334]   n.d. [mid 14th cent.]
Walter Saundres of Woodford and Sir William de Syde.

Walter has quitclaimed to William the land [etc.] which William had by grant of Walter in
Wodeford within the manor of Alkyntone.
Witnesses: John de Clyve, William Curteys, Robert Groundy, Richard le Chaloner, John Cuc.

A1/60/48 [GC 2608]   n.d. [mid 14th cent.]
Alice widow of Thomas Robat of Newport and Sir William de Syde.

Alice has granted to William, his heirs and assigns a parcel of land which was of the
curtilage of Robert Mareschal of Newport, and concedes to him a path called Leyelone, in
Alkyntone.
Witnesses: John de Clyve, Robert Groundy, John Cuppare, Richard Aleyn, Henry le Eyr.

A1/60/49 [GC 3306]   n.d. [mid 14th cent.]
Henry le Hayward of Newport and Sir William de Syde.

Henry has granted to William, his heirs and assigns a parcel of land in the field of
Wlmesworthy, which he had by grant of John de Lorwynge of Mettesdone, in Camme and
Alkyntone.
Witnesses: Robert Groundy, Richard Aleyn, Henry le Eyre, Thomas le Wor, Richard le Ferour.

A1/60/50 [GC 3324]   n.d. [mid 14th cent.]
Alice widow of Roger de Mortemer of Newport and Sir William de Syde.

Alice has granted to William, his heirs and assigns 1 a. of land in the field of Ryham, viz.
that which she had from Sir Thomas lord of Berkelee in exchange for 1 a. of land in the
field of Oldebury, in Alkyntone.
Witnesses: John de Clyve, Robert Groundy, Richard Aleyn, Henry le Heyr, William le Gryp.

Leases in Alkington
A1/60/51 [GC 3069]   Thurs. after St. Luke, 17 Edw. III [23 Oct. 1343]
William de Syde; and Richard Selewyne and Nicholas his son.

William has leased to Richard and Nicholas the holding in Wyke called Holtesholding
(except for the dovecot, the meadow called Smalemed, the grange [*grannettum*] called
Wythladdesgrof and a parcel of land called Wythladdescroft), in Alkyntone; for their lives,
rent 22*s.* a year.
Witnesses: William de Chiltenham, John de Clyve, Roger de Estham, Robert Groundy,
Stephen Kyneltre.
At: Berkeley.

A1/60/52 [GC 3177]   20 March 22 Edw. III [1348]
William de Syde; and Richard le Carpenter and John his son.

William has leased to Richard and John a messuage with a curtilage and 5 selions of land
in Neuport and 2½ a. of land in Ryham and Hamstal, in Alkyntone; for their lives, rent
9*s.* 2*d.* a year.
Witnesses: Stephen de Kyneltre, John de Swanleye, Richard Aleyn, Thomas Wor, Nicholas
Skot.
At: Newport.

ACQUISITION APPARENTLY IN BERKELEY
A1/60/53 [GC 3291]   n.d. [mid 14th cent.]
John Coby of Berkeley the elder and Sir William de Syde.

John has leased to William the croft which he had by lease of Walter son and heir of
Roger le Cuppere of Berkelee, in Berkelee.
Witnesses: Robert Groundy, Richard le Panit', John Sewaker, John Gamelef, John Byl.

ACQUISITION OF THE SAUL HOLDING IN CAM

A1/60/54 [GC 2745; *duplicate* GC 2746]   Sun. the feast of the Assumption of St. Mary,[1]
6 Edw. III [16 Aug. 1332]

Roger atte Stile of Cam and John called le Blake of the same.

Roger has leased to John, for 12*s.*, a parcel of his garden called Heriethehey with the house built on it; for life, rent 2*s.* a year.

Witnesses: John de Draykote, John de la Wodende, Robert Passelewe, Robert de Draykote, Walter Selymon.

At: Cam.

A1/60/55 [GC 2753; *duplicate* GC 3341]   Sun. after the Exaltation of Holy Cross, 6 Edw. III
[20 Sept. 1332]

Roger atte Stile of Cam and John called le Blake of Cam.

Roger has leased to John a parcel of his garden in Camme called Heriethehey beside the stream of Corietes Flodyete; for Roger's life, rent 12*d.* a year and 1 bu. of pears.

Witnesses: Robert Passelewe, Robert de Draykote, Roger of the hall (*de aula*), Walter Selymon.

At: Cam.

A1/60/56 [GC 2973]   5 July 14 Edw. III [1340]

Roger ate Stile of Cam and Sir William de Syde.

Roger has surrendered to William, his heirs and assigns a messuage, a garden called Herietheheye and 1½ a. of land in the fields of Nethere Camme in the furlong called Gorbrodlond, which Roger held for life of William by grant of Richard de Salle.

Witnesses: John de Clyve, Robert Groundy, William Curteys, Roger de Estham.

At: Berkeley.

A1/60/57 [GC 2555]   n.d. [mid 14th cent.]

John Seliman son of Walter Seliman of Cam and William de Syde.

John has leased to William, his heirs and assigns a messuage and croft formerly of Richard de Salle in Camme; to hold of the chief lord.

ACQUISITIONS IN HAM
The Earl half-acre of meadow in Parham

A1/60/58 [GC 644]   Michaelmas, 26 Edw. I [29 Sept. 1298]

Richard le Erl of Newport and Agnes his wife; and Richard ate Slo, son of Adam ate Slo, of Ham.

Richard and Agnes have leased to Richard ate Slo ½ a. of meadow in Perhamesmor; for the lives of Richard and his wife, for a certain sum of money.

Witnesses: Robert Bastard, Richard Averey, John Sewaker, John le Cuppere, Henry de Hamme, John Purlewent, Richard le Sopere.

A1/60/59 [GC 1701]   St. Barnabas, 2 Edw. II [11 June 1309]

Richard le Erl of Newport and Alice his daughter.

Richard has granted to Alice all his land in the field called Berclewode, beside the road from Weneswelle to Berkel', and all his land in the field called Kyngesfithele, and the reversion of ½ a. of meadow in Perham, held by Richard ate Slo for the lives of himself and Margaret his first wife; to her and her issue, rent to the chief lord 16*d.* a year.

Witnesses: John le Cuppare, Roger le Cuppare, Robert Bastard, Richard Pothering, Alan Marescall.

At: Newport.

---

[1] The feast of the Assumption, 15 Aug., fell on Saturday in 1332.

A1/60/60 [GC 2924]   Thurs. before St. Edmund the king, 12 Edw. III [19 Nov. 1338]
Alice le Erl, daughter and heir of Richard le Erl of Newport; and Robert Groundy of
Berkeley, Agnes his wife and Robert, Robert's son.

Alice has granted to Robert, Agnes and Robert all her land in the field called lesser
Berklewode, and also the reversion of ½ a. of meadow in Perhamme which Margery widow
of Richard ate Slo holds for life.
Witnesses: John Cuppere, Henry de Modybrok, Alexander de Bathe, John le Bil, William le
Vygnur, John Payn, John le Schipward.
At: Berkeley.

A1/60/61 [GC 3302]   n.d. [mid 14th cent.]
Robert Groundy of Berkeley and Sir William de Syde.

Robert has granted to William, his heirs and assigns ½ a. of meadow in Perhame which
he had by grant of Alice la Eorl in Hamme.
Witnesses: William de Chiltenham, John de Clyve, William Curteys.

The Lorridge holding
A1/60/62 [GC 783]   n.d. [late 13th cent.]
Adam de Lorewinge; and William de Mettesdone and Alice his wife.

Adam has granted to William and Alice all the land in his furlong called Aketre, next to
the road from Lorewinge to Berkeleye; rent 8*d.* a year, and they have given him £4 15*s.*
Witnesses: Robert de Bradeston, John de Crauleye, Thomas the serjeant (*serviens*), William
Capl', Richard de Wenden, Thomas Aleyn, Roger Coby.

A1/60/63 [GC 3322]   n.d. [mid 14th cent.]
Robert de Mettesdone, son and heir of Adam de Mettesdone, and John de Clyve.

Robert has granted to John, his heirs and assigns all his land in Aketre within the manor
of Hamme, viz. the land which Adam de Lorwynge granted to William de Mettesdone and
Alice his wife.
Witnesses: John de Milkesham, John de Egetone, John de Lorwynge, Stephen de Kyneltre,
Adam Purlewent.

A1/60/64 [GC 3290]   n.d. [mid 14th cent.]
John de Clyve and Sir William de Syde.

John has granted to William, his heirs and assigns all his land in Aketre within the manor
of Hamme, viz. the land which he had by grant of Robert son and heir of Adam de
Mettesdone.
Witnesses: William Curteys, Robert Groundy, Stephen de Kyneltre, Richard Aleyn, Henry
le Heyr.

ACQUISITIONS IN HILL
The Forthay holding
A1/60/65 [GC 2741]   Wed. after St. Valentine, 6 Edw. II [18 Feb. 1332]
Richard atte Fortheye of Rockhampton and Sir William de Syde.

Richard has granted to William, his heirs and assigns all the lands which he had by grant
of Thomas atte Fortheye, his brother, in Hulle.
Witnesses: John Capel, Thomas Aleyn, John de Swonhungre, John de Egeton, John Purlewent.
At: Hill.

A1/60/66 [GC 2742]   Wed. after St. Valentine, 6 Edw. III [18 Feb. 1332]
(1) William de Syde; (2) John de Clyve and Robert Groundy; (3) Richard atte Fortheye.

William has appointed John and Robert his attorneys to receive seisin of the lands which
he had by grant of Richard in Hulle.
At: Berkeley.

Fowler's land

A1/60/67 [GC 2995]   Sun. in Holy Trinity, 15 Edw. III [3 June 1341]
Robert le Foulare of Hill by Berkeley (Glos.) and William ate Polle.

Robert has granted to William, his heirs and assigns all the land and holdings, rents [etc.] that he had in fee within the said manor of Hulle; for the customary services to the chief lord.
Witnesses: William Martel, Gilbert Tynedane, Thomas Aleyn, Walter le Mareys, Richard Russel.
At: Hill.

A1/60/68 [GC 2996]   Sun. in Holy Trinity, 15 Edw. III [3 June 1341]
Robert le Voulare and John le Voulare his brother; and William ate Polle.

Robert and John have quitclaimed to William the lands and holdings which they had by lease of Thomas ate Fortheigh for their lives in Holecroft, within the manor of Hulle by Berkleigh (Glos.), and 1 a. of meadow called la Wyldepurye by lease of Gilbert Tynedane for their lives.
Witnesses: Gilbert Tynedane, William Martel, Thomas Aleyn, Richard Russel, Walter le Mareys.
At: Hill.

A1/60/69 [GC 3329]   n.d. [mid 14th cent.]
William atte Pulle of Hill and Adam Purlewent of Ham.

William has granted to Adam, his heirs and assigns all the lands and holdings in Hulle which he had by grant of John le Voulare and Robert his brother.
Witnesses: John son of Nicholas, John Purlewent, Walter Mareis, Richard Jussel [*recte* Russel], Thomas Aleyn.

A1/60/70 [GC 3330]   n.d. [mid 14th cent.]
Adam Purlewent and Sir William de Syde.

Adam has granted to William, his heirs and assigns the messuage and land which he had by grant of William atte Pulle, called Foulareslond, in Hulle by Berkelee.
Witnesses: John de Clyve, Robert Groundy, John Purlewent.

A1/60/71 [GC 1624]   n.d. [*temp.* Edw. III]
Gilbert Tyndone of Rockhampton and Sir William de Syde.

Gilbert has quitclaimed to William a meadow called P. . . ymede which William holds for life . . .
Witnesses: John de Clyve, William Curteys, Robert Groundy.

The Mandeware holding

A1/60/72 [GC 3120]   Thurs. after Holy Trinity, 19 Edw. III [26 May 1345]
William ate Pulle of Hill and Maud le Kynges.

William has granted to Maud, her heirs and assigns all the lands and holdings which he had by grant of William le Maundewere in Hulle.
Witnesses: Thomas Aleyn, Richard Russel, John Malot, Nicholas Thomas, John Waynter.
At: Hill.

A1/60/73 [GC 3313]   n.d. [mid 14th cent.]
Maud le Kynges of Hill and Sir William de Syde.

Maud has granted to William, his heirs and assigns all the lands and holdings which she had by grant of William ate Pulle of Hulle, in Hulle by Berkeleye, and which William ate Pulle had by grant of William le Maundewere.
Witnesses: John de Clyve, Robert Groundy, John Purlewent, John Bastard, Adam Purlewent.

A1/60/74 [GC 2602]   n.d. [mid 14th cent.]
Christine widow of William Maundewere of Bristol and Sir William de Syde.

Christine has quitclaimed to William her dower rights in the lands which were of William Maundewere and which William de Syde holds in Hulle by Berkelee.
Witnesses: None.

Other acquisitions
A1/60/75 [GC 2959]   Fri. before St. Laurence, 13 Edw. III [6 Aug. 1339]
William atte Pulle of Hill and Sir William de Syde.

William atte Pulle has granted to William de Syde, his heirs and assigns all the lands, holdings and reversions which he had by grant of Thomas atte Fortheye of Rochampton, in Hulle by Berkelegh.
At: Berkeley.

ACQUISITION OF THE KINGSTON HOLDING IN SLIMBRIDGE
A1/60/76 [GC 2247]   Wed. after the translation of St. Thomas [of Canterbury], 12 Edw. II
[12 July 1318]
Roger de Gosyntone; and John son of Nicholas de Kyngestone and Mabel his wife.

Roger has granted to John and Mabel, for a certain sum of money, 5 selions and a gore of land in the furlong called Dodyforlong, beside the road called Cammestrete leading from Cambrugge to Camme; to them and John's heirs.
Witnesses: Roger Archer, Walter de Gosyntone, William Botyler, John Duyk, Thomas de Kyngestone, Thomas Hallyng, Walter Oldelonde.
At: Gossington.

A1/60/77 [GC 3032]   Thurs. after St. Lucy, 16 Edw. III [20 Dec. 1342]
Thomas son of John de Kyngeston and Sir William de syde.

Thomas has granted to William, his heirs and assigns 5 selions and a gore of land in the furlong called Dodyforlong and all his meadow in Parva Lottesmor, which he had by grant of John de Kyngeston his father, in Slymbrugge.
Witnesses: John de Clyve, Robert Groundy, William le Botiller, John le Knyght, Nicholas de Bradeforde.
At: Slimbridge.

A1/60/78 [GC 3033]   Thurs. after St. Lucy, 16 Edw. III [20 Dec. 1342]
(1) William de Syde; (2) Robert Groundi and William Odyes; (3) Thomas son of John de Kyngestone.

William has appointed Robert and William his attorneys to receive seisin in his name of 5 selions and a gore of land in Dodyforlong and the meadow in Parva Lottesmor which he had by grant of Thomas in Slymbrugge.
At: Slimbridge.

A1/60/79 [GC 3038]   Thurs. the feast of St. Stephen, 16 Edw. III [26 Dec. 1342]
John de Kyngestone and Sir William de Syde.

John has quitclaimed to William 5 selions and a gore of land in the furlong called Dodyforlong and the meadow called Parva Lottesmore, which Thomas his son held in Slymbrugge.
Witnesses: John de Clyve, Robert Groundi, William le Botiller, John le Knyght, Nicholas de Bradeforde.
At: Slimbridge.

ACQUISITIONS IN WORTLEY AND ELSEWHERE
Grants by William de Coombe in Wortley, Nibley, Cam and Alkington
Joyesland in Wortley and Smallmead in Alkington

A1/60/80 [GC 1437; *duplicate* GC 1438]   n.d. [late Hen. III]
Roger Joye of Tresham; and William de Cumbe and Clarice his wife.

Roger has granted to William and Clarice and their issue a messuage and a half-virgate and a quarter-virgate of land in the vill of Wyrteleye, viz. that which he bought from Roger de Wyndeye; to them and their issue, and they have given him 40 marks.
Witnesses: Sir John de Chausy, Walter de Chaldefeld, John de Chalcleye, Laurence de Hildesleye, Geoffrey Wynebold.

A1/60/81 [GC 964]   n.d. [early 14th cent.]
Alice la Selye of Dangerville Wick and William de Cumbe.

Alice has granted to William all her meadow called Smalemede in the parish of Berkeleya with the dower which was her mother's; rent ½d. a year, and he has given her 40s.
Witnesses: Thomas le Archer, William de Knabbewell, William de Kyneltreo, Richard Dosy, William Daungervile, Walter Motun, Nicholas de Wodeford.

A1/60/82 [GC 1608]   n.d. [early 14th cent.]
William de Coumbe; and William his son and Walter, brother of William the younger.

William has granted to William and Walter a meadow called Smalemed within the manor of Berkel'; to hold of the lord of the fee, rent to Alice Hageleye ½d. a year, and to Margery her sister ½d. a year.
Witnesses: Peter de Stinchescumbe, William de Burgo, Warin son of William, Robert de Chirche, Michael le Venor.

A1/60/83 [GC 3035; *duplicate* GC 3036]   Thurs. the feast of St. Stephen, 16 Edw. III
                                                                          [26 Dec. 1342]
William son of William de Combe the younger and Sir William de Syde.

William de Combe has granted to William de Syde, his heirs and assigns a messuage and a half-virgate and a quarter-virgate of land called Joyeslond, with the reversion of all the lands and holdings held of him for lives or years, in Wurteleye within the manor of Wotton Underegge.
Witnesses: John de Clyve, Elias de Berleye, William Curteys, Geoffrey Neel, John de Combe.
At: Wotton-under-Edge.

A1/60/84 [GC 3037]   Thurs. the feast of St. Stephen, 16 Edw. III [26 Dec. 1342]
(1) William son of the William de Combe the younger; (2) Roger Groundy; (3) Sir William de Syde.

William de Combe has appointed Roger to give seisin in his name to William de Syde of a messuage and a half and a quarter of a virgate called Joyeslond in Wurtel', and of a messuage and 1 virgate of land in Wyke in Camme and 7 a. of meadow called Smalemed in Alkyntone, which William de Syde had by his gift.
At: Cam.

Willets ridding in Alkington

A1/60/85 [GC 3293]   n.d. [mid 14th cent.]
William son of William de Combe the younger and Sir William de Syde.

William de Combe has granted to William de Syde a rent of 2s. from John de Swanleye and Cecilia his wife for a croft beneath Mikkelwode called Wylotesruydingge, which they hold for their lives within the manor of Berkeleye, with the reversion of the croft after their deaths.
Witnesses: William de Chiltenham, John de Clyve, Elias de Berleye, William Corteys, Robert Groundi.

A1/60/86 [GC 3060]   Sat. the morrow of St. James, 17 Edw. III [26 July 1343]
William de Syde; and John de Swanleye and Cecilia his wife.

William has leased to John and Cecilia a croft called Wylotesrudynge in Alkyntone; for their lives, rent 2s. a year.
Witnesses: John Serjaunt, John Sewaker, Thomas Snyte, Thomas le Wor, Adam Purlewent, clerk.
At: Berkeley.

Others in Wortley and Nibley

A1/60/87 [GC 3118]   Tues. the Invention of Holy Cross, [19] Edw. III [3 May 1345]
. . . William de Combe of Wortley the elder and Sir William de Syde.

Agreement that the said John . . . to the said William a cellar below William's solar at the chief hall . . . and 6½ feet of land in la Impeheye . . . and 6½ feet of land in la Fysshwere . . . in exchange in the same vill of Worteleye.
Witnesses: . . . le Skay, William Curteys, Henry Peche, Geoffrey Neel.

A1/60/88 [GC 3294]   n.d. [mid 14th cent.]
William son of William de Combe the younger and Sir William de Syde.

William de Combe has granted to William de Syde a messuage with a curtilage at Barlichlone in Wurteleye and an annual rent of 4s. 6d. from Roger Hayl for 3 a. of land which he holds of William [de Combe] for his life, in Wurteleye, with the reversion of the land after Roger's death.
Witnesses: William de Chiltenham, John de Clyve, Elias de Berleye, William Corteys, Robert Groundi.

A1/60/89 [GC 3248]   n.d. [mid 14th cent.]
William son of William de Combe the younger and Sir William de Syde.

William de Combe has granted to William de Syde an annual rent of 3s. from Nicholas Damescolace for the lands which Nicholas holds of William [de Combe] in fee in Nubbeleye.
Witnesses: William de Chiltenham, John de Clyve, William Corteys, Elias de Berleye, Robert Groundy.

A1/60/90 [GC 3345]   n.d. [mid 14th cent.]
(1) William de Syde; (2) William Corteys; (3) William son of William de Combe.

William de Syde has appointed William Corteys to take seisin of all the lands and holdings which he had by grant of William de Combe in Wurteleye, Nubbeleye, Alkyntone and Berkeleye.

The Lovecock holding in Wortley

A1/60/91 [GC 2078]   Morow of the Purification, 9 Edw. II [3 Feb. 1316]
William de Cumbe, son and heir of William de Cumbe; and Nicholas Lovekoc, Eleanor his wife and Lucy their daughter.

William has attorned Adam de Tettepenne and Pavia his wife to render to Nicholas, Eleanor and Lucy an annual rent of a clove which they rendered to him for the holding which they have for Pavia's life, in Worteleye, which rent John Wyllam has sold to Nicholas, Eleanor and Lucy, with the reversion of the holding. [*In French.*]
At: Wortley.

A1/60/92 [GC 2443]   Fri. before the nativity of St. John the Baptist, 18 Edw. II
                                                               [21 June 1325]
William son and heir of William de Coumbe and Nicholas Lovecok of Wortley.

William has quitclaimed to Nicholas, his heirs and assigns a messuage and 4 a. of land in Wortelegh which Nicholas previously held of William for his life.

Witnesses: John de Olepenne, John de Bradeford, John de Milkesham, Thomas de Fallewolle, John le Skay of Nibley, Warin son of William, William Curteys, clerk.
At: Wotton.

A1/60/93 [GC 2454]   11 April 1326
John Bradeford of Dursley, chaplain; and Nicholas Lovecok of Wortley, Alice his wife and William and Juliana their children.

John has granted to Nicholas, Alice, William and Juliana the holding which he had by grant of Nicholas in Weorthel' within the manor of Wottone; to them and the issue of William and Juliana, with remainder to Nicholas and Alice and Nicholas's heirs.
Witnesses: Roger Joye, John le Chausi, Nicholas the clerk, John le Hore of Wotton, Thomas Wallewoll, William Warlemond, Roger Hayl.
At: Wortley.

A1/60/94 [GC 3213]   Tues. after St. Peter in cathedra, 23 Edw. III [24 Feb. 1349]
Geoffrey Craddock of Kingswood, called de la Halle, and Robert le Fysshere of Wotton.

Geoffrey has granted to Robert, his heirs and assigns all his lands and holdings in Wyrteleye within the manor of Wottone which were of Nicholas Lovecoke of Wryteleye.
Witnesses: William Curteys, Adam Legat, William Smalcombe, Thomas le Deyare, Thomas Matheu.
At: Wortley.

A1/60/95 [GC 3215]   Sat. after St. Matthew, 23 Edw. III [28 Feb. 1349]
Geoffrey Craddock of Kingswood, called de la Halle, and Robert le Fysshere of Wotton.

Whereas Geoffrey has enfeoffed Robert of the lands which were of Nicholas Lovecoke in Wyrteleye, Robert wills that if the half of the said lands, held by Geoffrey's sister Edith for her life, revert to Robert after her death, the charter of Geoffrey will be void.
At: Wortley.

A1/60/96 [GC 3214]   Sun. after St. Matthew, 23 Edw. III [1 March 1349]
Geoffrey Craddock of Kingswood, called de la Halle, and Robert le Fysshere of Wotton.

Geoffrey has quitclaimed to Robert all the lands that were of Nicholas Lovecoke in Wyrteleye.
Witnesses: Walter le Glovere, Adam Legat, William Smalcombe, Thomas le Dyare, Thomas Matheu.
At: Wortley.

A1/60/97 [GC 3967]   n.d. [mid 14th cent.]
Robert le Fisshare of Wotton and Sir William de Syde.

Robert has granted to William, his heirs and assigns all his lands, holdings [etc.] which he had by grant of Geoffrey Craddok, cousin and heir of Nicholas Lovecoke, in the vill of Wyrteleye by Wottone sub egge.
Witnesses: Elias de Berlegh, Geoffrey Neel, Adam Legat, Roger Hayl, Edward Grevel.

A1/60/98 [GC 3380]   Fri. after the conversion of St. Paul, 26 Edw. III [27 Jan. 1352]
William de Syde; and Simon Partrych and Edith his wife.

William has leased to Simon and Edith half of the holding which was of Nicholas Lovecoke in Wyrteleye within the manor of Wottone; for their lives, rent ½ mark a year; and he has also granted to Simon the reversion of the other half after Edith's death if he survives her, rent ½ mark a year, for his life.
Witnesses: Elias de Bereleye, Adam Legat, Geoffrey Neel, Robert le Visschare, Roger Hayl.
At: Wotton.

The Coombe plot beside le Welshearth in Wortley

A1/60/99 [GC 3027]   Sun. after All Saints, 16 Edw. III [3 Nov. 1342]
Elias de Combe and Thomas de Combe, son of William de Combe of Wortley.

Elias has granted to Thomas, his heirs and assigns a plot beside the curtilage which Thomas had by grant of his mother at le Welscherde; rent a rose a year.
Witnesses: Elias de Bereleye, John de Combe of Wortley, Nicholas Lovecoke, Roger Hayl, Peter Dewenysche.
At: Wortley.

A1/60/100 [GC 3029]   [Thurs.] before St. Edmund the archbishop, [16] Edw. III
                                       [14 Nov. 1342]
Elias de Combe and Thomas de Combe, son of William Combe of Wortley.

Elias has granted to Thomas a plot beside the curtilage which Thomas had by grant of his mother at le Welscherde; to him and his issue, rent a rose a year, with remainder to William and his heirs.
Witnesses: Elias de Berleye, John de Combe of Wortley, Nicholas Lovecok, Roger Hayl, Peter Devenysche.
At: Wortley.

A1/60/101 [GC 3030] Thurs. before St. Edmund the archbishop, 16 Edw. III [14 Nov. 1342]
Elias de Combe and Thomas de Combe, son of William de Combe of Wortley.

Elias has released to Thomas a curtilage in the vill of Worteleye beside le Welscherde, which Thomas had by grant of Joan his mother.
Witnesses: Nicholas Lovecoke, John de Combe, Roger Hayl.
At: Wortley.

A1/60/102 [GC 3084]   Tues. after St. Lucy, 17 Edw. III [16 Dec. 1343]
Adam Colewych of Wotton and Sir William de Syde.

Adam has leased to William a curtilage in the vill of Wrteleye beside le Welscherde, which he holds for life of Elias de Combe and Thomas son of William de Combe.
Witnesses: Elias de Berleye, William Curteys, Geoffrey Neel, Roger Dunyssh, Nicholas Lovecoke.
At: Wotton.

A1/60/103 [GC 3083]   Tues. after St. Lucy, 17 Edw. III [16 Dec. 1343]
Adam Colewych of Wotton and Sir William de Syde.

Adam has granted to William, his heirs and assigns, for a certain sum of money, a house plot in Wrtelegh which he had by grant of Thomas son of William de Combe of Wrtelegh.
Witnesses: Elias de Berleye, William Curteys, Geoffrey Neel, Roger Dunyssh, Nicholas Lovecoke.
At: Wotton.

The Shareshull lands in Wortley

A1/60/104 [GC 3046]   Fri. the feast of St. Valentine, 17 Edw. III [14 Feb. 1343]
Adam de Shareshulle, knight, and Bogo FitzWaryn.

Adam has granted to Bogo, his heirs and assigns all his lands and holdings which he had by grant of Elias de Coumbe in Worteley by Wottone.
Witnesses: John Chausy, John de Milkesham, Elias de Coumbe, John de Coumbe, Nicholas Lovecoke.
At: Wortley.

A1/60/105 [GC 3072]   n.d. [*c.* Nov. 1343]
Bogo FitzWaryn and Sir William de Syde.

Bogo has granted to William, his heirs and assigns all his lands and holdings which he
had by grant of Sir Adam de Shareshulle, knight, in Wortelegh by Wottone. [*Unfinished*]
Witnesses: William de Chiltenham, John de Clyve, Robert Groundy, Nicholas Lovekoc,
John de Combe.

A1/60/106 [GC 3073]   Mon. the morrow of All Souls, 17 Edw. III [3 Nov. 1343]
Bogo FitzWaryn and Sir William de Syde.

Bogo has granted to William, his heirs and assigns all his lands and holdings which he
had by grant of Sir Adam de Shareshulle, knight, in Wortelegh by Wottone.
Witnesses: William de Chiltenham, John de Clyve, Robert Groundy, Nicholas Lovekoc,
John de Combe.
At: Wortley.

A1/60/107 [GC 3074]   Mon. the morrow of All Souls, 17 Edw. III [3 Nov. 1343]
(1) William de Syde; (2) Robert Groundy; (3) Bogo fiz Waryn.

William has appointed Robert his attorney to receive seisin of the lands and holdings
which he had by grant of Bogo in Wortelegh.
At: Wortley.

The Heynes holding in Wortley

A1/60/108 [GC 3309]   n.d. [mid 14th cent.]
Richard Heynes of Woodmancote and Sir William de Syde.

Richard has granted to William all his holding in Worteleye within the manor of Wottone
sub Egge of the inheritance of Maud la Tornour his wife, which she inherited after the death
of Alice Alvard her mother.
Witnesses: William Corteys, Elias de Berle, Robert Groundi, John de Combe, Geoffrey
Neel.

A1/60/109 [GC 3346]   n.d. [mid 14th cent.]
(1) William de Syde; (2) Robert Groundy and Roger le Dunysshe; (3) Richard Heynes of
Woodmancote.

William has appointed Robert or Roger to receive seisin of the lands which he had by
grant of Richard in Worteleye within the manor of Wottone sub Egge.

A1/60/110 [GC 2611]   n.d. [mid 14th cent.]
John le Tornour, son and heir of Maud le Tornour, and Sir William de Syde.

John has quitclaimed to William the holding which William had by demise of Richard
Heynes of Wodemoncote in Worteleye in the manor of Wottone sub Egge.
Witnesses: William Corteys, Elias de Berle, Robert Groundy, John de Combe, Geoffrey
Neel.

Foundation of the chantries and passage of other lands to Thomas (III) Lord Berkeley

A1/60/111 [SC 509]   5 May 17 Edw. III [1343]
King Edward III and William de Syde.

The king has granted to William licence to grant in mortmain two messuages, 2 virgates
of land and 100*s.* rent in Berkele, Wotton and Alkyngton for the support of two chaplains in
the chapel of Neweport.
At: Westminster.

A1/60/112 [SC 508; *duplicate* SC 510]   5 May 17 Edw. III [1343]
King Edward III and William de Syde.

The king has granted to William licence to grant in mortmain two messuages, 2 virgates

of land and 100*s.* rent in Berkele, Wotton, Alkyngton and Hulle for the support of two chaplains in the chapel of Neweport.
At: Westminster.

A1/60/113 [SC 506; *duplicate* SC 507]   5 May 17 Edw. III [1343]
King Edward III and William de Syde.

The king has granted to William licence to grant in mortmain a messuage, 1 virgate of land and 50*s.* rent in Berkele, Camme and Slymbrigge for the support of a chaplain in the chapel of Cambrigge.
At: Westminster.

A1/60/114 [SC 505]   5 May 17 Edw. III [1343]
King Edward III and William de Syde.

The king has granted to William licence to grant in mortmain a messuage, 1 virgate of land and 50*s.* rent in Berkele and Camme for the support of a chaplain in the chapel of Cambrigge.
At: Westminster.

A1/60/115 [GC 3055]   10 July 1343
Wulstan [de Bransford], bishop of Worcester, and William de Syde.

The bishop has confirmed William's foundation of a chantry chapel of St. Maurice in Neweport, for the souls of Sir Thomas de Berkelee, Sir Maurice de Berkelee,[1] Sir Reginald de Cobham and Lady Joan his wife, Sir John Mautravers, Richard de Cestre, William de Chiltenham and Robert Groundy, and also for those of John, William's father, and Margaret his mother, Sir John Gyffard, Lady Margaret de Berkelee, Lady Margaret Gyffard and Sir John de Wylyntone and Lady Joan his wife.
At: Worcester.

A1/60/116 [SC 512]   30 Jan. 18 Edw. III [1344]
King Edward III and Thomas de Berkeley.

The king has granted to Thomas licence to alienate to William de Syde 100 a. of land, 10 a. of meadow, 4 a. of wood and 40*s.* rent in Alkyngton, in exchange for an identical quantity of land [etc.] in Wotton, Slymbrugge and Hull.
At: Westminster.

A1/60/117 [GC 3141; *duplicate* GC 3142]   Sat. 8 July 20 Edw. III [1346]
Thomas lord of Berkelee and William de Syde.

Thomas, by the king's licence, has granted to William a messuage, 1 virgate and 100 a. of land, 10 a. of meadow, 4 a. of wood and 40*s.* rent in Camme and Alkyntone, held in chief, in exchange for a messuage, 1 virgate and 100 a. of land, 10 a. of meadow, 4 a. of wood and 40*s.* rent in Camme, Alkyntone, Wottone and Slymbrugge, which William holds of Thomas. *Witnesses*: Sir Simon Basset, Sir Peter Corbet, William de Chiltenham, John de Clyve, Robert Groundy.
At: Berkeley.

A1/60/118 [SC 518]   10 July 20 Edw. III [10 July 1346]
Thomas lord of Berkeley and William de Syde.

Thomas has confirmed to William the grant of a messuage, 1 virgate of land which Robert de Hulmancote sometime held, and 50*s.* rent in Berkelee, Camme and Slymbrugge for the support of a chaplain in the chapel of Cambrugge.
At: Berkeley.

---

[1] 'Sir Maurice de Berkelee' is written twice, possibly for the son and the brother of Sir Thomas.

A1/60/119 [GC 2483]   n.d. [*c.* 1345]
(1) William de Syde; (2) the chaplain of Cambridge chantry; (3) Thomas lord of Berkele.

Whereas William granted a messuage, 1 virgate of land which Robert de Hulmancote formerly held and a rent of 50*s.* in Berkele, Camme and Slymbrugge, except 9 a. of meadow in Slymbrugge, to the chaplain and his successors of the chapel of Cammebrugge, by licence of the king and confirmation of the bishop of Worcester, which holding is held of Thomas, Thomas wills and concedes that the chaplain and his successors should hold the land in pure and perpetual alms without rendering services.
Witnesses: Sir Maurice de Berkelee, Sir Thomas de Bradeston, Sir Simon Basset, knights, William de Chiltenham, John de Clyve.

A1/60/120 [SC 486]   n.d. [*c.* 1342]
Thomas lord of Berkeley and William de Syde.

Whereas William has granted two messuages, 2 virgates and 100*s.* rent in Berkelee, Wotton and Alkynton for the support of two chaplains at the chapel of Neweport, and a messuage, 1 virgate and 50*s.* rent in Wotton for the support of a chaplain at the chapel of Worteleye, Thomas has confirmed these grants of lands held of him.
Witnesses: Maurice de Berkeley, Thomas de Bradeston, Simon Basset, knights, William de Chiltenham, John de Clyve.

A1/60/121 [GC 2583]   n.d. [mid 14th cent.]
Thomas lord of Berkelee and Sir William de Syde.

Thomas has quitclaimed to William all actions, real and personal, suits, quarrels and demands which he has against William, his heirs or executors.

A1/60/122 [GC 3276]   n.d. [mid 14th cent.]
Thomas lord of Berkelee and Sir William de Syde.

Thomas has quitclaimed to William all actions, quarrels and demands, real and personal [etc.]

A1/60/123 [GC 3251]   n.d. [mid 14th cent.]
Thomas vicar of Almondesbury; and Sir Walter Goldemere and John de Clyve.

Thomas has granted to Walter and John, and their heirs and assigns, all his lands and holdings in Slymbrugge, Wottone and Nybbelee, and elsewhere within the hundred of Berkelee, to which he succeeded by inheritance on the death of Sir William de Syde.
Witnesses: Sir Simon Basset, William de Chiltenham, Elias de Berleye.

THE GROUNDY HOLDING

The Groundy lands in Berkeley, Ham, Alkington and Hinton passed to Thomas (III) Lord Berkeley through his frequently used feoffees David de Melkesham, Walter Goldemere and John le Vey. See below, A1/61/22 [GC 3388], for evidence of the passage from those feoffees to Thomas, and A1/61/27 [GC 3301] for the grant to the feoffees.

ACQUISITION OF THE GOLD HOLDING IN NEWPORT

A1/61/1 [GC 2655]   Nativity of St. John the Baptist, 2 Edw. III [24 June 1328]
William le Golde of Wick; and Robert Groundi of Berkeley the elder and Sibyl his wife.

William has granted to Robert and Sibyl, and their heirs and assigns, his holding in Neuport which William de Merchse and Eleanor his wife formerly held.
Witnesses: Walter de Coumbe, John de Lorwyng, Adam de Mettesdone, Adam Moton, Stephen de Kyneltre, William Gryp, Adam le Heerde.
At: Newport.

A1/61/2 [GC 2709]   8 Sept. 4 Edw. III [1330]
Christine widow of William le Golde; and Robert Groundy of Berkeley and Sibyl his wife.

Christine has quitclaimed to Robert and Sibyl the holding at Neweport which they had by grant of William, within the manor of Alkyntone.

Witnesses: John de Lorewynge, Adam de Mettesdone, Adam Moton, Stephen de Kyneltre, William le Gryp.

At: Berkeley.

A1/61/3 [GC 2865]   Thurs. after St. Gregory, 11 Edw. III [13 March 1337]
Sibyl widow of Robert Groundy of Berkeley and Robert Groundy, her son.

Sibyl has granted to Robert the younger the holding in Neweport which she had by grant of William le Golde and Christine his wife.

Witnesses: Walter de Coumbe, Stephen Kyneltre, William le Gryp, John le Cuppere, William Jodde, John Fromylode, Henry le Eyre.

At: Berkeley.

ACQUISITIONS IN BERKELEY BOROUGH
The Noblepas holding

A1/61/4 [GC 2379; *duplicate* GC 2380]   The Invention of Holy Cross, 15 Edw. II
                                                                          [3 May 1322]

John son and heir of Richard Noblepas of Berkeley; and Richard atte Slo of Ham, Margery his wife and Maud their daughter.

John has granted to Richard, Margery and Maud his cottage in Berckel' with an adjacent plot of land measuring 16 by 16 perches, which cottage John the miller (*molen'*) had by grant of Richard his father; for their lives, rent a rose a year, and they have given him a certain sum of money.

Witnesses: Henry le Gardiner, Robert Groundi, Adam Pynel, William Iweyn, Thomas Page.

At: Berkeley.

A1/61/5 [GC 2665]   Mon. before the conversion of St. Paul, 2 Edw. III [23 Jan. 1329]
John son and heir of Richard Noblepas of Berkeley; and Robert Groundy of Berkeley and Agnes his wife.

John has granted to Robert and Agnes, and Robert's heirs and assigns, his holding in Berckel' with two plots of curtilage, and a plot of land beside the curtilage of Juliana, John's sister, and the reversion of a cottage and plot of land held for life by Richard ate Slo, Margery his wife and Maud their daughter.

Witnesses: Thomas Page, William Judde, Adam Pynel, Henry de Modybrok, Edward le Fromylode, John le Gardiner, Hugh le Proute.

At: Berkeley.

A1/61/6 [GC 2692]   Sun. after the Purification, 4 Edw. III [4 Feb. 1330]
Robert Groundy of Berkeley and Agnes his wife; and William ate Wode of Berkeley and Christine his wife.

Robert and Agnes have leased to William and Christine the holding in Berckel' which they had by grant of John Noblepas; for their lives, rent 4*s.* a year.

Witnesses: William Jodde, Edward de Fromelode, Henry de Modybrok, Adam Pynel, Nicholas Daungervyle, John le Webbe, William the miller (*molendin'*).

At: Berkeley.

A1/61/7 [GC 2755]   Michaelmas Day, 6 Edw. III [29 Sept. 1332]
Maud daughter of Richard ate Sloo, unmarried woman, and Edith her sister.

Maud has quitclaimed to Edith a cottage at Berckel' which she had by lease of John Noblepas.

Witnesses: John Capel, Nicholas Iweyn, Nicholas the clerk, Robert Bastard, John Purlewent.

At: Berkeley.

The Webbe holding

A1/61/8 [GC 2989]   Tues. the feast of St. Philip and St. James, 15 Edw. III [1 May 1341]
William le Webbe of Sherston; and Robert Groundy and Agnes his wife.

William has granted to Robert and Agnes, and their heirs and assigns, a messuage with a curtilage in Berkeleye.
Witnesses: John de Clyve, John le Cuppare, John le Bil, Alexander de Bathe, William Harreis, Robert Prikke, Adam Purlewent, clerk.
At: Berkeley.

A1/61/9 [GC 2990]   Sun. the feast of St. John before the Latin Gate, 15 Edw. III
[6 May 1341]
Juliana le Webbe of Berkeley and Robert Groundy.

Juliana has quitclaimed to Robert a messuage with a curtilage which he had by grant of William le Webbe, son and heir of Roger le Webbe of Scherston.
Witnesses: John Cuppare, Alexander de Bathe, John Bil, Henry de Modybrok, John le Webbe, John Gamylef, Adam Purlewent.
At: Berkeley.

A1/61/10 [GC 2613]   n.d. [mid 14th cent.]
Henry le Webbe of Berkeley and Robert Groundy.

Henry has quitclaimed to Robert a messuage with a curtilage in Berkeleye.
Witnesses: Robert Prikke, John Bil, Henry de Modibrok, William Clerkes, John Payn.

A1/61/11 [GC 2991]   Sun. the feast of St. John before the Latin Gate, 15 Edw. III
[6 May 1341]
Henry le Webbe of Berkeley and Robert Groundy.

Henry has quitclaimed to Robert a messuage with a curtilage which he had by grant of William le Webbe, son and heir of Roger le Webbe of Sherston.
Witnesses: John Cuppare, Alexander de Bathe, John Bil, Henry de Modybrok, John le Webbe, John Gamylef, Adam Purlewent.
At: Berkeley.

A1/61/12 [GC 2999]   Sat. the feast of the translation of St. Thomas the martyr, 15 Edw. III
[7 July 1341]
Robert Groundi; and Juliana le Webbe, Henry her son and Alice, Henry's wife.

Robert has leased to Juliana, Henry and Alice half of his messuage and curtilage in Berkeleye which he had by grant of William le Webbe of Scherston; for their lives, rent 12*d.* a year.
Witnesses: John le Webbe, Henry Swele, Richard le Fisschare, Thomas Sewaker, Richard le Webbe.
At: Berkeley.

Other holdings

A1/61/13 [GC 2822]   31 May, the feast of St. Petronilla, 9 Edw. III [1335]
Geoffrey Beoleye and Juliana his wife, daughter of Richard Noblepas of Berkeley; and Robert Groundy of Berkeley and Agnes his wife.

Geoffrey and Juliana have granted to Robert and Agnes, and Robert's heirs and assigns, two cottages with curtilages in Berkeleye.
Witnesses: John de Egetone, William de Swonhongre, William Jodde, John Cuppere, Edward de Fromylode, William Clerkes, John Fromylode, John Schipward, John Gomyles, Alexander de Bathe.
At: Berkeley.

A1/61/14 [GC 2867]   Sat. after St. Gregory, 11 Edw. III [15 March 1337]
Sibyl widow of Robert Groundy of Berkeley and Robert Groundy, her son.

Sibyl has granted to Robert the younger her one third of a house with a curtilage, which third is between the thirds of her sisters Isabel widow of Nicholas Coby and Juliana widow of Ralph le Cook, which they three had by grant of Rose Mounes, their mother.
Witnesses: John le Cuppere, William Jodde, John Fromylode, Robert le Schipward, John Gamyleof, Alexander de Bathe, John le Byk.
At: Berkeley.

A1/61/15 [GC 3042]   Fri. before the Purification, 17 Edw. III [31 Jan. 1343]
Robert Groundy; and Henry le Webbe, Alice his wife and John their son.

Robert has leased to Henry, Alice and John two cottages with a curtilages, beside the road from Berkel' to the chapel of St. Michael; for their lives, rent 12*d.* a year.
Witnesses: John le Webbe, Henry Swele, John Payn, John Bil, John Schipward.
At: Berkeley.

A1/61/16 [GC 3116]   Mon. in Easter week, 19 Edw. III [28 March 1345]
Edith daughter of Richard ate Slo, unmarried woman, and Robert Groundy.

Edith has surrendered to Robert and his heirs her status in a cottage in Berkeleye beside his holding.
Witnesses: Robert Prikke, John le Webbe, John Sley, John Payn, Adam Purlewent, clerk.
At: Berkeley.

ACQUISITIONS IN HAM
The Franklin holding in Berkeley Wood

A1/61/17 [GC 1554]   n.d. [*temp.* Edw. I]
Adam son of John Sutor of Berkeley; and Hugh le Fraunckeleyn and Agnes his wife.

Adam has granted to Hugh and Agnes 1 a. of land in the furlong called Berclewode, beside the king's highway above the fishpond called Smethemore; rent to the chief lord a rose a year, and they have given Adam a certain sum of money.
Witnesses: Walter Sewaker, John le Coppere, Walter le Coppere, Edward de Fromilode, William Bodde, William Purlewent, clerk.

A1/61/18 [GC 2866]   Thurs. after St. Gregory, 11 Edw. III [13 March 1337]
Walter le Fraunkelayn, son and heir of Hugh le Fraunkelayn of Berkeley, and Robert Groundy of Berkeley.

Walter has granted to Robert, his heirs and assigns 1 a. of land in the furlong called Berclewode; rent a rose a year to the chief lord.
Witnesses: John le Serjaunt, John de Lorewynge, Edward Fromylode, John le Cuppere, William Jodde, John le Schipward, Henry Modebrok.
At: Berkeley.

A1/61/19 [GC 3117]   Mon. after St. Philip and St. James, 19 Edw. III [2 May 1345]
Alice widow of Walter Fraunkeleyn of Berkeley and Robert Groundy of Berkeley.

Alice has quitclaimed to Robert her dower rights in 1 a. of land in the field called Beorkelewode.
Witnesses: William Capel, John Sewaker, Henry Madebroke, Edward Fromelode, John Schypward.
At: Berkeley.

The Sumpter holding

A1/61/20 [GC 2735]   Sun. the feast of St. Dunstan, 5 Edw. III [19 May 1331]
Richard son and heir of William le Someter, formerly burgess of Bristol, and Isabel widow of William his father.

Richard has granted to Isabel, her heirs and assigns all the lands and holdings which he inherited after the death of his father in Hamme by Berkeley, and also the reversion of 2 a. of land which John le Sergeaunt holds for life.

Witnesses: John de Clyve, John Wyth, John de Swonhungre, John Capel, Robert de Asschelworthy, Robert Groundy, William Judde.

At: Berkeley.

A1/61/21 [GC 2786]   Thurs. the morrow of the Purification, 8 Edw. III [3 Feb. 1334]
John Ceynte and Isabel his wife; and Robert Groundy of Berkeley and Agnes his wife.

John and Isabel have granted to Robert and Agnes, for a certain sum of money, the messuage with a curtilage, garden and croft which Isabel had by grant of Richard son and heir of William le Someter within the manor of Hamme by Berkeleye, and also 2 selions in Westfeld and 2 a. of land in Berkelwode which Isabel had by grant of Richard; to them and Robert's heirs and assigns.

Witnesses: John le Sergeant, John de Egetone, John le Gardyner, William Capel, John de Lorwynge, William Judde, Edward de Fromelode, Henry de Modybroke.

At: Ham.

A1/61/22 [GC 3388]   12 May 26 Edw. III [1352]
Thomas de Berkelee, lord of Berkeley; and Thomas Gylmyn, Maud his wife and Richard their son.

Thomas has leased to Thomas, Maud and Richard a messuage and various parcels of land called Sompteresholding which Robert Groundy previously held in Hamme; for their lives, rent 4*s.* a year.

Witnesses: John Serjant the elder, John Serjant the younger, Henry de Egetone, John ate Boure, William Modebroke.

At: Berkeley.

Other acquisitions

A1/61/23 [GC 2763]   Tues. the conversion of St. Paul, 7 Edw. III [25 Jan. 1334]
Walter le Cuppere, son and heir of Roger le Cuppere of Berkeley, and Robert Groundy of Berkeley.

Walter has granted to Robert an annual rent of 3*d.* from Juliana Noblepas and her issue for 3 selions of land in Westfelde within the manor of Hamme . . .

Witnesses: John le Sergeant, John Capel, John de Egeton, John de Lorewynge, John le Gardyner, William Jodde.

At: Berkeley.

A1/61/24 [GC 2764]   Tues. the conversion of St. Paul, 7 Edw. III [25 Jan. 1334]
Walter le Cuppere, son and heir of Roger le Cuppere of Berkeley, and Robert Groundy of Berkeley.

Walter has granted to Robert a plot of land in Westfeld within the manor of Hamme, beside the street called Mulleweye.

Witnesses: John le Sergeant, John Capel, John de Egeton, John de Lorewynge, John le Gardyner, William Jodde, Edward de Fromelode.

At: Berkeley.

A1/61/25 [GC 3092]   Thurs. after the Invention of Holy Cross, 18 Edw. III [6 May 1344]
Robert Groundy and John Broun.

Robert has granted to John, his heirs and assigns a selion of land beside the road from Swonhungre to Berkel'.

Witnesses: John le Serjaunt, William Gelemyn, William de Swonhungre, Thomas de Costone, Walter Mathew.

At: Wanswell.

Passage to feoffees

A1/61/26 [GC 2598]   n.d. [early Edw. III]
Robert Groundy and Sir Thomas ate Welle, chaplain.

Robert has granted to Thomas, his heirs and assigns all his lands and holdings in Berkelee, Hamme, Alkyntone and Hynetone, and elsewhere within the hundred of Berkelee.
Witnesses: William de Chyltenham, John de Egetone, John de Clyve, John Lorewynge, Roger le Clerk of Uley.

A1/61/27 [GC 3301]   n.d. [mid 14th cent.]
Robert Groundy; and David de Milkesham, vicar of Berkeley, Sir Walter Goldemere and John le Vey of Syde.

Robert has sold to David, Walter and John all his goods and chattels in the lands and holdings which they had by his grant in Berkelee, Hammc, Alkyntonc and Hynctone.

THE JUDD HOLDING

Many of the Judd lands in Berkeley, Ham and Alkington passed to the Marybrook family and from them to Thomas (IV) Lord Berkeley.

HOLDINGS IN ALKINGTON
The Moreville holding

A1/62/1 [GC 2350]   10 May 14 Edw. II [1321]
William de Morevile; and John Judde of Berkeley and Alice his wife.

William has granted to John and Alice, and John's heirs and assigns, all his land in Heyrithhethfelde which Walter Cole holds for a term of years, in Alkyntone; and they have given him a certain sum of money.
Witnesses: Richard de Avene, John de la Hay, William de Kyneltreo, William le Golde, William le Gryp, Edward de Fromelode, John Sewaker.
At: Berkeley.

A1/62/2 [GC 2381]   20 May 15 Edw. II [1322]
John de Morevile, son and heir of William de Morevile; and John Judde of Berkeley and Alice his wife.

John has quitclaimed to John and Alice the land which they had by grant of William his father at Heyrithhethfelde in Alkyntone.
Witnesses: Edward de Fromelode, John Sewaker, William de Kyneltre, William le Golde, William le Gryp.
At: Berkeley.

A1/62/3 [GC 2731]   Mon. after Michaelmas, 5 Edw. III [30 Sept. 1331]
John Morvyle and William Jodde of Berkeley.

John has quitclaimed to William three parcels of land in Herietteshaffeld in Alkintone.
Witnesses: John Gardyner, Robert Grondy, Edward de Fromelode, Adam de Mettesdone, Adam Moton.
At: Alkington.

Other holdings in Alkington

A1/62/4 [GC 1900]   1 Feb. 6 Edw. II [1313]
Thomas de Berkelee, lord of Berkeley; and John Jodde and Alice his wife.

Thomas has granted to John and Alice 4 a. 20 perches of land below the heath (*bruera*) in Alkyntone; to hold enclosed, to them and their issue, rent 5s. 4d. a year.
Witnesses: Richard de Avene, Maurice de Beoleye, Walter Sewaker, John le Cuppere, Henry le Gardener, Roger le Cuppere, William de Kyneltret.
At: Berkeley.

A1/62/5 [GC 1979]   St. Augustine, 7 Edw. II [26 May 1314]
John son of Walter de Lorwynge; and John Judde of Berkeley and Alice his wife.

John son of Walter has granted to John and Alice, and John's heirs and assigns, 1 a. of land in the field called Aketre.
Witnesses: John le Serjaunt, John Wyth, William Kyneltre, Adam Dangervyle, Adam de Metesdone, William Golde, William Gryp.
At: Alkington.

A1/62/6 [GC 2080]   7 Feb. 9 Edw. II [1316]
Thomas de Berkeleye, lord of Berkeley; and John Jodde and Alice his wife.

Thomas has granted to John and Alice 7½ a. 35 perches of land above the heath (*bruer'*) in Alkyntone; to hold enclosed, to them and their issue, rent 9*s*. 8*d*. a year.
Witnesses: Richard de Avene, John Wyth, William de Kyneltre, Geoffrey Motoun, William le Gryp.
At: Berkeley.

A1/62/7 [GC 2400]   St. Ambrose, 16 Edw. II [4 April 1323]
Henry le Gardiner of Berkeley; and John Judde of Berkeley and Alice his wife.

Henry has granted to John and Alice, and John's heirs and assigns, 1 selion of land in the field called Aketre.
Witnesses: Robert Groundi, William Gylemyn, John Sewaker, Adam Pynel, Thomas Page, William Kyneltre, Thomas the miller (*molendin'*).
At: Berkeley.

A1/62/8 [GC 2404]   St. John before the Latin Gate, 16 Edw. II [6 May 1323]
John son and heir of Ralph Walebroc of Newport; and John Judde of Berkeley and Alice his wife.

John has granted to John and Alice, and their heirs and assigns, a croft and four parcels of land which Richard Wynsum formerly held in Wyke, the land lying in Baynham.
Witnesses: Walter de Coumbe, John ate Hay, William Golde, Adam Daungervyle, William Kyneltre, Adam de Mettesdone, Adam Moton.
At: Wick.

A1/62/9 [GC 2644]   10 March 2 Edw. III [1328]
William de Baa and William Judde.

William de Baa has granted to William Judde all his land in the field called Aketre in Alkyntone.
Witnesses: Robert Groundy, John atte Churche, Edward de Fromelode, Thomas Page, John le Schipward.
At: Berkeley.

A1/62/10 [GC 2656]   Sun. after the translation of St. Thomas the martyr, 2 Edw. III
                                                                              [10 July 1328]
Hervey Kyllecote of Berkeley and William Jodde of Berkeley.

Hervey has granted to William a parcel of land in the field called Aketre.
Witnesses: John Wyht, John de Lorwyng, Robert Groundy, Adam de Mettesdone, Thomas Page, Adam Pynel.
At: Berkeley.

A1/62/11 [GC 2819]   St. John before the Latin Gate, 9 Edw. III [6 May 1335]
John de Lorwynge and William Judde of Berkeley.

John has quitclaimed to William a croft within the manor of Alkyntone.

Witnesses: John le Serjaunt, Walter de Coumbe, John de Egetone, Robert Groundy, Stephen de Kyneltre, John le Schypward.
At: Alkington.

HOLDINGS IN BERKELEY BOROUGH

A1/62/12 [GC 1999] 10 Oct. 8 Edw. II [1314]
Thomas de Berkeleye, lord of Berkeley; and John Jodde and Alice his wife.

Thomas has granted to John and Alice the holding in the borough of Berkeleye previously held of Thomas by Robert Akotyn and Roger Sutor of Bristol; to them and their issue, rent 10*s.* a year, with liberty to buy and sell merchandise in the port and marketplace of the borough.
Witnesses: John le Cuppere, Henry le Gardener, John Sewaker, Roger le Cuppere, Edward de Fromelode.
At: Berkeley.

A1/62/13 [GC 3537] St. Peter and St. Paul, 36 Edw. III [29 June 1362]
Thomas Judde, heir of William Judde of Berkeley; and John Gamul and Sibyl his wife.

Thomas has leased to John and Sibyl a burgage in the borough of Berkele, with access to the spring and the mill; for their lives, rent 12*s.* a year.
Witnesses: William Modibroke, John Coby, Thomas Goldhoppe, John Walbroke, Richard Grundi.
At: Berkeley.

HOLDINGS IN HAM

A1/62/14 [GC 2281] Sat. the eve of the nativity of St. John the Baptist, 12 Edw. II
[23 June 1319]
Hugh de Costone and William son of John Judde of Berkeley.

Hugh has granted to William, in free marriage with his daughter Margery, his holding in the borough of Berkeleye between the holdings of Robert Swele to the south and William Iweyn to the north, and three parcels of land of which one lies in the field called Ochongre, one in la Westfelde extending to the bridge called Smalebrugge, and the third in the same field, in Hamme; to them and their issue, rent 2*s.* a year and ½*d.* at Easter.
Witnesses: Richard le Serjaunt, William Gylemyn, William de Swonhongre, John le Cuppere, Henry le Gardener, Roger le Cuppere, John Sewaker.
At: Berkeley.

A1/62/15 [GC 2447] St. Matthew, 19 Edw. II [21 Sept. 1325]
Margaret widow of Robert Swele of Berkeley; and John Judde of Berkeley and Alice his wife.

Margaret has quitclaimed to John and Alice a parcel of land in the field called le Westfelde and 4 selions and a gore of land in the furlong called Lockedonne.
Witnesses: Henry le Gardiner, Robert Groundi, John Sewaker, Edward de Fromylode, Thomas Page, William Iweyn, Hugh le Proute.
At: Berkeley.

A1/62/16 [GC 2974] Wed. before St. Kenelm, 14 Edw. III [12 July 1340]
Henry son and heir of William Judde of Berkeley; and David le Schipward and Joan his wife.

Henry has leased to David and Joan his part of a messuage with a curtilage and two houses in the said curtilage, near his [Henry's] house called Tanhous;[1] for their lives, rent 3*s.* 4*d.* a year.
Witnesses: Robert Groundy, John Bil, Robert Prikke, John Payn, John Gomilef.
At: Berkeley.

---

[1] The house may be the later Tanhouse Farm in Ham.

A1/62/17 [GC 3536]   Mon. after the nativity of St. John the Baptist, 36 Edw. III
[27 June 1362]
Thomas Judde, son of the late William Judde of Berkeley, and William Modebroke of Berkeley.

Thomas has granted to William an annual rent of 6*d.* from Richard Scriveyn for a holding which he holds of Thomas for life and the reversion of the holding after Richard's death.
Witnesses: Henry de Egetone, John Byl, John Coby, Thomas Goldhoppere, John Walbroke.
At: Berkeley.

PASSAGE TO BERKELEY OF LANDS IN BERKELEY, HAM AND ALKINGTON

A1/62/18 [GC 3569]   10 March 39 Edw. III [1365]
Thomas Jeodde of Berkeley and William Modebroke of the same.

Thomas has quitclaimed to William the lands [etc.] that William had by grant of Thomas in Berkeleye, Hamme, Alkyntone and elsewhere within the hundred of Berkeleye.
Witnesses: Henry de Egetone, Walter Oldelond, Richard Gylemyn, Thomas Goldhoppe, Richard Skryveyn.
At: Berkeley.

A1/62/19 [GC 3312]   n.d. [mid 14th cent.]
Thomas Jeodde of Berkeley and William Modebroke of the same.

Thomas has quitclaimed to William all the lands, holdings, rents and reversions which William had by grant of Thomas in Berkeleye, Hamme, Alkyntone and elsewhere within the hundred of Berkeleye.
Witnesses: Henry de Egeton, Walter Oldelonde, Richard Gylemyn, Thomas Goldhoppe, Richard Skryveyn.

A1/62/20 [GC 3553]   Mon. after St. Oswald the archbishop, 38 Edw. III [4 March 1364]
William Modebroke of Berkeley and John Hulles of Gossington in Slimbridge.

William has leased to John a meadow called Juddesmor in Alkyntone beside Capeles moor and a croft called Juddescroft at the end of the field called Muchelaketreo; for his life, rent a rose a year.
Witnesses: Henry de Egetone, John Coby, John Byl, Thomas Goldhoppe, Richard Scriveyn.
At: Berkeley.

A1/62/21 [GC 3946]   Mon. the feast of St. Simon and St. Jude, 22 Ric. II [28 Oct. 1398]
Thomas de Berkeleye, lord of Berkeley; and John Dyere, Agnes his wife and Cecilia, Agnes's daughter.

Thomas has leased to John, Agnes and Cecilia, for John's good service, his holding with a garden in the borough of Berkel', a croft called Jodduscroft in the manor of Alkyntone, 5 selions of land in the field called Yonderaketre in the manor of Hamme and 3 selions of land in Hyderaketre in Hamme; for their lives, rent 1*d.* a year and the customary services.
Witnesses: William Smalcombe the younger, Geoffrey Skey, John Ekton the younger, Richard Ektone, Thomas Lucas.
At: Berkeley.

THE LORRIDGE HOLDING

Lands in Wick, Lorridge, Walgaston, Berkeley, Ham, Alkington and Halmore passed from John de Lorridge (*Lorewynge*) to Ralph Waleys in 1370 and from the Waleys heiress to Thomas (IV) Lord Berkeley in 1412. It appears that they then passed to Roger Bailly, who granted them to the Thorpes in 1454, although there is no definite link between Berkeley and Bailly.

LORRIDGE TO BERKELEY

A1/63/1 [GC 3617]   Thurs. before St. Petronilla, 44 Edw. III [30 May 1370]
John de Lorewynge; and Ralph Waleys and John Aleyn of Hill.

John has granted to Ralph and John the annual rents of 60*s.* from John Walton and Sibyl his wife for land at Wyke and Lorewynge, 6*s.* from John Gamul and Sibyl his wife for 4 a. of land in Walmegastone, 4*s.* 4*d.* from Walter Bekct and Katherine his wife for lands in Berkele and Hamme and 2*d.* from William Blanket and Isabel his wife for 1 a. of land in Alkyntone, with the reversions of all the holdings on their deaths, and rents of 5*s.* 4*d.* a year from John Sergeant of Monemouth for a croft called Gastonus by Yremongarislone at Halmare held in fee, 20*d.* from John Frig of Halmare for lands held in fee and 8*d.* from the chantry chaplain of Newport and his successors for land in Alkyntone.

Witnesses: Thomas fiz Nicolc, John Sergeaunt, John Oulpenne, Thomas Skay, Walter Oldelonde, John Archir, William Modebroke, Richard Gilmyn, John Ricardes.

At: Berkeley.

A1/63/2 [GC 3883; *duplicate* GC 3884]   Thurs. before St. Philip and St. James, 17 Ric. II
[30 April 1394]
John Webbe of Tockington and Thomas Lucas of Berkeley; and Master John Wike, rector of the church of St. Stephen, Bristol, William Cotes, vicar of Almondsbury, and John Balle, vicar of the church of St. Augustine, Bristol.

John and Thomas have granted to Master John, William and John, and their heirs and assigns, all the lands, holdings [etc.] in the enclosure called Lorwyngesclos within the hundred of Berkelee which they had by grant of Ralph Waleis.

Witnesses: Ralph Waleis, William Smalcombe, Edmund de Forde, John Trie, Richard Gilmyn.

At: Berkeley.

A1/63/3 [GC 3885; *duplicate* GC 3886]   Fri. the feast of St. Philip and St. James, 17 Ric. II
[1 May 1394]
(1) John Webbe of Tockington and Thomas Lucas of Berkeley; (2) William Pokulchurche and John Whytefeld; (3) Master John Wike, rector of the church of St. Stephen, Bristol, William Cotes, vicar of Almondesbury, and John Balle, vicar of the church of St. Augustine, Bristol.

John and Thomas have appointed William and John to give to Master John, William and John seisin of all their lands [etc.] in the enclosure called Lorwyngesclos in the hundred of Berkelee.

At: Berkeley.

A1/63/4 [GC 4013]   St. Augustine, 7 Hen. IV [26 May 1406]
Reginald Waleys, brother and heir of the late Ralph Waleys, and William son of John Wallere.

Reginald has leased to William the reversion of all the holdings at Wyke by Berkeley and elsewhere within the hundred of Berkeley which the said John Wallere holds for life by lease of Ralph Waleys; for his life, rent 10*s.* a year.

Witnesses: Thomas Stauntone, John FitzRobert, Thomas Wyth, William Gylmyn, Richard Scot.

At: Berkeley.

A1/63/5 [GC 4073]   Wed. the feast of St. Thomas the apostle, 14 Hen. IV [21 Dec. 1412]
William son of John Wallere; and John More and Margery his wife, daughter and heir of Reginald Waleys, brother and heir of Ralph Waleys.

Whereas William holds for life various lands and holdings in Wyke by Berkeley and elsewhere within the hundred of Berkeley, by grant of Reginald, the reversion of which after his death belongs to John and Margery, William has surrendered all the said lands to John and Margery.

At: Berkeley.

A1/63/6 [GC 4074] Fri. after St. Thomas the apostle, 14 Hen. IV [23 Dec. 1412]
John More and Margery his wife, daughter and heir of Reginald Waleys; and Thomas lord of Berkeley, knight.

John and Margery have granted to Thomas, his heirs and assigns a messuage, 1 carucate of land, 15 a. of meadow, 8 a. of wood and 7s. 8d. rent in Wyke, Lorewynge, Walmegarstone, Berkele, Hamme, Alkyntone and Halmare, which were of John de Lorewynge and Margery his wife, and all other lands [etc.] that they had in the said vills and elsewhere within the hundred of Berkeley.

Witnesses: Thomas FitzNicol, knight, John Grevell, John Rolves, Thomas Kendale, Thomas Stauntone.

At: Berkeley.

A1/63/7 [GC 4094] 8 Sept. 2 Hen. V [1414]
Maud widow of John Wallere, father of William Wallere, and Thomas Berkeley, lord of Berkeley.

Maud has surrendered to Thomas her right and claim in two crofts beside the road from Mabilyescroys to Cranhambrugge and her dower rights in all the lands of her late husband within Berkeley and Berkeleyhurnes.

At: Berkeley.

PASSAGE FROM ROGER BAILLY TO JOHN AND MARGARE THORPE

A1/63/8 [GC 4283] 1 May 32 Hen. VI [1454]
Roger Bailly; and John Thorppe and Margaret his wife.

Roger has granted to John and Margaret, and John's heirs and assigns, all his lands and holdings [etc.] in Berkeley, Wyke, Hyntone, Lorewynche, Wallmegarstun, Hamme, Alkynton and Halmere.

Witnesses: John Barre, knight, Maurice [Berkeley] de Beverston, knight, Edmund Yngylthorp, knight, Nicholas Poynes, Thomas Poyntes, John de Vele, Richard Venables, John Hervy, Richard Clavyld.

A1/63/9 [GC 4284; *duplicate of* A1/63/8 (GC 4283) *but in a different hand, with different witnesses*] 1 May 32 Hen. VI [1454]
Roger Bailly; and John Thorppe and Margaret his wife.

Roger has granted to John and Margaret, and John's heirs and assigns, all his lands and holdings [etc.] in Berkeley, Wyke, Hyntone, Lorewynche, Wallmegarstun, Hamme, Alkynton and Halmere.

Witnesses: Nicholas Poyntz, Thomas Mille, John Poyntz, esquires, Richard Venables, John Wyth, Richard Clayfeld, John Hervy, John Priour.

A1/63/10 [GC 4285] 29 June 32 Hen. VI [1454]
Nicholas Stanshawe, esquire; and John Thorppe and Margaret his wife.

Nicholas has granted to John and Margaret, and John's heirs and assigns, his status in all lands and holdings [etc.] in Berkeley, Wyke, Hyntone, Lorewynche, Wallmegarstun, Hamme, Alkynton and Halmere.

Witnesses: Nicholas Poyntz, Thomas Mille, John Poyntz, esquires, Richard Venables, John Wyth, Richard Clayfeld, John Hervy, John Priour.

A1/63/11 [GC 4286]   29 June 32 Hen. VI [1454]
Nicholas Stanshawe, esquire; and John Bullesdon and Alice his wife.

    Nicholas has granted to John and Alice all his lands and holdings [etc.] in Berkeley, Wyke, Hyntone, Lorewynche, Wallmegarstun, Hamme, Alkynton and Halmere.
Witnesses: Nicholas Poyntz, Thomas Mille, John Poyntz, esquires, Richard Venables, John Wyth, Richard Clayfeld, John Hervy, John Priour.

A1/63/12 [GC 4287; *duplicate of* A1/63/11 (GC4286) *but in a different hand, with different witnesses*]   29 June 32 Hen. VI [1454]
Nicholas Stanshawe, esquire; and John Bullesdon and Alice his wife.

    Nicholas has granted to John and Alice all his lands and holdings [etc.] in Bcrkeley, Wyke, Hyntone, Lorewynche, Wallmegarstun, Hamme, Alkynton and Halmere.
Witnesses: James lord of Berkeley, knight, Maurice Berkeley of Beverston, knight, John Barre, knight, Nicholas Poyntz, esquire, Thomas Poyntz, esquire, John de Vele, esquire, Richard Venables, John Wythe and Richard Lee.

THE GARDENER HOLDING

The holding consisted of holdings in Ham, Alkington, Berkeley and Berkeley borough brought together by Henry le Gardener and passed on by him to his younger son John. There is no evidence that it eventually passed to the Berkeley lords.

BERKELEY BOROUGH
Grants by Henry le Gardener to Thomas (II), 1316

    A curtilage
A1/64/1 [GC 2102]   1 June 9 Edw. II [1316]
Henry son of Adam le Gardener of Berkeley and Sir Thomas de Berkeleye, his lord.

    Henry has granted to Thomas, his heirs and assigns his curtilage between the holding of Robert Wyther and the curtilage of William le Gardener, extending to the croft of Roger le Cuppere above the sea wharf, with the reversion of the dower in the curtilage held by Alice widow of Robert le Gardener, his brother, in the borough of Berkeleye.
Witnesses: John le Cuppere, John Sewaker, John Martin, John Judde, John Page.
At: Berkeley.

A1/64/2 [GC 2108]   Thurs. the feast of the nativity of St. John the Baptist, 9 Edw. II
[24 June 1316]
William called le Gardener and Maud his wife; and Sir Thomas de Berkeleye, lord of Berkeley.

    William and Maud have rendered to Thomas and his heirs, for an annual rent of 3*s.* 6*d.* which Thomas has released to them, the curtilage which they had by grant of Thomas for their lives, beside the curtilage formerly of Henry le Gardener, and extending to the croft of Roger le Cuppere above the sea wharf, in Berkeleye.
Witnesses: Henry le Gardener, John le Cuppere, Roger le Cuppere, Adam Pynel, John Page.
At: Berkeley.

A1/64/3 [GC 2110]   1 July 9 Edw. II [1316]
Thomas de Berkeleye, lord of Berkeley, and Richard de Culmescote.

    Thomas has leased to Richard two curtilages which he had by grant of William called le Gardener and Henry son of Adam le Gardener, which extend to the croft of Roger le Cuppere above the sea wharf, in Berkeleye; to him and Alice his wife and John and Walter their sons, for their lives, rent 10*s.* a year, and Richard will build a house there.
Witnesses: John le Cuppere, Henry le Gardener, John Sewaker, Edward de Fromelode, Roger le Cuppere.
At: Berkeley.

A messuage

A1/64/4 [GC 2125]   20 Oct. 10 Edw. II [1316]
Henry son of Adam le Gardener of Berkeley and Sir Thomas de Berkeleye, lord of Berkeley.

Henry has quitclaimed to Thomas the messuage which he held of Thomas for life, opposite the house of Adam Pynel in the borough of Berkeleye.
Witnesses: John le Cuppere, Roger le Cuppere, Thomas Page, Adam Pynel, Henry de Kyllecote.
At: Berkeley.

A1/64/5 [GC 2131]   20 Nov. 10 Edw. II [1316]
Thomas de Berkeleye, lord of Berkeley, and Adam Pynel.

Thomas has granted to Adam the messuage and curtilage opposite his house, which Henry son of Adam le Gardener previously held of Thomas in the borough of Berkeleye; to him and his issue, rent 3*s.* a year.
Witnesses: John le Cuppere, Henry le Gardener, John Judde, Robert Groundi, John Sewaker, Roger le Cuppere, Henry de Kyllecote.
At: Berkeley.

Miscellaneous acquisitions by Henry

A1/64/6 [GC 896]   n.d. [late 13th cent.]
John le Cuppere of Berkeley and Henry called Gardiner.

John has granted to Henry a half-burgage in the new town of Berkel'; rent to the lord of Berkel' 6*d.* a year, and Henry has given John 40*s.*
Witnesses: John Sewaker, reeve, John Bonserjant, Walter Shipward, Henry le Cuppere, Walter le Cuppere, John Marescall, Richard le Savoner, clerk.

A1/64/7 [GC 2070]   Wed. the eve of the Circumcision, 9 Edw. II [31 Dec. 1315]
Henry le Gardener, son of Adam de Monemuth, and John de Coueleye.

Henry has granted to John, his heirs and assigns his house with a curtilage, with the reversion of the dower in the house held by Alice, widow of his brother Robert le Gardener, in the borough of Berkeleye.
Witnesses: John le Cuppere, John Sewaker, Roger le Cuppere, William Iweyn, John Martyn, Richard Noblepas, Henry de Killecote.
At: Berkeley.

The Scott holding

A1/64/8 [GC 1147]   Ascension Day, 35 Edw. I [4 May 1307]
Simunda daughter of Agnes Scote of Berkeley, unmarried woman, and Henry le Gardiner of Berkeley.

Symunda has granted to Henry her half-burgage in the vill of Berckel' which she had after the death of her mother, situated between the holdings of Edith Partrix and Cecilia sister of Symunda, for a certain sum of money.
Witnesses: John le Coppere, Walter Sewaker, Walter le Coppere, Richard Noblepas, Robert Swele, William Iweyn, Roger le Coppere.
At: Berkeley.

A1/64/9 [GC 1784]   Wed. the feast of St. Fabian and St. Sebastian, 4 Edw. II [20 Jan. 1311]
Cecilia Scote, daughter of Agnes Scote, unmarried woman; and Henry le Gardyner and Isabel his wife.

Cecilia has granted to Henry and Isabel a plot of land in Berckeleye which she inherited after the death of her mother, measuring 36 by 54 feet.

Witnesses: John le Cuppere, Roger le Cuppere, John Sewaker, William Budde, William Iweyn, John le Schipward, John le Vynour.
At: Berkeley.

A1/64/10 [GC 1806]   Sun. before the Annunciation, 4 Edw. II [21 March 1311]
Simunda daughter of Agnes Scote of Berkeley, unmarried woman, and Henry le Garden' of Berkeley.

Simunda has quitclaimed to Henry her half-burgage, which she had after the death of Agnes her mother, beside the holding of Cecilia her sister.
Witnesses: John le Cuppere, John Sewaker, Roger le Cuppere, William Iweyn, John le Schipward, John de Kyllecote, Hugh le Proute.
At: Berkeley.

A1/64/11 [GC 2624]   Fri. before Palm Sunday, 1 Edw. III [3 April 1327]
Henry le Gardiner and John his younger son.

Henry has confirmed to John, his heirs and assigns all the holdings in Berkel' which Henry Scote formerly held between the roads from the marketplace to the church and from the bridge called Locfastebrugg' to the marketplace.
Witnesses: Sir Henry de Cerneye, vicar of Berkeley, Robert Groundi, John Judde, John Sewaker, Edward de Fromylode, Adam Pynel, Thomas Page, Hugh le Proute, William Judde.
At: Berkeley.

A1/64/12 [GC 2647]   Sat. the feast of St. Ambrose, 1 Edw. III [4 April 1327]
Henry le Gardyner of Berkeley and John his younger son.

Henry has granted to John, his heirs and assigns all his holding with the buildings, which Henry Scote formerly held in Berkel' between the roads from the marketplace to the bridge called Locfastebrugge and from the marketplace to the church.
Witnesses: Robert Groundy, John Judde, John Sewaker, Edward de Fromylode, Thomas Page.
At: Berkeley.

Miscellaneous acquisitions by John

A1/64/13 [GC 2698]   31 March 4 Edw. III [1330]
Isabel daughter of Robert le Taillour of Berkeley, unmarried woman, and John le Gardyner of Berkeley.

Isabel has granted to John, for a certain sum of money, her holding in the vill of Berkeleye between the roads from the marketplace to Locfastebrugge and from the marketplace to the churchyard.
Witnesses: Robert Groundy, William Judde, Adam Pynel, Nicholas le Vynour, Henry de Madebrok.
At: Berkeley.

A1/64/14 [GC 2747]   2 April 6 Edw. III [1332]
Thomas [*blank, sc.* Bardulf] and Isabel his wife; and John le Gardyner of Berkeley.

Thomas and Isabel have granted to John, for a certain sum of money, all their holding in the town of Berkeleye between the roads from the marketplace to Locfastebrugge and from the marketplace to the churchyard. Endorsed: *Carta Thom. Bardulf de Herford.*
Witnesses: Robert Groundy, William Judde, Adam Pynel, Nicholas le Vynour, Henry de Madebroke.
At: Berkeley.

A1/64/15 [GC 2769]   Thurs. the feast of the Annunciation, 7 Edw. III [25 March 1333]
Geoffrey Martyn, clerk, and John le Gardiner.

Geoffrey has leased to John his holding with a shop and curtilage in the town of Berkel' next to John's holding to the north; for a term of 8 years, rent a rose a year.
At: Berkeley.

MISCELLANEOUS ACQUISITIONS BY HENRY IN HAM AND ALKINGTON

A1/64/16 [GC 1637]   Sun. the feast of St. Ambrose, 33 Edw. I [4 April 1305]
Isabel widow of John de Egetone; and Henry le Gardiner' and Sir Thomas de Berkelegh, her lord.

Isabel has quitclaimed to Henry and Thomas her dower rights in the land above Cheldinehulle in Westfeld next to Smethemor in Hynetone, which they had by grant of John her late husband; they have given her a certain sum of money.
Witnesses: Richard de Byselegh, Robert de Bradestone, Thomas de Beolegh, Thomas de Swonhungre, John de Alkelegh.
At: Berkeley.

A1/64/17 [GC 452]   Friday in Michaelmas, 1 Edw. I [29 Sept. 1307]
Thomas de Berkelegh, lord of Berkeley, and Henry le Gardener of Berkeley.

Thomas has granted to Henry the pasture at the north head of the fishpond of Smethemor which Isabel de Berkeley his aunt previously had by gift of Thomas de Berkeley his grandfather, her father, with all appurtenances in Hamme; to Henry, Isabel his wife and their issue, rent 5s. a year.
Witnesses: Robert de Bradeston, Thomas de Beol, Thomas de Swonhongre, Robert de Stanford, Geoffrey Neel.
At: Berkeley.

A1/64/18 [GC 1838]   Mon. before the nativity of St. Mary, 5 Edw. II [6 Sept. 1311]
Roger le Cuppere of Berkeley and Henry le Gardin' of Berkeley.

Roger has granted to Henry all his land above Opynchhul; to hold of the chief lord by the customary services.
Witnesses: John le Cuppere, John Sewaker, Edward de Fromilode, John le Schipward, Robert Groundy.
At: Berkeley.

A1/64/19 [GC 2081]   12 Feb. 9 Edw. II [1316]
William le Herde of Alkington and Henry le Gardyner of Berkeley.

William has granted to Henry 1 a. of meadow in the meadow called Matford, extending to the field called Oldeburi above the rhine there, in Alkyntone, as contained in his charter, and Henry grants that if William, his heirs or assigns, on the feast of St. Peter in chains [1 August] next coming, pays to Henry, his heirs or assigns 14s. then the said meadow with the said charter will be delivered to William, his heirs or assigns.
Witnesses: William le Gold, William de Kyneltre, John le Cuppere, John Jodde, John le Schipward.
At: Alkington.

A1/64/20 [GC 2521]   n.d. [c. 1300]
Henry le Grut of Berkeley and Henry called Gardiner of the same.

Henry le Grut has granted to Henry le Gardiner, his heirs and assigns, for a certain sum of money, all his land in the croft beyond Modibroc between the land of John Marescall and of John de Grantval.
Witnesses: Thomas Alein, Richard Averey, John Sewaker, Walter Schipward, Henry le Cuppere, Walter le Cuppere, Richard le Savoner, clerk.

A1/64/21 [GC 915]   n.d. [late 13th cent.]
William le Grut and Henry called Gardin' of Berkeley.

William has granted to Henry all his land at Lockedon within the manor of Hamme, between the land of Walter de Ulmo and Alilonde, and next to the road from Berkel' to Swonhungre; to hold of Thomas de Swonhungre at a rent of 10*d.* a year, and Henry has given William 40*s.*
Witnesses: Robert de Stan', Robert Wyther, Thomas Alein, Richard Averey, John Sewaker, John Bonserjant, Richard le Savoner.

A1/64/22 [GC 1342]   n.d. [*temp.* Edw. I]
John de Egetone and Henry le Gardiner of Berkeley.

John has granted to Henry the ditch with a hedge at Alilond which lies between John's land and Henry's land; Henry has given him 2*s.*
Witnesses: Thomas Serjant, Geoffrey Nel, Nicholas Nel, Adam Hatholf, John Sewaker, John Cuppere, Henry Grout.

A1/64/23 [GC 1629]   n.d. [*temp.* Edw. I]
John son of John Bonserjant of Berkeley and Henry called Gardinar' of Berkeley.

John has granted to Henry all his land in la Westfeld of Berkel', lying in the furlong called Alilond; rent to the chief lord 2*d.* a year, and Henry has given John 40*s.*
Witnesses: John Sewaker, John le Cuppere, Henry le Cuppere, Walter le Cuppere, Richard le Sopere.

HOLDING IN HAM AND ALKINGTON: BARR CROFT, ACTREE, DUDMOOR, HOLMEAD
The Barr lands in Ham

Grant by Adam at Barr
A1/64/24 [GC 1162]   n.d. [*temp.* Edw. I]
Adam ate Barre of Berkeley; and Henry le Gardiner of Berkeley and Isabel his wife.

Adam has granted to Henry and Isabel a plot of land in Berk', with the buildings on it, to the south of Adam's house, containing at the back 12½ feet, and in the front, to the west towards the hedge, 18 feet, and being 56 feet long; also a curtilage 40 by 31½ feet; for their lives, rent 4*d.* a year and they have given him 27*s.*
Witnesses: Thomas Alein, Walter Shipward, John Sewaker, John Bonserjant, Henry le Cuppere, Richard le Savoner, Henry Grout, clerk.

A1/64/25 [GC 585]   3 Sept. 1291
Maud ate Barre, daughter and heir of Adam ate Barre of Berkeley, widow; and Henry le Gardiner of Berkeley and Isabel his wife.

Maud has quitclaimed to Henry and Isabel all the lands which they had by grant of Adam her father in Berkeley.
Witnesses: Robert de Stone, Thomas Alein, Walter Shipward, John Sewaker, John Bonserjant, Henry Cuppere, Richard Noble, Walter le Cuppere, Henry Grout.
At: Berkeley.

Grants by Maud at Barr
A1/64/26 [GC 860]   n.d. [late 13th cent.]
Maud daughter and heir of Adam ate Barre of Berkeley, unmarried woman, and Henry called Gardiner.

Maud has granted to Henry, for a certain sum of money, 4 selions of land in the croft beyond Modibroc, next to the land of St. Augustine's Abbey called la Leye; rent ½*d.* a year.
Witnesses: Thomas Alein, Richard Averey, Henry Cuppere, John Cuppere, Richard Savoner.

A1/64/27 [GC 1164]   n.d. [*temp.* Edw. I]
Maud daughter and heir of Adam ate Barre of Berkeley, unmarried woman, and Henry le
Gardiner' of Berkeley.

Maud has granted to Henry, for a certain sum of money, all her land in the upper furlong
in her croft next to Modibroc; rent 1*d.* a year to the chief lord of the fee.
Witnesses: Robert de Stan', Thomas Alein, John Sewaker, Walter Cuppere, Roger Tannare,
Henry Grout.

A1/64/28 [GC 1603]   n.d. [*temp.* Edw. I]
Maud daughter and heir of Adam de la Barre of Berkeley, unmarried woman, and Henry
Gardin' of Berkeley.

Maud has granted to Henry all her land in the croft beyond Modibroc; rent to the lord of
the fee 8*d.* a year, and Henry has given Maud 10*s.*
Witnesses: Robert de Stone, Richard de Wyke, Thomas de Swonhungre, Thomas Alain,
John Sewaker, Richard Averey, Richard le Savoner.

A1/64/29 [GC 1163]   n.d. [*temp.* Edw. I]
Maud daughter and heir of Adam ate Barre of Berkeley, unmarried woman; and Henry
called Gardin' of Berkeley and Isabel his wife.

Maud has granted to Henry and Isabel her land in the croft next to Modibroc and the
reversion of the lands there held by Alice her mother in dower; they have given Maud £4.
Witnesses: Robert de Stan', Robert de Bradeston, John de Crauleye, Thomas de
Swonhungre, John Sewaker, Richard Averay, John le Cuppere, John Bonserjant, Richard le
Sopere.

A1/64/30 [GC 1165]   n.d. [*temp.* Edw. I]
Maud daughter and heir of Adam ate Barre of Berkeley and Henry le Gardiner' of Berkeley.

Maud has granted to Henry 10 selions of land between her land and the field called la
Lye; rent 4*d.* a year to the chief lord of the fee, and he has given her 10*s.*
Witnesses: Robert de Stane, Thomas Alein, John Sewaker, Henry Cuppere, William de
Modebrok.

A1/64/31 [GC 666]   n.d. [*c.* 1291]
Maud daughter and heir of Adam ate Barre and Henry called Gardin' of Berkeley.

Maud has granted to Henry an annual rent of 1*d.* from John de Gauntval and Sibyl his
wife for 3 selions of land in a croft beyond Modibroc.
Witnesses: Robert de Stone, Robert Wither, Thomas Alein, Richard Averay, John Sewaker.

A1/64/32 [GC 2092]   1 April 9 Edw. II [1316]
Henry le Gardener and his lord, Sir Thomas de Berkeleye, lord of Berkeley.

Henry has granted to Thomas and his heirs a rent of 12*d.* a year from Henry and his heirs
for the land which was of Adam de la Barre in Hamme, and for this Thomas has released to
Henry and his heirs suit to his court of Hamme and his hundred of Berkeleye.
Witnesses: John Capel, John de la Hay, John le Serjaunt, John Wyth, John Sewaker.
At: Berkeley.

A1/64/33 [GC 2093]   1 April 9 Edw. II [1316]
Walter Saundres and Juliana his wife; and their lord, Sir Thomas de Berkeleye, lord of
Berkeley.

Walter and Juliana have granted to Thomas and his heirs a rent of 12*d.* a year from Henry
le Gardiner and his heirs for the land which was of Adam de la Barre in Hamme, and for
this Thomas has released to Henry and his heirs suit to his court of Hamme and his hundred
of Berkeleye.

Witnesses: John Capel, John de la Hay, John le Serjaunt, John Wyth, John Sewaker.
At: Berkeley.

A1/64/34 [GC 2121]   7 Sept. 10 Edw. II [1316]
Thomas de Berkeleye, lord of Berkeley, and Henry le Gardener.

Whereas Henry and his heirs are bound to Thomas and his heirs in an annual rent of 12*d.* by a charter of Henry's, Thomas has released the rent to him for his life.
Witnesses: John le Cuppere, John Sewaker, Edward de Fromelode, Roger le Cuppere, Adam Pynel.
At: Berkeley.

Marshall lands in Barr croft
A1/64/35 [GC 667]   n.d. [*c.* 1291]
Alice widow of Adam ate Barre of Berkeley and Henry le Gardiner of Berkeley.

Alice has quitclaimed to Henry her dower rights in land in the croft of John Marscall.
Witnesses: Robert de Stone, Thomas Alein, John Sewaker, Walter Shipward, Henry Grout.

A1/64/36 [GC 1931]   Fri. before the nativity of St. John the Baptist, 6 Edw. II [22 June 1313]
Mabel widow of John Marescall of Berkeley and Robert son of the said John Marescall.

Mabel has quitclaimed to Robert her rights in the croft called Barrecroft, except for one third in dower for her life.
Witnesses: John le Cuppere, John Sewaker, Henry le Gardyner, John le Vygnur, Roger le Cuppere.
At: Berkeley.

A1/64/37 [GC 1949]   14 Oct. 7 Edw. II [1313]
Robert son of John Marescall of Berkeley and Henry le Gardener.

Robert has granted to Henry all his land at la Barrecrofte by Berkelee, in the manor of Hamme.
Witnesses: Thomas de Stone, John Capel, John le Cuppere, Roger le Cuppere, John Sewaker, Robert Averay, John le Schippard.
At: Berkeley.

Shoyar lands in Barr croft
A1/64/38 [GC 1961]   26 Jan. 7 Edw. II [1314]
Robert son and heir of John le Schoyare of Berkeley;[1] and Henry le Gardener and Isabel his wife.

Robert has granted to Henry and Isabel all his land in Barrecroft by Berkelee, with the reversion of the portion held in dower by William le Taillour and Mabel his wife, widow of Robert's father John, which croft he inherited on the death of his father, in Hamme.
Witnesses: Thomas de Stone, John Capel, John le Cuppare, John Sewaker, Roger le Cuppare, John le Schippard, William le Somyter.
At: Berkeley.

A1/64/39 [GC 2373]   St. Laurence, 15 Edw. II [3 Feb. 1322]
Mabel de Fromylode, widow of John de la Schoyare of Berkeley, and Henry le Gardiner of Berkeley.

Mabel has quitclaimed to Henry her dower rights in a parcel of land in Barrecroft.
Witnesses: John le Cuppere, John Judde, Roger le Cuppere, Thomas Page, Adam Pynel.
At: Berkeley.

---

[1] It is possible that Robert son and heir of John le Shoyar was the same man as Robert son and heir of John Marshall, recorded above in A1/64/36–7.

Sumpter lands in Barr croft

A1/64/40 [GC 2340]   Mon. the feast of the Purification, 14 Edw. II [2 Feb. 1321]
William le Someter and Henry le Gardyner of Berkeley.

   William has granted to Henry, his heirs and assigns 4 selions of land lying beside the vill
of Berkelee in the field called Barrescrofte, and Henry has given him a certain sum of
money.
Witnesses: John le Coppere, John Judde, William attan Abbeye, Robert Bastard, John atte
Hay.
At: Berkeley.

A1/64/41 [GC 2341]   Mon. the feast of the Purification, 14 Edw. II [2 Feb. 1321]
(1) William le Someter; (2) Richard his eldest son; (3) Henry le Gardyner of Berkeley.

   William has appointed Richard his attorney to give seisin to Henry of 4 selions of land in
Barrescrofte, as in his charter.
At: Berkeley.

Three selions in Dudmoor

A1/64/42 [GC 426]   n.d. [*c*. 1310]
Walter called Schipward of Berkeley; and Henry le Gardiner and Isabel his wife.

   Walter has granted to Henry and Isabel, for their lives, 3 selions of land in the manor of
Hamme in the furlong called Didemere between the land of Sir Peter son of Warin and
Richard ate Slo, for a certain sum of money.
Witnesses: John le Coppere, Richard le Coppere, John Sewaker, Robert Bastard, Nicholas
Iweyn.

Meadow in Holmead in Ham

A1/64/43 [GC 862]   n.d. [late 13th cent.]
Richard Averey of Berkeley and Henry Gardin'.

   Richard has granted to Henry, for a certain sum of money, his meadow in Holemed
between the meadow of the lord of Berkeley and of Richard le Wyne; rent 1*d*. a year.
Witnesses: Thomas Alein, John Sewaker, Henry le Cuppere, John le Cuppere, Richard le
Savoner.

A1/64/44 [GC 845]   n.d. [late 13th cent.]
Richard le Wyne and Henry called Gardiner of Berkeley.

   Richard has granted to Henry, for a certain sum of money, ½ a. of meadow in Holemed.
Witnesses: John Sewaker, Robert Averey, John le Cuppere, Henry and Walter le Cuppere,
Richard le Sopere, clerk.

Grant of the combined holding to John

A1/64/45 [GC 2620]   Wed. the feast of the Annunciation, 1 Edw. III [25 March 1327]
Henry le Gardyner of Berkeley and John his younger son.

   Henry has granted to John, his heirs and assigns the holding which he had by grant of
Adam ate Barre and John le Shoyare, lying near Berkel', called Barrycroft, also 2 a. of land
in the manor of Alkyntone in the field called la Moreaketre, 3 selions of land in the manor
of Hamme in the field called Dyddemere beside the land of Sir Nicholas de Kyngestone and
all his meadow in Holemed in the manor of Hamme.
Witnesses: John de Egetone, John de Swonhungre, John Judde, Robert Groundy, Edward de
Fromylode, John Sewaker.
At: Berkeley.

A1/64/46 [GC 2621]   The Annunciation, 1 Edw. III [25 March 1327]
Henry le Gardener of Berkeley and John his younger son.

   Henry has granted to John, his heirs and assigns his croft called Barrycrofte which he had by grant of Adam ate Barre and his croft in the same place which he had by grant of John le Schoyare near Berckel', also 2 a. of land in the greater Aketre, 3 selions in the field called Dyddemere and all his meadow in Holemede.

Witnesses: John de Egetone, John de Swonhungre, John Judde, Robert Groundy, Edward de Fromylode, John Sewaker.

At: Berkeley.

A1/64/47 [GC 2626]   Mon. after St. Philip and St. James, 1 Edw. III [4 May 1327]
Henry le Gardyner of Berkeley and John his younger son.

Henry has quitclaimed to John the holdings with a house, buildings and a croft which he had by grant of Adam ate Barre and John le Shoyare near Berkel', the croft of which holding is called Barrycroft, and 2 a. of land in the manor of Alkyntone in the field called la Moreaketre, 3 selions of land in the manor of Hamme in the field called Dyddemere and his meadow in Holemede in the manor of Hamme.

Witnesses: John de Egetone, John de Swonhungre, John Judde, Robert Groundy, Edward de Fromylode, John Sewaker.

At: Berkeley.

HOLDING IN HAM AND ALKINGTON: ACTREE, ALILAND, LUGDOWN, WESTFIELD AND MATFORD
The Herriots' meadow in Matford

A1/64/48 [GC 907]   n.d. [*temp*. Edw. I]
Alice widow of Thomas Flambert of Newport and Henry called Gardin'.

Alice has granted to Henry, for a certain sum of money, her part of 1 a. of meadow in Matford which she inherited after the death of William Herieth her father, between the river of Matford and the field called Oldebur'.

Witnesses: Robert de Stan', Robert de Bradeston, Walter Moton, Walter the weaver (*textor*), Robert Grip, William Pathering, Richard le Sopere, clerk.

A1/64/49 [GC 956]   n.d. [*temp*. Edw. I]
William Clerk of Rudgwick and Alice Flambard, his wife; and Walter Motun of Wick.

William and Alice have granted to Walter all the portion of land in Baynham which Alice had after the death of her sister, and ¼ a. of meadow in Mateford at Beme.

Witnesses: Richard de Avene, Nicholas de Wodeford, William Gold, William de Keneltre, Thomas de Lorewenge, John Mason, Maurice Bernard.

A1/64/50 [GC 786]   n.d. [*temp*. Edw. I]
Walter Moton of Wick and Henry called Gardiner of Berkeley.

Walter has granted to Henry all his land and meadow in Kyngesfithele, and ¼ a. of meadow in Matford which he had from Walter called Webbe of Swanleye and Joan his wife, and which descended to William and Joan after the death of Maud sister of Joan, and ¼ a. of meadow in Matford at la Beme which he had from William Clerk of Ruggewyk and Alice his wife . . . Alice Flambart his wife which descended after the death of the said Maud, Alice's sister.

Witnesses: Richard de Avene, William le Gold, William de Kyneltre, John Coppere of Berkeley, Roger le Coppere, Robert Grundy, John Judde.

A1/64/51 [GC 1488]   n.d. [*temp*. Edw. I]
William de Morevile of Nibley and Isabel his wife; and Henry le Gardiner of Berkeley.

William and Isabel have granted to Henry all their land and meadow in Kyngesfithele, and a plot of meadow in Matford, which they inherited after the death of Maud, sister of Isabel; he has given them a certain sum of money.

Witnesses: Richard de Avene, Walter Moton, William le Gold, John Coppere, Roger le Coppere.

A1/64/52 [GC 1699]   Tues. the eve of St. Barnabas, 2 Edw. II [10 June 1309]
Joan Herieth and Henry le Garden' of Berkeley.

   Joan has quitclaimed to Henry the meadow called Matford which she inherited after the
death of William Herieth her father.
Witnesses: William de Kyneltre, Adam de Mettesdone, John le Cuppere, Roger le Cuppere,
John le Schipward.
At: Berkeley.

A1/64/53 [GC 2199]   Tues. the feast of St. Luke, 11 Edw. II [25 Oct. 1317]
Joan Herieht of Newport, widow of Walter le Webbe of Swanley, and Henry le Gardiner of
Berkeley.

   Joan has quitclaimed to Henry, his heirs and assigns her meadow in Matforde in various
places, in Alkyntone.
Witnesses: Walter Sewaker, John Capel, John ate Hay, William Golde, William Kyneltre,
Adam de Mettesdone, William Grip.
At: Newport.

Lands in Actree

Grants by Nicholas Thedulf to the Gardeners
A1/64/54 [GC 974]   n.d. [early 14th cent.]
Nicholas Thedulf; and Henry called Gardin' of Berkeley and Isabel his wife.

   Nicholas has granted to Henry and Isabel 17 selions and a gore with a fore-earth at each
end, in Aketre; and they have given him 40*s*.
Witnesses: Richard Averey, John Sewaker, Richard le Sopere, William de Kineltre, Robert
le Grip.

A1/64/55 [GC 1622]   n.d. [early 14th cent.]
Nicholas Thedulf of Alkington and Henry called Gardin' of Berkeley.

   Nicholas has granted to Henry, for a certain sum of money, 26 selions of land with fore-
earths, ditches and hedges, in the furlong called Aketre in the manor of Alkinton; rent to the
lord of the fee a rose a year.
Witnesses: Robert de Stane, William Capel, Thomas Alein, John le Cuppere, Richard le
Sopere.

A1/64/56 [GC 1559]   n.d. [early 14th cent.]
Nicholas Thedulf of Alkington; and Henry called Gardin' of Berkeley and Isabel his wife.

   Nicholas has granted to Henry and Isabel all his land called Aketre, beside the rhine of
Cronhammessciche, which he had in exchange from Sir Maurice lord of Berkel'; rent to the
lord of Berkeley 1*d.* a year, and they have given Nicholas 10 marks.
Witnesses: Robert de Stane, Robert de Bradestone, Thomas de Swonhungre, Walter Moton,
William de Mettesdone, Adam Godmon, William de Kineltre, Robert Grip, Richard le
Sopere, clerk.

A1/64/57 [GC 975]   n.d. [early 14th cent.]
Nicholas Thedulf of Alkington; and Henry called Gardin' of Berkeley and Isabel his wife.

   Nicholas has granted to Henry and Isabel all his land called Aketre above the rhine of
Kronammessach; to hold of the lord of Berkel', rent 1*d.* a year, and they have given
Nicholas 10 marks.
Witnesses: Walter Moton, William de Kineltre, Robert le Grip, Thomas Martin, Richard le
Savoner, clerk.

   Grants by others
A1/64/58 [GC 1734]   Mon. after St. Mark the evangelist, 3 Edw. II [27 April 1310]
Richard Noblepas of Berkeley and Henry le Gardiner of Berkeley.

Richard has granted to Henry 3 selions of land in Aketre beside the king's highway at Mabeliecroyz above Crenhamsiche.

Witnesses: John le Cuppere, Roger le Cuppere, William Iweyn, John le Schipward, John the miller (*molend'*).

At: Berkeley.

A1/64/59 [GC 2175]   Holy Trinity, 10 Edw. II [29 May 1317]

Thomas the miller (*molendinar'*) of Berkeley, and Henry le Gardiner of Berkeley.

Thomas has granted to Henry, his heirs and assigns a selion of land in the field called Aketre, beside the road from Berkel' to Lorwynge above Cronhamessiche, and Henry has given him a certain sum of money.

Witnesses: John le Coppare, John Jodde, Robert Groundi, John Sewaker, Edward de Fromilode, Roger le Coppare, John le Vyngnur.

At: Berkeley.

Grant of the combined holding to John

A1/64/60 [GC 2459]   St. Barnabas, 19 Edw. II [11 June 1326]

Henry le Gardiner of Berkeley and Sir Henry de Cerneye, vicar of Berkeley.

Henry le Gardiner has granted to Henry de Cerneye, his heirs and assigns two crofts of land, one called Aketre in the manor of Alkyntone and the other called Alylond in the manor of Hamme, and all his land in the field called Lockedonne, a parcel of land in la Westfelde, and 1 a. of meadow in the meadow of Matforde; and Henry de Cerneye has given him a certain sum of money.

Witnesses: John le Serjaunt, John Capel, John de Egetone, John de Swonhungre, Walter de Coumbe, John Judde, William Kyneltre.

At: Berkeley.

A1/64/61 [GC 2462; *duplicate* GC 2463]   Tues. after St. Bartholomew, 20 Edw. II
                                                                    [26 Aug. 1326]

Henry le Gardiner of Berkeley and John his younger son.

Henry has granted to John, his heirs and assigns two crofts of land, one called Aketre in the manor of Alkyntone and the other called Alylond in the manor of Hamme, and all his land in the field called Lockedonne in the manor of Hamme, a parcel of land in la Westfelde in the manor of Hamme, and 1 a. of meadow in the meadow of Matforde.

Witnesses: John le Serjant, John Capel, John de Egetone, John de Swonhungre, Walter de Coumbe, John Judde, William Kyneltre.

At: Berkeley.

A1/64/62 [GC 2464]   Fri. in the decollation of St. John the Baptist, 20 Edw. II [29 Aug. 1326]

Sir Henry de Cerneye, vicar of Berkeley, and John younger son of Henry le Gardiner of Berkeley.

Henry has quitclaimed to John the lands [etc.] which he had by grant of Henry le Gardiner, and for his greater security has handed over the charter.

Witnesses: John le Serjaunt, John de Egetone, John de Swonhungre, John Wyht, John Judde.

At: Berkeley.

A1/64/63 [GC 2622]   The Annunciation, 1 Edw. III [25 March 1327]

Henry le Gardener of Berkeley, and John his younger son.

Henry has quitclaimed to John two crofts, one called Aketre in the manor of Alkyntone and the other called Alylonde in the manor of Hamme, and also all his land in Lockedonne, a parcel of land in la Westfelde and 1 a. of meadow in Mattforde.

Witnesses: John le Serjaunt, John Capel, John de Ecketone, John de Swonhungre, Walter de Coumbe, John Judde, William Kyneltre.
At: Berkeley.

A1/64/64 [GC 2623]　　　　　　　　Sat. after the Annunciation, 1 Edw. III [28 March 1327]
Henry le Gardener of Berkeley and John his younger son.

　　Henry has quitclaimed to John two crofts, one called Aketre in the manor of Alkyntone and the other called Alylonde in the manor of Hamme, and also all his land in Lockedonne, a parcel of land in la Westfelde and 1 a. of meadow in Mattforde.
Witnesses: John de Swanhungre, John de Egetone, William Kyneltre, John Judde, Robert Groundy, Thomas Page, John de Fromelode.
At: Berkeley.

JOHN LE GARDENER AND HIS SUCCESSORS

A1/64/65 [GC 2418]　　　　　　　　　St. Gregory, 17 Edw. II [12 March 1324]
Alice daughter of Maud ate Barre of Berkeley, widow, and John son of Henry le Gardiner of Berkeley.

　　Alice has quitclaimed to John all the inherited right which she may have in all lands and holdings in the liberty of Berckel'.
Witnesses: John Judde, Robert Groundy, Adam Pynel, John Sewaker, Thomas Page, William Iweyn, William Bodde.
At: Berkeley.

A1/64/66 [GC 2785]　　　　　　　St. Edward the Confessor, 7 Edw. III [5 Jan. 1334]
Walter le Cuppare of Berkeley and John le Gardyner of Berkeley.

　　Walter has granted to John, for a certain sum of money, 4 selions of land in the field called Nokeshulle.
Witnesses: John le Serjaunt, John de Swonhongre, John Capel, John de Egetone, Robert Groundy, William Judde, Edward de Fromelode.
At: Berkeley.

A1/64/67 [GC 4131]　　　　　　　　St. Thomas the apostle, 8 Hen. V [21 Dec. 1420]
William Dolyf, son and heir of Philip Dolyf; and Maurice Clayvile, Alice his wife and Richard their son.

　　Whereas, on the above date, William leased to Maurice, Alice and Richard his croft called Barryescroftys and a lane beside the said croft, for their lives, rent 13s. 4d. a year, he has warranted the croft and lane to them.
Witnesses: Richard Scot, Richard Gilberd, David Pakkere, Thomas Romeron.

THE COSTON HOLDING

The holding, in Ham, Saniger, Wanswell, Acton, Berkeley borough and Alkington, was built up by Hugh de Coston, a villein tenant who took his surname from Coston, a Leicestershire manor which came to Thomas (II) Lord Berkeley with his wife Joan de Ferrers *c.* 1280. After the death of Hugh's son Thomas and Thomas's son Thomas, the holding seems to have passed to Thomas Judd, Hugh de Coston's grandson, Hugh's daughter Margery having married William Judd (see above, A1/62/14 [GC 2281]), but whether by sale or by inheritance is not clear (see below, A1/65/34 [GC 3534]). It may then have passed with other of the Judd lands to the lord of Berkeley, but there is no evidence.

GRANT OF HUGH BY THOMAS (II) LORD BERKELEY TO ROBERT DE STONE 1286

A1/65/1 [GC 523]　　　　　　　　　St. Calixtus, 14 Edw. I [14 Oct. 1286]
Thomas lord of Berkeley and Robert de Stanes.

Thomas has granted to Robert his villein [*nativus*] Hugh de Coston, son of Alice de Coston, and his progeny.

At: Wenden.

ACQUISITIONS IN ALKINGTON, BERKELEY BOROUGH AND ACTON

A1/65/2 [GC 2530]   n.d. [*c.* 1300]

Thomas son and heir of Walter the miller (*molend'*) of Berkeley and Hugh de Costone.

Thomas has granted to Hugh, his heirs and assigns all his land in Juelesaketre, which he had by grant of Sir John de Wyke, chaplain; rent 6*d.* to the lord of Berkel', and Hugh has given Thomas 30*s.*

Witnesses: Robert de Bradeston, John de Crauleye, Thomas le Serjant, Thomas Alein, Walter Moton, William de Mettesdone, Adam Godmon, Robert Grip.

A1/65/3 [GC 2262]   Mon. before the translation of St. Wulfstan, 12 Edw. II [15 Jan. 1319]

Adam Elyot of Hinton; and Hugh de Costone, Alice his wife Alice and Thomas and John their elder sons.

Adam has quitclaimed to Hugh, Alice, Thomas and John, for their lives, ½ qr. of wheat and 1½ qr. of beans and peas in which they are bound each year in rent for 7 a. of land in Netherehethfelde, between the lanes called Irmongareslone and Windmullelone.

Witnesses: William Gilemin, Richard Serjaunt, Nicholas Neel, Alan Aunger, John Duyk.

At: Wanswell.

A1/65/4 [GC 1397]   n.d. [*temp.* Edw. I]

Henry Grout and Hugh de Costone.

Henry has quitclaimed to Hugh the holding in Berk' between the holding of Richard le Coppere and the holding of Robert Swele.

A1/65/5 [GC 1996]   Sun. in Michaelmas, 8 Edw. II [29 Sept. 1314]

Isabel widow of Adam le Hayward of Hinton and Hugh de Costone.

Isabel has leased to Hugh a croft called Henegarstone in Egetone; to Hugh and Alice his wife for a term of 12 years.

Witnesses: [Robert] de Stanforde, Richard le Serjant, John le Serjant, William Gylemyn, William in the Hurne, Robert le Wyghtteladde, William Hert.

At: Berkeley.

ACQUISITIONS IN HAM
Land in Broad croft from John de Acton

A1/65/6 [GC 615]   n.d. [*c.* June 1296]

John de Egeton and Hugh de Coston.

John has enfeoffed Hugh with 5 selions of land in the field called Bradecroft and 2 selions in the same field, as in his charter now in the hands of Sir Walter de Frouc', vicar of Berkeley; John or his attorney will give to Hugh or his attorneys 32*s.* in Berkeley church on the nativity of St. John the Baptist, 24 Edw. I [24 June 1296] and will receive the said charter from the vicar.

Witnesses: Robert de Stone, Robert Wither, Geoffrey Neel, Adam Hadulf, John Sewaker, Henry Cuppere, Henry Grout.

A1/65/7 [GC 1730]   St. Denis, 3 Edw. II [8 April 1310]

William de la More and his brother Thomas, sons of Loretta de Weneswelle; and Hugh de Costone and Alice his wife.

William and Thomas have quitclaimed to Hugh and Alice whatever they may have inherited after the death of Loretta their mother in the lands and holdings which Hugh had by grant of John de Egetone.

Witnesses: Robert de Bradestone, Robert de Berk', Thomas de Beoleye, Robert Wyther, Geoffrey Neel, Nicholas Neel, William Purlewent, clerk.
At: Berkeley.

Meadow in Bulwick meadow from Robert Avery

A1/65/8 [GC 1892]   All Saints, 6 Edw. II [1 Nov. 1312]
Robert Averay of Berkeley; and Hugh de Costone and Alice his wife.

Robert has enfeoffed Hugh and Alice of all his meadow in Bolewyke, for 4 marks which Hugh has given him, on the understanding that if, at Michaelmas next following, Robert pays to Hugh the 4 marks the charter is void, but if he fails to pay part or all of the sum, the charter stands.
Witnesses: Thomas de Stone, John Sewaker, Robert de Stanford, Alan Aunger, Nicholas Neel, William Purlewent, clerk.
At: Berkeley.

A1/65/9 [GC 2067]   Sun. after the Conception of St. Mary, 9 Edw. II [14 Dec. 1315]
Robert Averay; and Hugh de Costone, Alice his first wife and Thomas and John their eldest sons.

Robert has leased to Hugh, Alice, Thomas and John his meadow in Bolewyk in Hamme; for their lives, rent a rose a year.
Witnesses: Robert de Stanford, William Gylemyn, Nicholas Neel, John Sewaker, Thomas le Meleward.
At: Berkeley.

A1/65/10 [GC 3182]   Mon. in Michaelmas, 22 Edw. III [29 Sept. 1348]
Thomas Costone and John le Hert of Hinton.

Whereas Thomas has leased to John 1 a. of meadow in Bolewyke for his life, John wills that if Thomas pays to him, at Berkeleye at Michaelmas in 4 years following, 30*s.* the lease will be void.
Witnesses: John Serjaunt, John de Egetone, William de Swonhongre, William Gilemyn, William Andreus.
At: Saniger.

Land in Lugdown from Robert le Shoyar

A1/65/11 [GC 1963]   Sun. before the Purification, 7 Edw. II [27 Jan. 1314]
Robert le Schoyar of Berkeley and Hugh de Costone.

Robert has granted to Hugh, his heirs or assigns a parcel of land in Lokkedonne in Hamme.
Witnesses: John le Cuppere, John Sewaker, Robert de Stanforde, William Gylemyn, Matthew Hatholf.
At: Berkeley.

A1/65/12 [GC 2432]   St. Thomas the apostle, 18 Edw. II [21 Dec. 1324]
William de Boutone and Mabel de Fromylode his wife; and Hugh de Costone.

William and Mabel have quitclaimed to Hugh land in Lokedonne beside the road from Berckel' to Swonhungre called le Muleweye, which Mabel held in dower after the death of John le Schoyare, formerly her husband.
Witnesses: John le Serjaunt, John de Egetone, John de Swonhungre, William Gylemyn, Nicholas Neel, John Sewaker, Edward de Fromylode.
At: Berkeley.

Other acquisitions

A1/65/13 [GC 861]   n.d. [late 13th cent.]
Richard Averey of Berkeley and Hugh de Coston.

Richard has granted to Hugh, for a certain sum of money, 2 selions of land in the furlong called Ochungre near the land of Peter son of Warin, extending towards Boggethurne; to hold of the chief lord of the fee.

Witnesses: Sir Walter vicar of Berkeley, John Sewaker, Walter le Cuppere, John le Cuppere, Richard le Sopere.

A1/65/14 [GC 882]   n.d. [late 13th cent.]
John Bonserjant of Berkeley and Hugh de Costone.

John has granted to Hugh 1 a. of land in le Westfeld in the furlong called Hopinghul; rent 4*d.* a year.

Witnesses: Robert de Stan', Thomas de Swonhungre, Richard Averey, John Sewaker, Henry le Cuppere, John le Cuppere, John de Asselworth.

A1/65/15 [GC 632]   Sun. after the Exaltation of Holy Cross, 25 Edw. I [15 Sept. 1297]
Alice Heriet, widow of Thomas Flambard of Newport, and Hugh de Coston.

Alice has quitclaimed to Hugh the lands which Hugh had by grant of Thomas de Swonhungre in the field called Alilond.

Witnesses: Robert de Stone, Thomas de Swonhungre, William Capel, Walter Moton, Geoffrey Neel, John Sewaker, John Coppare, Henry Coppare, Henry Grout.
At: Berkeley.

A1/65/16 [GC 1230; *duplicate* GC 1231]   n.d. [*temp.* Edw. I]
Thomas lord of Berkel' and Hugh de Coston.

Thomas has leased to Hugh 1 a. of land in a croft outside Berkel', next to the land of St. Augustine's Abbey, which he had by grant of John Sewaker; to him and his issue, rent 7½*d.* a year.

Witnesses: Robert de Stone, Robert Wyth', Thomas Alain, John Bonserjant, Walter Schipward.

A1/65/17 [GC 990]   n.d. [early 14th cent.]
Richard le Wyne of Berkeley and Hugh de Coston.

Richard has granted to Hugh, for a certain sum of money, all his land in Westfeld; rent a rose a year if required.

Witnesses: Thomas Alein, Richard Averey, John Sewaker, Henry and John le Cuppere.

A1/65/18 [GC 971]   n.d. [early 14th cent.]
Thomas de Swonhungre and Hugh de Coston.

Thomas has granted to Hugh, for a certain sum of money, all his land in Westfeld between the land of Walter de Tresham and William Snite, called Lutelealilonde, also all his land above Lockedon above the road from Berkel' to Swonhungre; rent 1*d.* a year.

Witnesses: Robert de Stan', William Capel, Robert Wyther, Thomas Alein, Richard Averey, John Sewaker, Geoffrey Neel.

A1/65/19 [GC 1655]   Ascension Day, 1 Edw. II [23 May 1308]
Juliana widow of Hervi de Hamme and Hugh de Costune.

Juliana has granted to Hugh, for a certain sum of money, 7 selions of land containing 1 a. in the furlong called Plankehulle within the manor of St. Augustine's at Berkeleye; to hold of the chief lord.

Witnesses: Robert de Berkeleye, Robert de Bradeston, Geoffrey Neel, Nicholas Neel, Alan Aunger, Thomas de Lorewinge, Richard Sune.

A1/65/20 [GC 1954; *duplicate* GC 1955]   Mon. before St. Katherine, 7 Edw. II [19 Nov. 1313]
Robert Aufrey of Berkeley and Hugh de Costone.

Robert has leased and mortgaged to Hugh 1 a. of land in Dolefeldeshull, for 20*s.*; and if Robert fails, in whole or in part, to repay the 20*s.* to Hugh by Michaelmas next following, the land will remain to Hugh and Alice his wife.

At: Berkeley.

A1/65/21 [GC 2399]   The Annunciation, 16 Edw. II [25 March 1323]
Henry Kyllekote of Berkeley and Hugh de Costone.

Henry has granted to Hugh, his heirs and assigns 5 selions of land, one in greater Berklewode and four in the furlong called Plaunckehull.

Witnesses: John le Serjaunt, John Capel, William Gylemyn, John Sewaker, John Judde, Nicholas Neel, Richard de Stanford.

At: Berkeley.

A1/65/22 [GC 2446]   St. Bartholomew, 19 Edw. II [24 Aug. 1325]
William Arthur of Berkeley and Hugh de Costone.

William has quitclaimed to Hugh the annual rent of 1*d.* which Hugh pays for 2 selions of land in Bercklewode.

Witnesses: Henry le Gardiner, John Sewaker, John Judde, Nicholas Neel, Richard de Stanford.

At: Berkeley.

ACQUISITION OF THE SKINNER HOLDING IN SANIGER

A1/65/23 [GC 720]   n.d. [*temp.* Edw. I]
Hugh de Coston and Henry the skinner (*pellipar'*).

Hugh has leased to Henry the messuage with a curtilage, garden and croft in Swonhungre which he had from Hervey de Hamme; to hold of Hervey de Hamme, for life, rent to Hugh 4*s.* 6*d.* a year.

Witnesses: Thomas de Swonhungre, John de Egeton, Geoffrey Neel, Nicholas Neel, John de Asselworth.

A1/65/24 [GC 919]   n.d. [late 13th cent.]
Walter son of Hervey de Hamme and Juliana daughter of Robert Gamel of Saniger, his mother.

Walter has granted to Juliana the holding, viz. a messuage, curtilage and croft in Swonhungre, which Henry le Skynnare held; to hold of the chief lord of the fee.

Witnesses: Thomas le Serjent, Geoffrey Neel, Richard le Serjant, Robert de Stanford, Alan Aung', John le Serjant.

A1/65/25 [GC 439]   n.d. [*temp.* Edw. I]
Juliana daughter of Robert Gamel of Saniger, widow, and Hugh de Coston.

Juliana has granted to Hugh a holding of a messuage, a curtilage and a croft in Swonhangre, which Henry le Skynnere once held; to hold of the chief lord of the fee for the due services, viz. 9*d.* a year.

Witnesses: Robert de Bradeston, Robert de Berkeleye, Thomas le Serjaunt, Geoffrey Neel, Nicholas Neel, Richard le Serjaunt, Robert de Stanford, Alan Aunger.

A1/65/26 [GC 2563]   n.d. [early 14th cent.]
Walter son of Hervey de Hamme by Berkeley and Hugh de Costone.

Walter has quitclaimed to Hugh a messuage, curtilage and croft in Swonhongre, which Henry le Skynnere formerly held.

Witnesses: Geoffrey Neel, Nicholas Neel, Robert de Stanford, Alan Aunger, Geoffrey de Boele.

ACQUISITIONS IN WANSWELL
Croft in Dolefield

A1/65/27 [GC 1398]   n.d. [*temp.* Edw. I]

William le Grout and Henry son of Henry Grout.

William has granted to Henry all the land in the croft called Dolfeld in the vill of Weneswelle, beside the road from Berk' to Hynetone; to hold of the chief lord of the fee, rent 6*d.* a year, and Henry has given him 3½ marks.

Witnesses: Robert de Stone, Thomas Alein, Thomas de Swonhungre, John de Egetone, Adam Hadulf, Roger Coby, Walter Shipward, Henry Cuppere.

A1/65/28 [GC 2520]   n.d. [late 13th cent.]

Henry Grut of Berkeley and Hugh de Costone.

Henry has granted to Hugh his croft at Weneswell beside the road from Berkel' to Hiniton; and for this Hugh has granted to Henry all his land in Juelesaketre and 1 a. of land in a croft beyond Modibroke in exchange.

Witnesses: Robert de Stane, Thomas de Swonhungre, Thomas Alein, Richard Averey, John Sewaker, Walter Schipward, Walter le Cuppere.

A1/65/29 [GC 2503]   n.d. [late 13th cent.]

Hugh de Costone and Henry Grut.

Hugh has granted to Henry, his heirs and assigns all his land in Juelesaketre beside Juelessciche and 1 a. in the croft beyond Modibroke; for this Henry has granted to him a croft at Weneswell in exchange.

Witnesses: Robert de Stone, Thomas de Swonhungre, Thomas Alein, Richard Averey, John Sewaker, Walter Scipward, Walter le Cuppere, Richard le Savoner, clerk.

A1/65/30 [GC 2319]   Mon. the eve of the nativity of St. John the Baptist, 13 Edw. II [23 June 1320]

William son of William le Grout and Hugh de Costone.

William has quitclaimed to Hugh, his heirs and assigns 4 a. of land in the field called Dolefeld and 1 selion of land in Berkelewode beside the road from Hynetone to Berkeleye, above the fishpond of Smethemor, in Hamme.

Witnesses: Richard le Sergeant, William de Schokerwych, Alan Aunger, John le Cuppere, Henry le Gardener, John Judde, Roger le Cuppere.

At: Berkeley.

A1/65/31 [GC 2739]   St. Nicholas, 5 Edw. III [6 Dec. 1331]

Hugh de Costone and Thomas his son.

Hugh has granted to Thomas a croft of land called Dolfeld beside the road from Swonhungre to Weneswelle; to him and his issue.

Witnesses: John le Serjaunt, John de Swonhungre, John de Egetone, William Gylemyn, Richard de Stanford, Nicholas Neel.

At: Wanswell.

Other

A1/65/32 [GC 652]   Sun. in the Invention of Holy Cross, 27 Edw. I [3 May 1299]

Agnes de la Faude, widow of William de la Faude, and Hugh de Coston.

Agnes has quitclaimed to Hugh all the lands and holdings in Waneswell which she had from Hugh for her life.

Witnesses: Thomas le Serjant, Richard le Serjant, John de Asselworthe, William Gilemyn, William de Webbel', clerk.

At: Berkeley.

A1/65/33 [GC 2756]   St. Matthew, 6 Edw. III [21 Sept. 1332]
Hugh de Costone and Thomas his son and heir.

Hugh has granted to Thomas all his holding in Weneswelle in Hamme; to him and his issue.

Witnesses: John le Serjaunt, John de Swonhungre, William de Swonhungre, John de Egetone, William Gylemyn, Nicholas Neel.
At: Wanswell.

A1/65/34 [GC 3534; *duplicate* GC 3535]   27 May 36 Edw. III [1362]
Thomas Judde; and William le Kyng, Edith his wife and John and William their sons.

Thomas has leased to William, Edith, John and William a croft at le Wyte Croys in Waneswelle, which he had after the death of Thomas son and heir of Thomas de Costone; for their lives, rent 5*s.* a year.
Witnesses: John Serjaunt, John Aleyn, Henry de Egetone, Walter Matheu, John Herne.
At: Berkeley.

THE SALTMARSH HOLDING

The Saltmarshes (*de salso marisco, de Sautemareys*) were a knightly family in the 12th and 13th centuries, appearing frequently as witnesses to Berkeley and other local charters, but had fallen in status by the early 14th century when John de Saltmarsh granted to Thomas (III) Lord Berkeley his lands in Woodford and Ham.

A1/66/1 [SC 244]   10 Kal. of March 1238 [20 Feb. 1239]
Sir Thomas de Berkeley and Maurice son of Hugh de Saltmarsh (*de salso marisco*).

Thomas has granted to Maurice all the land at Wudeford which Walter Puthering held, in exchange for the land in the park of Hocleia which Maurice claimed but has now relinquished.
Witnesses: Sir Richard de Clifford, Peter de Stintescumbe, Walter Cavell, John de Wudeford, Maurice de Stanes, William Veel (*Vitulus*), Adam Russel.

A1/66/2 [GC 350]   n.d. [1243 × 1261]
Maurice lord of Berkeley and Maurice de Saltmarsh (*de salso marisco*).

Maurice de Berkeley has quitclaimed to Maurice de Saltmarsh 20*s.* of the annual rent of 23*s.* which he renders for his holding in Wodeford, so that Maurice de Saltmarsh and his heirs shall have the holding for 3*s.* a year; and if he dies without issue then the 20*s.* will revert to Maurice de Berkeley and his heirs.
Witnesses: Sir Nicholas son of Roger, Roger de Lokinton, [Richard?] de Cromhale, Walter de Burgo, Henry de Berkeley, Robert de Hales, steward, Maurice de Stanes, Adam Flaumbard, William son of Robert, Nicholas le Rus, John de Egeton, Andrew de Bradeston, Thomas Mathias.

A1/66/3 [GC 687]   n.d. [1243 × 1261]
Maurice lord of Berkel and Maurice de Saltmarsh (*de salso marisco*).

Maurice de Berkel has granted to Maurice de Saltmarsh 35½ a. of arable land, 4¼ a. of pasture and 1 a. of meadow in his manor of Alcrinton, viz. all the furlong called Kingesham below his court in Wodeford for 7 a., and all the furlong of Oldebur' lying outside the park of Ocle on the south side, for 22 a., and 4½ a. in Echedon outside the wood of Inwod and 2 a. in the same field, and 4¼ a. of pasture and 1 a. of meadow in Brademed, viz. all of Brademed, all of the land, persons, and progeny of Gilbert de Wodeford and Herebet le Syvier, and an annual rent of 40*s.* which John de Wodeford paid to Maurice [de Berkeley]'s ancestors for his holding in Wodeford and Hunteneford; to him and his issue, rent a pair of gloves a year or 1*d.*

Witnesses: Sir Nicholas son of Roger, Roger de Lokinton, Richard de Cromhal, Walter de Burgo, Henry de Wik, Robert de Hales, steward of Berkeley, Maurice de Stanes, Adam Flambard, William son of Robert, Nicholas le Rus, John de Egeton, Andrew de Bratheston.

A1/66/4 [GC 1550]   n.d. [late Hen. III]
Maurice de Stanes and Maurice de Saltmarsh (*de salso marisco*).

Maurice de Stanes has quitclaimed to Maurice de Saltmarsh the mill of Wudeford, which was anciently called the mill of Aukeringtone, and has granted to him 2 perches of land beside it.
Witnesses: Sir William le Maunsel, Jordan de Budeford, Peter de Wike, Philip de Leyc', John de Bradeston, Nicholas de Crauleye, Adam Coby, John de Egeton, William Maudut, Henry de Baton', Henry de Haweye, Robert [de Stane], Maurice's son, Robert Caudel, Nicholas de Caldewell, Adam Flambard, Robert le Bastard.

A1/66/5 [GC 1549]   n.d. [*c.* 1262]
Maurice de Stane and Sir Maurice de Saltmarsh (*de salso marisco*).

Maurice de Stane has granted to Maurice de Saltmarsh the meadow in Eygeht, 4 selions of land in the upper ham and 1 selion in the same ham; rent 1*d.* a year, and Maurice has given him 3 marks.
Witnesses: Sir Richard de Wygorn, steward of Berkeley, Sir Nicholas vicar of Berkeley, William de Mathem, Peter de Wyke, Thomas the serjeant (*serviens*), John de Egeton, Nicholas de Crauleygh, Robert Caudel, Ralph de Angervill, Walter Sely.

A1/66/6 [SC 419]   n.d. [*temp.* Hen. III]
Eve la Wlbetere, daughter of Walter le Wlbetere, and Sir Maurice de Saltmarsh (*de salso marisco*), knight.

Eve has granted to Maurice the meadow above the marsh (*super mars*) between the meadow of William de Stane, son of Walter the clerk of Stane, and the meadow of Ralph de Northblone; rent a clove a year, and Maurice has given her 2 marks. Endorsed: *Alkyngton*.
Witnesses: Sir Roger de Lokinton, Sir Walter de Burgo, knights, Master William Taney, steward of Berkeley, Andrew de Brotheston, Maurice de Stane, John Egeton, Robert Bastard, Adam Flamberd.

A1/66/7 [SC 370]   n.d. [*temp.* Hen. III]
Geoffrey the forester (*forestarius*) and Maurice de Saltmarsh (*de salso marisco*).

Geoffrey has sold to Maurice ½ a. of meadow in Longomede, lying between the meadow of the said Maurice and Hegeruding, for 15*s.* Endorsed: *Alkynton*.
Witnesses: William Mansel, John de Wudeford, Maurice de Stane, William Kavel, William de Stane, Robert the forester (*forestarius*), Thomas Scoth, Robert Chaudel, Thomas the clerk of Tortwr[th], who wrote this charter.

A1/66/8 [GC 1507]   n.d. [late Hen. III]
Mabel Pelthein and Maurice de Saltmarsh (*Salsomar'*).

Mabel has granted to Maurice the services of Ralph Norslane for his holding in the vill of Stanes, and 2 a. of land in the same vill, 3 selions in la Heyvore Hamme and ½ a. of meadow in Matford; further, the services of Hugh of the bridge (*de ponte*) for his holding in Stanes, with the dower of Eve, her mother, of la Hamme; rent a pair of gloves price 1*d.*, or 1*d.*, a year.
Witnesses: William le Mansel, Roger de Lokinton, Sir Nicholas vicar of Berkeley, Maurice de Stanes, Ralph Dangerwill, Hugh the clerk, Hugh of the bridge, Thomas de Tyrinham.

A1/66/9 [SC 401]　　　　　　　　　　　　　　　　　　　　　n.d. [*temp.* Hen. III]
Maurice de Saltmarsh (*de salso marisco*) and Nicholas the miller (*molendinarius*).

Maurice has quitclaimed to Nicholas and his wife, for their lives, the land which he once held as a customary tenant (*nomine custumarii*) in Wodeford; they will pay him 2*s.* a year in rent; for which they have given him 23*s.*
Witnesses: Nicholas de Wodeford, Robert Caudel, Richard Bochard, William the smith, Richard the clerk.

A1/66/10 [GC 2518]　　　　　　　　　　　　　　　　　　n.d. [early 14th cent.]
Philip le Gleche of Woodford and John de Saltmarsh (*de salso marisco*).

Philip has granted to John, his heirs and assigns a messuage in Wodeford in the high street, and also ½ a. of land in Stone above la Hamme.
Witnesses: Robert de Bradestone, Adam le Waleys, Warin FitzWilliam, Roger atte Garstone, Richard de Wyke, John de Bradelegh, William de Trobrugge.

A1/66/11 [GC 2660]　　　Wed. the eve of the nativity of St. Mary, 2 Edw. III [7 Sept. 1328]
(1) John de Sautemareys; (2) Thomas de Arondel and John de Baggeworth; (3) Sir Thomas de Berkelee, lord of Berkeley, and Margaret his wife.

John has appointed Thomas and John to give seisin to Thomas and Margaret of all the lands, holdings, rents [etc.] which he had in Hamme, Alkyntone and Wodeforde, as in his charter.
At: Bristol.

A1/66/12 [GC 3258]　　　　　　　　　　　　　　　　　　　n.d. [mid 14th cent.]
Thomas lord of Berkelee; and John Baron and Edith his wife.

Thomas has leased to John and Edith all the lands and holdings which he had from John Sautemareys in Wodeforde, except for the mill, the pond and 2 a. of meadow, the rents, and the plot of pasture where the beasts carrying corn to the mill graze; for their lives, rent 4 marks a year.

UNIDENTIFIED MANORS

A1/67/1 [SC 60]　　　　　　　　　　　　　　　　　　　　n.d. [late 12th cent.]
Fulk de Bristollo and Robert son of William de Astona.

Fulk has granted to Robert all his land of Wika; rent 5*s.* a year, for which Robert has given him 10*s.*, and to Aufria his wife a gold coin, and 12*d.* for relief when it happens.
Witnesses: Siuard the proud (*superbus*), Humphrey the proud, Richard the clerk of Compton (*Cumtonia*), Elias de Catecumba, Peter de Stihelvei, Nicholas son of Raher, Stephen the maiden (*virgo*) or the small (*parvus*), Thomas Prethor, Richard de Chenecote, Alduin Prethor, Simon Their, Eliot de Hambroc, Robert the Irish (*Hiberniensis*), Chunther the German (*Alemannus*).

A1/67/2 [SC 346]　　　　　　　　　　　　　　　　　　　　n.d. [*temp.* Hen. III]
Thomas de Berkeley and Stanley Priory.

Thomas has granted to the priory the land which John Blunt held of him; and has also confirmed a rent of 24*s.* in the vill of B. . . [which was granted to them by?] Maurice de Berkeley his father.
Witnesses: . . . son of Richard, Peter de Stintescumbe, Richard de Couele, Thomas de . . ., Robert de Couele, Robert de la Planke, Hugh the baker (*pistor*), . . .

A1/67/3 [GC 731]　　　　　　　　　　　　　　　　　　　　n.d. [late 13th cent.]
William the tailor (*cissor*) and Richard le Shipward of Berkeley.

William has granted to Richard 5 selions of land with two fore-earths which William had from Walter the skinner (*pellipar'*), between the land of Walter the miller (*molendarius*) and

Richard's land of the fee of St. Augustine's Abbey, Bristol; for this Richard has granted to him 4 selions of land, as in his charter.

Witnesses: Philip de Leycestre, Peter de Wyk, Thomas the serjeant (*serviens*), Geoffrey Neel, John Sewaker, Thomas Kavel, Thomas Aleyn.

A1/67/4 [GC 780]   n.d. [late 13th cent.]
Richard called Marschall of Berkeley; and William Hodde of Berkeley and Agnes his wife.

Richard has granted to William and Agnes 2 selions of his curtilage; rent ½*d.* to the chief lord of the fee, and they have given Richard certain monies.

Witnesses: John le Coppere, Walter Sewaker, Walter le Coppere, Roger le Coppere, William le Graunt, Hugh le Frankeleyn, William Purlewent.

A1/67/5 [GC 1251]   n.d. [*temp.* Edw. I]
Thomas de Boeleye and Sir Thomas de Berkeleye, lord of Berkeley.

Thomas de Boeleye has granted to Thomas de Berkeleye a rent of 2*d.* a year from John de Kynggeston and William son of Robert for holdings which they previously held of him.

Witnesses: Robert de Bradestone, Thomas le Sergant, Robert Wyter, Henry de Camme, Maurice de Camme.

A1/67/6 [GC 1739]   Mon. before St. Augustine, 3 Edw. II [25 May 1310]
Thomas son of Richard de Wike and Robert Aufrey.

Agreement between Thomas and Robert concerning Thomas's chase and Robert's pasture rights. [*In French.*]

Witnesses: Sire Maurice de Berkeleye, John Champeneys, Robert de Berk', Robert de Bradestone, John Sewaker, Edward de Fremelode.

At: Berkeley.

A1/67/7 [GC 2501]   n.d. [early 14th cent.]
(1) John Chaumpeneys; (2) Sir Maurice [de Ber]keleye; (3) Alice, widow of . . .

Whereas John is bound to Alice by a certain bond in 20 marks for Sir Maurice . . . his attorney, in the said writing contained, but the said Alice wills . . . keleye enfeoffs the same Alice in 13 a. of land, a half-acre . . . wood, with appurtenances, and with the rents and services of Henry Gry. . . [St. Peter in?] cathedra, the bond will be . . .

Witnesses: . . . inthecombe, Richard Wythemore, Simon ate Broke.

A1/67/8 [SC 503]   Sunday after the translation of St. Thomas [of Canterbury], 13 Edw. III
[11 July 1339]
(1) Thomas de Berkeley; (2) John le Coppare of Berkeley; (3) John son and heir of Roger de Gosynton.

Thomas has appointed John le Coppare to receive seisin of the lands and holdings which John son and heir of Roger had granted to him.[1]

At: Berkeley.

A1/67/9 [GC 3707]   Palm Sunday, 51 Edw. III [22 March 1377]
Maud Topyn of Berkeley, widow, and Thomas Golthoppe.

Maud has quitclaimed to Thomas a holding which she previously held for life by grant of the said Thomas.

At: Berkeley.

A1/67/10 [GC 3780]   4 Dec. 8 Ric. II [1384]
Thomas Berkele, lord of Berkeley, and John Rande.

Thomas has granted to John, his heirs and assigns the holding which Robert Mellere,

---

[1] The appointment may relate to A1/45/11–14, above.

Margaret his wife and John and William their sons had for their lives by grant of Maurice de Berkele, his father; rent 2*s*. 1*d*. a year.
Witnesses: John Elys, John Pake, John Nortone, Walter Claneford, John Herry.

A1/67/11 [GC 3785]   Fri. after St. Mark, 8 Ric. II [28 April 1385]
(1) Sir Thomas de Berkeleye, lord of Berkeley; (2) Ralph Coke; (3) John Sergeaunt of Stone.

Thomas has appointed Ralph to give seisin to John of an annual rent of £12 from various of Thomas's tenants, in exchange, as in a certain indenture made between them.

A1/67/12 [GC 3977]   Fri. after St. Mary Magdalen, 1 Hen. IV [23 July 1400]
William Otclyve, parson of Cromhall, and Robert Coryet, clerk; and John Bannebury of Gloucester.

Whereas William and Robert quitclaimed to John all the lands in Gloucestershire, Somerset, Berkshire, London and Bristol that they had by grant of Thomas de Berkeley of Berkeley, knight, John has granted that if William and Robert pay £400 to John at Michaelmas next the quitclaim shall be void.

A1/67/13 [GC 4158]   St. Brice, 7 Hen. VI [13 Nov. 1428]
(1) John Swonhungre the elder; (2) John Byrden chaplain and William Brown of Berkeley; (3) John Swonghungre, son of John the elder.

John Swonhungre the elder has appointed John Byrden and William to deliver seisin to John Swonhungre the younger of all the lands, holdings [etc.] which he had by grant of Maud his mother, as in his charter.
At: Berkeley.

A1/67/14 [GC 4159]   18 Dec. 7 Hen. VI [1428]
Sir James de Berkeley, knight and lord of Berkeley, and Lady Isabel his wife and lady of Berkeley (Glos.); and John Reve and Joan his wife.

James and Isabel have leased to John and Joan a messuage and 1 virgate of land called Jameres, a toft and half-virgate called Lyllebroke and a toft and half-virgate called Puthey; for their lives, with remainders to their sons William, Thomas, John, Walter and Richard for their lives, successively, rent 14*s*. a year.
Witnesses: John Douve, John Dadsynton, John Edmund, Thomas Lode.
At: Berkeley Castle.

MISCELLANEOUS PERSONAL TRANSACTIONS BETWEEN TENANTS OF THE HONOUR

A1/68/1 [GC 2394]   Translation of St. Thomas the martyr, 16 Edw. II [7 July 1323]
Robert Averay of Berkeley and Henry le Gardiner of Berkeley.

Robert has quitclaimed to Henry all quarrels, merchandise and transgressions between himself and Henry from the coronation of King Edward, son of King Edward I, to the feast of the translation of St. Thomas the martyr 16 Edward II, and Henry has quitclaimed to Robert all quarrels, merchandise and transgressions [etc.]
Witnesses: John le Serjaunt, Roger le Cuppere, John Sewaker, Edward de Fromylode, William Gylemyn, Robert Groundy, William Iweyn.
At: Berkeley.

A1/68/2 [GC 3468]   Wed. after St. Matthew, 32 Edw. III [28 Feb. 1358]
Edmund Aubrai of Worcester and William Modebroke of Berkeley.

Edmund is bound to William in £40 to be paid in Bristol at Easter next.
At: Bristol.

A1/68/3 [GC 3507]   15 Aug. 34 Edw. III [1360]
Nicholas Holte and Margaret Sebryth, daughter and heir of Richard Sebryth; and Robert le Baille and Margaret his wife.

Nicholas and Margaret have received from Robert and Margaret all the goods and chattels [*itemised*] of Richard which remained in the custody of Margaret le Baille after Richard's death.
Witnesses: Robert de Middeltone, Walter Huet, Walter Jakemon.
At: Arlingham.

A1/68/4 [GC 4203]   St. Calixtus, 15 Hen. VI [14 Oct. 1436]
William Mulward the younger of Slimbridge (Glos.); and John Byforde, Thomas Gylmyn, Richard Bernard and Henry Yngram.

William is bound to John, Thomas, Richard and Henry in £3 10s.

2: BERKELEY LANDS OUTSIDE THE HUNDRED

CHILDREY (BERKS.)

Thomas (III) Lord Berkeley (d. 1361) had two interests in Childrey, both of which were short-lived. In 1329 Walter and Eugenia de Hamme quitclaimed their life-interest in the holding referred to in the charter below to John Mautravers, whose rights were granted to Nicholas de la Beche in the following year when Mautravers fled abroad and forfeited his lands.[1] Thomas de Berkeley also acquired there a meadow which he forfeited in 1322; it was farmed at 9s. a year while in the hands of the king and Thomas received the same rent in 1327.[2] In 1338 he granted all his interests there to Nicholas de la Beche and his wife Margery, an outright grant of a mill and 18 a. of land, and a quitclaim of all mills, lands, meadows, rents and services.[3]

A2/1/1 [GC 2347]   Three weeks after Easter, 14 Edw. II [10 May 1321]
Thomas son of Maurice de Berkele and Margaret his wife (by Richard de Salle); and Thomas de Luda and Margaret his wife.

Final concord concerning a messuage and 1 carucate of land, 18 a. and 1 rood of meadow and 16s. 10d. rent in Chelreye; Thomas and Margaret de Luda have acknowledged the right of Thomas and Margaret de Berkele, to them and the heirs of Thomas, after the death of Walter de Hamme and his wife Eugenia who hold it for their lives, of the inheritance of Margaret de Luda; Thomas and Margaret de Berkele have given them £20.
At: Westminster.

YEWDON, IN HAMBLEDEN (BUCKS.)

Yewdon was never actually held by Thomas (III) de Berkeley. It had been settled on Amicia by her father Hugh Peverel in 1286 and she still held it in 1346, after the death of her husband Miles de Beauchamp in 1338. Amicia seems to have married secondly Henry de Montfort (as in the charters), and in 1345 Henry's son Reginald de Montfort agreed with Thomas de Berkeley that if Henry and Amicia acquired the manor in fee Thomas would be free of the obligation of giving Reginald a knight's robes each year for his life (as below). In 1350 Reginald quitclaimed the manor to Thomas, as did Reginald de Reyny in 1351, although after Henry's death Thomas quitclaimed the manor to Amicia. The relevant

---

[1] *VCH Berks.* iv. 275.
[2] *CMR* no. 872; BCM SR 39 (cf. below, A4/2/7).
[3] *CCR* 1337–9, 522.

charter is undated so it is difficult to judge the sequence of events. In 1354 Thomas sold the reversion to Thomas Doyly.[1]

A2/2/1 [GC 3109]   4 Jan. 18 Edw. III [1345]
Reginald de Monte forti, knight, and Thomas de Berkele, lord of Berkeley.

Whereas Thomas is bound to Reginald in a furred robe of the sort of his knights annually, from his manors of Bedemenystre, Portbur' and Portesheved (Som.) and Wottone (Glos.), for Reginald's life, he has granted that if Sir Henry de Monteforti, his father, and Amicia his wife, acquire the manor of Ivedon (Bucks.), to them and their issue, so that Thomas cannot implead them, the bond will be void.
At: Wotton-under-Edge.

A2/2/2 [GC 3271]   n.d. [mid 14th cent.]
Thomas lord of Berkelee and Amicia widow of Sir Henry de Montfort.

Thomas has quitclaimed to Amicia the manor of Ivedene.

A2/2/3 [GC 3370]   Wed. the feast of St. Margaret the virgin, 25 Edw. III [13 July 1351]
Reginald de Reyny and Sir Thomas lord of Berkelee.

Reginald has quitclaimed to Thomas the manor of Ivedene and all lands, holdings [etc.], which Amicia de Beauchamp had in Iveden and Hameldone [*with seals of all witnesses*].
Witnesses: John de la Ryvere, knight, William de Chyltenham, John de Clyve, Hugh de la Boure, John de Asschebury, Walter de Hurste.
At: Berkeley.

HIGH BRAY (DEVON)

Bought by FitzHarding from William de Breouse (below, A2/3/1 [SC 9]), the manor was granted by Thomas (I) Lord Berkeley (d. 1243) to his nephew Osbert Giffard, younger son of Thomas's sister Maud and her husband Elias Giffard (III) (d. 1190).[2] It was to revert, in exchange for Foxcote (Som.), on the death of Robert (II) de Berkeley's widow Lucy (below, A2/3/4 [SC 168]). Lucy died in 1234, and Thomas granted it to his younger son Thomas (below, A2/3/5 [GC 1220]) who died without issue between 1243 and 1247, when it presumably reverted to Thomas's eldest brother Maurice (II) Lord Berkeley (d. 1281). The dower settlement for Maurice's mother Joan, widow of Thomas (I) covered Thomas's lands in Gloucestershire, Somerset and Devon (above, A1/1/70 [GC 1200]). In 1250–1 Maurice was impleaded by William de Fourd for half a hide of land in East Bray, a suit decided in Maurice's favour after trial by battle, but Bray does not appear in Berkeley hands later.[3] See also above, A1/11/14 [SC 240].

A2/3/1 [SC 9]   n.d. [*c.* 1150 × 1160]
William de Braiosa and Robert FitzHarding.

William has granted Bray to Robert, except for the land which Furland held, in fee, to hold as one quarter of a knight's fee, and has received Robert's homage.
Witnesses: Hugh de Hesla, William de Mompinchun, Hamon de Merlai, Alan son of Buci, Payn the clerk, Durand de [Br]ai; on the part of Robert, Maurice his son, Odo son of William, Alan de Furnellis, Adam de Saltemareis, Nigel son of Arthur, Osbert Martre, Walter son of Albert.

---

[1] *VCH Bucks*. iii. 49; *CCR 1354–60*, 310.
[2] *GEC* v. 639, 649–53.
[3] Smyth, i. 133.

A2/3/2 [SC 10]   n.d. [*c.* 1150 × 1160]
William de Braiuse and Maurice son of Robert FitzHarding.

William has confirmed to Maurice his grant of Brai to Robert, and has received the homage of Maurice; in acknowledgement of Maurice becoming his man, William has given him a gold ring with a sapphire.

Witnesses: Philip de Braiose, Walter de Braiose, Philip his brother, William de Folcellis, Elias son of Bernard, Herbert the chamberlain; on the part of Maurice, William de Cliftone, Master Maurice, Osbert le Martre, William Stut, Osbert Gule.

A2/3/3 [SC 89]   n.d. [*c.* Michaelmas 1209]
Robert de Berkele and Ralph de Bray.

Robert has granted to Ralph all his land of Bray for a term of 15 years beginning at Michaelmas, 11 John; rent 100*s.* a year.

Witnesses: Roger de Berkeley, Adam son of Nigel, Bernard de Cromhale, Bernard de Stanes, Henry the chaplain, Swigin the chaplain, Thomas de Tiringham, Maurice son of Nigel, Thomas de Lovent, William de Rotomag' now sheriff, Robert de Albamara, William de Raleg', Walter Giffard, Ranulf de Albemara, John Cole.

A2/3/4 [SC 168]   n.d. [1220 × 1226]
Thomas de Berkeley and Osbert Gyffard, his nephew.

Thomas has granted to Osbert the reversion of the land of Foxcote after the death of Lucy the widow (*mulieris*) who holds it in dower, and Osbert has agreed to restore to Thomas the land of Bray after the death of Lucy, and will answer to Maurice, eldest son of Thomas, for all services from Foxcote and Bray except for the service of a pair of gilt spurs or 6*d.* every Easter.

Witnesses: Sir William Briguere, Sir Maurice Gaunt, Elias Giffard, Stephen de Segrave, Sir William de Pontdelarch, Thomas de Thiringham, Maurice son of Nigel, John de Heketon, Hubert de Vaus.

A2/3/5 [GC 1220]   n.d. [1236 × 1243]
Thomas de Berkel' and Thomas de Berkel', his son.

Thomas the elder has granted to Thomas the younger all the land of Bray by Suthmultun, in fee, as a quarter of a knight's fee.

Witnesses: Sir Nicholas son of Roger, Richard de Clifford, Peter de Stintescumbe, Henry de Berkel', Richard de Couel', William de Berkel', Simon de Ollepenn, Nicholas Ruffus, Elias the butler (*Pincerna*).

GREAT EASTON (ESSEX)

Great Easton and Maddington (Wilts.) were held by the Moigne family and were acquired temporarily by Thomas (III) Lord Berkeley in wardship during the minority of Henry son of John Moigne (d. 1342).[1] Henry (d. 1374) married Joan le Veel, Thomas's stepdaughter, so Thomas probably acquired the marriage of the heir as well as the wardship of his lands.[2] See also below, A2/94/1 [GC 3056].

A2/4/1 [GAR 341] Manorial account   June to Michaelmas, 17 Edw. III [1343]

SAFFRON WALDEN (ESSEX)

The charter is included among the Wenden charters in the Great Cartulary.[3]

A2/5/1 [SC 148]   n.d. [late 13th cent.]
Robert the Scot (*Scoticus*) of Walden; and William son of William de Udlisford and Margaret his wife.

[1] *CIPM* viii, no. 365; ix, no. 595.
[2] Ibid. xiv, no. 79; *CCR* 1381–5, 442.
[3] BCM SB 10, f. 338v.

Robert has granted to William and Margaret a house in the parish of Waledon with 9½ perches of land; rent 14*s.* a year, and other conditions.
Witnesses: William de Ripa, Ranulf Harying, John son of Geoffrey de Wenden, Henry son of Waryn, Philip Hyleberd, John Abraham, Stephen the clerk.

WENDENS AMBO (ESSEX)

The manor of Great Wenden came to the Berkeleys as the marriage portion of Isabel, wife of Maurice (II) (d. 1281). She was the daughter of Richard FitzRoy, a bastard son of King John, and Rose, daughter and heir of Robert de Dover, of Chilham (Kent). A charter of Richard and Rose is recorded in the Great Cartulary.[1] The manor was augmented in the mid 14th century by that inveterate investor in land, Thomas (III) Lord Berkeley, who bought a rent of £10 from John de Bartlow and a number of other smaller holdings from the Bartlow inheritance. It was sold in 1404 by Thomas (IV) to William Loveney.[2] The parishes of Great Wenden and Little Wenden were united as Wendens Ambo in 1662.

BERKELEY ACQUISITIONS

The Bronesho holding in Newport

A2/6/1 [GC 1262; *duplicate* SC 323]   n.d. [*temp.* Edw. I]
Edmund son of Henry de Bronesho and Roger son of Walter the glover (*gantator*) of Newport.

Edmund has granted to Roger, for 4½ marks, 3½ a. of land in the vill of Neuport in the field called Northfield, beside the road called Nortunewei; rent 7*d.* a year.
Witnesses: Quentin son of Warin, John Quentin, John le Flemeng, William son of Alan, John Abraham, Laurence son of Ranulf, John de Aula Petrina, Thomas de Witthiton, clerk, William Agar, Alexander de Wallington, Stephen the clerk, Robert de Bronesho.

A2/6/2 [GC 2519]   n.d. [1307 × 1312?]
Roger son of Walter the glover (*cyrotecar'*) of Newport and Sir Thomas de Berkeley.

Roger has granted to Thomas, his heirs and assigns, 7 a. of land in the vill of Newport beside the road called Nortonewey . . . one head above the king's highway from Newport to the bridge of Odelesford; [rent] . . . [Peter Gaveston] earl of Cornwall, lord of Newport, a rose a year; for this Thomas has granted to him 14 a. of land of his demese in the vill of Wendene Magna for his life.
Witnesses: Geoffrey de Waledone, William Pou[en?], Warin Quyntyn, Master Richard de Beauchamp (*de Bello Campo*), Richard Quyntyn, Sir Miles master of the hospital of St. Leonard, . . . Wenden, William Adwyne, Stephen the clerk.

Bartlow holdings

Aveline Bartlow's holding

A2/6/3 [GC 2726]   Thurs. the feast of St. Mark, 5 Edw. III [25 April 1331]
John de Berklowe and Aveline his daughter.

John has granted to Aveline 6 a. of land lying in 6 plots, and 1 a. of meadow called Goseholm; for her life, for the service of a rose a year.
Witnesses: John vicar of Wenden, John Sake, Walter de Norton, John Andreu, John Bole, John Godwyne, John the smith.
At: Wenden.

A2/6/4 [GC 2900]   Mon. after Easter, 13 Edw. III [29 March 1339]
Avelina de Berklawe and Sir Thomas de Berklee.

Avelina has attorned to Thomas for the service of a rose a year and for her fealty for 6 a.

---

[1] BCM SB 10, f. 396v.
[2] *CCR* 1402–5, 308, 311, 314, 318.

of land and 1 a. of meadow in the vills of Wendene Magna and Parva, which she holds of Thomas for her life, by assignment of John son and heir of John de Berklawe.
At: Great Wenden.

Agnes Giffard's holding

A2/6/5 [GC 1968]   Thurs. the feast of St. Peter in cathedra, 7 Edw. II [22 Feb. 1314]
Thomas Lenveyse and Emma his wife and Richard de Aldeby and Alice his wife; and John de Berkelawe.

Thomas, Emma, Richard and Alice have granted to John 1 rood of meadow of the inheritance of Emma and Alice in the vill of Wendene in Clanefordemade.
Witnesses: Richard de Wendene, John Andrew, Robert Pake, Walter de Northone, Philip de Northone, John de Mundeford, Roger Berthelot, clerk.
At: Wenden.

A2/6/6 [GC 2859]   28 Nov. 10 Edw. III [1336]
John Berklowe and Agnes Giffard, his maid (*ancilla*).

John has granted to Agnes a garden within his enclosure in the vill of Wenden, lying between the great gate and the holding formerly of William Aldwyne, and 6 a. of land lying in 5 plots, with the long house called the byre (*boveria*) in the said garden; for her life, rent a pair of gloves or *2d.* a year.
Witnesses: Sir John vicar of Wenden, John Pake, Walter de Nortone, Robert Brite, John Franceys, chaplain.
At: Wenden.

A2/6/7 [GC 2882]   30 June 11 Edw. III [1337]
John de Berkelowe and Agnes Giffard, his maid.

John has granted to Agnes 1 rood of land sometime of William Aldwyne which John acquired from Thomas Veisy and his wife Emma in the vill of Magna Wendene; for her life, rent a rose a year.
Witnesses: John vicar of Great Wenden, John 'my son', Anselm vicar of Chishill, John Lord, chaplain, John Pake.
At: Great Wenden.

A2/6/8 [GC 2905]   Mon. before Ascension, 12 Edw. III [18 May 1338]
John de Berklowe and Agnes Giffard, his maid.

Whereas John recently granted to Agnes a garden within his enclosure in the vill of Wendene by his great gate, and 6 a. of land and 1 rood of meadow, he has now granted to Agnes free access through the said gate.
At: Great Wenden.

A2/6/9 [GC 2941]   Mon. after Easter, 13 Edw. III [29 March 1339]
Agnes Giffard and Sir Thomas de Berklee.

Agnes has attorned to Thomas for the service of a rose a year and for her fealty for 6 a. of land in the vills of Wendene Magna and Parva, which she holds of Thomas for her life, by assignment of John son and heir of John de Berklawe.
At: Great Wenden.

A2/6/10 [GC 2942]   Thurs. in Easter week, 13 Edw. III [1 April 1339]
Agnes Giffard and Sir Thomas de Berklee.

Whereas John de Berklawe lately granted to Agnes part of his messuage and 6 a. of land in Magna Wendene and Parva Wendene for her life, and the reversion of the holding belongs to Thomas by assignment of John son and heir of the said John, Agnes has surrendered the holding to Thomas and has quitclaimed it to him.

Witnesses: Roger de Barlee, John Flambard, John de Wyditone, John Beauchamp, John Bole, John Pake, Walter de Nortone, John Hubert.
At: Great Wenden.

Margaret de Daventry's holding

A2/6/11 [GC 2975]   6 Aug. 14 Edw. III [1340]
Margaret de Daventre and Sir Thomas de Berkle.
    Margaret has received from Thomas, by the hand of Geoffrey atte Hawe his bailiff of Wenden, 13*s*. 4*d*. for her lands which John de Berklawe demised to Thomas in the said vill, for the term of St. Peter in chains, 14 Edw. III [1 Aug. 1340].
At: Catmere End.

A2/6/12 [GC 2983]   1 Jan. 14 Edw. III [1341]
Margaret de Daventre and Sir Thomas de Berkle.
    Margaret has received from Thomas, by the hand of Geoffrey atte Hawe his bailiff of Wenden, 13*s*. 4*d*. for her lands which John de Berklawe demised to Thomas in the said vill, for the term of Christmas, 14 Edw. III [1340].
At: Catmere End.

Various

A2/6/13 [GC 2938]   7 March 13 Edw. III [1339]
William Taney and John son and heir of John de Berklawe.
    William has quitclaimed to John all the lands and holdings which John inherited after the death of his father in the vills of Wendene Magna and Parva.
Witnesses: John Flambard, John de Wyditone, John Bole, John Andrew, John de Beauchamp, Walter de Nortone, John Pake, John Hubert.
At: Great Wenden.

A2/6/14 [GC 2937]   7 March 13 Edw. III [1339]
John son and heir of John de Berkelawe and Sir Thomas de Berkelee.
    John has granted to Thomas, his heirs and assigns, a rent of £10 a year from all his lands and holdings in the vills of Wendene Magna and Parva.
Witnesses: John Pake, John Bele, John Andrew, Walter de Nortone, John Beauchamp, John Hubert, Stephen Foule.
At: Great Wenden.

Other Berkeley acquisitions

A2/6/15 [GC 446]   n.d. [*temp*. Hen. III]
William son of John de Wendene and Sir Maurice de Berkele.
    William has granted to Maurice a half-acre of land in the vill of Wendene, in exchange for another half-acre in the vill.
Witnesses: Sir [William] Pucin, Sir William de Langetut, Sir John de Derveres, William de Ripar', . . . Richard son of Robert, Richard son of Michael, John son of Geoffrey.

A2/6/16 [SC 353]   n.d. [*temp*. Hen. III]
Maurice de Berkele and Robert of the cross (*de Cruce*).
    Maurice has granted to Robert 2 selions of land with buildings on it, in exchange for 3 selions lying between the land of Thomas de la More and the king's highway. Endorsed *Wenden*.
Witnesses: Peter de Wyke, Richard de Wyke, Gilbert de Lynch, Richard de Sancta Brigida, Robert son of Guy, Walter de Fromlode, Walter Sely.

A2/6/17 [GC 1522]   n.d. [late Hen. III]
William de Ripar' and Sir Maurice de Berkel'.

William has quitclaimed to Maurice the meadow which he has in Estmersh.
Witnesses: Quentin de Neuport, John Quyntyn, Peter de Wendene, Peter de Bouketre, John Chyleham, Walter Sely, clerk, of Berkeley.

A2/6/18 [GC 315]   Wed. before St. Barnabas, 52 Hen. III [6 June 1268]
William Wrenne, miller, and Sir Maurice de Berkeley.

William has quitclaimed to Maurice the mill in the vill of Magna Wenden which he had by charter of Maurice for his life.

A2/6/19 [GC 1590]   n.d. [late Hen. III]
Edith widow of William Wrenne; and Sir Maurice de Berkele and Isabel his wife.

Edith has quitclaimed to Maurice and Isabel 1 a. and 3 roods of land in the parish of Wendene.
Witnesses: John le Blunt, Peter de Wendene, Geoffrey de la Holte, William de Wendene, smith, John Man.

A2/6/20 [GC 2512]   n.d. [late Hen. III]
Richard de Ewelle and Sir Maurice de Bercle.

Richard has granted that Maurice is not bound to warrant Richard and his heirs against Isabel, Maurice's wife, and her heirs for the land which Richard bought from Maurice.
Witnesses: Sir Richard de Dauny, Ralph de Sentosi, Walter de Creppinges, Richard de Herlawe, Ralph son of Richard de Farenham, William de Huppewyk, Geoffrey de Mores, John Lovel, William de Ware, Robert de Dunderle.

A2/6/21 [GC 418]   n.d. [early Edw. I]
Reginald de la Revere and Sir Thomas de Berkele, knight.

Reginald has granted to Thomas a messuage in the parish of Wenden which was of Ranulf Haryng and which abuts on the river of the mill called Twygrind and the road to Waledon Monachorum.
Witnesses: Sir Robert de la Rokele, Geoffrey Sitadoun of Walden, William Poucyn, Master Richard de Neuporte, William Aldwyne, John de Northone, John Man, Robert de Wenden.

A2/6/22 [GC 1414]   n.d. [*temp.* Edw. I]
Richard de Hokerhelle of Great Wenden and Sir Thomas de Berkle, knight.

Richard has granted to Thomas, for 40*s.* and half a quarter of corn, a messuage in Magna Wendene, beside the great road from Magna Wenden to Arkesden; rent 8*d.* a year to the chief lord of the fee.
Witnesses: Robert de Wendene, William Aldwyn, John Man, Reginald de Ripar', John de Norton, Bartholomew by Weston, Robert the clerk.

A2/6/23 [GC 4002]   26 Feb. 5 Hen. IV [1404]
Thomas Berkeley, lord of Berkeley, Thomas Evesham, William Coventre, William Oteclyf, clerk, and John Scot clerk; and John Ederyk and William Loveney, esquire.

Whereas Thomas, Thomas, William, William and John have granted to John and William a rent of 50 marks a year, to them and William's heirs and assigns, from the manor of Cerney (Glos.), John and William have granted that if they and Margaret wife of William, and William's heirs and assigns, hold peacefully the manor of Graunde Wenden (Essex), which was recently Thomas Berkeley's, they will quitclaim the rent. [*In French.*]

Account rolls

A2/6/24 [GAR 345]   n.d. [1310 × 1319]

A2/6/25 [GAR 346]   9–10 Edw. III [1335–6]

Leases

A2/6/26 [GC 465]   Wed. after St. Valentine, 3 Edward [20 Feb. 1275]
Maurice de Berkele and Isabel daughter of Walter the smith (*faber*) of Wenden Parva.

Maurice has granted to Isabel, for a certain sum of money, the messuage called Deyephuel and 1 a. and 3 roods of land, of which the western head abuts on the road to Fissemere and the eastern head on the river running to Kekesbregge, to her and her issue; rent 4*s.* a year.

Witnesses: Sir William son of Ralph de Pebemers, knight, Richard de Wendene, Thomas de Bello Campo, Robert . . . , John Man, Walter the cook, John Andrew.

A2/6/27 [GC 513]   Mon. after St. Philip and St. James, 12 Edw. I [8 May 1284]
Thomas de Berkel, knight, and Ralph de Bedemonstre.

Thomas has granted to Ralph and his first wife, for their lives, a messuage and 10 a. of land, which Silvester son of Jordan held in the vill of Wendene Magna; rent 4*s.* a year.

Witnesses: Geoffrey Setadun, John le Blunt, Robert de Stanes, William Aldwyne, John de Nortone, John Man, Bartholomew Byweston, Luke de Claneford, Alexander the clerk.
At: Wenden.

A2/6/28 [GC 1755]   Sun. after St. Peter and St. Paul, 3 Edw. II [5 July 1310]
Maurice de Berkele; and Reginald vicar of Wenden and Agnes his sister.

Maurice has granted to Reginald and Agnes 3 roods of meadow in Wendene at Kekesbregge, for their lives, rent 16*d.* a year.

Witnesses: Richard de Wendene, Thomas de Beauchamp, John Andr', Robert Pake, Roger de Rypariis, John Man, Richard the clerk.
At: Portbury.

A2/6/29 [GC 2019]   Sun. after St. Valentine, 8 Edw. II [16 Feb. 1315]
Maurice de Berkelee; and Philip son of Robert Schingkel of Wenden Magna and Felicity his wife.

Maurice has granted to Philip and Felicity and their issue the messuage which Robert atte Welle formerly held of Maurice in Wendene, beside the stream called Pottokespet; rent to Robert atte Welle for his life 3*s.* a year, and to Maurice and his heirs 3*s.* 4*d.* a year.

Witnesses: Robert de Rupell, Richard de Wendene, Robert Pake, John Andreu, Walter de Norton, Walter le Bolee, Richard the clerk.
At: Wenden.

A2/6/30 [GC 3518]   2 Feb. 35 Edw. III [1361]
Maurice son of Thomas de Berkele; and Walter Elys and Denise his wife.

Whereas Maurice de Berkele, grandfather of Maurice, and Thomas his son granted to John Hormand and Mabel his wife the holding which John atte Mede and Maud his mother held in villeinage in Wendene, to [John and] Mabel and their issue at a rent of 16*s.* a year, and because Thomas son of John and Mabel has died without issue and the holding has reverted to Maurice, Maurice has granted the reversion of the holding to Walter and Denise and their issue, at the same rent.

Witnesses: John Beauchamp, Gilbert Lenveyse, John de Wydinton, Richard Botiller, John de Norton.
At: Wenden.

OTHER INTERESTS

A2/6/31 [GC 903]   n.d. [late 13th cent.]
William de Ripar': and William Wrenne and Margaret his wife.

William has granted to William and Margaret 1½ a. of land in the vill of Wendene abutting on the royal street from Neuport to Hykelington, and on the street from Odelesford to Kekesmellin; rent 18*d.* a year, and they have given him ½ mark.
Witnesses: Quentin de Neuport, John Quent', John Ab[ra]ham, Simon de Sancto Michaele, Philip Yleberd, Peter de Wenden, John son of Geoffrey, William Aldwyn, Alexander the clerk.

A2/6/32 [SC 341]   n.d. [*temp.* Hen. III]
Joan daughter of Alan Aildred and Walter son of Rose of the cross (*de Cruce*) of Wenden.

Joan has granted to Walter part of her messuage and the whole of her croft in Magna Wenden, and a rent of 4*d.* which John son of Walter Scoce of Wenden owes her, for 22*s.* which he gave her and a rent of 9*d.* a year.
Witnesses: Richard son of Michael, Roger Sangrinel, William de Ripariis, Quentin son of Warin, Hugh son of Emelen, Simon de Sancto Michaele, John son of Geoffrey, Richard son of Robert, Hamon Peverel, Adam de London, William son of John, Stephen the clerk.

A2/6/33 [SC 292]   n.d. [*c.* Michaelmas 1246]
Richard de Katthemere and Rose his wife; and Geoffrey son of Ralph de Wenden and Maud his wife.

Richard and Rose have granted to Geoffrey and Maud a messuage with a croft at Hokerhull in Wenden, for ½ mark, from Michaelmas 30 Hen. III for 9 years, at a rent of 12*d.* a year.
Witnesses: Matthew de Wenden, William de Ripa, Roger Sangrinel, Simon de Sancto Nicholao [*recte* Michaele?], John son of Geoffrey, Peter de Blanketre, Philip Ylebert, William Ylebert, John the clerk.

A2/6/34 [GC 564]   n.d. [early Edw. I]
Nicholas de Poucine and Bartholomew . . .

Nicholas has granted to Bartholomew . . . half-virgate which Thomas son of Metlefrein held in Claneford . . . ; rent 5*s.* a year.
Witnesses: . . . de Wenden, Richard de Wenden, Abboldus de Wenden, . . . John son of Richard, James son of William, Michael de Wenden, . . .

A2/6/35 [GC 838]   n.d. [late 13th cent.]
Peter de Wendene, son of Stephen de Wendene, and Robert de Tunderle.

Peter has granted to Robert, for a certain sum of money, all his messuage and lands, meadows, rents [etc.] in the vill of Wendene Magna.
Witnesses: Robert de Torleye, Michael le Pucyn, John de Wach . . . , Geoffrey de Ambredone, William de Gerdele, Robert de Gerdele, William de Ripa, John Gefray, . . . , Philip de Norton', William Aldwyne, Jordan Biwestene, . . .

ABSON (GLOS.)

William de Cheltenham was the principal officer of Thomas (III) (d. 1361) and Maurice (IV) (d. 1368) Lords Berkeley, and sold to Maurice (IV) his manors of Little Marshfield and Purton (below, pp. 473, 480). This is probably significant in view of the remainder to Maurice, son of Maurice (IV), mentioned in this charter but lands here are not found in Berkeley hands later.

A2/7/1 [GC 3585; *duplicate* GC 3586]   Mon. after St. Matthew, 40 Edw. III [28 Sept. 1366]
Robert Aleyn and William Smalcombe, and William de Chiltenham and Eleanor his wife.

Robert and William have leased to William and Eleanor all the lands and holdings [etc.] which they had in Abbedestone by grant of William; to William and Eleanor and William's issue, with remainder to William son of John de Lench and his issue, and Maurice son of Sir Maurice de Berkele lord of Berkeley and his heirs and assigns.
Witnesses: John Stanshawe, John de Wottone, Richard le Mohoun.
At: Abson.

ACTON ILGER (GLOS.)

The history of the Berkeley interest in Acton is complicated, partly because of a confusion between Iron Acton and Acton Ilger (a vill in Iron Acton, now lost) and partly because of a number of fractions of holdings. By 1086 Iron Acton was divided into two manors which were later in different hundreds. One of the manors was held by a tenant named Ilger and this was the Acton bought by Robert FitzHarding and his son Maurice. It later passed to Maurice's daughter Maud when she married Elias Giffard of Brimpsfield and from her to Giffard's nephew Osbert who in 1247 paid a rent of 40*s*. to his uncle for Acton.[1] The principal landholder in Acton at the end of the 13th century seems to have been Henry de Mareys who paid rents of 20*s*. a year to St. Bartholomew's, Gloucester, and of 40*s*. a year to Osbert Giffard. The 40*s*. rent was sold by Giffard to Joan Russell, and passed from her to John Hales and finally, in 1297, to Thomas (II) Lord Berkeley. Berkeley also acquired the 20*s*. rent which Mareys paid to St. Bartholomew's and another rent of 5*s*. paid by William de Hildesleigh to St. Bartholomew's. Hildesleigh's holding seems to have passed to St. Mark's hospital, Bristol, at some time between 1326 and 1348: the rent of 5*s*. was released to the hospital by Thomas (III) Lord Berkeley in 1348–9.[2]

The rent of 60*s*. a year paid for the Mareys holding was paid to Ham manor so it can be traced in the accounts of that manor, and the holding seems to have been called the 'manor' of Acton Ilger. Henry de Mareys had died before the rental of 1323 was made and left a number of heirs although John de Acton (lord of the manor of Iron Acton) acquired five-sixths of the holding and paid 50*s*. a year for it to Ham manor. By 1330 the remaining sixth was held by Sir Richard de Ryvers at an increment of 10*s*. a year beyond the original rent of 10*s*., and was probably entered as owing 20*s*. a year on the new rental made in 1340 (unfortunately not extant). This portion may have been that acquired by Thomas de Berkeley from John and Margaret le Freman by Oct. 1330 (below, A2/9/1 [GC 2710]), although it is described as a fifth portion and not a sixth, which Thomas would then have been able to re-lease at a higher rent. How long it stayed in Ryvers's hands is not clear but in 1353 the holding was seemingly re-acquired by Thomas de Berkeley, apparently from Sir John de Acton. As a sixth of the manor of Acton Ilger it continues to appear in the accounts until 1378. The tenants of this sub-manor paid rents of 11*s*. 4*d*. a year until around 1362, and of 8*s*. 4*d*. thereafter, and from 1365 the land was farmed at 10*s*. a year. Maurice de Berkeley's inquisition *post mortem* of 1368 records that he held a sixth of the manor, being rents of 66*s*. 8*d*.[3] By the time of the 1378 rental the five-sixths was still paying 50*s*. a year, John Parsons owed 10*s*. a year from one-sixth of the manor, and three other tenants paid rents amounting to 8*s*. 4*d*., and it is recorded that this (one-sixth) used to render 20*s*. a year.

Although the rents were paid to Ham manor the holding was apparently not considered as part of the manor (and so was not settled with it in tail male in 1349) since in 1375 it was

[1] Jean Manco, 'Iron Acton: a Saxon nucleated village', *TBGAS* cxlii (1995), 89–97.
[2] *Cartulary of St. Mark's Hospital, Bristol*, ed. C. D. Ross (Bristol Record Society xxi, 1959), 411–12. Thomas de Berkeley quitclaimed to St. Mark's a rent of 5*s*. for a messuage and 1 virgate of land with appurtenances in Iron Acton in exchange for 10 a. of land in la Lee beside Thomas's park at Over.
[3] The figure was actually 68*s*. 4*d*., being 50*s*. a year from the five sixths, 8*s*. 4*d*. a year from the tenants of the one sixth and 10*s*. a year from the tenant of the one sixth of 'demesne'.

mortgaged, with other unentailed lands in Purton (Glos.) and elsewhere.[1] See also above, A1/1/47, A1/1/62 [GC 4146*, GC 4427*], which mention holdings in Iron Acton and Acton Ilger in Berkeley hands (although disputed) in 1425 and 1482. It is not clear exactly which Hampton is referred to in the first charter, although Hanham is presumably the manor within the parish of Bitton and Acton is Acton Ilger. According to Smyth, Maurice immediately leased Hanham and Hampton to tenants.[2]

A2/8/1 [SC 15]   n.d. [*temp.* Hen. II]
Richard Foliot and Maurice son of Robert FitzHarding.

Richard has granted to Maurice the land of Accatone, the land of Hanam and the half-hide of Hamtona, with all liberties [etc.]; held of Humphrey de Bohun; Maurice's father has paid 20 marks in acknowledgement.[3]
Witnesses: William earl of Gloucester, Hubert the steward, Robert de Almari, Gregory de Turre, Elias the chamberlain (*camberarius*), Robert de Saltmarsh (*de saltemaresco*), Boso, Jordan son of Harding, Elias son of Harding, David son of Gudbmundi.

A2/8/2 [SC 12]   n.d. [*c.* 1155]
(1) Humphrey de Bohun; (2) Richard Foliot; (3) Robert FitzHarding.

Humphrey has confirmed the grant by Richard to Robert in Acton.
Witnesses: Margaret de Bohun, Humphrey de Sancto [Vigore], William de Buhun, Robert Fronte, Walter Hussey (*Hosatus*), Richard de Buhun, William son of Geoffrey, Richard [de Warwick] abbot of Bristol, Odo son of William, Nicholas son of Robert, Robert his brother, Adam de Saltemareis, Osbert Martra.

A2/8/3 [GC 916]   n.d. [late 13th cent.]
Sir Osbert Gyffard, knight, and Joan Russell.

Osbert has granted to Joan a rent of 40*s.* from Henry de Marreys of Hyrenacton; rent a rose a year.
Witnesses: Sir Roger le Rus, knight, Sir Philip de Mattesdene, knight, Henry de Ruwes, Henry de Bares, John de Cumbe, Ralph de Lucy, William le Warenir.

A2/8/4 [GC 2552]   n.d. [late 13th cent.]
Joan Russel and John de Halis.

Joan has demised to John, and quitclaimed, the rent of Henry de Marisco which she had by grant of Sir Osbert Giffard, and has granted to him the documents of the gift.
Witnesses: Henry de Tisteldene, Henry de Marisho, Elias de Filton, Roger de Hildeslegh, Henry of the ash (*de fraxino*), John son of Stephen de Actone, Walter le Tanaur, who have all attached their seals (*signa*).

A2/8/5 [GC 1402]   n.d. [*c.* May 1297]
John de Hales and Sir Thomas de Berkel'.

John has granted to Thomas a rent of 40*s.* a year from Henry de Mareys for his holding in Irene Acton which he had by grant of Joan Russel, who was enfeoffed by Sir Osbert Gyffard.
Witnesses: Sir Robert de Berkel', John de Welinton, Robert le Veel, knights, John de Ripar', Robert de Stane, Richard de Byseleie, Robert de Bradeston, William de Wauton, Robert de Bittlescumb, Robert le Vayre, Roger de Hyldesleye, Thomas de Swonungre.

A2/8/6 [GC 629]   Sun. after St. John before the Latin Gate, 25 Edw. I [12 May 1297]
Henry de Mareys and Sir Thomas de Berkel.

Henry, by grant of John de Hales, voluntarily attorns to Thomas, his lord, in 26*s.* 8*d.*

---

[1] Below, p. 482.
[2] Smyth, i. 77.
[3] *Transcript*: Jeayes, pp. 10–11.

annual rent while Lady Joan Rossel lives and after her death in the full rent of 40s. for his holding in Irenactone; which rent of 40s. was assigned to her by Sir Osbert Gyffard and of which Joan remitted to him 13s. 4d. for her life.

Witnesses: Sir Robert de Berkeleye, Robert le Veel, knights, William de Wauton, Robert de Bytlescumbe, Robert de Ston, Richard de Byseleye, Robert de Bradeston, Thomas de Swonhungre, Robert Wyther.

At: Berkeley.

A2/8/7 [GC 1134]   24 Oct. 34 Edw. I [1306]
Prior John [de Oak] and the brothers and sisters of St. Bartholomew's hospital, Gloucester; and Sir Thomas de Berkeleye, lord of Berkeley.

The prior and the brothers and sisters have granted to Thomas a rent of 25s. a year in Irenacton, viz. from Henry le Mareys 20s. and from William de Hildeslegh 5s.; and Thomas has given them 25 marks.

Witnesses: Sir John de Wylynton, Sir Thomas le Boteler, Sir William de Wauton, Sir Peter Crok, knights, Robert de Berkeleye, Robert de Bradestone, Thomas de Beoleye, Robert de Butlescombe, John de la Haye.

At: Berkeley.

A2/8/8 [GC 1135]   25 Oct. 34 Edw. I [1306]
Prior John and the brothers and sisters of St. Bartholomew's hospital, Gloucester; and Henry de Mareis.

The prior and the brothers and sisters inform Henry that they have enfeoffed Sir Thomas de Berkeleye, lord of Berkeley, with his rent.

At: Berkeley.

A2/8/9 [GC 1136]   25 Oct. 34 Edw. I [1306]
Prior John and the brothers and sisters of St. Bartholomew's hospital, Gloucester; and William de Hildeslegh.

The prior and the brothers and sisters inform William that they have enfeoffed Sir Thomas de Berkeleye, lord of Berkeley, with his rent.

Witnesses: At: Berkeley.

A2/8/10 [GC 4057; *later copy* GC 4058]   Fri. before Epiphany, 12 Hen. IV [2 Jan. 1411]
Thomas lord of Berkeley and John Whytyng, carpenter.

Thomas has granted to John a messuage and 1 virgate of land with appurtenances in Actone Ylgere which was of Walter de Smytheley; to John and his issue, by knight service viz. wardship, marriage, relief and suit to the court of Hamme, rent 5s. 4d. a year.

Witnesses: Robert Poyntes, William Bayly of Frampton, John Stynchecombe, Walter Whytehowse, Robert Stynchecombe.

At: Iron Acton.

IRON ACTON (GLOS.)

For the background of the Berkeleys' interests in Iron Acton, see above, p. 428, Acton Ilger.

A2/9/1 [GC 2710]   Three weeks after Michaelmas, 4 Edw. III [20 Oct. 1330]
Thomas de Berkeleye; and John le Freman and Margaret his wife.

Final concord concerning one fifth of a messuage and 2 carucates of land in Irenacton; Thomas has acknowledged the right of Margaret, and John and Margaret have granted the holding to Thomas.

At: Westminster.

A2/9/2 [GRR 17] Rental of Iron Acton   20 Edw. III [1346]

AWRE (GLOS.)

This manor, with its advowson and Bledisloe hundred with which it was associated, was acquired by the Berkeleys in the early 14th century in two halves. The first was granted to Maurice (III) (d. 1326) by his lord Aymer de Valence, earl of Pembroke, in 1308 and the second came with Margaret Mortimer as part of her marriage portion when she married the young heir Thomas (III) (d. 1361) in 1319.[1] Since it was settled on Margaret and Thomas and their issue it was not settled in tail male in 1349 along with the ancient patrimony and, as a consequence, passed in 1417 to Thomas (IV)'s daughter Elizabeth, countess of Warwick, and not to Thomas's nephew and heir male, James Lord Berkeley. As a result, presumably, there are few charters concerning the manor in the archive. Other holdings purchased by the lords at neighbouring Blakeney and Etloe (below, pp. 436, 457) were often associated with the manor. See also above, A1/1/18 [GC 3206], and below, A2/77/13–14 [GC 4005, SC 581].

THE PAYNEL OR BOHUN HOLDING

There is no known connection between William Paynel and the Bohuns of Midhurst, so it is assumed that Paynel had bought this holding or the reversion. John de Bohun had died in 1284: his widow was Joan, daughter and heir of Bartholomew de la Chapelle, and she eventually died in 1328.[2]

A2/10/1 [GC 3513]   n.d. [*c.* 1307]
William Paynel, knight; and Sir Thomas de Berkeley and Joan his wife.

William has granted to Thomas and Joan, and the heirs and assigns of Thomas, all his lands and holdings, rents, services, and villeins, their issue and chattels, in the vill of Aure (Glos.), with the pasture called le Warth on the other side of the Severn, with the reversion of the dower held by Joan widow of John de Boun, which holding was previously held by John de Boun, father of John.
Witnesses: Sir Thomas de Gardinis, sheriff of Gloucester, Walter de Gloucestre, escheator, Nicholas de Ba, Nicholas de Kyngestone, John Lovel, William de Wautone, Hugh de Audeleye, knights, William Hathewy, Richard le Blund, Walter de Nasse, Hugh de Bray, Ralph Hathewy.

A2/10/2 [GC 1645; *duplicate* GC 1646]   Epiphany, 1 Edw. II [6 Jan. 1308]
Joan widow of Sir John de Baun, lord of Midhurst, and Sir Thomas lord of Berkele, knight.

Joan has quitclaimed to Thomas her dower in a manor with appurtenances in Aure and Blakeneye (Glos.), and Thomas has given her a certain sum of money.
Witnesses: Sir John Lovel, Sir William de Wauton, Sir John Bisshop, Sir Thomas le Boteler, Sir Nicholas de Baa, knights, William Hathewy, Robert de Berkele, Robert de Bradeston, Richard le Whyte of Awre.
At: London.

OTHER

A2/10/3 [GC 1681]   Sun. the feast of the Purification, 2 Edw. II [2 Feb. 1309]
Thomas de Berkelee, lord of Berkeley; and William son of Laurence, carpenter, and Isabel his wife.

Thomas has granted to William and Isabel half a messuage and curtilage which was of Walter Grym in Aure; to them and their issue, rent 21*d.* a year.
Witnesses: Richard le Whyte, Walter de Nasse, John de Aure, Roger de Blydeslowe, John atte Churche.
At: Berkeley.

---

[1] *Genealogist*, N.S. xxxv (1919), 96–7, citing B.L. Harl. MS. 1240, f. 41v.; BCM GAR 255 (above, A1/51/50).

[2] *GEC* ii. 199–201; x. 322–8. William Paynel was summoned to parliament 1304–15 and died without issue in 1317.

A2/10/4 [GC 2293]   1 Dec. 13 Edw. II [1319]
Thomas de Berkeleye, lord of Berkeley, and Sir Thomas de Berkeleye, lord of Awre, his
grandson [*nepos*].

Thomas the elder has leased to Thomas the younger all his lands and holdings in Aure
and Blakeneye, with rents and services [etc.], for his life, rent £10 a year, and Thomas
the younger has granted to Thomas the elder, his grandfather [*avus*], the profits of the
pasture rights in la Warth pertaining to the lordship of Aure, and will restore to John de
Berkeleye, his brother, after the death of Thomas the elder, eight oxen price £8, one wagon
price 10*s.*, two mares price 20*s.*, and the vesture of 32 a. sown with wheat, price 64*s.*, the
which goods and chattels Thomas the younger received from Thomas the elder, to the use
of John.
Witnesses: Sir John Mautravers, Sir Nicholas de Kyngestone, Sir William de Wautone,
knights, John FitzNichol, Thomas de Bradeston, Walter de Nasse, John de Aure.
At: Berkeley.

AYLBURTON (GLOS.)

Not to be confused with manor of Elberton in Berkeley Herness, the holdings acquired here
by Thomas (III) seem to have been incorporated into a newly created manor of Yorkley and
appear in valors and inquisitions post mortem of the later 14th century as 'Tutnalls and
Purton' (see below, p. 503).

BERKELEY INTERESTS

Schovelbrodacre meadow

A2/11/1 [GC 3068]   Mon. after St. Luke, 17 Edw. III [20 Oct. 1343]
Walter le Moul of Aylburton and Sir Thomas lord of Berkeleye.

Walter has granted to Thomas, his heirs and assigns, 1 a. of meadow called
Schovelbrodaker in Ailbertonesmerssh in Ailbertone.
Witnesses: William Bray, Philip Longe, Walter Dauste, John Elys, Richard de Peulesdone.
At: Aylburton.

A2/11/2 [GC 3325]   n.d. [mid 14th cent.]
Walter lord of Nasse and John son of Thomas le Forester of Lydney.

Walter has granted to John, his heirs and assigns 1 a. of meadow in the marsh of
Aylbertone in the place called Scovelebrodacree.
Witnesses: Walter Home, Walter de Auste, Walter son of Stephen, Thomas le Forester,
William de Bray.

A2/11/3 [GC 2497]   n.d. [mid 14th cent.]
Isaac atte Broke of Aylburton and Sir Thomas lord of Berkeleye.

Isaac has quitclaimed to Thomas 1 a. of meadow in Ailberton called Schovelebredacre
which John le Forister formerly held.
Witnesses: Walter de Auste, William Bray, John de Nasse, John Chyffon of Aylburton,
Walter le Moul.

The Forester holding

A2/11/4 [GC 2968]   Sun. after the Annunciation, 14 Edw. III [26 March 1340]
John le Forester of Lydney and Sir Thomas lord of Berkeleye.

John has granted to Thomas, his heirs and assigns all his meadow lying in the marsh of
Aylbryghton, viz. that which he had by grant of his mother Joan le Forester.
Witnesses: William Bray, Philip le Longe, Walter Dauste.
At: Aylburton.

A2/11/5 [GC 3298]   n.d. [*c.* 1340]
Joan le Forester of Lydney and Sir Thomas lord of Berkeleye.

Joan has quitclaimed to Thomas the meadow in the marsh of Aylbryghton which Thomas had by grant of John le Forester her son, in the said vill of Aylbryghton.

OTHER INTERESTS

A2/11/6 [GC 725]   n.d. [late 13th cent.]
William Clerk, son of Robert the priest; and John Was of Wenna and Edith his wife, William's daughter.

William has granted to John and Edith 2 a. of arable land lying in the place called Wrthi and a certain piece of meadow which pertains to it, the land lying next to William's meadow which is above the bank of the water of Diveleys; rent ½*d.* and John has given him 17*s.* 9*d.* Endorsed: *Alburton.*
Witnesses: William son of Richeman and Philip his brother, John son of Agnes, Richard Payn, William Flandeus of Wenna, Cradoc Kendelan, . . .

A2/11/7 [GC 1054]   Wed. the feast of St. Leonard, 31 Edw. I [6 Nov. 1303]
Philip Hurel; and Walter son of Stephen and Margery daughter of Richard Malemort.

Philip has granted to Walter and Margery a certain messuage and curtilage in the vill of . . . , with the dower when it falls in; also 4 a. of land and a half-acre of meadow, of which 2 a. of land lie next to the water called Neuwarne and the road called la [Heynorande], 2 a. of land lie next to the footpath to Poltone, and the half-acre of meadow in Smethevurlong; Walter and Margery have given him 100*s.*
Witnesses: Walter lord of Nasse, Thomas the forester, Richard Edy, John le Moul, Thomas Ody.
At: Lydney.

A2/11/8 [GC 2218]   The Purification, 11 Edw. II [2 Feb. 1318]
Agnes daughter of Walter de Blakeneye, widow; and Elias son of Henry le Gardiner of Berkeley and Agnes his wife.

Agnes has granted to Elias and Agnes, and their heirs and assigns, all the land which she inherited in the field called Wyke beside the land of her sister Isabel and the road from Nasse to Pyritone, with the reversion of the land of that holding held in dower by her mother Helen.
Witnesses: Walter de Nasse, John Waryn, Richard Edii, Walter le Walische, Richard ate Wele.
At: Purton.

A2/11/9 [GC 2431]   St. Andrew, 18 Edw. II [30 Nov. 1324]
Richard ate Wele and Henry le Gardiner of Berkeley.

Richard has leased to Henry and his heirs, for 30*s.*, all his land called le Ruydyng lying beside the Severn, and between Caldewelle to the north and Richard's grove to the south, but if Richard or his attorney pays the 30*s.* to Henry then the land will revert to Richard, and if the land is sown at the time then Henry or his assigns shall have the crop.
Witnesses: Walter de Nasse, William Waryn, Philip Waryn, Gilbert le Welische, Walter ate Hurste.
At: Purton.

A2/11/10 [GC 3076]   Tues. the feast of St. Martin, 17 Edw. III [11 Nov. 1343]
William Oldelynche and William le Bray.

Whereas William le Bray granted to William Oldelynche all the meadow in Oxenemor which William le Bray had by grant of William Hathewy of Rodmor, as in his charter, William Oldelynche has granted that if William le Bray warrants the meadow to him for 10 years, he will return the charter.
At: Lydney.

BEACHLEY, IN TIDENHAM (GLOS.)

The charters show a neat progression of tenure from Nicholas FitzRoger to Thomas (III) de Berkeley through five changes of ownership, missing direct evidence only of the passage from Tropyn to de la Marche. Another holding acquired by Thomas at Tidenham in the same area included lands in Beachley (below, A2/44/15–18 [GC 3514, GC 914, GC 2597, GC 3040]).

A2/12/1 [GC 400]   n.d. [late Hen. III]
Nicholas son of Roger and Robert de Betesleya.

   Nicholas has granted to Robert all the land which William Ruathlay once held in the vill of Betesleya and half of the fishery called Mideimistestower; rent 7*s.* 7½*d.* a year.
Witnesses: Walter Walding, Thomas Walding his son, Cradoc Walens, Adam Walens, Walter Torel, Peter Tursteyn, Nicholas Tursteyn his son, Robert Burdon, Adam the smith (*faber*), archer, Robert the smith, Walter Seli de Striguil.

A2/12/2 [GC 603]   Mon. the morrow of St. Peter in chains, 22 Edw. I [2 Aug. 1294]
Henry son of Reginald de Betesleye and John Tumbrel, burgess of Bristol.

   Whereas Henry has granted to John all his land in Betesleye with messuages, buildings and fisheries and his part of the ferry of Betesleye, for 50 marks, he has now bound himself and his heirs in 100*s.* to the chief lord of the fee and in 50 marks to John and his heirs or assigns, for any claim he or his heirs may make.
Witnesses: John ap Howel, steward of Beachley, John de Newent, Adam Waunsi, Thomas de Filtone, John de Betesleye.
At: Bristol.

A2/12/3 [GC 2157]   Sat. before the Annunciation, 10 Edw. II [19 March 1317]
John Tumbrel and John Tropyn.

   John Tumbrel has granted to John Tropyn, his heirs and assigns his messuage, 18 a. of land, his portion of the ferry of Betesleye and half of a fish-weir, in the vill of Betesleye, which he had by grant of Henry de Betesleye.
Witnesses: Roger de Seynt Mor, William Deraunt, Master Ralph de Seynt Mor, William de Dernevorde, John de la Lee.
At: Beachley.

A2/12/4 [GC 2672]   28 Feb. 3 Edw. III [1329]
Joan widow of Richard de la Marche called Shakel and Sir Thomas lord of Berkeleie.

   Joan has quitclaimed to Thomas the lands and holdings which Richard formerly had and held in Betysleye, and the ferry of the same vill.
Witnesses: William de Derneforde, William Bendevyle, Meurice de Kemmeys, Philip de la More, John Herlofe.
At: Beachley.

A2/12/5 [GC 2744]   Sun. after St. Gregory, 6 Edw. III [15 March 1332]
Adam Reymond and Sir Thomas lord of Berkeley.

   Adam has quitclaimed to Thomas a messuage and 18 a. of land with meadow, a ferry, fisheries [etc.] adjacent, which Richard de la Marche sometime held in Beteslegh and all the lands and holdings which Thomas has in the same vill.
Witnesses: William de Derneforde, John de la Lee, Philip de Beteslegh, Nigel de Beteslegh, Adam de Auste.
At: Beachley.

A2/12/6 [GC 2772]   Wed. the feast of St. Augustine, 7 Edw. III [26 May 1333]
Edward son of Howel of Beachley and Sir Thomas lord of Berkelee.

Edward has quitclaimed to Thomas a messuage and 18 a. of land with adjacent meadow, a ferry and fishery which Richard de la Marche formerly held in Betesleye, and also all the other lands and holdings which Thomas has in the same vill.

Witnesses: William de Derneforde, John de la Lee, Philip de Betesleye, Nigel de Betesleye, Adam de Auste.

At: Beachley.

A2/12/7 [GC 2780]   Wed. one week after Michaelmas, 7 Edw. III [6 Oct. 1333]
Rose widow of John Tumbrel, formerly burgess of Bristol, and Sir Thomas lord of Berkeleye.

Rose has quitclaimed to Thomas her dower rights after the death of John in all the lands, holdings, ferry and fisheries which were of John in Beteslegh.

Witnesses: Roger Turtle, John de Axebrugge, Robert Gyene, John atte Walle, John le Tournour.

At: Bristol.

A2/12/8 [GC 2781]   Wed. one week after Michaelmas, 7 Edw. III [6 Oct. 1333]
Rose widow of John Tumbrel, formerly burgess of Bristol, and Sir Thomas lord of Berkeleye.

Rose is bound to Thomas in 40*s.* a year for her life at her Bristol house at Key'am.

Witnesses: Roger Turtle, John de Axebrugge, Robert Gyene, John atte Walle, John le Tournour.

At: Bristol.

A2/12/9 [GC 2796] Sun. after the nativity of St. John the Baptist, 8 Edw. III [26 June 1334]
Sir Thomas lord of Berkelee and Philip Fryk.

Thomas has leased to Philip a messuage and 18 a. of land with meadow, a ferry and fisheries adjacent, viz. the holding which Richard de la Marche formerly held in Beteslegh; for his life, rent 100*s.* a year; and Philip is to maintain the holding, ferry-boat and fisheries in their present condition; his mainpernors for the payment of the rent are Edward Howel and Robert de Rillebury, and Thomas may distrain not only on the said holding in Beteslegh but also on the lands of Edward and Robert in Barewe.

Witnesses: Roger de Estham, John Wyth, Edmund de Lyouns, William Arthur, John de Trye.

A2/12/10 [GC 2480]   n.d. [mid 14th cent.]
Thomas lord of Berkelee and Sir Thomas ap Adam, knight.

Thomas de Berkelee has granted to Thomas ap Adam and his issue all his land, holding and ferry at Betesleye; rent 10 marks a year, with remainder to Thomas de Berkelee and his heirs if Thomas ap Adam dies without issue.

Witnesses: Sir John Tracy, Sir Simon Basset, knights, William de Chyltenham, John Serjant, John Clyve.

BENTHAM, IN BADGEWORTH (GLOS.)

A holding here was acquired in or before 1333 when it was being administered jointly with Upton St. Leonards and it seems from the joint account of 1333–4 (below, A2/46/7 [GAR 323]) that various holdings had been purchased, including two from Roger Mautravers and William de Bentham. In the second transaction below, William de Syde may have been acting as agent for Thomas (III) Lord Berkeley and William Sewyn may have been the William de Bentham mentioned in the account. By 1345–6 the holding in Bentham was being administered jointly with Westonbirt and in 1346 it was entailed with Leckhampton and Down Hatherley. It passed to Thomas (III)'s younger son John de Berkeley of Beverstone. See below, pp. 468, Down Hatherley, 477, Over, 487, Syde, and 499, Westonbirt.

A2/13/1 [GC 328]   *c.* May 55 Hen. III [1271]
William Urry of Bentham and Roger Sewyn.

William has leased to Roger 3 selions of land from May 55 Hen. III for 9 years; and
Roger has given him 18*d.*
Witnesses: William the huntsman (*venator*), William de Benetham, John Cropet, Peter
Damyselle, Richard the clerk.

A2/13/2 [GC 2755*]   One week after St. Hilary, 6 Edw. III [20 Jan. 1333]
William de Syde (by John de Wynston); and William Sewyn and Alice his wife.

Final concord, made one week after St. Michael [6 Oct. 1332] and granted one week after
St. Hilary, concerning 2 messuages, 70 a. of land, 3 a. of meadow and 10*s.* of rent in
Beggeworthe, Magna Benetham and Shurdynton; William and Alice have acknowledged
the right of William, and quitclaim for themselves and the heirs of Alice; William has given
them £40.
At: Westminster.

BERWICK, IN HENBURY (GLOS.)

Maurice (III) Lord Berkeley (d. 1326) leased from Roger Crok, son and heir of Sir Peter
Crok, two thirds of his manors of Olveston and Berwick and was holding them when he
forfeited his lands in 1322.

A2/14/1 [GC 592]   Thurs. after the Annunciation, 21 Edw. I [26 March 1293]
William Chaumpeneys and Sir Peter Crok, knight.

William has inspected the grant by Edward de Leye to Peter of a certain holding which
Edward had by William's grant, for Peter's life, and has warranted it.
Witnesses: Henry Vynipeny, Walter le Fouler, Nicholas de Berewyk, John de la Cumbe,
John de Howell.
At: Berwick.

BLAKENEY (GLOS.)

Holdings here were bought by Thomas (II) and Thomas (III) and were probably
incorporated into the manor of Awre and passed from Thomas (IV) (d. 1417) to his
daughter Elizabeth, countess of Warwick. See also above, p. 431, Awre.

BERKELEY INTERESTS
Holding in Essetemore

A2/15/1 [GC 953]   n.d. [early 14th cent.]
Nicholas Pouke of Essetemore and John Loviesone of Little Dean.

Nicholas has granted to John one part of his land and garden in Essetemore, next to the
road from Lydeneye to Gloucestria, to hold of the chief lord of the fee. Endorsed:
Blakeneye.
Witnesses: Walter Aley[n], William Balle, Gilbert Godewyne, John le Hore, Henry Waleys.

A2/15/2 [GC 1878]   10 May 5 Edw. II [1312]
John Lovesone of Little Dean and Sir Thomas de Berkelee, lord of Berkeley.

John has granted to Thomas his garden with a small meadow adjacent, which he had by
grant of Nicholas Pouke of Essetemore, in Essetemore, as in his charter, beside the road
from Lydneie to Gloucestre.
Witnesses: Walter de Nasse, Richard le White of Awre, Thomas de Stone, Thomas de
Bradestone, Hugh de Bray, John de Aure, John Baderon.
At: Blakeney.

The Longe holding

A2/15/3 [SC 384]   n.d. [*temp.* Edw. I]
Laurence le Longe of Blakeney; and Richard son of Walter de Blakeneye and Alice his wife.

Laurence has granted to Richard and Alice all the messuages, gardens [etc.] which he purchased from Thomas de Blakeneye and John le Hore in the manor of Blakeneye; to hold of the lord of the fee by the services laid down in the charters.
Witnesses: Richard Blund of Awre, Roger de Blydeslowe, Thomas de Blakeneye, Philip le Gaynore, Walter son of John, John son of Loue.

A2/15/4 [GC 2166]   4 May 10 Edw. II [1317]
Richard de Blakeneye and Sir Thomas de Berkeleye, lord of Berkeley.
Richard has granted to Thomas, his heirs and assigns the messuage with a garden and curtilage which he had by grant of Laurence le Longe in Blakeneye.
Witnesses: Walter de Nasse, Thomas Blakeneye, Roger de Blydeslowe, Henry Waleys, Philip le Gaynare, Walter son of John, Walter Crompe.
At: Blakeney.

The Palmer holding

It is possible that Adam Palmer can be identified with the Adam Jordan of A2/15/12 [GC 1138], especially as Juliana Palmer's father was surnamed Jordan: see A2/15/6 [GC 2817].

A2/15/5 [GC 2816]   Fri. after St. Ambrose, 9 Edw. III [7 April 1335]
Adam Palmar' of Blakeney and Nicholas Holeforde.

Adam has quitclaimed to Nicholas, his heirs and assigns all lands, holdings [etc.] at Blakeneye in the parish of Aure.
Witnesses: John de Aure, John Wite, Henry Croumpe, John Bletheslowe, Gilbert Jolif.
At: Blakeney.

A2/15/6 [GC 2817]   Palm Sunday, 9 Edw. III [9 April 1335]
Juliana Palmar' of Blakeney and Nicholas de Holeforde.

Juliana has quitclaimed to Nicholas the lands [etc.], which . . . Jordan, her father, formerly held, and which he had by grant of T[homas de Ber]keleye at Blakeneye.
Witnesses: John Boxe, John Blytheslowe, John de Aure, John Wite, Henry Croumpe.
At: Awre.

A2/15/7 [GC 1416]   n.d. [after 1335]
Nicholas de Holeford and Sir Thomas lord of Berkeleye.

Nicholas has granted to Thomas the messuage, garden, curtilage and 3½ a. of land which he had by grant of the same Thomas, and which Adam le Palmar' previously held, in Blakeneye.
Witnesses: James atte [Box], John de Blideslowe, William Bray, Walter de Auste, William Waryn.

A2/15/8 [GC 3266]   n.d. [mid 14th cent.]
Thomas lord of Berkel'; and John atte Churche and Robert Bollock.

Thomas has appointed John and Robert to receive seisin of a messuage, garden, curtilage and 3½ a. of land which he had by grant of Nicholas de Holeford in Blakeneye.

The Giffard holding

A2/15/9 [GC 1245]   n.d. [*temp.* Edw. I]
John son of Walter de Blakeneye and William le Wodar of Blakeney.

John has granted to William a messuage with a curtilage and croft, which Ralph Giffard formerly held in the vill of Blakeneye, lying between the king's highway from Blakeneye to

Aure and the land which Walter his father formerly held; rent 12*d.* a year and William has given him 25*s.*

Witnesses: Thomas de Blakeneye, Robert Levard, Hugh the weaver, Henry Robelard, Thomas Lovejore, J[ohn] the clerk.

A2/15/10 [GC 1385]   n.d. [*temp.* Edw. I]
Gilbert Godewine of Blakeney and Clarice his wife; and John Huge of Blakeney.

    For 30*s.*, Gilbert and Clarice have granted to John the messuage with curtilage and croft which Ralph Giffard formerly held in the vill of Blakeneye; rent 12*d.* a year to the chief lord of the fee.

Witnesses: Roger de Blid', Robert de Blid', Adam de Blid', Henry Waleis, John Eudas, John clerk.

A2/15/11 [GC 1721]   1 March 3 Edw. II [1310]
Thomas de Berkelee, lord of Berkeley, and John Hugh.

    Thomas has leased to John the building plot and curtilage which was of Ralph Giffard in Blaken'; for his life, rent 3*s.* a year.

Witnesses: Robert de Berkelee, Robert de Bradestone, Hugh de Bray, Walter de Nasse, Richard le White of Awre, John Baderon, William Mensk.

At: Blakeney.

Other

A2/15/12 [GC 1138]   6 Dec. 35 Edw. I [1306]
Thomas de Berkeleg', lord of Berkeley, and Adam Jordan.

Thomas has granted to Adam a messuage, garden and curtilage with 3 a. of land which Badekoc Jordan, Adam's father, previously held in Blakeneye; to him and his issue, rent 3*s.* a year.

Witnesses: Richard le Whyte, Elias de Blakeneye, Elias Wynter, Roger de Blydeslowe, Walter le Waleys.

At: Berkeley.

OTHER INTERESTS

A2/15/13 [GC 2364]   Mon. the feast of St. Matthew, 15 Edw. II [21 Sept. 1321]
Hugh son of Walter le Smyth of Blakeney and William Broun of Carswell.

    Hugh has granted to William, his heirs and assigns, his croft in Blakeneye lying between Churchegrove and Smythfeld, and between the stream and Hugh's curtilage.

Witnesses: Walter de Nasse, John de Aure, Roger de Blideslowe, John Baderon, John le Whyte of Awre, Robert le Bray, Adam de Blideslowe.

At: Blakeney.

BLEDISLOE HUNDRED (GLOS.)

This hundred was associated with Awre manor and its advowson, acquired by the Berkeleys in two halves in the early 14th century. See above, p. 431, Awre, and also above, A1/1/18 [GC 3206], and below, A2/77/14 [SC 581].

A2/16/1 [GC 2862]   Tues. the eve of the Circumcision, 10 Edw. III [31 Jan. 1336]
John de Wylintone and Robert Upehulle.

    John has appointed Robert his attorney to do suit for him to the hundred of Blydeslowe for his manor of Poltone.

At: Yate.

A2/16/2 [GAR 415] Bailiff's account   10–11 Edw. III [1336–7]

BRISTOL (GLOS.)

Bristol was part of Gloucestershire until 1373, when it became a county of itself. The Berkeleys had various holdings there from the earliest days, Robert FitzHarding being a merchant of Bristol.

BERKELEY INTERESTS
Chantry in St. Augustine's Abbey

A2/17/1 [GC 2878]   Fri. the morrow of Corpus Christi, 11 Edw. III [20 June 1337]
Thomas lord of Berkele and Roger de Coumbe, chaplain celebrating in the church of St. Augustine's Abbey.

Thomas has granted to Roger, celebrating for the souls of Margaret his late wife and of himself after his death, a messuage with appurtenances in the vill of Bristoll in Bradestrete.
At: Bristol.

A2/17/2 [SC 517]   20 May 20 Edw. III [1346]
Ralph [Ash] abbot of St. Augustine's, Bristol, and Thomas lord of Berkeley.

The abbot has granted to Thomas the house inside the abbey gate which Thomas had built for the use of the chaplain who will celebrate in the abbey church masses for Thomas's soul.
At: The Chapter House.

A2/17/3 [SC 521; *duplicate* SC 522]   20 April 22 Edw. III [1348]
Thomas de Berkeley and St. Augustine's Abbey.

Thomas has granted 2 messuages and 20*s.* rent to a chaplain to sing in St. Augustine's Abbey for the soul of Margaret his wife and for himself, with conditions on the behaviour of the chaplain. Confirmed by Bishop Wulstan [Bransford] of Worcester at Herdebur', 25 April 1348,[1] and by John the prior at Worcester, 27 April 1348.
Witnesses: Sir Maurice de Berkeley, the grantor's eldest son, Sir Thomas de Bradeston, Sir John de Acton, Sir Simon Basset, William de Cheltenham.
At: Berkeley.

A2/17/4 [SC 544]   Mon. after the Assumption, 40 Edw. III [17 Aug. 1366]
Maurice de Berkelee, lord of Berkeley, and William de Wynchecommbe, chaplain.

Maurice has granted to William, for his life, the holding next to the gate of St. Augustine's and a garden and dovecot in Bradestret, for his support in celebrating divine service in the monastery of St. Augustine's for the soul of Margaret his mother.
At: Berkeley.

Redcliffe Street

A2/17/5 [SC 58]   n.d. [*c.* 1200]
Alice de Berkelai and St. Augustine's Abbey.

Alice has granted to the abbey a house and land in Redeclive Street, Bristol, on the Avon side, which Maurice her lord gave her, and which he had bought from Ralph Thurimund, for her soul's health and with the concurrence of Robert de Berkeley her son, who has released her from every service excepting the landgable.[2]
Witnesses: Sir Robert de Berk', Hugh le Petit, Philip de Berkelai, Reginald and Richard, chaplains, Master Peter de Paris, Walter Blundus.

A2/17/6 [SC 56]   n.d. [1190 × 1215]
Alice widow of Maurice de Berkeley and Thomas de Berkeley her son.

Alice has granted to Thomas her land in Redcliff Street which she bought from Alsi de

---

[1] Cf. *Reg. Bransford*, 907.
[2] *Transcript*: *St Augustine's Cartulary*, no. 532.

Bathonia, and which Gerard son of Richard the smith held; landgable rent 7*d.* a year.

Witnesses: W[illiam] abbot of Kingswood, John abbot of St. Augustine's, Roger de Berkeley, Philip and Oliver his brothers, Maurice, Henry and William his brothers, Master Peter de Paris, Master Maurice de Slimbrugg, Reginald de Gosinton, Maurice son of Nigel, Reginald and William, chaplains, Hugh the clerk and Elias his brother.

A2/17/7 [GC 884]   n.d. [late 13th cent.]
The hospital of St. John, Bristol, and Sir Thomas de Berkeley, knight.

Stephen, master of the hospital, and the brothers and sisters have granted to Thomas a rent of 22*d.* a year from William de Burgo of Nubelegh for land which Roger the skinner (*pelliparius*) formerly held in Nubelegh, in exchange for Thomas's remission to them of 22*d.* from the rent of 10*s.* 3½*d.* which they owe him for landgable rent for various land in Redeclyve Street.

Witnesses: Sir John de Sancto Laudo, Sir Roger de Lokinton, knights, Thomas de Lyuns, William de Lyuns, William de Gatecombe.

A2/17/8 [SC 570]   18 Jan. 22 Ric. II [1398]
Thomas Forster, baker, burgess of Bristol, and Thomas de Berkeley, lord of Berkeley.

Thomas Forster has quitclaimed to Thomas de Berkeley a burgage in the street of Redeclyve in Bristol.

Witnesses: John Canynges, mayor of Bristol, Robert Bakster, sheriff, John Banbury, William Wermyster, John Stevens, Walter Seymore.
At: Bristol.

A2/17/9 [GC 3956]   4 April 22 Ric. II [1399]
Thomas Berkele, lord of Berkeley, knight; and Hugh Scryven, burgess of Bristol and Alice his wife.

Whereas Thomas by a writ of escheat recently recovered from John Verschford and Margaret his wife a messuage in the suburb of Bristoll in Redeclyvestrete, which Joan daughter of John de Wycombe recently held of Thomas de Berkele, knight, his grandfather, by knight service, Thomas has granted to Hugh and Alice the said messuage; to them and Hugh's issue, rent 6*d.* a year.

Witnesses: Master Simon Uphull, Henry Brynt, Robert Lygh.
At: Bristol.

A2/17/10 [GC 4001]   Sun. after the Annunciation, 4 Hen. IV [1 April 1403]
Thomas Berkeley, lord of Berkeley; and John Sharpe burgess of Bristol, Joan his wife and John his eldest son.

Thomas has granted to John, Joan and John a holding in Redeclyvestret, which John Rowbergh formerly held, extending from the road in front to the water called Avene behind, between the holdings of John Chastel of Cornestret and a 'comyne slype'; for their lives, rent a red rose a year.

Witnesses: John Stevenns, mayor of Bristol, Thomas Knappe, John Barstaple, William Freme, William Wermynstre.
At: Bristol Castle.

A2/17/11 [SC 577]   Sat. after St. Thomas the apostle, 10 Hen. IV [22 Dec. 1408]
John Sutton and John Redence for Thomas lord of Berkeley; and John Fisher, mayor of Bristol.

At the request of John Sutton and John Redence, the mayor has inspected a charter of Robert de Berkelai viz. Robert has confirmed 1 a. of land near the mill of Trivele, which Thuri the embroiderer (*brodderius*) held, to William the chaplain of Redclive, son of Edric the plumber (*plumbarius*), to hold at a rent of 12*d.* a year, as in Robert's father's charter;

and further has granted to William another 3 a. near the mill at a rent of 3*s.* a year.
Witnesses: [to Robert's charter] Walter de Insula, Bernard de Stanes, Robert Warre, Walter the chaplain, Adam son of Nigel, Maurice his brother, William de Bructun, Walter Scugge, Adam the clerk, John son of Heward, Ivo the baker.
At: Bristol.

The Arblaster holding

A2/17/12 [GC 2760]   Wed. after St. Thomas the archbishop, 6 Edw. III [30 Dec. 1332]
Walter atte Pyle and Sir Thomas de Berkeleye, lord of Berkeley.

Walter has granted to Thomas, his heirs and assigns, for a certain sum of money, a quarter of a burgage, which John le Arblaster sometime held in the vill of Bristoll in the street of Bradestret, which he inherited after the death of John son of John le Arblaster.
Witnesses: Roger Turtle, mayor of Bristol, Robert Gyene, John de Axebrugge, John atte Walle, William le Tayllour.
At: Bristol.

A2/17/13 [GC 2778]   Wed. the feast of Michaelmas, 7 Edw. III [29 Sept. 1333]
Thomas lord of Berkelee; and Thomas Pennarth, burgess of Bristol, and Margaret his wife.

Thomas has leased to Thomas and Margaret the messuage with appurtenances which John le Arblaster formerly held in Bradestret in the vill of Bristoll; for their lives, rent 40*s.* annually.
Witnesses: Roger Tortle, mayor of Bristol, Stephen le Spicer, Henry Babbecari, Robert Helhurste, Walter Hervy.
At: Berkeley.

The Hospitaller holding

A2/17/14 [SC 516]   20 May 1345
Philip de Thame, prior of the hospital of St. John of Jerusalem, and Thomas de Berkeley.

The prior has granted to Thomas 4 a. of land in the suburb of Bristol, near the manse of the prior and Augustinian friars at Bristol, in exchange for a messuage in the same suburb, between the house of Sir John Fraunceys, chaplain, and a holding of the Friars.
At: Shingay (*Shenegeye*).

A2/17/15 [GC 3132]   20 Feb. 1345, 20 Edw. III [1346]
Thomas lord of Berkelee; and the prior and friars hermit of St. Augustine, Bristol.

Thomas has granted to the friars 4 a. of land in the suburb of Bristoll which he had by grant of brother Philip de Thame, prior of hospital of St. John of Jerusalem in England.
At: Berkeley.

Shops in St. Thomas Street

A2/17/16 [GC 4056]   Fri. after St. Thomas the martyr, 12 Hen. IV [2 Jan. 1411]
Thomas lord of Berkeley; and John Rederys of Bristol and Margaret his wife and Hugh Vincy of the same and Margery his wife.

Thomas has granted to John and Margaret and Hugh and Margery 6 shops with gardens in the suburb of Bristol in SeinThomasstrete between the garden of Sir Thomas Broke, knight, and the lane called Houndenlane; to John and Margaret and their issue, and Hugh and Margery and their issue, rent 6*d.* a year.
At: Berkeley.

A2/17/17 [GC 4065]   Mon. before All Saints, 13 Hen. IV [26 Oct. 1411]
Thomas Berkeley, lord of Berkeley, and John Rederyce, burgess of Bristol.

Thomas has granted to John 3 shops in the suburb of Bristoll in the street called Seint Thomas Strete; to him and his issue, rent 3*d.* a year, with remainders to Richard Rederyce and his issue, John Rederyce the younger and his issue, William Rederyce *alias* Marchall and his issue, Thomas Rederyce *alias* Marchall and his issue, Thomas Rederyce and his issue, Thomas Berkeley and his heirs.

At: Berkeley.

A2/17/18 [GC 4066]   Mon. before All Saints, 13 Hen. IV [26 Oct. 1411]
Thomas Berkeley, lord of Berkeley, and Hugh de Vyncy, burgess of Bristol.

Thomas has granted to Hugh 3 shops . . . in the street called Seynt Thomas Strete beside the shops which John Rederys holds of Thomas . . . ; to him and his issue, rent 3*d.* a year, with various remainders.

Other

A2/17/19 [SC 61]   n.d. [late 12th cent.]
Nicholas son of Robert and St. Augustine's Abbey, Bristol.

Nicholas has granted to the abbey, which was founded by his father, the land which he held in Bristol near the church of St. Werburg, for the souls of himself, his father, mother and wife, with the consent of Henry, his son and heir, who has a tiercel for an acknowledgement.[1]

Witnesses: Richard the chaplain, Guy de Troi, Ala wife of the said Nicholas, Henry his son, Jordan Henry's brother, Reginald de Sancto Leodegario, Hugh Martra, Hugh Capreole, Clement, and Reginald the cook.

A2/17/20 [SC 49]   n.d. [*temp.* Ric. I]
Robert de Berchele and Jordan son of John the bishop (*episcopus*) of Bristol.

Robert has notified to all his friends and all honest men of Bristol his grant to Jordan of all that fee which he holds of Herbert de Sancto Quintino in Bristol, within the town walls; rent 38*s.* annually.

Witnesses: Richard de Clifford, Ralph Musard, Richard de Chohull, Bernard de Stanes, Henry de Saltmarsh (*salsomar'*), Walter the chaplain, Maurice and Henry, brothers of Robert, Peter Warr, John son of John the bishop, William the chaplain of Redecl[ive], Elias son of E. de Merleberg', Simon de Olopenne, Hugh de Camma, Robert Bastard, Walter Snige.

A2/17/21 [SC 163]   n.d. [1218 × 1220]
Robert de Berkelai, son of Maurice de Berkelai, and St. Augustine's Abbey, Bristol.

Robert has granted to the abbey all his lands within the walls of Bristol, viz. that which Richard Coterel, Elias son of Alfred, Laurence the butcher (*macellarius*), William Curteluve, William de Penris, Thomas son of Alfred, Elias Clut, Gilda, Robert de Oxonia, Walter de Paris, Thomas Rufus, Richard Burg', Robert Bernardus, Robert la Warra, Everard Francing, William Cordewain', and Hawise Longbord hold of him, for the celebration of the anniversaries of himself, Juliana his wife and Lucy his second wife.[2]

Witnesses: Sir R[ichard] abbot of Keynsham, H— prior of Keynsham, Jordan la Warra, Roger Cord', Peter la Warra, Roger Ailard, William Blakeman, Philip Long, Robert Seuari.

A2/17/22 [GC 2273]   Sat. after St. Ambrose, 12 Edw. II [7 April 1319]
Sir Maurice, knight, son of Sir Thomas de Berkeleye; and Richard le Bolour of Hereford and Joan his wife.

An agreement that Richard and Joan will bring a suit against Roger de Apperleye for a shop in the draper's quarter [*Draperia*] of Bristol, and against Christine de Calne holding a messuage in St. Mary Street, Bristoll, and against John de Calne holding 5 shops in Wynchestret, and Thomas de London, tailor, holding a shop in the fishmarket [*Piscaria*] of Bristoll, from which ought to be paid 1 mark rent to Richard and Joan, and against Hugh de Longebrugge holding a messuage above the Avene in Bristoll, to recover the holdings and rent, at the costs of Maurice and his council and to use no other council, and when the

---

[1] *Transcript*: *St Augustine's Cartulary*, no. 84.   [2] *Transcript*: ibid. no. 123.

holdings are recovered, Richard and Joan will enfeoff Maurice and his heirs of the said holdings, and Maurice will give them £10; for his greater security, they are bound to him in a recognisance of £100 which will be cancelled when they have completed the agreement.
Witnesses: Sir John Mautravers, Sir William de Wauton, Sir Nicholas de Kyngeston, knights, William Colewich, Thomas de Bradestone, Roger de Berleye, John de Coueleye.
At: Berkeley.

A2/17/23 [GC 3751]   . . . 4 Ric. II [1380–1]
William Cheddre of Bristol . . . and Sir Thomas de Berkelee, lord of Berkeley.
    William . . . has surrendered to Thomas all . . . holdings with appurtenances . . . of the fee of Thomas in Bristuyt . . . [*In French.*]
Witnesses: . . . Thomas Beaupyne, John Stanys, Henry . . . , John Wyderoue.
At: Bristol.

A2/17/24 [GC 4028]   12 Oct. 10 Hen. IV [1408]
Walter Wale of Wraxall (Som.) and Sir Thomas lord of Berkeley.
    Walter has quitclaimed to Thomas a messuage with a cellar and a shop built on it in the suburb of Bristol in Toukarstreet, which was of John Bunt, late burgess of the vill, and 4 shops in Templestreet.
Witnesses: John Fisshere, mayor of Bristol, John Leycestre and John Sharpe, bailiffs, Richard Bueton, John Boys.
At: Bristol.

A2/17/25 [GC 4063]   Fri. after the translation of St. Thomas [the archbishop], 12 Hen. IV
[10 July 1411]
Thomas de Berkeley, lord of Berkeley; and William Pays, burgess of Bristol, and Alice his wife.
    Thomas has granted to William and Alice his holding in the suburb of Bristoll in the street called Templestret, which John de Gosebourne lately held for life; to them and their issue, with remainder to Richard Mason of Naylsey and his issue, and Thomas lord of Berkeley and his heirs.
At: Berkeley.

BERKELEY ADMINISTRATIVE DOCUMENTS
Rent-collectors' accounts
A2/17/26 [GAR 416]   25 Feb. 24 Edw. III to Michaelmas 30 Edw. III [1350–6]
Four rolls attached at the head.
A2/17/27 [GAR 417]   35–7 Edw. III [1361–3]
Two rolls attached at the head.
A2/17/28 [GAR 418]   37–8 Edw. III [1363–4]
Rentals
A2/17/29 [GRR 26]   n.d. [*c.* 1300]
Landgable rents of Thomas de Berkele, in Radeclyvestret and Toukernestret.
A2/17/30 [GRR 29]   n.d. [*temp.* Edw. II]
For Thomas de Berkeley; unfinished, not divided into streets; includes the house of Sir Maurice de Berkeley.
A2/17/31 [GRR 27]   21 Edw. III [1347]
Rents of the lord Thomas de Berkele within and without Redcliff Gate; items are 'within the gate of Redeclyve', Fuller Street, Templar Street and St. Thomas Street.
A2/17/32 [GRR 28]   1366
Rents of the lord [Maurice] de Berkele within and without Redcliff Gate; items are 'within the gate of Redeclyve', Fuller Street, Templar Street and St. Thomas Street.

OTHER INTERESTS
The Wombstrong holding in St. Thomas Street

A2/17/33 [SC 420]   n.d. [*temp.* Hen. III]
Hugh Womestrang and Leticia his wife; and Richard Womestrang, their son.

Hugh and Leticia have granted to Richard the rent of 5*s.* due from Richard the miller for land in la Langerewe in the parish of St. Thomas, a suburb of Bristol; rent 2*d.* to be paid to the lord of Berkeley, and Richard has given them 4 marks.
Witnesses: Richard the draper, reeve of Redcliffe, William Seuare, Master Thomas Auverey, John the clerk, James his brother, Roger le Taverner, Ralph the tanner, William Lovel, Thomas Ruffus, John of the temple (*de Templo*), notary public.

A2/17/34 [GC 1587]   n.d. [*temp.* Edw. I]
Richard Womestrang, son of Hugh Womestrang, and Robert de la Cornere.

Richard has granted to Robert all his land in the street of St. Thomas in the suburb of Bristoll'; rent ½ mark a year, and to the hospital of St. John of Radecliva 3*s.*; Robert has given him 40*s.*
Witnesses: John Gilbert, William de Berwyk, William Seuare, Reginald de Panes, John de Witethorthe, Robert de Aiston, John de Malmesbur', reeve of Redcliffe, Alexander Knicht, Walter Long (*Longus*), Walter de Bedmenistre, Thomas Young (*Juvenis*), William de Ouvers, Ralph le Tanner, Nicholas the baker, Walter the dyer, John the Irishman (*Hyberniens'*).

The Marlwood holding in Broad Street

A2/17/35 [GC 2748]   4 April 5 Edw. III [1331]
Henry Clete, burgess of Bristol, and Juliana his wife; and Walter de Merlewode of Thornbury.

Henry and Juliana have quitclaimed to Walter . . . in the vill of Bristoll' in the street called Bradestret.
Witnesses: [John] Daxebrugge, mayor of the vill of Bristol, John atte Walle, Henry de Fro[mpton], stewards of the vill, Roger Plofe and Henry Babbekary, bailiffs of the vill, William le Taillour, Walter Hervy, Peter Muntestephene, Roger de Seyntmor, Nicholas de Seyntmor, John de Boiffeld, Richard de [Calne], clerk.
At: Bristol.

A2/17/36 [GC 2727]   . . . St. Botoloph, 5 Edw. III [*c.* 17 June 1331]
Walter de Morlewode and Robert Williames of Berkeley.

Walter has granted to Robert, his heirs and assigns half of a holding in the vill of Bristoll in Bradestrete, and Robert has given him a certain sum of money.
Witnesses: John de [Axebrugge], mayor of Bristol, John atte Walle and Henry de Frompton, stewards of the vill, Roger Plofe and Henry Babbecari, [bailiffs] of the vill, Roger Turtle, William le Tayllor, Walter le Copere, Nicholas de Seymor, William de Bolkyngton, Walter Hervy, Richard de Calne.
At: Bristol.

The Canynges chantry

A2/17/37 [SC 618]   14 April 8 Edw. IV [1468]
King Edward IV and William Canynges, merchant, of Bristol.

The king has granted to William licence to alienate certain rents in Bristol for the support of his chaplain at St. George's altar in the church of St. Mary, Redcliff, for the souls of the king and Elizabeth the queen [and others].
At: Westminster.

A2/17/38 [SC 619]   24 Oct. 8 Edw. IV [1468]
William Canynges, merchant of Bristol, and Thomas Hallkesock.

William has founded a perpetual chantry at the altar of St. George in the parish church of St. Mary Redcliffe, Bristol, and has appointed Thomas chaplain of the same.

Witnesses: Philip Mede, mayor, Robert Straunge, sheriff, John Godard and John Nancotham, bailiffs, John Shipward the elder, William Coder, William Spenser, Henry Chestre, Robert Bolton, Thomas Oseney.

At: Bristol.

Other

A2/17/39 [SC 52]   Ash Wednesday after the death of John de Constantiis,
                                                      bishop of Worcester [3 March 1199]
Walter son of Herbert le Werra and Thomas his brother.

Partition between the two brothers of property in Bristol.

Witnesses: John la Werra, David la Werra, Robert la Werra, clerk, Roger Werra, brother of the same John, Thomas the chaplain of Cnolla, Roger the cordwainer (*corduwanarius*), Jordan le Eveske, John de Cnolla.

A2/17/40 [GC 834]   n.d. [late 13th cent.]
Albreda daughter of Geoffrey the vintner of Bristol and Lewis de Langport.

Albreda, for lack of advice and aid from Jordan Ledbet' her husband, in her urgent necessity, has sold to Lewis the rent of 1 mark from Radeclive Street, and he has given her 10 marks for her sustenance in the absence of her husband; warranty given in the presence of the hundred of Radcliffe.

Witnesses: Sir Philip Long (*Longus*), Thomas his son, Vincent son of Hermer, William Blakeman, reeve, Adam de Deverel, Richard Bernard, Hugh Womestrang, Thomas Harcing, Matthew Palmer, Hugh of the bridge (*de ponte*), David the baker.

A2/17/41 [GC 567]   n.d. [early Edw. I]
Nicholas de Schidwene and William, son of his sister Margery.

Nicholas has granted to William all the land which he has in the parish of St. Mary, Redcliff, lying between the land of Alan Mogge and the road to the mill of Trivele; rent to the chief lord of the fee 2*s.* a year; and William has given him 20*s.*

Witnesses: Everard le Fraunceys, mayor of Bristol, Thomas Koker, reeve of Redcliffe Street, John de Seinde, John de Legh, Robert le Brid, Peter the smith, Nicholas the clerk.

A2/17/42 [GC 1941]   n.d. [1313]
Robert Darcy, sheriff of Gloucester.

Note of a visit by Robert to Bristol in connection with a royal writ of Thurs. the morrow of the Assumption, 7 Edw. II [16 Aug. 1313] to Bartholomew de Badlesmere for the release of prisoners held in Bristol.

A2/17/43 [GC 2799]   Sun. before St. Peter in chains, 8 Edw. III [31 July 1334]
Robert de Wryngton and Gilbert Pokerel.

Robert is bound to build a stone wall on the plot of land which he acquired from Gilbert, between Gilbert and himself

At: Bristol.

CANONBURY (GLOS.)

The manor, which had belonged to St. Augustine's Abbey, Bristol, was bought by Henry Lord Berkeley (d. 1613) in 1570–1. According to Smyth, it was the only monastic land acquired by the family after the Reformation. The capital messuage lay close to the town of Berkeley and the manor was composed of lands throughout the hundred granted by members of the Berkeley family and their tenants over several centuries.

ACCOUNT ROLLS

A2/18/1 [GAR 288] View	Michaelmas–Easter, 34–5 Edw. I [1306–7]
A2/18/2 [GAR 289]	11 June–Michaelmas 35–6 [*sic*] Edw. I [1307]
A2/18/3 [GAR 290]	2–3 Edw. II [1308–9]
A2/18/4 [GAR 291]	9–10 Edw. II [1315–16]
A2/18/5 [GAR 292]	Michaelmas–Hilary 3 Edw. III [1329–30]
A2/18/6 [GAR 293]	14–15 Ric. II [1390–1]
A2/18/7 [GAR 294]	15–16 Ric. II [1391–2]
A2/18/8 [GAR 295]	1–2 Hen. V [1413–14]
A2/18/9 [GAR 296]	3–4 Hen. V [1415–16]
A2/18/10 [GAR 297]	6–7 Hen. V [1418–19]
A2/18/11 [GAR 298]	3–4 Hen. VI [1424–5]
A2/18/12 [GAR 299]	6–7 Hen. VI [1427–8]
A2/18/13 [GAR 300]	8–9 Hen. VI [1429–30]

Rental

A2/18/14 [GRR 30]	May 14 Edw. IV [1474]

Court Rolls

A2/18/15 [GCR 12]	Morrow of St. Martin, 10 Edw. I [12 Nov. 1282]
A2/18/16 [GCR 13]	Morrow of St. Denis, 13 Edw. I [10 Oct. 1285]
A2/18/17 [GCR 14]	Mon. after St. Luke, 14 Edw. I [21 Oct. 1286]
A2/18/18 [GCR 15]	Sat. the eve of St. Andrew, 3 Edw. II [29 Nov. 1309]
A2/18/19 [GCR 16]	Thurs. after St. Mark, 3 Edw. II [30 April 1310]
A2/18/20 [GCR 17]	Tues. before St. George, 4 Edw. II [20 April 1311]
A2/18/21 [GCR 18]	Sat. the feast of St. Thomas the bishop, 5 Edw. II [2 Oct. 1311]
A2/18/22 [GCR 19]	Fri. after St. Mark, 6 Edw. II [27 April 1313]
A2/18/23 [GCR 20]	17 April 7 Edw. II [1314]
A2/18/24 [GCR 21]	Sun. before St. Tibertius and St. Valerianus, 13 Edw. II [13 April 1320]
A2/18/25 [GCR 22]	Fri. . . . 14 Edw. II [1320–1]
A2/18/26 [GCR 23]	Thurs. the feast of St. Leonard, 20 Edw. II [6 Nov. 1326]
	Tues. after St. Mark, 1 Edw. III [28 April 1327]
A2/18/27 [GCR 24]	Fri. the feast of St. Denis, 1 Edw. III [9 Oct. 1327]
	Mon. after St. Tiburtius and St. Valerianus, 2 Edw. III [18 April 1328]
A2/18/28 [GCR 25]	Fri. the feast of St. Simon and St. Jude, 2 Edw. III [28 Oct. 1328]
	Sat. the feast of St. John before the Latin Gate, 3 Edw. III [6 May 1329]
A2/18/29 [GCR 26]	St. Denis, 5 Edw. III [9 Oct. 1331]
	Wed. the feast of St. John before the Latin Gate, 6 Edw. III [6 May 1332]
	Wed. the feast of St. Mary Magdalene, 6 Edw. III [22 July 1332]
A2/18/30 [GCR 27]	Tues. after Michaelmas, 6 Edw. III [6 Oct. 1332]
	Fri. before St. Philip and St. James, 7 Edw. III [30 April 1333]
A2/18/31 [GCR 28]	Thurs. before St. Denis, 7 Edw. III [7 Oct. 1333]
	Sat. the feast of St. George, 8 Edw. III [23 April 1334]
A2/18/32 [GCR 29]	Fri. after Michaelmas, 9 Edw. III [6 Oct. 1335]
	Thurs. 19 April 10 Edw. III [1336]
A2/18/33 [GCR 30]	Mon. after Michaelmas, 12 Edw. III [5 Oct. 1338]
A2/18/34 [GCR 31]	Tues. after St. Ambrose, 13 Edw. III [6 April 1339]

A2/18/35 [GCR 32]		Wed. after Michaelmas, 14 Edw. III [4 Oct. 1340]
		Thurs. after St. Mark, 15 Edw. III [26 April 1341]
A2/18/36 [GCR 33]		Sat. 11 Oct. 17 Edw. III [1343]
		Thurs. after the Invention of Holy Cross, 18 Edw. III [6 May 1344]
A2/18/37 [GCR 34]		8 Oct. 18 Edw. III [1344]
		7 April 19 Edw. III [1349]
A2/18/38 [GCR 35]		Mon. after Michaelmas, 19 Edw. III [3 Oct. 1345]
		Sat. after the Invention of Holy Cross, 20 Edw. II [6 May 1346]
A2/18/39 [GCR 36]		Wed. after St. Calixtus, 20 Edw. III [18 Oct. 1346]
		Invention of Holy Cross, 21 Edw. III [3 May 1347]
A2/18/40 [GCR 37]		. . . 23 Edw. III [1349]
A2/18/41 [GCR 38]		Thurs. after St. Thomas the apostle, 24 Edw. III [23 Dec. 1350]
	Hocktide court	29 May 25 Edw. III [1351]
A2/18/42 [GCR 39]	Michaelmas court	18 Oct. 25 Edw. III [1351]
	Hocktide court	16 April 26 Edw. III [1352]
A2/18/43 [GCR 40]	Michaelmascourt	Wed. after All Saints, 26 Edw. III [7 Nov. 1352]
	Hocktide court	24 April 28 Edw. III [1354]
A2/18/44 [GCR 41]		27 Nov. 28 Edw. III [1354]
	Hocktide court	2 May 29 Edw. III [1355]
A2/18/45 [GCR 42]	Michaelmas court	27 Oct. 29 Edw. III [1355]
	Hocktide court	22 May 30 Edw. III [1356]
A2/18/46 [GCR 43]	Michaelmas court	30 Nov. 30 Edw. III [1356]
A2/18/47 [GCR 44]	Hocktide court	20 June 31 Edw. III [1357]
A2/18/48 [GCR 45]	Michaelmas court	23 Oct. 31 Edw. III [1357]
	Hocktide court	32 Edw. III [1358]
A2/18/49 [GCR 46]	Michaelmas court	3 [Nov. ?] 32 Edw. III [1358]
	Hocktide court	30 May [33 Edw. III, 1359]
A2/18/50 [GCR 47]	Michaelmas court	15 Oct. 33 Edw. III [1359]
		13 April 34 Edw. III [1360]
A2/18/51 [GCR 48]	Michaelmas court	24 Nov. 34 Edw. III [1360]
A2/18/52 [GCR 49]		Fri. after St. Lucy, 35 Edw. III [Dec. 1361]
A2/18/53 [GCR 50]	Michaelmas court	17 Oct. 35 Edw. III [1361]
	Hocktide court	25 April 36 Edw. III [1362]
A2/18/54 [GCR 51]	Michaelmas court	5 Nov. 36 Edw. III [1362]
	Hocktide court	8 April 37 Edw. III [1363]
A2/18/55 [GCR 52]		Wed. the eve of St. Thomas the apostle, 37 Edw. III [20 Dec. 1363]
A2/18/56 [GCR 53]		Sat. after the Annunciation, 38 Edw. III [30 March 1364]
A2/18/57 [GCR 54]		Sat. after Michaelmas, 38 Edw. III [5 Oct. 1364]
A2/18/58 [GCR 55]	Hocktide court	Fri. in Easter week, 39 Edw. III [18 April 1365]
A2/18/59 [GCR 56]		Sat. the eve of St. Thomas the apostle, 39 Edw. III [20 Dec. 1365]
A2/18/60 [GCR 57]	Hocktide court	4 May 41 Edw. III [1367]
A2/18/61 [GCR 58]	Michaelmas court	Mon. after St. Luke, 41 Edw. III [25 Oct. 1367]
A2/18/62 [GCR 59]	Michaelmas court	Sat. after St. Luke, 42 Edw. III [21 Oct. 1368]
A2/18/63 [GCR 60]	Hocktide court	Thurs. the morrow of St. Mark, 43 Edw. III [26 April 1369]
A2/18/64 [GCR 61]		12 Sept. 43 Edw. III [1369]
A2/18/65 [GCR 62]	Hocktide court	Wed. after Ascension, 44 Edw. III [29 May 1370]
A2/18/66 [GCR 63]	Michaelmas court	5 Nov. 44 Edw. III [1370]

A2/18/67 [GCR 64] Hocktide court	Wed. after St. Mark, 46 Edw. III [28 April 1372]
A2/18/68 [GCR 65]	26 Oct. 46 Edw. III [1372]
A2/18/69 [GCR 66]	19 May 47 Edw. III [1373]
A2/18/70 [GCR 67] Michaelmas court	Thurs. after St. Martin, 47 Edw. III [17 Nov. 1373]
A2/18/71 [GCR 68] Michaelmas court	23 Oct. 48 Edw. III [1374]
A2/18/72 [GCR 69] Hocktide court	27 April 50 Edw. III [1376]
A2/18/73 [GCR 70] Michaelmas court	6 Nov. 50 Edw. III [1376]
A2/18/74 [GCR 71] Michaelmas court	4 Nov. 1 Ric. II [1377]
A2/18/75 [GCR 72] Michaelmas court	13 Dec. 2 Ric. II [1378]
A2/18/76 [GCR 73] Hocktide court	18 May 2 Ric. II [1379]
A2/18/77 [GCR 74] Michaelmas court	2 Nov. 4 Ric. II [1380]
A2/18/78 [GCR 75] Michaelmas court	Sat. after Michaelmas, 5 Ric. II [5 Oct. 1381]
A2/18/79 [GCR 76] Hocktide court	24 April 5 Ric. II [1382]
A2/18/80 [GCR 77] Michaelmas court	Fri. after Michaelmas, 6 Ric. II [3 Oct. 1382]
A2/18/81 [GCR 78] Hocktide court	30 April 6 Ric. II [1383]
A2/18/82 [GCR 79] Michaelmas court	8 Oct. 7 Ric. II [1383]
A2/18/83 [GCR 80] Hocktide court	17 April 7 Ric. II [1384]
A2/18/84 [GCR 81] Michaelmas court	Tues. before St. Simon and St. Jude, 8 Ric.II [25 Oct. 1384]
A2/18/85 [GCR 82] Hocktide court	11 April 8 Ric. II [1385]
A2/18/86 [GCR 83] Michaelmas court	Mon. before All Saints, 10 Ric. II [29 Oct. 1386]
A2/18/87 [GCR 84] Hocktide court	Fri. after St. John before the Latin Gate, 10 Ric. II [10 May 1387]
A2/18/88 [GCR 85]	Sat. before St. Luke, 12 Ric. II [17 Oct. 1388]
A2/18/89 [GCR 86]	8 May 12 Ric. II [1389]
A2/18/90 [GCR 87]	. . . after Michaelmas, 14 Ric. II [1390]
A2/18/91 [GCR 88] Hocktide court	Thurs. after St. Mark, 14 Ric. II [27 April 1391]
A2/18/92 [GCR 89] Michaelmas court	22 Nov. 15 Ric. II [1391]
A2/18/93 [GCR 90] Hocktide court	Wed. before St. Petronilla, 15 Ric. II [29 May 1392]
A2/18/94 [GCR 91] Michaelmas court	19 Oct. 16 Ric. II [1392]
A2/18/95 [GCR 92] Hocktide court	22 April 16 Ric. II [1393]
A2/18/96 [GCR 93] Hocktide court	22 April 16 Ric. II [1393]
A2/18/97 [GCR 94]	Fri. the feast of St. Philip and St. James, 17 Ric. II [1 May 1394]
A2/18/98 [GCR 95]	Tues. after St. Luke, 18 Ric. II [20 Oct. 1394]
A2/18/99 [GCR 96]	Wed. after St. Mark, 18 Ric. II [28 April 1395]
A2/18/100 [GCR 97]	13 Oct. 19 Ric. II [1395]
A2/18/101 [GCR 98]	10 Oct. 20 Ric. II [1396]
A2/18/102 [GCR 99]	5 May 20 Ric. II [1397]
A2/18/103 [GCR 100] Michaelmas court	2 Oct. 21 Ric. II [1397]
A2/18/104 [GCR 101] Hocktide court	8 May 21 Ric. II [1398]
A2/18/105 [GCR 102] Michaelmas court	13 Jan. 22 Ric. II [1399]
A2/18/106 [GCR 103] Hocktide court	10 April 22 Ric. II [1399]
A2/18/107 [GCR 104] Hocktide court	6 May 1 Hen. IV [1400]
A2/18/108 [GCR 105] Michaelmas court	22 Oct. 3 Hen. IV [1401]
A2/18/109 [GCR 106]	4 April 3 Hen. IV [1402]

A2/18/110 [GCR 107] Hocktide court	Thurs. the morrow of St. Mark, 4 Hen.IV [26 April 1403]
A2/18/111 [GCR 108]	. . . after the Invention of Holy Cross, 5 Hen. IV [May 1404]
A2/18/112 [GCR 109]	12 June 9 Hen. IV [1408]
A2/18/113 [GCR 110]	9 April 11 Hen. IV [1410]
A2/18/114 [GCR 111]	4 Oct. 14 Hen. IV [1412]
	3 May 1 Hen. V [1413]
A2/18/115 [GCR 112]	9 Oct. 4 Hen. VI [1425]
	24 April 4 Hen. VI [1426]
A2/18/116 [GCR 113]	18 Oct. 5 Hen. VI [1426]
	8 May 5 Hen. VI [1427]
A2/18/117 [GCR 114]	8 Oct. 6 Hen. VI [1427]
A2/18/118 [GCR 115] Hocktide court	14 May 6 Hen. VI [1428]
A2/18/119 [GCR 116]	20 Nov. 11 Hen. VI [1432]
	St. Mark, 11 Hen. VI [25 April 1433]
A2/18/120 [GCR 117]	Oct. 18 Hen. VI [1439]
A2/18/121 [GCR 118]	12 May 24 Hen. VI [1446]
A2/18/122 [GCR 119]	19 Oct. 25 Hen. VI [1446]
A2/18/123 [GCR 120]	1 May 26 Hen. VI [1448]
A2/18/124 [GCR 121]	14 Dec. 29 Hen. VI [1450]
A2/18/125 [GCR 122]	25 May 29 Hen. VI [1451]
A2/18/126 [GCR 123]	4 Nov. 30 Hen. VI [1451]
A2/18/127 [GCR 124]	6 May 30 Hen. VI [1452]
A2/18/128 [GCR 125]	24 Oct. 36 Hen. VI [1457]
A2/18/129 [GCR 126]	. . . 37 Hen. VI [1458–9]
A2/18/130 [GCR 127]	. . . 38 Hen. VI [1459–60]
A2/18/131 [GCR 128]	11 Oct. 39 Hen. VI [1460]
	7 May 1 Edw. IV [1461]
A2/18/132 [GCR 129]	Fri. before St. Simon and St. Jude, 1 Edw. IV [23 Oct. 1461]
	11 May 2 Edw. IV [1462]
A2/18/133 [GCR 130]	. . . 2 Edw. IV [1462]
	Morrow of the Invention of Holy Cross, 3 Edw. IV [4 May 1463]
A2/18/134 [GCR 131]	9 Oct. 22 Edw. IV [1482]
	[23 Edw. IV, 1483]

SOUTH CERNEY AND CERNEY WICK (GLOS.)

South Cerney and Cerney Wick were bought by Thomas (IV) Lord Berkeley from the last Aymer Lord St. Amand (d. 1402). The first Aymer de St. Amand (d. 1241) was probably a younger son of a minor Norman lord and his wife, the daughter of Walter de Verdon, sheriff of Essex and Hertfordshire 1218–20. While the eldest son William stayed in Normandy, Aymer and his brother Guy came to England to join the royal service and take up the family's inheritance from their kinsman Ralph son of Walter de Verdon, and by 1239 William had quitclaimed to Aymer the lands in England of Ralph de Verdon and of their brother Guy (who was still living in 1237).[1] From the Verdons Aymer inherited lands in Oxfordshire and also South Cerney.[2]

[1] *GEC* xi. 295–6.
[2] *VCH Oxon.* ix. 4, 16, 46, 60.

South Cerney and Cerney Wick occasionally occur as two manors but more usually as one.[1] The last Aymer had a son and heir apparent, Aymer, who died without issue between 25 June and 28 Nov. 1401.[2] The inquisition post mortem on the older Aymer recorded that he and his wife were not seized of the manor at his death in 1402 although it had been regranted to them for their lives, with reversion to the feoffees, by the feoffees to whom Aymer had granted it in 1398 (below, A2/19/9 [GC 3944]).[3] In 1404 Thomas de Berkeley offered a rent of 50 marks from 'Cerney' as a surety for his sale of Wendens Ambo. South Cerney and Cerney Wick lay 2 miles east of Shorncote (then Wilts., now Glos.), which Thomas bought in 1414, and all three were among the lands granted to feoffees three weeks before Thomas's death in 1417 (below, A2/77/14 [SC 581]), which appear to have been intended for his nephew and heir male, James. The settlement of Cerney Wick in 1412 (below, A2/19/11 [SC 578]) may also have been intended for James's benefit. Most of the lands involved in the entail of 1417 were the subject of a dispute with the heir general, Thomas's daughter Elizabeth, and her husband Richard Beauchamp, earl of Warwick. Warwick was holding South Cerney at his death in 1439 and it was later held by the Nevilles through one of his daughters by Elizabeth.[4]

THE ST. AMAND MANOR

A2/19/1 [SC 59]   n.d. [late 12th cent.]
Margaret de Buhun and Ralph de Verdun.

Margaret has granted to Ralph the land of Cernai which William de Chaisne held of her by the service of one knight's fee, Ralph to perform the same service; also Margaret has confirmed to Ralph 6 a. of land which her brother Henry gave him, and 6 a. which she herself has given him to improve his land and holding.

Witnesses: William de Pinkeny, Richard de Abenesse, Humphrey the chaplain, William de Hasweia, Griffin son of Reginald, Matthew nephew of the Lady, John de Vehun, Thomas son of Payn, William de Amenesches.

A2/19/2 [SC 402]   n.d. [early Hen. III]
Annora widow of Sir Walter de Verdun and Aymer de Sancto Amando.

Annora has granted to Aymer the messuage in Cernay which Walter gave her in free dower, in exchange for the new messuage which Aymer has given to her in the same vill.

Witnesses: Sir Thomas de Saunford, Sir Stephen de Harnhulle, Sir Miles parson of Cerney, Anselm de Sancto Germano.

A2/19/3 [GC 839]   n.d. [early Hen. III]
Anora de Weredun and Sir Aymer de Sancto Amando.

Anora has granted to Aymer 3 half-acres which she had from William le Fraunceys in Westgarstone. Endorsed: *Sarneye*.

Witnesses: Walter Frari, William Sori, John of the marsh (*de marisco*), Miles le Fraunkeleyn, Michael de Stoke.

A2/19/4 [SC 443]   n.d. [late Hen. III]
Arnulf Byset, lord of Preston, and Aymer de Sancto Amando.

Arnulf has granted to Aymer the homage, service and fealty due from Anselm de Sancto

---

[1] e.g. *CIPM* v, no. 272; vii, no. 286; xv, no. 582.

[2] *GEC* xi. 301.

[3] *CIPM* xviii, no. 800. That Thomas de Berkeley's uncle John and a close associate Sir Thomas FitzNichol witnessed the charter of 1398 may indicate that the settlement involved the grant of the reversion of the manor to Thomas de Berkeley. Aymer's widow Eleanor lived until 1426; the manor may have been granted to Berkeley soon after Aymer's death.

[4] Rudder, *Glos.* 327.

Germano for the holding which he has in Cerneye, Aymer to perform the necessary service to the chief lord of the fee, viz. a quarter of one knight's fee.
Witnesses: Sir Roger [de Rodmarton] abbot of Cirencester, Sir William de Kaynes, Sir John Paaynel, Sir Richard parson of Cerney, John le Frankelein of Cerney, Simon de Stok of Cerney, William le Franceyg' of Cerney, William le Burgeys, Robert de Clendone.

A2/19/5 [GC 717]   n.d. [late 13th cent.]
Ralph de Cerneye, son of Anselm de Sancto Germano, and Aymer de Sancto Amando.

Ralph has granted to Aymer 1 virgate in the vill of Cerneye which he had by grant of Anselm his father.
Witnesses: Sir Roger abbot of Cirencester, William son of Odo, Sir Richard rector of Cerney, Hugh de Basco, Roger . . . of Rakeburn, John le Frankelin, William le Frankelein, Simon de Stok, William le Burgess.

A2/19/6 [SC 454]   17 March 6 Edw. I [1278]
King Edward I and Aymer de Sancto Amando.

Licence, at the request of Robert son of John, steward of the household, to Aymer to divert the public way which goes through Cerney past his gate, in order for him to build a bridge beyond his fishpond.
At: Quenington.

A2/19/7 [GC 2386]   Sun. after St. Margaret the virgin, 16 Edw. II [25 July 1322]
John de Sancto Amando; and William Bythewatere and Alice his wife.

John has leased to William and Alice the holding in Southcerneye which was of Maud, sister and heir of Nicholas le Frenshe, also a rent of a rose a year from 6 a. of land which Henry le Taillur and his wife Juliana hold for life of John in the same vill, with the reversion of the land; for their lives, rent 6*s*. 8*d*. a year.
Witnesses: Jordan de Baudyntone, William Archebauld, John de Sloghtere, Michael de Stoke, Walter de Auneford, clerk.
At: South Cerney.

A2/19/8 [GC 3893]   The Circumcision, 18 Ric. II [1 Jan. 1395]
Aymer de Sancto Amando; and John atte Halle of South Cerney and Agnes his wife.

Aymer has leased to John and Agnes a messuage and a half-virgate of land, with a water-mill adjacent in the same vill, which John previously held of Aymer; for their lives and 7 years, rent 20*s*. a year.
At: South Cerney.

A2/19/9 [GC 3944]   1 Sept. 22 Ric. II [1398]
Aymer de Sancto Amando; and Henry Ingepenne, William Tudderle, clerk, and Philip Shipiere.

Aymer has granted to Henry, William and Philip his manor of Suthcerneye and CerneyWyke, and all his possessions in Gloucestershire.
Witnesses: John de Berkele and Thomas FitzNicholl, knights, William Erchebaud, Thomas Tresham, Nicholas Punter, William Walley, William Aillewyne.
At: South Cerney.

A2/19/10 [SC 569]   1 Sept. 22 Ric. II [1398]
(1) Aymer de Sancto Amando, knight; (2) Henry Ingepenne, William Tudderle, clerk; and Philip Shipiere; (3) the tenants of South Cerney and Cerney Wick.

Aymer has granted to Henry, William and Philip his manor of Suthcerneye and CerneyWyke, and all his tenants should attorn to them.

A2/19/11 [SC 578]   15 May 13 Hen. IV [1412]
William Hankeford, knight, Robert son of Robert Hull, Henry Popham and Robert son of
John Hull, knight; and Thomas de Berkeley, lord of Berkeley.

William, Robert, Henry and Robert have granted to Thomas the manor of Wyke (Wilts.),
which they had by grant of William Esturmy, knight, to Thomas; for his [life?] [*damaged*].
Witnesses: Walter Hungerford, William Chayne, knights, William Stourton, Thomas
Calston, Walter Beauchamp.
At: Wyke.

THE STURTON HOLDING

The large number of charters at the Castle concerning the holding suggest that Thomas (IV)
Lord Berkeley purchased the holding at some time after 1409.

A2/19/12 [GC 959]   n.d. [early 14th cent.]
Aymer de Sancto Amando and Thomas de Sturtone.

Aymer has granted to Thomas that he may enclose his croft lying to the east of his house
in the vill of Cerneye.
Witnesses: Master Ralph de Sturtune, Miles the franklin, Jordan Burgeys of Badminton,
William French (*Franciscus*), Michael de Stokes, Jordan Child, Richard Wethay.

A2/19/13 [GC 1370]   n.d. [early 14th cent.]
Miles called the franklin of Cerney, William French (*Franciscus*) of the same, Jordan called
Burgeys of Badminton, and Michael de Stokes; and Thomas de Sturtune.

Miles, William, Jordan and Michael have granted to Thomas their common rights in his
croft to the east of his house in the vill of Cerneye so that he may enclose it.
Witnesses: Master Ralph de Sturtune, Bartholomew Archebaud, Walter de Hankintune, John
de Cotes, William Hinder, Jordan Child, John de Caumpedene.

A2/19/14 [GC 929]   n.d. [late 13th cent.]
John le Marchant of Bourton and Thomas de Sturtone.

John has granted to Thomas, in free marriage with Alice his sister, all his lands and
holdings in the vill of Suthcerney; rent a rose a year; to them and their issue, and if they die
without issue then the land shall revert to John.
Witnesses: Walter Frury of Down Ampney, John de Grantebrugge of Cricklade, John of the
marsh (*de marisco*) of Up Ampney, William Franceys, Miles de Cerney, Robert de Startone,
Bartholomew Archebaud, William le Oyselor.

A2/19/15 [GC 911]   n.d. [late 13th cent.]
Miles the franklin of South Cerney and Thomas de Sturtone.

Miles has granted to Thomas 3 a. of arable land in Suthcerneye: 1 a. between Heyeweye
and Bradeweye, 3 fardels in la Suthgarstone, a half-acre next to la Greneweye at John's
mill, and 3 fardels at Boxwelle; and also the half-virgate of meadow which William
Bargodin held; rent a rose a year, and Thomas has given him 4 marks.
Witnesses: Bartholomew Archebaud, John de Hankintone, John of the marsh (*de marisco*),
Walter brother of Walter de Hankintone, John de Caumpedene, William French
(*Franciscus*) of Cerney.

A2/19/16 [SC 561]   Fri. before St. George, 7 Ric.II [22 April 1384]
Aymer de Sancto Amando and Agnes Pyke of Cerney.

Aymer has manumitted his villein (*nativa*) Agnes.
At: West Woodhay [Berks.].

A2/19/17 [GC 3788]   Nativity of John the Baptist, 9 Ric. II [24 June 1385]
William Lyente, son of Richard Lyente of Highworth, and William Noty the younger.

William Lyente has granted to William Noty, his heirs and assigns all the lands, holdings [etc.] in the vill of Southsarneye which he had by grant of Agnes Pyke, widow of Thomas Stortone; for Agnes's life.

Witnesses: John Cosyn, Nicholas Pouter, John Campedene, William atte Halle, John Herteshorne, John Meleward, Thomas Tresham of Siddington, Thomas Stokes.

At: South Cerney.

A2/19/18 [GC 3789]   Mon. the feast of St. John and St. Paul, 9 Ric. II [26 June 1385]
Agnes Pyke, widow of Thomas Stortone of South Cerney, and William son of Richard Lyente of Highworth (Wilts.).

Agnes has granted to William all the lands, holdings [etc.] in the vill of Southsarneye which she had by grant of Sir Nicholas vicar of South Cerney; for the term of her life, rent 12*d.* a year.

Witnesses: William Noty, Henry Hykady, John Herteshorn.

At: South Cerney.

A2/19/19 [GC 3790]   Mon. the feast of St. John and St. Paul, 9 Ric. II [26 June 1385]
(1) Agnes Pyke, widow of Thomas Stortone of South Cerney; (2) Gilbert Dooge of Henley on Thames and John son of Walter Lyente of Highworth; (3) William son of Richard Lyente of Highworth.

Agnes has appointed Gilbert and John to deliver seisin to William of all her lands, holdings [etc.] in South Sarneye.

At: South Cerney.

A2/19/20 [GC 3791]   St. Peter the apostle, 9 Ric. II [29 June 1385]
Agnes Pyke, widow of Thomas Stortone, and William Noty the younger.

Agnes has quitclaimed to William all the lands, holdings [etc.] which she and Thomas had by grant of Richard de Stoke and John Edmond in the vill of Southsarneye.

At: South Cerney.

A2/19/21 [GC 3792]   Thurs. after St. Peter the apostle, 9 Ric. II [6 July 1385]
William Lyente, son of Richard Lyente of Highworth, and William Noty the younger.

William Lyente has quitclaimed to William Noty the lands, holdings [etc.] which he had by grant of Agnes Pyke, widow of Thomas Stortone, in the vill of Southsarneye.

At: South Cerney.

A2/19/22 [GC 3793]   20 July 9 Ric. II [1385]
William Lyente of Highworth and William Noty the younger of South Cerney.

William Lyente is bound to William Noty in £20 to be paid at Michaelmas next.

A2/19/23 [GC 3799]   St. Juliana the virgin, 9 Ric. II [23 Feb. 1386]
William Lyente of Highworth and William Noty the younger of South Cerney.

William Lyente has quitclaimed to William Noty all actions in respect of 12 marks which he owed him, the which 12 marks have been paid.

At: Cricklade.

A2/19/24 [GC 4003]   Tues. after St. Petronilla, 5 Hen. IV [3 June 1404]
John Noty, son and heir of William Noty, and Robert Colyns.

John has granted to Robert, his heirs and assigns, all the lands, holdings, rents [etc.] which he inherited in the vill of Southsarneye after the death of William Noty his father.

Witnesses: William Aylewyn, Alexander Langeneye, Geoffrey Hydeman, John Rageor, John atte Mulle.

At: South Cerney.

A2/19/25 [GC 4004]   Thurs. after St. Petronilla, 5 Hen. IV [5 June 1404]
John Colles and his wife Margaret; and Robert Colyns.

John and Margaret have quitclaimed to Robert lands and holdings in Southsarneye called Schermannestenement.

Witnesses: Alexander Langeleye, William Aylewyn, Geoffrey Hydemon, John atte Mulle, John Rageor.

At: South Cerney.

A2/19/26 [GC 4038]   20 June 10 Hen. IV [1409]
Robert Colynes and John atte Halle of South Cerney (Glos.).

Robert has granted to John, his heirs and assigns, all his lands, holdings [etc.] in Southcerneye which he had by grant of John Noty, son and heir of William Noty.

Witnesses: Robert Poynes, William Aylewyne, John Bovy, John Gage, Geoffrey atte Hyde, John Smyth.

At: South Cerney.

A2/19/27 [GC 4042]   14 Nov. 11 Hen. IV [1409]
Robert Colyns and John atte Halle of South Cerney (Glos.).

Robert has quitclaimed to John the lands and holdings in Southcerneye which he had by grant of John Noty, son and heir of William Noty.

Witnesses: Robert Poynes, William Aylewyne, John Bovy, John Gage, Geoffrey atte Hyde, John Smyth.

At: South Cerney.

OTHER

A2/19/28 [SC 372]   n.d. [*temp.* Hen. III]
John le Frankelein of Cerney and Walter Dubedent.

John has granted to Walter a messuage with a garden, in the croft which used to belong to Richard Slide; rent 2*s.* a year, and Walter has given John 2*s.*

Witnesses: Sir Miles parson of Cerney, Anselm de Sancto Germano, Walter Frankelan of Driffield, William le Burgeis of Cerney.

A2/19/29 [GC 897]   n.d. [late 13th cent.]
Walter Dulbedent of Cerney and William Peruding.

Walter has granted to William, in free marriage with his daughter Maud and for the sustenance for his life which William has provided, a messuage with a curtilage in the vill of Cerneye; rent 2*s.* a year to the chief lord of the fee.

Witnesses: Sir Richard parson of Cerney, Roger Harang of Siddington, John the franklin of Cerney, Simon de Stokes, William le Burgeys, William le Franceys, Richard de Cerneye, clerk.

A2/19/30 [GC 968]   n.d. [early 14th cent.]
Agnes de Stok of South Cerney and Robert de Puryton, merchant.

Agnes has granted to Robert, for 10 marks, 6½ a. of arable land in the vill of Southcerneye, with the rent of 2 free tenants, Henry le Taylour and John de Estsex, viz. ½*d.* and ¼*d.* a year respectively, the land lying as follows: a fardel at Westdoune, a half-acre at Hodyngbroc, a half-acre at Amelamesweye, a half-acre at Bryanuscrofte, a half-acre at 'le lytele horte', a half-acre against the high street, a half-acre at le Vernforlonge, a half-acre at Amecomesforlonge, a half-acre at Soutlongelonde, a half-acre at Beggarushulle, a half-acre at Northgarstone, a fardel at Brynqelake, a fardel at le Wykebruggehende, a fardel at Vernham, a fardel in le Estlynwarde and a fardel at Heyzeweyusonde.

Witnesses: Master John de Baudynton, John de Sloutere, Robert Barbost of Siddington, Simon le Frankeleyn of Driffield, John le Mareys of Ampney.

A2/19/31 [GC 3929]   Tues. after the nativity of St. John the Baptist, 21 Ric. II
[26 June 1397]
Henry Gosyntone of Slimbridge; and Thomas Pypere, chaplain, and Henry Taylur, clerk.

Henry has granted to Thomas and Henry, and their heirs and assigns, all his lands and holdings in Southcerneye and CerneyeWyke within the hundred of Crouthorne.
Witnesses: Nicholas Panter, William Wodeforde, John Haralt, John ate Mulle, John Bayly.
At: South Cerney.

A2/19/32 [GC 3318]   n.d. [late 14th cent.]
William atte Halle and others; and Walter Lyente.

William, William Hertheven, Richard Bertone, John Heose, Robert Taillour, William Borghton, Walter Curteys, John Churchey, Maurice Boch', Peter Smyth, William Morcote and William Weysangere of the vill of Heyworth have testified that Walter Lyente, father of John Lyente, was born a bastard.

COMPTON GREENFIELD (GLOS.)

Smyth states that Thomas (III) Lord Berkeley (d. 1361) created a manor here by purchases from various lords in 1330 and 1331, and the charter below (A2/20/1 [GC 2997]) shows that Thomas had certainly acquired an interest here before 1340, but the manor held by his widow Katherine at her death in 1386 (actually two thirds of the manor with the reversion of the other third) was probably one which had come from the Hereward inheritance of Joan, wife of Thomas's nephew Maurice, a younger son of Maurice de Berkeley of Stoke Giffard.

The Hereward inheritance consisted of the manors of Compton Greenfield (Glos.), Pencarrow (Cornw.), and Deep Moor, Dodscott and Blinsham (Devon).[1] William Hereward married Douce, sister of Walter Stapledon, bishop of Exeter (d. 1326), and of Richard Stapledon (d. 1332). Richard had married Joan, daughter and coheir of Serlo Hay, and Serlo's father Walter Hay had granted lands in Pencarrow, Chapel Amble and Rose (Cornw.) to Joan and her issue, with remainder to her sister Thomasine, who married Bartholomew Penhirgard, and her issue. Despite that settlement, in 1306 Richard and Joan sold the lands to his brother Walter, whose right was acknowledged by fines of 1317 and 1320, and by the latter of which he granted them back to Joan and Richard and Richard's heirs, with remainder to Walter's sister's husband William Hereward, thereby overriding the entail created by Walter Hay. In 1318 William Hereward bought the manor of Compton Greenfield (Glos.) from Bartholomew de Greneville and his wife Anne, and in 1320 this too was settled, through Walter Stapledon, on William and his issue, with remainder to Richard Stapledon and his issue and William's right heirs. In April 1328 a fine between Bartholomew le Seneschal and William's son William Hereward and his wife Elizabeth settled the manors of Deep Moor and Dodscott, with 40 messuages in Great Torrington (Devon), on William and Elizabeth and their issue, with remainders to Thomas Hereward for life and his son Robert for life, and then to Reginald son of John le Sore and his issue. Joan, daughter and heir of William and Elizabeth, was married to Maurice de Berkeley by 1351, when Maurice brought an assise of novel disseisin against John Penhirgard, grandson of Bartholomew and Thomasine, for the Cornish lands. Penhirgard pleaded the entail by Walter Hay but the jurors at Launceston found for Berkeley and awarded him £20 damages. At Easter 1354 the manors of Deep Moor, Dodscott, Blinsham, Pencarrow and Compton Greenfield were settled on Maurice and Joan and their issue, and in Dec. 1354 John Brok of 'Radeclif' quitclaimed to Maurice and Joan all messuages, lands and holdings in Blinsham and Great Torrington which they held of Joan's inheritance.[2] In Feb. 1356 all the manors except, significantly,

---

[1] M. Buck, *Politics, Finance and the Church in the Reign of Edward II: Walter Stapledon, Treasurer of England* (Cambridge, 1983), 22–4, 32.
[2] Devon CRO 1148 M/T.

Pencarrow, were again settled on Maurice and Joan and their issue, but this time with remainder to Maurice's uncle Thomas Lord Berkeley and his wife Katherine and their male issue, before Joan's right heirs. Maurice campaigned with the Black Prince in 1359 but had died by April 1371 when John de Wylington, as lord of Umberleigh (Devon), quitclaimed to Elizabeth, widow and executrix of Maurice (IV) Lord Berkeley, and her co-executors the marriage and custody of the body of Maurice, son and heir of Maurice de Berkeley of Compton Greenfield.[1] Joan Hereward is said to have died without issue,[2] and the young heir may not have been her son, but in 1373 half a fee at Dodscott was said to be held by the heir of Maurice de Berkeley.[3] By 1386 Compton Greenfield had passed to Katherine de Berkeley and the Devon lands were divided between Joan's four aunts or their issue.[4]

A2/20/1 [GC 2997]   21 June, 14 Edw. III [1340]
William de la Marsche, rector of the chapel of Compton Greenfield, and Sir Thomas de Berkeleye, lord of Berkeley.
    William has released to Thomas the tithes paid to the chapel from a pasture called le Herdelese within the said manor of Comptone from the purparty of Thomas.
At: Berkeley.

A2/20/2 [GC 3477]   Sun. after Michaelmas, 32 Edw. III [30 Sept. 1358]
Sir Maurice de Berkeleye, lord of Compton Greenfield, and Thomas de Berkeleye, lord of Berkeley.
    Maurice has leased to Thomas 52 a. of meadow called Herdeslese in Comptone; for life, rent a rose a year for 9 years, and thereafter £20 a year.
At: Berkeley.

A2/20/3 [SR 36]
Copies of five final concords:
(i) One month after Easter, 35 Edw. I [23 April 1307], Bartholomew de Grenvyle and Anne his wife; and William Giffard, concerning the manor of Compton Greynvyll and the chapel of the same manor, settled on Bartholomew and Anne and the heirs of Bartholomew;
(ii) One week after Michaelmas, 12 Edw. II [6 Oct. 1318], William Hurward; and Bartholomew de Grenevill and Anne his wife, concerning the manor of Compton Grenevill and the advowson of the chapel of the same manor. Bartholomew and Anne have acknowledged the advowson and one-third and two-thirds of two-thirds of the manor to be the right of William, and they grant the reversion of one-third of two-thirds of the manor, held by Richard de Thoverton and Katherine his wife in dower, to William, for 100 marks;
(iii) One week after Trinity 13 Edw. II [1 June 1320], Walter de Stapelton, bishop of Exeter and William Herward concerning the manor of Compton Greynevyle, rent of 1 lb. of pepper and half a knight's fee in Almyngton and the advowson of the chapel of the said manor. Walter has granted the above, except for one-third of two-thirds of the manor, and the reversion of the one-third, held by Richard de Thunverdon and Katherine his wife in dower, to William and his issue, with remainders to Richard de Stapelton and his issue and to the right heirs of William;
(iv) Three weeks after Easter 28 Edw. III [4 May 1354], Maurice son of Maurice de Berkeley, knight, and Joan his wife; and William Corbrugge and Richard Warbulton concerning the manors of More, Dodescote and Blemesham (Devon), Pencarrou (Cornw.) and Compton Grenevyll (Glos.), settled on Maurice and Joan and their issue, with remainder to the right heirs of Joan

----

[1] Smyth, i. 257, 376; below, A5/10/7 [GC 3631].
[2] Pole, *Devon*, 231, 395.
[3] *CIPM* xiii, no. 268 (p. 243).
[4] Lysons, *Magna Britannia*, p. clxvi; Pole, *Devon*, 231, 395.

(v) Morrow of the Purification 30 Edw. III [3 Feb. 1356], Maurice de Berkele, knight, and Joan his wife; and John Vey, clerk, and William de Corbrigge concerning the manors of More, Dodescote and Blemesham (Devon), and the manor of Compton Grenevyll (Glos.) and the advowson of the chapel of the same manor, settled on Maurice and Joan and Joan's issue, with remainder to Thomas son of Maurice de Berkeley the elder, knight, and Katherine his wife and the heirs male of their bodies, and the right heirs of Joan.

ETLOE (GLOS.)

The holdings in Etloe purchased by Thomas (II) Lord Berkeley (d. 1321) were usually considered as appurtenances of the manor of Awre (Glos.). See also above, pp. 431, Awre, 436, Blakeney, and below, p. 480, Purton.

BERKELEY INTERESTS

A2/21/1 [GC 1597]   n.d. [early 14th cent.]
Elias Wynter of Etloe; and Sir Thomas de Berkelee, lord of Berkeley, and Joan his wife.

Elias has granted to Thomas and Joan a messuage with a garden, curtilage and croft, with the reversion of the dower of Juliana Wynter, his mother, and the reversion of the messuage, garden and curtilage held for life by Christine Martin, in Ettelowe, the croft lying in the field called Brokkeholebecbesfeld, beside the road from la Wyle to Brokkeholesbeche.
Witnesses: Sir John de Wylynton, Elias de Aylberton, Walter de Nasse, Hugh de Bray, Richard le Whyte of Awre, John de Aure, Robert de Bradeston, Robert de Berkelee, Robert Wyther.

A2/21/2 [GC 2155]   Sun. after St. Matthew, 10 Edw. II [27 Feb. 1317]
Thomas Hatholf of Etloe and Sir Thomas de Berkel', lord of Berkeley.

Thomas Hatholf has granted to Thomas de Berkel', his heirs and assigns all his lands and holdings in Ettelowe within the manor of Aure.
Witnesses: Walter de Nasse, John ate Boxe, Roger de Blideslowe, Richard Edy, John le White, John Bauderon, Thomas le Forester.
At: Etloe.

OTHER INTERESTS

A2/21/3 [GC 1246]   n.d. [*temp.* Edw. I]
Roger son of Walter de Blakeneye and William Biut of Etloe.

Roger has granted to William a messuage with a curtilage, garden and croft, containing 4 a., in Ettelowe, in the field called Brocholebechesfeld, next to the common road from la Wele to Brocholebeche; rent 6*d.* a year, and William has given him 3½ marks.
Witnesses: Philip Baderun, Robert de Aure, Henry Crumpe, Robert le Ward, Richard Blundus, Henry Waleys, Thomas le Kobbenave.

A2/21/4 [GC 1247]   n.d. [*temp.* Edw. I]
Walter de Blakeneye and Philip his son.

Walter has granted to Philip 4 a. of land in Hettelowe, viz. those which he had from Walter atte Burowe in exchange, in 5 plots in Brocholebechesfeld between the Severn and the road from Hettelowe to Pyriton; rent a rose a year, and Philip has given him 4 marks.
Witnesses: John de Aust, John le Scot, Robert de Aure, Philip Badrun, Walter de Aura, Thomas de Blakeney, Henry Crumpe.

A2/21/5 [GC 2366]   Michaelmas, 15 Edw. II [29 Sept. 1321]
John de Aure and Henry le Gardiner of Berkeley.

John has leased and demised at farm to Henry all his holding with houses, lands, meadows [etc.] in Ettelowe, which Richard le Heerde and Walter atten Assche of Ettelowe formerly held, in Ettelowe; from Michaelmas for a term of 5 years, the rent that which pertains to the holding.

Witnesses: Walter de Nasse, John Waryn, John le Wythe of Awre, Roger de Blydeslowe, Walter le Walsche.

At: Etloe.

FALFIELD, IN THORNBURY (GLOS.)

Isabel de Clare (d. 1338), second wife of Maurice (III) (d. 1326), had a holding in Falfield at Mars (presumably the Marsh), and her stepson Thomas (III) had also acquired a holding there by 1329 if the holding mentioned in the Ham account of that year (BCM GAR 119; cf. above, A1/24/128) was different from Isabel's. From 1333 to 1360 it was administered with Alkington (BCM GAR 23–45; cf. above, A1/3/125–45) and in 1352 it was entailed on Thomas's younger son Edmund and his brothers, with Barrow Gurney, Cheddar and Tickenham (Som.). It consequently passed to John de Berkeley of Beverston. See also below, p. 514, Barrow Gurney.

A2/22/1 [GC 2099]   Wed. the feast of Whitsun, 9 Edw. II [2 June 1316]
John le Bruyn of Falfield and William Payn of Oldbury.

   John has granted to William his meadow called Alresmede in the vill of Fallefelde within the [manor] of Thornbury; for his life, and after his death to his executors or assigns for a term of 20 years, rent ½*d.* a year.

Witnesses: John Chaumpeneys, John le Longe, Walter le Mason, Robert de Southmede, Elyas de Heneys.

At: Falfield.

A2/22/2 [GC 2876]   15 June 11 Edw. III [1337]
(1) Thomas lord of Berkele; (2) John de Clyve; (3) Isabel widow of Sir Maurice de Berkele (Thomas's father) and Thomas son of Thomas.

   Thomas has appointed John to deliver to Isabel and Thomas the younger seisin of all his lands and holdings in Falefeld, which he had by grant of William Payn.

At: Berkeley.

FRAMPTON ON SEVERN (GLOS.)

The rent of 22 marks from the manor (which was acquired in 1303) was paid to the manor of Hurst in Berkeley Herness and was entailed with that manor in jointure on Maurice (IV) and Elizabeth Despenser on their marriage in 1338. As a result it formed part of the settled estate which passed to Thomas (IV)'s nephew and heir male James Lord Berkeley on Thomas's death in 1417. On the death of the tenant Robert (II) FitzPayn in 1354, the manor passed to his daughter and heir Isabel, who married Sir John de Chideock (d. 1388), and her son Sir John. That John died in 1390 leaving a son (a third John) aged 12, who was married in the same year to Eleanor, daughter and heir of Sir Ivo FitzWarren. FitzWarren was granted the manor for a term of nine years by Chideock's feoffees for the sustenance of John and Eleanor.[1] The charters below show that there is no justification for the claim made by Smyth, and followed by GEC, that Isabel wife of Robert Lord FitzPayn was a daughter of Sir John de Clifford. See also above, A1/1/31, A1/1/33–4, A1/1/47 [GC 4384, GC 4412–13, GC 4146*].

BERKELEY INTERESTS

A2/23/1 [GC 1044]   Easter Monday, 31 Edw. I [8 April 1303]
Richard de Clyfford, son and heir of Sir John de Clyfford, and Sir Thomas de Berkelee, lord of Berkeley.

   Richard has granted to Thomas the annual farm of 3*s.* 4*d.* in which Robert son of Payn

---

[1] *GEC* v. 450–8.

and Isabel his wife are bound for their lives, with robes for Richard, Sarah his wife and their children and household, for the rent of £18 5s. a year from Peter Flori for the manor of Frompton sur Severne, which Peter holds for life, along with the reversion of the manor after Peter's death and the dower of Margery, Richard's mother, when it falls in, which Robert and Isabel have for their lives by grant of Richard; and Richard will grant to Thomas the reversion of the manor after the deaths of Robert and Isabel, Peter and Margery, for which Thomas has given him 100 marks and will enfeoff him in his manor of Wyke juxta Erlyngham along with the fishery called le Berewewater in the Severn, to Richard and Sarah and Richard their eldest son for their lives, and will give to Richard 3½ marks a year for robes for himself and his groom, and to Sarah 40s. for her robe, and 60 marks for Richard's daughters Katherine and Maud, and maintenance for his younger son Nicholas. [*In French.*]

Witnesses: Hugh de Veer, Robert le FizPaeyn, John Abadam, Walter de Gloucestre, Thomas de Gardyns, Thomas le Botyller, John Lovel of Snorscomb, John Basset, Peter Crok, knights, Robert de Bradestone, Robert de Bettlescombe, Richard de Byselee, Thomas de Styntescombe.

At: Berkeley.

A2/23/2 [GC 1046]   Sun. one week after Easter, 31 Edw. I [14 April 1303]
Richard de Clyfford, son and heir of Sir John de Clyfford, and Sir Thomas de Berkelee, lord of Berkeley.

Richard has granted to Thomas all the rents and services which Sir Robert son of Payn and Isabel his wife pay to Richard, for their lives, for a rent of £18 5s. a year from Peter Flori for the manor of Frompton super Sabrina, with the reversion of all the lands and holdings of the same manor after the deaths of Peter and of Margery, Richard's mother, which Robert and Isabel had by his grant for their lives, and the reversion of the manor after the deaths of Robert and Isabel, Peter and Margery.

Witnesses: Sir Hugh de Veer, Sir Robert son of Payn, Sir John Abadam, Sir Walter de Glouc', Sir Thomas de Gardinis, Sir Thomas le Boteler, Sir John Lovel of Snorscomb, Sir John Basset, Sir Peter Crok, knights, Robert de Bradestone, Robert de Bettlescombe, Richard de Byselee, Thomas de Styntescombe.

At: Berkeley.

A2/23/3 [GC 1049]   Fri. after St. Peter and St. Paul, 31 Edw. I [5 July 1303]
Thomas de Berkeleye, knight, and Richard son of John de Clyfford.

Richard has acknowledged the right of Thomas in the manor of Frompton super Severne (Glos.) before the king's justices in the Bench at York, which manor Peter de Flory holds for life by grant of the said John, so that the manor remains after the death of Peter to Robert le FizPayn and Isabel his wife, for their lives, and one third of the manor held in dower by Margery, widow of John de Clifford; further Richard has confirmed to Thomas the rent of £20 16s. from Robert and Isabel for their lives and the rent of 8 robes for him and his household [*familiares*]; for this acknowledgement, Thomas acknowledges that he is bound to Richard in 32 marks for his daughters, to support Richard's son as a scholar until aged 16, and will give seisin to Richard and his wife Sarah in a rent of 6½ marks a year in Gloucestershire for their lives.

Witnesses: Sir William de Bereford, John Lovel of Snorscomb, John de Bradeford, Anthony de Bradeneye, Henry Scrup, William de Herle, Richard de Asbsheby, Richard de Roden[ey], William de Brocworth.

At: York.

A2/23/4 [GC 1070]   One week after Trinity, 33 Edw. I [20 June 1305]
Thomas de Berkeleye and Richard son of John de Clifford.

    Final concord, made at York the morrow of St. John the Baptist, 32 Edw. I [25 June 1304]
and granted and recorded one week after Trinity, 33 Edw. I, concerning the manor of
Frompton super Sabrinam; Richard has acknowledged the manor to be the right of Thomas,
which Robert son of Payn and Isabel his wife hold for life, and Thomas has given Richard
£200.
At: Westminster.

A2/23/5 [GC 3272]   One week after Michaelmas, 33 Edw. I [6 Oct. 1305][1]
Robert son of Payn and Thomas de Berkeley the elder.

    Copy of final concord concerning the manor of Fromptone super Sabrinam; Robert has
acknowledged the manor to be the right of Thomas, and Thomas has granted it to Robert
and Isabel his wife and Robert's issue; rent 22 marks a year to Thomas and his heirs;
contingent reversion to Thomas.

A2/23/6 [GC 3920]   Sun. after St. Gregory, 20 Ric. II [18 March 1397]
Ivo FitzWaryn, knight, and his lord of Berkelegh.

    Ivo has appointed his lord of Berkelegh to govern his manor of Fromptone super
Sebrinam, and receive all the profits except the wood, from Michaelmas next to the
Michaelmas following for one year, and orders all his ministers to obey the lord.
At: Frampton.

A2/23/7 [SR 37]
Copies of three final concords:
(i) [as above, A2/23/5 (GC 3272)];
(ii) [as above, A2/23/4 (GC 1070)];
(iii) Two weeks after Easter, 22 Edw. I [2 May 1294], William Bysshop and Richard son of
John Clifford, concerning one third of the manor of Frumton super Sabrinam; William has
acknowledged the one third to be the right of Richard, who will pay William 100*s.* a year
for William's life.

OTHER INTERESTS

A2/23/8 [GC 2250]   Tues. the feast of St. James, 12 Edw. II [25 July 1318]
Peter le King of Frampton and Odo de Actone.

    Peter has granted to Odo, his heirs and assigns, his furlong called Heyweyesforlong beside
the road called Heywey, with a croft at la Wodende called Mulewardescroft in Frompton.
Witnesses: William de Clifford, Robert Warner, Stephen de Draicote, Warin son of William,
John Duyk, Richard de Salle of Epney, Nicholas de la Newelonde, John Lokare, Walter
Vrenshe, John le Vowel.
At: Frampton on Severn.

GLOUCESTER (GLOS.)

    Strangely, although it may be assumed that the Berkeley family had interests in the shire
town long before, the evidence of any interest there is limited to four charters, the earliest of
which is dated 1313. The enfeoffment carried out by Thomas (IV) three weeks before his
death in 1417 mentions purchases in Gloucester and it is probable that the bulk of the rest of
the surviving charters gives a better indication of the degree of the family's interests there.

BERKELEY INTERESTS

A2/24/1 [GC 2397]   Mon. the feast of St. Gregory, 6 Edw. II [12 March 1313]
John de Aysselworthe and Sir Maurice de Berkel'.

_____
[1] Date supplied from PRO CP 25/1/75/39, no. 250.

John has granted to Maurice for his [John's] life a rent of 10*s*. and if this fails, he wills that Maurice and his bailiff may distrain for the arrears of the rent on his shop in Glouc' opposite le Munesmyth.

Witnesses: William de Aston and Edmund de Banerton, bailiffs of Gloucester, Walter le Spiser, William de Ryouns, William de Hertford.

At: Gloucester.

A2/24/2 [GC 2116]   4 Aug. 10 Edw. II [1316]

Alexander de Lideneye, burgess of Gloucester, and Sir Maurice de Berkeleye, son of Sir Thomas de Berk'.

Alexander has granted to Maurice, his heirs and assigns his holding in Egbrugge Street and a shop in the same street, which his mother Christine granted to him and Jordan de Hengham.

Witnesses: Andrew de Pendock, Owen de Wyndeslesor, Robert Stanedissh, William de Riouns, William de Marklee, Walter le Spicer, John de Northwych.

At: Gloucester.

A2/24/3 [GC 3985]   4 Nov. 3 Hen. IV [1401]

Thomas Berkeleye, lord of Berkeley; and William Plomer and Edith his wife.

Thomas has leased to William and Edith, for the good service of William, a burgage and 6 shops adjacent in Gloucestre in the parish of St. Michael; for their lives, rent 12*d.* a year.

At: Wotton.

A2/24/4 [GC 4044]   1 Jan. 11 Hen. IV [1410]

Thomas Berkeleye, lord of Berkeley, and William More of Gloucester and Edith his wife.

Thomas has leased to William and Edith, for the good service of William, a burgage and 6 shops in Gloucestre in the parish of St. Michael, and also a holding in the parish of St. Aldate in the lane called Oxbodelane; for their lives, rent 12*d.* a year.

At: Wotton.

OTHER INTERESTS

Passage of rents and holdings from Richard de Monmouth to William Ryouns

A messuage and two shops in the shambles

A2/24/5 [GC 908]   n.d. [1295]

John Flori, son of Robert Flori of Gloucester, and John son of John de Monemuwe, formerly burgess of Gloucester.

John Flori has quitclaimed to John de Monemuwe an empty place in the shambles of Gloucester which he (John de Monemuwe) received from John (Flori).

Witnesses: William Croc and John Lucus, bailiffs of Gloucester, Robert Honsom, William Chose, Reginald le Draper, John de Aure, John Franceys.

A2/24/6 [GC 643]   Mon. in St. Tiburtius and St. Valerianus, 26 Edw. I [14 April 1298]

John son of John de Monemue, formerly burgess of Gloucester; and William de Ryouns of Gascony, merchant, and Amicia his wife.

John has leased to William the messuage with a shop to the east of the entrance with the garden, curtilage etc., which John his father lived in, in Gloucestre, opposite the place called le Menesmyth; for their lives, rent 38*s.* a year.

Witnesses: Walter le Severne and William de Wychtfeld, bailiffs of Gloucester, Robert de Hansom, Stephen Brun, Hugh Pyioun, John Flory, John de Aure, Robert de Lassyndon, William de Redenhale.

At: Gloucester.

A2/24/7 [GC 2533]   n.d. [*c.* April 1298]
Richard son of John de Monemwe, formerly burgess of Gloucester; and William de Ryouns of Gascony, merchant, and Amicia his wife.

Richard has quitclaimed to William and Amicia for their services, for their lives, a messuage with a shop to the east of the entrance which his father John formerly inhabited in Glouc' opposite le Muntsmith, which they had by grant of John his brother for their lives.
Witnesses: Walter le Sevarne and William de Wytfeld, bailiffs of Gloucester, Stephen Broun, Hugh Pigon, John Florye, Henry le Taylor, Walter de Bykenore, Thomas Craft, skinner, William de Redenhale.

A2/24/8 [GC 1084]   Mon. after St. Hilary, 33 Edw. I [18 Jan. 1305]
Richard de Monemuwe, son of John de Monemuwe, formerly burgess of Gloucester; and William de Ryons, burgess and merchant of Gloucester, and Amicia his wife.

Richard has received from William and Amicia £51 6*s.* 8*d.* which they ought to render of a certain annual rent of 38*s.* for a messuage and a shop, which they have for their lives, opposite the place called la Mundsmyth, viz. for 24 years from Christmas A.D. 1304 or 33 Edw. I.
Witnesses: William de Withfeld and William de Hertford, bailiffs of Gloucester, Robert Honsom, Stephen Broun, Walter de Bykenore, Hugh Pigon, Thomas Craft.
At: Gloucester.

A2/24/9 [GC 1643; *duplicate* GC 1642]   Michaelmas Day, 1 Edw. II [29 Sept. 1307]
Richard son and heir of John de Monemuth, late burgess of Gloucester, and William de Ryuns, burgess of Gloucester.

Richard has leased to William, for £10, a shop in Glouc', situated in front of the holding which William holds of him, opposite la Munesmith; from Michaelmas 1 Edw. II for a term of 20 years, rent a rose a year.
Witnesses: John de Northwych, John de Coumbe, bailiffs of Gloucester, Walter de Bikenore, Stephen Broun, Hugh Pyiun, Thomas de Bernwod, Roger de Tuekesbury.

A2/24/10 [GC 1731]   Sat. the eve of Easter, 3 Edw. II [18 April 1310]
Richard de Monemuth, son of heir of John de Monemuth, late burgess of Gloucester, and William de Ryuns, merchant.

Richard has quitclaimed to William, for a certain sum of money, a messuage in Gloucestre opposite la Munesmith, with 2 shops next to the entrance to the hall of the messuage, which William and Amicia his wife previously held for their lives, of Richard.
Witnesses: Walter le Espic' and Peter de la Hulle, bailiffs of Gloucester, Robert Pope, William de Hertford, Hugh Pyiun, William de Teukesbury, John de Ashelworth.
At: Gloucester.

A2/24/11 [GC 2532]   n.d. [1309–10]
Richard de Monemuth, son and heir of John de Monemuth formerly burgess of Gloucester, and William de Ryuns, burgess of Gloucester.

Richard has granted to William, for a certain sum of money, a shop in Glouc' beside the entrance to William's hall opposite la Munesmith, and an annual rent of 10*s.* from the shop which Robert Peyt, Alice his wife and Roger their son hold for their lives, and a rent of 1*d.* from the shop which Leticia Sake holds for life, with the reversion of the shops and a rent of 8*s.* from the shop which Denise de Maurthyn holds for a term of 34 years opposite la Munesmith in the shambles (*mascecraria*) with the reversion, and a rent of 12*s.* from the shop which Roger de Teukesbury holds in the shambles for a term of 12 years, with the reversion.
Witnesses: Walter Lespicer and Peter de la Hulle, bailiffs of Gloucester, Robert Pope, William de Hertford, Hugh Pyiun, William de Teukesbury, John de Ashelworth.

A2/24/12 [GC 1732; *duplicate* GC 1733]   Thurs. the feast of St. George, 3 Edw. II
[23 April 1310]

William de Ryuns, burgess of Gloucester, and Richard de Monemuth, son and heir of John de Monemuth, late burgess of Gloucester.

Whereas Richard has quitclaimed to William and Amicia his wife a messuage and 2 shops opposite la Munesmith which they held for life, and has granted to them a shop to the west of the entrance to the hall of his holding, and rents of 10*s.* from Robert Peyt, Alice his wife and William their son for a shop held for their lives, and 1*d.* from Leticia Zake for a shop held for life, and 8*s.* from Denise de Mawerthy for a shop held for 34 years, and 12*s.* from Roger de Teukesbury for a shop held for 12 years, with the reversion of the said shops at the end of the respective terms, William wills that if Richard or his attornies pay to him, his heirs or executors 12 marks at Christmas next following and £11 4*s.* 5*d.* at the Easter following William will give up his claim to the rents and reversions.

At: Gloucester.

A2/24/13 [GC 1770]   Thurs. after Michaelmas, 4 Edw. II [1 Oct. 1310]

Richard de Monemuth, son and heir of John de Monemuth, late burgess of Gloucester, and William de Ryuns, burgess of Gloucester.

Richard has granted to William, for a certain sum of money, a shop in Gloucestre in the shambles.

Witnesses: Walter le Spec' and Peter de la Hulle, bailiffs of Gloucester, Stephen Broun, William de Hertford, Thomas de Penedok, Roger de Teukesbur', John de Upton.

At: Gloucester.

A2/24/14 [GC 1769]   Fri. after Michaelmas, 4 Edw. II [2 Oct. 1310]

Richard de Monemuth, son and heir of John de Monemuth, late burgess of Gloucester, and William de Ryuns, burgess of Gloucester.

Richard has quitclaimed to William 2 shops in Gloucestre, in the shambles.

Witnesses: Walter le Spec' and Peter de la Hulle, bailiffs of Gloucester, Stephen Broun, William de Hertford, John de Aschelworth.

At: Gloucester.

The Tewkesbury rent (see also above, A2/24/11–12 [GC 2532, GC 1732])

A2/24/15 [GC 1032]   Wed. the feast of St. Valentine, 30 Edward [14 Feb. 1302]

Richard de Monemwe, son of John de Monemwe, formerly burgess of Gloucester, and Roger de Theokesbur'.

Richard has remitted to Roger 12*d.* of the 15*s.* a year which Roger renders for his holding in the shambles (*masecaria*) of Glouc'.

Witnesses: Roger le Heybarare and Robert [*altered from* Roger] the spicer (*apothecar'*), bailiffs of Gloucester, Walter de Bykenore, Thomas Craft, Hugh Pygon, Germand de Tonebrugg, William de Theok'.

At: Gloucester.

A2/24/16 [GC 1126]   Sun. before the nativity of St. John the Baptist, 34 Edw. I
[19 June 1306]

Richard de Munemuth, son and heir of John de Munemuth, formerly burgess of Gloucester; and Roger de Teukesbur' of Gloucester, butcher, and Agnes his wife.

Richard has leased at farm to Roger and Agnes the annual rent of 14*s.* which they pay for the holding in the shambles (*bocharia*) of Gloucester, from the feast of the nativity of St. John the Baptist [24 June] for 26 years, for a certain sum of money.

Witnesses: William de Hereford and Robert de Goldhulle, bailiffs of Gloucester, Hugh Peioun, Thomas de Bernwode, John de Combe, Roger le Heyberare, Stephen Broun.

At: Gloucester.

The Peyt rent (see also above, pp. 461–3)

A2/24/17 [GC 1718]   Tues. after St. Lucy, 3 Edw. III [16 Dec. 1309]
Richard de Monemuwe, son of John de Monemuwe, late burgess of Gloucester, and Robert Peyt, butcher, Alice his wife and William their son.

Richard has leased to Robert, Alice and William, for a certain sum of money, his shop opposite la Mundsmyth in front of the hall of William de Ryons; for their lives, rent 6*s.* a year.
Witnesses: Walter the spicer (*apothecarius*) and Peter de la Hulle, bailiffs, William de Ryons, Stephen Broun, William de Hertford, Roger de Wygemor, Thomas de Penedoc.
At: Gloucester.

A2/24/18 [GC 2531]   Tues. after St. Lucy, 3 Edw. II [16 Dec. 1309]
Richard de Monemuwe, son of John de Monemuwe, formerly burgess of Gloucester; and Robert Peyt, butcher, Alice his wife and William their son.

Richard has granted to Robert, Alice and William, for a certain sum of money, his shop opposite le Mundsmyth; for their lives, rent 6*s.* a year to the church of the Blessed Virgin of Graselon', and 2*s.* a year to Richard and his heirs.
Witnesses: Walter the spicer (*apothecarius*), Peter de la Hulle, bailiffs of Gloucester, William de Ryons, Stephen Broun, William de Hertford, Roger de Wygemore, Thomas de Penedok.
At: Gloucester.

Other

A2/24/19 [GC 1818]   Mon. after Easter Day, 4 Edw. II [12 April 1311]
Richard son and heir of John de Monemue, burgess of Gloucester, and William de Ryouns.

Richard is bound to William in £100 to pay him or his attorney at Gloucestre at the nativity of St. John the Baptist [24 June] next following, under the terms of the statute of merchants made at Actone Burnel and at Westminster.
At: Hereford.

A2/24/20 [GC 2717]   Mon. after St. Thomas the martyr, 4 Edw. III [31 Dec. 1330]
Richard de Monemuth, son and heir of the late John de Monemuth, late burgess of Gloucester, and William de Ryuns, burgess of Gloucester.

Richard has granted to William, for a certain sum of money, an annual rent of 10*s.* from a holding formerly of Roger de Teukesburi, butcher, in the shambles (*bocharia*) of the vill of Gloucestre.
Witnesses: Stephen Broun and Roger Heved, bailiffs of Gloucester, William le Spicer, Richard Schot, Roger de Ryuns, Walter de Boyfelde, John de Lilletone.
At: Gloucester.

A2/24/21 [GC 2978]   Fri. the eve of St. Simon and St. Jude, 14 Edw. III [27 Oct. 1340]
Richard son of John de Monemuta, late burgess of Gloucester, and William de Ryouns, burgess of Gloucester.

Richard has quitclaimed to William the holding with houses, buildings, shops [etc.], in the vill of Gloucestre in the south part of la Munsmyth, also 10*s.* rent from a shop which Roger le Tekysbury, butcher, formerly inhabited, also an oven with 2 stalls in Ebruggestret opposite le Lichlone, 3*s.* rent from a holding in Smythestrete, 2*s.* 8*d.* rent from a holding in Bridelone and two 12*d.* rents in Ebruggestret.
Witnesses: John Cheverel and Robert le Walour, bailiffs of Gloucester, Richard Shot, William Gruyn, William le Spicer.
At: Gloucester.

Cornwallis holdings

A2/24/22 [GC 1306]   n.d. [*temp.* Edw. I]
Henry called le Cornwaleys, burgess of Gloucester, and Margery his daughter.

Henry has granted to Margery the holding which John de Froucestre holds of him in the suburb of Gloucester, viz. in Bartone; to her and her issue.
Witnesses: Walter Sevare, Walter de Bikenor, Robert Cornish (*Cornubiensis*), John White (*Albus*), Hugh the clerk, John le Sureys, Walter the weaver (*textor*).

A2/24/23 [GC 1713]   Sun. after Michaelmas, 3 Edw. II [5 Oct. 1309]
William de Hertford of Gloucester; and Margery, Agnes and Joan, daughters and heirs of Henry le Cornwalleys of Gloucester.

William has granted to Margery, Agnes and Joan a rent of 6*d.* in Gloucestre from a shop in the Cordwainery (*Coyseria*).
Witnesses: Walter le Espicer, Peter de la Hulle, bailiffs, William de Wyghtfeld, Robert de Goldhull, Stephen Broun, Alexander de Penedok, Thomas de Penedok.
At: Gloucester.

A2/24/24 [GC 1849]   Thurs. after All Saints, 5 Edw. II [4 Nov. 1311]
Agnes daughter of Henry le Cornwalleys, late burgess of Gloucester, and Joan her sister.

Agnes has quitclaimed to Joan the curtilage which Alice their mother left to Joan in her last will.
Witnesses: Walter le Espicer and Nicholas de Housom, bailiffs of Gloucester, Robert de Standish, John Lucas, Stephen Broun, Robert le Cornwalleys, John de Froucestre.
At: Gloucester.

Dunning holdings

A2/24/25 [SC 139]   n.d. [early 13th cent.]
Richard son of Walter Kadifor and David Dunning.

Richard has granted to David, for 24 marks, all his land lying between that of Richard Burg' and that of John son of Osbert; rent 1 lb. of cumin a year at Christmas.
Witnesses: Richard Burg' and Thomas Oie, reeves, John the draper, John de Gosediches, Laurence son of Richard, Maurice Palmer, Arnold Dunning, John Dunning.

A2/24/26 [SC 310]   n.d. [*c.* 1250]
Richard son of Walter Kadifer, of Gloucester, and Alice widow of David Dunyng the younger of Gloucester.

Richard has confirmed to Alice and her heirs by David the land in Gloucester which lies between the land which was of Richard the burgess and the land which was of John son of Osbert, as in the charter made between Richard and David; rent 1 lb. of cumin a year, and for the confirmation Alice gave Richard 3 marks.
Witnesses: Richard Ayllard, Peter the burgess, Henry the burgess, William de Simeri, Stephen Cornish (*Cornubiensis*), reeve of Gloucester, Walter Hoth, Richard Blund, Walter Payn, Richard of the cellar (*de sellario*), Payn the burgess, Vincent Fardayn.

A2/24/27 [SC 121]   n.d. [early 13th cent.]
Aumfelisia daughter of John son of Osbert of Gloucester and Richard son of David Dunning of Gloucester.

Aumfelisia has quitclaimed to Richard, for 3*s.*, the lands which Walter Kadifor and David Dunning bought from Osbert the butcher (*carnifex*) and from John, Aumfelisia's father.
Witnesses: Henry the burgess, Richard Kadifer, Walter Wain, Walter de Pinnekote, Robert Bel hoste, William Gille, Geoffrey de Bathonia.

A2/24/28 [GC 1341]   n.d. [*c.* 1258?]
Maud daughter and heir of David Dunning of Gloucester; and William de Watford and
Alice his wife, Maud's mother.

Maud has granted to William and Alice all the land which David her father held opposite
'del munescmythe' of Gloucester, further an oven (*furnum*) with 3 shops in Smith Street
(*vicus fabrorum*), the land in the Jewry (*Judaismus*) of Gloucester between St. Michael's
church and the land which was of William Bruton, the land between the Jew's school and
the land which was of Bovenfaunt the Jew, the land in the Jewry between the land of the
priory of Llanthony by Gloucester and the land of Walter Bruton, all the land and buildings
in the west street; and rents of 22*s.*, 12*d.*, 5*s.*, 24*s.*, 3*s.* 6*d.*, 4*s.* from land in Travayllon, 5*s.*,
3*s.*, 4*s.* in the mercery (*merceria*), 3*s.*, 7*s.*, 9*d.*; to them and Alice's heirs; rent 2*s.* a year.
Witnesses: Roger le Onveyse and William de Chiltenham, bailiffs of Gloucester, Hugh de la
Hingeshame, John Simund, William de Toek, Alexander del Broc, Richard Fraunceys,
Thomas Burgeys, Thomas de Evesham, Geoffrey Russel, John Payn.

A2/24/29 [GC 899]   n.d. [late 13th cent.]
Maud daughter and heir of David Dunning of Gloucester and William de Watfortd.

Maud has granted and confirmed to William the grant which she made to William of
holdings and rents in Glouc'.
Witnesses: Roger le Enveyse and William de Chiltenham, bailiffs of Gloucester, John
Frimund, William de Toek, Walter de Saundon', Thomas de Evesham, Richard the clerk.

The Kingswood Abbey holding

A2/24/30 [SC 201]   n.d. [early Hen. III]
Kingswood Abbey and Ralph the fisher (*piscator*).

The abbey has granted to Ralph the land in Gloucestria which Lady Edith Slane gave in
alms to the abbey, which lies beyond the bridge of Gloucester between the hospital and the
outer rampart; rent 3*s.* a year.
Witnesses: Roger chaplain of St. Nicholas, Roger son of Cecilia, Robert Toli, Richard
Burgeis, Henry Caln, William son of Katherine, Simon son of Alfred, William son of Joel,
Gilbert the baker (*pistor*), Faricius.

A2/24/31 [SC 189]   n.d. [early Hen. III]
The monks of Kingswood Abbey and Roger son of Cecilia.

The monks have granted to Roger certain land in Gloucester which was of Ralph son of
Wibert and the land which Roger bought from his brother Nicholas, to hold at an annual
rent of 8*s.*; and Roger grants to the monks the land which Edith Slane gave them near
Gloucester Castle at an annual rent of 2*s.*
Witnesses: William Russel, reeve, Roger the chaplain, Richard Burgeis, Elias the palmer
(*palmarius*), Robert Tholi, Richeman son of Hernisus, William son of Katherine, John de
Huth. . ., Gilbert the baker (*pistor*), Walter son of Sevar.

Compton holdings

A2/24/32 [GC 3750]   Sat. the feast of St. Thomas the apostle, 5 Ric. II [21 Dec. 1381]
Thomas Comptone, burgess of the vill of Gloucester, and Joan his wife; and Walter
Shypton, butcher, burgess of the same.

Thomas and Joan have granted to Walter, his heirs and assigns their holding in the
shambles (*bocheria*) of Glouc' opposite la Munesmyth, and other holdings and rents.
Witnesses: Richard Baret and Richard Asshewell, bailiffs, William Heyberare, William
Crooke, Roger Resceyvour, Walter Markeley, John But, cordwainer.
At: Gloucester.

A2/24/33 [GC 3752; *duplicate* GC 3752*]   One week after St. Hilary, 5 Ric. II [20 Jan. 1382]
Walter Schiptone; and Thomas Comptone and Joan his wife.

Copy of final concord concerning 12 shops, 2 tofts, 28s. 8d. rent and rent of 1 lb. of pepper in Gloucestre and the suburbs; Thomas and Joan have acknowledged the right of Walter by their gift, and he has given them 100 marks.
At: Westminster.

A2/24/34 [GC 3786]   8 May 8 Ric. II [1385]
Walter Messuntre, burgess of the vill of Gloucester; and William Thomeworthe and Thomas Gregory chaplain.

Walter has quitclaimed to William and Thomas an annual rent which he recently had by grant of Thomas Comptone, burgess of the same.
Witnesses: John Pope and Roger Balle, bailiffs of the vill of Gloucester, William Harleye, Thomas Salysbury, Robert Tounesende.
At: Gloucester.

A2/24/35 [GC 3809]   Mon. 1 Oct. 10 Ric. II [1386]
Walter Shypton, burgess of Gloucester, and Thomas Comptone, burgess of Bristol.

Walter has granted to Thomas, his heirs and assigns all the lands, holdings, rents, and other appurtenances in the vill of Glouc' and the suburbs, except one holding and 4 shops in Gorelane, which John Comptone holds for life, and which he had by grant of the said Thomas and Joan his wife.
Witnesses: John Comptone and Robert Walaur, bailiffs of Gloucester, William Heybere, John Heved, Roger Receyvour, William Crook, John Pope.
At: Gloucester.

A2/24/36 [GC 3810]   5 Oct. 10 Ric. II [1386]
Walter Shypton, burgess of Gloucester, and Thomas Comptone, burgess of the same.

Walter has quitclaimed to Thomas all the lands and holdings in the vill of Glouc' and the suburbs which he recently had by grant of Thomas and Joan his wife.
Witnesses: John Comptone and Robert Walaur, bailiffs of Gloucester, John Heved, Richard Bart, Roger Receyvour, John Bannebury, Thomas Prestebury.
At: Gloucester.

A2/24/37 [GC 3894; *duplicate* GC 3895]   Mon. the feast of the Invention of Holy Cross,
                                                           18 Ric. II [3 May 1395]
Thomas Comptone, burgess of Gloucester; and Sir William Thomeworthe and Sir Thomas Gregory, chaplains.

Thomas has granted to William and Thomas, their heirs and assigns all his holdings, with houses, shops, rents [etc.], within and without the borough of Glouc'.
Witnesses: John Pope and Roger Balle, bailiffs of Gloucester, Richard Baret, William Crook, Edward Tamrun, William Harley, Thomas Salesbury, Robert Tounesende.
At: Gloucester.

A2/24/38 [GC 3896; *duplicate* GC 3897]   6 May 18 Ric. II [1395]
Thomas Comptone, burgess of Gloucester; and William Thomeworthe and Thomas Gregory, chaplains.

Thomas has quitclaimed to William and Thomas all his holdings [etc.] within and without the borough of Glouc'.
Witnesses: John Pope and Roger Balle, bailiffs of Gloucester, William Harleye, Thomas Salesbury, Robert Tounesende, Robert Swaynefeys.
At: Gloucester.

Other holdings

A2/24/39 [GC 1388]   n.d. [1265 × 1285]

Sibyl de la Grave; and German de Tonebrugge, burgess of Gloucester, and Mabel his wife.

Sibyl is bound to German and Mabel in 100 marks which he expended on her behalf during her case regarding her claim and inheritance of the land of la Grave next to Gloucester, and will pay the said 100 marks to German or Mabel or their assigns, at Glouc' in his house, within 8 days after receiving from him seisin of the land of la Grave.

Witnesses: Alexander de Bykenor and Ralph de Potel, bailiffs of Gloucester, John Pain, John Corwaleis, Walter de Sandon, Robert de Houtsun, Philip le Spicer, Peter Florie, John le Kerewerthin, Philip de Hatherl', Thomas de Henesh, John de Munemuwe, William Chose.

A2/24/40 [GC 665]   n.d. [1263–4]

John Asse, son of Hugh Asse, and Ralph le Surreys, burgess of Gloucester.

John has granted to Ralph all his garden lying between the land of Luke Cornish (*Cornubiensis*) and the land of James de Longeneya and extending to Fulbrock, and a curtilage; Ralph has given him 8 marks.

Witnesses: William de Chelteham and Philip le Spicer, bailiffs of Gloucester, Luke Cornish (*Cornubiensis*), Robert Foly, John Fage, John Asse, John Cornish, John le Surreys, John de Brochamton, William de Thigewrth, Philip Kyng, John the clerk.

A2/24/41 [GC 3559]   Fri. after the translation of St. Thomas the martyr, 38 Edw. III
[12 July 1364]

Robert Dene and John Bokeler of Gloucester.

Robert has quitclaimed to John the holding with a curtilage in Gloucestre in the lane called Oxebodelone, extending from the said lane to the north to the lane called Rosselone to the south.

Witnesses: William le Heyberere and William Croke, bailiffs of Gloucester, Thomas Wyot of Gloucester, merchant, Richard de Rycestre, Thomas Muleward, William de Heyhamstede, baker, William del Oke.

At: Gloucester.

A2/24/42 [GC 3609*]   7 Sept. 43 Edw. III [1369]

Adam ap Howell, chaplain, and William Sygryth; and Robert Palet and Katherine his wife.

Adam and William have granted to Robert and Katherine all their holdings in Wottone . . . Gloucestre and Elmor, which they had by grant of the said Robert; to them and Robert's issue . . . remainder to Helen daughter of Robert and her issue. Copy, dated at the king's court of Westminster, Easter term, 12 Ric. II [May 1389].

Witnesses: . . . John Monemouth of Paganhill, Richard his son, John Coweley, Walter Brownyng, John . . ., Thomas de Byseley.

At: Wotton.

DOWN HATHERLEY (GLOS.)

The holding was bought by Thomas (III) Lord Berkeley from Roger de Burghill at the same time as he was dealing with Burghill over the Herefordshire manors of Burghill and Tillington (below, p. 504). It appears to have been temporarily granted to Thomas's servant William de Syde and it was probably entailed, with Leckhampton and Bentham, in 1346, as is suggested by the statement that Thomas *bought* holdings in the three places in that year, 'in the names of his said Servants Goldmere, Syde and others'.[1] The manors of Over and King's Weston were certainly subject to a settlement in that year, and Bentham was granted

[1] Smyth, i. 328, probably misinterpreting a charter no longer extant which formed part of a settlement of that date.

to feoffees with the two manors, further implying that Bentham (and therefore probably Down Hatherley and Leckhampton also, since they were associated with Bentham in the statement) was entailed at the same time (above, p. 435). The three holdings of Down Hatherley, Leckhampton and Bentham were again associated in 1363, with the manors of Syde and Westonbirt, as the only lands purchased by Thomas (III) in which his widow Katherine did not have jointure and in which she was therefore claiming dower (below, p. 488). Like all the rest, Down Hatherley passed to her son John de Berkeley of Beverston.

A2/25/1 [GC 2632*]   Morrow of All Saints, 1 Edw. III [2 Nov. 1327]
Thomas de Berkel'; and Roger de Burghull and Sibyl his wife.
    Final concord concerning 1 carucate of land in Dounhatherle, which William de Hathewy and Agnes his wife hold for their lives; Roger and Sibyl have acknowledged the right of Thomas, and have granted to him the reversion after the deaths of William and Agnes; Thomas has given Roger and Sibyl 10 marks.
At: York.

A2/25/2 [GC 2848]   Mon. after St. Barnabas, 10 Edw. III [17 June 1336]
(1) Thomas lord of Berkel'; (2) William Hathewy; (3) Sir William de Syde.
    Whereas William Hathewy has granted to William de Syde, for ½ mark, the villein Walter Mays with his issue and chattels, and also all the land that Alice Mays, mother of Walter, formerly held in villeinage in Dounhatherly, for the lives of William [Hathewy] and Agnes his wife, Thomas has quitclaimed the said villein and land to William [de Syde].
Witnesses: William de Chiltenham, Robert Dabetot, Henry de Clifford, John de Clyve, Thomas Pricke.
At: Berkeley.

A2/25/3 [GC 3252]   n.d. [*c*. June 1336]
William Hathewy and Sir William de Syde.
    William Hathewy has sold to William de Syde, for a certain sum of money, all his goods and chattels in the lands and holdings which Alice Mays recently held of him in villeinage in Dounhatherley.

HILLSLEY, IN HAWKESBURY (GLOS.)

William de Cheltenham clearly sold the advowson of the chapel of St. Giles to the Berkeley lords, and most probably to Maurice (IV) (d. 1368), to whom he sold the manors of Little Marshfield and Purton and the advowson of Purton chapel. Thomas (IV) died holding the advowson of the chapel in 1417. See also above, A1/1/62 [GC 4427*].

GRANTS BY WILLIAM DE CHELTENHAM

A2/26/1 [GC 2962]   Two weeks after Michaelmas, 13 Edw. III [13 Oct. 1339]
William de Chiltenham; and Walter de Hortone and his wife Eleanor.
    Final concord concerning a messuage, 2 carucates of land, 3 a. of meadow and 24*s.* of rent in Haukesbury; Walter and Eleanor have granted it to William, and have quitclaimed her dower; William has given them £20.
At: Westminster.

A2/26/2 [SC 542]   n.d. [*c*. Michaelmas 1365]
Abbot Peter [de Broadway] and the abbey of Pershore; and William de Chiltenham.
    Whereas William is the patron of the chantry chapel of St. Giles, Hildesley, and whereas it has been destroyed by pestilence, the abbey has granted him licence to grant 3 messuages, 3 virgates of land, a mill and 20*s.* rent in Hildeslee and Sedlewode, which he holds of them, for the support of the chantry.

A2/26/3 [SC 543]   Mon. after Michaelmas, 39 Edw. III [6 Oct. 1365]
William de Chiltenham and John Wouweston, chaplain of St. Giles's chantry.

By licence of the king and Pershore Abbey, William has granted to John and his successors in the chapel of St. Giles of Hildesleye, 3 messuages, 3 virgates of land, a mill and 20s. rent in Hildesleye and Sedlewode, for the souls of himself and his ancestors and the lords of Berkeley.

Witnesses: Elias Berleye, John Joye, Thomas Skay, Robert Chalkleye, Nicholas Chausy.
At: Pucklechurch.

LEASES BY THE CHAPLAINS

A2/26/4 [GC 3672]   Thurs. [*sic*] the feast of the Circumcision, 48 Edw. III [1 Jan. 1375]
John Wonastone, chantry chaplain of Hillsley, and John Hontteleye.

John Wonastone has leased to John Hontteleye a messuage with curtilage and 6 a. of land in Hildesleye; for his life, rent 4s. a year.

Witnesses: Geoffrey Wynnebolt, John Pyghe, Richard Pope, Roger Barabast, Richard Newemon.
At: Hillsley.

A2/26/5 [GC 4344]   Michaelmas, 7 Edw. IV [29 Sept. 1467]
Robert Shypper, chaplain of Hillsley chantry; and John Stane and Joan his wife.

Robert has leased to John and Joan the holding in Hyldysley in which they live; to them and their son Richard, for their lives, rent 13s. 4d. a year.

A2/26/6 [GC 4361]   2 March 49 Hen. VI and 1 of the re-adeption [1471]
Robert Schypper, chaplain of the Hillsley chantry; and Edward Hore, Alice his wife and Robert his son.

Robert has leased to Edward, Alice and Robert a messuage, 1 virgate of land and a meadow called Wastmede in Sedylwode; for their lives, rent 20s. a year.

Witnesses: Thomas Forster, John Stane, William Slyke.
At: Hillsley.

LAUNCESPLACE IN HAWKESBURY, MORETON VALENCE AND TYTHERINGTON

A2/26/7 [GC 3170]   Wed. after the conversion of St. Paul, 22 Edw. III [30 Jan. 1348]
Walter Launce of Moreton Valence; and Nicholas le Heyward of Putloe, Edith his wife and John their son.

Walter has granted to Nicholas, Edith and John, and their heirs and assigns, all his lands and holdings [etc.], within the manor of Mortone Valence, also all his lands [etc.], in the vill of Haukesbury which he inherited after the death of his brother John, and the reversion of lands and holdings in the vill of Tyderyntone which Roger Heynes and Margery his wife hold for life.

Witnesses: Richard Fraunceys, Nicholas Ket, John atte Gorste, Walter de Stanedysch, John de Clyfford, Peter le Frensch.
At: Moreton Valence.

A2/26/8 [GC 3171]   Wed. after the conversion of St. Paul, 22 Edw. III [30 Jan. 1348]
(1) Walter Launce; (2) John le Chapmon of Epney; (3) Nicholas le Heyward of Putloe, Edith his wife and John their son.

Walter has appointed John to give seisin to Nicholas, Edith and John of the lands in Mortone Valence, Haukesbury and Tyderyntone.

Witnesses: Richard Fraunceys, Nicholas Ket, John atte Gorste, Walter de Stanedysch, John de Clyfford, Peter le Frensch.
At: Moreton Valence.

A2/26/9 [GC 4171]   St. Martin, 11 Hen. VI [11 Nov. 1432]
John Selewode, chaplain of the Hillsley chantry; and John Gardyner of Upton and Alice his wife.

John Selewode has leased to John and Alice the messuage called Launcesplace in Stoke with the croft and garden; for their lives, rent 8*s.* a year.
Witnesses: Thomas Wynbold, Richard Russell, John Baldon, Richard Hunteley.
At: Hillsley.

OTHER

A2/26/10 [SC 94]   n.d. [1203 × 1210]
Henry Levet and Master Absolom de Almoneremunstre, rector of Hawkesbury.

After arbitration by W[illiam] abbot of Bordcslcy, W[illiam de Verdun] archdeacon of Gloucester and R[alph de Evesham] prior of Worcester, arbitrators appointed by Pope Innocent III, Henry and Absolom have agreed concerning a chapel built in Henry's court in Hildesley and parish rights belonging to Haukesbury church.
Witnesses: Henry chaplain of Hampton, Richard chaplain of Stretford, William de Eth', Philip chaplain of Haukesbury, Master Gilbert de Elsecote, Richard parson of Bradeforde, Maurice the clerk of Almonemunstre, Bunduphilip the clerk of Wyth, Richard de Ecdesale, William his son, Stephen de Upton, William son of Robert de Coldecote, Alard the clerk, Walter the clerk of Hildesley, William le Skay, John Madina, John de Chalkesley, Walter de Upton.

HORTON (GLOS.)

Thomas (IV) Lord Berkeley (d. 1417) bought from Robert Stanshawe and Isabel his wife a messuage, 20 a. of land, 8 a. of meadow and 5 a. of wood in Horton and Yate, a transaction formalised in a fine of Easter 1412.[1] It formed part of the lands granted by him to feoffees three weeks before his death: below, A2/77/14 [SC 581].

A2/27/1 [GC 3257]   n.d. [early 15th cent.]
Thomas Berkeley, lord of Berkeley, and Nicholas Alderlegh.

Thomas has granted to Nicholas, for his good services, a toft with land, meadow [etc.], in the vill of Horton and Yate which Thomas recently acquired from R. Stanshawe; for his life . . . [*Unfinished*].

LECKHAMPTON (GLOS.)

Although there is no record of the purchase of the holding by Thomas (II) Lord Berkeley (d. 1321) it may be the same as that held earlier by Thomas de Monmouth, since it paid the same rent to the same landlord (Fécamp Abbey). It was granted to Maurice (III)'s younger son John de Berkeley, who forfeited it in 1322 and died without issue in 1336, when the holding reverted to his eldest brother Thomas (III). Thomas then entailed it, with Down Hatherley and Bentham, in 1346 and it passed to the Beverston cadet line: see also above, p. 468, Down Hatherley, and below, p. 487, Syde.

A2/28/1 [GAR 304] Account roll   11–12 Edw. III [1337–8]

LYDNEY (GLOS.)

See below, p. 503, Yorkley.

THE WEBBE HOLDING

A2/29/1 [GC 3100]   12 Sept. 18 Edw. III [1344]
John son of William le Webbe of Lydney and Sir Thomas, lord of Berkelee.

John has granted to Thomas, his heirs and assigns 2 a. of land in the field called Inlond,

[1] PRO CP 25/1/79/85, no. 57.

which he had by grant of Walter son of Stephen de Nasse, in Lydeneye.
Witnesses: William Bray, Philip Longe, James de Boxe, John le Whyte, Henry Crompe.
At: Lydney.

A2/29/2 [GC 3715]   n.d. [*c.* Sept. 1344]
John Stephenes of Nass and Sir Thomas, lord of Berkelee.

John has quitclaimed to Thomas 2 a. . . ., which Thomas had by grant of John le Webbe of Neuwarth in Lydeneye.
Witnesses: William de Chiltenham, Philip le Longe, Henry Crompe, John de Clyve, John de Auste.

THE BOTER HOLDING

A2/29/3 [GC 3355]   n.d. [*c.* 1345]
(1) John Boter; (2) Sir Robert de Home, vicar of Lydney, Robert Groundy and Henry le Gardiner; (3) Sir Thomas, lord of Berkelee.

John has appointed Robert, Robert and Henry to give seisin to Thomas of 3½ a. of meadow in Lydeneye and an annual rent of 7*s.* 9*d.*

A2/29/4 [GC 3310]   n.d. [*c.* 1345]
Richard de Home and Sir Thomas, lord of Berkelee.

Richard has quitclaimed to Thomas 3½ a. of meadow in Lydeneye and a rent of 7*s.* 9*d.*, which Thomas had by grant of John Boter in Lydeneye.
Witnesses: William Bray, John de Auste, Philip le Longe, William Waryn, Thomas de Home.

A2/29/5 [GC 1417]   n.d. [*c.* 1345]
(1) Richard de Home; (2) Sir John Boter; (3) Sir Thomas de Berkelee.

Richard has rendered up to John, to the use of Thomas, 3½ a. of meadow which he had by grant of Robert Boter, father of John, for his life; and further has rendered up to John a rent of 7*s.* 9*d.* in Lydeneye, which he held of John for life.

A2/29/6 [GC 3122]   Feast of the Assumption, 19 Edw. III [15 Aug. 1345]
Richard Home of Lydney and John Boter parson of Staunden.

Richard has quitclaimed to John a rent of 7*s.* 9*d.* a year in the parish of Lyden', and 3½ a. of meadow in the same parish which he had for his life by grant of Robert Bot', beside the meadow of Sir Thomas de Berkeleye, knight.
Witnesses: William Bray, Philip le Longe, William Waryn, Thomas Home, Walter Achard.
At: Lydney.

A2/29/7 [GC 3123]   Wed. after the Assumption, 19 Edw. III [17 Aug. 1345]
Sir Robert de Home, vicar of Lydney, and Sir Thomas, lord of Berkelee.

Robert has received from Thomas, by the hand of Sir Philip de Hurste, chaplain, 20 marks, and Robert has granted to Thomas 3½ a. of meadow and an annual rent of 7*s.* 9*d.* in Lydeney of the inheritance of Sir John Boter. [*In French.*]
At: Berkeley.

THE WARYN HOLDING IN LYDNEY, TUTNALLS AND NASS

A2/29/8 [GC 3351]   n.d. [*c.* 1350]
Thomas Waryn, son and heir of Henry Waryn of Lydney, and Sir Thomas, lord of Berkele.

Thomas Waryn has granted to Thomas de Berkele, his heirs and assigns, all the lands, holdings, rents and reversions which he had in Lydeneye, Tokenhale and Nasse of the fee of Philip de Mondevylle.
Witnesses: Sir Edmund de Clyvedon, Sir Simon Basset, knights, William de Chiltenham, John de Clyve, John Joce, and Philip le Longe.

A2/29/9 [GC 3352]   n.d. [*c.* 1350]
Thomas Waryn, son and heir of Henry Waryn of Lydney, and Sir Thomas, lord of Berkele.

Thomas Waryn has granted to Thomas de Berkele, his heirs and assigns all the lands, holdings, rents and reversions which he had in Lydeneye, Tokenhale and Nasse of the fee of Philip de Moundevylle, which he recovered by an assize of novel disseisin at Gloucester.
Witnesses: Sir Edmund de Clyvedon, Sir Simon Basset, knights, William de Chiltenham, John de Clyve, John Joce, and Philip le Longe.

A2/29/10 [GC 3243]   Sat. after St. Peter in chains, 24 Edw. III [7 Aug. 1350]
(1) Thomas Waryn, son and heir of Henry Waryn of Lydney; (2) Philip le Longe and Walter Auste; (3) Sir Thomas, lord of Berkele.

Thomas Waryn has appointed Philip and Walter to give seisin of all the lands, holdings, rents [etc.], which he had in Lydeneye, Tokenhale and Nasse to Thomas, lord of Berkele.
At: Berkeley.

LITTLE MARSHFIELD (GLOS.)

Smyth records that the manor was acquired by Thomas (III) and granted to his servant William de Cheltenham for life, but he says the same of the manor of Purton (below, p. 480) which Cheltenham certainly purchased and sold to Maurice (IV) Lord Berkeley (d. 1368). It is likely, therefore, that the reversion of Little Marshfield was also bought by Maurice (IV) from Cheltenham, for settlement on Maurice's younger son James. James died in 1405 leaving his son James to succeed as his brother Thomas (IV)'s heir male in 1417. Little Marshfield, together with Daglingworth and a moiety of Brokenborough (Glos.) and the lordship of Talgarth (Brecon.) were the subject of a number of settlements in the 1430s on James's three younger sons, Thomas, James and Maurice, although in Nov. 1440 Brokenborough and Daglingworth, and in Jan. 1441 Little Marshfield, were granted by James and his wife Isabel to Nicholas Poyntz and his wife Elizabeth. The grant was later the subject of a dispute between Maurice (V), the last surviving son of James Lord Berkeley, and his son Maurice (VI) on the one hand, and a later Nicholas Poyntz on the other, the solution to which was that Maurice was to have Daglingworth and half of the moiety of Brokenborough while Poyntz was to have Little Marshfield and the other half of the moiety of Brokenborough.

A2/30/1 [GC 924]   n.d. [early 14th cent.]
Felicia de Heydune, widow of Sir Richard de Heydune, knight, and Richard de Heydune, her son.

Felicia has granted to Richard all her land in Parva Marsfeld, which she and her late husband had by grant of the late Sir Gilbert de Clare, earl of Gloucester and Hertford, with the dower of Joan de Turbervile, widow of John de Turbervile, when it falls in.
Witnesses: Sir John de la Ryvere, Sir William Russel, knights, Richard Bacun, Thomas Payn, Robert le Bayllif, William de Dauntesey, Peter le Bule.

A2/30/2 [GC 2465]   Sun. before All Saints, 19 Edw. II [27 Oct. 1325]
Richard de Heydone, son of Sir Richard de Heydone, knight; and Alexander de Hunsingowere and Isabel his wife.

Richard has granted to Alexander and Isabel his manor in Westmarsfeld (Glos.) with all the appurtenances; for their lives, rent £10 a year, with remainder to Isabel de Hingstrugge and her issue at the same rent while Richard lives, with successive contingent remainders to Alexander son of John de Heydone and his issue, to Felicia daughter of the said John de Heydone and her issue, to Richard son of John de Heydone and his issue, and to the grantor's own right heirs.
Witnesses: Sir Robert de Noers, Sir John Gerberge, knights, Philip de Noethone, John

Daunce, John de Snoyshil, Hugh de Heyhawe of Norfolk, and John de Staundene, Thomas Wittokesmede, Thomas Payn of Gloucestershire.
At: 'Stiburde'.

A2/30/3 [GC 3593]   Mon. after St. John before the Latin Gate, 41 Edw. III [10 May 1367]
William de Westhale and William Smalcombe; and William de Chiltenham.

   William de Westhale and William Smalcombe have leased to William de Chiltenham the manor of Parva Marsfelde, for his life, with remainder to Maurice de Berkele, lord of Berkeley, for life, and to James his son and his male issue, James's brother Maurice and his male issue, and the right heirs of Maurice de Berkele, lord of Berkeley.
Witnesses: Sir John Tracy, Sir Nicholas de Berkele, knights, John Serjant, John Stanschawe, John Joye.

A2/30/4 [GC 4270]   17 Sept. 29 Hen. VI [1450]
(1) Nicholas Poyntz esquire and Elizabeth his wife; (2) John Stokes and John Bury; (3) Maurice Berkeley of Beverston, knight, Maurice Denys, Matthew de la Hay, esquires, Thomas Gilmyn and John Andrews.

Nicholas and Elizabeth have appointed John and John to deliver seisin to Maurice, Maurice, Matthew, Thomas and John of their manor of Parva Mersshefeld (Glos.), as by their charter dated 17 Sept. 29 Henry VI.

MINCHINHAMPTON (GLOS.)

Lucy de Tytherington granted all her lands in Minchinhampton and in St. Chloe and Dryleaze (both in Minchinhampton) to Thomas (III) Lord Berkeley around 1350: below, A2/37/17 [GC 3347]; cf. A2/37/12, 14 [GC 2367, GC 2940]. See also above, A1/1/47 [GC 4146*].

JENETESCROFTE

A2/31/1 [GC 966]   n.d. [*temp.* Edw. I]
Walter Spilemon of Rodborough and John son of Roger Mael.

   Walter has granted to John his meadow called Hokedemede with his assart of Amberley and a rent of 8*d.* from John for Chenetescrofte, in exchange for the rent of Richard Wyt and John le Neveue; rent 14*d.* a year for Amberley and 8*d.* a year for Chenetescrofte.
Witnesses: Elias de Rodeber', John Achard, John de Seyncleye, Richard de Nayleswrthe, Alan de Forewode, John de Chalcforde, William Houtemer.

A2/31/2 [SC 395]   n.d. [*temp.* Edw. I]
William de Ponte and John Mayel.

   William has quitclaimed to John a croft and assart called Jenetescroft which he held from Walter Spilemon.
Witnesses: Henry de Lupiate, John de Chalford, John de Sentleye.

A2/31/3 [GC 1473]   n.d. [early 14th cent.]
John Mael of St. Chloe and Justine his daughter.

   John has granted to Justine two assarts, one called Longerudingg' and the other called Chenetescrofte, for 4 marks, to her and her issue.
Witnesses: Adam Spilemon, John de Rodeber', John de Seyntel', Richard Elivant, William de Sentel'.

A2/31/4 [GC 2477]   n.d. [early Edw. III]
John de Bentham; and William de Tydryntone and Lucy his wife.

   John has granted to William and Lucy, their heirs and assigns, his two crofts in the manor of Munechenehamtone, one called Langgerudynge and the other called Jetuscroft.
Witnesses: Hugh de Rodberwe, Elias de Aylbryntone, Robert Kynne, Richard Toumbes, Thomas Elivaunt.

OTHER

A2/31/5 [SC 186]   n.d. [early Hen. III]

John de Seyncleye and William son of Walter Symon.

John has granted to William the messuage in Hamton Monialium which Walter used to hold, the land called le Duppemor near the Wodecroft, pasture for 2 oxen and one horse [etc.]; rent 5*s.* 6*d.* a year and William has given John 2 marks.

Witnesses: John Bachard, Walter Spyleman, Thomas de Rodebur', John Mahel, Richard de Nayleswrthe.

MURCOTT AND HARTPURY (GLOS.)

The holding at Murcott and Hartpury remained with the cadet line based at Wymondham (Leics.) and was again entailed by a later Berkeley holder in 1374, with the Arlingham rents and fisheries which Thomas (II) Lord Berkeley also granted to his younger son Thomas, the founder of the branch. See above, A1/11/11 [SC 483].

A2/32/1 [GC 1912]   24 April 6 Edw. II [1313]

(1) James de Berkeleye; (2) William de Gamage and John de Helyon; (3) William Durant.

James has appointed William and John his attorneys to take seisin from William of a messuage, land, meadow, pasture, toft and rent in Morkote and Hardepirie, which were of Richard de Byseleye and which William recovered against Richard and his wife Rose in the court of St. Briavell, and has granted to James.

At: Berkeley.

A2/32/2 [GC 1920]   12 May 6 Edw. II [1313]

William Durant and Master James de Berkelee.

William has quitclaimed to James the messuage, land, meadow, pasture, wood and rent in Morcote and Hardepurie which he recovered against Richard de Biseleie and Rose his wife in the court of St. Briavell, and afterwards demised to James.

Witnesses: Sir John de Buttone, Sir Miles de Rodeberwe, Sir William de Wauton, knights, Walter de Nasse, Peter de Helion, John de Helion, William de Gamage, Ralph Hathewy, Richard le Blount of Awre.

At: Gloucester.

A2/32/3 [GC 1922]   24 May 6 Edw. II [1313]

James de Berkelee, son of Sir Thomas de Berkelee, and Sir Thomas his lord and father.

James has granted to Thomas the messuage, land, meadow, pasture, wood and rent in Morcote and Hardepurie which he had by demise of William Durant and which William recovered against Richard de Biseleie and Rose his wife in the court of St. Briavell.

Witnesses: Sir John de Buttone, Sir Miles de Rodeberwe, Sir William de Wauton, knights, Walter de Nasse, Peter de Helion, John de Helion, William de Gamage, Ralph Hathewy, Richard le Blount of Awre.

At: Berkeley.

A2/32/4 [GC 1925]   1 June 6 Edw. II [1313]

Richard de Biseleie, Rose his wife and Hugh their son; and Sir Thomas de Berkelee, lord of Berkeley.

Richard, Rose and Hugh have quitclaimed to Thomas a messuage, land, meadow, pasture, wood and rent in Morcote and Hardepurie, which Thomas had by grant of Master James de Berkelee, his son, and which James had by demise of William Durant.

Witnesses: Sir John de Buttone, Sir Miles de Rodeberwe, Sir William de Wauton, knights, Walter de Nasse, Peter de Helion, John de Helion, Roger de Aldewike, John Notelyn, William de Gamage, Ralph Hathewy, John de la Hay.

At: Berkeley.

A2/32/5 [GC 1981]   1 June 7 Edw. II [1314]
Sir Thomas son of Sir Thomas de Berkeleye; and William de Gamage and Isabel his wife.

Thomas has leased to William and Isabel, for their lives, his holding at Morcote and Hardepurie; rent £4 a year, beginning at the Nativity of St. John the Baptist, 7 Edw. II [24 June 1314].
Witnesses: Peter de Helion, Walter de Nasse, Odo de Acton, John le Boteler, John de Abbehale, Richard de Haydon, Ralph Hathewy.
At: Berkeley.

A2/32/6 [GC 2007]   1 Feb. 8 Edw. II [1315]
Thomas de Berkeleye, lord of Berkeley; and William Gamage and Isabel his wife.

Thomas has inspected the charter of his son Thomas de Berkeleye to William and Isabel concerning Thomas's holding at Morcote and Hardepurie, and has confirmed it; and if the said Thomas the younger dies without male issue, or if his male issue dies before William and Isabel, then the holding ought to revert to Thomas the elder and the rent of £4 a year will be paid to Thomas the elder and his heirs.
Witnesses: Peter de Helyon, Walter de Nasse, John le Botiler, Thomas de Bradeston, Peter de Styntescombe, Walter Sewaker, John le Serjant.
At: Berkeley.

A2/32/7 [SC 488]   12 May 17 Edw. II [1324]
King Edward II; and Robert de Aston and John de Hampton.

The king orders Robert and John to hold an inquiry into the terms of an agreement made by Thomas de Berkeley the elder with Hugh de Bysele, for Hugh's support as one of Thomas's esquires.
At: Westminster.

A2/32/8 [SC 489]   Wed. after Trinity, 17 Edw. II [13 June 1324]
Inquisition held before Robert de Astone and John de Hamptone, by order of the king's writ, concerning the grant of support as one of his esquires by Thomas de Berkeley the elder to Hugh de Biseleye, in return for a grant by Richard de Biseleye, Hugh's father, to Thomas of a messuage and 1 carucate in Morcote and Hardpirie, value 6 marks a year, which Thomas later granted to his son Thomas; the support of Hugh valued at 106*s.* 5½*d.* a year, or 3½*d.* a day, of his man at 45*s.* 7½*d.* a year, or 1½*d.* a day, and of the horse 76*s.*, or 2½*d.* a day, and two furred robes a year at Christmas and Whitsun or 36*s.*; total £13 4*s.* 1½*d.*
At: Bristol.

A2/32/9 [GC 2579]   n.d. [1346 × 1358]
Thomas lord of Berkelee; and Philip Holeberwe, vicar of Hartpury, and Adam Thynchul.

Thomas has leased to Philip and Adam the custody of all the lands and holdings which were of Sir John de Berkelee at Morcot' in Hardepyrye which are in Thomas's hands through the minority of the heir of the said John; to hold until the full age of the heir, rent 5 marks a year.

NAILSWORTH (GLOS.)

The charter below is presumably connected with Thomas (III)'s acquisitions from the Mael family in neighbouring Minchinhampton and St. Chloe.

A2/33/1 [GC 1536]   n.d. [*temp.* Edw. I]
William Savyn of Nailsworth; and John Mayel and Nichola his wife.

William has leased to John and Nichola, for their lives, half of his mill in Neylesworth; rent 3*d.* a year.
Witnesses: Adam Spilemon, John de Chalford, Richard Helindunt, Thomas de la Hortene, Richard . . .

NASS, IN LYDNEY (GLOS.)

See below, p. 503, Yorkley.

A2/34/1 [GC 3154]   14 Nov. 20 Edw. III [1346]
Sir Thomas de Berkele, lord of Berkeley, and Walter de Nasse, lord of Nass.

Whereas Walter is bound to Thomas in a rent of 26s. 8d. a year from his manor of Nasse, Thomas wills that if Walter pays the rent annually until £12 2s. 8d. is paid, then the bond will be void.
At: Nass.

OVER, IN ALMONDSBURY (GLOS.)

Over was one of the manors granted by FitzHarding to his son Robert and was bought by Thomas (III) from Thomas ap Adam, Robert's descendant, in 1330. Like most of Thomas (III)'s purchases, it was entailed on his younger sons and passed to the cadet line of Beverston. See also above, pp. 147, Beverston, 298, King's Weston.

UNDATED ENTAIL OF OVER, KING'S WESTON AND BENTHAM

A2/35/1 [GC 3277]   n.d. [mid 14th cent.]
Thomas lord of Berkelee; and William de Syde and Walter Goldemere.

Thomas has granted to William and Walter, and their heirs and assigns, all the lands, holdings, rents [etc.], which he has in Ovre, Kyngeswestone and Benetham (Glos.).
Witnesses: William de Chiltenham, John de Clyve, Henry de Clyfford, Robert Groundy, William Curteys.

A2/35/2 [GC 3344]   n.d. [mid 14th cent.]
(1) William de Syde and Walter Goldemere; (2) Thomas de Sambourne; (3) Thomas lord of Berkelee.

William and Walter have appointed Thomas de Sambourne to receive seisin of the lands, holdings, rents, villeins and all other goods and chattels which they had by grant of Thomas de Berkelee in Ovre, Kyngesweston and Benetham (Glos.).

ENTAIL OF OVER, 1344

A2/35/3 [GC 3105]   Tues. the feast of St. Andrew, 18 Edw. III [30 Nov. 1344]
(1) Walter Goldemere; (2) Sir William de Tettebur' chaplain; (3) William de Syde.

Walter has appointed William de Tettebur' to give seisin to William de Syde of the manor of Overe.
At: Berkeley.

A2/35/4 [GC 3106]   Tues. the feast of St. Andrew, 18 Edw. III [30 Nov. 1344]
(1) William de Syde; (2) William Curteis, Robert Groundy and Thomas de Samborne; (3) Walter Goldemere.

William has appointed William, Robert and Thomas to receive seisin of the manor of Overe which he had by grant of Walter Goldemere.
At: Berkeley.

ENTAIL OF OVER AND KING'S WESTON, 1349

A2/35/5 [GC 3225]   Two weeks after Easter, 27 Edw. III [7 April 1353]
Thomas son of Maurice de Berkele, Katherine his wife and Thomas their son; and Thomas de Besseford, parson of Beverston, Roger de Estham and John le Vey, clerk.

Final concord, made a month after Easter 23 Edw. III [10 May 1349] and granted two weeks after Easter 27 Edw. III, concerning the manors of Ovre and Kyngesweston, which William de Side holds for life; Thomas and Roger have granted the reversion after William's death to Thomas and Katherine and Thomas and the male issue of Thomas the son, with remainder to the male issue of Thomas and Katherine, and of Ovre to the right heirs of

Thomas the father, and of Kyngeswestone to Alphonse de Berkeleye[1] and his male issue, and the right heirs of Thomas the father.
At: Westminster.

A2/35/6 [GC 3222]   n.d. [c. April 1353]
(1) Maurice, eldest son of Sir Thomas de Berkeleye, lord of Berkeley; (2) [the said] Thomas de Berkeleye, Katherine his wife and Thomas their son; (3) Thomas de Besseford, parson of Beverston, Roger de Estham and John le Vey, clerk.

Maurice has ratified the agreement made in the king's court at Westminster at Easter 23 Edw. III and afterwards at Easter 27 Edw. III [as above, A2/35/5 (GC 3225)].
Witnesses: Sir Thomas de Berkeleye of Uley, Sir Simon Basset, Sir Peter de Veel, Sir John Tracy, knights, William de Chiltenham.

LEASES

A2/35/7 [GC 3245]   Mon. after All Saints, 24 Edw. III [8 Nov. 1350]
Sir William de Syde and Sir Thomas, lord of Berkelee.

William has leased to Thomas the manors of Kyngeswestone and Ovre for the life of William; rent 40 marks a year.
Witnesses: Sir Simon Basset, William de Chiltenham, Thomas de Gydeforde, John de Clyve, Robert Groundy.
At: Berkeley.

A2/35/8 [GC 2582]   n.d. [1330 × 1350]
Thomas lord of Berkeleye; and John Olyfer and Edith his wife.

Thomas has leased to John and Edith a messuage and 10 a. of land which Alice Rycheman previously held in Overe; for their lives, rent 12s. a year to Thomas for his life and after his death to his son Thomas and his male issue, and John and Edith have given Thomas 10 marks.

A2/35/9 [GC 3269]   n.d. [mid 14th cent.]
Thomas lord of Berkelee; and Thomas Lovote and Christine his wife.

Thomas has leased to Thomas and Christine a messuage and a half-virgate of land which John Lovote, father of Thomas, previously held by charter of Sir Thomas ap Adam in Ovre; for their lives, rent 16s. a year.
Witnesses: Thomas Gydeford, Robert Polyng, Thomas Lovote, John Stoke, Thomas Mareys.

A2/35/10 [GC 3357]   12 Jan. 24 Edw. III [1351]
Sir Thomas lord of Berkelee; and Robert Polyng, Joan his wife and Alice their daughter.

Thomas has leased to Robert, Joan and Alice the lands and holdings which Adam Neel previously held in the manor of Ovre; for their lives, rent 26s. 8d. a year.
Witnesses: Edmund de Brokenbergh, Ralph le Waleys, John Pesshun, William atte Wode, Thomas Mareys, John atte Wode.
At: Over.

A2/35/11 [GC 3358]   20 Jan. 24 Edw. III [1351]
Thomas lord of Berkelee and lord of Over and John le Mareys.

Thomas has leased to John and his first wife the holding which Henry Batecoke formerly held in the manor of Overe in the salt marsh; for their lives, rent 16s. a year.
Witnesses: John de Westone, Thomas Gideforde, Richard de Halkeleye, Thomas de Hawe, John Pessoun, Thomas le Mareys.
At: Over.

---

[1] Alphonse was probably a younger son of Thomas (III)'s younger brother Maurice de Berkeley of Stoke Gifford who had died, apparently at the siege of Calais, in Feb. 1347, leaving a young family.

A2/35/12 [GC 3367]   Mon. after St. Barnabas, 25 Edw. III [13 June 1351]
Thomas lord of Berkelee and of Over and John Stodfolde.

Thomas has leased to John and his first wife the holding which Robert Stodfolde his father formerly held in the salt marsh within the manor of Overe, except for 7 a. of land in the west part of Cheselepulle; for their lives, rent 12s. 7d. a year.
Witnesses: John de Westone, Thomas Gedforde, John Pessoun, Thomas le Mareys, John le Mareys.
At: Over.

A2/35/13 [GC 3407]   10 Nov. 27 Edw. III [1353]
Thomas de Berkelegh, lord of Berkeley; and Richard Dodyng and Juliana his wife.

Thomas has leased to Richard and Juliana the messuage and 10 a. of land and meadow which Robert le Leche sometime held in Overe; for their lives, rent 10s. a year.
Witnesses: Edmund de Brokenbergh, Ralph Waleys, John Pesscham, Thomas Mareys, Thomas Lovete.
At: Over.

A2/35/14 [GC 3431]   10 July 29 Edw. III [1355]
Thomas lord of Berkele; and William Dodyng, Edith his wife and William their son.

Thomas has leased to William, Edith and William a messuage and a half-virgate of land, which Edith widow of John Tillare previously held of Thomas in Overe; for their lives, rent 14s. a year.
At: Over.

A2/35/15 [GC 4174; *duplicate* GC 4175]   Christmas Eve, 12 Hen. IV [24 Dec. 1433]
James Berkeley, knight, lord of Berkeley; and John Cosham, Christine his wife and Thomas his son.

James has leased to John, Christine and Thomas a half-acre toft with land [etc.] in the east part of Cheselpull and a half acre of land in Chilsan; for their lives, rent to Almondsbury chantry 3s. 2d. a year.
At: Almondsbury.

ACCOUNT ROLLS

A2/35/16 [GAR 314]   n.d. [1334–5]
A2/35/17 [GAR 315]   11–12 Edw. III [1337–8]
A2/35/18 [GAR 316]   Michaelmas–12 June 20 Edw. III [1345–6]
A2/35/19 [GAR 317]   12 June–Michaelmas 20 Edw. III [1346]
With two indentures dated Michaelmas 19 Edw. III and 12 June 20 Edw. III, and a memorandum of fines.
A2/35/20 [GAR 318]   n.d. [1346–7]

OTHER

A2/35/21 [GC 2834]   Sun. after St. Andrew, 9 Edw. III [3 Dec. 1335]
Elias de Aylbertone and Joan his wife; and Sir Thomas de Berkeleye, lord of Berkeley.

Elias and Joan have quitclaimed to Thomas an annuity of £10 from the manor of Overe (Glos.) for their lives, which they had by grant of Sir Thomas ap Adam.
Witnesses: Thomas de Agmundesham, Henry de Brokworth, Robert Dapitot, John son of Nichol, Walter de Cumbe, John de Clyve, William de Tyderintone.
At: Berkeley.

A2/35/22 [GC 2873]   1 June 11 Edw. III [1337]
Thomas lord of Berkelee and Sir William de Tettebury, chaplain of Over chapel.[1]

---

[1] Thomas founded a chapel at Over in 1337, shortly after the death of his first wife Margaret Mortimer: Smyth, i. 334; cf. below, A2/35/23 [SC 514].

Thomas has granted to William and his successors celebrating in Thomas's chapel of Ovre a rent of 16s. a year from the manor of Ovre, for the life of John atte Walle of Ovre and Maud his wife.
At: Over.

A2/35/23 [SC 514]   12 March 19 Edw. III [1345]
King Edward III and Thomas de Berkele.

The king has granted to Thomas licence to grant a messuage and 2 virgates of land in Overe, which he holds of the Crown in chief, for the support of a chaplain in the chapel at Overe to celebrate divine service every day for the souls of Thomas and Margaret his late wife.
At: Westminster.

PURTON, IN LYDNEY[1] (GLOS.)

Purton was bought by Maurice (IV) Lord Berkeley from William de Cheltenham (who had bought it from Thomas ap Adam in 1328) and, although it was possibly intended for a younger son, Maurice, who died early (see above, p. 473, Little Marshfield), it passed to Thomas (IV). As it was not entailed, it probably passed in 1417 to Thomas's daughter Elizabeth, countess of Warwick. That would explain, in part at least, the account from Newland of 1436–7 for the earl of Warwick. See also above, pp. 147, Beverston, and below, p. 527, Portbury.

THE AP ADAM MANOR

A2/36/1 [GC 2445]   Sun. after St. James, 19 Edw. II [28 July 1325]
Thomas ap Adam, son and heir of John ap Adam, and John de Walton.

Thomas has granted to John all the holdings which he has in Puriton (Glos.) held of him in villeinage, with the villeins, and the rents and services of all the free tenants, and the lordship over them, and all other profits pertaining to the lordship, viz. the ferry, fisheries [etc.]; for his life.
Witnesses: Thomas de Rodeberewe, John de Boxe, Richard de Salle, John de Trye, John Sergeaunt, Henry le Gardener, John Teste.
At: Purton.

A2/36/2 [GC 1571]   n.d. [1326 × 1330]
John de Walton; and William de Chiltenham and Eleanor his wife.

John has leased to William and Eleanor all the lands, holdings [etc.], which he had in Puryton by demise of Sir Thomas ap Adam, for their lives, to hold of Thomas by the customary services.
Witnesses: Sir Thomas lord of Berkel', Sir Thomas de Gornay, knights, John Wyth, William Capel, Edward Howel, John de Clyve.

A2/36/3 [GC 2650]   4 May 2 Edw. III [1328]
Thomas ap Adam; and William de Chyltenham and Eleanor his wife.

Thomas has granted to William and Eleanor the manor of Pyriton by Lydeneye, to them and William's heirs.
Witnesses: John de Swonhongre, John de Egeton, John de Clyve.
At: Beverston.

A2/36/4 [GC 2712]   One week after Michaelmas, 4 Edw. III [6 Oct. 1330]
William de Chiltenham and his wife Eleanor (by John de Chiltenham); and Thomas ap Adam.

Final concord concerning the manor of Purytone by Newenham; William has

---

[1] To be distinguished from Purton in Hinton; the two hamlets called Purton lie little more than 1 mile apart, on opposite banks of the Severn.

acknowledged the right of Thomas by his gift, and Thomas grants the manor to William and Eleanor and William's heirs.
At: Westminster.

A2/36/5[GC 3573]   Mon. after Michaelmas, 39 Edw. III [6 Oct. 1365]
William de Chiltenham and Sir Maurice de Berkele, lord of Berkeley.
   William has granted to Maurice, his heirs and assigns, the advowson of the chapel of St. Leonard of Piryton by Aure.
Witnesses: John Joce the elder, John Joce the younger, John Gayner, Thomas Gayner, Walter de Auste.
At: Berkeley.

A2/36/6 [GC 3577]   Sat. after the conversion of St. Paul, 40 Edw. III [30 Jan. 1366]
William de Chiltenham; and Sir Maurice de Berkele, lord of Berkeley, and William Smalcombe.
   William de Chiltenham has granted to Maurice and William Smalcombe all his lands, holdings [etc.] in Piryton by Aure; to them and Maurice's heirs and assigns.
Witnesses: John Serjaunt, John Aleyn of Hill, John Joce, John de Auste, Thomas Gayner.
At: Berkeley.

A2/36/7 [GC 3576]   Sat. [after] the conversion of St. Paul, 40 Edw. III [30 Jan. 1366]
William de Chiltenham; and Sir Maurice de Berkele, lord of Berkeley, and William Smalcombe.
   William de Chiltenham has granted to Maurice and William Smalcombe all his lands, holdings [etc.] in Piryton by Aure and in Ettelowe; to them and Maurice's heirs and assigns.
Witnesses: John Aleyn of Hill, John Joce, John de Auste, Thomas Gayner.
At: Berkeley.

A2/36/8 [GC 3578]   6 Feb. 40 Edw. III [1366]
Maurice de Berkele, lord of Berkeley, and William Smalcombe; and William de Chiltenham.
   Maurice and William Smalcombe have leased to William de Chiltenham all their lands [etc.] in Piriton by Aure and in Ettelowe which they had by grant of William; for his life, rent a rose a year.
Witnesses: John Joce, John de Auste, Thomas Gayner.
At: Berkeley.

A2/36/9 [GC 3579]   12 Feb. 40 Edw. III [1366]
William Smalcombe and Sir Maurice de Berkele, lord of Berkeley.
   William has quitclaimed to Maurice all the lands [etc.] in Piryton by Aure and in Ettelowe which he and Maurice had by grant of William de Chiltenham.
At: Berkeley.

A2/36/10 [GC 3594]   Mon. the feast of St. Nicholas, 41 Edw. III [6 Dec. 1367]
William de Chiltenham and Sir Maurice de Berkele, lord of Berkeley.
   Whereas Maurice leased to William the manor of Pyrytone to hold for life with reversion to Maurice, William has surrendered to Maurice all his status in the manor, to hold to him and his heirs quit of William and his heirs.
Witnesses: John Gayner, John de Auste, John Stepenus, Walter de Auste, Thomas Gayner.
At: Berkeley.

A2/36/11 [GAR 426]   15–16 Hen. VI [1436–7]
Accounts of the reeve, hayward, beadle and receiver of the Forest of Dean; for the earl of Warwick.

MORTGAGE, 1375

The mortgage involved holdings at Tutnalls, Acton Ilger, Slimbridge, Bristol (Glos.), Steep Holme, Christon and Uphill and the advowson of Brean (Som.), as well as Purton; these were virtually the only lands inherited by Thomas (IV) that were not entailed in some way and so, presumably, the only ones which he could use as security for the loan. See also below, p. 516, Bedminster.

A2/36/12 [GC 3677]   15 Feb. 49 Edw. III [1375]
Thomas de Berkelee, lord of Berkeley; and William Cheddre of Bristol, Roger Seward, William's brother, and John Stanes of Bristol.

Whereas Thomas has granted to William, Roger and John, and their heirs and assigns, all the lands [etc.] which he had in Purytone, Tokkenhale and Actone Ulger, with the reversion of all the lands and holdings which Ralph Waleys holds for life in Slymbrugge (Glos.), and also all the lands and holdings which he had within the county of Bristuyt, and the island called Stepholm with the appurtenant lands and holdings within the hundred of Wynterestoke (Som.), and the advowson of Breen; William, Roger and John grant that if Thomas pays to Robert Cheddre of Bristuyt or the said William Cheddre 400 marks, viz. at Christmas next 200 marks and at Easter next 200 marks, they will re-grant to him all the said lands except Stepholm and the appurtenant lands and the advowson of Breen, which they will grant to Sir Richard Dacton for his life, with reversion to Thomas. [*In French.*]
At: Bristol.

A2/36/13 [GC 3687]   Mon., Christmas Eve, 49 Edw. III [24 Dec. 1375]
Sir Thomas de Berkele, lord of Berkeley; and Robert Cheddre of Bristol and William Cheddre the elder of Bristol.

Whereas Thomas has granted to William, Roger Seward, William's brother, and John Stanes of Bristol, and their heirs and assigns, all the lands [etc.] which he had in Purytone, Tokkenhale and Actone Ulger, with the reversion of all the lands and holdings which Ralph Waleys holds for life in Slymbrugge (Glos.), and also all the lands and holdings which he had within the county of Bristuyt, and the island called Stepholm with the appurtenant lands and holdings within the hundred of Wynterestoke (Som.), and the advowson of Breen, for the payment of 400 marks, Robert and William have received 200 marks in part payment. [*In French.*]
At: Bristol.

A2/36/14 [GC 3705]   18 Feb. 51 Edw. III [1377]
Thomas de Berkele, lord of Berkeley; and William Cheddre of Bristol the elder, Roger Seward, William's brother, and John Stanes of Bristol.

Whereas Thomas recently granted to William, Roger and John all his lands [etc.] in Kyngestone, Gosyntone and Hurst in the manor of Slymbrugge (Glos.), and all his lands [etc.] in the suburbs of Bristuyt and within the county of Bristuyt, and also all his lands [etc.] in Puritone . . . hundred of Bliddeslowe (Glos.), and all his lands [etc.] in Acton Ulger in the same county, they have granted and surrendered to him the estate which they had in the said lands, and have quitclaimed them to him. [*In French.*]

ST. CHLOE, IN MINCHINHAMPTON (GLOS.)

All the Mael family's holdings within the large manor of Minchinhampton, at St. Chloe, Dryleaze and Hampton itself, were apparently granted *c.* 1350 by the coheir Lucy de Tytherington to Thomas (III) Lord Berkeley. They were administered as a separate manor of St. Chloe, and except for those which can definitely be attributed to Hampton, are included below. In 1362 the manor was farmed to Philip de Rodborough and the rent appears in the valor of 1389. The holding had previously passed from William and Roger Mael to Roger's son John and grandsons Robert and Richard but eventually passed to Robert's daughter and coheir Lucy, who married William de Tytherington.

A2/37/1 [SC 371]   n.d. [*temp.* Hen. III]
John de Forwude and William Mael.

With the consent of his wife and heirs, John has granted to William his meadow between Ellemoreesfeld and 'the water'; rent 6*d.* a year and the royal service which pertains to so much land in his holding of Hamtune; for which grant William has given to John 8*s.* and a crannock of corn, to his wife 12*d.* and to Walter his eldest son 12*d.*
Witnesses: John Spileman, Walter his son, William de Rodeberge, Robert de Livant, Walter de Neileswurde, Roger Meinard, Richard de Aldewike, Henry Hardewine, Mauger de Kolecumbe.

A2/37/2 [GC 714]   n.d. [late 13th cent.]
The abbess and convent of Holy Trinity, Caen,[1] and William Mael.

The abbess and convent have confirmed to William, for his service, the virgate of land which Payn his grandfather held at Drueleya in their manor of Hamton, and afterwards Mael son of Payn; rent 10*s.* a year.
Witnesses: John de Garlemont, Peter Achard, Henry Hardwin, Richard de Avening, Elias de Seincl', Walter Spilemon, Richard de Livant, Walter de Neilleswure.

A2/37/3 [GC 298]   44 Hen. III [1259–60]
Thomas son of Richard Scimound and Roger Mael.

Thomas has granted to Roger an assart (*rudinga*) of arable land at Sencley, which lies below Heyruding and which he received from John son of Elias de Sencley, containing 2½ a. of the customary measure of the vill of Hampton; rent to the chief lord 10*d.* a year; Roger has given him 18*s.*

Witnesses: John Achard, Thomas de Roduber, Walter Spileman, A. his son, William son of Gilbert, John Horston, John Schir', William de Berna.

A2/37/4 [GC 300]   A.D. 1260 [1260–1]
John de Sencleya and Roger Mael.

John has granted to Roger an assart at Sencel viz. that which Thomas de Berna held of him, below Hemeruding, containing 2½ a., in the manor of Hampton, rent 10*d.*; Roger gave him ½ mark for the grant.
Witnesses: Richard de Aldewyk, John Achard, Thomas de Rodeberg, Walter Spileman, Roger de Forewod, Walter de Nayleswrd, John de Warelemond, William Hardwyn, John de Chalkford, William Blaking, Robert his son, Gerard de Hampton who wrote this charter.

A2/37/5 [GC 777]   n.d. [late 13th cent.]
Roger Mael and William son of Gilbert Warin.

Roger has leased to William and his first wife, for their lives, a messuage, curtilage and croft, except a new house built in the croft, and 3 a. of land; rent 4*s.* a year, and they have given him 40*s.*
Witnesses: Peter Achard, Walter Spilemon, Elyas de Seyncleye, Walter de Nayleswrthe, John de Nayleswrthe.

A2/37/6 [GC 1476]   n.d. [early Edw. I]
Roger Mael and Richard son of William Hunderwod.

Roger, with the assent of his son and heir John, has leased to Richard and his first wife, for their lives, the messuage with a curtilage and land which William his father sometime

---

[1] The nuns of Caen held most of the large manor of Hampton; 'Minchin' means a nun.

held of Roger Mael; rent 4*s.* 5*d* a year, and Richard has given him 20*s.*
Witnesses: John Achard, Walter Spilmon, John de Sencley, Henry Elyvant, Robert of the churchyard (*de cimiterio*).

A2/37/7 [GC 776]   n.d. [*c.* 1260]
Roger Mael; and Thomas son of Richard Symonis and Basilia his wife.

    Roger, with the assent of his wife, has leased to Thomas and Basilia, for 4*s.*, a messuage which Roger Swele formerly held, and 1½ a. of land; for their lives, rent 2*s.* a year.
Witnesses: Thomas de Rodebarwe, John Achard, Elyas de Seyncleye, John de Seyncleye, his son, Walter de Nayleswrthe, John de Nayleswrthe, Roger de Forewode.

A2/37/8 [GC 1472]   n.d. [*temp.* Edw. I]
John Mael and William son of Thomas de Grangia.

    John has granted to William a messuage and croft and a half-acre of land in the long assart, and two other half-acres; for his life, rent 2*s.* a year and the support of one man working at John's harvest for 3 days, and William has given him 13*s.* 4*d.*
Witnesses: Adam Spilemon, John de Seyncleye, John de Chalkford, Richard Elivant, Thomas de la Hore Stane.

A2/37/9 [GC 1474]   n.d. [early 14th cent.]
John Mael and Robert his son.

    John has granted to Robert the messuage with a curtilage and a half-acre of land which Elias de la Berne formerly held of John at farm; rent a pair of white gloves a year.
Witnesses: John de Seynceley, Richard de Neyleswrthe, William brother of John de Seynceleye, William de Warlemond, Alan de Forewode.

A2/37/10 [GC 1735]   Sun. after St. Philip and St. James, 3 Edw. II [3 May 1310]
John Mayel of St. Chloe; and Robert and Richard Mayel, his two sons.

    John has granted to Robert and Richard a messuage with all the lands, holdings, gardens, rents [etc.] which he had and held at Seyncleye within the manor of Hampton Monialium (Glos.); for their lives, and to Robert's issue, with remainder to John and his heirs.
Witnesses: Adam Spilemon, John de Chalkford, Gilbert de Naylesworth, Richard de Elyvaunt, Richard Kynnes, Samson Caperon, Thomas de Horesten.
At: St. Chloe.

A2/37/11 [GC 1475]   n.d. [early 14th cent.]
Robert and Richard Mayel; and John Mayel of St. Chloe, their father.

    Robert and Richard have granted to John the hall, great chamber, cellar, kitchen and dovecot of a holding at Sencleye next to [D]ruyleye, which John previously granted to them, and the herbage and half of the fruits of the garden; for his life.
Witnesses: Adam Spilemon, Richard Kyme, Richard Elivaunt, Samson Caperon, Thomas de Horestone.

A2/37/12 [GC 2367]   1 Oct. 15 Edw. II [1321]
Richard Mayel; and Thomas Toky and Christine his wife, daughter of Robert Mayel, and William de Tyderinton and Lucy his wife, daughter of Robert Mayel.

    Richard has leased to Thomas, Christine, William and Lucy and their heirs a messuage with all the lands and holdings [etc.] which he had at Seyncley within the manor of Hamptone Monialium (Glos.), for his life, by grant of John Mayel his father.
Witnesses: John Spilmon, Thomas de Rodeberwe, John de Avenyng, Richard de Kynnes, Samson Caperon, Thomas de la Horstane, William de Forzwode, Alexander de Avenyng, Robert Braunche.
At: St. Chloe.

A2/37/13 [GC 2857]   Fri. the feast of All Saints, 10 Edw. III [1 Nov. 1336]
William de Tyderyngton and Lucy his wife; and Alice de Bodebrok of Nailsworth and
William her son.

William and Lucy have leased to Alice and William a messuage with a curtilage and a
green croft and a plot of land called Penchey and a plot called la Bosche, and 1 a. of land in
the field towards Senkeleye by le Lupeyate, and 1 a. of land in le Homfeld; for their lives,
rent as before.
Witnesses: John Spilman, Thomas de Rodbergh, Richard de Coumbe, Henry Olvant, John
Coterich.
At: St. Chloe.

A2/37/14 [GC 2940]   Easter Sunday, 13 Edw. III [28 March 1339]
Walter Toky, son and heir of Thomas Toky of Hartpury; and William de Tyderyntone and
Lucy his wife.

Whereas a water-mill with appurtenant land and meadow in the liberty of the king's
barton by Gloucestre descended after the death of Christine, mother of Walter, to Walter
and to Lucy, now the wife of William, and was divided between them, but there was dispute
in the king's court prosecuted by William and Lucy, William and Lucy have granted to
Walter the other part of the mill [i.e. the part not held by Walter], land and meadow, and
Walter has granted to them all the lands and holdings which he inherited from Christine in
Seyncle within the manor of Munchenehamptone (Glos.), and 3 plots of land within the
liberty of the king's barton by Gloucestre, and 3 a. of meadow there.
Witnesses: Robert Dapitot, Henry de Clifford, William ate Merssh, William Pope, John de
Bryghthamton, Robert Sage, Robert Prycke.
At: King's Barton.

A2/37/15 [GC 3164]   Sat. the feast of Michaelmas, 21 Edw. III [29 Sept. 1347]
Lucy de Tydryngton, widow of William de Tydryngton the elder; and Richard ate Berue and
his wife Agnes.

Lucy has leased to Richard and Agnes a messuage in Sencleye, which William ate Berue,
Richard's father, held for his life, with a croft called M . . .; for their lives, rent 3*s*. 3½*d*. a
year.
Witnesses: . . . Hugh de Rodberewe, Robert Kynne, Richard Coumbes, John Elvaunt.
At: Gloucester.

A2/37/16 [GC 3201]   Sun. the feast of St. Thomas the apostle, 22 Edw. III [21 Dec. 1348]
Lucy de Tydryntone, widow of William de Tydryntone, and Robert Wattes, son of Ralph
Wattes.

Lucy has leased to Robert a messuage with a curtilage and croft and 2½ a. of land in
Sencleye; for life, rent 2*s*. 6*d*. a year.
At: St. Chloe.

A2/37/17 [GC 3347; *duplicate* GC 3348]   n.d. [mid 14th cent.]
Lucy widow of William de Tydryntone and Sir Thomas, lord of Berkelee.

Lucy has granted to Thomas, his heirs and assigns, all her lands and holdings in
Sencleye, Druweleye and Munchenehampton.
Witnesses: Sir Thomas de Berkelee of Coberley, Sir Simon Basset, knights, William de
Chiltenham, Elias de Ailberton, Hugh de Rodeberwe.

A2/37/18 [GC 3512]   n.d. [mid 14th cent.]
Thomas lord of Berkelee; and Robert le Walkere, Joan his wife and John their son.

Thomas has leased to Robert, Joan and John 1½ a. 1 rood of meadow called Longemede
in Sencleye; for their lives, rent 10*s*. 6*d*. a year.

A2/37/19 [GAR 320] Manorial account   Michaelmas, 36 Edw. III for 42 weeks [1362–3]

SIDDINGTON (GLOS.)

It is likely that the holding in Siddington was associated with the St. Amand manor of South Cerney and Cerney Wick (Glos.), bought by Thomas (IV) Lord Berkeley *c*. 1399: cf. above, pp. 449–50.

A2/38/1 [GC 3524]   Wed. the feast of the nativity of the Virgin Mary, 35 Edw. III
                                                                                 [8 Sept. 1361]
Joseph le Glovere of Cirencester and Agnes his wife; and Aymer de Sancto Amando, knight.

Joseph and Agnes have granted to Aymer, his heirs and assigns all their lands and holdings in Southyntone.
Witnesses: Geoffrey Ailwyne, Richard atte Hide, James le Grys, Walter atte Gate, Richard le Boun, John Fraunkeleyn.
At: Siddington.

SNEEDHAM, IN UPTON ST. LEONARDS (GLOS.)

German de Tonbridge sold all his lands in Sneedham and Upton St. Leonards to Maurice (III) Lord Berkeley in 1317 and all the lands were administered as the manor of Upton St. Leonards. See below, A2/46/1–2 [GC 2208–9].

A2/39/1 [GC 419]   n.d. [*c*. 1280]
William le Ryche, son of William le Ryche of Sneedham, and John Payn, burgess of Gloucester.

William has granted to John all his holding in Scnedehame and John has given him 8 marks.
Witnesses: Master Stephen de Glastonia, warden of the king's barton, Miles the clerk, Philip de Haytherleye, Henry de Ruwel, Robert de la Grave, Henry de Lassbrwe, Henry de Bares, William Geraud.

A2/39/2 [SC 190]   n.d. [*c*. 1280]
William le Ryche, son of William le Ryche of Sneedham, and John Payn, burgess of Gloucester.

William has granted to John all his holdings in Scnedhame and in return John will provide William with a crannock of corn every 6 weeks, a garment every year and a house to live in; if he fails, the bailiffs of King's Barton hundred will distrain on John.
Witnesses: Master Stephen de Glastonia, keeper of the king's barton, Miles the clerk, Philip de Haytherleye, Henry de Ruwes, Robert de la Grave, Henry de Lasseberuwe, Henry de Bares, William Geraud.

A2/39/3 [GC 489]   Tues. the eve of Ash Wednesday, 8 Edw. I [5 March 1280]
Mabel de Eynesford, widow of William le Ryche of Upton, and John Payn, burgess of Gloucester.

Mabel has quitclaimed to John all the lands which her late husband held, and John has given her 12*s*.
Witnesses: Sir Henry, rector of church of St. Michael, Gloucester, Philip de Haytherleye, Robert de la Grave, Henry de Ruwes, Henry de Lasseberwe, Philip de Matisdon, Henry de Bares, John Cornish (*Cornubiens'*) and Walter de Saundon, burgesses of Gloucester, Jordan de Harnhull, reeve of the queen's barton of Gloucester, Nicholas the clerk.
At: Gloucester.

A2/39/4 [GC 950]   n.d. [early 14th cent.]
William Payn, son of John Payn of Gloucester; and German de Tounbrug' and Mabel his wife.

William has granted to German and Mabel a half-virgate in Snedham; rent a rose a year, and they have given him 5 marks.
Witnesses: Sir Roger le Rus, Sir Philip de Mattisdon, Henry de Reues, Philip de Hatherleye, Henry de Bares.

A2/39/5 [GC 1521]   n.d. [*temp.* Edw. I]
William le Riche, son and heir of Geoffrey le Riche of Sneedham; and German de Tonebrugge and Katherine his wife.

William has granted to German and Katherine a messuage and a half-virgate, and rent of 7*d.* in the vill of Snedham, within the king's barton of Gloucestre; they have given him £10.
Witnesses: William le Gardinis, William Waleys, Richard de Apperleye, John de Hatherleye, Gilbert de Riews, Robert Mayel, Walter Pope.

KING'S STANLEY (GLOS.)

The manor was granted by Aymer le Despenser to John Giffard of Brimpsfield and his wife Aveline in Nov. 1311. The grant was made without the king's licence, and the manor was taken into the king's hands and granted in Dec. 1312 to Thomas (II) de Berkeley.[1] In June 1314 the king's council was called in order to examine the business pending in the King's Bench between the king and John Giffard over the manor of King's Stanley at the suit of Thomas de Berkeley.[2] Giffard was pardoned for the unlicensed acquisition in April 1315 and the manor was restored to him.[3] See also below, p. 510, Great Rollright.

A2/40/1 [GC 1971]   5 April 7 Edw. II [1314]
Thomas de Berkelee, lord of Berkeley, and Maurice de Berkelee, his son.

Thomas has granted to Maurice his right and claim in the manor of Kynggestanleye, which he had by grant of the king, and also in the inn (*l'ostel*) which he had from Sir Robert le fiz Water in Londres, and in a rent of 40*d.* from Elias le Ferrour of Kynggestanleye, so that Maurice will grant the said manor to Thomas his son when he is knighted, for his life, or the value of the manor, and if he sells the manor to Sir John Giffard or another for cash, Milicent his daughter will have the same cash in aid of her marriage. [*In French.*]
Witnesses: Sir Thomas de Gurnay, Sir William de Wautone, Sir Roger Pychard, knights, . . . de Actone, William de Gamage, John de Olepenne, John Notelin.
At: Berkeley.

SYDE (GLOS.)

The manor was forfeited by John Giffard of Brimpsfield in 1322, but was granted back to his mother Margaret for her life.[4] By 1339 the reversion after her death had been acquired by Thomas (III) Lord Berkeley.[5] The manor was settled on Thomas's younger son Thomas in 1349 with Westonbirt.[6] The two manors may have been settled earlier, possibly in 1344 (see below, A2/41/2 [GC 3103], A2/49/1 [GC 3102]). Unlike most of Thomas's other acquisitions, however, it was not held in jointure by his widow Katherine and she had dower in it after his death (below, A2/41/3 [GC 3538]). It passed eventually to her son John and the cadet line of Beverston.

[1] *CFR* 1307–19, 158, 160.
[2] J. C. Davies, *The Baronial Opposition to Edward II* (Cambridge, 1918), 334.
[3] *GEC* v. 645 n.
[4] *VCH Glos.* vii. 228–9.
[5] PRO CP 25/1/77/62, no. 162.
[6] PRO CP 25/1/77/67, no. 295.

A2/41/1 [GC 3061]   Wed. before St. Bartholomew, 17 Edw. III [20 Aug. 1343]
(1) William de Syde; (2) Robert Groundy; (3) Ralph Cole of Syde, chaplain.

William has appointed Robert his attorney to deliver to Raph seisin of all the lands and holdings, goods and chattels, which he recently had by grant of Ralph in Syde. [*In French*.]
At: Westonbirt.

A2/41/2 [GC 3103]   26 Oct. 18 Edw. III [1344]
(1) William de Syde; (2) John le Veye; (3) Sir Thomas, lord of Berkel'.

William has appointed John to give seisin to Thomas of the manor of Syde with the advowson and all the goods and chattels there.
At: Berkeley.

A2/41/3 [GC 3538]   22 April 37 Edw. III [1363]
Thomas Moigne, sheriff of Gloucester, to John Shardelowe, his itinerant bailiff, and Adam Legat.

Whereas Katherine widow of Thomas son of Maurice de Berkele the elder, has recovered seisin, against John son of the said Thomas, of one third of the manor of Syde and of 4 messuages, 3 carucates and 1 virgate of land, 15 a. of meadow, 43 a. of pasture, 18 a. of wood and £7 13s. 3d. rent in Syde, Westonebret, Dounhatherleye, Lekhamptone, and Bentham, as of her dower, the sheriff orders John and Adam to give her full seisin as soon as possible, following the king's writ of 6 Feb. 37 Edw. III.
At: Gloucester.

A2/41/4 [GAR 321] Two manorial accounts
                    Michaelmas to St. Andrew, 19 Edw. III [29 Sept. to 30 Nov. 1345]
St. Andrew, 19 Edw. III to Michaelmas, 20 Edw. III [30 Nov. 1345 to 29 Sept. 1346]

THORNBURY (GLOS.)
BERKELEY INTERESTS

A2/42/1 [GC 4147]   Mon. before St. Simon and St. Jude, 4 Hen. VI [22 Oct. 1425]
Isolda Frenshe, daughter and heir of John Chese, and John Frenshe, her son and heir, of Thornbury; and John Rolves.

Isolda and John have quitclaimed to John Rolves a messuage with a curtilage and croft in Thornbury, and one third of 1 a. of land near the park [etc.].
Witnesses: Robert Poyntz, Nicholas Stanshawe, Nicholas Alderlegh, John Foort, William Perns.
At: Thornbury.

A2/42/2 [GC 4153]   Mon. after St. James, 5 Hen. VI [28 July 1427]
John Rolves of Hope (Glos.), esquire, and William Berkeley, son of James Berkeley, lord of Berkeley.

John has granted to William, after the death of himself and Joan his wife, all his lands, holdings [etc.] in the vill of Thornebury and within the tithing of Kyngton within the lordship of Thornebury in the said county.
At: Berkeley.

A2/42/3 [GC 4436]   10 May . . . Edw. IV [c. 1463]
(1) William Berkeley, knight, son and heir of James Berkeley, lord of Berkeley; (2) John Haydon; (3) Maurice Berkeley, William's brother.

William has appointed John to deliver seisin to Maurice . . . rents, reversions and services which he had by grant of John Rolves of Hope (Glos.), esquire, . . . of Kyngton within the lordship of Thornbury.
At: Thornbury.

HALEWELL MEAD (HALEMEAD CROFT)

A2/42/4 [GC 3409]   Tues. after St. Agatha, 28 Edw. III [11 Feb. 1354]
John Northalle and John Dumbelton.

John Northalle has granted to John Dumbelton, his heirs and assigns his meadow called Halewellemed; rent 2*s.* a year to the church of St. Mary of Thornbury for a lamp, and the customary services to the chief lord.
Witnesses: Walter Marchal, John Veel, . . .
At: [Thornbury?]

A2/42/5 [GC 3604]   Mon. [*sic*] Christmas Eve, 42 Edw. III [24 Dec. 1368]
Alice Douniltone, widow of John Douniltone, burgess of the vill of Thornbury; and Walter Marchald, burgess of the same, and Agnes his wife.

Alice has granted to Walter and Agnes, and their heirs and assigns, her croft called le Halemed; rent 2*s.* a year to sustain a lamp in the church of St. Mary of Thornbury.
Witnesses: Simon Pengrisch, John Tannere and John Barthelot, bailiffs of the vill, John Chese, John Veel, Thomas Diare, Thomas Pennok, Robert Southmed.
At: Thornbury.

CAVENHULL CROFT

A2/42/6 [GC 1547]   n.d. [*temp.* Edw. I]
William Skydie and Maud Paty his wife; and Nicholas Paty, son of William Paty of Thornbury.

William and Maud have granted to Nicholas the croft with a meadow and appurtenances in the fee of Thornbur' called Cavenhull; Nicholas has given them a certain sum of money.
Witnesses: Stephen de Saltmarsh (*de salso marisco*), William de Westbrok, Stephen Beaubras, Nicholas le Forester, Thomas le Tannere, Thomas le Scrivein, John the baker (*pistor*), Walter Gasterus.

A2/42/7 [GC 965]   Friday after the feast . . . [*unfinished*] [early 14th cent.]
Maud Skydie, widow of William Skydie, and Nicholas Paty her brother.

Maud has quitclaimed to Nicholas a croft with a meadow [etc.] in the fee of Thornbur' called Cavenhull, which she and her late husband previously granted to him; for a certain sum of money.
At: Bristol.

A2/42/8 [GC 1619]   n.d. [*temp.* Edw. I]
Nicholas Paty, son of Alice Pati of Thornbury; and Adam le Palmare and Alice his wife.

Nicholas has granted to Adam and Alice the croft called Cavenhull in the manor of Thornbury; for their lives, rent 12*d.* a year.
Witnesses: William de Westbrok, John Long (*Longus*), Robert [Sudmede], John the baker (*pistor*), Walter Gasterus.

A2/42/9 [GC 2909]   Fri. after Whit Sunday, 12 Edw. III [5 June 1338]
Maud daughter of Walter le Mareschal of Thornbury and Walter le Mareschal her brother.

Maud has granted to Walter her brother her holding in Thornbiri, which she had by legacy of their father, and Walter has given her a certain sum of money.
Witnesses: Simon le Clerk of Thornby, Thomas le Baker, William Forester, William Huwes, Richard de Garderoba, John Chese, John de Derlington, clerk.
At: London.

A2/42/10 [GC 2970]   Sun. before St. Philip and St. James, 14 Edw. III [30 April 1340]
Nicholas Paty and Walter Marischal.

Nicholas has quitclaimed to Walter a croft with a meadow called [Cavenhulle] in the manor of Thornebury which William Skydie formerly held.
Witnesses: Simon Clerke, Thomas Bakere, Walter Fishpul, William Tannare, William Forister.
At: Thornbury.

OTHER

A2/42/11 [GC 3139]   Mon. the feast of St. Philip and St. James, 20 Edw. III [1 May 1346]
Edward Forster of Thornbury and William Mildemay of Falfield.

Edward has granted to William, his heirs and assigns a house with a curtilage beside the gate of Edward's holding in the vill of Thornbury.
Witnesses: John Sandford, bailiff of the vill, Walter Marischal, Richard le Clerk, William Chepmon, Simon Fleshewar.
At: Thornbury.

A2/42/12 [SR 150] Customs of Thornbury manor   4 Hen. VII [1488–9]

THORNBURY BOROUGH (GLOS.)

Maurice (V) Lord Berkeley married Isabel, daughter and eventually heir of Philip Mead.

THE CORNER HOLDING

A2/43/1 [GC 4208]   Fri. before St. Martin, 16 Hen. VI [8 Nov. 1437]
Robert Hawkyns of Thornbury; and William atte Were, John Benet and William Symmes.

Robert has granted to William, John and William his corner holding, being a half-burgage, in the high street of Thornbury, which John Stynchecombe lately held.
Witnesses: John Cocker and William atte Were, bailiffs of the borough, William Piers, John Frensshe, Thomas the clerk.
At: Thornbury.

A2/43/2 [GC 4209]   10 Oct. 17 Hen. VI [1438]
William atte Were, John Benet and William Symmes; and John Danyell of Thornbury.

William, John and William have granted to John Danyell, his heirs and assigns the corner half-burgage holding which they had by grant of Robert Hawkyns in the high street of the borough of Thornbury.
Witnesses: John Frensshe, John Ernesburgh, Thomas the clerk.
At: Thornbury.

A2/43/3 [GC 4276]   Mon. after St. Martin, 30 Hen. VI [15 Nov. 1451]
John Danyell of Thornbury; and Humphrey Mede and Joan his wife.

John has granted to Humphrey and Joan, and their heirs and assigns, his half-burgage corner holding in the borough of Thornbury, which he had by grant of William Symmes, William Were and John Benet.
Witnesses: John Frensshe and John Adam, bailiffs of the borough, William Piers, John Erneburgh, Thomas de Thornbury, clerk.
At: Thornbury.

A2/43/4 [GC 4278]   30 Jan. 30 Hen. VI [1452]
John Danyell, burgess of Thornbury (Glos.), and Humphrey Mede, weaver of the said vill.

John has quitclaimed to Humphrey all actions, suits, quarrels and demands, real and personal.
At: Thornbury.

A2/43/5 [GC 4318]   Mon. after Michaelmas, 2 Edw. IV [4 Oct. 1462]
Humphrey Mede; and William Baylle of Tytherington and Robert Lyndesey of the same.

Humphrey has granted to William and Robert, and their heirs and assigns, his half-burgage corner holding in the high street of Thornbury, which he had by grant of John Danyell.

Witnesses: Thomas Bray and William Hilpe, bailiffs of the borough, John Parker, Stephen Baschirche, Thomas Morgan.
At: Thornbury.

A2/43/6 [GC 4319]   Mon. after St. Gregory, 3 Edw. IV [14 March 1463]
William Baylle of Tytherington and Robert Lyndesey of the same; and Edmund More, Juliana his wife and Richard Hulpe.
    William and Robert have granted to Edmund, Juliana and Richard, and their heirs and assigns, their half-burgage corner holding in the high street of Thornbury, which they had by grant of Humphrey Mede and he by John Danyell.
Witnesses: John Crokehorn and Edward Roburgh, bailiffs of the borough, John Adam, Thomas Smyth, Thomas Morgan.
At: Thornbury.

A2/43/7 [GC 4320]   Mon. after St. Gregory, 3 Edw. IV [14 March 1463]
(1) William Baylle of Tytherington and Robert Lyndesey of the same; (2) William Hulpe; (3) Edmund More, Juliana his wife and Richard Hulpe.
    William and Robert have appointed William Hulpe to deliver seisin to Edmund, Juliana and Richard of their half-burgage corner holding in the high street of Thornbury, which they had by grant of Humphrey Mede and he by John Danyell.
At: Thornbury.

A2/43/8 [GC 4321]   Tues. after St. Gregory, 3 Edw. IV [15 March 1463]
William Baylle of Tytherington and Robert Lyndesey of the same; and Edmund More, Juliana his wife and Richard Hulpe.
    William and Robert have quitclaimed to Edmund, Juliana and Richard their half-burgage corner holding in the high street of Thornbury, which they had by grant of Humphrey Mede and he by John Danyell.
Witnesses: John Crokeham and Edward Roburgh, bailiffs of the borough, John Adam, Thomas Smyth, Thomas Morgan.
At: Thornbury.

A2/43/9 [GC 4323]   2 June 3 Edw. IV [1463]
Humphrey Mede of Kingswood (*Kingsworth*) (Glos.); and Edmund More and Juliana his wife.
    Humphrey has quitclaimed to Edmund and Juliana all actions, real and personal.

A2/43/10 [GC 4354]   Eve of the conception of the Virgin Mary, 8 Edw. IV [7 Dec. 1468]
Juliana Moore, widow of Edmund Moore of Thornbury (Glos.); and John Jamys and Elizabeth Jamys, his wife, of Thornbury.
    Juliana has granted to John and Elizabeth, and their heirs and assigns, her half-burgage corner holding in the high street of Thornbury, which she and Edmund and Richard Hulpe had by grant of William Bailly and Robert Lyndesey of Tydryngton (Glos.).
Witnesses: Master John Drover, clerk, Thomas Bray the elder, John Adams.
At: Thornbury.

A2/43/11 [GC 4355]   4 Jan. 8 Edw. IV [1469]
Juliana Moore, widow of Edmund Moore of Thornbury (Glos.); and John Jamys and Elizabeth Jamys, his wife, of Thornbury.
    Juliana has quitclaimed to John and Elizabeth, and their heirs and assigns, her half-burgage corner holding in the high street of Thornbury, which she and Edmund and Richard Hulpe had by grant of William Bailly and Robert Lyndesey of Tydryngton (Glos.).
At: Thornbury.

A2/43/12 [GC 4377]					13 Dec. 13 Edw. IV [1473]
Thomas Smyth and Elizabeth Jamys of Thornbury; and John Jamys of Thornbury.

Thomas and Elizabeth have granted to John, his heirs and assigns, all their corner half-burgage holding in the high street of Thornbury, which they had by grant of Juliana Moore of Thornbury.
Witnesses: Thomas Bray the elder, John Heydon, John Ernebrowgh.
At: Thornbury.

A2/43/13 [GC 4379]					7 Feb. 13 Edw. IV [1474]
John James of Thornbury (Glos.), yeoman, and Maurice Barclay, esquire.

John has granted to Maurice, his heirs and assigns his corner half-burgage holding in the high street of Thornbury which he and Elizabeth James, his late wife, had by grant of Juliana More, widow of Edmund More.
Witnesses: Maurice Denyes, esquire, John Adams, Thomas Bray.
At: Thornbury.

A2/43/14 [GC 4380]					10 Feb. 13 Edw. IV [1474]
John James of Thornbury (Glos.), yeoman, and Maurice Barclay, esquire.

John has quitclaimed to Maurice, his heirs and assigns his corner half-burgage holding in the high street of Thornbury, which Maurice had by his grant.
Witnesses: Maurice Denyes, esquire, John Adams, Thomas Bray.
At: Thornbury.

A2/43/15 [GC 4389]				Mon. after All Saints, 14 Edw. IV [7 Nov. 1474]
Thomas Steward of Rockhampton (Glos.), clerk, and Thomas Bray of Thornbury, gentleman; and Maurice Berkeley, esquire, son of James late lord of Berkeley.

Thomas and Thomas have granted to Maurice their holding in the high street of Thornbury, lying in length between the high street and le Portrey Broke, and the corner half-burgage holding in the high street, and other parcels of land, which they had by grant of Maurice; to Maurice and his wife Isabel, and their issue, with remainder to the right heirs of Maurice.
Witnesses: Maurice Berkeley of Stoke, Maurice Deonyce, Richard Forster, esquires.

OTHER

The charter has the same date as that above (A2/43/15 [GC 4389]) by which the corner holding, acquired by Maurice a few months earlier, was settled on Maurice and Isabel.

A2/43/16 [SC 631]				Mon. after All Saints, 14 Edw. IV [7 Nov. 1474]
Philip Mede, burgess of Bristol, and Richard his son and heir; and Maurice Berkeley, esquire, son of James late lord Berkeley, and Isabel his wife.

Philip and Richard have granted to Maurice and Isabel several holdings and burgages in Thornbury, to them and their issue, with reversion to Philip's right heirs.
Witnesses: William Spencer, John Hawlis, Maurice Berkeley of Stoke, Maurice Deonyce, Richard Forster.

TIDENHAM (GLOS.)

Thomas (III) Lord Berkeley acquired the holding from Thomas son of Hugh de Gurney and apparently granted it in 1342 to Thomas ap Adam's sons Robert and Hamon in successive tail general, with remainder to Thomas ap Adam's heirs,[1] possibly in exchange for ap Adam's quitclaim of rents for his land in Beachley.[2]

---

[1] *GEC* i. 181 n.; BL Harl MS 6079, f. 108d.
[2] Below, A2/44/18 [GC 3040]; and see above, pp. 434–5, Beachley.

A2/44/1 [GC 518; *duplicate* GC 1281]   14 Feb. 13 Edw. I [1285]
Bertram son and heir of Philip Champeneys and John son of Reginald ap Adam.

Bertram has granted to John a messuage in the place called Quigelynysfee in the manor of Tudeham between the Severn and the Wye, with all appurtenances, to hold of the chief lord of the fee and rendering a clove a year; for this John has acquitted him of 200 marks in which he is bound to Peter the Jew of Strugull [i.e. Chepstow] for the debts of his father Philip. Endorsed: *Gorste*.

Witnesses: Sir Walter de Redesham, steward of Chepstow, Sir Robert de Gamages, Sir John Martel, Sir Thomas de Hunteleye, Philip Denebaud, William Derneford, Walter Waldyng, Robert de Auste, Maurice Torel, Philip le Waleys, Hugh le Harloter, Nicholas de Wyrwode.
At: Chepstow.

A2/44/2 [GC 589]   5 Sept. 20 Edw. I [1292]
Roger le Bygod, earl of Norfolk and marshal of England, and John ab Adam.

Roger has granted to John, for his service, a park within the parish of Tudenham, so that he may enclose his wood and his holdings.
At: Chepstow.

A2/44/3 [SC 459]   13 May 22 Edw. I [1294]
Roger le Bygod, earl of Norfolk and marshal of England, and John ab Adam.

Roger has granted to John a weekly market on Wednesdays at his manor of Betesle, and an annual fair on the vigil, day and morrow of St. Margaret the virgin [19–21 July], and free warren in all his demesne lands of Betesle and la Gorste.

Witnesses: Sir Ralph abbot of Tintern, Sir Thomas de Berkele, Sir Maurice de Berkele his son, Sir John Bluet, knights, Sir William de Beccles, Roger's chancellor, Philip le Waleys, Philip de la More.
At: London.

A2/44/4 [GC 1272]   n.d. [*temp.* Edw. I]
Roger Bygod, earl of Norfolk and marshal of England, and John son of Reginald ab Adam.

Roger has granted to John all the lands and rents which he had by grant of Philip Chaumpeneys, between the Wye and the Severn in the parish of Todeham; rent a clove a year.

Witnesses: Sir Bartholomew de Mora, Sir Robert son of Payn, knights, Philip Denebaud, Nicholas de Wirwode, Robert de Aust.

A2/44/5 [GC 712; *duplicate* GC 1271]   n.d. [*c.* 1292]
Roger Bygod, earl of Norfolk and marshal of England, and John son of Reginald ab Adam.

Roger has granted to John all the land with rents which he acquired from Peter Maynard of Strugull, between the Wye and the Severn in the parish of Todeham; rent a red rose a year. Endorsed: *carta com. mareschall de ten. Maynard de la Gorste*.

Witnesses: Sir Bartholomew de Mora, Sir Robert de Gaumages, Sir John Martel, Sir Thomas de Hontele, Sir Walter de Reddesham, steward of Chepstow Castle, knights, Philip Denebaud, William de Sancto Petro, Nicholas de Runeston, Walter de Bendevile.

A2/44/6 [GC 1479]   n.d. [*temp.* Edw. I]
Peter Maynard of Chepstow and John son of Reginald ab Adam.

Peter has quitclaimed to John all the lands and holdings which were of Sir Roger le Bygod, earl of Norfolk and marshal of England, next to le Grost in the manor of Tudeham, which the earl later enfeoffed to John.

Witnesses: Walter Walding, Maurice Thorel, Philip le Waleys, Robert de Aust, Adam de Wyrwode.

A2/44/7 [GC 1253]   n.d. [*temp.* Edw. I]
Henry Bordon and John son of Reginald ap Adam.

Henry has granted to John a messuage and curtilage with 19 a. of land in the vill of Tudeham in Sothebury, of which 6½ a. lie above le Redeclive, beside the road from la Gorste to Betesleya, 4 a. beside the land called Baggesgrof and the land called Haycroft, 5½ a. in the field called Charrudyng, 1½ a. in the field called Humpelgate and 1½ a. in the field of Sothebury; John has given him 8 marks.

Witnesses: Walter Waldyng, Maurice Torel, Robert de Auste, Adam de Wyrwode, Philip le Waleys, William Rugelyn, Henry Repe, William Repe, John de Bestesley.

A2/44/8 [GC 1159]   n.d. [*c.* 1300]
John son of Reginald ap Adam; and John Repe and Eleanor his wife.

John has granted to John and Eleanor the messuage and curtilage which Henry Burdon held in Suthebury in the vill of Tudeham; for their lives, rent 2*s.* a year and two suits to his court of Betesleya.

Witnesses: Adam de Wyrwod, William Rugelyn, John de Betesleya, Henry Repe, William Repe, Richard de Walewere, Adam of the park.

A2/44/9 [GC 1072]   Mon. before Lammas Day, 22 Edw. I [26 July 1294]
Philip Tursteyn and John ap Adam, his lord.

Philip has granted to John 6 a. of arable land in the furlong called Heryngbrugge, next to the fishpond; rent a rose a year, and John has given him 4 marks.

Witnesses: Walter Waldyng, Maurice Torel, Robert de Auste, William Cosiner, Adam le Parker.

At: Chepstow.

A2/44/10 [GC 1025]   Thurs. after St. Andrew, 30 Edw. I [7 Dec. 1301]
Sarah le Waleys and John Apadam.

Sarah has granted to John all her wood in Puriesgrove in la Gorste next to the land of le Scrynor, with an annual rent of 2*d.* from William Cosiner and Laurence de Peresfelde; John has given her 1 mark.

Witnesses: Adam atte . . . , John Herlof, John Tomberel, Thomas de Pirtone, John de Betesleg'.

A2/44/11 [GC 978]   n.d. [*c.* 1300]
Philip Thursteyn and Sir John son of Reginald ap Adam.

Philip has granted to John a messuage with appurtenances at la Gorste in the parish of Tudenham, of the fee of John or otherwise, and has granted to him all his right in all burgages, rents [etc.] in the vill of Strugull; John has given him 20 marks.

Witnesses: Ralph Hathewy, steward of Chepstow, Philip de la More, Walter de Bendevile, Leyson ap Morgan, John de la Lee, Walter Walding, Maurice Torel, Robert de Aust, Adam de Wirwode, Adam Wauncy.

A2/44/12 [GC 951]   n.d. [*c.* 1300]
Laurence de Perisfeld and Alice daughter of John Thorstayn, his wife; and Sir John son of Reginald ap Adam.

Laurence and Alice have granted to John 2 a. of arable land and a third of an acre of wood in the place called Pyrelond at la Gorste which was of John Thorstayn, in exchange for lands and holdings at Sothb. . . from William Rugelyn, which he formerly held of John ap Adam.

Witnesses: Ralph Hathewy, steward of Chepstow, Walter Bendevyle, Walter Waldyng, Robert de Auste, Philip de Auste, Adam de Wyrwode, Adam Wanci.

A2/44/13 [GC 1663]   St. Margaret the virgin, 2 Edw. II [13 July 1308]
John ap Adam and Maud Thorsteyn, daughter of Philip Thorsteyn.

John has granted to Maud a messuage and curtilage which the said Philip once held in the parish of Tudynham; for her life, rent 12*d.* a year, and she has given him 20*s.*
Witnesses: Robert de Auste, Maurice Torel, Walter Waldyng, Adam de Wyrewode.
At: Aylburton.

A2/44/14 [GC 2683]   Sun. before the Assumption of the Virgin Mary, 3 Edw. III
                                                                    [13 Aug. 1329]
Thomas ap Adam, lord of Beverston, and Sir Thomas de Gurnay, knight, son of Hugh de Gurnay.

Thomas ap Adam has quitclaimed to Thomas de Gurnay the vill of Beteslegh in the parish of Tudynham, and also the advowson of the chapel of St. Toci in the Severn by Beteslegh, and also for all the lands, holdings [etc.] of la Gorste in the parish of Tudenham.
Witnesses: William de Derneford, Adam le Akatour, Thomas Waldyng, Adam de Pultone, Nigel de Beteslegh.
At: Beachley.

A2/44/15 [GC 3514]   n.d. [mid 14th cent.]
Thomas de Gournay of Harptree, knight, and Sir Thomas, lord of Berkelee.

Thomas de Gournay has granted to Thomas de Berkelee, his heirs and assigns, all the lands and holdings, rents [etc.] which he had in Betesleye, Gorste, Tudenham and elsewhere within the lordship of Strugull.

A2/44/16 [GC 914]   n.d. [early Edw. III]
(1) Thomas de Gournay of Harptree, knight; (2) Edward Houwel of Beachley and John le Cuppere of Berkeley; (3) Sir Thomas, lord of Berkeleye.

Thomas de Gournay has appointed Edward and John to give seisin to Thomas de Berkeley of all the lands, holdings, reversions and appurtenances which he has in Betesleye, Gorste, Tudenham and elsewhere within the lordship of Strugull, as in his charter to Thomas.

A2/44/17 [GC 2597]   n.d. [early Edw. III]
Thomas de Gournay of Harptree, knight, to his tenants of Beachley, Gorst and Tidenham.

Thomas de Gournay instructs his tenants of Betesleye, Gorste, Tudenham and elsewhere within the lordship of Strugull to submit to Sir Thomas, lord of Berkelee, as he has granted to Thomas de Berkelee all his lands and holdings, rents, reversions and the services of all his tenants, free and villein, in the said vills.

A2/44/18 [GC 3040]   25 . . . , 16 Edw. III [1342]
Thomas ap Adam and Sir Thomas de Berkeleye, lord of Berkeley.

Thomas ap Adam has quitclaimed to Thomas de Berkeleye all rents [etc.] from lands and holdings which Thomas [de Berkeleye] holds in Betesleye.
At: Berkeley.

TOCKINGTON (GLOS.)

The surviving charters show that Thomas (III) Lord Berkeley bought the reversion of the large and valuable manor from the feoffees of the impoverished and debt-ridden Sir Nicholas Poyntz (d. 1376), though Thomas is said to have bought it in 1355 from one Piers

Chilworth, who was holding it for the repayment of Poyntz's debts.[1] Thomas was holding the manor in 1361, and his executors' account records that Ralph de Stafford, earl of Stafford, forgave a fine of £40 for the manor to Thomas's heir Maurice (IV) Lord Berkeley.[2] As the grant of the reversion shows, it was entailed in the same way as the rest of Thomas's purchases, his widow Katherine holding it in jointure until her death in 1386; it later passed to her son John and the cadet line of Beverston.

A2/45/1 [GC 2162]   Mon. the morrow of Easter, 10 Edw. II [4 April 1317]
Hugh Poyntz, lord of Curry Mallet, and Nicholas Poyntz, son of Puncius de la Launde Peroune.

Hugh has granted to Nicholas a house in the vill of Tokintone with a curtilage and 6 marks annual rent from tenants [*named*] in the vill; for life, rent 7*d.* a year, and for this Nicholas has granted to Hugh and his heirs all his lands and holdings in Tokintone and Wytleigh.
Witnesses: John de Alkeleye, Roger Corbet, John de Brokeneborghe, John Corbet, Robert de Hawe.
At: Tockington.

A2/45/2 [GC 3328]   n.d. [mid 14th cent.]
Nicholas de Poyntz, lord of Curry Mallet; and William de Brythleye and Maurice de Chiltenham.

Nicholas has granted to William and Maurice, and their heirs and assigns, the manor of Tokyntone with the advowson of the chapel there, the knights' fees [etc.].
Witnesses: Sir Thomas de Bradeston, Sir Simon Basset, knights, William de Chiltenham, John Serjant, John de Clyve.

A2/45/3 [GC 3287]   n.d. [mid 14th cent.]
William de Brythleye and Maurice de Cheltenham; and Sir Nicholas de Poyntz, lord of Curry Mallet.

William and Maurice have granted to Nicholas the manor of Tokynton with the advowson of the chapel, knights' fees [etc.]; for his life, with reversion to Thomas lord of Berkel' and Katherine his wife and their male issue, remainder to the right heirs of Thomas.

Witnesses: Sir Thomas de Bradeston, Sir Simon Basset, knights, William de Chiltenham, John Serjaunt, John de Clyve.

UPTON ST. LEONARDS (GLOS.)

Upton was the only major acquisition of the 14th century which remained with the main line of the Berkeleys. It was entailed with the rest of Berkeley Herness in 1349 (above, pp. 4–6) and consequently passed from Thomas (IV) Lord Berkeley to his nephew and heir James in 1417. (For other charters connected with the holding of German de Tonbridge, see above, pp. 486–7, Sneedham.)

A2/46/1 [GC 2209]   Fri. after St. Lucy, 11 Edw. II [16 Dec. 1317]
German de Tonebrugge and Maurice de Berkel', son and heir of Sir Thomas de Berkel'.

German has granted to Maurice and his heirs all his holding of Opton Sancti Leonardi by Gloucestria, and all his holding in Snedam in Opton, with the appurtenances.
Witnesses: Sir John le Rous, Sir William de Wauton, Sir William Maunsel, knights, John le Boteler, William Waleys of Woolstrop, Walter de Wylton, Richard de Salle.
At: Upton St. Leonards.

[1] Smyth, i. 330; J. Maclean, 'The Manor of Tockington', *TBGAS* xii. 135; *GIPM* v. 309.
[2] BCM GMR 17 (cf. below, A4/2/28).

A2/46/2 [GC 2208]   Fri. after St. Lucy, 11 Edw. II [16 Dec. 1317]
(1) Maurice de Berkeleye, knight, son of Sir Thomas de Berkel'; (2) William Gamage and William de Berleye; (3) German de Tonebrugge.

Maurice has appointed William and William his attorneys to take siesin of the lands and holdings which he had by grant of German in Opton Sancti Leonardi and Snedam.
At: Upton St. Leonards.

A2/46/3 [GC 3379]   20 Nov. 25 Edw. III [1351]
Sir Thomas lord of Berkelee and Sir William de Side.

Thomas has leased to William all his lands, holdings, rents [etc.] in Uptone by Gloucestre; for his life, rent 100*s.* a year.
At: Wotton.

A2/46/4 [GC 3574]   Mon. after Michaelmas, 39 Edw. III [6 Oct. 1365]
William de Chiltenham, on behalf of the lord of Berkele, and William Elkyn of Nibley.

William de Chiltenham has leased to William Elkyn at farm for a term of 10 years all the lands and holdings of the lord of Berkele in Uptone, saving to the lord the pleas and perquisites, fines and heriots, wardships and marriages, and William shall have from the lord for the first year 6 oxen price £6, 4 quarters of wheat for seed, 6 quarters of pulse and 6 quarters of oats which he shall repay to the lord at the end of the first year, or their price, at the choice of the lord and his council, and he also has one wagon price ½ mark etc. [*itemised*].

A2/46/5 [GC 3833]   Sun. the feast of St. Stephen, 13 Ric. II [26 Dec. 1389]
Thomas de Berkeleye, lord of Berkeley; and John Webbeleye, Agnes his wife and John and John their eldest sons [*sic*].

Thomas has leased to John, Agnes, John and John his manor of Optone by Gloucestre, with all the appurtenances except the fines, wardships, marriages, reliefs, escheats, homages and reversions of holdings in fee tail; for their lives, rent £6 13*s.* 4*d.* a year.
Witnesses: Ralph Waleys, John Brounyng, William Heyberare, William Alre.
At: Wotton.

A2/46/6 [GC 3941]   20 May 21 Ric. II [1398]
Thomas Berkeley, lord of Berkeley, and John Banbury of Gloucester.

Thomas has granted to John, for his good service, the reversion of all the lands, holdings [etc.] which John Webbeleye holds for life by demise of Thomas in Uptone Leonard (Glos.), with a rent of 10 marks a year at present; for his life, rent a red rose a year.
At: Berkeley.

A2/46/7 [GAR 323]   7–8 Edw. III [1333–4]
Manorial account of Upton St. Leonards and Bentham.

WESTCOTE (GLOS.)

Robert Lord Berkeley (d. 1220) granted Westcote to Bradenstoke Priory.[1] The charter below was copied into the Great Cartulary,[2] from which the words between square brackets have been supplied to fill lacunae.

[1] *CCR* 1226–57, 161.
[2] BCM SB 10, f. 274.

A2/47/1 [SC 170]   n.d. [1190 × 1220]
Peter de Iweleia and Robert de Berkelai.

Peter has granted to Robert his land of Westcote and also Elias, his man; Robert pays an acknowledgement of 8 marks and one [robe and one horse] value 2 marks.

Witnesses: Henry the chaplain, Hugh chaplain of Lorridge (*Lorilinga*), William de Pontearche, John de [Iweleie], Adam son of Nigel, Henry de Coueleia, Bernard de Stanes, Harding de Hunteneford, Maurice son of Nigel, Elias de Bevingtuna, Maurice his son, Bernard de Brothestan, Hugh de Salso Marisco.

LAWRENCE WESTON (GLOS.)

The holdings here were merged with those at King's Weston (above, p. 298) to become the secondary manor of King's Weston, which passed to the Beverston cadet line.

A2/48/1 [GC 2002]   Thurs. before St. Thomas the apostle, 8 Edw. II [19 Dec. 1314]
Peter de Styntescombe; and William Golde and Edith his wife.

Peter has granted to William and Edith, for a certain sum of money, all his land and pasture and meadow which he has in the marsh of Westone Sancti Laurencii in the furlong called Lockyngham, in a small meadow between the sea and the meadow of Madham; for their lives, rent 5*s.* a year, and they are responsible for the sea-wall between the sea and the said land.

Witnesses: William le Botiler, Florentinus de Stoke, Thomas Jurdon, Walter Golde, Richard de Mora, clerk.

At: Lawrence Weston.

A2/48/2 [GC 2034]   Wed. the feast of St. George, 8 Edw. II [23 April 1315]
Peter de Styntescoumbe; and Roger Sely of Redland (*Thriddelonde*) and Maud his wife.

Peter has leased to Roger and Maud, for their lives, a plot of land at Lolleye in the parish of Westbur', and others at Radforlong, Dodeden, Rokkesdene, and le Westcroft, a plot of meadow in the marsh of Hembury, and plot of pasture in le Westcroft and la Grove, with half of the trees there; rent 2*s.* a year.

Witnesses: Richard de Stoke, Florentinus de Stoke, William de Thriddelonde, John de Cumbe, William Lamberd.

At: Redland.

A2/48/3 [GC 2056]   Sun. after Michaelmas, 9 Edw. II [5 Oct. 1315]
Peter de Styntescoumbe and Sir Maurice de Berkeleye.

Peter notifies his tenants, free and otherwise, of Weston Sancti Laurencii by Hembury, that he has enfeoffed Maurice of all his lands and holdings, rents [etc.] in the said vill.

At: Berkeley.

A2/48/4 [GC 2295]   Mon. the feast of St. Silvester, 13 Edw. II [31 Dec. 1319]
Maurice de Berkeleye, son of Sir Thomas de Berkeleye, knight, and John de Berkeleye, his son.

Maurice has granted to John all his holding in Westone Sancti Laurencii (Glos.), with the appurtenances, and with the reversion of the lands and holdings which Joan widow of William le Veyihn holds in dower; to John and his male issue, rent a rose a year.

Witnesses: Sir William de Suhtleye, Sir William de Wautone, knights, John de Button, John de Alcleye, John de Combe.

At: Wotton.

A2/48/5 [GC 3133]   26 Feb. 20 Edw. III [1346]
(1) William de Syde; (2) Nicholas de Faireford, chaplain; (3) Master Simon le Botiller, prebendary and chancellor of the cathedral church of Wells.

William has appointed Nicholas to receive seisin of a parcel of land in Westone Sancti Laurencii by Hembury in Salso Marisco which he had by grant of Simon.
At: Berkeley.

WESTONBIRT (GLOS.)

On many occasions William de Syde acted as a feoffee for Thomas (III) Lord Berkeley, so that the first charter below may not record Thomas's acquisition of the manor. A number of newly acquired manors were entailed in the autumn of 1344, including Syde (apparently) and Over (Glos.) and Elston (Wilts.), and it is likely that Westonbirt was one of them. It was certainly entailed on a younger son in 1349 with Syde,[1] the second charter below probably being a grant in that connection. Thomas's widow Katherine claimed dower in it (above, A2/41/3 [GC 3538]) and it eventually passed to her son John and the cadet line of Beverston. The account of 1286–7 below (A2/49/3 [GAR 324]) was of a manor held by John de Wylington (d. 1338) and apparently not that acquired by Thomas de Berkeley, since John's son and heir Ralph held a manor there at his death in 1348.[2] John's mother-in-law Margaret Giffard acquired another manor there in 1316 from Maud Brut, Alice her sister and Laurence Tresham, seemingly coheirs, and granted it in 1327 to John, who in 1332 petitioned for its restoration after it had been taken into the king's hands in 1331 following Edward III's coup of 1330.[3] His son Ralph sold parts of the Giffard inheritance to Thomas (III) de Berkeley and his brother Maurice: below, p. 540, Elston.

A2/49/1 [GC 3102]   18 Oct. 18 Edw. III [1344]
Thomas de Berkel', lord of Berkeley, and Roger atte Yate, clerk.

Thomas has appointed Roger to receive seisin of the lands, holdings and reversions in Westonbrut, and all the goods and chattels there, as in the charter of Sir William de Syde to Thomas.
At: Berkeley.

A2/49/2 [GC 3194]   Sat. after St. Edmund the king, 22 Edw. III [22 Nov. 1348]
(1) Thomas son of Maurice de Berkelee; (2) Robert Burgolon of Beverston; (3) Thomas de Besford, parson of Beverston, Roger de Estham and John le Vey, clerk.

Thomas has appointed Robert to receive seisin of the manor of Westone Brut which he had by grant of Thomas, Roger and John.
At: Beverston.

A2/49/3 [GAR 324] Manorial account   Michaelmas 14 Edw. I to 11 June 15 Edw. I
                                                                    [1286–7]
A2/49/4 [GAR 325] Manorial account of Westonbirt and Bentham   19–20 Edw. III
                                                                    [1345–6]

WICKWAR (GLOS.)

The Barbastre manor in Wickwar was settled by William Lord Berkeley on himself and his wife Joan in 1477 (see above, p. 7) and had presumably been purchased since 1440, either by his father or himself. There is no evidence of its purchase despite a good succession of charters recording its passage from the Orescoiz family to William de Stures, to the Barbastres and eventually to Richard Massenger.

---

[1] PRO CP 25/1/77/67, no. 295.
[2] *CIPM* ix, no. 103.
[3] *CIM* ii, no. 1291.

THE BARBASTRE MANOR

A2/50/1 [SC 66]   n.d. [late 12th cent.]
Richard son of Elias Orescoiz and Walter de Stures.

Richard has granted to Walter, with Agatha his kinswoman, a half-virgate of land, which Walter son of Edward held, and half of Benleigemore, which the same Walter held, in the vill of Wiche; rent 1 lb. of pepper at Michaelmas.

Witnesses: Thomas and William, brothers of the lord, Lady Ida, wife of the lord, Roger le Scai, Lioffus de Wic', Robert son of Archibald, Roger de la Hethe, Roger de Rivers (*de Ripariis*), Ernald Barbast, Walter de Suint', Richard clerk of Suit', Richard and Henry sons of Lioffus, Thomas clerk of Dudinton, Elias chaplain of Wick, Robert de Cromale, William the chaplain.

A2/50/2 [GC 969]   n.d. [early 14th cent.]
William Storing; and Philip Barbast, son of Thomas Barbast, and Alice, William's daughter.

William has granted to Philip and Alice all his lands and the holding of his inheritance in the vill of Wykewarr, viz. that which Richard son of Elias Erescoyt granted to Walter de Stores with Agatha his kinswoman.

Witnesses: Jordan de Holdeburie, Laurence de Hildesle, John de Chalkesle, Reginald de Tonwelle, John de Brokeneborewe.

A2/50/3 [GC 655]   Wed. after the nativity of St. John the Baptist, 27 Edw. I [1 July 1299]
Roger son of Thomas Barbastre of Wickwar and Alice widow of Philip Barbastre, his late brother.

Roger has granted to Alice all his lands and holdings in the vill of Wykewarre for her life.

Witnesses: Sir Roger le Warr, Sir John de Actone, Sir William de Wauton, knights, John de la Hay, Adam Camupe of Winterbourne.

At: Wickwar.

A2/50/4 [GC 1698]   Wed. after St. Petronilla, 2 Edw. II [4 June 1309]
Roger son of Thomas Barbastre of Wickwar and Alice widow of Philip Barbastre of Wickwar.

Roger has quitclaimed to Alice all the lands which she holds for life by his demise in Wikewarr.

Witnesses: Roger Corbet of Earthcott, John de Alkeleye, Roger Camps of Winterbourne, William Colewich of Charfield, William de la Hay, Adam Blacwyne of Oudeby, Robert Russel of Kibworth, William de Kylyngworth, William Foaurcoun of [Smeeton] Westerby.

At: Kibworth

A2/50/5 [GC 1710]   Sun. after the decollation of St. John the Baptist, 3 Edw. II
[31 Aug. 1309]
Roger son of Philip Barbastre of Wickwar and Alice widow of Philip Barbastre.

Roger has granted to Alice a messuage and 1 virgate of land in Wikwarre, viz. that which Roger son of Thomas Barbastre formerly held; for her life, rent 1*d.* a year.

Witnesses: Roger Corbet of Earthcott, John de Alkeleye, William Colewith, William de la Hay, William Bousihan.

At: Wickwar.

A2/50/6 [GC 2234]   St. Mark, 11 Edw. II [25 April 1318]
Thomas son of Philip Barbastre and Roger son of Philip Barbastre, his brother.

Thomas has quitclaimed to Roger, his heirs and assigns, a messuage and a half-virgate of land in Wykewarr', which William de Stoure granted to Philip Barbastre and Alice, Thomas's mother, and which Alice in her widowhood granted to Roger.

Witnesses: William de la Hay, John de Alkeleye, John de Staundone, John de Chiltone, Andrew de Didinham.
At: Wickwar.

A2/50/7 [GC 3187]   Sun. after St. Luke, 22 Edw. III [19 Oct. 1348]
Roger Barbastre of Wickwar and Emma Barbastre, his sister.
   Roger has leased to Emma a plot of land in le Westcrofte, extending above Caldewellestreme; for her life and one year, rent 4*d.* a year.
Witnesses: Geoffrey de Langetone, Geoffrey Wynebaud, John ate Slo of Doddington, William le Forester, William le Bosce.
At: Wickwarr.

A2/50/8 [GC 3393]   Eve of St. John the Baptist, 26 Edw. III [23 June 1352]
(1) Roger Barbast of Wickwar; (2) Thomas le Tornor; (3) Richard Barbast and Alice his wife.
   Roger has appointed Thomas to give seisin to Richard and Alice and their issue, of 1 carucate of land in Wykewarr'.
Witnesses: Reginald de Colne, Henry de Strode, William le Best.
At: Wickwar.

A2/50/9 [GC 3394]   St. John the Baptist, 26 Edw. III [24 June 1352]
Roger Barbast; and Richard son of Lucy Barbast and Alice his wife.
   Roger has granted to Richard and Alice and their issue all the lands and holdings which he had by grant of Alice Barbast, late his mother; rent for Roger's life 5 marks a year.
Witnesses: Nicholas Wynebaud, John Joye, John ate Sloe, William West', Nicholas Bourham.
At: Wickwar.

A2/50/10 [GC 3596]   Fri. after St. S[cholast]ica, 42 Edw. III [11 Feb. 1368]
Walter le Parker of Stanton Harcourt and John Barbast of Wickwar.
   Walter has quitclaimed to John all personal actions.
At: Gloucester.

A2/50/11 [SC 545]   St. Benedict, 1369 [4 Dec. 1369]
Nicholas prior of the Austin Friars, Bristol; and John Barbast and Alice his wife.
   Nicholas has promised to John and Alice, in return for their generosity to his order, certain spiritual benefits.
At: Bristol.

A2/50/12 [GC 3726]   4 July 2 Ric. II [1378]
Eve Barbast, daughter of Alexander Barbast of Wickwar, and Thomas Tornour of Wickwar.
   Eve has quitclaimed to Thomas the lands and holdings which she had by inheritance in Wykewarre.
Witnesses: Richard le Vale, William Beste, Thomas the clerk (*clerus*).
At: Wickwar.

A2/50/13 [GC 3760]   Mon. before the Annunciation, 6 Ric. II [23 March 1383]
Richard Vale of Wickwar and Edith Barbast of the same.
   Richard has granted to Edith, her heirs and assigns a burgage in the borough of Wykewar', which he had by grant of Henry atte Home.
Witnesses: John Barbast, John Haddecombe, William Aylward, John Stanbourne, William le Beste.
At: Wickwar.

A2/50/14 [GC 4205]   Holy Innocents, 15 Hen. VI [28 Dec. 1436]
Joan Barabast of Gloucester and Richard Messenger, her son and heir.

Whereas Edith Barabast, sister of Joan, held . . . within the lordship of Wykewarre when she died which Joan inherited, Joan has appointed Richard to take seisin.
At: Gloucester.

A2/50/15 [GC 4214]   10 March 18 Hen. VI [1440]
John Vale, chaplain, David Massynger, John Wynslade, burgess of Gloucester, and John Brayn; and Richard Egton of Newport and Thomas Wodeward.

John, David, John and John have granted to Richard and Thomas, and their heirs and assigns, all the land, holdings [etc.] in Wykewarr (Glos.) which they had by grant of Richard Massynger.
Witnesses: Thomas Staunton, John Oldelond, John Hervy, John Dosy, Robert Wytt.
At: Wickwar.

THE LEGAT HALF-VIRGATE

A2/50/16 [GC 3540]   Sun. before Corpus Christi, 37 Edw. III [28 May 1363]
Nicholas Bourham, son and heir of the late John Bourham of Wickwar; and Adam Legat of Wotton-under-Edge and Margery his wife.

Nicholas has granted to Adam and Margery, and Adam's heirs and assigns, a messuage and half-virgate in Wykewarre, which William Bourham had by grant of Sir Roger le Warre, lord of Wykewarre.
Witnesses: Sir Peter de Veel, John Sergeant the younger, William Heneg, Richard Vale of Wickwarr, Thomas le Tornour of the same.
At: Wickwar.

A2/50/17 [GC 3541]   Fri. after Corpus Christi, 37 Edw. III [2 June 1363]
Nicholas Bourham, son and heir of the late John Bourham of Wickwar; and Adam Legat of Wotton-under-Edge and Margery his wife.

Nicholas has quitclaimed to Adam and Margery a messuage and half-virgate in Wykewarre, which William Bourham had by grant of Sir Roger le Warre, lord of Wykewarre, and also a messuage with a curtilage to the west of the half-virgate.
At: Wickwar.

A2/50/18 [GC 3615]   26 March 44 Edw. III [1370]
John de Stanshawe and Adam Legat.

Whereas John was impleaded for a half-virgate of land which he held of Adam in Wykewarre, Adam has vouched and warranted it to him for his life. [*In French.*]
At: Wotton.

BOROUGH HOLDINGS

A2/50/19 [GC 3602]   Sun. after . . . 42 [Edw. III, *c.* 1368]
John . . . and . . .

John has quitclaimed to . . . in the borough of Wykewarr, which burgage and a half he had by grant of . . . for the term of his life.
Witnesses: . . . John Wythur.
At: Wickwar.

A2/50/20 [GC 3661]   Fri. after St. Laurence, 47 Edw. III [12 Aug. 1373]
Agnes Bryd and John Robynes.

Agnes has granted to John, his heirs and assigns a burgage with appurtenances in the borough of Wykewarre.
Witnesses: Richard Vaal, Richard Stanbourne, Thomas Tournor.
At: Wickwar.

THE IVORY HOLDING

A2/50/21 [GC 4078]   St. Nicholas [*unfinished*] [mid 14th cent.]
Adam Ivory of Kingswood and Roger de Hortone.
    Adam has quitclaimed to Roger 3 crofts in the lordship of Haukesbury.
Witnesses: Elias Chalkeley, John atte Halle, Nicholas Wynebaud, John atte More.
At: Hawkesbury.

A2/50/22 [GC 3440]   Mon. after the Purification, 30 Edw. III [8 Feb. 1356]
John Baiouse; and John Doly, vicar of Hawkesbury, and William his brother.
    John has quitclaimed to John and William the lands and holdings which were of Adam
Ivory in Haukesbury and Wikewarre.
Witnesses: Richard de Chalkele, John Joye, John Wynebald, Laurence de Wike, William
Best, Thomas Tornor.
At: Hawkesbury.

A2/50/23 [GC 3454]   Fri. the feast of St. Martin, 30 Edw. III [11 Nov. 1356]
John Doly, vicar of Hawkesbury, and William Doly, his brother; and Isabel daughter and
heir of William Ivory of Hawkesbury.
    John and William have quitclaimed to Isabel all the lands and holdings which Adam
Ivory formerly held in the vills of Haukesbury and Wykewarr at le Sterte.
Witnesses: William de Cheltenham, John Joye, John Wynbald, John Trageys, and Richard
Trageys.
At: Hawkesbury.

YATE (?) (GLOS.)

The manor was acquired by the Berkeley family late in the 15th century and, after the
Castle had passed to Henry VII, it became the family's principal residence. See also above,
p. 471, Horton.

A2/51/1 [GC 2807]   Wed. after Epiphany, 8 Edw. III [11 Jan. 1335]
(1) John de Wylyngton, lord of Yate; (2) Thomas de Sancto Maniseo and Joan his wife;
(3) Sir William de Wautone, knight.
John has assigned Thomas and Joan to attorn their homage and fealty to William.
At: Yate.

YORKLEY (GLOS.)

A number of small holdings at Aylburton, Purton, Newland, Lydney, Tutnalls, Nass and
Yorkley, bought by Thomas (III) Lord Berkeley between 1340 and 1350 (see above,
pp. 432, 471, 477, 480), seem to have been combined into a manor which was called
Yorkley. After Thomas's death the 'manor' seems to have been abandoned and by 1368 it
was represented by two holdings at Tutnalls and Purton, which consisted mostly of rents.

A2/52/1 [GC 3002]   Thurs. after the decollation of St. John the Baptist, 15 Edw. III
                                                                    [30 Aug. 1341]
(1) Thomas lord of Berkeleye; (2) Adam Purlewent and John ate Churche of Purton;
(3) John Bray.
    Thomas has appointed Adam and John to receive in his name seisin of the lands and
holdings which Thomas had by grant of John Bray in Pirtone, Newelond and Yarkeleye in
the Forest of Dean, as in his charter. [*In French*.]
At: Berkeley.

A2/52/2 [GAR 326]   19–20 Edw. III [1345–6]
Manorial account in two rolls (Michaelmas 19 Edw. III to 27 May, and 27 May to
Michaelmas 20 Edw. I), and an indenture of inventory, attached at the foot.

BURGHILL (HEREFS.)

Thomas (III) Lord Berkeley attempted to acquire the reversion of the manors of Burghill and Tillington through an agreement with Roger de Burghill which is reflected in the first four charters below. By the agreement Roger granted the manors to Thomas who regranted them to Roger and his wife Sibyl and their issue, with reversion to Thomas if they died without issue. Thomas was bound in £3,000 to ensure that he made the regrant, and the Berkeley receiver's account for 1327 records that Roger received £100 for, in effect, granting the reversion to Thomas.[1] The agreement had evidently lapsed by 1336 (below, A2/53/5 [GC 2844]), and Roger's lands passed to the Eylesford family: in 1336 Roger granted the reversion of his manor of Westbury on Severn (Glos.) to William de Eylesford,[2] and William's son John de Eylesford died in 1396 holding Tillington of Thomas (IV) Lord Berkeley.[3] References to Burghill in the account rolls for Ham manor cease after 1336; they evidently relate to small holdings temporarily in Thomas (III)'s possession, for which accounts survive for 1332–4. That Thomas was in an almost unassailable position as Mortimer's son-in-law at the time of the agreement of 1327, and that he was still on trial for complicity in the death of Edward II in 1336 when it had lapsed, suggest the possibility that Roger's role was not entirely voluntary and that he took the opportunity to back out.

AGREEMENT ABOUT BURGHILL AND TILLINGTON, 1327

A2/53/1 [GC 2632**; *duplicate* GC 2632***]   One week after St. John the Baptist,
                                                              1 Edw. III [1 July 1327]
Roger de Burghull and Sibyl his wife; and Thomas de Berkeleye.
    Final concord concerning the manors of Burghull and Tullynton; Roger has acknowledged the right of Thomas by his gift, and for this Thomas has granted the manors to Roger and Sibyl and their issue, to hold of Thomas and his heirs, rent a rose a year; if they die without issue, the manors will remain to Thomas and his heirs.
At: York.

A2/53/2 [GC 2633]   9 July 1 Edw. III [1327]
Roger de Bourghull and Sir Thomas de Berkeleye.
    Roger has granted to Thomas, his heirs and assigns all his manor of Tullyntone and two thirds of the manor of Bourghull (Herefs.).
Witnesses: Sir Gilbert Talebot, Sir Richard de Baskervile, Sir Reginald de Abbehale, knights, William Gamage, Adam Lucas, Henry de Hulle, Henry de Chaxhulle.
At: Gloucester.

A2/53/3 [GC 2634]   9 July 1 Edw. III [1327]
Roger de Bourghulle and Sir Thomas de Berkele.
    Whereas Thomas is bound to Roger in £3,000 to be paid at the feast of St. Peter in chains [1 Aug.] next following, Roger wills that if Thomas grants to Roger and Sibyl his wife the manors of Tullyntone and two thirds of the manor of Bourghull in the king's court, to them and their issue, he will give up to Thomas the bond of £3,000.
At: Gloucester.

A2/53/4 [GC 3284]   . . . July . . . Edw. III [*c.* 1327]
Thomas lord of Berkeleye and [Henry] de Rokhulle.
    Thomas has appointed Henry to receive seisin of the manor of Tullynton and two thirds of the manor of Bourghull.

---

[1] BCM SR 39 (below, A4/2/7).
[2] PRO CP 25/1/77/61, no. 129.
[3] PRO C 136/87, no. 22.

A2/53/5 [GC 2844]   15 April 10 Edw. III [1336]
Roger de Bourghull and Sir Thomas son of Maurice de Berkeleye.

   Roger has released to Thomas all personal actions, viz. of debts, contracts, tripartite covenants [etc.] [*In French.*]

At: Tillington.

HOLDINGS IN BURGHILL

A2/53/6 [GC 1263]   n.d. [late 13th cent.]
Roger de Burchulle, lord of Tillington, and Walter his son.

   Roger has quitclaimed to Walter 2 messuages in Hulle and 30 a. of land.

Witnesses: Robert de Bere, Simon de Crowenhulle, Henry Moris, William de Miners, John Germasyn, Richard Rostot, Roger Lucas, Simon de Ledelawe, clerk.

A2/53/7 [GC 1268]   n.d. [late 13th cent.]
Roger de Burghulle, lord of Tillington, and Walter de Burghulle, his son.

   Roger has granted to Walter, for his laudable service, the messuage which Henry de Burghulle, Roger's brother, formerly held in the vill of Burghulle, with the garden and croft and land in the fields called Poddynghullesfeld and Coppedethorne, and the land within the ditch called le Parkesdyche, and his land of Horneshulle; further his land in the field called Upfeld and in the field called Conynghullesfeld with le Stokkyng, and the land within the ditch called le Oldedych, and 16 a. in le Ruevorlong, and half of his wood called le Mynerspark, next to the wood of Henry de Burghulle, Roger's son, and 4 a. of meadow in Lugheye, half of his pasture of Conemars and Puldesturne and Lolukedene, and rents of 50*s.*; for his life.

Witnesses: Richard de Hampton, Walter de Evereus, knights, Walter de Frene, Thomas le Wafre, Andrew de Chandos, Walter de Burghope, Richard de Bagyngdene, Robert de la Bere, Richard de Hoggeshawe.

A2/53/8 [GC 2654; *duplicate* GC 3415]   Fri. after St. Barnabas, 2 Edw. III [17 June 1328]
Roger de Boruhulle and Sir Thomas lord of Berkeleye.

   Roger acknowledges a messuage, 1 carucate of land and 60*s.* of rent which Walter de Boruhulle holds for life by demise of Roger de Boruhulle, Roger's grandfather, in the manors of Boruhulle and Tulynton (Herefs.), and a rent of £4 which John de Merchston holds for life by demise of Roger the younger in the same manors, and 4 a. of wood which Adam Lucas holds for a term of 20 years by demise of Roger the younger, and all reversions of holdings held of him for terms of lives or years in the said county, to be the right of Thomas, and concedes that all the holdings ought to revert to Thomas after the deaths of Walter, John, Adam [etc.].

Witnesses: John de Oulepenne, Peter de Styntescombe, Elias de Fyltone, John Mylkesham, Richard de Beodelescombe.

At: Gloucester.

A2/53/9 [GC 2662]   Sun. after All Saints, 2 Edw. III [6 Nov. 1328]
(1) Thomas lord of Berkeleye; (2) John de Clyve and Richard de Harsefeld; (3) Roger de Bourghull.

   Thomas has appointed John and Richard to receive the attornments of all the tenants of Roger in Herefs. who hold for terms of lives or years, which Roger granted to Thomas. [*In French.*]

At: Berkeley.

A2/53/10 [GC 2667]   20 Feb. 3 Edw. III [1329]
Adam Lucas and Thomas de Berkeleye, lord of Berkeley.

   Adam has attorned to Thomas for the wood and pasture which he holds for a term of

years by demise of Roger de Borghulle and the reversion of which Roger has granted to Thomas and his heirs.
At: Berkeley.

A2/53/11 [GC 2668]   20 Feb. 3 Edw. III [1329]
(1) Roger de Borghulle; (2) Adam Lucas; (3) Thomas de Berkeleye, lord of Berkeley.

Whereas Roger granted to Adam a plot of wood and pasture in the manor of Borghulle for a term of 20 years, and Roger then granted the reversion of the said wood and pasture to Thomas and his heirs, and Adam has attorned to Thomas, Thomas has granted that Adam may hold the said wood and pasture for the said term.
At: Berkeley.

A2/53/12 [GC 2673]   . . . Feb. 3 Edw. III [1329]
John de Mersshtone and Eleanor his wife; and Thomas de Berkeleye, lord of Berkeley.

John and Eleanor have attorned to Thomas for the [lands] which John holds for life by demise of [Roger de] Borghulle and of which Roger has granted the reversion to Thomas.
At: [Berkeley].

A2/53/13 [GC 2669]   Wed. the feast of St. Peter in cathedra, 3 Edw. III [22 Feb. 1329]
Walter de Borghulle and Sir Thomas, lord of Berkel'.

Walter has attorned to Thomas for all the lands and holdings which he holds for life by demise of Roger de Borghulle his ancestor, the reversion of which Roger has granted to Thomas and his heirs.
At: Berkeley.

A2/53/14 [GC 2670]   Wed. the feast of St. Peter in cathedra, 3 Edw. III [22 Feb. 1329]
(1) Thomas lord of Berkel'; (2) Hugh de Stoke; (3) Walter de Borghulle.

Thomas has appointed Hugh to receive in his name the fealty of Walter for the holding which Walter holds for life by demise of Roger de Borghulle.
At: Berkeley.

A2/53/15 [GC 3286]   n.d. [c. 1329]
Roger de Bourghull and Thomas son of Maurice de Berkeleye.

Roger has quitclaimed to Thomas the lands and holdings which Thomas holds in Bourghull, which Walter son of Roger de Bourghull formerly held.
Witnesses: William de Eylnsford, knight, John Bot', parson of Staunden, Richard de Laber, Adam Lucas, Philip de Marstone.

MANORIAL ACCOUNTS

A2/53/16 [GAR 347]   6–7 Edw. III [1332–3]
A2/53/17 [GAR 348]   7–8 Edw. III [1333–4]

CANNON BRIDGE (HEREFS.)

See above, p. 504, Burghill.

A2/54/1 [GC 2426]   Sun. before St. Kenelm, 18 Edw. II [15 July 1324]
Roger son of Roger de Bourghull and Agnes daughter of Gerard de Eylesford.

Roger has sold to Agnes, for a certain sum of money, custody of the lands and heir of Walter Ilour in Canonebrugg' until the full age of the heir.
At: King's Pyon.

EYNESBURY (HUNTS.)

Eynesbury came to the Berkeleys with Joan de Ferrers, wife of Thomas (II) Lord Berkeley (d. 1321). Joan's mother Margaret was one of the three daughters and heirs of Roger de Quincy, earl of Winchester, and although Margaret's own third of the manor descended in the Ferrers family, she acquired the portion of one of her sisters, which was settled on Thomas and Joan.[1] It was later settled on their second son Thomas, who established the cadet branch in Leicestershire (see below, this page, Coston.)

A2/55/1 [SR 25]
Copies of charters relating to the families of the Quincy earls of Winchester and the Ferrers earls of Derby.

AUSTIN, IN EYNSFORD (KENT)

The manors of Austin (*Orkesdon*) and Chiddingstone, with other holdings in Aldington, Boardfield, Shelve and 'Shardmarsh', were settled on Joan, daughter of Thomas (III) Lord Berkeley, in jointure with her husband Reginald Cobham, and it appears that Thomas was one of the feoffees for the transaction.[2] The lands do not otherwise appear in Berkeley hands. The Great Cartulary records another grant by Cobham to his feoffee Thomas de Fitlyng of the manor of Prynkham and holdings in 'Stonhurste' and East Grinstead (Surrey) and holdings in 'Nongare', Cooling and Cliffe, Stoke, Hoo, Bromhey, Frindsbury, 'Weldham', Halstow, 'Neuheth' and Hadlow (Kent).[3]

A2/56/1 [GC 3013]   19 June 16 Edw. III [1342]
(1) Reginald de Cobham; (2) his tenants; (3) Sir Thomas, lord of Berkeleye.
   Whereas Reginald has granted his manors of Orkesdon and Chidingstone and his holdings in Bourdefelde, Schelve and Aldintone and his marsh of Schardemersche to Thomas, as in his charter, he wills that his tenants attorn to Thomas for their fealties and services [etc.]
At: Berkeley.

A2/56/2 [GC 3017]   . . . June 16 Edw. III [1342]
Reginald de Cobham and [Thomas] lord of Berkeleye.
   Reginald has granted to [Thomas] all his goods and chattels in the manors of Orkesdon and Chedingstone, in the holdings of . . . and Aldintone and in the marsh of Schardemersche.

A2/56/3 [GC 3018]   1 July 16 Edw. III [1342]
Thomas de Berkeleye and William Curteys.
   Thomas has appointed William to receive in his name seisin of the manors of Orkesdone and Cheddyngstone, and holdings in Bourdefeld, Schelve and Aldyntone and of the marsh of Shardemerssh, as in the charter to himself and Thomas de Fitlyng.

COSTON (LEICS.)

Coston was brought to Thomas (II) Lord Berkeley by his wife Joan de Ferrers. Like her other manor of Eynesbury (Hunts.), it was settled on their second son Thomas and descended in the cadet branch which he founded in Leicestershire.[4]

A2/57/1 [SC 369]   n.d. [1260 × 1262]
Robert de Ferrers, son and heir of William de Ferrers, late earl of Derby, and Joan de Ferrers, his sister.
   Robert has granted to Joan and her issue the manor of Caston (Leics.), to hold at a rent of [100 gold threads].[5]
Witnesses: Sir Roger de Quency, earl of Winchester, Sir Richard de Clare, earl of

---

[1] *VCH Hunts*. ii. 273.
[2] *CPR 1361–4*, 129; *CCR 1360–4*, 231.
[3] BCM SB 10, f. 345.
[4] Ibid. f. 351.
[5] The lacuna has been filled from the copy in the Great Cartulary, BCM SB 10, f. 350v.

Gloucester, Sir Simon de Montfort, earl of Leicester, Sir Thomas de Ferrers, Robert's uncle, William de Ferrers, Robert's brother, William de Oyli, knight, Roger de Luvetot, . . .

A2/57/2 [GC 847]   n.d. [late 13th cent.]
Thomas de Berkelee, lord of Berkeley, and Maurice de Berkelee, his son.

Thomas has granted to Maurice the rent of a pair of gold spurs, which Thomas de Berkelee, son of Thomas, renders for the manors of Coston (Leics.) and Eynesbur' (Hunts.) *Witnesses*: Sir Roger le Brabazon, Sir John Hamelyn, Sir Nicholas son of Ralph, knights, Roger le Brut, Robert de Tothale, William Launcelyn, Thomas de Stapelho.

WYMONDHAM (LEICS.)

The purchaser was Thomas de Berkeley of Coston and Eynsbury, second son of Thomas (II) Lord Berkeley and Joan de Ferrers. He married Isabel, daughter and heir of Sir John Hamelyn of Wymondham.

A2/58/1 [GC 2258]   Morrow of St. Martin, 12 Edw. II [12 Nov. 1318]
Thomas de Berkele; and John de Charneles of Wymondham.

Copy of final concord concerning a messuage and 1 carucate of land in Wymundeham and Thorp; John has acknowledged the right of Thomas, and for this Thomas has granted the land to John for his life, with reversion to Thomas.
At: Westminster.

LONDON, ATHELINGSTRETE

The charter, with several others relating to it, appears in the Great Cartulary although the Berkeley connection is not apparent. The Lisles had a holding in London of St. Bartholomew's Priory but it lay in the parish of St. Sepulchre.[1] The grant by Joan de Huntingfield mentioned in the charter is dated 10 Oct. 1336 like that charter, which describes her as the late Joan, and records that she and her late husband had acquired the holding from John de Waledone and his wife Margery. By Jan. 1371 the holding, then described as two shops with a solar built over it in Athelardeslane, was held by Thomas Bonet's widow Cecilia, then married to Adam Haket, citizen of London. Thomas Bonet's heir was his nephew Thomas, son of his brother John, and the nephew had granted the reversion to Thomas Coston, 'pouchemaker' and citizen, who had then granted the reversion to Adam Fermer and Robert Mannoer, 'cultellar' and citizen.[2]

A2/59/1 [GC 2850]   Thurs. after St. Faith, 10 Edw. III [10 Oct. 1336]
John son and heir of Sir Walter de Huntyngfeld, knight; and Thomas Bonet and John Bonet, his brother, citizens and boatmen of London.

John has quitclaimed to Thomas and John a holding which they had by grant of the late Joan, widow of the said Walter his father, in the parish of St. Gregory near the church of St. Paul, London, in Athelingstrete.
Witnesses: Reginald de Conductu', mayor of the city of London, John de Northall called le Clerk, Simon de Turnham, John Tornegold, Richard de Pynnore, Roger de Bernes, William de Rotenhale, William le Haptere, John de Hales, Henry Brenge.
At: London.

CRANFORD (MIDDX.)

Cranford was divided between two manors, Cranford St. John, held by the Knights Templar and later by the Knights Hospitaller, and Cranford le Mote. Both manors, with lands in Heston and East Bedfont, were bought in 1618 by Elizabeth, widow of Sir Thomas

---

[1] BCM SB 10, f. 353v., a rent payment in 1366.
[2] Ibid. ff. 352–353v.

Berkeley (d. 1611) and descended in the Berkeley family thereafter.[1]

THE HICKBRED OR ATTE WELLE HOLDING

A2/60/1 [GC 3080]   Wed. before the conception of the Virgin Mary, 17 Edw. III
[3 Dec. 1343]
Roger de Salyngg and Alan de Tothulle of East Bedfont.
   Roger has granted to Alan, his heirs and assigns his curtilage in the vill of Craunford,
which he had by grant of William atte Sperte.
Witnesses: William atte Wodehalle, Gregory atte Wyke, Richard atte Ford, John le
Chapman, Edmund Trewe, John le Parker, John West.
At: East Bedfont.

A2/60/2 [GC 3564]   Sun. after St. Martin, 38 Edw. III [17 Nov. 1364]
Alan de Tothull and Robert de Blatherwyk.
   Alan has granted to Robert, his heirs and assigns, a messuage with a garden and 2 a. of
land with meadow in Craunford.
Witnesses: Ralph Hikkebrid, Edmund Trewe, William Hikkebrid.
At: Cranford.

A2/60/3 [GC 3567]   Sun. the feast of the Purification, 39 Edw. III [2 Feb. 1365]
Robert de Blatherwike and Ralph Hikbrid of Cranford.
   Robert has granted to Ralph, his heirs and assigns a messuage and 2 a. of land in
Craunford.
Witnesses: Edmund Trewe, William Michel, William Hikbrid, John Agger.
At: Cranford.

A2/60/4 [GC 3742]   Friday the feast of St. Laurence the martyr, 4 Ric. II [10 Aug. 1380]
Ralph ate Welle of Cranford and William his son.
   Ralph has granted to William, his heirs and assigns, a messuage with a garden and 2 a. of
land in Craunford.
Witnesses: William Michel, Hugh Bakwelle, Richard atte Solere, John Veysy, John
Symme.
At: Cranford.

A2/60/5 [GC 3840]   St. Matthew, 14 Ric. II [21 Sept. 1390]
Ralph atte Welle of Cranford; and William of Cranford his son, cordwainer, and Agnes his
wife.
   Ralph has granted to William and Agnes, their heirs and assigns, 2½ a. of land in le
Northfeld of Craunford.
Witnesses: John Symme, William Mychell, John Pellyng, Hugh Bakwelle, Richard Soler.
At: Cranford.

A2/60/6 [GC 4374]   1 March 12 Edw. IV [1473]
Thomas Brecchemer of Harlington (Middx.), husbandman, and William atte Welle *alias*
William Hickebrid of Cranford, son and heir of Thomas atte Welle *alias* Thomas Hickebrid.
   Thomas has demised to William all the lands, holdings [etc.] in Craneford and Heston
which he [Thomas] and the late John Veysy of Hardyngton[2] had by grant of the said
Thomas atte Welle, father of William.
Witnesses: William Weylond of Cranford, Nicholas atte Moote of the same, Richard Veysy
of Hardington, John Bischop of the same, the elder, Nicholas Molle of the same, Robert

---

[1] *VCH Middx.* iii. 179–80.
[2] 'Hardington' was an early form of the place-name Harlington: *VCH Middx.* iii. 261; cf. Ekwall,
Dict. of Eng. Place-Names.

Hobard of the same, Roger Tayler of the same.
At: Cranford.

CRANFORD ST. JOHN

Edmund earl of Cornwall (d. 1300), first cousin of King Edward I, held the manor of
Isleworth. Part of the manor, Osterley and Heston, eventually passed to the daughters
and heirs of Sir Michael Stanhope, of whom, Elizabeth married George Lord Berkeley
(d. 1658).[1] For the Stanhope lands see below, pp. 936–45.

A2/60/7 [SC 463]   3 Dec. 28 Edw. I [1299]
Edmund earl of Cornwall; and the master and brethren of the Knights of the Temple of
Solomon in England and their tenants of Cranford.

   Edmund has granted to the brethren and their tenants common of pasture and heathland
within the hundred of Isleworth, viz. from Cranford to the vill of Twickenham in length,
and from Babworth Bridge to Hundesloue in breadth.
Witnesses: Hugh abbot of Hayles, Walter de Ailesburie, Roger de Marlow, William Mole,
Edmund's steward of Berkhampstead.
At: Hailes.

GREAT ROLLRIGHT (OXON.)

Great Rollright had formed part of the estate of the Despenser family but they lost many of
their lands. Sir Adam (d. 1295) sold two other manors in addition to his mortgage of Great
Rollright to Robert and Philip Burnell (below, A2/61/1 [GC 536]), and his son Aymer sold
King's Stanley (above, p. 487) and another.[2] The king's grant of Great Rollright to Maurice
(III) Lord Berkeley may have been made to compensate for the Berkeleys' loss of King's
Stanley to John Giffard of Brimpsfield (above, p. 487); it is perhaps significant that Adam
Despenser's quitclaim to Maurice was made at Brimpsfield: below, A2/61/2 [GC 2101].
Maurice is said to have forfeited Great Rollright in 1322,[3] but the Burnells evidently
regained or retained the manor: Robert Burnell's sister and heir Maud and her husband John
de Haudlo, who had livery of the Burnell inheritance in Feb. 1316, had livery of Great
Rollright in May 1317.[4] See also below, H1/9/1 [GC 4095]. The Berkeley retainer William
de Gamages at his death in 1346 held a manor in Great Rollright which may have been the
Berkeleys', granted to him by Thomas (III) Lord Berkeley.[5]

A2/61/1 [GC 536]   Sun. after Easter, 16 Edw. I [4 April 1288]
Robert Burnel, bishop of Bath and Wells, and Philip Burnel; and Sir Adam le Despenser,
knight.

   Adam has enfeoffed Robert and Philip in the manor of Magna Rollingdryth (Oxon.), for
£55 11*s.* ½*d.*, and after 8 years they will restore the manor to Adam and his heirs.
At: London.

A2/61/2 [GC 2101]   1 June 9 Edw. II [1316]
Aymer le Despenser, son and heir of the late Sir Adam le Despenser, and Sir Maurice de
Berkeleye.

   Aymer has quitclaimed to Maurice and his heirs the manor of Rollingrygt Mangna
(Oxon.) with the advowson of the church, which was of his ancestors and later came into
the hands of the king, who demised it to Maurice.
Witnesses: Sir Richard Dammary, Sir John Mautravers the younger, Sir William de

---

[1] *VCH Middx*. iii. 103, 109.
[2] *GEC* iv. 287–8.
[3] Smyth, i. 274.
[4] *GEC* vi. 400.
[5] *CIPM* viii, no. 678.

Wautone, Sir Thomas de Byngham, knights, William de Brocworth, Robert de Presteburi, John de Elkeston, William de Gamage, Adam le Mareschal of Cirencester.
At: Brimpsfield.

ROCKHILL (SALOP.)

Thomas (III) Lord Berkeley is said to have bought holdings in 'Rochull, Whitton, Grete and Stoke' (Rockhill, Whitton, Greete and Stoke) in 1330 from John Blake and his wife Petronilla[1] but there is no surviving charter to support the statement other than those of 1330 and 1332 below. Greete and Whitton lie together, just over the border from Eastham (Worcs.), and they may have been administered from the manor at Eastham, which included rents from holdings at nearby Tenbury Wells (Worcs.), Burford and Overton (Salop.)

A2/62/1 [GC 1823]   Mon. the feast of the Invention of Holy Cross, 4 Edw. II [3 May 1311]
John son of William le Blake of Rockhill and Henry son of Robert de Rochulle.
    John, with the assent of Petronilla his wife, has granted to Henry all the holding which was of Simon de Rochulle, brother of Henry, in Rochulle; to him and his issue.
Witnesses: Henry de Rok', William Coterel, Philip le Proude of . . ., Geoffrey de Rochulle, Hugh Tunni, Thomas Aubyn, Nicholas de Stoke.
At: Rockhill.

A2/62/2 [GC 2211]   Tues. after St. Thomas the martyr, 11 Edw. II [3 Jan. 1318]
Henry de Rok'; and Margery le Blake and Nicholas her son.
    Henry has granted to Margery and Nicholas, and their heirs and assigns, for a certain sum of money, all his meadow at le Bruehe and 8 selions of land above le Bruehe. Endorsed: *Rokhulle* [*in a contemporary hand*].
Witnesses: Reginald de Stoke, John le Blake, Geoffrey de Rochulle, Thomas Aubyn, Philip Stengket.
At: Stoke.

A2/62/3 [GC 516]   Sun. after one week after the Purification, 13 Edw. II [10 Feb. 1320]
Robert Bagard and Henry de Rochulle.
    Robert has agreed that Henry should make a new road in Rochulle, and Henry has agreed that Robert should have access to the spring of Caldewelle in Henry's enclosure.
At: Rockhill.

A2/62/4 [GC 2339]   Mon. after St. Hilary, 14 Edw. II [19 Jan. 1321]
Robert Bagard and Henry de Rochull, clerk.
    Robert has granted to Henry, his heirs and assigns, for a certain sum of money, 9 selions of land in Rochulle.
Witnesses: John le Blake of Rockhill, Geoffrey of the same, Reginald de Stoke, John Simon of Greete, Nicholas le Blake of Stoke.
At: Rockhill.

A2/62/5 [GC 2716]   Wed. the feast of St. Stephen, 4 Edw. III [26 Dec. 1330]
John le Blake of Rockhill and Sir Thomas, lord of Berkel'.
    John has granted to Thomas, his heirs and assigns, 9 a. of land in Rokhulle, of which 4 a. lie in the furlong called Heetheshale and 5 a. in the furlong called Rudynge.
Witnesses: Richard Moyl, Reginald de Stoke, Hugh atte Boure, Geoffrey de Rokhulle, Simon le Muneter.
At: Rockhill.

----

[1] Smyth, i. 329.

A2/62/6 [GC 2749]   4 June 6 Edw. III [1332]
Thomas lord of Berkelee and John Greyel.

Thomas has appointed John his attorney to receive seisin of a messuage and 4 parcels of
land in Rokhulle, viz. of that holding which was formerly of Agnes Blake, as in the charter
of John de Greote, vicar of Little Hereford.
At: Berkeley.

STOKE (SALOP.)

See above, p. 511, Rockhill.

A2/63/1 [GC 1365]   n.d. [*temp.* Edw. I]
Agnes, lady of Stoke, widow of Walter Black (*Nig'*) of Eastham, and William her son.

For 100*s.*, Agnes has granted to William the land which Henry Wendut formerly held of
her in the vill of Stoca; rent 16*d.* a year.
Witnesses: Hugh Carbonel, Peter lord of Greete, William Coterel, William Bonet, Osbert
[Inuges], Hugh son of Peter, John Black (*Niger*) of Yarkhill (*Jachul*).

A2/63/2 [GC 2322]   Mon. before St. Margaret, 14 Edw. II [14 July 1320]
Richard de la Crose of Stoke and Henry the clerk of Rockhill.

Richard has granted to Henry, his heirs and assigns, for a certain sum of money, 1 a. of
land in Stoke at Plumleyesiche, beside Henry's land.
Witnesses: John le Blake of Rockhill, Reginald de Stoke, Geoffrey Peris of Rockhill, John
Simond of Greete, Nicholas le Blake of Stoke.
At: Stoke.

LONG ASHTON (SOM.)

The holdings here were closely associated with Bedminster (below, p. 516) and presumably
passed with Bedminster manor to Elizabeth countess of Warwick on the death of her father
Thomas (IV) Lord Berkeley. The Gatcombe holding will have reverted to Thomas (III)
Lord Berkeley, as its lord, after the king had had his year and a day of waste when it was
forfeited by the felon John de Gatcombe.[1] See also below, p. 527, Portbury.

A2/64/1 [GC 1697]   Trinity Sunday, 2 Edw. II [25 May 1309]
John called le Coffrer of Ashton and William Masseday.

John has granted to William 4 a. of land in the field called Bridewellefelde.
Witnesses: John de Baiocis, Robert Bavent, Matthew de Snoudone, Robert de Ryllebury,
John Sprot, Oliver Testewode, Robert de Brouton.
At: Ashton.

A2/64/2 [GC 2719]   1 March 5 Edw. III [1331]
Thomas lord of Berkelee; and John de Snoudone and Eleanor his wife.

Thomas has leased to John and Eleanor the holding which John le Coffrer formerly held
in Asshtone; for their lives, rent 26*s.* 8*d.* a year.
Witnesses: Edmund de Lyouns, Edward Howel, John de Lamyntone, Robert de Rillebur',
Robert de Boryton.
At: Berkeley.

A2/64/3 [GC 3193]   Wed. after St. Martin, 22 Edw. III [12 Nov. 1348]
Eleanor de Snowdon, widow of John de Snowdon, and Richard le Teyn.

Eleanor has granted to Richard, his heirs and assigns 7 a. of land in the field called le
Redfeld, and the croft called le Brodebreche in Dongfyleyswyke.
Witnesses: John Gatecumbe, Edmund de Leyouns, Robert de Bentone, John atte Clyve,
Edward atte Pole.
At: Ashton.

---

[1] *CPR* 1358–61, 98.

THE GATCOMBE HOLDING IN ASHTON AND KENCOTE

A2/64/4 [GC 3474]   Wed. before St. Margaret the virgin, 32 Edw. III [18 July 1358]
John de Gadecoumbe; and Sir William Pykeslegh, rector of Backwell, and Sir John de Buri, chaplain.

John has granted to William and John, and their heirs and assigns, all his lands, holdings and rents in Aysschton by Bristoll.
Witnesses: Edmund de Lyons, Richard Artur, Thomas Lang, William de Whytyngton, John de Lamyngton.
At: Ashton.

A2/64/5 [SC 532]   3 Oct. 32 Edw. III [1358]
King Edward III and John de Bekynton, escheator for Somerset.

Whereas, for £4 given by Nicholas le Carpenter of Cadebury, the king has granted to him the year, day and waste in a house and 2 carucates of land in Asshton and Kennecote which were forfeited by John de Gatcombe, outlawed for felony, and which have been valued at 80*s.* of which 30*s.* is the waste, the king now orders John de Bekynton to hand it over to Nicholas.
At: Westminster.

A2/64/6 [SC 533]   12 Oct. 32 Edw. III [1358]
Nicholas le Carpenter of Cadbury and Lord Thomas de Berkeley.

Whereas the king granted to Nicholas the year, day and waste of a messuage and 2 carucates of land in Asthon and Kennecote forfeited by John de Gatecombe for felony, he has now granted the same to Thomas, for a certain sum of money.

A2/64/7 [GC 3614]   23 March 44 Edw. III [1370]
John de Gatecombe of Ashton by Bristol; and Sir John de Bury and John Stanford, chaplains, and Richard atte Stoke.

 John has granted to John, John and Richard, and their heirs and assigns, all his lands, holdings [etc.] in Longeaschtone by Bristoll.
Witnesses: Walter Laurence, Ralph Damysel, Richard the Theyne, William Neel, William atte Pole, Ralph de Yeule, Thomas atte Mulle.
At: Bedminster.

A2/64/8 [GC 3624]   9 Sept. 44 Edw. III [1370]
John de Bury, chaplain, and John de Gatecombe of Ashton by Bristol.

Whereas John de Gatecombe granted to John de Bury all his lands [etc.] in Longeaschtone by Bristoll, John de Bury has granted that if John de Gatecombe pays to him in the church of Holy Trinity, Bristoll, at the feast of All Saints [1 Nov.] next, 100*s.*, the charter of the grant will be vacated.
At: Bristol.

OTHER

A2/64/9 [GC 2783]   Fri. after St. Lucy, 7 Edw. III [17 Dec. 1333]
John de Meryen and Sir Thomas, lord of Berkeleye.

John has attorned for his fealty to Thomas for the manor of Ashtone Daundo which he holds of Thomas. [*In French*.]
At: Ashton Dando.

A2/64/10 [GC 3127*]   Thurs. after St. Hilary, 19 Edw. III [19 Jan. 1346]
Sir Thomas, lord of Berkelee, and Edmund de Lyouns of Ashton.

Thomas has granted to Edmund, his heirs and assigns all the lands, holdings, rents [etc.] that Thomas Roules of Bedministre and Christine his wife held of him in Asshton for their lives, viz. the holding called Lyouneshammes, in exchange for lands, holdings [etc.] held by Walter le Daye and John his son, Henry Bat and Hawise his wife and John Spore and Thomas his son for their lives, of Edmund, in the vill of Bedministre.

Witnesses: Andrew de Bromptone, Robert de Feylond, William Scovyle, John atte Clyve, John de Snoudone.

At: Portbury.

A2/64/11 [GC 3951]   16 March 22 Ric. II [1399]
Thomas Berkeley, lord of Berkeley, and Thomas Lyons of Ashton.

Thomas Berkeley has granted to Thomas Lyons an annual rent of 13*s.* 4*d.* from holdings in Assheton which John Cokket holds for life, with the reversion of the holdings after John's death; for Thomas Lyons's life, rent a red rose a year.

At: Portbury.

BARROW GURNEY (SOM.)

Robert, son of Robert FitzHarding and known as Robert de Weare, married Hawise, daughter and heir of Robert de Gurney of Barrow and Englishcombe (Som.). The manors descended to her daughter Eve and to her son Robert 'de Gurney' and thence from the Gurneys to John ap Adam and his son Thomas.[1] Barrow was one of the manors bought by Thomas (III) Lord Berkeley from Thomas ap Adam in 1330 and it was entailed by Berkeley on his younger son Edmund and his brothers, passing eventually to John and the cadet line of Beverston. See also above, p. 147, Beverston.

THE BERKELEY MANOR

A2/65/1 [GC 2767]   28 Feb. 7 Edw. III [1333]
Walter de Romesie and Sir Thomas de Berclegh.

Walter acknowledges that he holds of Thomas, who has the right which was of Sir Thomas de Appadam in the manor of Barewe, 3 messuages, 2½ virgates and 4 a. of land in the vill of Barewe, by knight service, in the right of Katherine his wife. [*In French.*]

At: Oakley.

A2/65/2 [GC 2821]   20 May 9 Edw. III [1335]
The prioress and convent of Barrow; and Sir Thomas lord of Berkelee.

Whereas the prioress and convent are bound to Thomas to find annually a fold of 360 sheep on the land of Thomas in his manor of Barewe, Thomas has quitclaimed to the convent the fold, and they will celebrate annually on the last day of May for the anniversary of Sir Maurice de Berkelee, Thomas's father, and on 5 Dec. for the anniversary of Lady Eve his mother, for the anniversaries of himself and Margaret his wife, and will pay 2*s.* 6*d.* for a pittance on the anniversary of Maurice, and the same for the anniversaries of Eve, Thomas and Margaret.

At: Portbury.

A2/65/3 [GC 2917]   Wed. after St. Peter in chains, 11 Edw. III [6 Aug. 1337]
Thomas lord of Berkele and Sir William de Syde.

Whereas Thomas leased to William, for his life, the manor of Barewe (Som.), with the wood and underwood of the manor except the great oaks and other trees, Thomas has now granted that William may have all the timber of the said manor for his life.

Witnesses: William de Chiltenham, John de Clyve, Roger de Estham, John Wyth, William Capel.

At: Berkeley.

---

[1] Smyth, i. 52–4; *GEC* i. 179–81.

A2/65/4 [GC 3064**]   Two weeks after Michaelmas, 17 Edw. III [13 Oct. 1343]
Thomas son of Maurice de Berkele, knight, and William de Syde; and Elias de Aylbrighton
and Joan his wife.

Final concord concerning the manor of Barwe; Elias and Joan have acknowledged the
right of Thomas, and have quitclaimed the manor to him for themselves and Joan's heirs,
and will warrant his right; Thomas has given them 100 marks.
At: Westminster.

A2/65/5 [GC 3094]   Fri. after St. Aldhelm, 18 Edw. III [28 May 1344]
(1) William de Syde; (2) William Curteys; (3) William de Compton, clerk.

William de Syde has appointed William Curteys to receive seisin of the lands and holdings
which he had by grant of William de Compton in Barewe Gournay, as in his charter.
At: Bristol.

A2/65/6 [GC 3246]   Mon. after St. Martin, 24 Edw. III [15 Nov. 1350]
Sir William de Syde and Sir Thomas, lord of Berkelee.

William has leased to Thomas the manor of Barwe; for the life of William, rent 20 marks
a year.
Witnesses: Edmund de Lyouns, John de Gatecombe, Thomas de Ryllebury, John Bavent,
Walter Buryman.
At: Bedminster.

A2/65/7 [GC 3603]   n.d. [*c.* June 1352]
Maurice son and heir of Sir Thomas de Berkeleye lord of Berkeley; and William Syde and
Walter Goldmere.

Maurice has ratified and confirmed the covenant made at Westminster at Trinity 26 Edw.
III between Thomas de Berkeleye, and William Syde and Walter Goldemere, concerning the
manor of Barwe and 2 messuages and 3 carucates of land in Cheddre and Tykenham (Som.),
and a messuage and 1 carucate of land in Faleveld (Glos.), whereby Thomas acknowledged
the manor and the messuage and carucate of land at Faleveld to be the right of William and
Walter by his gift, and William and Walter granted the said manor and holding to Thomas for
life, and further they grant the reversion of a messuage and 2 carucates of land in the vill of
Cheddre, which John de Actone, knight, held for life, and a messuage and 1 virgate [*sic*] of
land in the vill of Tykenham, which Roger de Estham held for life, of the inheritance of the
said William, to Thomas for life, with remainder to his son Edmund and his male issue, the
male issue of Thomas and his wife Katherine, and the right heirs of Thomas, saving the
customary services from Barwe and Tykenham to the hundreds of Portbur' and Harclyve.

MANORIAL ACCOUNTS

A2/65/8 [GAR 358] Two rolls attached at foot
                    Michaelmas, 6 Edw. III to St. John before the Latin Gate, 7 Edw. III
                                                          [29 Sept. 1332 to 6 May 1333]
                    St. John to Michaelmas, 7 Edw. III [6 May to 29 Sept. 1333]
A2/65/9 [GAR 359]   10–11 Edw. III [1336–7]
A2/65/10 [GAR 360]   23–4 Edw. III [1349–50]

THE BURCY HOLDING

A2/65/11 [GC 1264]   n.d. [*temp.* Edw. I]
Laurence Burci of Barrow; and Isabel atte Whitecrofte and Margaret her daughter.

Laurence has leased to Isabel and Margaret a cottage with a curtilage in his enclosure,
which Gounote la Shuppisci previously held, for their lives, rent 12*d.* a year.
Witnesses: Joceus de Bayoure, Robert Bavent, John Sprot, Thomas Wombestrang, William
de Marleboure.

A2/65/12 [GC 2864]   Fri. after St. Scholastica, 11 Edw. III [14 Feb. 1337]
Laurence Burcy and Eleanor his wife; and Richard Kruys and Lucy his wife.

Whereas Richard and Lucy have granted to Laurence and Eleanor all their land and holdings in the vill of Barwe Gornay, to them and their heirs and assigns, Laurence and Eleanor will that, if Richard and Lucy pay to them 5s. a year for the lives of Laurence and Eleanor, the land will revert to Richard and Lucy on the deaths of Laurence and Eleanor.
Witnesses: John Bavent, Robert de Rillebury, John de Lamyngton, William Gilbert, William de Bernewode.
At: Barrow Gurney.

BARTON (SOM.)

The holding is not mentioned by name in Berkeley hands later, and the assumption is that it was merged with the holding at nearby Edingworth (below, p. 524), which was also settled on Maurice de Berkeley (of Stoke Giffard), second son of Maurice (III) Lord Berkeley and his wife Eve la Zouche.

A2/66/1 [GC 1144]   2 Ides of Jan. 35 Edw. I [12 Jan. 1307]
William son of Hugh Malerbe; and Sir Maurice de Berkele, Eve his wife and Maurice their son.

William has quitclaimed to Maurice, Eve and Maurice all the land and holdings [etc.] which were of William son of Bartholomew de Wyntred in Barton and Wynescombe.
At: Shipham.

BEDMINSTER (SOM.)

Bought by Robert FitzHarding before he acquired the lordship of Berkeley, Bedminster was one of the principal manors of the Berkeley patrimony. The overlordship passed from Robert of Gloucester to the Clares and, after the division of the Clare lands in 1317, to the Despensers through the younger Despenser's wife Eleanor de Clare. Eleanor married secondly William la Zouche, who was thus the lord in 1334 (see below, A2/67/10 [GC 2793]). In 1289 the manor was settled on Maurice (III) Lord Berkeley and his first wife Eve la Zouche in jointure and tail general.[1] As a result, on the death of Thomas (IV) in 1417 it passed to his daughter Elizabeth, countess of Warwick. See also above, pp. 419, Yewdon, 512, Long Ashton, and below, p. 527, Portbury.

MORTGAGE, 1375

The three documents imply that Thomas (IV) Lord Berkeley obtained a loan of 400 marks, using as security a temporary grant of the manor to four merchants who in turn raised a loan from another merchant. See also above, A2/36/12–14 [GC 3677, GC 3687, GC 3705].

A2/67/1/ [GC 3681]   Sat. after St. George, 49 Edw. III [28 April 1375]
William Cheddre of Bristol, merchant; and Richard de Actone, knight, Ralph Waleys, Walter Laurence and William Smalcombe, merchants of Glos. and Som.

Whereas Richard, Ralph, Walter and William are bound to William Cheddre in a statute staple bond of 800 marks as security for payment of 400 marks, William has received from them 100 marks for the Easter term in part payment of the 400 marks.
At: Bristol.

A2/67/2 [GC 3685]   Thurs. after Michaelmas, 49 Edw. III [4 Oct. 1375]
William Cheddre of Bristol, merchant; and Richard de Actone, knight, Ralph Waleys, Walter Laurence and William Smalcombe, merchants of Glos. and Som.

Whereas Richard, Ralph, Walter and William are bound to William Cheddre in a statute

---

[1] Smyth, i. 244.

staple bond of 800 marks as security for payment of 400 marks, William has received from them 100 marks for the Michaelmas term in part payment of the 400 marks.
At: Bristol.

A2/67/3 [SC 551]   8 Feb. 51 Edw. III [1377]
Richard Dacton, knight, Walter Laurence, Ralph Waleis, and William Smalcombe; and Thomas de Berkele, lord of Berkeley.

Whereas Thomas recently granted to Richard, Walter, Ralph and William the manor of Bedmynstre, they have now granted it back to him and quitclaim to him any right they have in it. [*In French.*]

OTHER BERKELEY INTERESTS

A2/67/4 [SC 5]   n.d. [*c*. 1153]
Henry duke of Normandy and Robert FitzHarding.

Henry has confirmed to Robert the grant to him by Robert earl of Gloucester of the land of Bedminster.
Witnesses: Manasser Bis[et], steward, Henry de Oilleio, Henry Hussey (*Hosatus*), Hugh de Piris, Payn Carbonell.

A2/67/5 [GC 3321]   n.d. [late 12th cent.]
Maurice son of Robert and the hospital of St. John of Redcliffe.

Maurice has granted to the hospital a rent of 2*s*. from land near the Pill. [*14th-cent. copy*].
Witnesses: Walter de Dunstanvilla, William Priest (*Presbiter*), Adam de Salso Marisco, John the dean, Master Maurice, Master Henry, Jordan la Warre, Herbert and David his brothers, James son of Farden Hemoro, Richard the smith, Richard Sergant.

A2/67/6 [SC 95]   n.d. [*temp.* John]
Walter de Dunstanville, canon and rector of Bedminster, and Sir Robert de Berkelai.

Walter has granted to Robert the offices of a chaplain in the oratory which Robert has built in his court of Bedminster, and Robert has granted to Walter a curtilage and messuage in Bedminster worth 3*s*. a year, which Edric holds, with Edric and his wife.
Witnesses: J[ohn] abbot of St. Augustine's, R . . . , Henry dean of Portbury, William chaplain of Redcliffe, Philip chaplain of Bedminster, . . . , Henry the chaplain, Gilbert the chaplain, Ralph Musard, John de Merstun, Oliver de Berkeley, William . . . , William Dessuble, Walter Snigga.

A2/67/7 [GC 1299]   n.d. [*temp.* Edw. I]
Walter Cole and Sir Thomas de Berkel'.

Walter has granted to Thomas a rent of ½*d*. a year from John of the mill (*de Molend'*).
Witnesses: Sir William de Ovill, knight, Thomas de Fylton, Richard Scappe, John Young (*Juvenis*), John Goce, clerk.

A2/67/8 [GC 1885]
Sun. the morrow of the nativity of St. John the Baptist, 5 Edw. II [25 June 1312]
William Tyard, burgess of Bristol, and Sir Maurice de Berkeleye.

William has granted to Maurice 3 a. of meadow in Bedmynystre, in the meadow of Adderclyve.
Witnesses: William de Odyham, Thomas Artur, Hugh Cryps, John Goce, John Brounyng.
At: Bedminster.

A2/67/9 [GC 2499]   n.d. [mid 14th cent.?]
Thomas son and heir of John Brounyng of Bedminster and Sir Thomas lord of Berkelee.

Thomas Brounyng has granted to Thomas de Berkelee, his heirs and assigns, all the land, holdings, rents [etc.] which he has in Bedminstre (Som.).
Witnesses: Roger Turtle, Roger Beauner, William atte Grene, Henry Goce, Thomas Rolves.

A2/67/10 [GC 2793]   22 May 8 Edw. III [1334]
Richard de Creckelade, keeper of the fees (*custos feodorum*) of William la Zousch and
Eleanor his wife, and Thomas de Berkele, lord of Berkeley.

Richard has received from Thomas 50*s*. for his relief after the death of Maurice de
Berkele, his father, for the manor of Bedeminstre, which he holds of William and Eleanor
of the inheritance of Eleanor for the service of half a knight's fee; and has also received
10*s*. for the marriage of the said Eleanor's eldest daughter.
At: Berkeley.

A2/67/11 [GC 2877]   Fri. the morrow of Corpus Christi, 11 Edw. III [20 June 1337]
Thomas lord of Berkele and Roger de Coumbe, chaplain celebrating in the church of St.
Augustine's Abbey, Bristol.

Thomas has granted to Roger, celebrating for the souls of his late wife Margaret and of
himself after his death, an annual rent of 30*s*. from the manor of Bedminstre, for the life of
Roger.
At: Bristol.

A2/67/12 [GC 3354]   n.d. [late 14th cent.]
Roger Whitewode of Norton Malreward, nephew and heir of Alice Cole, late the wife of
Richard Cole, and Thomas de Berkele lord of Berkeley.

Roger has quitclaimed to Thomas the lands and holdings [etc.] which were of Richard
Cole in Bedmynstre by Bristoll.

LEASES

A2/67/13 [SC 147]   n.d. [early 13th cent.]
Robert de Berkeley and Walter Snigge.

Robert has granted to Walter the quarter-virgate at Bedministre which Arthur held; rent
4*s*. a year, acknowledgement 1 silver mark.
Witnesses: Robert Young (*Juvenis*), Adam son of Nigel, Richard de Cuhill, Bernard de
Stanes, Walter the chaplain, Maurice son of Nigel, Simon de Olepenne, Robert Bastard,
Roger the goldsmith (*aurifaber*).

A2/67/14 [SC 295]   Fri. after the translation of St. Thomas [7 July] 1247
Maurice de Berkeley and the abbey of Blanchland (*Blanchalanda*).

Maurice has granted to the abbey the mill, messuage and land which Ailward the miller
held of Roger de Berkeley, Maurice's [great] uncle, in Bedminster, at a rent of 20*s*. a year,
and has quitclaimed to the abbey all suit to his hundred court, for the souls of himself and
his wife Isabel.
Witnesses: Sir Maurice de Saltmarsh (*de salso marisco*), Sir Jordan la Ware, William de
Beaumont (*de Bello Monte*), Master William Taney, steward of Berkeley, Hillary de
Champfleur (*de Campo Florido*), Walter son of Alan, Stephen de Lyons, Walter Sely, clerk.
At: Berkeley.

A2/67/15 [GC 1240]   n.d. [*temp.* Edw. I]
Thomas lord of Berkel' and William le Vayre.

Thomas has leased to William 1 virgate of land in Thomas's manor of Bedminstre, which
Thomas Schoche formerly held of Thomas in villeinage, except the land and meadow
which Adam Kade holds of Thomas; to William and Alice his first wife, for their lives, rent
20*s*. a year, and they have given him 40*s*.
Witnesses: Sir William de Ovile, Thomas de Lyons, Walter Cole, Master John de Morvile,
John Goce, Richard Scappe, Richard le Vayre, Richard Turmon.

A2/67/16 [GC 3160]   12 May 21 Edw. III [1347]
Thomas lord of Berkel' and William de Godewyne, chaplain, keeper of the house of St. Katherine of Bedminster by Bristol.

Thomas has leased to William a plot of land containing 2½ a. in the field called Sauncetre in the manor of Bedmenestre; for his life, rent 3s. a year.
At: Bedminster.

A2/67/17 [GC 3179]   26 March 22 Edw. III [1348]
Thomas lord of Berkeleye; and Roger Beauner of Bristol and Randolph his son.

Thomas has leased to Roger and Randolph the holding with 1 virgate of land, which Richard Averey formerly held of Thomas in Bedmynstre; for their lives, at the customary rent.
At: Berkeley.

A2/67/18 [GC 3500]   10 Jan. 33 Edw. III [1360]
Thomas de Berkele, lord of Berkeley; and John Sprakemon and Eleanor his wife.

Thomas has leased to John and Eleanor all the lands and holdings which he had by grant of the same John and Eleanor in Bedminstre, for a term of 100 years, but if either dies within the term then the land will revert to Thomas.
At: Bedminster.

A2/67/19 [GC 3501]   12 June 34 Edw. III [1360]
Thomas lord of Berkele; and John Webbe and Maud his wife.

Thomas has leased to John and Maud the house which Simon Swaynesheys previously held opposite the cross of Bedmenstre in Bedmenstre; for their lives, rent as Simon paid.
Witnesses: Thomas atte Mulle, John Castelaker, Ralph de Yevele, Simon Lodar, Thomas . . .
At: Bedminster.

A2/67/20 [GC 3502]   12 June 34 Edw. III [1360]
Thomas lord of Berkele and Thomas Waleys.

Thomas has leased to Thomas Waleys a messuage and 1 virgate of land, which Simon Russel previously held in Bedmenstre; for his life, rent 26s. 8d. a year.
Witnesses: Ralph de Yevele, Thomas atte Mulle, John Arthur, John Webbe, . . . , Richard Torinssh.
At: Bedminster.

A2/67/21 [GC 3279]   n.d. [late 14th cent.]
Thomas de Berkeley, lord of Berkeley; and William Tarre and Sibyl his wife.

Thomas has demised to William, Sibyl and their eldest son a messuage and 1 a. of land called Heylond with the market-stall (*schameles*) which Elias Romyn formerly held in Bedmynstre; for their lives, rent 6s. 8d. a year, and William will not be appointed reeve, rent-collector or tithingman.
Witnesses: Richard Dacton, knight, Robert Cheddre, Thomas atte Mulle, John Tybbes, Ralph Thevele.

A2/67/22 [GC 4070]   20 Jan. 13 Hen. IV [1412]
Thomas de Berkelee, lord of Berkeley; and Richard Powlysham, Joan his wife, John Powlysham, his son, and Alice, John's wife.

Thomas has leased to Richard, Joan, John and Alice the reversion of a messuage with garden containing 1 a. of land, after the death of Thomas Mayons, in Bedmynstre in north street; for their lives, rent 5s. a year.
Witnesses: Ralph Yevyle, John Mannyng, Walter Mannyng, Thomas Sely, Robert Loder.

A2/67/23 [GC 4103]   Fri. after the translation of St. Thomas the martyr, 3 Hen. V
                                                                                    [12 July 1415]
Thomas de Berkeley, lord of Berkeley; and Richard Bortone, fuller (*toukere*), burgess of
Bristol, Joan his wife and Robert their eldest son.

    Thomas has leased to Richard, Joan and Robert a messuage with 2 a. of land in the vill of
Bedmynstre by Bristoll beside the high road; for their lives, rent 7*s*. 6*d*. a year.
Witnesses: John Rederyse, Hugh Vyns, Thomas Mayes, Richard Poulesham, Robert
Redewelle.
At: Bedminster.

MANORIAL ACCOUNTS

A2/67/24 [GAR 361]   30–4 Edw. III [1356–60]
Four rolls (for 1356–7, 1357–8, 1358–9 and 1359–60) attached at the head.

OTHER INTERESTS

A2/67/25 [SC 27]   n.d. [*temp.* Hen. II]
King Henry II and St. Augustine's Abbey, Bristol.

    Copies of three deeds relating to a mill which the king allowed the canons of St.
Augustine's to build and hold on the water of Trivel in the royal fee of Bedminster.[1]

A2/67/26 [GC 1524]   n.d. [*temp.* Edw. I]
Robert son of Alfred and Agatha his daughter.

    Robert has granted to Agatha and her issue, in free marriage, the land which William
Burnel sometime held and a plot of land lying below the grove of John le Frankelayn; rent
9*d*. a year.
Witnesses: Adam parson of Wraxall, Stephen de Capenore, Robert de Weston, Richard de
Karswell, Richard Beket, Elias le Fua.

A2/67/27 [GC 1508]   n.d. [*temp.* Edw. I]
John le Perour, son of the late William le Perour of Bedminster, and Richard Romayn.

    John has granted to Richard a half-acre of meadow which Elyas Danyel formerly held of
the St. Katherine's Hospital, Bristol, lying in Norperwademore, between the pasture of Sir
Maurice de Berkelye and the pasture of St. John's Hospital, Bristol; rent a rose, red or
white, a year, and 6*d*. to St. Katherine's Hospital; Richard has given him 10*s*.
Witnesses: Hugh Crisp (*Crispus*), John of the mill (*de molendino*), Henry Martyn, John
Gose, Matthew le Vayre, Ralph the hayward (*messor*), Thomas Purs.

A2/67/28 [GC 444]   n.d. [*temp.* Hen. III or Edw. I]
John la Warre of Bristol and Adam de la Hope.

    John has granted to Adam certain of his land above Cuderigge between two roads, one
which divides the land of Legha and the land of Cuderigge, and the other which goes to
Wrockeshale, with pasture and 2 a. of meadow and all his land of Dodinghulle and his
grove called Litelcomesgrove; rent 1*d*. a year, and Adam has given him 100*s*.
Witnesses: William Artur, Robert de Weston, William le Bret, Robert de Feghelonde,
Richard de Carswelle, William le Franc, John son of Adam, Philip de Carswell, Thomas
Neel.

BEDMINSTER HUNDRED (SOM.)

Robert FitzHarding acquired the adjacent hundreds of Bedminster, Portbury and Hartcliff
and granted them to his younger son Robert, but Thomas (I) Lord Berkeley (d. 1243)
bought the reversion from Robert's son and heir Maurice de Gant (below, A2/68/2 [SC 101]).
Portbury hundred was entailed in tail male, along with the manor, by Thomas (III), but
Bedminster and Hartcliff hundreds, possibly because they were settled in jointure and tail

---

[1] *Transcript of one deed*: *St Augustine's Cartulary*, no. 9.

general in 1289 with the manor of Bedminster, were not. Consequently, on the death of Thomas (IV) in 1417, Bedminster and Hartcliff hundreds passed to his daughter, the countess of Warwick.

BEDMINSTER, HARTCLIFF AND PORTBURY HUNDREDS

A2/68/1 [SC 234]   n.d. [1220 × 1230]
Thomas de Berkeley and Maurice de Gant.

Thomas has inspected the grant by Robert, his grandfather, to Robert his [Robert's] son of the three hundreds which the earl of Gloucester gave him, viz. those of Portbury, Bedmunistre and Hareclive, to hold of him [Robert] for a rent of 1 mark a year, and confirms it to Maurice de Gant.
Witnesses to the original grant: Henry [de Berkeley] archdeacon of Exeter, Nicholas his brother, William prior of St. Augustine's, John de Cogan, Walter his brother, Henry de Saltemar', William son of Elias, Robert de Hanum, Rainald son of Drogo, Adam de Cuntevile.
Witnesses: Sir D[avid] abbot of St. Augustine's, Sir Richard Siward, Sir Jordan la Warre, Sir Walter de Tilli, Sir John de Alneto, Adam de Budiford, Gilbert de Hendun, Henry de Venn.

A2/68/2 [SC 101]   n.d. [1220 × 1230]
Maurice de Gant and Thomas de Berkeley.

Maurice has granted to Thomas the reversion after his death of the three hundreds which Robert FitzHarding granted to Robert the younger (*juvenis*), Maurice's father, viz. those of Bedminster, Portbury and Harcliffe, if Maurice should die without an heir.
Witnesses: Sir William Briwere, Sir Stephen de Segrave, Sir William de Pontearche, Richard de Troham, Osbert Giffard, Thomas de Tyringeham, Maurice son of Nigel.

ADMINISTRATIVE DOCUMENTS

A2/68/3 [GAR 409] Bailiff's account   46–7 Edw. III [1372–3]
Bedminster, Hartcliff and Portbury hundreds.

Court rolls, Bedminster hundred
A2/68/4 [GCR 198] Twelve courts   42–3 Edw. III [1368–9]
A2/68/5 [GCR 199] Eighteen courts   44–5 Edw. III [1370–1]
A2/68/6 [GCR 200] Sixteen courts   45–6 Edw. III [1371–2]

BROCKLEY (SOM.)

The first three of the grantees below were prominent servants of the Berkeley family, as were, among the witnesses, John de St. Lo and Edmund de Clevedon. The manor of Brockley was held by the Ashton family. Lands in the parish, which Sir Robert de Ashton held in 1367, are said to have descended to the Berkeleys.[1] If so, the Berkeleys concerned were probably the cadet branch of Beverston founded by John, younger son of Thomas (III). John in 1368 married Eleanor, daughter and heir of Sir Robert de Ashton (d. 1383), and although Eleanor soon died without issue John retained some of Sir Robert's lands.

A2/69/1 [GC 3560]   Tues. before St. Margaret [the virgin], 38 Edw. III [16 July 1364]
John de Brokkeleygh, son and heir of the late Roger de Brokkele'; and Richard de Actone, knight, Robert de Coueleye, parson of Slimbridge, Walter Lauerence and John Bays.

John has granted to Richard, Robert, Walter and John all the lands [etc.] which he inherited in Brokkeleygh after the death of his father.
Witnesses: Theobald de Gorges, John de Sancto Laudo, Edmund de Clivedone, knights, Edmund de Keu, Richard le Thein, William de Whitingtone, Robert de Foilond.
At: Chelvey.

---

[1] J. Collinson, *History and Antiquities of the County of Somerset* (Bath, 1791), ii. 120–1.

CHARLTON, IN WRAXALL (SOM.)

Thomas (IV) Lord Berkeley made a number of small acquisitions within Portbury hundred (below, pp. 527, Portbury, 534, Walton-in-Gordano, 535, Weston-in-Gordano, 536, Wraxall), towards the end of his life, which he appears to have intended for his nephew and heir male, James, heir to the manor and hundred of Portbury. The acquisitions, to which that in Charlton was attached, formed part of a settlement made by Thomas three weeks before his death: see below, A2/77/14 [SC 581]).

A2/70/1 [GC 3766]   Tues. the morrow of St. Andrew, 7 Ric. II [1 Dec. 1383]
Walter Carswill and Amicia his wife; and Sir Thomas de Berkeleye and Margaret his wife.

   Walter and Amicia have quitclaimed to Thomas and Margaret messuages, lands and holdings in Banecombe within the manor of Cherletone, and also the reversion of . . . held for life in dower.
Witnesses: Thomas Gouytz, Thomas Halghewill, Nicholas Cotelond, Ralph Gernays, . . .
At: Charlton.

A2/70/2 [GC 3773]   Tues. the morrow of St. Mark, 7 Ric. II [26 April 1384]
Alice widow of Walter Carswill; and Sir Thomas de Berkeleye and Margaret his wife.

   Alice has quitclaimed to Thomas and Margaret all the lands and holdings in Banecombe in the manor of Cherletone which they recently acquired from Walter, with the reversion of the holding which Margery Turtele holds for life in dower.
Witnesses: Thomas Govytz, John Wolhay, Thomas Halghewill, John Irlaund, Ralph Prestecote.
At: Charlton.

CHATLEY (SOM.)

The acquistions in Chatley and Tellisford made by Robert (II) Lord Berkeley (d. 1220) are not found in Berkeley hands later and were probably subinfeudated. In the mid 14th century a rent of a pair of shoes for a messuage and 1 carucate of land in Chatley was paid to Bedminster manor.[1]

A2/71/1 [SC 85]   n.d. [1200 × 1212]
Ivo de Teveleford and Robert de Berkeleia.

   Ivo has granted to Robert, his man (*affidatus*), 1½ virgates with a wood, in Chatteleg' and the half-virgate which Richard son of Svetric holds in Teveleford, together with Richard himself and his two sons, Walter and Hugh, at a fee-farm rent of 6*d.* a year; and further has granted pasture for 100 sheep, 4 cows and 8 oxen; Robert has paid an acknowledgement of 8 marks to Ivo, 22*s.* to Ivo's son Robert and ½ mark to Ivo's son Henry.
Witnesses: Mauger bishop of Worcester, William abbot of Kingswood, Walter prior of Bath, William Marshal, earl of Pembroke, Roger de Berkeley, Henry de Monteforti, Roger and Hubert his brothers, John de Erleia, Henry of the furlong (*de cultura*), Guy of the furlong, Ranulf de Thoringtun, Maurice de Berkeley, Mahu Turpin, William de Balun, Robert la Warra, Oliver de Berkeley, Philip and Eustace his brothers, Geoffrey de Chausi, Harding de Hunteneford.

A2/71/2 [SC 86]   n.d. [*temp.* John]
Ivo de Teveleford and Robert de Berkelai.

   Ivo has granted to Robert, his man (*affidatus*), 1½ virgates and a wood in Chatleg', and the half-virgate in Teveleford which Richard son of Svetric holds, with rights of pasture [as above, A2/71/1 (SC 85)]; rent 6*d.* a year.

---

[1] BCM GAR 361 (above, A2/67/24).

Witnesses: the abbot of Kingswood, the prior of Bath, Sir Roger de Berkele, Henry de Monteforti, Roger and Hubert his brothers, J[ohn] de Erlega, Henry of the furlong (*de cultura*), Guy of the furlong, Ranulf de Thoringn', Robert de Thoringn', Maurice de Berkeley, Mahu Turpin, Ranulf Garnun, Robert le Ware, Oliver de Berkeley, Philip and Eustace his brothers, Geoffrey de Chausi, Harding de Hunteneford, Hugh de Bradeleg', William le Scai of Tresham, Bartholomew de Olepenn.

A2/71/3 [SC 84]   A.D. 1204
Ivo de Tablesford and Robert de Berkeley.
    Ivo has granted to Robert a half-virgate in Cacheleie, which Godwin held, and his wood there; Robert has given an acknowledgement of 6*s.*.
Witnesses: Robert prior of Bath, Robert . . . , Thomas son of William, [Roger] de Berkeley, Oliver de Berkeley, William Dessuble, Adam . . . , Henry of the furlong (*de cultura*), . . . his son, Walter Snigga, Bernard de Stanes, Maurice son of Nigel, . . . de Crauleia, James . . .

CHEDDAR (SOM.)

The reversion of the manor was granted to Thomas (III) Lord Berkeley by Sir John de Acton in 1346, and in 1352 Thomas settled the reversion (of a messuage and two carucates of land) on his younger son Edmund and his brothers.[1] It eventually passed to Thomas's younger son John and the cadet line of Beverston.[2] See also above, A2/65/7 [GC 3603].

CHRISTON (SOM.)

Lands in Christon and Uphill, the advowson of Brean and the island of Steep Holme formed one holding which had been acquired by Thomas (III) Lord Berkeley by 1332 when Walter Bursey quitclaimed it to him. It had previously been held by one John Bursey, who had acquired it from Thomas's great-uncle Robert de Berkeley (of Arlingham).[3] It was not entailed by Thomas and having passed to his son Maurice (IV) and grandson Thomas (IV) was available for the mortgage in 1375 (above, p. 482). Sir Maurice Wyth (below, A2/72/2 [SR 31]) was the second husband of Elizabeth, widow of Maurice (IV) Lord Berkeley.

A2/72/1 [SC 217]   n.d. [late Hen. III]
Thomas de Muncketon and the church of St. Michael in Steep Holme.
    Thomas has granted to the church all his land in Curcheston, viz. a half-virgate sometime held by Ailmar Boving, which Robert son of Richard gave to him and which John de Keu and Agacia daughter and heir of the said Robert, his wife, confirmed to him.[4]
Witnesses: . . . Sparkeford, Robert and Elias his brothers, Richard son of Arthur, Adam Wallense, John his son, Geoffrey the serjeant (*serviens*), . . . priest of Loxton, Humphrey de Bagewrke, Hugh de Auxe, Adam his son, Henry de Begeton.

A2/72/2 [SR 31]
Copies of three leases of lands in Christon and Uphill:
(i) by Sir Maurice Wyth and Elizabeth his wife, to William Pynchard of Loxton, Alice his wife and John their son, of a holding in Crytheston by Banewell, for Elizabeth's life; rent 8*s.* a year and heriot; dated at Portbury, the feast of St. Nicholas, 2 Ric. II [8 Dec. 1378];
(ii) by Maurice de Berkeley, lord of Portbury, to John Ive and Alice his wife, of a holding in Crikeston as Robert Parsayea held it; for their lives, rent 8*s.* a year; dated at Portbury, Sun. after the decollation of St. John the Baptist, 28 Edw. III [31 Aug. 1354];
(iii) by Maurice de Berkeley, lord of Portbury, to Richard Oldemyxon, Anne his wife and William his brother, of a messuage and half-virgate in Uphulle, which John Howes held; for

[1] PRO CP 25/1/199/24, no. 61.
[2] PRO C 135/156, no. 12; C 139/35, no. 50.
[3] *Reg. Shrewsbury*, 90; *Reg. Drokensford*, 211.
[4] *Transcript*: Jeayes, pp. 73–4.

their lives, rent 2*s.* a year for the first two years and thereafter 30*s.* 4*d.* a year, and heriot; dated at Portbury, Sun. the feast of St. Hilary, 26 Edw. III [13 Jan. 1353].

EDINGWORTH (SOM.)

Edingworth and Milverton (Som.) were brought to Maurice (III) Lord Berkeley by his wife Eve la Zouche on their marriage in 1289.[1] They were settled on their second son Maurice (of Stoke Giffard), whose grandson Maurice (d. 1400) sold them to his second cousin Thomas (IV) Lord Berkeley. See also below, A2/76/1 [GC 3900], A2/90/3 [SC 493].

A2/73/1 [GC 3948]   12 Jan. 22 Ric. II [1399]
Thomas Berkeley, lord of Berkeley, and Thomas Arthur, knight.

   Thomas Berkeley has granted to Thomas Arthur all his lands, holdings [etc.] in Yedenworth (Som.), which were of Maurice de Berkeley, knight, in exchange for all Thomas Arthur's lands, holdings [etc.] in Weston in Gordano.
Witnesses: John Bluet, Ralph Damesell, Nicholas More, Geoffrey Lang the elder, Robert Foyland.
At: Portbury.

A2/73/2 [GC 3952]   12 March 22 Ric. II [1399]
(1) Thomas Berkeley, lord of Berkeley; (2) John Rolves; (3) Thomas Arthur, knight.

   Thomas Berkeley has appointed John to deliver seisin to Thomas Arthur of all his lands, holdings [etc.] in Yedenworth.
At: Portbury.

FOXCOTE (SOM.)

Maurice (I) Lord Berkeley (d. 1190) granted the manor to his younger son Maurice, a grant which was later confirmed by Maurice's eldest son and heir Robert (d. 1220) on the condition that it would revert to Robert if Maurice died without issue by his wife.[2] As it was later held in dower by Robert's widow Lucy, the manor presumably duly reverted on Maurice's death. Maurice bought a meadow there and then granted it, with other lands in Cam (Glos.), to St. Augustine's Abbey, but the abbey later granted the lands back to Robert. By 1227 Robert's brother and heir Thomas (I) Lord Berkeley (d. 1243) had promised the reversion of the manor on Lucy's death to his nephew Osbert Giffard in exchange for the Devon manor of High Bray, and Osbert died in 1237 holding Foxcote. His son Osbert granted it, with the rest of his lands, to his son, also Osbert, in 1284.[3] In 1316 Foxcote was held by John de Kingston,[4] by the mid 14th century the rose rent for the manor was paid to Bedminster and by 1373 the manor was held by Thomas Kyngston of John de Berkeley (of Beverston).[5] See also above, pp. 152, Cam, 420, High Bray.

A2/74/1 [SC 18]   n.d. [1175 × 1180]
Humphrey de Bohun and Maurice son of Robert.

   Humphrey has granted to Maurice the land of Foxcote in fee, to hold as half a knight's fee; if unable to warrant the land to Maurice he will, in place of it, given an equal portion of land in his manor of Wogasia; in acknowledgement of his grant Maurice has given to Humphrey a gold ring and to the countess Margaret, his wife, an ounce of gold.
Witnesses: Richard [de Warwick] abbot of St. Augustine's, William prior of the same, William son of Geoffrey, Henry de Buhun, the grantor's brother, Robert de Vernon, Reginald de Sumerford, Eustace the chamberlain, William Brito, Eudes de Sancto Salvatore, Ralph the

---

[1] Smyth, i. 244.
[2] Ibid. 100; BCM SR 1 (above, A1/2/48), nos. 57, 61.
[3] *GEC* v. 649 n., 651.
[4] *Feud. Aids*, iv. 323.
[5] BCM GAR 361 (above, A2/67/24); *CIPM* xiii, no. 167 (pp. 136–7).

butler (*Pincerna*), Adam son of Nigel, Adam de Saltmarsh (*de salso marisco*), Osbert Martra, Richard de Elmedon, Herbert Werra, Maurice the clerk, Roger de Weston, Maurice son of Nigel, Ralph de Scay, Ralph Francis, John Pulla, William de Hanum.

A2/74/2 [SC 120]   n.d. [1200 × 1210]
Baldwin de Ekewike and Maurice de Berkelei.

Baldwin has granted to Maurice all his meadow under Foxcote lying between Foxcote and Pekelinge, for the service of a pair of iron spurs a year.
Witnesses: Henry de Monteforti, Roger his brother, Richard Cotele, William de Balun, Robert la Warre, William Mal . . ., . . ., Thomas de Foxcote.

A2/74/3 [SC 71]   n.d. [*c*. 1200]
Baldwin de Ekewike and Maurice de Berkelei.

With the assent of William his heir, Baldwin has granted to Maurice the meadow which he held on the bank of the river near Foxcote, lying between Foxcote and Pekelinge; rent a pair of iron spurs at Michaelmas; Maurice has given to Baldwin 3 silver marks, to Avice his wife a silver fermail, and to William his heir a silver ring.
Witnesses: Henry de Monteforti, Roger his brother, Richard Cotele, William de Balun, Robert la Warre, William Malreward, Ernald de Balun, William chaplain of Horton, Thomas chaplain of Foxcote, Alexander de Monteforti.

A2/74/4 [SC 81]   n.d. [1200 × 1212]
John abbot of St. Augustine's Abbey and Lord Robert de Berkeleya.

John has granted to Robert all the lands which Maurice his brother bought and gave to the abbey in his last will, viz. the land lying between Beoleyebroc as it flows down to Widipulle and the water of Cambrigge, the land called Snitelega, a rent of 18*d*. due from Juliana de Slinbrigga, the meadow called Littlemed of the fee of Roger de Berkeley, 2 a. in Fulemore of the fee of Eggetuna, and a meadow in Foxchota which Maurice held of Baldwin de Ekewich.
Witnesses: Mauger bishop of Worcester, William de Verdun, archdeacon of Gloucester, Henry dean of Bristol, Master Robert de Clipstun, Master Stephen de Schalopesburia, Master Philip de Brai, Robert de Roppeleya, Thomas de Thiringeham, Maurice son of Nigel, Thomas de Loventa, Henry chaplain of Berkeley.

KINGSTON SEYMOUR (SOM.)

In 1317 Maurice (III) Lord Berkeley acquired a third of the manor of Kingston Seymour, with a third of the advowson, and settled it on his second son Maurice (of Stoke Giffard). It descended in the son's cadet line[1] until 1485 when it was sold to Maurice de Berkeley, later Lord Berkeley (d. 1506). See also below, A2/90/3 [SC 493].

THE MANOR

A2/75/1 [GC 2210]   Thurs. the morrow of St. Thomas the apostle, 11 Edw. II
                                                                         [22 Dec. 1317]
Philip de Wyke and Maud his wife; and Sir Maurice de Berkelee, son and heir of Sir Thomas de Berkelee.

Philip and Maud have granted to Maurice one third of the manor of Kingestone Seymor with a third of the advowson of the church.
Witnesses: Sir John de Clyvedon, Sir Simon de Aston, Sir Thomas de Gorneye, Sir Geoffrey de Hautevile, knights, William Douvile, William Arthur, John de Gatecumbe, Robert de Feulonde, Robert Bavent.
At: Bedminster.

---

[1] *CIPM* ix, no. 46; xi, no. 10.

A2/75/2 [GC 2235]   Mon. before St. George, 11 Edw. II [17 April 1318]
Laurence de Sancto Mauro, son and heir of Maud de Sancto Mauro, and Sir Maurice de Berkel', son and heir of Sir Thomas de Berkel'.

Laurence has quitclaimed to Maurice, his heirs and assigns one third of the manor of Kyngestone Seymor with the advowson of one third of the church, viz. the third which Philip de Wyke and Maud his wife held.
Witnesses: Sir John de Clyvedone, Sir Simon de Asschtone, Sir Geoffrey de Hautevyle, knights, William Arthur, William de Skouvyle, Nicholas de Keu, Baldwin Pyke.
At: Portbury.

A2/75/3 [GC 2261]   Sun. the morrow of Epiphany, 12 Edw. II [7 Jan. 1319]
Maurice de Berkele, knight, son of Sir Thomas de Berkele, and Sir Thomas de Berkele, his lord and father.

Maurice has granted to Thomas all his holding in Kyngeston Seynt Moor, with the advowson of one third of the church, which he had by grant of Laurence de Seynt Moor.
Witnesses: Sir John de Clyvedone, Sir Simon de Ashton, Sir Richard de Rodeneye, knights, William Arthur, Robert de Freulond, William de Capenore.
At: Portbury.

A2/75/4 [GC 3435]   Tues. the morrow of the Exaltation of Holy Cross, 29 Edw. III
[15 Sept. 1355]
(1) Thomas de Berkele of Uley; (2) Thomas Brid; (3) Sir Robert parson of Uley.

Thomas de Berkele has appointed Thomas Brid to deliver seisin of the manor of Kyngestone Saintmaur (Som.) with the appurtenances to Sir Robert. Sealed with the seal of his very dear and good friend Sir Simon Basset. [*In French*.]
At: Uley.

A2/75/5 [GC 4442]   5 May 2 Ric. III [1485]
Thomas Lymeryke and John Joce, feoffees of William Berkeley of Weoley (Worcs.), knight; and Maurice Berkeley of Thornbury, esquire.

Thomas and John, at the instance of William, have demised to Maurice, his heirs and assigns, the manor of Kyngeston Seymour (Som.) with the appurtenances, which they, along with the late Thomas Burdet, esquire, and John Dauntsey, had by grant of William.
Witnesses: Thomas Hykkes, rector of Kingston Seymour, Thomas Snygge, Thomas Smythe of Thornbury, John Kemysse, William Large.

MANORIAL ACCOUNT ROLLS

A2/75/6 [GAR 362]	1–2 Hen. VI [1422–3]
A2/75/7 [GAR 363]	2–3 Hen. VI [1423–4]
A2/75/8 [GAR 364]	3-4 Hen. VI [1424–5]
A2/75/9 [GAR 365]	5–6 Hen. VI [1426–7]
A2/75/10 [GAR 366]	8–9 Hen. VI [1429–30]
A2/75/11 [GAR 367]	11–12 Hen. VI [1432–3]
A2/75/12 [GAR 368]	12–13 Hen. VI [1433–4]
A2/75/13 [GAR 369]	15–16 Hen. VI [1436–7]
A2/75/14 [GAR 370]	18–19 Hen. VI [1439–40]
A2/75/15 [GAR 371]	19–20 Hen. VI [1440–1]
A2/75/16 [GAR 372]	20–1 Hen. VI [1441–2]
A2/75/17 [GAR 373]	21–2 Hen. VI [1442–3]
A2/75/18 [GAR 374]	24–5 Hen. VI [1445–6]

A2/75/19 [GAR 375]	25–6 Hen. VI [1446–7]
A2/75/20 [GAR 376]	26–7 Hen. VI [1447–8]
A2/75/21 [GAR 377]	27–8 Hen. VI [1448–9]
A2/75/22 [GAR 378]	31–2 Hen. VI [1452–3]
A2/75/23 [GAR 379]	34–5 Hen. VI [1455–6]
A2/75/24 [GAR 380]	37–8 Hen. VI [1458–9]
A2/75/25 [GAR 381]	38–9 Hen. VI [1459–60]
A2/75/26 [GAR 382]	7–8 Edw. IV [1467–8]
A2/75/27 [GAR 383]	8–9 Edw. IV [1468–9]
A2/75/28 [GAR384]	10–11 Edw. IV [1470–1]
A2/75/29 [GAR385]	14–15 Edw. IV [1474–5]

COURT ROLLS

A2/75/30 [GCR 201]	26–7 Hen. VI [1447–8]
A2/75/31 [GCR 202]	33 Hen. VI [1454–5]

MILVERTON (SOM.)

See above, p. 524, Edingworth, and below p. 539, Brigmerston.

A2/76/1 [GC 3900]   Mon. after Michaelmas, 19 Ric. II [4 Oct. 1395]
Thomas de Berkeley, lord of Berkeley; and William Pope and Joan his wife.

Thomas has leased to William and Joan all the land and meadow which William Helyare previously held in Mylverton, viz. 12 a. of land in an enclosure called Hatcheshull, 2 a. in an enclosure opposite Mortemeresyate,[1] 2 a. in Fayrecroft, 1 a. in Loveboundeswell [etc.]; for their lives, rent 20s. 6d. a year.
Witnesses: John Lorty, knight, John Rolfes, Thomas Frye, George atte More, John Hatche.
At: Berkeley.

A2/76/2 [GC 4060]   Mon. before St. Barnabas, 12 Hen. IV [8 June 1411]
Thomas Berkeley, lord of Berkeley; and John Muskham, Joan his wife and William their son.

Thomas has granted to John, Joan and William the reversion of all the land and meadow which William Pope and Joan his wife hold for their lives in Mulverton (Som.), except the wood and pasture in Hatcheshull; for their lives, rent 26s. 8d. a year.
At: Berkeley.

A2/76/3 [GC 4061]   Tues. after St. Barnabas, 12 Hen. IV [16 June 1411]
Thomas Berkeley, lord of Berkeley; and John Devenysch and Thomas Hurdyng.

Thomas has leased at farm to John and Thomas all his purparty of the manor of Mulvertone; for their lives, rent £7 a year.
At: Berkeley.

PORTBURY (SOM.)

Acquired by Robert FitzHarding, Portbury was one of the two principal manors of the Berkeley patrimony in Somerset but, unlike Bedminster (which had been settled in jointure and tail general in 1289), it was settled in tail male by Thomas (III) Lord Berkeley in 1350, with its hundred.[2] On the death of Thomas (IV) Lord Berkeley in 1417 it passed to his nephew and heir male James. See also above, A1/1/35 [GC 4446], A2/2/1 [GC 3109].

---

[1] The Mortimer earls of March held a manor in Milverton, their interest and that of the Zouches or Berkeleys deriving from the Breouse inheritance: see below, p. 539.
[2] *Somerset Fines, 1347–99*, 21.

BERKELEY INTERESTS

A2/77/1 [SC 13]   n.d. [*c.* 1150 × 1160]
Richard de Moreville; and Robert FitzHarding and Maurice his son.

Richard has acquitted Robert and Maurice of their relief for half of the manor of Portbury, which they hold of him.

A2/77/2 [SC 69]   n.d. [*c.* 1190]
Herbert de Morevilla and Robert de Berkeleia son of Maurice de Berkel'.

Herbert has confirmed to Robert that part of Portbury which Richard his brother gave to Robert FitzHarding, Robert's grandfather, and which Robert's father Maurice and grandfather Robert held of them, for the service of half a knight's fee; Herbert has received Robert's homage and relief.
Witnesses: John [abbot] of St. Augustine's, William [abbot] of Keynsham, William [abbot] of Kingswood, William earl of Salisbury, William Marshal, Ivo de Morevill, William and Roger his sons, William chaplain of Morevill, Richard son of Herbert, Henry brother of Herbert's wife, Walter the chaplain, Henry the chaplain, John le Warre, William de Suble, William Cotele, Walter Snigg, Gilbert son of Osmund, Hugh de Camme, Richard the smith.

A2/77/3 [GC 811; *duplicate* GC 812]   n.d. [*c.* 1200]
William de Saltmarsh (*de salso marisco*) and Robert de Berkel', his lord.

William has granted to Robert all the land which he had at Portburi, which Richard de Moraville gave to Adam de Saltmatsh his grandfather, for the service of 2½ virgates, for which Robert has given him in exchange lands near Berkel'; rent 12*d.* a year.
Witnesses: Sir Nicholas Puinz, William de Moravilla, Nicholas de Limesia, Adam son of Nigel, Richard son of Arthur, William de Karswell, Henry and Alexander, chaplains of Berkeley, Robert le Horder, Maurice son of Nigel, John le Bret, John de Egetun.

A2/77/4 [SC 376]   n.d. [*temp.* Edw. I]
Adam de la Hope and Sir Thomas de Berkeley, lord of Portbury.

Adam has granted to Thomas the holding which John de la [Chuth] held in Portbury.
Witnesses: John de Clyvedon, Richard Artur, knights, William de Bradeford, William de Capenore, John le Pike, . . . , William Wale.

A2/77/5 [GC 623]   Morrow of Epiphany, 25 Edw. I [7 Jan. 1297]
Thomas de Berkel; and John atte Yate of Carswell and Lucy his wife.

Thomas has leased to John and Lucy, for their lives, the messuage, curtilage and 1 a. of land previously held of Isabel de la Hope and of John Welle, and 1½ a. of land in the west field of Carswell; rent 7*s.* 6*d.* a year, the customary services and suit to the hundred court of Portbury.
Witnesses: Robert de Stan, Richard de Bisel', Richard Broun, William Wale, Nicholas the clerk.
At: Portbury.

A2/77/6 [GC 2681]   18 June 3 Edw. III [1329]
Isabel widow of Sir Maurice de Berkel' and Sir Thomas de Berkel', lord of Berkeley.

Isabel has quitclaimed to Thomas the manor and hundred of Portbur' and all the holdings which Thomas holds in Somerset except her holding in Kinggestone Seintmor.
Witnesses: Sir William de Wautone, knight, Thomas de Rodberewe, Robert de Aston, John de Milkesham, John Lidyerd, John le Skai of Nibley.
At: Wotton.

A2/77/7 [SR 32]

Copies of:

(i) inspeximus by King Edward III, dated [20] Jan. 18 Edw. III [1344], of his licence to Thomas de Berkeley to grant to William de Syde 100 a. of land, 10 a. of meadow, 4 a. of wood and 40s. rent in Alkington, held in chief, in exchange for similar quantities of land etc. which William holds of Thomas;

(ii) exemplification, dated 8 May 19 [? Hen. VI, 1441], at the request of James Berkeley, knight, of an inspeximus by King Edward III of his licence, dated 6 Feb. 19 Edw. III [1345], to Thomas de Berkeley to alienate in mortmain 40 a. of land and 20s. rent in Portbury, Eston and Bedmenstre [as below, A2/77/8].

A2/77/8 [GC 3114]   6 Feb. 19 Edw. III [1345]

King Edward III and Thomas de Berkele.

The king has granted licence to Thomas to grant a messuage, 40 a. of land and 20s. rent in Portbury, Eston and Bedemenstre, held in chief, to the chapel of St. Katherine of Katerine Pulle by Bristoll.

At: Westminster.

A2/77/9 [GC 3239*]   6 June 24 Edw. III [1350]

Maurice de Berkelee, knight, son of Sir Thomas, lord of Berkelee; and Sir William de Syde, Sir Walter Goldemere and Sir John le Vey.

Maurice has granted to William, Walter and John his manor of Portbur' (Som.) and all his lands and holdings in Portesheved and Wroxhale, which he had by grant of the said Sir Thomas for his life; to them for his life.

Witnesses: Sir Edmund de Clyvedon, William de Chiltenham, Edmund de Lyouns, Robert de Aisshtone, Andrew Basset.

At: Berkeley.

A2/77/10 [GC 3240]   6 June 24 Edw. III [1350]

(1) Maurice de Berkelee, knight, son of Thomas lord of Berkelee; (2) Sir Hugh vicar of Portbury and Walter le Cook of Portbury; (3) Sir William de Syde, Sir Walter Goldemere and Sir John le Vey.

Maurice has appointed Hugh and Walter his attorneys to give seisin to William, Walter and John of the manor of Portbur' (Som.) and all his lands and holdings in Portesheved and Wroxhale.

At: Berkeley.

A2/77/11 [GC 3241]   11 June 24 Edw. III [1350]

Thomas lord of Berkelee; and Sir William de Syde, Walter Goldemere and John le Vey.

Thomas has quitclaimed to William, Walter and John the manor of Portbur' and lands and holdings in Portesheved and Wroxhale (Som.), which they had by grant of Maurice de Berkelee, knight, son of Thomas, for Maurice's life.

Witnesses: Sir Edmund de Clyvedon, William de Chiltenham, Edmund de Lyouns, Robert de Aisshtone, Andrew Basset.

At: Berkeley.

A2/77/12 [GC 3242]   Wed. before the nativity of St. John the Baptist, 24 Edw. III
                                                              [23 June 1350]

Maurice de Berkelee, knight, and his lord Sir Thomas lord of Berkelee, his father.

Maurice has granted to Thomas, for Maurice's life, an annual rent of £100 from Maurice's manor of Portbur'.

At: Berkeley.

A2/77/13 [GC 4005]¹   10 June 5 Hen. IV [1404]

Thomas de Berkeleye, lord of Berkeley, knight; and Nicholas Bubbewyth, clerk, Thomas Knolles, citizen of London, Thomas Rede, William Coventre, William Wheteley citizen of London, Robert Burdon and John Bonjon, vicar of Berkeleye.

Thomas has granted to Nicholas and the others, and their heirs and assigns, his manor of Portbury in Gordene with the appurtenances in Portbury and with the hundred of Portbury, the manor of Bedemenstre with the appurtenances in the vills of Bedemenstre and Bristoll with the hundreds of Bedemenstre and Hareclefe, the manors of Walton and Chorlton in Gordene with the appurtenances and the advowson of Walton and all his lands, holdings [etc.] in the parish of Wroxhale, the manor of Westone in Gordene with the appurtenances and with his lands [etc.] in Porteshede (Som.), and the manor of Aure with appurtenances and the hundred of Bledeslowe and lands, holdings [etc.] in Pyrytone and Tokenhale, with the advowson of the chantry of Pyrytone, and all the lands [etc.] which he recently acquired in the vills of Wottone sub Egge, Berkeley, Hyntone, Swonongre, Hamme and Gloucestre (Glos.), and in Favalore and Offyngton (Berks.). Not sealed.

Witnesses: Thomas FitzNicol, knight, John Bluwet, William Wermentre, John Bays, George Longe, Robert Poyns, Ralph Whytyngtone, James Spersholte.

A2/77/14 [SC 581]   Thurs. the feast of the nativity of St. John the Baptist, 5 Hen.V
                                                                [24 June 1417]

Thomas lord of Berkeley; and Walter Poole, Gilbert Deneys, knights, Thomas Knolles, citizen of London, Thomas Rugge, John Grevell, Robert Greyndour and Thomas Sergeant, esquires.

Thomas has granted to Walter and the others all the lands, holdings, reversions, services [etc.] which he has bought in Berkeley, Wotton, Gloucester, South Cerney, Cerneyswike, Aure, Erlingham and Horton, and in Berkeley and Bledislow hundreds (Glos.), all the holdings which he has in London, all the lands [etc.] which he has bought in Portbury, Porteshed, Weston, Bedminster, and in Bedminster and Portbury hundreds (Som.), and all the lands [etc.] which he has bought in Sharnecote and Chicklade (Wilts.), together with the advowsons of St. Andrew's church in Baynard's Castle, London,² of Chicklade, Porteshed and Walton, and the patronage and advowson of Kingswood Abbey.

Witnesses: Thomas FitzNicoll, John Pauncefoot, knights, Robert Poynes, Edmund Bassett, Thomas Kendale.

At: Berkeley.

A2/77/15 [GC 4162]³   22 Aug. 7 Hen. VI [1429]

James de Berkele, knight, lord of Berkeley; and Richard de la Mare, John Brygge, esquires, Edmund Moreys and Thomas Lyghtfote.

Whereas James granted to Richard, John, Edmund and Thomas the manors of Portbury (Som.) and of Alkyngton (Glos.), they have granted that if when James dies John Merbury of Herefs., esquire, has not been satisfied of the 900 marks in which James is bound to John

---

¹ This charter bears a strong similarity to the following one, the settlement of 1417, but for the notable exception of Bedminster and Awre, and may have been an early uncompleted attempt at a settlement. Bedminster had been settled in tail general in 1289 and Awre in jointure and in tail general in 1319, and were therefore excluded from the 1417 settlement. As the charter is not sealed, it may be a forgery, part of the Warwicks' attempts to recover the lands which Thomas (IV) Lord Berkeley appears to have intended for his nephew James.

² Bought by Thomas (IV) Lord Berkeley for £120 in 1394 from Walter Lord FitzWalter, whose great-great-grandfather Robert had sold Berkeley Inn to Thomas (II) Lord Berkeley: BCM SB 10, f. 239 and v.

³ On 21 Aug. John Merbury and his wife Agnes and other feoffees granted the lordship of Talgarth to James; in 1420 James's mother and her fourth husband had granted it to Merbury and feoffees.

by various bonds made 18 Aug. 7 Hen. VI, and if Richard, John, Edmund and Thomas then hold the said manors without impediment from James to apply the profits to the said debt for the use of John Merbury, then the said charter of enfeoffment shall be void.

A2/77/16 [GC 4259]   5 June 25 Hen. VI [1447]

William Berkeley, knight, and Nicholas Poyntz, esquire; and John [de Mowbray] duke of Norfolk, Edward Gray and James Ormounde, knights, Thomas Danyell, John Howarde, John Wyngefelde, Robert Wyngefeld and William Brandon esquires.

Whereas James Berkeley, lord of Berkeley, knight, lately demised at farm to William and Nicholas the manor of Portbury (Som.), with all his other lands in the said county, for a term of 40 years starting at Whitsun 18 Hen. VI [15 May 1440], William has granted to John and the others his status in the said land.

A2/77/17 [GC 4353]   24 Oct. 8 Edw. IV [1468]

Thomas Campeden, chaplain, and Richard Badeham; and William Berkeley, lord of Berkeley, knight, and Joan Wylughby, daughter of Katherine duchess of Norfolk.

Thomas and Richard have granted to William and Joan the manor of Portebury (Som.) which they had by grant of William; to them and the male issue of William, with remainder to his right heirs, on the condition that if William marries Joan around Christmas next, then the present charter will be void.

PORTBURY CHANTRY

A2/77/18 [GC 2878*]   24 June 11 Edw. III [1337]

Thomas lord of Berkelee and William [Godwyne], vicar of Portbury.

Thomas has granted to William and his successors a rent of 8s. in Portbur' from the holding which Elizabeth de Carswelle holds of Thomas, for the anniversary of the Lady Eve, Thomas's mother, and Margaret, Thomas's late wife, and of Sir William Godwyne, vicar of Portbur'.

At: Portbury.

A2/77/19 [GC 2879]   24 June 11 Edw. III [1337]

Thomas lord of Berkelee and William Godwyne, vicar of Portbury.

Thomas has leased to William a half-acre of pasture at Dichlese in la Estmede in Portbur', for his life, celebrating for the souls of Eve, Thomas's mother, Margaret Thomas's late wife, and himself.

At: Portbury.

ADMINISTRATIVE DOCUMENTS

A2/77/20 [GAR 388] Manorial account   Michaelmas to 24 June 13 Edw. II [1319–20]

A2/77/21 [GC 4346]   19 Nov. 7 Edw. IV [1467]

William lord Berkeley, knight, and Richard ap Adam, bailiff of Portbury.

William has received from Richard, in part payment of the fines within the lordship of Portbury, £6 6s. 8d. Not sealed. [In English.]

PORTISHEAD (SOM.)

A third of the manor of Portishead was acquired by Maurice (III) Lord Berkeley, probably in 1311.[1] It descended in the main line, being entailed with Portbury in 1350.[2] See above, A1/1/77 [SC 580], A2/2/1 [GC 3109], A2/77/11 [GC 3241]; below, A2/83/2 [GC 3989*].

SOCK DENNIS (SOM.)

One of the many purchases made by Thomas (III) Lord Berkeley for the benefit of his

[1] Smyth, i. 273; BCM SR 39 (below, A4/2/7); PRO CP 25/1/198/16, no. 3.
[2] PRO C 135/199, no. 9; C 136/58, no. 1.

younger sons, it passed to his son John and the cadet line of Beverston.[1]

A2/78/1 [GC 3434]   n.d. [c. 1355]
Grimbald Pauncevot and Sir Thomas, lord of Berkelee.

Grimbald has granted to Thomas the reversion of half of the manor of Sokke (Som.), which Lady Clemence Pauncevot holds in dower of his inheritance after her death; to Thomas for life, with reversion to his son Edmund and his male issue, remainder to Maurice, brother of Edmund and son of Thomas and Katherine his wife, and his male issue, the male issue of Thomas and Katherine and the right heirs of Thomas.
Witnesses: Sir Edmund de Clyvedone, Sir Walter de Rodeneye, knights, William de Chiltenham, Edmund Lyouns, John de Clyve.

A2/78/2 [GC 3433]   16 Aug. 29 Edw. III [1355]
(1) Thomas lord of Berkele, Katherine his wife and Edmund their son; (2) Robert de Couelegh and John Vag'; (3) Lady Clemence Pauncefot, lady of Hasfield.

Thomas, Katherine and Edmund have appointed Robert or John to receive seisin of the manor of Socke (Som.) as in the charter of Clemence. [*In French.*]
At: Berkeley.

STEEP HOLME (SOM.)

The island formed one holding with land at Christon (above, p. 523) and Uphill (below, p. 533) and the advowson of Brean (Som.).

A2/79/1 [SC 430]   5 Ides of April [9 April] 1260
William [de Bitton] bishop of Bath and Wells.

William has declared that, for the more frequent celebration of divine service at the religious place called Stepholm, which, with the island of Stepholm, was granted to the Austin canons of Stodlegh by R. de Tregoz, the prior of Studley shall appoint two canons at least to reside in the island.[2]
At: Charlcombe.

TELLISFORD (SOM.)

See above, p. 522, Chatley.

A2/80/1 [SC 83]   n.d. [c. 1200]
Ivo de Tevellesford and Robert de Bercel'.

Ivo has granted to Robert 4½ a. of land in Tevellesford; Robert has given him a cow in acknowledgement.
Witnesses: Henry de Monteforti, John de Erlega, Richard de Cotela, Roger de Monteforti, Guy of the furlong (*de cultura*), Richard the parker (*parcarius*), Thomas de Bodinc.

A2/80/2 [SC 64]   n.d. [c. 1200]
Philip son of Elias Wace and Robert de Berchelai.

Philip has granted to Robert 1 virgate of land in Tablesford, which John son of Walter Wace held; rent 1 lb. of cumin at Christmas.
Witnesses: Henry de Munford, Roger de Munford, Master Reginald de Herlega, Richard the parker (*parc'*) of Hinton (*Hentona*), James the cottar (*cocellus*), William de Hagelega, John de Craulega, Herebert de Echewicha, Baldwin de Hechewicha, Robert son of Ivo.

---

[1] PRO C 135/156, no. 12; C 139/35, no. 50; *CCR* 1360–4, 232.
[2] *Transcript*: Jeayes, pp. 134–6.

A2/80/3 [SC 416]   n.d. [mid 13th cent.]
Philip Wace and Thomas de Berkeleia.

Philip has confirmed to Thomas the virgate of land which John Wace, his uncle, sold to Sir Robert de Berkelay in Tefleford; rent 1 lb. of cumin a year; Thomas has given Philip 1 mark in acknowledgement.

Witnesses: John Bonet, Geoffrey de Laurtun, Payn de Waltun, Thomas de Tefleford, Elias de Tefleford, Richard the parker (*parcarius*), Peter de Stintecumbe, Richard de Couleg', Thomas de Tiringham, John de Crauleg', Richard Lestut.

TICKENHAM (SOM.)

Thomas (III) bought a messuage and 4 virgates from Thomas ap Adam,[1] in addition to the holding acquired from John de Manners. In 1352 the reversion of a messuage and 1 carucate of land held for life by Roger de Estham, a servant of Thomas, was settled on Thomas's younger son Edmund and his brothers; it passed to Thomas's son John and his cadet line at Beverston.[2] See also above, p. 458, Falfield.

A2/81/1 [GC 2646]   Tues. after Easter, 2 Edw. III [5 April 1328]
Thomas ap Adam, lord of Beverston, and John Londoniar, burgess of Bristol.

Whereas Thomas and Fulk, Thomas's sons, have leased to John all the lands and holdings in Tykenham which they had by grant of Thomas the elder for the term of his life, Thomas has confirmed the grant.

At: King's Weston.

A2/81/2 [GC 3320]   n.d. [mid 14th cent.]
Alice widow of Robert de Maners and Sir Thomas, lord of Berkelee.

Whereas John de Maners granted to Thomas the reversion of all the lands and holdings which Alice holds for life in Tykenham of John's inheritance, she has attorned to Thomas.

Witnesses: Sir Edmund de Clyvedone, knight, Matthew de Clyvedone, Richard de Clyvedone, Richard Arthur, Andrew Basset.

A2/81/3 [GAR 389] Manorial account: two rolls attached at the foot, Michaelmas, 7 Edw. III to the feast of the nativity of St. John the Baptist [29 Sept. 1333 to 24 June 1334] and St. John to Michaelmas, 8 Edw. III [24 June to 29 Sept. 1334].

UPHILL (SOM.)

See above, p. 523, Christon.

A2/82/1 [SC 110]   n.d. [*temp.* John]
William son of Robert son of Martin and Robert son of Richard, knight.

William has confirmed the grant by Robert of 1 virgate of land in Huppilla, which Ailric de Rewa held, to the church of St. Michael of Stepholm island.

Witnesses: Robert de Langatot, Robert de Sancta Cruce, Richard de Bichefauda, Thomas his brother, Warin de Morcellis, Schep' de Audewic, William the clerk of Cuantona, William Bodin.

A2/82/2 [SC 50]   n.d. [*temp.* John]
Robert son of Richard and the brethren of St. Michael of Stepholm.

Robert has granted to the brethren as much of the church of St. Nicholas of Uppilla as can belong to a lay person.[3]

Witnesses: David dean of Bleaden (*Bleden'*), Walter de Kywestoc, Richard chaplain of

[1] GRO D1866/T18, T19.
[2] PRO C 139/35, no. 50.
[3] *Transcript*: Jeayes, p. 23.

Cardiff, Richard the clerk of the marsh (*de marisco*), Nicholas the clerk, John the clerk of East Brent (*Estbrenta*), Thomas de la Ville, Jordan de Greinton, Hugh Vassal, Richard de Lockeston, Richard son of Geoffrey, Hugh de Uppilla, Ralph the clerk.

A2/82/3 [SC 104]   n.d. [*temp.* Hen. III]
John de Keu and the brethren of the island called Stepholm.

  John has confirmed to the brethren the half-virgate of land in Uphulla which his ancestor Robert son of Richard granted to the brethren, viz. that which Ailric de Rewa held, with the right of grinding at the mill in the vill and pasture for 4 cows and 20 sheep.[1]
Witnesses: A. chaplain of Broclegha, Gervase de Locaston, Daniel chaplain of Loxton, A. chaplain of Christon, Jordan the chaplain, Hugh Vassal, Reginald the Irish (*Iberniensis*), Robert de Sparkeford, Robert de Perrers, Thomas de Muneketon, Geoffrey Vassal, Richard de la Hull.

WALTON-IN-GORDANO (SOM.)

See also above, A2/77/13–14 [GC 4005, SC 581].

ACQUISITIONS BY THOMAS (IV) LORD BERKELEY

A2/83/1 [GC 3179*]   One month after Easter, 22 [Ric. II, 27 April 1399]
John Walters, clerk, and John Rolves; and Thomas [Longe] and Petronilla his wife.

  Copy of final concord concerning the manor of Waltone in Gordano and the advowson; Thomas and Petronilla have acknowledged the right of John Walters by their gift to him and John Rolves, except for a messuage and a half-virgate of land in the same manor, and warrant for themselves and Petronilla's heirs; John has given them 100 marks.
At: Westminster.

A2/83/2 [GC 3989*]   24 Aug. 2 Hen. IV [1401]
King Henry IV and Thomas Berkeley, lord of Berkeley.

  The king, of special grace, has granted to Thomas free warren in his demesne lands within his manors of Waltone, Westone, Porteshed and Charlton by Wroxhale (Som.).
At: Westminster.

A2/83/3 [GC 3997]   Fri. before St. George, 3 Hen. IV [21 April 1402]
Thomas Berkeley, lord of Berkeley; and Richard Sparwe, Christine his wife, John Sparwe, his son, and Milicent, John's wife.

  Thomas has leased to Richard, Christine, John and Milicent the holding which Richard previously occupied and held in the manor of Waltone; for their lives, rent 12*s.* a year.
Witnesses: Thomas Artour, knight, John Bleuet, Ralph Poevale, John Gauge, John Morcok.
At: Walton.

OTHER INTERESTS

A2/83/4 [GC 2748*]
15th-cent. copy of two deeds:
(i) Brian de Bromtona and Edmund his son.   n.d. [14th cent.]
  Brian has granted to Edmund all his land of Walton, in demesne and in rents; to him and his issue, rent 1*d.* a year.
Witnesses: Sir Hugh de Crofte, Sir John de Lyngeyn, Sir Simon de Burl', Sir Ralph de Bakeputz, Robert de Westona, William Artur, Stephen de Capenore, Roger de Cangl', Thomas son of William de Cornwayl, William the chaplain;
(ii) Andrew de Bromton and Joan his wife; and Nicholas de Brente, vicar of Chard.
                                                   One month after Easter 6 Edw. III [17 May 1332]
  Final concord concerning the manor of Waltone in Gordeno and the advowson of the church, two thirds held by Nicholas and the reversion of one third held in dower by Cecilia

---

[1] *Transcript*: Jeayes, pp. 41–2.

widow of Thomas de Bromtone; Andrew has acknowledged the right of Nicholas by his gift, and Nicholas has granted the two thirds and the reversion of the one third to Andrew and Joan.
At: Westminster.

A2/83/5 [SC 550]   1 Feb. 1374
John [Harewell], bishop of Bath and Wells, and Ralph Damesel.

The bishop has granted to Ralph that he may have a portable altar in a chapel in his house at Walton in the parish of Stoke super Mare.
At: Dogmersfield.

WEARE (SOM.)

Robert FitzHarding granted Weare to his younger son Robert.

A2/84/1 [SC 47]   n.d. [*temp.* Ric. I]
John count of Moret[ain] and Robert son of Robert FitzHarding.

John has confirmed to Robert the vill of Were, which Juliana de Bantona granted to Robert's father Robert FitzHarding, to hold for the service of one knight, as Juliana's charter and the confirmation of King Henry declare.
Witnesses: William de Wenn[eval], Hamon de Val[oniis], John the marshal (*marescallus*), William de Buchet, Theobald Walter, William son of John, Henry de Munfort, Roger de Novoburgo, William de Viliers, John de Bonavilla, Robert le Francois, Master Peter de Littel.
At: 'Cranebr''.

WESTON-IN-GORDANO (SOM.)

See also above, A2/73/1 [GC 3948], A2/77/13–14 [GC 4005, SC 581].

A2/85/1 [GC 2243]   Wed. after St. John the Baptist, 11 Edw. II [28 June 1318]
Simon de Asschton, knight, and Sir Maurice de Berkeleye, son and heir of Sir Thomas de Berkel'.

Simon has granted to Maurice, his heirs and assigns, for a certain sum of money, a rent of 10*s.* a year from a messuage and a half-virgate which Robert de Snoudon holds for life of Simon in Weston in Gordene, with the reversion of the holding, and a rent of 10*s.* a year from a messuage and a half-virgate which Walter de Lamynton and Eleanor his wife hold for their lives, in the same vill, with the reversion of the holding after their deaths.
Witnesses: Sir Ralph de Gorges, Sir John de Clyvedone, knights, William Arthuyr, William de Capenore, William de Bradeford, Philip de Wyke, Brian le Fry.
At: Portbury.

A2/85/2 [GC 3955]   One month after Easter, 22 Ric. II [27 April 1399]
John Walters, clerk, and John Rolves; and Thomas Longe and Petronilla his wife.

Final concord concerning the manor of Weston in Gordano and the advowson of the church; Thomas and Petronilla have acknowledged the right of John Walters by their gift to him and John Rolves, except for a messuage and half-virgate of land; John and John have given them 100 marks.
At: Westminster.

A2/85/3 [GC 4068]   . . . Hilary, 13 Hen. IV [*c.* 13 Jan. 1412]
Thomas de Berkelee, lord of Berkeley, and William Sore of Weston-in-Gordano.

Thomas has leased to William the holding with land [etc.], . . . John Burnel formerly held in Westone aforesaid; for his life, rent 6*s.* a year.
Witnesses: Ralph Percevale, John Coker, Thomas Tylly, John Gage, . . .

A2/85/4 [GC 4069]   St. Wulfstan, 13 Hen. IV [19 Jan. 1412]
Thomas de Berkelee, lord of Berkeley, and William Carpenter of Weston-in-Gordano and Joan his wife.

Thomas has leased to William and Joan the reversion of all the lands [etc.] which Walter Carpenter, William's father, holds of Thomas for his life within the lordship of Westone aforesaid; for their lives, rent 7s. a year.
Witnesses: Ralph Percevale, John Coker, Thomas Tylly, John Gage, Thomas Brian.
At: Portbury.

WINTERHEAD (SOM.)

The holding is not found later in Berkeley hands, and may have been merged with the nearby holding at Edingworth, which was also settled on Maurice (of Stoke Giffard), the second son of Maurice (III) Lord Berkeley and Eve la Zouche.

A2/86/1 [GC 1086]   2 Feb. 33 Edw. I [1305]
William son of William de Wyntred; and Sir Maurice de Berkeleye, Eve his wife and Maurice their son.

William has quitclaimed to Maurice, Eve and Maurice the lands which he has inherited or might inherit in Wyntred and Wynescumbe.
Witnesses: Sir John le Waleys, Sir Richard Arthur, Sir Simon de Ashton, Sir John de Wyke, knights, William Malerbe, Roger de le Pulle, Adam le Hundredmon.
At: Winterhead.

WORLE (SOM.)

Richard Mead was the brother-in-law of Maurice (V) Lord Berkeley.

A2/87/1 [GC 4357]   1 Aug. 9 Edw. IV [1469]
(1) Richard Thomelyn *alias* Richard Cutteler; (2) Richard Mede of Bristol and Thomas Hogges of Tickenham (Som.); (3) Maurice Berkeley, esquire, son of James Berkeley, lord of Berkeley.

Richard has appointed Richard and Thomas to deliver seisin to Maurice of all the lands, holdings [etc.] in the parishes of Newton, Kewestoke, Weston super Mare, Worle and elsewhere in Somerset and Bristol which he inherited after the death of his mother Elizabeth, one of the daughters and heirs of John Wikyng, son and heir of the late Geoffrey Wikyng, and his wife Isabel Fraunceys.

WRAXALL (SOM.)

The Berkeley family had a holding in Wraxall as early as 1350 (see above, A2/77/9–11 [GC 3239*, GC 3240–1]) but the purchases of Thomas (IV) Lord Berkeley were part of those apparently designed to enhance the inheritance of his nephew and heir male, James (see above, p. 522, Charlton). Maurice (V) Lord Berkeley married Isabel, daughter of Philip Mead.

BERKELEY INTERESTS

A2/88/1 [GC 3953]   15 March 22 Ric. II [1399]
Thomas Norton of Bristol the elder and Thomas Berkeley, lord of Berkeley.

Thomas Norton has granted to Thomas Berkeley and his heirs a messuage called Whelpesplace in the parish of Wroxhale, with the reversion of 4 a. of meadow in Newmede in the said parish, as Elias Spelly formerly acquired them of John Blount, knight.
Witnesses: Thomas Arthur, Edward Seymore, knights, John Bluwet, Geofrey More, Nicholas More, George Lange the elder.
At: Portbury.

A2/88/2 [GC 4345]   20 Oct. 7 Edw. IV [1467]
Philip Mede of Bristol, merchant, Isabel his wife and Richard their son; and Maurice
Bercley, esquire, and Isabel his wife.

   Philip, Isabel and Richard have leased to Maurice and Isabel the holding in Feylond in
the parish of Wroxsale called Medeisplace; for a term of 20 years, rent 45s. 8d. a year.
Witnesses: Richard Arthur, esquire, Ralph Percevale, Thomas Feylond.

GAGE CLOSE

A2/88/3 [GC 1486]   n.d. [*temp.* Edw. I]
Humphrey de Monte; and Thomas son of Roger Gaugy and Isabel his wife, daughter of
Miles de Sancto Mauro.

   Humphrey has confirmed the grant by Miles to Thomas in free marriage with Isabel his
daughter of all his lands with appurtenances in the parish of Wraxhale, which Miles bought
from Humphrey.
Witnesses: Sir Edmund de Brompton, knight, Sir Roger de Evesham, Robert de la Berghe,
Robert de Feghelond, William de Carswelle.

A2/88/4 [GC 2943]   Mon. before St. Tiburtius, 13 Edw. III [12 April 1339]
William de Osmynton, parson of Stoke super Mare, and Thomas de Aschelwourth, vicar of
Clevedon; and John Gaugy the younger and Eleanor his wife.

   William and Thomas have granted to John and Eleanor all the rents, customs and services
which John Gaugy the elder renders to them annually for the lands and holdings which he
holds of them for his life in the manor of Wroxhale, with the reversion of the lands; to them
and their issue, with remainder to the right heirs of John Gaugy the elder.
Witnesses: Andrew de Brompton, Robert de Feylonde, John Mogge, William de Bury,
William Wale, Henry Wale, John Tynte.
At: Wraxall.

A2/88/5 [GC 3737]   Mon. after the nativity of St. John the Baptist, 4 Ric. II [25 June 1380]
John Gauge the younger of Walton and Eleanor his wife; and Walter Lauerans of Capenor
and Eleanor his wife.

   John and Eleanor have leased to Walter and Eleanor all their lands, meadow and pasture
within the lordship of Wroxhale within the limits of the land called Gageclos, except the
wood; for their lives, rent 14s. a year.
Witnesses: Ralph Parsyvale, John Morecoke, William Glastingbury, Richard Wykford, John
Forster.
At: Wraxall.

A2/88/6 [GC 3762]   Mon. after the Assumption of the Blessed Virgin Mary, 7 Ric. II
                                                                   [17 Aug. 1383]
John Gage of Walton-in-Gordano and John Mareys of Capenor.

   Whereas all the wood, except the timber, of John Gage within the enclosure called
Gageclos in the parish of Wroxale in the hundred of Portbury is in the hands of John
Mareys from the feast of the Purification of the Virgin Mary [2 Feb.] next following for 4
years, John Gage has granted that John Mareys may cut and sell the timber, paying to John
Gage 20s. for each year.
Witnesses: Robert Bryen, Thomas Tylly, Richard Chapele, John Serjaunt, Thomas
Weddman.
At: Portishead.

THE MORVILLE HOLDING

A2/88/7 [SC 203]   n.d. [early Hen. III]
William de Morevile and Laurence de Sancto Mauro.

William has granted to Laurence, in marriage with his daughter Hawise, a house called Woderige, with Walter de Woderige and all his issue, half of the wood called Nadderhurste, a certain moor outside the wood, and pasture for 20 pigs; to Laurence and Hawise's issue, and if Hawise dies without issue, the land will revert to William or his heirs.

Witnesses: Matthew de Clivedune, Roger de Sancto Mauro, Richard son of Arthur, Roger de Morevile, Richard de Capenor, John la Warre, Peter of the marsh (*de marisco*), Philip de Nerberth, Henry de Bikeford, Brian le Brech, Reginald de Remesby, Nicholas de Capenor, William de Sancto Mauro, Elias de Wrokeshale, Eustace his son.

A2/88/8 [GC 814]   n.d. [late 13th cent.]
Hawise de Sancto Mauro, widow, and John de Sciptone.

Hawise has granted to John, in free marriage with Eleanor her daughter, all the holding and rent which she had in free marriage from William de Morevile her father in the manor of Worckeshale, viz. the holding called Woderigge and the wood called Naderhurste, and the road from the messuage to the river, and mast for 20 pigs and in the warren of Naillesy, with remainder to Laurence, son of Eleanor by her first husband, after the death of John and Eleanor.

Witnesses: Sir Edmund de Bremtone, William Brun, Robert de Fealande, John Wale, Stephen de Aistone, William de Carssewelle, John de Lydeard.

OTHER INTERESTS

A2/88/9 [GC 512]   St. Ambrose, 12 Edw. I [4 April 1284]
Isabel de la Hope, widow, and John de la Churche and Helen his wife.

Isabel has granted to John and Helen and their issue a quarter-virgate of land with a messuage, curtilage [etc.], which John Crede held in the manor of Wroxale at Cherulton; to hold of Robert le Warre, rent to Robert a rose a year.

Witnesses: Robert de Feolond, John Wale, William de la Forde, William de Carswelle, Ralph Brun.

At: 'Le Hope'.

A2/88/10 [GC 542]   St. Silvester, 17 Edw. I [31 Dec. 1288]
John Wale of Wraxall and Alice his daughter.

John has granted to Alice a messuage, garden, curtilage and 7 a. of meadow and pasture, which Richard le Wythe and Isabel his wife hold for their lives in the vill of Wroxale, also a messuage, curtilage and 2½ a. of land which Robert in le Reke and Margery his wife formerly held of him, also a messuage and curtilage and plot above Naylesey which Hugh the tiler formerly held of him, and a messuage, curtilage and 2 a. which Walter Gerneys above la Hulle formerly held of him; to her and her issue, to revert to him if she dies without issue.

Witnesses: Robert de Stonlonde, Thomas Gauge, Thomas Mogge, Philip of the ash (*de fraxeno*), Robert le Proute, Thomas called Noreys, John de Howelle, clerk.

At: Wraxall.

A2/88/11 [GC 2115]   Tues. after St. James, 10 Edw. II [27 July 1316]
Ralph de Gorges, lord of Wraxall, and Henry de Rokhulle.

Ralph has granted to Henry, for a certain sum of money, custody of all the lands and holdings which were of William Malet in Wroxhale until the full age of William's heir, with the marriage of the heir.

Witnesses: Robert de Foylonde, Robert Bavent, Thomas Nel, Richard Tynte, Walter Mogge.

At: Wraxall.

A2/88/12 [SR 33]

Copies of two deeds:

(i) quitclaim by Ralph de Gorges to William de Bury of the holding which William held of Ralph in the vill of Wroxhale [n.d.];

(ii) lease by Theobald de Gorges, knight, to John de Bury, chaplain, of the holding which Robert Kyngwest previously held in Naylesheye in the manor of Wroxhale; for life, rent 20s. 4½d. a year; also to John and Alice his sister, of the holding which William Bury previously held in Wraxhale, 1 a. which William le Grat once held in Langhalre above Nayleseye and 2 a. of meadow next to le Parkwalle; for their lives, rent 10s. a year; dated at Wraxall, Tues. after St. John before the Latin Gate, 24 Edw. III [11 May 1350].

MONEWDEN (SUFF.)

The reversion of the manor was part of the purchase made by Thomas (III) Lord Berkeley from Thomas ap Adam in 1330, and was sold by Thomas (III) to Isabel Hastings in 1332 for 100 marks.[1] Isabel was a daughter of the elder Despenser and the widow of John Lord Hastings (d. 1313) and of Ralph de Monthermer (d. 1325).[2] The manor passed to her son by Hastings, from whom the cadet line of Hastings of Elsing descended.[3]

A2/89/1 [GC 2456]   Thurs. the feast of St. James, 19 Edw. II [25 July 1325]

Thomas ap Adam, son and heir of John ap Adam, and Lady Isabel de Hastinges, recently wife of Sir Ralph de Monte Hermii.

Thomas has demised to Isabel his manor of Monewedene (Suff.) with the advowson of the church of the vill; to hold for her life, rent 1d. a year.

Witnesses: Sir William de Weylond, Sir Roger de Bylneye, Sir Ralph de Bockynge, knights, Benedict Oliver, William de Hoo, John his son, John le Warde.

At: East Tytherley (*Tudderleigh*)[4].

A2/89/2 [GC 2695]   4 March 4 Edw. III [1330]

Thomas ap Adam and Sir Thomas, lord of Berkeleie.

Thomas ap Adam has granted to Thomas de Berkeleie the reversion of all the lands and holdings which Isabel de Hastyngs holds of him for her life in Mundene.

Witnesses: Sir Maurice de Berkel', Sir John de Clyvedone, Sir Geoffrey de Hauteville, knights, Andrew de Brompton, John Perceval.

At: Portbury.

BRIGMERSTON (WILTS.)

Brigmerston and Milston (Wilts.) came to Maurice (III) Lord Berkeley in 1289 with his wife Eve la Zouche, and they were settled on their second son, Maurice (of Stoke Giffard), with the other lands which she had brought in Edingworth and Milverton (Som.). They descended in the son's cadet line. The Great Cartulary records the grant of the two manors by Milicent de Montalt to her daughter Eve, at a rent of £30 a year during Milicent's life.[5] Milicent, sister and coheir of George Cauntelo (d. 1273), married Eudo de la Zouche.[6]

A2/90/1 [GC 545]   Mon. before the nativity of St. John the Baptist, 17 Edw. I
[20 June 1289]

Milicent de Monte Alto and Eve la Zousche.

[1] *CPR* 1327–30, 507; *CCR* 1330–3, 424, 529.
[2] *GEC* vi. 348–9.
[3] Ibid. 352–87.
[4] Cf. *VCH Hants*. iv. 515.
[5] BCM SB 10, f. 321v.
[6] *GEC* xii (2), 938.

Milicent has received from Eve, her daughter, the £30 annual rent for the manors of Britmerston and Mildeston which she holds of her.
At: London.

A2/90/2 [GC 545*]   n.d. [1289]
Seal of Milicent de Monte Alto, charter torn away.
Endorsed in 19th century hand: . . . *de Monte . . . la Souche filie . . . Berkeley filio . . . Berkeley de qui . . . in liberu' maritag'*.

A2/90/3 [SC 493]   Thurs. after the Annunciation, 3 Edw. III [30 March 1329]
Thomas lord of Berkeley and Maurice his brother.

Whereas Maurice, father of Thomas, granted to Maurice, Thomas's brother, lands and holdings in Brithmerston (Wilts.) and in Milverton and Edenworth and the reversion of lands and holdings in Kingeston Seymor (Som.), and lands in Bradele and Cumbe and the reversion of the land which Eleanor de Bradelee holds for life in the manor of Wotton, to Maurice the younger and his male issue, Thomas has confirmed these grants.
Witnesses: Peter le Veel, William de Wauton, knights, Peter de Styntescumbe, John de Melkesham, Elias de Filton.
At: Berkeley.

CHICKLADE (WILTS.)

Sir John de la Ryvere in 1350 granted to Thomas (III) Lord Berkeley the reversion of a messuage and 1 carucate of land, which passed in the main line.[1] Thomas (IV) Lord Berkeley bought the advowson and 1 a. of land in 1380 and made a presentation to the church in 1411,[2] and the advowson formed part of the 1417 settlement (above, A2/77/14 [SC 581]). After Thomas's death in 1417 it presumably passed to his daughter Elizabeth, countess of Warwick.

A2/91/1 [GC 3462]   10 April 31 Edw. III [1357]
Ralph [de Stafford] earl of Stafford, lord of Tonbridge, and his very dear cousin Sir Thomas, lord of Berkelee.

Ralph has quitclaimed to Thomas all actions, quarrels and demands which he has for the lands and holdings which Thomas had by grant of Sir John de la Ryvere in Wilts. because of a statute merchant bond made by the said John.
At: Ludlow.

ELSTON, IN ORCHESTON ST. GEORGE (WILTS.)

Elston was part of the Giffard of Brimpsfield inheritance which was forfeited to the Crown by John Giffard (executed in 1322), and was granted to John Mautravers in 1329 and then, after it was forfeited by him in 1330, to Maurice de Berkeley (of Stoke Giffard) in 1334.[3] Maurice did not receive all the Giffard lands, however, and Elston was granted to Ralph de Wylington, with whom Maurice exchanged the manors of Corton and Ashton (Wilts.) for Orcheston and a moiety of Elston by a fine of Michaelmas 1338.[4] His brother Thomas (III) Lord Berkeley acquired the other half of Elston from Ralph by a fine of Nov. 1339,[5] and possibly Maurice surrendered his claim to half in favour of his brother. Elston was settled on Thomas's younger sons and passed in the cadet line of Beverston.[6] Alphonse de Berkeley was probably a younger son of Maurice and his wife Margery de Vere.

---

[1] *Wilts. Fines, 1327–77*, no. 379; PRO C 135/199, no. 9; C 136/58, no. 1; C 138/28, no. 50.
[2] Smyth, ii. 13; *Reg. Hallum*, no. 224.
[3] *CPR 1334–8*, 42, 563; *CFR 1327–37*, 423; *CCR 1337–9*, 370, 549.
[4] *Wilts. Fines, 1327–77*, no. 199.
[5] Ibid. no. 229.
[6] PRO C 139/35, no. 50.

A2/92/1 [GC 2944]   1 May 12 Edw. III [1338]

Ralph de Wylyngton[1] and Maurice de Berkele, knight.

Ralph has acknowledged the right of Maurice in the manor and advowson of Orchestone and half the manor of Elestone, held for life by Margaret widow of John Giffard of Brimesfeld in dower, of Ralph's inheritance, and has granted the reversion of the manors to Maurice.

Witnesses: Nicholas de la Beche, knight, Richard Pyck, William de Chiltenham, John de Chiltenham.

At: Orcheston.

A2/92/2 [GC 3107; *duplicate* GC 3108]   Thurs. after St. Andrew, 18 Edw. III [2 Dec. 1344]

William de Syde and Walter Goldemere; and Sir Thomas, lord of Berkelee.

William and Walter have granted to Thomas half of the manor of Elyston (Wilts.); for his life, with remainder to his son Thomas and his issue, and the right heirs of Thomas the elder.

Witnesses: William de Chiltenham, John de Clyve, William Curteys, Robert Groundy, Henry Peche.

At: Berkeley.

A2/92/3 [GC 3156]   3 March 21 Edw. III [1347]

Thomas lord of Berkelee; and Sir William de Syde and Walter Goldemere.

Thomas has granted to William and Walter, and their heirs and assigns, all his lands and holdings in Elistone by Orchestone (Wilts.).

At: Wotton-under-Edge.

A2/92/4 [GC 3223]   n.d. [*c.* 12 April 1349]

Maurice de Berkeleye, eldest son of Sir Thomas de Berkeleye, lord of Berkeley; and the said Thomas, William de Syde and Walter Goldemere, chaplain.

Maurice has ratified the agreement made in the king's court at Westminster at Easter 23 Edw. III between Thomas and William and Walter concerning half of the manor of Elyston, in which Thomas acknowledged the right of William, by his grant to William and Walter, and William and Walter granted the half-manor to Thomas for life, with remainder to Alphonse de Berkeleye and his male issue, Thomas son of the said Sir Thomas and his male isssue, the male issue of Sir Thomas and his wife Katherine, and the right heirs of Sir Thomas.

Witnesses: Sir Thomas de Berkeleye of Uley, Sir Simon Basset, Sir Peter de Veel, Sir John Tracy, knights, William de Chiltenham.

LANGLEY BURRELL (WILTS.)

The manor passed to Reginald de Cobham and his wife Joan, daughter of Thomas (III) Lord Berkeley. They held it in jointure at Reginald's death in 1361.[2]

A2/93/1 [GC 3064]   Thurs. before the nativity of the Virgin Mary, 17 Edw. III
                                                                    [4 Sept. 1343]

John de la Mare of Langley Burrell, knight, and Thomas son of Maurice de Berkelee, knight.

John has granted to Thomas, his heirs and assigns, his manor of Langele Burel with the advowson and all appurtenances except for 1 carucate of land in Tydryngton which is not parcel of the manor.

Witnesses: Robert Selyman, knight, Geoffrey Gascelyn, William Caillewey, Ralph de Cokelberugh, Henry de Cosham.

At: Langley Burrell.

---

[1] Ralph was Margaret Giffard's grandson: his mother Joan, wife of John de Wylington, was Margaret's daughter by her first husband, John de Neville of Essex (d. 1282): *GEC* v. 643; ix. 483–4.

[2] *CIPM* xi, no. 59.

A2/93/2 [GC 3063]   Fri. before the nativity of the Virgin Mary, 17 Edw. III [5 Sept. 1343]
(1) Thomas son of Maurice de Berkelee, knight; (2) John de la Mare of Langley Burrell, knight; (3) Reginald de Cobham, knight.

Whereas Thomas is bound to John for a robe and 10 marks a year, John has granted that the bond will be void when Reginald enters into a bond to him for a furred robe of the sort of his knights and 10 marks a year.
At: Langley Burrell.

A2/93/3 [GC 3075]   5 Nov. 17 Edw. III [1343]
Sir Thomas, lord of Berkele, and John de la Mare, lord of Langley Burrell.

Whereas Thomas has, with John's assent, presented Richard de Malmesbur' to the church of Langelee Burel, John has granted that neither Thomas nor his heirs shall be challenged if he makes a presentation without John's assent. [*In French.*]
At: Langley Burrell.

A2/93/4 [GC 3081]   Fri. the eve of St. Lucy, 17 Edw. III [12 Dec. 1343]
John de Lamare of Langley Burrell, knight, and Thomas son of Maurice de Berkele, knight.

John has received from Thomas a furred robe of the sort of his knights, for which Thomas is bound to John for his life. [*In French.*]
At: Wotton-under-Edge.

A2/93/5 [GC 3064*]   Two weeks after St. Hilary, 18 Edw. III [27 Jan. 1344]
John de la Mare of Langley Burrell, knight, and Thomas son of Maurice de Berkeley, knight.

Final concord, made three weeks after Michaelmas, 17 Edw. III [20 Oct. 1343], and granted and recorded two weeks after St. Hilary, 18 Edw. III, concerning the manor of Langley Burel with the appurtenances except for the advowson; John has acknowledged the right of Thomas by his gift, and Thomas has granted it to John for life, with remainder to Reginald de Cobeham and Joan his wife and Reginald's issue, Thomas son of Thomas and his issue, and Thomas and his heirs.
At: Westminster.

MADDINGTON (WILTS.)

See above, p. 421, Great Easton.

A2/94/1 [GC 3056]   17 June 17 Edw. III [1343]
Juliana widow of John de Moigne of Shipton Moyne and Sir Thomas, lord of Berkelee.

Juliana, executrix of her late husband, has sold to Thomas all the wheat growing in all the lands which were of John in the manors of Wynterbourne Madyngton (Wilts.) and of Eystanes atte Monte (Essex), and also all the spring crops growing in Wynterbourne Madyngton.
At: Berkeley.

A2/94/2 [GAR 396] Manorial account   29 May–Michaelmas, 17 Edw. III [1343]
A2/94/3 [GAR 397] Manorial account   19–20 Edw. III [1345–6]

SHELDON (WILTS.)

The unusual agreement of 1351 probably resulted from Geoffrey Gascelyn's debts.[1]

A2/95/1 [GC 3375]   Sat. before St. Denis, 25 Edw. III [8 Oct. 1351]
Geoffrey Gascelyn and Thomas de Berkelee, lord of Berkeley, knight.

---

[1] See "A 'Rising' Lord and a 'Declining' Esquire: Sir Thomas de Berkeley III and Geoffrey Gascelyn of Sheldon", *BIHR* vol. 61, no. 146 (1988), 345–56.

Geoffrey has granted to Thomas all his goods and chattels in the manors of Shuldone, Chippenham, Lolledon and Westlone.

At: Bristol.

A2/95/2 [GC 3376]   Sun. the feast of St. Denis, 25 Edw. III [9 Oct. 1351]
Geoffrey Gascelyn and Thomas de Berkelee, lord of Berkeley, knight.

Geoffrey has leased to Thomas the manors of Shuldone, Chippenham, Lolledon and Westlond, with the hundreds of Chippenham, Bisshopuston and Dunlewe and the fair and market of the vill of Chippenham and all his other lands and holdings within the said hundreds except the manor of Budestone; for Thomas's life, rent 20 marks a year for the first 2 years, £20 a year for the following 5 years, and £100 a year thereafter, and during the first 7 years Geoffrey will have maintenance in Thomas's household for himself, a groom and a horse in the same manner as Thomas's esquires, or 10 marks a year if Thomas dies within 7 years.

Witnesses: Sir Edmund de Clyvedone, Sir Simon Basset, Sir Thomas de Gornay, knights, John de Clyve, John de Strete.

At: Berkeley.

A2/95/3 [GC 3377]   Sun. the feast of St. Denis, 25 Edw. III [9 Oct. 1351]
(1) Geoffrey Gascelyn; (2) John de Asschebury and Thomas Dreu; (3) Thomas de Berkelee, lord of Berkeley, knight.

Geoffrey has appointed John and Thomas Dreu to give seisin to Thomas de Berkelee of the manors of Shuldone, Chippenham, Lolledone and Westlond, with the hundreds of Chippenham, Bysshopustone and Donlewe and the market and fair of the vill of Chippenham.

At: Bristol.

A2/95/4 [SC 530]   12 Dec. 25 Edw. III [12 Dec. 1351]
King Edward III and Thomas son of Maurice de Berkeley.

The king has pardoned Thomas for acquiring from Geoffrey de Gascelyn, for life, the manors of Shulden, Chippenham and Lolledon, and the hundreds of Chippenham, Bisshopeston and Donlewe, at a rent of 20 marks a year for the first 2 years, £20 a year for the following 5 years and £100 a year thereafter until the end of Thomas's life.

At: Westminster.

A2/95/5 [GC 3470]   Mon. after the Annunciation, 32 Edw. III [26 March 1358]
Thomas de Berkeleye, lord of Berkeley, and Geoffrey Gascelyn.

Whereas Thomas holds for life, by grant of Geoffrey, the manors of Shuldone, Chippenham, Lolledone and Westlond, with the hundreds of Chippenham, Bisshoppeston and Dunlewe and the market and fair of the vill of Chippenham, at a rent of £100 a year after a 7 year term, Geoffrey has granted that, at the end of the 7 year term, Thomas for the 5 years following shall pay 20 marks a year and Geoffrey shall have maintenance for himself, his groom and horse in Thomas's household as an esquire or 10 marks a year.

Witnesses: William de Chiltenham, Bogo FitzWaryn, John de Clyve.

At: Berkeley.

SHORNCOTE (WILTS.)

Thomas (IV) Lord Berkeley appears to have intended this manor, along with the nearby manor of South Cerney and Cerney Wick and other holdings, for his nephew and heir male by means of a grant to feoffees made three weeks before his death. Like South Cerney, however, it passed instead to his daughter Elizabeth, countess of Warwick. See above, p. 450 and A2/77/14 [SC 581].

A2/96/1 [GC 3686]   Tues. after the conception of the Virgin Mary, 49 Edw. III
                                                                              [11 Dec. 1375]
Hugh de Rodebergh, cousin and heir of Thomas de Rodebergh, knight, and John ap Adam,
son and heir of Thomas ap Adam, knight.
    Hugh has quitclaimed to John the manor of Cernecote (Wilts.).
Witnesses: William de Weorstone, Robert de Chorlton, Richard de Erdelegh, John Walraunt,
Henry Cane.

A2/96/2 [GC 3980]   20 Nov. 2 Hen. V [1414]
John ap Adam of Llanllowell and Margaret his wife; and Thomas Berkeley, lord of
Berkeley.
    John and Margaret have granted to Thomas, his heirs and assigns their manor of
Cernecote with appurtenances (Wilts.).
Witnesses: Robert Poyntz, John Rolves, Henry Crooke, John Polayne, John Smarte.
At: Wotton.

A2/96/3 [GC 3981]   20 Nov. 2 Hen. V [1414]
(1) John ap Adam of Llanllowell and Margaret his wife; (2) Adam ap Gryffitz, chaplain;
(3) Thomas Berkeley, lord of Berkeley.
    John and Margaret have appointed Adam to deliver seisin to Thomas of the manor of
Cernecote with appurtenances (Wilts.).
At: Wotton.

A2/96/4 [GC 4098]   20 Nov. 2 Hen. V [1414]
John ap Adam of Llanllowell and Margaret his wife; and Thomas Berkeley, lord of
Berkeley.
    John and Margaret have granted to Thomas, his heirs and assigns all their lands, holdings
[etc.] in the vill and lordship of Sharnecote (Wilts.).
Witnesses: Robert Poyntz, John Rolves, Henry Crooke, John Polayne, John Smarte.
At: Wotton.

A2/96/5 [GC 4099]   24 Nov. 2 Hen. V [1414]
John ap Adam of Llanlowell and Margaret his wife; and Thomas Berkeley, lord of Berkeley.
    John and Margaret have quitclaimed to Thomas the manor of Cernecote (Wilts.), and also
all the lands and holdings there.
Witnesses: Robert Poyntz, John Rolves, Henry Crook, John Polayne, John Smarte.
At: Wotton.

SOPWORTH (WILTS.)

It appears from the Wotton account of 1307–8 (BCM GAR 255; cf. above, A1/51/50) that
Sopworth was granted to Maurice (III) Lord Berkeley, for his life, by his lord, Aymer de
Valence, earl of Pembroke, in 1308. It presumably reverted to Pembroke on Maurice's
forfeiture in 1322 or to Pembroke's coheirs on Maurice's death in 1326.

A2/97/1 [GAR 319] Manorial account   5–6 Edw. II [1311–12]

EASTHAM (WORCS.)

Eastham is mentioned in accounts of Ham between 1345 and 1349 and Clevelode between
1345 and 1353, and both manors were of the inheritance of William de Siddington
(d. 1303), whose heirs were a nephew, Richard le Porter, and two sisters, married to Walter
Blount and William de Doverdale. The Eastham account records the payment of a rent to
William Doverdale, and in 1372 one of the Porter coheirs quitclaimed Clevelode to John de
Berkeley, who had by that date inherited it from his father Thomas.[1] The account records

---

[1] *VCH Worcs.* iv. 187, 267.

the payment of rents from Tenbury Wells and Rochford (Worcs.) and from nearby Burford and Overton (Salop.). Clevelode descended in the Berkeley cadet line of Beverston, but Eastham did not pass to John and may have been sold.[1]

A2/98/1 [GC 3327]   n.d. [mid 14th cent.]
Richard le Porter, lord of Eastham, and John de Clyve, constable of Berkeley Castle.

   Richard has granted to John, his heirs and assigns, his part of the park of Estham, with all his ground and land in the said park.
Witnesses: Hugh de la Boure, William Symond, Robert de Coueleye.

A2/98/2 [GC 3278]   n.d. [mid 14th cent.]
(1) Thomas lord of Berkelee; (2) John Pywaw and Robert de Merston; (3) William de Syde, John le Tornor, Hugh de la Boure and John de Clyve.

   Thomas has appointed John and Robert to give seisin to William, John, Hugh and John of all the lands, holdings, rents and reversions which he has in Ekyntone, Clyvelode and Estham.

A2/98/3 [GC 1464]   n.d. [*c.* 1340]
Edward le Longe and Walter Philip.

   Indenture of inventory of all goods, stock, equipment [etc.] on a manor [*unnamed*], on the occasion of Edward handing over to the new reeve Walter.

A2/98/4 [GC 3356]   n.d. [mid 14th cent.]
Memorandum of goods left at Estham, viz. in the hall, including 1 bucket, 4 trestles, 1 bushel measure for corn, 1 damaged plough, 6 oxen, 1 horse, 7 geese, hay and straw.

A2/98/5 [GC 2987]   Sun. after St. Gregory, 15 Edw. III [18 March 1341]
(1) Thomas de Berkeleye, lord of Berkeley; (2) Richard le Porter of Eastham; (3) Roger de Estham.

   Thomas has appointed Richard to receive in his name seisin of the lordship, homage, rents and services of William de Overtone and others [*named*] for the holdings which they held of Roger in Bureford and Overtone, of which Roger enfeoffed Thomas. Endorsed: *Estham*.
At: Berkeley.

A2/98/6 [GAR 398] Manorial account   n.d. [1342–3]

ECKINGTON (WORCS.)

Eckington was granted in 1288 by Sir William Poer to Walter Berthover at rents of £30 a year to himself and 13 marks a year to the overlords, Westminster Abbey. It was recovered in 1297 by Poer's daughter Aline, who granted it to Edmund Lord Mortimer of Wigmore and his wife Margaret. In 1315 the reversion on Margaret's death was granted by Roger Lord Mortimer to his brother John, who died three years later, long before his mother Margaret (d. 1334). By 1333 it had passed to Thomas (III) Lord Berkeley, who married Roger's daughter in 1319. The two surviving accounts show the manor still paying the rent of 13 marks to Westminster Abbey and receiving rents from Pirton and Whittington (Worcs.) with profits of a court at Pirton. Thomas sold the manor in 1358, possibly to help with paying the ransom of his son Maurice (IV), captured at Poitiers.[2] See also above, A2/98/2 [GC 3278].

A2/99/1 [GAR 399] Manorial account   10–11 Edw. III [1336–7]
A2/99/2 [GAR 400] Manorial account   n.d. [1342–3, from internal evidence]

---

[1] PRO C 136/38, no. 10; C 139/35, no. 50.
[2] *VCH Worcs*. iv. 70.

ROECLIFFE (YORKS.)

In 1504–5 Thomas (V) Lord Berkeley (d. 1533) married Eleanor, daughter of Sir Marmaduke Constable and widow of John Ingleby, son and heir apparent of Sir William Ingleby, both of Yorkshire. Her Ingleby jointure, settled on their marriage in 1489, consisted of the manors of Spridlington (Lincs.) and lands in Roecliffe, Skelton and East Harlsey (Yorks.) as in the charter of enfeoffment below.[1] Marjory Lady Welles, presumably Sir William Ingleby's mother, was the daughter of Sir James Strangeways of Harlsey Castle, in Osmotherley (Yorks.), and the widow of Richard Lord Welles and Willoughby and of John Ingleby.[2]

A2/100/1 [GC 4467]   22 Sept. 5 Hen. VII [1489]
William Ingilby, knight, Marjory Lady Welles, widow, George Strangways, clerk, Richard Acclon, gentleman, and William Arcehode, parson of Marston; and John Ingilby.

William, Marjory, George, Richard and William have granted to John, eldest son of William Ingilby, knight, and Eleanor his wife, daughter of Marmaduke Constable, knight, all the lands, holdings [etc.] in Rowcliffe, Skelton and Estharlesaye (Yorks.), which they had by grant of the said William Ingilby; to John and Eleanor for their lives.
At: Roecliffe.

3: LANDS OF OTHER ESTATES WITH A BERKELEY CONNECTION

The muniments include a few groups of charters which are concerned with the estates of other families that were connected with the Berkeleys by marriage. Two of the groups, those of the Clifford and Mautravers estates, appear in very similar circumstances. Two sisters of Thomas (III) Lord Berkeley (d. 1361) and his brother Maurice married Robert Lord Clifford and John Lord Mautravers, and all the charters in those groups are concerned very closely with the affairs of the sisters' sons. The third group, concerned with the Veel inheritance, contains some documents that can certainly be associated with the marriage of Thomas (III) Lord Berkeley to Katherine, widow of Peter le Veel (d. 1343), but others that appear to be too late for that association.

THE CLIFFORD ESTATE

Isabel, sister of Thomas (III) Lord Berkeley, married in 1328 Robert Lord Clifford (d. 1344). The Cliffords of Westmorland were a cadet branch of the Cliffords of Clifford (Herefs.), descended from Roger, younger son of Walter Clifford (d. 1221), who was granted the manors of Bridge Sollers (Herefs.) and Tenbury Wells (Worcs.) by his father. Roger's elder brother Walter died in 1263 leaving a daughter and heir Maud, then widow of William Longespée (d. 1256–7) but shortly to be abducted by John Giffard of Brimpsfield. Roger lived on until 1286 and his son and heir apparent, Roger (II) (d.v.p. 1282), made an excellent marriage with Isabel, daughter and coheir of Robert de Vipont (d. 1264), which established the Cliffords as lords in the north.[3] Roger (II)'s son Robert, born in 1274, succeeded his grandfather in 1286 and his mother in 1291, and had seisin of their lands in 1295. Two years later his great-uncle Richard FitzJohn died without issue, and he and his aunt Idonia, the other daughter of Vipont, were coheirs to a quarter part of the FitzJohn inheritance as Vipont had married Isabel, one of the four sisters of FitzJohn. After some dispute between the coheirs, FitzJohn's twelve English manors were divided between them and livery was granted in Oct. 1299, Clifford and Idonia receiving the manors of Moulton (Northants.), Winterslow (Wilts.) and the reversion of Shalford (Surrey)

[1] Smyth, ii. 227–8; *GEC* ii. 137.
[2] *GEC* xii (2), 667.
[3] Ibid. iii. 291.

which was held until her death in 1332 by FitzJohn's widow Emma. Each of the four purparties also included ten townships in the cantred of the Isles in Thomond.

Robert was granted Skipton-in-Craven (Yorks.) by the king in 1310 but was killed at Bannockburn. His eldest son Roger (III) had only just had seisin when he became involved in the Despenser war and was executed after Boroughbridge in 1322. His heir was his brother Robert (II), born in 1305, to whom the inheritance was restored in 1327 and who married Isabel Berkeley in 1328. Her brother Thomas had agreed to pay £500 for Robert's marriage in Jan. 1327, being under the impression that Robert was under age; he was later discharged of this debt and gave 1,050 marks as a portion with Isabel.[1] Robert's great-aunt Idonia had married Roger de Leyburn (d. 1284) and then John de Cromwell (d. 1335) but died without surviving issue in 1333. She had settled her Westmorland (Vipont) lands on her nephew Robert (I) de Clifford in 1308, but her portion of the FitzJohn lands and others passed to Edward Despenser, younger son of the younger Despenser (who was the grandson of her cousin Isabel, daughter of William Beauchamp, earl of Warwick, by Maud, sister of Richard FitzJohn, Isabel having married Patrick Chaworth and the elder Despenser).

Four of the six charters are concerned with the settlements made by Robert (II) shortly before his death in May 1344 on his three sons, Robert (III), Roger and Thomas. Skipton had been settled on himself and Isabel in 1338.[2] Maltby (Yorks.) and Severn Stoke (Worcs.) had been involved in the arrangements for the marriage of his heir Robert to Euphemia, daughter of Ralph Neville, in April 1343.[3] His moiety of Shalford (Surrey) and Tarrant Rushton with associated holdings (Dorset) and the manors of Bridge Sollers (Herefs.) and Tenbury Wells (Worcs.) had been granted to feoffees in Jan. 1344 for regrant to himself for life, with remainder to his younger sons Roger (Bridge Sollers and Tenbury Wells) and Thomas (Shalford and Tarrant Rushton). His Westmorland lands had been granted to feoffees in Feb. 1344 for regrant to himself for life, with remainders to the eldest son Robert and his issue, Roger and his male issue, Thomas and his male issue and his own right heirs, but he had died before the regrant.[4] Isabel, who held Skipton in jointure, was assigned a third of the Westmorland, Cumberland and Northumberland lands in dower (valued respectively at £53, £5 and £30 approximately), and also lands in Ireland, the remaining two-thirds of the Cumberland and Northumberland lands being granted to her brother Maurice de Berkeley to hold in wardship.[5] Robert (III) died without issue in 1345 and his brother and heir Roger proved his age in August 1354; in the following year he acknowledged that he had received all the charters which his uncle Thomas de Berkeley had had in his custody during Roger's minority, so it seems that Thomas took over the wardship after his brother's Maurice's death in 1347. Some of the charters, clearly, were

---

[1] *CMR* 1326–7, no. 990; *CCR* 1327–30, 286, 388; Smyth, i. 272–2.

[2] His attempt in 1337 to settle the lordship on his sons Robert and Roger and his own right heirs had been disallowed, because the royal grant of 1310 had been to his father and his issue, and the remainder to his right heirs would have jeopardised the king's reversionary rights: *CPR* 1334–8, 345, 406.

[3] In Robert's inquisition *post mortem* of 1344, Severn Stoke was held by grant of Neville for a term of three years, and Maltby was held by Neville for eight and a half years with reversion to Robert the younger and Euphemia: *CIPM* viii, no. 531.

[4] On 10 Nov. the feoffees were summoned to the king as he had been deprived of the wardship because, at Robert's death, the lands were held by the feoffees and had not been regranted: *CCR* 1343–6, 633. The feoffees gave a third of the lands to Isabel.

[5] The wardship was granted in Oct. 1344 at £36 a year less than the extents: *CFR* 1337–47, 381; *CPR* 1343–5, 298; 1345–8, 11.

not restored to Roger. Isabel married secondly Thomas de Musgrave, one of Clifford's feoffees mentioned in the charters, and died in July 1362.[1]

SHALFORD (SURREY)

A3/1/1 [GC 3089]   21 Jan. 17 Edw. III [1344]
Robert de Clifford, lord of Westmorland, to his tenants of Shalford and Tarrant Rushton.

Whereas Robert has granted his parts of the manors of Shaldeford and of Tarent Russeton to Thomas de Musgrave and Thomas de Oustone, parson of Severnestoke, he commands that his tenants attorn to Thomas and Thomas. [*In French.*]
At: Hart [co. Durham].

A3/1/2 [GC 3090]   23 Feb. 18 Edw. III [1344]
(1) Thomas de Ouston, parson of Severn Stoke; (2) John Mandefout; (3) Robert de Clifford, lord of Westmorland.

Thomas has appointed John to receive seisin of part of the manor of Schaldford (Surrey) which he and Thomas de Musgrave had by Robert's grant. [*In French.*]
At: Tarrant Rushton.

SEVERN STOKE (WORCS.) AND MALTBY (YORKS.)

A3/2/1 [GC 3099]   17 Aug. 18 Edw. III [1344]
Sir Maurice de Berkele and William de Corbrigge.

Maurice has received from William three indentures concerning Severne Stoke and Maltby, sealed with the seal of Sir Ralph de Nevile.
At: Berkeley.

TENBURY WELLS (WORCS.) AND BRIDGE SOLLERS (HEREFS.)

The first charter recites the descent of the Cliffords of Westmorland from the Cliffords of Clifford. Thomas (III) Lord Berkeley also had holdings in Tenbury Wells, the rents of which were paid to his manor of Eastham nearby,[2] and the charter of 1313 below may relate to the Berkeley land rather than the Clifford manor. The charter of 1456, dated at Berkeley, is clearly connected with the Berkeley estate but its relationship to the others is unknown.

THE CLIFFORD MANORS

A3/3/1 [GC 3098]   Eve of the Assumption, 18 Edw. III [14 Aug. 1344]
Sir Maurice de Berkeley, lord of Brimpsfield and brother of the Lady de Clifford, and William de Corbrig'.

Maurice has in William's custody a charter of Walter de Clifford granting to Roger de Clifford his manor of Brug'; and another of Walter, with the assent of his wife Agnes and his son and heir Walter, granting to Roger his son the manor of Tamedebr', to him and his issue; and another of Walter de Clifford confirming to Roger his brother the grants by Walter his father of Tamedebr'; and a writing of Maud Longesspy, daughter and heiress of Walter, confirming to Roger son of Roger son of Walter de Clifford the manor of Tamdebr'; and a letter of attorney of Robert de Clifford, lord of Westmorland, to Sir John chaplain of the chapel of the manor of Tamedebr, Hugh Plasse and Richard Matheu to receive seisin of the manors of Tamedbr and Brugge supra Weye; and an order from Robert to his tenants of Tamedberi and Brugge supra Wye to attorn to Thomas de Musgrave and Thomas de Oustone, parson of Severn Stoke. [*In French.*]
At: Brimpsfield.

---

[1] *CPR* 1343–5, 477; *CIPM* xi, no. 312. Her son Roger had seisin of her dower lands in Aug. 1362, and of the lands which she held in Ireland in dower and fee tail in June 1363: *CCR* 1360–4, 353, 480.
[2] BCM GAR 398 (above, A2/98/6).

OTHER INTERESTS

A3/3/2 [GC 1901]   Tues. the morrow of St. Agatha, 6 Edw. II [6 Feb. 1313]
Edith Baret and William de Cornedal.

Edith has quitclaimed to William a burgage in the vill of Themedebur', which was of William de Bykeleye.

Witnesses: Roger Reginald, Jordan de Cornedal, William Abel, William de Home, Roger de la Pole.

At: Tenbury Wells.

A3/3/3 [GC 4289]   20 Jan. 34 Hen. VI [1456]
John Holte the elder, son and heir of Roger Holte of Tenbury (Worcs.), and Thomas Holte.

John has quitclaimed to Thomas a messuage with a curtilage in Temdebury, a burgage with a curtilage between the holdings called Maywode and Wynchestre, and 2 shops in the high street, which were of Roger his father; rent to John while he lives 13*s*. 4*d*. a year.

Witnesses: Maurice Berkeley, esquire, Richard Acton, esquire, Edward Hopton, esquire, Thomas de la Hay, esquire, John Hopton, John Mumford, chaplain, Robert Holte.

At: Berkeley.

THE MAUTRAVERS ESTATE

Milicent, daughter of Maurice (III) Lord Berkeley (d. 1326) and sister of Thomas (III) Lord Berkeley (d. 1361) and of Maurice de Berkeley of Stoke Gifford (d. 1347), was married about 1314 to John Mautravers the younger (d. 1364). John's career was a spectacular one.[1] He took part with the Berkeleys in the Despenser war of 1321–2 and forfeited his lands in 1322 as a result, fleeing abroad. He returned with Isabella and Mortimer in 1326 and quickly became a major supporter of the new regime, being appointed one of the keepers of Edward II at Berkeley Castle with his brother-in-law Thomas Lord Berkeley. In 1329, for these and other services, he was granted the inheritance which the last Giffard of Brimpsfield had forfeited in 1322, and was summoned to parliament in 1330. He then became involved in the earl of Kent's so-called conspiracy and had to flee abroad again in the summer of 1330. In the following November Edward III staged his dramatic coup at Nottingham Castle, and one of his first independent acts was to pursue the matter of his father's death. As a result, Mautravers had to stay abroad for the next twenty years.

His father, concerned for the future of his own inheritance, in 1338–9 entailed it all on his grandson, the younger John's eldest son and the nephew of Thomas and Maurice de Berkeley. The close involvement of the Berkeleys in this action is shown by the appearance of five Berkeley retainers as witnesses to one of the charters, dated at Lytchett Matravers. The settlement avoided the problem of the immediate heir being an exiled felon with a price on his head. At the same time Maurice de Berkeley, who had been granted many of the Giffard lands shortly after Mautravers had forfeited them, entailed them also on his nephew.[2] At his death in 1347 these manors were said to be held in fee simple: an inquiry was started but nothing came of it, possibly because the nephew, John (III) Mautravers,

[1] *GEC* viii. 580–6.

[2] In March 1339 he had licence to settle the manors of King's Stanley, Rockhampton, Stonehouse, Stoke Gifford and Walls (Glos.) and Corton, Sherrington, Codford, Stapleford and Ashton (Wilts.): *CPR* 1338–40, 239. Eight of the manors and two lordships in the Welsh March had been granted to him for life, at the extent, in Nov. 1334; in 1337 six of them, with the reversion of four more currently held by a Giffard widow, were regranted to him in fee without a farm; he seems to have exchanged Corton and Ashton with Ralph de Wylington for Elston and Orcheston (also of the Giffard inheritance): *CPR* 1334–8, 42, 563; 1338–40, 238–9, 400, 446; *CFR* 1327–37, 423; *CCR* 1337–39, 370, 549.

died in Jan. 1349.[1] The grandfather, John (I) Mautravers, had died in 1341, and John (III)'s one-year-old son and heir, Henry, had died by Feb. 1350, leaving two sisters, Joan, aged about eight, and Eleanor, aged about five. The final turn of the regicide's life came in June 1351 when, having busied himself on the king's behalf in the Low Countries during the late 1330s and 1340s, his outlawry was annulled, and he was fully restored in Feb. 1352. Milicent de Berkeley had died by Feb. 1331 when John was married to Agnes de Bereford, but he was evidently grateful for the consideration shown to his son during his exile and repaid the compliment by settling three of the Giffard manors on Thomas de Berkeley, son and heir of his late brother-in-law, Maurice.[2] At his death in 1364 the three manors descended to Thomas, but the rest of his estate was divided between his granddaughters. Joan married Sir John de Keynes and Sir Robert Rous but died without issue *c.* 1397, and Eleanor married John d'Arundel, younger son of Richard earl of Arundel. Her grandson was the heir male of Thomas earl of Arundel in 1415.

LANGTON MATRAVERS (DORSET)

In March 1339 John (I) Mautravers obtained the king's licence to enfeoff Henry Furneux, parson of Slimbridge, and Thomas de Homer with the manors of Woolcombe, Langton Matravers, Lytchett Matravers and Witchampton (Dorset), Coate, Somerford and Hill Deverill (Wilts.), Yeovil (Som.) and Woodchester (Glos.).[3] His intention was to settle the lands on his grandson: see above, p. 549.

A3/4/1 [GC 2914]   Wed. the morrow of the translation of St. Thomas the martyr,
12 Edw. III [8 July 1338]

John Mautravers the elder; and Henry de Fourneaux, Hugh Fyllol and Thomas de Homere.

John has sold to Henry, Hugh and Thomas all his goods in the manors of Wodechastre and Rotburgh (Glos.), Somerforde, Cotes and Deverel (Wilts.) and Wychamptone, Langetone and Wolecombe (Dorset) for £200, which he has received from them.
At: Lytchett Matravers.

PHILIPSTON, IN WIMBORNE ALL SAINTS (DORSET)

A3/5/1 [GC 2529]   n.d. [*temp.* Edw. II]
John Mautravers the younger and Sir Maurice de Berkele, knight.

John has granted to Maurice, his heirs and assigns, his manor of Phelipestone with all the appurtenances.
Witnesses: Sir Robert abbot of Milton Abbas, Sir William de Wytefeld, Sir Peter son of Reginald, knights, Henry de Gussich, Richard le Wolff, John de Brideport, John le Butiller.

RODBOROUGH, IN MINCHINHAMPTON, AND WOODCHESTER (GLOS.)

See also above, A3/4/1 [GC 2914].

A3/6/1 [GC 2913]   Fri. after the translation of St. Thomas the martyr, 12 Edw. III
[10 July 1338]

John Mautravers the elder; and Henry de Furneaux, Hugh Filol and Thomas de Homere.

John has granted to Henry, Hugh and Thomas, their heirs and assigns, his manor of Wodechastre (Glos.), with the advowson of the church, and also a messuage, 1 carucate of

---

[1] *CCR* 1346–9, 481; *CIPM* ix, no. 46; *CPR* 1348–50, 240; *GEC* viii. 581.
[2] *CPR* 1354–8, 74; PRO CP 25/1/77/69, nos. 344, 350. Agnes de Bereford was the daughter of William de Bereford, Chief Justice of the Common Pleas, and the widow of Sir John d'Argentine (d. 1318) and of Sir John de Nerford (d. 1329). In 1354 she was coheir of her brother Edmund de Bereford, and had no issue by Mautravers or Nerford. She died in 1375 and her heir was her son John d'Argentine, her Nerford lands reverting to Margery, wife of John Brewes, who was the daughter of John de Nerford, son of Sir John's brother Thomas.
[3] *CPR* 1338–40, 238–9.

land, 10 a. of meadow and 20 a. of pasture in Rodburgh in the manor of Menechenehampton.
Witnesses: Thomas de Bradestone, Peter de Veel, Simon Basset, knights, William de
Chiltenham, Thomas de Rotburgh.
At: Lytchett Matravers.

WALLS, IN STOKE GIFFARD (GLOS.)

Walls was one of the manors of the Giffard of Brimpsfield inheritance which, having
been forfeited by the last Giffard lord in 1322, was granted first to John Mautravers in
1329 and then to Maurice de Berkeley in 1334. The lands were restored to Mautravers
in 1351 but he then settled Walls, with Rockhampton and Stoke Gifford, on his Berkeley
nephew and on his death in 1364 they duly descended to that cadet line. John de Cailly was
declared to be Giffard's heir in 1329 for the purpose of allowing him to quitclaim to
Mautravers.

A3/7/1 [GC 1694]   Sun. after St. Mark, 2 Edw. II [27 April 1309]
Adam de Cailly, knight, and John de Cailly his brother.
    Adam informs John that, whereas he granted to John a messuage and 2 carucates of land
in Glos. called la Walles within the manor of Giffardesstoke for life, he has now enfeoffed
Lady Margaret, widow of Sir John Giffard of Brymesfeld, and John Giffard, Sir John's son
and heir, and John de Cailly must now do them fealty.
At: 'Grauntebrugg'.

A3/7/2 [GC 1695]   Mon. after St. Mark, 2 Edw. II [28 April 1309]
John de Cailly; and Lady Margaret, widow of Sir John . . ., and John Gyffard, son and heir
of Sir John Gyffard.
    John de Cailly has . . . granted and remitted to Margaret and John . . . 2 carucates of land
called la Walles in the manor of Gyffardestoke in the county of . . . which he holds by
demise of . . . Sir Adam . . . viz. for a quarter of one knight's fee.
Witnesses: Sir John de Wylington, John de Akton, Richard de . . ., Elias de Fylton, William
de Doudeswelle, William de Brokworth, Robert de Prestle . . .
At: 'Cauntebrugg'.

HILL DEVERILL (WILTS.)

See also above, p. 550, Langton Matravers.

A3/8/1 [GC 2907]   Fri. after St. Augustine, 12 Edw. III [29 May 1338]
John Mautravers the elder; and Henry de Furneaux, Hugh Filol and Thomas de Homere.
    John has granted to Henry, Hugh and Thomas 3 messuages, 1 carucate of land, 10 a. of
meadow, 100 a. of wood and all his pasture in the vill of Hulle Deverel, and all his chattels,
and all his villeins and their issue, and the homage, rents and services of tenants [*named*]
in Hulle Deverel, Smalebrouk, Herteleye, Asschegore, Deverel Langebrugge and
Codeforde.
Witnesses: William Filol, Reginald de Kyngestone, John Strong the younger, Richard
Bryan, John de Dulr'.
At: Lytchett Matravers.

PERSONAL

The exploit of kidnapping the Gloucestershire coroners was carried out by Mautravers with
his brothers-in-law, Thomas (III) and Maurice de Berkeley, in 1319. It was one of the
means by which they tried to avoid justice for having illegally hunted in the park of Aymer
de Valence at Painswick (Glos.) in the previous year.

A3/9/1 [SC 479]   7 March 13 Edw. II [1320]
King Edward II and John Mautravers the younger.

Pardon to John for arresting John de Morton, Richard de Compton, William de Holt and William de Colwich, the king's coroners for Gloucestershire, and preventing them from performing their duties.

At: Canterbury.

THE VEEL ESTATE

The Veels were a prominent gentry family in 14th- and 15th-century Gloucestershire. Peter (II) (d. 1343) and his son, Peter (III) (d. 1391), were closely involved with the Berkeley lords and, indeed, Thomas (III) Lord Berkeley married Peter (II)'s widow, Katherine de Clevedon, in 1347. That may account for some of the Veel charters being in the Castle, as she brought with her a number of manors which she held in jointure and dower, including portions of the manors of Norton Fitzwarren (Som.) and Lariharn (unidentified). The documents in the Berkeley archive reveal a connection with Sir Nicholas de Kingston, made famous in a paper by K. B. McFarlane.[1]

The Veels were descended from Geoffrey le Veel who had married by 1206 Maud, daughter of Harding, son of Elias FitzHarding, and so a great-niece of Robert FitzHarding; she was the daughter and heir of Denise de Huntingford and brought Huntingford, in Wotton under Edge (Glos.), to Geoffrey.[2] They rose to prominence in the person of Sir Robert le Veel (d. 1298 × 1301), son of Robert, son of Geoffrey and Maud, who made his fortune in the service of Gilbert de Clare, earl of Gloucester (d. 1295).[3] The earl granted him the manor of Swanbourne (Bucks.) in 1274, and he acquired Littlecote, in Stewkley (Bucks.), and Lisworney, with the castle of St. Fagans, near Cardiff, both by 1275, and Charfield (Glos.), near Huntingford, by 1278 when it was settled on him and his wife Hawise in jointure.[4] He had three, possibly four, sons, Peter, Robert, Bogo and possibly Thomas.[5] In 1275 he settled Lisworney on his son Peter and his wife Hawise; in the same year he was acting in Littlecote with his son Robert; and Swanbourne passed to another

[1] McFarlane, *Collected Essays*, 45–55.

[2] Robert FitzHarding granted to his brother Elias a hide of land in Huntingford to hold as a quarter of a fee, and on Maud's marriage to Geoffrey her cousin Robert (II) de Berkeley (Robert FitzHarding's grandson) granted her lands in free marriage, including two assarts in Michaelwood Chase. In 1205–6 the king confirmed to Geoffrey the lands which he had been granted with Maud by Robert in marriage, the lands which she had inherited from her father and all the lands which she had inherited from her mother in Huntingford. These passed to their son Robert and to his son Sir Robert: Smyth, i. 16; iii. 37, 147, 234–5, 238. The elder Robert witnessed a charter of Kingswood Abbey in 1246–7, and Sir Robert another three in the period 1262–75: below, F1/5/3, 6–8 [SC 293, GC 1195, SC 449, GC 1526].

[3] Sir Robert was alive on 27 Dec. 1298 but had died by 26 May 1301 when his widow Hawise had licence to remarry: above, A1/18/3 [SC 461]; *CPR 1291–1301*, 595. For his connection with Gloucester, including acting as his executor, see *CCR 1288–96*, 126; *CPR 1291–1301*, 19, 140, 292.

[4] *VCH Bucks*. iii. 423–4; PRO CP 25/1/75/31, no. 32. In 1286 William de Wauton quitclaimed Charfield to Robert and Hawise (P.R.O. CP 25/1/75/33, no. 80), which seems to indicate that Robert had acquired the manor, and a 16th-century inquisition stated that the manor had been granted by John Meysy to Robert and his male issue. The earls of Gloucester were overlords of Littlecote and Robert may have had that manor by the earl's grant also. Robert and his son Robert were pursuing a suit against Alice widow of Hugh de Dunster in 1275, and one of the Roberts was holding the manor in 1284–6. For Swanbourne and Lisworney, see below, pp. 557–8.

[5] A Thomas le Veel was granted two messuages in Berkeley by Maurice (II) Lord Berkeley, which he later granted to Thomas (II) in 1306; he witnessed a charter in Alkington in Dec. 1304, and in July 1321 his widow Edith was granted a plot of land at Wick Dangerville, in Alkington, by Thomas (II), to her and her issue: above, A1/4/3, 37 [GC 2362, GC 1080], A1/12/11 [GC 1118].

son, Bogo (clearly named after his lord's brother). It is not clear which of the sons was the eldest but Peter and Robert appear to have died without issue as Lisworney and Littlecote passed to Peter (II), son of Bogo. Bogo had married Joan, daughter and coheir of Sir Peter FitzWarren of Ablington, Alton and Penleigh (Wilts.), Hamfallow in Ham (Glos.) and Norton Fitzwarren (Som.), but was dead by 1310 when Joan was his widow.

By 1319 Joan had married Sir Nicholas de Kingston of Tortworth and Oldbury (Glos.). The evidence of Joan's identity is provided by the succession to the manors of Hamfallow, Charfield and Swanbourne, by a series of charters concerning Wickstowe in Ham and by other charters from Ham manor. The sub-manor of Hamfallow within the large manor of Ham (Glos.), which had been held by Peter FitzWarren in 1285 and 1288, was held by Joan le Veel in 1310 and by Kingston *c.* 1320 and in 1325–6, and it later passed to Peter le Veel.[1] In 1338 Peter le Veel quitclaimed to William FitzWarren and his wife and son lands in Wickstowe (in Hill or Ham) which William had had by demise of Alice FitzWarren, Peter's aunt, and Alice is in the same series of charters described as daughter and coheir of Sir Peter FitzWarren (who had bought the holding in 1281), and as Alice, wife of Sir Adam de Sharesull.[2] Alice and Joan were therefore the daughters and coheirs of Sir Peter FitzWarren, Joan was the mother of Peter (II) le Veel and Alice married Adam de Shareshull.

That Joan the mother of Peter le Veel was the widow of Bogo le Veel is indicated by other charters in the Castle (above, A1/24/14–15 [GC 1722, GC 1758]) which mention holdings in 1310 of Joan, widow of Bogo le Veel. In the same year Joan le Veel was holding Hamfallow, formerly of Peter FitzWarren. The descent of Swanbourne (below, p. 557) shows that Bogo was a son of Sir Robert, and it was Bogo's son Peter (d. 1343) who succeeded to the Veel family lands as well as the FitzWarren lands of his mother. The Veel lands included Charfield, which in 1316 was held by Peter le Veel, a minor in the custody of Ralph Monthermer,[3] and in 1320 the advowson of Charfield was held by Sir Nicholas de Kingston in the right of his wife's dower.[4] Combined with his tenure of Hamfallow, the evidence shows beyond doubt that Kingston's wife Joan of 1319 and 1324 was Joan, daughter and coheir of Sir Peter FitzWarren, widow of Bogo le Veel and father of Peter (II) le Veel.

Sir Nicholas de Kingston and his first wife Margaret acquired manors in Kingston Bagpuize and Ashdown (Berks.) and lands in Pusey (Berks.). He later granted Kingston Bagpuize to his elder brother Sir John, and *c.* 1300 exchanged Ashdown and Pusey for the Gloucestershire manors of Tortworth and Redland, near Bristol, with Sir William Maunsel. He was granted free warren in both and a market at Tortworth in 1304, but apparently later exchanged Redland for the manor of Oldbury and adjacent holdings. Kingston witnessed charters for Thomas (II) Lord Berkeley on six occasions between July 1304 and Dec. 1319, acted as arbitrator on his behalf in a dispute with Kingswood Abbey in May 1303, and was pardoned an amercement of 3*s.* 4*d.* in the hundred court of Berkeley in 1316–17.[5] He was one of Thomas's household which travelled to Leicestershire in 1318 for

---

[1] Ham account rolls (cf. above, p. 202); the rent of 24*s.* and 1 lb. of cumin for Hamfallow was paid to the Berkeley lords by Sir Nicholas de Kingston in 1325–6, and the entry does not change until 1339–40 when it was said to have been paid by his 'heirs', and then by Veel; from 1347 it was not paid, being owed by Veel's widow Katherine, then wife of Thomas de Berkeley.

[2] Above, A1/35/2–3 [GC 2920–1], 5 [GC 2982]. Alice had granted the holding to one William FitzWarren, his wife Clarice and their son William, whose relationship to Sir Peter FitzWarren, Alice's father, is not clear. Other lands in Billow, in Cam (Glos.), and Birdham and West Itchenor (Sussex) were included in Sir Peter's purchase in 1281: above, A1/35/1 [GC 497].

[3] *Feud. Aids*, iv. 269.

[4] *Reg. Cobham*, 234.

[5] Above, A1/2/39 [GC 1116], A1/9/5 [SC 470], A1/11/10–11 [GC 1980, SC 483], A1/48/7 [SC 468], A2/10/4 [GC 2293], A2/17/22 [GC 2273]; BCM GAR 111 (above, A1/24/119).

the marriage of the lord's younger son Thomas to a local heiress,[1] but he was not exclusive in his service to Berkeley. He was granted two robes a year from Siston (Glos.) by Sir Alan Plokenet of Kilpeck but these ceased to be paid in 1313 and in 1320 he tried to recover them through an assise of novel disseisin.[2] In 1309 he witnessed a charter of John Giffard of Brimpsfield, and in 1311 Robert FitzPayn arranged for him to be sheriff.[3] He was sheriff twice, in 1308 and again 1312–13, knight of the shire for Gloucestershire in 1306 and 1315, keeper of the peace in 1314, and tax-collector and assessor in 1313, 1316 and 1319.[4] He is not recorded as active after May 1324, and in November that year he was said to be 'incapacitated by age'.[5] The statement that he outlived Henry Burghersh, bishop of Lincoln, who died in Dec. 1340, is probably an error, being made in an inquisition of 1504.[6] His heirs were said to hold Hamfallow before Michaelmas 1340.[7] His wife Joan had presumably died by 1338 when Peter le Veel confirmed the grants of his aunt Alice de Shareshull.

In 1319 Kingston settled his lands on himself and Joan in jointure, and again in 1324 with remainder to Henry Burghersh for life and then to Joan's son Peter le Veel and his wife Cecilia and their issue.[8] Peter was a minor in 1316 when Charfield was in the custody of Ralph Monthermer, and Cecilia bore him a son, Peter (III), in 1327.[9] In July 1330 he settled Lisworney on himself and Cecilia and their male issue, and Charfield, Tortworth and Huntingford were settled in the same way. Cecilia was dead by 1337 when Ablington and Alton, with a rent of 20s. in Figheldean (Wilts.), were granted by Alice and Adam de Shareshull to Peter and his second wife, Katherine.[10] Penleigh was settled in 1340 on Alice and Adam.[11] Peter died in March 1343, drowning at sea, and leaving his son Peter by Cecilia and a son John (aged six) and daughter Joan by Katherine.[12] In 1347 Katherine married Thomas (III) Lord Berkeley (d. 1361) and in 1350 they acquired Penleigh from the Shareshulls, with remainder to Katherine's heirs by Veel.[13] Tortworth and Oldbury had passed after Kingston's death to Peter (II), who had sold Swanbourne and Littlecote in 1337 to Sir John de Moleyns.[14]

Following many changes, possession of the estate stabilised after 1343: Lisworney, Charfield and Huntingford (which had been held by Sir Robert), Tortworth and Oldbury (which had passed to Peter and Cecilia from Kingston), and Norton Fitzwarren (which Peter had inherited from his mother Joan) descended to Peter's elder son Peter (III);

---

[1] He witnessed a charter dated at Wymondham (Leics.), the inheritance of the son Thomas's wife, in June 1318 by which Thomas (II) granted some Glos. lands to his son and his new wife; the other witnesses included Thomas (II)'s eldest son and heir Maurice (III), and were all prominent members of his household and retinue: A1/11/11 [SC 483].

[2] Saul, *Knights and Esquires*, 96.

[3] McFarlane, *Collected Essays*, 55 n.; *Saul, Knights and Esquires*, 160.

[4] McFarlane, *Collected Essays*, 54 n.

[5] Ibid. 49.

[6] *CIPM Hen. VII*, ii, no. 757. The inquisition states that Hawise, wife of Sir Robert le Veel, did not survive her husband, who in fact left a widow Hawise; it is not impossible that he had two wives called Hawise.

[7] BCM GAR 124–5 (above, A1/24/133–4).

[8] PRO CP 25/1/76/50, no. 205; CP 25/1/76/54, no. 318.

[9] *Feud. Aids*, iv. 269; *CIPM* viii, no. 466.

[10] *CIPM* xiv, no. 215.

[11] *VCH Wilts.* viii. 159.

[12] *CIPM* viii, no. 466.

[13] *CIPM* xvi, no. 215; *Wilts. Fines 1327–77*, 376; *VCH Wilts.* viii. 159.

[14] *VCH Bucks.* iii. 423–4, 429–30. The conveyance was completed in 1339, but Moleyns forfeited his lands in 1340. They were restored in 1345 but Peter (III) managed to recover them and sold them again in 1352. In 1348–50 Katherine, Peter (II)'s widow, was claiming half the manor of Littlecote against Moleyns as having been settled on Peter and her and their issue.

Ablington and Alton, along with Penleigh after 1350, and Hamfallow and Veel Hall in Plympton (Devon) were held in jointure by Katherine and were to pass to her children by Peter (II).[1] Katherine also had a third of Norton Fitzwarren and Lariharn and possibly other lands, and in 1344 was claiming a third of Huntingford and Oldbury against Joan, widow of Henry le Veel who may have been another son of Peter (II).[2] In 1384 Peter (III) and his son Thomas confirmed the jointure lands to Katherine and her issue, possibly in return for her surrender of her dower lands, none of which are mentioned in the inquisition taken when she eventually died in 1386, 43 years after Peter.[3] Shortly before, John, her son by Peter, had died without issue and the heir to the lands was Sir John Moigne, the son of Katherine's daughter Joan and Sir Henry Moigne. The Moignes held Shipton Moyne (Glos.), Great Easton (Essex), Maddington (Wilts.) and Owermoigne (Dorset).[4] On the death of John Moigne, Sir Henry's father, in 1342 Thomas de Berkeley had acquired the wardship of his lands, and he seems also to have had the marriage of the heir, as Henry married Thomas's stepdaughter Joan. Henry proved his age in 1350 and died in 1374 leaving John, his eldest son and heir, to inherit Ablington, Alton, Penleigh, Plympton and Hamfallow on Katherine le Veel's death in 1386.

Sir Peter (III) le Veel had by 1358 married Elizabeth, daughter of Thomas Lord Bradestone (d. 1360), and Tortworth was settled on them and their male issue. Peter was succeeded in 1391 by his son Thomas, a younger son John apparently having been granted Norton, which he was trying to recover by force in 1393.[5] Thomas was succeeded by his son John (d. 1457–8), who in 1449 settled Lisworney on himself and his wife Alice with remainder in halves to their second and third sons William and John and their issue. In 1474 their eldest son Robert quitclaimed the manors to his mother Alice and his brothers.[6] Alice also held Tortworth and Oldbury in jointure. Robert left a daughter Alice who married

[1] When the land in Plympton was acquired is unknown. In 1343 it was described as a £10 rent; by 1386 as 20 messuages, 5 ferlings of land, a quantity of meadow and wood, and £16 of rents: *CIPM* viii, no. 466; xvi, no. 214.

[2] For Katherine's claim to Huntingford and Oldbury, Smyth, iii. 239; for her portions of Norton and Lariharn, below pp. 557–8. Henry le Veel is not otherwise mentioned but he appears to have been connected with Henry Burghersh, bishop of Lincoln, who had a remainder under Sir Nicholas de Kingston's settlement of 1324. A relationship of Kingston and the Veels with Burghersh, though not known to be recorded, may explain why a son of Peter's was called Henry. None of the lands which passed to Peter (III) were held in chief and in 1344–5 his body and part of his lands were in the wardship of Bartholomew Burghersh, Henry's brother and heir, and other parts of his lands were in the hands of six others, including Thomas Lord Berkeley, of whom he held Huntingford: *Year Book, 17 and 18 Edw. III*, 343 n. 7.

[3] *CCR 1381–5*, 442; *CIPM* xvi, nos. 214–17.

[4] Those manors had been held by Henry Moigne (d. 1315), along with half of the manor of Beckhampton (Wilts.) of the inheritance of his wife Joan, who held all the other manors in jointure. Their son John was a minor but by the time Joan died in 1340 she had evidently conveyed Owermoigne to John, as it does not appear in her inquisition *post mortem* and John's son Henry was born there in 1328. Beckhampton was not mentioned either, but instead there was a rent of 10 marks from 'Lideshulle' (Hants.). John died in 1342, leaving a widow Juliana. Thomas de Berkeley acquired the wardship of the son Henry, and accounts remain in the Castle for Great Easton (June to Michaelmas 1343) and Maddington (29 May to Michaelmas 1343, and 1345–6); the earlier Maddington account records the payment of the 10-mark rent from 'Lodeshulle' by Edward St. John, and Shipton is mentioned in the Ham account of 1348–9; on 17 June 1343 Juliana sold the crops growing at Easton and Maddington to Berkeley. Henry died in 1374, and in 1384 his surviving children by Joan were John, Henry, William, Elizabeth (wife of Sir Alan Cheyne), Agnes and Edith: *CIPM* v, no. 514; viii, nos. 275, 365; ix, no. 595, xiv, no. 79; *CCR 1385–9*, 118; above, A2/94/1 [GC 3056].

[5] *CPR 1392–6*, 359.

[6] Smyth, iii. 235.

David Matthew, but Charfield and Huntingford (and half of Lisworney, with Tortworth and Oldbury, after Alice's death) passed to his brother William, as they were all held in tail male. William died in March 1493 leaving a son William aged 11. The manors were then occupied by David Matthew, who died in 1504 leaving four daughters, Katherine, Elizabeth, Anne and Margaret, aged 14, 13, 11 and 10. In Jan. 1505 an inquisition confirmed that the four manors were held in tail male and were the inheritance of William, son of William,[1] who by then was of age.

KINGSTON BAGPUIZE (BERKS.)

The manor of Kingston Bagpuize was held by the Bagpuize family until William (d. 1290 × 1292), son and heir of John Bagpuize, sold it. As well as in his undated grant of the manor to Nicholas de Kingston and his wife Margaret (below, A3/10/1 [GC 2614]), William is recorded in 1290 as granting to John de Kingston (Nicholas's elder brother) and his heirs a messuage and 2 carucates of land there in exchange for rents in Wiltshire, a messuage and 1 carucate being confirmed by Kingston to Alice de Bagpuize, William's mother, for life; in 1292 Nicholas de Kingston and his wife Margaret quitclaimed to John de Kingston a messuage and 1 carucate of land and all her right in the land formerly of William de Bagpuize in Kingston Bagpuize.[2] That may suggest that Margaret had inherited a claim to lands there from William, possibly as his sister, although the grant of the manor had been made by William to Nicholas and Margaret and Nicholas's heirs. Thereafter it passed to the descendants of John de Kingston.[3] That Margaret and Nicholas were in possession of another of William's manors, Ashdown, in Compton (Berks.), by 1296 may, in the light of William's grant to them of Kingston Bagpuize, have resulted not from inheritance by Margaret but from a simple sale by William.[4] Before June 1297 Nicholas and Margaret had also acquired a holding in Pusey (Berks.) formerly of William Fokeram; at the time Fokeram acknowledged the right of Henry son of Richard de Puseye in a messuage and 4 virgates of land in Pusey, with the service of Nicholas and Margaret for the holding which Fokeram had previously held in the same vill.[5]

A3/10/1 [GC 2614]   n.d. [late 13th cent.]
William de Bagepuiz, son and heir of Sir John de Bagepuiz; and Nicholas de Kyngistone and Margaret his wife.
    William has granted to Nicholas and Margaret, and Nicholas's heirs and assigns, all his manor of Kyngistone and all his holdings which he had after the death of John his father within the said manor, with the dower of the Lady Alice de Bagepuz; they have given him certain necessaries, as in a cirograph made between them.

[1] *CIPM Hen. VII*, ii, nos. 757, 833. The two inquisitions, one on the death of David Matthew in May 1504 and one 'of concealments' in Jan. 1505, give slightly different accounts of the early settlements. According to the first, all four manors were held in tail general, while according to the second (presumably correct, as the manors did pass to Robert's brother William in the first instance) they were held in tail male. The first said that Tortworth and Oldbury were settled on Kingston with remainder (after Burghersh) to Peter (II) and Cecilia and their issue, the second that they were settled on Peter and Cecilia and their male issue, and later settled on Peter (III) and his wife Elizabeth and their male issue, and later still on John and Alice and their male issue; under the initial settlement by Kingston they were to pass to Peter and Cecilia and their issue. Similarly, Charfield was said to have been granted in the first place to Sir Robert le Veel and his male issue, passed to his son Peter and grandson Peter (II) and was settled on Peter (II) and Cecilia and their male issue, and Huntingford to have been settled on Peter and Cecilia and their male issue.
[2] McFarlane, *Collected Essays*, 50–1; *VCH Berks*. iv. 350.
[3] *VCH Berks*. iv. 350.
[4] Ibid. 18; McFarlane, *Collected Essays*, 50–1.
[5] Berkshire Record Office, D/E Bp T1 m. 3d.

Witnesses: Sir Richard de Seyn Walry, Sir John de Lanham, Sir Richard de Coleshulle, Sir, William Focram, Sir Thomas de Lye, Sir Robert Achard, Sir Richard de Pusie, Sir Robert de Etone, knights, William de Spersholte, John de Kyngistone, Philip de Fifhide, William de Worthe, John de Spersholte, William de Raumpayn, John de Cheveneye, Ralph de Haddeleye, Thomas de Barry, John le Coumbere, John Geffrey.

SWANBOURNE (BUCKS.)

The manor, which came to be known as Clifford's Manor, was held of the earls of Gloucester by the abbot of Woburn, and of the abbot by the prior of Newnham. In 1278–9 it was stated that the earl had dispossessed the prior and granted the land to Robert le Veel. It passed to his son Bogo le Veel, and to his son Peter (II) who alienated it in 1337 to Sir John de Moleyns.[1]

A3/11/1 [SC 450]   25 Feb. 1273 [1274]
G[ilbert] de Clare, earl of Gloucester and Hertford, to his tenants of Swanbourne.
   Gilbert notifies his tenants of Swaneburne that he has granted to Sir Robert le Veel a messuage and 1 carucate of land there, which his mother[2] formerly held in dower.
At: Abingdon.

CHARFIELD (GLOS.)

A3/12/1 [GC 431]   n.d. [early Edw. I]
Walter Tyson of Charfield and Sir Robert le Veel.
   Walter has granted to Robert a meadow called le Brockmede in the manor of Charfeld; Robert has given him 3½ marks.
Witnesses: Sir William le Maunsel, knight, John de Meysi, Elyas de Cumbe, Peter de Stintescumbe, Bartholomew de Olepenn, Ivo de Cumbe, Richard de Colewych.

TORTWORTH (GLOS.)

A3/13/1 [GC 4456]   17 Jan. 3 Hen. VII [1488]
David Mathowe, esquire, and Alice his wife, daughter and heir of Robert Veel of Tortworth (Glos.); and Elizabeth Swanle, daughter of Thomas, late of Nibley.
   David and Alice have leased to Elizabeth their holding in Tortworthy called Brokworthysplace, which Maurice Elyott lately held beside Damarybruge; for her life, rent 8*s.* a year, and if Elizabeth dies then they lease the holding to her mother Joan Swanle.
Witnesses: Thomas Cothryngton of Sodbury, gentleman, John Pulford, Thomas Knyght.
At: Tortworth.

NORTON FITZWARREN (SOM.)

A3/14/1 [GAR 386]   [1342–3]
Account from Michaelmas to the Sunday after the Purification of the Virgin Mary 17 Edw. III [9 Feb. 1343], for 19 weeks, and similarly for Lady Katherine de Veel from the said Sunday to Monday before St. Luke [12 Oct.] for [35] weeks.
A3/14/2 [GAR 387] Manorial account   n.d. [1343–4]

LISWORNEY (GLAM.)

A3/15/1 [SR 144]
Abstracts of seven charters concerning the manor of Lisworney (*alias* Llysworney) with the castle of St. Fagans and the advowson of the church of St. Fagans:

---

[1] *VCH Bucks*. iii. 429. In 1348–50 Katherine, widow of Peter le Veel (d. 1343) was claiming half the manor of Littlecote (Bucks.), which was near Swanbourne, against John de Moleyns, on the grounds that it had been settled on her and Veel and their issue; this was a Veel manor and it stayed with the main line: *VCH Bucks*. iii. 424 n.

[2] Maud de Lacy (d. 1287). Gilbert had livery of her dower lands in March 1289: *GEC* v. 700, 706.

(i) [n.d.] John Soer, son and heir of William Soer . . . Lisworney in Glamorgan with the castle and the advowson of the chapel of St. Fagan, to Sir Robert le Veele;

(ii) St. Martin 3 Edw. I [11 Nov. 1275]; grant of the above by Robert le Veele to Peter his son and Hawise his wife and their issue;

(iii) 26 July 4 Edw. III [1330]; Peter le Veel, knight, to Richard Colewyth, rector of Charfield;

(iv) 31 July 4 Edw. III [1330]; Richard Colewyth to Peter de Veel, knight, and Cecilia his wife and their male issue;

(v) 2 April 27 Hen. VI [1449]; John Veel (lord of St. Fagans and Lisworney) to David Levelyan, parson of the church, and John Turburvile;

(vi) 3 June 27 Hen. VI [1449]; David Lewelyn and John Turburvile to John Veele, esquire, and Alice his wife for their lives, with remainder, as to one half, to William Veele their second son and his issue, remainder to John Veel their third son, remainder to the right heirs of John the elder, and, as to the other half, to John the third son and issue, remainder to William the second son, remainder to the right heirs of John the elder;

(vii) 4 June 14 Edw. IV [1474]; quitclaim by Robert Veel, John's son and heir, to Alice his mother and William and John his brothers.

LARIHARN (UNIDENTIFIED)

A3/16/1 [GAR 422] Manorial account   22 Aug.–Michaelmas, 20 Edw. III [1346]
Portion of the manor belonging to Lady Katherine le Veel.

PERSONAL

A3/17/1 [GC 3467]   Thurs. the eve of the Purification, 32 Edw. III [1 Feb. 1358]
Peter de Veel, knight, and Thomas de Bradeston, knight.

Whereas Peter is bound to Thomas in £120 to be paid at . . . John the Baptist next coming, Thomas has granted that if Peter acquires within two years . . . Michaelmas after this date to Peter and his wife Elizabeth and their issue an annual rent of 100*s.* or . . . to the value of 100*s.* a year, with remainder to Thomas if they die without issue, the bond of £120 shall be void.
At: Winterbourne.

A3/17/2 [GC 3691]   14 March [50 Edw. III, 1376]
Peter le Veel and Thomas le Veel, knights, merchants of Glos.; and John Daundesey and Edward Dalyngrigge, knights, brother Robert Bourtone and Thomas Broun.

Peter and Thomas are bound to John, Edward, Robert and Thomas, executors of Sir Edward le Despenser, in £400 for merchandise purchased from them.
Witnesses: Henry Warner and William Erlyngham, burgesses of Bristol.
At: Bristol.

4: ESTATE AND HOUSEHOLD ADMINISTRATIVE DOCUMENTS

HOUSEHOLD DOCUMENTS

A4/1/1 [SR 58; SR 59 *a translation*]   5 Aug. to 10 Sept. 2 Edw. III [1328]
Account of Henry Peche, supervisor of the household at Berkeley while the lord and his retinue (*familia*) were staying at Bradley.

A4/1/2 [SR 60]   24 April to Sun. before the nativity of the Blessed Virgin Mary
[4 Sept.] 2 Edw.III [1328]
Account of Sir Thomas de Schypton, the lord's wardrober.

A4/1/3 [SR 61] Various rolls   [1328]
(i) 'Expenses of the lord at Berkeley and Bradley going to Portbury' 2 Edw. III, Monday 7 Nov. and the following Tuesday at Berkeley, Wednesday to the following Monday

inclusive at Bradley; 'expenses of the lord and lady of Clyfford coming to Berkeley', Thursday before St. Martin [10 Nov.], Thursday, Friday and Saturday; dorse 'Saturday 26 Nov. expenses of the lord in his coming to . . .', Sunday and Monday breakfast before the lord went to Portbury. Sum 73*s*. 4½*d.*

(ii) [No heading.] Daily expenses starting on [Tuesday] 29 Nov. continuing through to Thursday [22 Dec.?], dorse Friday [23 Dec.?] to Tuesday [3 Jan. 1329?], followed by entries under headings 'Lardar', 'Old lardar' and 'Sheep carcases', entries for Wednesday–Saturday [4–7 Jan.?] and an unfinished entry for Sunday. Sum 32*s*. 3½*d.*

(iii) 'Expenses of the lord's retinue (*familia*) staying at Berkeley after the return of the lord to Portbury', Friday the morrow of Michaelmas 2 Edw. III [30 Sept. 1328]; daily expenses until Monday [16 Oct.]. Sum 2*s*. 2¼*d.*

(iv) 'Expenses of the the lord', Sunday before St. Peter in cathedra [21 Feb.] at Berkeley, expenses of Monday to Wednesday. Sum 11*s*. 0¼*d.*

(v) [No heading.] Daily expenses from Sunday after St. Dunstan [23 Oct.?] to the following Monday in Advent [28 Nov.] and to the following Monday [*further membranes torn away*].

(vi) [No heading.] Daily expenses from Sunday before Hilary [8 Jan. 1329?] for six weeks to Saturday, then from Wednesday [St. Peter in cathedra, 22 Feb. 1329?] to the following Wednesday, with marginal note that Sunday, Monday and Tuesday not here because in the roll of the lord's expenses [i.e. (iv)].

(vii) 'Expenses of the household after the return of the lord to Portbury', Wednesday 10 May to Sunday 21 May [1329?]. Sum 4*s.*

(viii) [No heading.] Daily expenses from 'Tuesday' for six weeks. Sum 3*s*. 5¼*d.*

A4/1/4 [SR 63]   1 Edw. III [1327]
Chamberlain's account: account of John Averey, chamberlain, concerning journeys to London and elsewhere; sum owing at end of account 4*s*. 7¾*d.*

A4/1/5 [SR 62] Chamberlain's account   [1328]
[No heading.] First entry, for arrears, reads, 'Received 4*s*. 7¾*d.* from the arrears of John Averary, chamberlain of the lord, of his account of the preceding year'; account of the lord and his retinue travelling in the north and then to Woodstock in the spring of 1328.

A4/1/6 [SR 64]   [1345–6]
Household account of victuals, spices, cloth, etc. expended in the household over the year.

ROLLS AND ESTATE MANAGEMENT DOCUMENTS
INDENTURES FOR LIVERIES OF CASH
A4/2/1 [GMR 18]   Fri after St. Mark, 9 Hen. VI [27 April 1431]
Indenture of liveries of cash made by John Upton, auditor of [James] lord of Berkeley, with memorandum of details of one entry.

A4/2/2 [GMR 19] Two documents   Michaelmas and Dec. 15 Hen. VI [1436]
(i) Memorandum of cash received from ministers of the estate by John Upton, auditor, at Michaelmas 15 Hen. VI, and how expended;
(ii) Memorandum of cash delivered to [James] lord of Berkeley from various hands at the audit, Dec. 15 Hen. VI, by John Upton, auditor.

A4/2/3 [GMR 20] Two documents   Michaelmas and Dec. 17 Hen. VI [1438]
(i) Memorandum of cash received in the coffers of [James] lord of Berkeley from ministers, by the hand of John Upton, auditor, at Michaelmas 17 Hen. VI;
(ii) Memorandum of cash delivered to the lord by John Upton, at Dec. 17 Hen. VI.

A4/2/4 [GMR 21]   Jan. 27 Hen. VI [1449]
Memorandum of cash received by John Belde, auditor of Lord James de Berkeley.

A4/2/5 [GMR 22]   Michaelmas, 28 Hen. VI [29 Sept. 1449]
Memorandum of cash received by John Belde, auditor of Lord James de Berkeley.

ACCOUNTS AND RECEIPTS

A4/2/6 [GMR 46] Cofferer's account   [1293]
Receipts of Thomas Alein from Fri. after Hilary 21 Edw. I [16 Jan. 1293] until Easter next,
and from Easter to St. Giles [1 Sept.], with fines at Easter and Whitsun and the lawday of
Berkeley hundred, etc.

A4/2/7 [SR 39; SR 40 *a translation*]   Circumcision 20 Edw. II [1 Jan. 1327]
Receiver's account   to Michaelmas 1 Edw. III [1327]

A4/2/8 [GAR 424]   n.d. [1332–3]
Account of receiver John de Clyve   (dated from internal evidence)

A4/2/9 [GAR 425]   Michaelmas 32–3 Hen. VI [1453–4]
Account of William Eyffan, receiver of Lord James de Berkeley

A4/2/10 [GMR 23]   21 Edw. IV [1481–2]
Receipts from the Berkeley estate, viz. Ham, Hinton, Slimbridge, Sages, Hurst, Wotton
borough, Berkeley borough, Portbury, Wotton, Portishead and Portbury hundred, Coaley,
Cam, Horton and Arlingham, Berkeley hundred, Alkington.

RENTALS

A4/2/11 [SB 22] Rental of the whole honour   [1288]

A4/2/12 [GRR 6]   Nov. year 17 [?]
Extract from rental (totals owed at each term from each manor). [GMR 24 is the lower half
of the document, now united with GRR 6].

A4/2/13 [GRR 24]   Michaelmas, 15 Hen. VI [29 Sept. 1436]
Rental of lands and holdings of Philip Waterton in Berkeley.

VALORS

A4/2/14 [SR 67]   Michaelmas, 9 Ric. II [1385]
Valor of manors of Lord Thomas de Berkeley taken at Michaelmas 1385, including some of
the Lisle lands.

A4/2/15 [GMR 30]   Michaelmas, 13 Ric. II [1389]
Valor of manors of Lord Thomas de Berkeley taken at Michaelmas 1389, including some of
the Lisle lands.

A4/2/16 [GMR 31]   Michaelmas, 17 Hen. VI to April following [1438–9]
Valor of the Berkeley estate.[1]

A4/2/17 [GMR 32]   Michaelmas, 5 Edw. IV [29 Sept. 1465]
Valor of the Berkeley estate.

GRANTS OF VILLEINS

A4/2/18 [GC 517]   St. Valentine, 13 Edw. I [14 Feb. 1285]
Thomas lord of Berkeley and Roger Gouby.
   Thomas has granted to Roger his villein Henry son of Ralph le Gardiner.
Witnesses: Robert de Stanes, William Capel', Richard de Wenden, Thomas Aleyn, John de
Cramial.
At: Portbury.

---

[1] This document is probably connected with the death of Richard Beauchamp, earl of Warwick
(d. April 1439).

A4/2/19 [GC 1223] n.d. [*c.* 1300]
Thomas lord of Berkele and Robert de Berk[ele], his nephew.

Thomas has granted to Robert his villein Robert, son of Ralph le Gardener of Berkeley, with all his issue and chattels.
Witnesses: Robert de Stan, Robert de Bradeston, Peter de Styntescumb, William Capel, Thomas de Swonhungre, Thomas de Boeleie, William de Burg'.

A4/2/20 [SC 482] n.d. [*c.* 1300]
Robert de Berkele and Berkeley church.

Robert has freed Robert son of Ralph le Gardiner, of Berkeley, late his villein, which he had of the gift of Lord Thomas de Berkeley, his uncle, and has quitclaimed to the church of Berkeley the payment of a silver penny for the lamp at the Holy Cross of that church.
Witnesses: Robert de Stone, Robert de Bradeston, Peter de Stintescumbe, William Capel', Thomas de Swonhungre, Thomas de Boeleye, William de Burgo.

GRANTS OF WARDSHIP AND MARRIAGE

A4/2/21 [GC 2688] 1 Nov. 3 Edw. III [1329]
Thomas lord of Berkeleie and William de Cheltynham.

Thomas has granted to William the wardship of the lands and holdings of John son of Robert de Oulepenne, nephew and heir of John de Oulepenne, and the marriage of the said John son of Robert, during his minority, and if he dies before reaching full age, the wardship and marriage of the next heir. [*In French.*][1]
At: Berkeley.

A4/2/22 [GC 3842] Mon before St. Nicholas, 14 Ric. II [5 Dec. 1390]
Thomas de Berkeley, lord of Berkeley, and John Coueleye.

Thomas has granted to John the marriage of John Swonhongre, son and heir of Elias Swonhongre, which came to Thomas because Elias held of Thomas by knight service. [*In French.*]
At: Wotton.

MISCELLANEOUS

A4/2/23 [GC 534] Wed. after the translation of St. Wulfstan, 16 Edw. I [21 Jan. 1288]
Thomas de Berk[eley], lord of Berkeley, and Thomas de Swonhongre.

Thomas is bound to Thomas in 40*s.* in allowance of what he has paid on behalf of the lord of Hulle (see below, A4/2/24 [GC 537]).
At: Berkeley

A4/2/24 [GC 537] Fri. before St. Barnabas, 16 Edw. I [4 June 1288]
Sir Thomas de Berkel and Nicholas son of Ralph, lord of Tickenham.[2]

Memorandum that on the above day, in the presence of Roger de Cumbe, Robert de Stane, Thomas de Swonungre and others, it was calculated between Thomas and Nicholas what cash Thomas had paid for Nicholas in various particulars for the grove of Tykeham which Thomas had bought from Nicholas, viz. to various merchants and burgesses of Bristol £[2], and Sir G. de Sandiacre, sheriff of Glos., 100*s.*, Stanley Priory 5 marks, the lord the Earl Marshal . . . marks, Thomas de Swonhongre 40*s.*. . . in £10 6*s.* 8*d.* (see above, A4/2/23 [GC 534]).

A4/2/25 [GMR 25] 8 Edw. II [1314–15]
Rents, entry fines and increments paid in various Glos. manors, viz. Berkeley, . . ., Alkington, Hurst, Slimbridge, Cam, Ham, Arlingham.

---

[1] *Transcript*: Smyth, iii. 311.
[2] Also lord of Hill and Nympsfield (Glos.).

A4/2/26 [GAR 411]   3 March 17 Edw. II to Michaelmas 20 Edw. II [1324–6]
Account of John Frelond, custodian of Berkeley honour.[1]

A4/2/27 [GMR 16]   36 Edw. III [1362]
Goods and chattels bought by Lord Maurice de Berkeley and Lady Katherine de Berkeley from the executors of the late Thomas Lord Berkeley.

A4/2/28 [GMR 17]   36–8 Edw. III [1362–4]
Account of sales by the executors of the late Thomas Lord Berkeley to Maurice lord Berkeley, 36 Edw. III, and repayments by Maurice made in 37 and 38 Edw. III.

A4/2/29 [SC 582]   21 July 5 Hen. V [1417]
King Henry V; and John Harewell, John Barton the younger and John Baysham, clerk.
   By mainprise of Thomas Berkeley, clerk, and Richard Catyrmayn, esquire, the king has granted to John, John and John custody of all the lands which came into the king's hands on the death of Thomas lord of Berkeley, rendering the extent at the Exchequer.
At: Waltham.

A4/2/30 [GRR 7]   Tues. before Whit Sunday, 9 Hen. V [6 May 1421]
List of tenants and rents for the recognition court of James de Berkeley in the presence of William Payn, sub-steward, and Robert Stanshawe, chief steward.

A4/2/31 [SB 10]
'The Great Cartulary'. A cartulary of 399 folios, the bulk being in a single hand, mid 15th century, with some later additions. It is concerned chiefly with the Lisle lands, although the first 84 folios relate to manors within the lordship of Berkeley. It was probably made for Richard Beauchamp, earl of Warwick (d. 1439).

A4/2/32 [SB 75]   n.d. [mid 14th cent.]
Copies of documents relating to the title and inheritance of Maurice (IV) Lord Berkeley, including schedules of (p. 4) knights' fees; (pp. 8–15, 21–6) services in labour and kind [in French]; (p. 19) totals of rents; and (p. 20) fees and wardships belonging to the lordship.

5: BERKELEY PERSONAL DOCUMENTS

MARRIAGES

THE CLIFFORD MARRIAGE, 1328

Isabel, daughter of Maurice (III) Lord Berkeley (d. 1326), was married in 1328 to Robert Lord Clifford (d. 1344). After Robert's death her brothers Maurice (d. 1347) and later Thomas (III) Lord Berkeley (d. 1361) obtained the wardship of Robert's sons and heirs, Robert (d. 1345, a minor) and Roger (of age in 1354). For the Clifford charters which, despite the quittance below (A5/1/3 [GC 3430]), remained in the Castle from the time of this wardship, see above, pp. 546–9.

A5/1/1 [GC 2653]   1 June 2 Edw. III [1328]
Robert de Clifford, lord (seignor) of Westmorland, and Sir Thomas lord (seignor) of Berkeley.
   Robert has received from Thomas 500 marks in part payment of 1,050 marks in which Thomas is bound by a recognisance. [In French.]

A5/1/2 [GC 2671]   28 Feb. 3 Edw. III [1329]
Robert de Clifford, lord of Westmorland, and Sir Thomas lord of Berkeley.
   Robert has received from Thomas 100 marks at the term of the Purification 3 Edw. III, in part payment of 1,050 marks in which Thomas is bound by a recognisance. [In French.]
At: Skipton-in-Craven.

---

[1] During the forfeiture of Maurice (III) Lord Berkeley 1322–6.

A5/1/3 [GC 3430]   10 July 29 Edw. III [1355]
Roger de Clyfford, lord of Westmorland, and Sir Thomas lord of Berkele, his uncle.

Roger has received from Thomas all the charters, writings, bonds, acquittances and all other muniments which Thomas had in his custody during Roger's minority. [*In French*.] At: Berkeley.

MARRIAGES OF JAMES AND MAURICE, SONS OF JAMES DE BERKELEY (d. 1405)

James and Maurice were the nephews, and James the heir male, of Thomas (IV) Lord Berkeley (d. 1417). For St. John's request in 1412 for an exemplification of the 1349 entail in tail male of the Berkeley estate, see also above, A1/1/23 [SC 579]. It is not known whether the St. John marriages were concluded, but James certainly married one of Stafford's daughters, although she did not live long.

A5/1/4 [GC 4047]   29 April 11 Hen. IV [1410]
Thomas de Berkeley, baron, and John SeintJohn, knight.

Whereas Thomas is bound to John in £600, John wills that the bond shall be void if Thomas dies without male issue and if John does not maintain James and his brother Maurice, heirs male of Thomas, whose marriages were granted by Thomas to John; and whereas John is bound to Thomas in £600, Thomas wills that the bond shall be void if John marries James or Maurice to any other than his daughters. [*In French*.]

A5/1/5 [GC 4092]   25 July 2 Hen. V [1414]
Humphrey de Stafforde, knight, of Dorset, and Thomas de Berkeley, lord of Berkeley, knight.

Whereas Humphrey is bound to Thomas and his executors in 600 marks, Thomas has granted that, as Humphrey has the marriage of James son of James de Berkeley, knight, brother of Thomas, by grant of Thomas, the which James son of James is heir male apparent to Thomas for the entailed inheritance, Humphrey will maintain James in an appropriate style until he has his inheritance, and if Humphrey will marry James to one of his daughters the bond will be void.

MARRIAGE OF MAURICE, SON AND HEIR OF MAURICE (V) LORD BERKELEY (d. 1506)

Maurice the son was the future Maurice (VI) Lord Berkeley (d.s.p. 1523).

A5/1/6 [SC 645]   28 Jan. 2 Ric. III [1485]
Maurice Berkeley, esquire, of Thornbury, and William Berkeley, knight, of Stoke Gifford.

An indenture made between Maurice and William for the marriage of Maurice, son and heir apparent of Maurice of Thornbury to marry Katherine, William's daughter, at the nativity of St. John the Baptist [24 June], and that William shall pay to Maurice of Thornbury 40 marks, and Maurice son of Maurice shall stay with William until his full age.

A5/1/7 [GC 3768]   31 Jan. 2 Ric. III [1485]
William Berkeley of Stoke Gifford (Glos.), knight, and Maurice Berkeley of Thornbury (Glos.), esquire, brother and heir of William [de Berkeley] earl of Nottingham.

William is bound to Maurice in 1,000 marks to be paid at the Annunciation [25 March] next. The bond will be void if William carries out all the obligations in a bond of 28 Jan.

OTHER MARRIAGES

A5/1/8 [SC 602]   25 July 35 Hen. VI [1457]
John [Talbot] earl of Shrewsbury and James Lord Berkeley.[1]

James will marry Joan, the earl's sister, and the earl will obtain an obligation of £1,000 in which James is bound to the king and deliver it to James on the day of the marriage or

---

[1] This alliance was part of the settlement of the Great Dispute. Joan later married Edmund Hungerford.

before, and the earl will pay 100 marks and provide suitable apparel for his sister, and be a good lord to the councillors, tenants and servants of James, and will help and support James by his advice, and James will make a settlement of £120 a year on himself and Joan.

A5/1/9 [GC 4401]   6 June 15 Edw. IV [1475]
William Berkley, knight, Lord Berkley; and Anne countess of Pembroke, Walter Devereux, knight, Lord Ferrers, James Baskervile, Henry Bodrugan, knights, and Simon Milborne, esquire.

Whereas Anne, Walter, James, Henry and Simon are bound by nine several obligations in the sum of £500, of this date, to William, William wills that if Mary Herbert, one of Anne's daughters, who is to marry Thomas Berkely, knight,[1] William's son and heir, dies before the due dates on any of the bonds, the bonds shall be void. [*In English*.]

A5/1/10 [GC 4426]   16 Jan. 20 Edw. IV [1481]
Edward Dudley; and William lord of Berkley and Joan his wife.[2]

Edward has received from William and Joan 100 marks in part payment of 500 marks, as in an indenture dated 6 Dec. 20 Edw. IV [1480].
At: Epworth.

MILITARY AFFAIRS
A5/2/1 [SC 574]   7 Oct. 4 Hen. IV [1402]
Thomas lord of Berkeley and Henry Talbot, esquire.

Thomas and Henry have agreed that Henry will deliver to Thomas 24 Scottish prisoners taken by Henry on the sea coast near Barnstaple (Devon), during Sept. 3 Hen. IV [1401], in which Thomas has a legal interest because of the force of war made by his barge, his soldiers and sailors on the sea, and for a certain sum of money paid to Henry by Thomas.
At: Lincoln.

A5/2/2 [SC 575]   1 May 5 Hen. IV [1404]
King Henry IV and Thomas lord of Berkeley, Admiral of the South and West.

An indenture made between them that Thomas will stay with the king for a quarter of a year, with 300 men-at-arms, viz. 5 bannerets, 11 knights and 285 esquires, and will have 7 ships, 7 barges and 7 ballingers [etc.].
At: Westminster.

A5/2/3 [SR 88]   n.d. [15th cent.]
Number of archers and billmen in the various townships of Gloucestershire.

RELIGIOUS AFFAIRS AND PATRONAGE
ST. AUGUSTINE'S ABBEY, BRISTOL
The abbey, founded by Robert FitzHarding, continued to receive the support of the family.

A5/3/1 [SC 36]   n.d. [*c*. 1190]
Robert son of Maurice de Berkeley and St. Augustine's Abbey.

Robert has confirmed to the abbey all the grants made by his father and grandfather.
Witnesses: William abbot of Kingswood, William chaplain of Redcliffe (*Redecliva*), Walter chaplain of the castle, Albert the chaplain, Adam son of Nigel, Matthias son of Daniel Rufus, Bernard de Stanes, Hubert de Saltmarsh (*de salso marisco*), Robert Bastard, Walter Snigga.

A5/3/2 [SC 495]   20 Aug. 4 Edw. III [1330]
Thomas lord of Berkeley and St. Augustine's Abbey.

Thomas has inspected the charter of his grandfather Thomas and his father Maurice to the

---

[1] Thomas was aged five at the time and died very shortly afterwards.

[2] Edward was the grandson and heir apparent of John Sutton, Lord Dudley, and married Cecilia, the daughter of William's wife Joan Strangeways by her first husband, William Willoughby.

abbey (above, A1/51/3 [SC 475]) and has confirmed it.

Witnesses: John de Wylyngton, Ralph de Wilyngton, John de Clyvedon, Thomas de Gournay, Geoffrey de Hautevyle, knights, William Arthur, Andrew de Brompton, Edmund de Lyouns, Humphrey de Scovylle.

At: Portbury-in-Gordano.

LONGBRIDGE HOSPITAL, BERKELEY

The hospital, near the Castle, was founded by Maurice (I) Lord Berkeley (d. 1190).

A5/3/3 [SC 28]   n.d. [1185 × 1191]

(1) Berkeley church; (2) the abbot of St. Augustine's, Bristol; (3) Longbridge Hospital; (4) Maurice de Berkeley.

An agreement that the chaplain of the hospital (which Maurice had built at Longbridge) should do fealty to Berkeley church in the presence of the abbot and Maurice; that he should neither do nor suffer harm to the church; that the brothers of the hospital should be allowed to have the offerings at the church on the feasts of St. John the Baptist and St. Mary Magdalene; that the brothers should have decent burial there.

Witnesses: William [de Saltmarsh] bishop of Llandaff, Lady Alice de Berkeley, Robert de Berkeley, Richard, Henry, Maurice and William his brothers, Adam son of Nigel, Adam de Saltemareis, Bernard de Stana, Master Peter, Albert the chaplain, Reginald the chaplain, Walter the chaplain, Elias de Sautemars, Maurice son of Nigel, Mael de Tormertun, Robert de Slohter.

A5/3/4 [GC 1202]   n.d. [late Hen. III]

Maurice de Berkel' and the Hospital of Holy Trinity, Longbridge.

For the souls of himself and his wife Isabel, Maurice has granted to the hospital the croft called Aketre which Adam Coby held of Maurice, next to the king's highway from Longebrugge to Lorewinge, and the land called Dersleye which he had by grant of William de Wyk, with an annual rent of 5*s.* from William de Wyk; rent, in the name of Maurice and his heirs to the chief lord of Fromtun, 4*s.* a year for a pasture called la Sterte.

Witnesses: William de Matheme, Walter de Egetun, John de Crawel', Robert de Bradeston, Thomas de Swonhungre.

BENEFITS GRANTED BY POPE URBAN VI TO THOMAS (IV) LORD BERKELEY (d. 1417)

A5/3/5 [SC 553]   Nones of July 2 Urban VI [7 July 1379]

Pope Urban VI; and Thomas de Berkeley, lord of Berkeley, and Margaret his wife.

The pope has granted to Thomas and Margaret a portable altar and licence to celebrate masses.

At: Rome.

A5/3/6 [SC 554; *duplicate* SC 555]   Nones of July 2 Urban VI [7 July 1379]

Pope Urban VI; and Thomas de Berkeley and Margaret his wife.

The pope has granted to Thomas and Margaret, licence to choose for themselves a private confessor.

At: Rome.

CARTULARIES

A5/3/7 [SB 1]   n.d. [late 13th cent.]

Cartulary of St. Augustine's Abbey, called the Red Book.[1]

A5/3/8 [SB 39]   n.d. [14th cent.]

Cartulary of a chantry in St. Andrew's church, Berkeley.

---

[1] See the printed edition, *St Augustine's Cartulary*.

A5/3/9 [SB 18]   n.d. [late 14th cent.]
Brief register of Croxton Kerrial Abbey (Leics.).

OTHER

A5/3/10 [SC 96]   n.d. [*temp.* John]
Prior Roger and the convent of Christ's Church, Twinham; and Robert de Berkeley.

The prior and convent have granted to Robert a daily mass to be said for all the faithful departed and agree to add another canon to the church to sing it, and will add Robert's name to the list of founders.

A5/3/11 [SC 600]   5 Oct. 34 Hen. VI [1455]
James lord of Berkeley; and the sisters and convent of St. Mary Magdalene, near Bristol.

James has granted licence to the sisters to elect another prioress in the place of Joan Waleys, deceased.
At: Berkeley.

A5/3/12 [SC 652]   23 March 3 Hen. VII [1488]
Prioress Elizabeth and Wallingwells Priory (the convent of Our Lady within the Parke of Carlton, otherwise called Wallyng Welles); and William [de Berkeley] Earl Marshal and of Nottingham.

Indenture of covenant agreeing that the priory shall take William as one of their founders, shall perform the usual offices in his honour, shall pray for the souls of his father and mother and of Jane his late wife, and for the good estate of Anne his wife and of Thomas [Stanley] earl of Derby; and William shall discharge the priory of a rent of 36*s.* due to him and his heirs.
At: . . .

A5/3/13 [SC 654]   21 Sept. 1489
Prior Robert of St. Mary's, Worcester, and William marquis of Berkeley.

The prior has admitted William into the society and fraternity of the priory, with all privileges of masses, etc., for the souls of James and Isabel, his father and mother, of Joan his late wife, and of himself and Anne his wife.
At: . . .

PUBLIC DUTIES

A5/4/1 [SC 515]   Eve of Palm Sunday, 19 Edw. III [19 March 1345]
The report relating to Bristol of Thomas de Berkeley and his associates commissioned to inquire who and how many persons in Gloucestershire hold lands or rents of the value of 100*s.* up to £1,000.
At: Bristol.

A5/4/2 [GC 4249]   27 July 23 Hen. VI [1445]
James Berkeley, lord of Berkeley, knight and J.P. for Glos.; and Robert Clavyle of Uley, constable of the peace in Berkeley hundred, and John ap Adam, constable of the peace in Dursley borough.

James orders Robert and John to attach Nicholas Bedow of Wodemancote (Glos.) and his son John Bedow.
At: Berkeley Castle.

GRANTS OF TITLES, OFFICES AND ANNUITIES TO WILLIAM
LORD BERKELEY (d. 1492)

TITLES

A5/5/1 [SC 637]   21 April 21 Edw. IV [1481]
King Edward IV and William Lord Berkeley.

The king has granted to William the title of viscount, viz. to be viscount of Berkeley, to him and his male issue.

Witnesses: Thomas [Bourgchier] cardinal archbishop of Canterbury, Thomas [Rotherham] archbishop of York, chancellor, J[ohn Russell] bishop of Lincoln, keeper of the privy seal, E[dmund Audley] bishop of Rochester, Richard [Plantagenet] duke of York, Richard [Plantagenet] duke of Gloucester, Henry [Bourgchier] earl of Essex, treasurer, Anthony [Woodville] Earl Rivers, William Hastings, chamberlain, Thomas Stanley, steward of the household.
At: Westminster.

A5/5/2 [SC 640]   28 June 1 Ric. III [1483]
King Richard III and William Viscount Berkeley.
   The king has granted to William the title of earl of Nottingham, to him and his male issue.
Witnesses: Thomas [Bourgchier] cardinal archbishop of Canterbury, the bishops of London [Thomas Kempe], Bath and Wells [Robert Stillington] and Lincoln [John Russell], Henry [Stafford] duke of Buckingham, John [de la Pole] duke of Suffolk, William [FitzAlan] earl of Arundel, Henry [Percy] earl of Northumberland, John Dudley and Thomas Stanley.
At: Westminster.

A5/5/3 [SC 643]   2 July 2 Ric. III [1484]
King Richard III and the sheriff of Nottingham and Derby.
   Whereas the king has raised William to the rank of earl of Nottingham, he authorises the sheriff to pay to William the sum of £20 a year from the revenue of the county of Nottingham.
At: Westminster.

A5/5/4 [SC 653]   28 Jan. 4 Hen. VII [1489]
King Henry VII and William Earl Marshal and Nottingham.
   The king has granted to William the dignity and title of marquess of Berkeley.[1]
Witnesses: The archbishops of Canterbury and York [John Morton and Thomas Rotherham], J[ohn Russell] bishop of Lincoln, R[ichard Fox] bishop of Exeter, keeper of the privy seal, Jasper [Tudor] duke of Bedford, the king's uncle, John [de la Pole] duke of Suffolk, John [de Vere] earl of Oxford, great chamberlain, Thomas [Stanley] earl of Derby, constable, John Dynham of Dynham, treasurer, Robert Willoughby de Broke, steward of the household.
At: Westminster.

LANDS AND OFFICES

A5/5/5 [SC 597]   22 March 26 Hen.VI [1448]
John [de Mowbray] duke of Norfolk [etc.], and William Berkeley, knight, his kinsman.
   John has granted to William, for his good service, for life, all his lordships, castles, manors, lands, holdings, rents and services in Ireland; rent a rose a year.
At: Ipswich.

A5/5/6 [SC 605]   4 Dec. 39 Hen.VI [1460]
Anne duchess of Buckingham[2] and William Berkeley, knight.
   Of her special affection for him, Anne has appointed William as master of the deer and overseer of her parks, forests, chases and warrens in Glos., for his life.
At: London

A5/5/7 [SC 607]   6 July 1 Edw. IV [1461]
Anne duchess of Buckingham and William Berkeley, knight.
   For his good and gratuitous services, Anne has appointed William to the office of steward of her manor of Thornbury (Glos.).

---

[1] Folded into the letters patent is the undated petition for the grant, SC 653.2.
[2] Anne Stafford was the sister of Richard Nevill, earl of Warwick and of Salisbury, and of Cecilia duchess of York and Katherine duchess of Norfolk.

ANNUITIES

A5/5/8 [GC 4397]   11 May 15 Edw. IV [1475]
William Hastynges, Lord Hastings, knight, and William Berkeley, knight, Lord Berkeley.

   William Hastynges has received from William Berkeley 100*s*. in full satisfaction of a certain annuity previously granted by Berkeley to Hastynges, the which sum is for the term of the Annunciation.

A5/5/9 [SC 639]   5 March 23 Edw. IV [1483]
King Edward IV and William, Viscount Berkeley.

   The king has granted to William, for his attendance at the council, an annuity of 100 marks for life, 50 marks from the customs of Bristol and 50 marks from the tonnage and poundage of the port of London.
At: Westminster

ROYAL PARDONS

A5/6/1/ [GC 471*]   4 Edw. I [1275–6]
King Edward I and Thomas de Berkele.

   Extract made in 25 Edw. I [1296–7] from a Great Roll of 4 Edw. I:
(i) Thomas de Berkele renders account of 500 marks of a fine for hunting, sureties Ralph de Sandwico and Robert FitzPayn; pardoned 500 marks by special grace of the king;
(ii) Thomas de Berkele owes £20 for hunting offences, pardoned.

A5/6/2 [SC 601]   1 Nov. 34 Hen. VI [1455]
King Henry VI and James lord of Berkeley, also called James Berkeley of Berkeley, knight.

   The king has issued a general pardon to James for all crimes, transgressions [etc.].
At: Westminster.

A5/6/3 [SC 603]   10 Jan. 36 Hen. VI [1458]
King Henry VI; and James lord Berkeley and Joan his wife.

   The king has pardoned James and Joan for their crimes, transgressions [etc.].
At: Westminster.

A5/6/4 [SC 604]   17 March 36 Hen. VI [1458]
King Henry VI and William Berkeley, knight, son and heir of James lord Berkeley.

   Henry has pardoned William for all his transgressions, offences [etc.].
At: Westminster.

A5/6/5 [SC 606]   1 May 2 Edw. IV [1462]
King Edward IV and William Berkeley, of Portbury, or of Thornbury, or of Berkeley.

   Edward has pardoned William for all transgressions, offences [etc.].
At: Westminster.

A5/6/6 [SC 638]   20 June 12 Edw. IV [1472]
King Edward IV and the sheriff of Gloucester.

   The king notifies the sheriff of his pardon to William lord Berkeley of 20 May last for all transgressions, offences [etc.], committed by him up to 30 Sept. last.
At: Westminster.

A5/6/7 [SC 642]   10 March 1 Ric. III [1484]
King Richard III and William earl of Nottingham.

   The king has pardoned William for all transgressions [etc.].
At: Westminster.

A5/6/8 [SC 644]   9 Dec. 2 Ric. III [1484]
King Richard III and William earl of Nottingham.
   The king has pardoned William for all transgressions [etc.] committed by him up to
16 Nov. last.
At: Westminster.

QUITCLAIMS FOR ACTIONS

A5/7/1 [GC 4331]   8 May 5 Edw. IV [1465]
David Williams of Chawyld (Wilts.), yeoman, and Maurice Berkeley, esquire.
   David Williams has quitclaimed to Maurice all actions, real and personal.

A5/7/2 [GC 4350]   19 June 8 Edw. IV [1468]
John Morley, citizen and tailor of London, and William lord of Berkeley, knight.
   John has quitclaimed to William all actions, real and personal.

A5/7/3 [GC 4403]   19 July 15 Edw. IV [1475]
Matthew Philipp, knight, late guager of the city of London, and William Berkelee, late of
Portbury (Som.), knight, *alias* late of Berkeley (Glos.).
   Matthew has quitclaimed to William for all actions.

DEBTS, BONDS AND ACQUITTANCES

A5/8/1 [GC 3510]   Fri. the feast of St. Leonard, 34 Edw. III [6 Nov. 1360]
Robert Partrich of Elmestree (*Ailmendestre*) and Sir Thomas de Berkeleye, lord of Berkeley.
   Robert is bound to Thomas is £20 to be paid at Berkele at Easter next.
At: Wotton.

A5/8/2 [GC 3528]   Thurs. after Michaelmas, 35 Edw. III [30 Sept. 1361]
Maurice son of Sir Thomas lord of Berkelee, and John de Hoghtone; and Richard
[FitzAlan] earl of Arundel.
   Whereas Maurice and John are bound to Richard in £200, Richard has granted that if
Maurice and John pay £100 at Arundel on the eve of Easter next, the bond shall be void.
At: London.

A5/8/3 [GC 3794]   St. Mary Magdalene, 9 Ric. II [22 July 1385]
(1) Elias de Thorpe, citizen and skinner of London; (2) William Knyght, citizen and
fellmonger, and David Lovelich; (3) Sir Thomas lord of Berkeley.
   Elias has appointed William and David to demand, recover and receive from his noble
lord Thomas £46 17s. 3d. of his, due for various goods made and delivered to the use of his
said lord. [*In French.*]
At: London.

A5/8/4 [GC 3973]   7 May 1 Hen. IV [1400]
John Whatele, citizen and mercer of London, and Sir Thomas lord of Berkeley.
   John has received from Thomas £100 in part payment of £198 18s. 1d.
At: London.

A5/8/5 [GC 4176]   29 April 12 Hen. VI [1434]
William Dawtre, citizen and mercer of London, and James Berkeley, lord of Berkeley.
   William has received from James, by the hand of his consort the Lady Isabel, £10 in part
payment of a greater sum.
At: London.

A5/8/6 [GC 4216]   St. Simon and St. Jude, 19 Hen. VI [28 Oct. 1440]
Nicholas Poyntz, esquire, and James Berkeley, lord of Berkeley, knight.

Nicholas has lent to James £113 payable at Michaelmas. [*In English, with 19th-cent. transcription.*]

A5/8/7 [GC 4306]						26 Aug. 38 Hen. VI [1460]
Maurice Berkeley of Beverston (Glos.), esquire, and Thomas Catour of the same, yeoman; and John Kendall, gentleman.
	Maurice and Thomas are bound to John in £6, payable at Christmas next.

A5/8/8 [GC 4341]						15 Aug. 7 Edw. IV [1467]
William Berkeley, knight, lord of Berkeley (Glos.), Thomas Berkeley of Berkeley, esquire, and Richard ap Adam of Portbury (Som.), gentleman; and Edmund Warter, esquire.
	Whereas William, Thomas and Richard are bound to Edmund in 270 marks by a bond dated 11 Aug. 7 Edw. IV, Edmund has granted that if they pay the 270 marks at 10 marks each Easter and Michaelmas until the full sum is paid, the bond shall be void.

A5/8/9 [GC 4349]						9 Feb. 7 Edw. IV [1468]
Walter Bayle of Woodford by Berkeley (Glos.) and William lord of Barkeley, knight.
	Walter is bound to William in £10, payable at the feast of the Annunciation [25 March] next.

A5/8/10 [SC 620]						10 June 9 Edw. IV [1469]
William Lord Berkeley; and John Roger and John Bleche, collectors of the subsidy of tonnage and poundage in the port of London.
	William has acquitted John and John for 50 marks, being the half-yearly instalment of 100 marks a year which the king granted to Joan, sometime wife of William Willoughby, now wife of William Berkeley.
At: . . .

A5/8/11 [GC 4370]						20 July 12 Edw. IV [1472]
Richard Parker of Wotton-under-Edge (Glos.), labourer, Walter Harpesham of the same, tailor, and John Whytmore of Bradley in the same county, husbandman; and Thomas Berkeley, esquire.
	Richard, Walter and John are bound to Thomas in £20 payable at the feast of St. Laurence [the martyr?, 10 Aug.] next.

A5/8/12 [GC 4373]						11 June 13 Edw. IV [1473]
John Everard of Hinton (Glos.), husbandman, and Thomas Berkeley, esquire.
	John is bound to Thomas in £10 payable at Michaelmas next.

A5/8/13 [GC 4393]						1 Feb. 14 Edw. IV [1475]
William Baker of Combe (Glos.), husbandman, and William Berkeley, knight, Lord Berkeley.
	William Baker is bound to William Berkeley in £10, payable at Easter [26 March] next.

A5/8/14 [GC 4398]						1 June 15 Edw. IV [1475]
Robert Brownyng of Coaley (Glos.), husbandman, and William Berkeley, knight, lord of Berkeley.
	Robert is bound to William in £20 payable at Michaelmas next.

A5/8/15 [GC 4383]						5 June 15 Edw. IV [1475]
John Brownyng the younger of Coaley (Glos.), husbandman, and William Berkeley, knight, Lord Berkeley.
	John is bound to William is £20, payable at Michaelmas next.

A5/8/16 [GC 4399]						5 June 15 Edw. IV [1475]
Thomas Bayly of Coaley (Glos.), labourer, and William Berkeley, knight, lord of Berkeley.
	Thomas is bound to William in £20 payable at Michaelmas next.

A5/8/17 [GC 4400]   5 June 15 Edw. IV [1475]
John Mylward of Coaley (Glos.), husbandman, and William Berkeley, knight, lord of Berkeley.
  John is bound to William in £20 payable at Michaelmas next.

A5/8/18 [GC 4406]   27 June 16 Edw. IV [1476]
William Berkeley, knight, lord of Berkeley, William Try of Hardwick, esquire, Walter Skay
of Nibley, esquire, and Richard Thorpe of Wanswell, gentleman; and Henry Cote, citizen
and goldsmith of London.
  Whereas William, William, Walter and Richard are bound to Henry in £56 13s. 4d.
payable at Michaelmas, Henry wills that if they pay, in the parish church of St. Vedast in
Faryndon ward in London, as follows, viz. at Michaelmas 5 marks, at Easter 5 marks, and
so from feast to feast until the sum is fully paid, the bond will be void.

A5/8/19 [GC 4422]   12 July 20 Edw. IV [1480]
William Brandon, knight, Thomas Sheryngham of Southwark (Surrey), yeoman, and Robert
Morley of the same, yeoman; and William Berkley, knight, lord Berkeley.
  William, Thomas and Robert are bound to William in £40, payable at Michaelmas A.D.
1481.

A5/8/20 [GC 4428]   17 May 21 Edw. IV [1481]
Thomas Barkeley, esquire, and William Viscount Barkeley.
  Thomas is bound to William in £1,000 payable at Christmas.

A5/8/21 [GC 4429]   17 May 21 Edw. IV [1481]
Maurice Kynge of Cam (Glos.), yeoman, and William Viscount Barkeley.
  Maurice is bound to William in 1,000 marks, payable at Christmas.

A5/8/22 [GC 4430]   9 Sept. 22 Edw. IV [1482]
Walter Gibbes of Frampton-on-Severn, weaver, and William Viscount Berkeley.
  Walter is bound to William in 40 marks, payable at Michaelmas A.D. 1483; [dorse] on
condition that the bond is void if Walter pays 20 marks at that date.

A5/8/23 [GC 4468]   25 May 5 Hen. VII [1490]
Thomas Creyford of Wotton (Glos.), yeoman, and William Marquess Berkeley.
  Thomas is bound to William in £20, payable at the nativity of St. John the Baptist
[24 June] next.

A5/8/24 [GC 4469]   26 Oct. 6 Hen. VII [1490]
Robert Bernard, Robert Gibbson, Robert Sele, William Osburn, William Knyght of Sileby
(Leics.), husbandmen, and Roger Gulden of the same, clothier (*pannar'*); and William
Marquess Berkeley.
  Robert, Robert, Robert, William, William and Roger are bound to William Berkeley in
£100, payable at St. Nicholas [6 Dec.] next; [dorse] on condition that if Richard Milling and
John Milling, William Berkeley's bailiffs, faithfully execute the conditions of the indentures
made between them and William at Swalclyff on 20 Oct. the bond shall be void.

CADET BRANCHES
ROBERT, LORD OF WEARE
Robert was the second son of Robert FitzHarding.

A5/9/1 [SC 8]   n.d. [1158]
King Henry II and Robert son of Robert FitzHarding.
  The king has granted to Robert the vill of Malmesbury with the castle, lands and
hundreds pertaining to it, in fee, at a rent of £13 10s. a year, for which grant Robert has
given to the king 100 marks and has become his man.[1]

---

[1] *Transcript*: *TBGAS* cix. 137. The charter is probably spurious. There is no evidence to suggest
that the grant took effect.

Witnesses: Thomas our chancellor, William brother of Reginald, Richard de Hummaz, Manasser Biset, steward, Walter de Dunstanvill, Peter de Beucamp, Robert de Wattevil.

A5/9/2 [SC 46]   n.d. [*temp*. Ric. I]
John count of Mortain (*Moreton*) and Robert son of Robert FitzHarding.

John has quitclaimed to Robert the services which Robert owes to John from his land until John repays to Robert the 60 marks which Robert lent to William earl of Gloucester.
Witnesses: Stephen Rid[el], Hamon de Valoun, Ralph Morin, John le Werre, Ralph de Arden, Henry de Munford, Master Alard.

A5/9/3 [SC 229]   n.d. [1216 × 1230]
David abbot of St. Augustine's, Bristol, and Sir Maurice de Gaunt.

Agreement between the abbot and Maurice concerning Maurice's provision of wheat, beans, peas, oat flour and rents for bread and pottage for 100 paupers admitted daily to the almonry which Maurice built for the abbey, and in return the services of a chaplain to pray for his soul and those of his father, mother and wife.
Witnesses: Sir Robert de Gurnay, Sir Jordan Warr', Sir William the chamberlain, Sir Gilbert de Schipton, Peter Warr', Roger Aillard, William the clerk, Henry Aki, Richard Warr', Philip Long, Robert Farthein, John Warr', William de Hida, Adam de Budiford.

JOHN DE BERKELEY OF BEVERSTON

John (1351–1428) was the youngest of the four sons of Thomas (III) by his second wife Katherine le Veel, the only one Thomas's younger sons to survive his father. Thomas settled on him an extensive estate consisting of nearly all the manors which he had purchased, of which the chief was Beverston (Glos.). John's first wife was Eleanor, daughter and heir apparent of the Somerset knight Sir Robert de Ashton, but Eleanor died without issue before her father.

A5/9/4 [GC 3609]   27 Aug. 43 Edw. III [1369]
The executors of Lady Katherine de Berkel', lady of Wotton, and John de Berkel' her son.

John will claim from the executors of Katherine, of her goods and chattels, only the following articles, viz. a silver hanaper with a cover enamelled with the arms of Berkel', six cups enclosed within an ewer engraved with the arms of Berkel', six dishes of silver and six saucers and six pans of silver, and all the things which he had by demise of the lord his father; item, the goods that John had through Eleanor recently his wife, viz. a quilt cover of sendal powdered with blue roses, a bed of blue embroidered with the arms of Sir Robert Dasshton (viz. one coverlet, a half-tester, six embroidered covers and three plain), three worsted curtains, one pair of lintels [etc.], which Robert had by grant of Lady Katherine and which Robert gave to Eleanor his daughter and she demised to John her husband, a bowl with cover with a rose in enamel of the arms of Berkel' and Cobeham, and two gold rings; item, of the goods which Katherine had demised to John and which her executors will deliver to him when he is of age, viz. one quilt of sendal tulle, five covers of tulle, one mattress, one pair of curtain lintels, one sendal pillow, and other things. [*In French.*]
Witnesses: Walter Burgh, Nicholas Kyngescote, Adam Legat, Walter Benyimin, Sir John Oldelonde.
Sealed by Henry Warner and Nicholas de Kyngescote, John's esquires, because John is within age.
At: Wotton.

A5/9/5 [GC 3803]   Fri. the morrow of Ascension, 9 Ric. II [1 June 1386]
Walter Burnel, rector of Brean; and Sir John de Berkeleye, knight, Henry Waryner and William Smalcombe.

Walter has quitclaimed to John, Henry and William, executors of Lady Katherine de Berkeley, lady of Wotton, all actions.
At: Berkeley.

A5/9/6 [SC 568] 20 March 18 Ric. II [1395]
John de Berkeley, knight, and William Smalcombe the younger.

John has appointed William to be his steward of all his manors, lands and holdings in Glos. [*In French*.]

A5/9/7 [GC 2693] 8 Feb. 4 Edw. IV [1465]
King Edward IV; and Maurice Berkeley of Beverston, Walter Langley, Edmund Blount, John Poyntes, Roger Kemys, Thomas Whityngton, Thomas Morgan and Thomas Frensshe.

The king orders Maurice, Walter, Edmund, John, Roger, Thomas, Thomas and Thomas, or any two of them, to try Richard Forde, a prisoner in Gloucester Castle.
At: Westminster.

MARGARET DAUGHTER OF THOMAS (II) LORD BERKELEY
A5/9/8 [SC 458] 6 Feb. 20 Edw. I [1292]
King Edward I; and Thomas FitzMaurice and Margaret his wife.

Edward has granted to Thomas and Margaret the lands in Waterford and Desmond, and the custody of Dungarvan Castle, which were leased by King John to Thomas son of Anthony, and by King Henry III to John son of Thomas, and were recovered recently in a suit by King Edward from Thomas FitzMaurice, kinsman and heir of the said John; to hold at a farm of 200 marks a year.
Witnesses: R[obert Burnell] bishop of Bath, A[nthony Bek] bishop of Durham, W[illiam de Louth] bishop of Ely, Edmund the king's brother, William de Valencia, the king's uncle, Gilbert de Clare, earl of Gloucester and Hertford, Henry de Lacy, earl of Lincoln, Robert de Tibetot, Walter de Beauchamp (*de Bello Campo*), Gilbert de Briddeshale.
At: Westminster.

VARIOUS
A5/10/1 [SR 102] [after 1351]
Pedigree of Berkeley, damaged at the top and beginning with the marriage of Thomas (II) Lord Berkeley and Joan de Ferrers, ending in Jan. 1351/2 with the birth of John, youngest son of Thomas (III) Lord Berkeley and his second wife Katherine.

A5/10/2 [SR 105] [15th cent. or later]
Genealogy of the Berkeley family to *temp*. Edw. IV.

A5/10/3 [SR 97] 5 Hen. VII [1489–90]
Pedigree of the Berkeley family.

A5/10/4 [SR 139; *a 14th-cent. copy* SR 140] Easter, 15 Edw. I [April 1287]
Pleas of *Quo warranto* before William de Saham, Roger Loveday and John Metingham, at Gloucester, concerning Thomas de Berkeley, Malmesbury Abbey, Richard de Crupes, the bishop of Hereford, Peter Corbet and Fécamp Abbey.

A5/10/5 [GC 1649] Ash Wednesday, 1 Edw. III [27 Feb. 1327]
The abbot of St. Augustine's, Bristol, and Thomas de Berkel', lord of Berkeley.

The abbot has delivered to Thomas and the executors of the will of Maurice de Berkel', viz. Thomas, Sir William de Brynton, John Chaumpeneys and Henry de Rokhull, all the charters, goods and chattels which were recently by command of the king's father seized at Brustuyt, and were in the custody of the abbey, including gold and silver items, relics, rubies, emeralds, sapphires, paternosters, gold crosses, rings, a book called *Breton*', quires of the *Legende des seintz*, an iron chest containing charters and other things.

A5/10/6 [SC 536]   28 Oct. 1360

Notification by John count of Saarbrücken (*Sairebruche*), on behalf of John de Bouch, knight, of the release of Sir Morizes de Berquelee, John de Bouch's prisoner, for a ransom of £1,080, for which Henry duke of Lancastre and Sir Francis de Hale are pledges [*in French*], with notarial authentication [*in Latin*].[1]

Witnesses: Audruyn abbot of Cluny, the duke of Lancaster, Sir Francis de Hale, Master Peter de Courbeton, prior of Grantehanp, Sir Guy de Brien, Sir William de Graitton, knights. At: Calais.

A5/10/7 [GC 3631]   24 April 45 Edw. III [1371]

John de Welyntone, lord of Umberleigh, knight, and Lady Elizabeth, widow of Maurice son of Thomas de Berkele, lord of Berkeley, Maurice's executrix.

John has quitclaimed to Elizabeth and her co-executors, John Sergeant, William de Chiltenham and John Hille, for the marriage and custody of the body of Maurice son and heir of Maurice Berkele of Comptone Greneville.[2]

A5/10/8 [SC 546]   14 Kal. of Aug. 46 Edw. III [19 July 1372]

Sibyl abbess of Wilton and Lady Elizabeth Berkeley.

Sibyl has received from Elizabeth, by the hand of Ralph Cok, 40 marks which Elizabeth owed to her. At: Wilton.

A5/10/9 [GC 2860]   St. Andrew, 10 [Ric. II, 30 Nov. 1386?]

Sir Maurice de Berkele and William de Grenevile.

Maurice has received from William various items of silverware and napery [*detailed*] which William had had in his custody. [*In French.*] At: Dodmarsh.

A5/10/10 [GC 4112]   25 Aug. 5 Hen. V [1417]

Henry Foldford and William Polayn.

Henry has paid for the expenses of the jurors for the inquisition *post mortem* of Thomas lord of Berkeley, by the escheator of Devon and Cornwall, £4 2s. 9d. Attached is a list of the expenses totalling that sum. At: Exeter.

A5/10/11 [SC 625]   2 May 10 Edw. IV [1470]

John Shipward the elder, mayor of Bristol, and a jury [*named*]; and Philip Mede and John Shipward the younger.

Whereas certain persons have slandered Philip and John by alleging that they sent armed assistance to Lord Berkeley against Lord Lisle, the mayor and jury have judged that there is no ground for the slander and that Philip and John are persons of good name and fame. At: . . .

A5/10/12 [SC 635]   18 Sept. 1477

John Pembroke, master, and Lord Berkeley, owner, of the merchant ship, *George of Berkeley*.

A charter for the *George of Berkeley* to sail between Bristol and Bordeaux, and conditions. At: . . .

---

[1] *Transcript*: Jeayes, pp. 168–70, mistaking the count's identity.
[2] For this Maurice, above, p. 455, Compton Greenfield.